THE ELEMENTS
OF
PHYSICAL CHEMISTRY

By

SAMUEL GLASSTONE

Professor of Chemistry, Boston College

FOURTH PRINTING

D. VAN NOSTRAND COMPANY, Inc.

TORONTO   NEW YORK   LONDON

NEW YORK

D. Van Nostrand Company, Inc., 250 Fourth Avenue, New York 3

TORONTO

D. Van Nostrand Company (Canada), Ltd., 228 Bloor Street, Toronto 8

LONDON

Macmillan & Company, Ltd., St. Martin's Street, London, W.C. 2

First Published, March 1946

Reprinted, August 1946, March 1947, April 1948

PRINTED IN THE UNITED STATES OF AMERICA

To V.

PREFACE

As its title implies, the purpose of this book is to present, in the words of Webster's Dictionary, "an outline regarded as containing the fundamental features" of physical chemistry. It is an introductory text intended not only for students who propose to specialize in chemistry, but also for those who require some knowledge of the principles of physical chemistry in connection with their studies of physics, engineering, metallurgy, biology, medicine, geology, etc. Without equivocation, the treatment is meant to be elementary and to be suitable for a first course in physical chemistry for the average, rather than the exceptional, student. The emphasis is, therefore, on simplicity and clarity, the author's purpose being to present the material in such a form as to help the reader obtain an understanding of the essential concepts and ideas of modern physical chemistry.

As an aid to both teacher and student, all new terms, names of laws, and other important topics are printed in bold-face type. The actual statements of laws and of fundamental results and conclusions are given in italics, so that they may be impressed on the mind of the reader. Although the mathematics employed does not go beyond the most elementary calculus, mathematical results are also stated in words, wherever it is feasible, for the benefit of readers with a limited knowledge of the calculus.

Each chapter is provided with a number of review questions covering all the essential points in the text, and two sets of problems to which answers are given at the end of the book. Within each set repetition has been avoided as far as possible, so that every problem serves to illustrate or test a separate point; the two sets, however, duplicate one another fairly closely. Teachers should find that this scheme lends itself to a variety of uses. In addition to these problems, based directly on the material in each chapter, and those worked out in the text, a number of miscellaneous problems of a variety of types have been added.

In order to encourage the beginning student to do some outside reading, without discouraging him by the difficulty of the material, the somewhat novel procedure has been adopted of giving references only to papers published in the *Journal of Chemical Education*. This journal, intended for students as well as teachers, is one to which the student should be introduced at the earliest opportunity. The references are to the fifteen years from 1930 through 1944; they cover a wide range of physicochemical topics, and in them the reader will be directed to papers in other journals. Further information and references to the subjects dealt with in this book may be found, if required, in the writer's "Textbook of Physical Chemistry."

v

In preparing the present book the author has drawn upon his varied experience as a teacher and writer. In addition, he has had the benefit of advice from two other experienced teachers, his friends Professor A. E. Stearn and Dr. E. B. Sanigar, to whom he is greatly indebted for reading the manuscript and for making many valuable suggestions. To Dr. Sanigar thanks are also due for his careful reading of the galley proofs and for checking the answers to most of the problems. In conclusion, the writer wishes once again to express his gratitude to his wife for reading the proofs and for her continued help in innumerable ways.

SAMUEL GLASSTONE

BERKELEY, CALIF.
November 1945

CONTENTS

CHAPTER I

INTRODUCTION: ATOMIC THEORY

THE NATURE OF PHYSICAL CHEMISTRY

1a. The Scope of Physical Chemistry.—Although the nature of the problems that fall within the scope of **physical chemistry** is well recognized, it is nevertheless not an easy matter to give a simple and precise definition of this subject. Chemistry has been described as the science which deals with matter and its transformations, in contrast to physics which is concerned largely with energy and its transformations. Physical chemistry may be regarded as an intermediate field involving the study of the interactions between matter and energy. However, this definition is not complete enough to include all the topics that are generally regarded as being properly in the realm of physical chemistry, and the situation may well be considered from another point of view. Inorganic chemistry and organic chemistry deal primarily with the actual nature of the material changes occurring in chemical reactions. In physical chemistry, on the other hand, the influence of physical factors, such as temperature, pressure, concentration, electricity, light, etc., both on the reacting substances and on the reactions, is of primary interest; the objective is the understanding of the fundamental nature of chemical change. It is thus reasonable to describe physical chemistry as being concerned with *the elucidation or clarification of the principles underlying those transformations of matter known as chemical reactions*, through a study of the physical properties of the reacting substances and of the effect of physical changes on the reactions themselves.

In the light of the foregoing definition, the treatment of physical chemistry as given in this book will commence with a brief review of the basic laws of chemical combination that have been known since the early part of the nineteenth century, and which led to the development of the modern concept of atoms and molecules. The internal structures of these building stones of the chemist will then be considered, and it will be seen that it is possible in this manner to understand the different ways in which atoms can combine to form molecules. Although matter is ultimately composed of molecules and atoms, and these of even smaller units, namely electrons, protons and neutrons, the substances that take part in chemical reactions are generally encountered in the form of gas, liquid or solid, or perhaps in solution. Consequently, in the further study of physical chemistry the properties of the various forms of matter, both in the pure state and in mixtures, will be taken up from a number of different points of view. With this general background, the student will be in a position to consider actual chemical reactions, and to examine the factors which determine the direction, velocity and extent of a chemical change. In this manner it is hoped to justify the assertion that physical chemistry deals with the fundamental principles that underlie all chemical transformations, irrespective of whether inorganic or organic substances are involved.

1b. Scientific Method.—Before proceeding to the more detailed consideration of the various topics, as just outlined, it is desirable to say a few words about the methods of physical chemistry. Essentially, the study of this subject provides one of the best illustrations of the use of what is called the **scientific method.** To start with, experiments are performed, and the results of the observations, i.e., the empirical data, relating to a particular phenomenon are collected. An attempt is then made to generalize these results in the form of a simple statement or mathematical expression known as a **law;** so long as further experiments bring to light no exceptions, the law is regarded as holding good. Sometimes, as in the case of the influence of temperature and pressure on the volume of a gas, more accurate observations show that the laws which were originally proposed are approximate and are applicable under certain restricted conditions only. In other instances, as, for example, with the laws of thermodynamics, no exceptions are known.

The next stage in the application of the scientific method is to put forward a **hypothesis** with the object of explaining the experimental observations, or of accounting for the general law which summarizes them. It is, of course, doubtful whether a complete "explanation" of observed phenomena is ever possible; after all, the fundamental concepts of matter and energy cannot really be "explained." What a hypothesis generally attempts, therefore, is *an interpretation of the experimental facts in terms of simpler or more easily understood phenomena.* In other words, the purpose of the hypothesis is to state the causes which lead to the observed effects. These causes themselves have underlying causes, and it is the object of science to trace them, step by step, as far back as possible; the ultimate aim is the unification of all phenomena into one scheme. This is being gradually achieved in chemistry, for example, by the use of the concepts of the electron, the proton and the neutron; even though the exact nature of these structural units cannot be explained, the resulting systematization has, nevertheless, proved of great value.

1c. Hypothesis and Theory.—It may happen that two or more alternative hypotheses are proposed to account for certain experimental facts. A familiar illustration is provided by the phenomenon of burning or combustion in air. Two hypotheses, one based on the supposed existence of "phlogiston" and the other on the idea of combination with oxygen, were suggested. In the course of time it became evident that the latter hypothesis offered a more satisfactory interpretation of the observations than did the former. The phlogiston hypothesis of combustion was consequently discarded, and it ceased to have any but historical interest. When a particular hypothesis has withstood the test of many experiments, while the others have been eliminated or proved to be unsatisfactory in one way or another, it is referred to as a **theory.**

Although a distinction should strictly be drawn between the terms hypothesis and theory, it is nevertheless the common practice to regard them as having the same significance. It is probably true to say that the use of the term "hypothesis" is decreasing in modern scientific writings, and the word "theory" is employed almost exclusively in this connection. One reason for this preference, in spite of its not being strictly correct, lies partly in the fact that the adjective "hypothetical" has acquired the significance of referring to something that is imaginary. The same, objection, however, does not apply to the adjective "theoretical," and such expressions as the "theoretical treatment" of a subject, or the "theoretical approach" to a problem can be used without misunderstanding.

It should be apparent from what has been said that there is nothing that is necessarily permanent about a theory. A satisfactory theory must be able to correlate all the known facts concerning a particular phenonenon or set of phenomena, and also predict new ones. If there exist proven facts which are not in harmony with the theory, or the theory makes predictions which are later found to be incorrect, then that particular theory must be modified or discarded in favor of another. Sometimes an unsatisfactory theory has to be retained, simply because the necessary improvement or alternative is not immediately evident. This was the case, for example, in connection with certain properties of salt solutions, i.e., the strong electrolytes. In the course of time, however, suggestions were made for modifying the theory, which had been known for many years to be inadequate, so as to bring it into better agreement with the observed facts. Even now, in spite of the great advances that have been made, it is realized that the theory is still incomplete. Sometimes a theory can be modified, as just indicated, but in other cases it may have to be discarded altogether. In any event, a theory is retained only as long as it proves useful in the correlation and interpretation of experimental data, for that is its prime function in the operation of the methods of science.

The Atomic Theory

2a. Elements and Compounds.—Although nearly half a million different chemical substances are known, it is now realized that there are actually only ninety-two distinct species from which these thousands of substances are composed. The simple species or types of matter are known as **elements,** and the chemical combination of two or more elements in a variety of possible ways leads to the formation of the many **compounds** which either exist in nature or have been prepared in the laboratory. Until the beginning of the present century, an element could be defined in a simple manner as a form of matter which could not in any way be split up into other forms of matter. The discovery of the phenomena of radioactivity, and the realization of the universal occurrence of electrons (see Chapter II), showed that this definition had to be modified; this necessity has been emphasized in recent years by the development of methods whereby one element can be changed into another. However, as will be seen shortly, radioactive changes are spontaneous and cannot be controlled by any known methods, while most processes used for artificial disintegration and transmutation of elements involve the use of electrically charged particles moving with high velocity under the influence of potentials of millions of volts. Such procedures can hardly be considered to be in the same category as ordinary chemical changes, and so it is possible to define an element as *a form of matter which cannot be decomposed into, nor be produced from, simpler forms of matter by means of ordinary chemical reactions.* As indicated above, a compound is a substance produced by the union of two or more elements as the result of a chemical reaction.

2b. The Fundamental Laws of Chemical Combination.—The combination of elements to form compounds, and chemical reactions generally, are governed by four simple laws. These laws may be regarded as fundamental, for without them there could have been no science of chemistry as it is to-day. The four laws, which are based on the results of many experiments, will be enunciated and discussed briefly in turn.

I. Law of Conservation of Mass.—Within the limits of experimental error, *the total mass of a reacting system is unchanged as the result of a chemical reaction.* In other words, *there can be no loss or gain of matter accompanying a chemical change.* Every properly balanced chemical equation is based on this law, for since matter can neither be created nor destroyed, every item that appears on one side of the equation must be represented on the other side, and vice versa. Were it not for the experimental fact of the conservation of matter, chemical equations, and the calculations based on them, would not be possible, and the science of quantitative analysis could not have been developed.

It may be pointed out that according to modern views the law of conservation of mass must be interpreted properly in order for its true significance to be understood. It seems certain that if a sufficiently accurate and sensitive balance were available, and all sources of error could be eliminated, it would be found that many chemical reactions were actually accompanied by a loss or gain of weight. This result would, nevertheless, not be contrary to the law of conservation of mass in its complete sense. The reason for this is to be found in the realization that *mass and energy must be regarded as equivalent.* If a chemical change is accompanied by either a loss or gain of energy, for example, in the form of heat, such as is generally the case, there must be a corresponding loss or gain of weight, respectively. The equivalence of mass and energy is expressed by means of the equation

$$E = mc^2, \tag{2.1}$$

where E is the energy and m is its mass equivalent; c is the velocity of light. If m is in grams and c in cm. per sec., i.e., 3×10^{10} cm. per sec., then the energy E will be given in ergs; to convert this to calories, the result should be divided by 4.184×10^7, as will be seen in § 23a. It follows, therefore, that equation (2.1) may be written in the form

$$E = m \times (3 \times 10^{10})^2 = 9 \times 10^{20} m \text{ ergs}$$

$$= \frac{m \times (3 \times 10^{10})^2}{4.184 \times 10^7} = 2.15 \times 10^{13} m \text{ calories.} \tag{2.2}$$

For a reaction involving about 100 grams of chemical substances, an energy change of 100,000 calories would be moderately large, and the corresponding mass equivalent would be given by equation (2.2) as

$$100,000 = 2.15 \times 10^{13} m$$

$$m = 4.65 \times 10^{-9} \text{ gram.}$$

If the heat is evolved in the given reaction, the weight should consequently be decreased by this amount; on a total mass of the order of 100 grams, or even of 1 gram, this change would, of course, be undetectable by any known means.

It is obvious, therefore, that the law of conservation of mass, in its simple form, will hold for all chemical reactions within the limits of any experimental accuracy that is possible at present. There are certain changes, associated with the transmutation of elements, in which very large amounts of energy are concerned; it will be seen in § 8d that in such cases the corresponding change in weight is no longer insignificant. As already stated, however, these transformation processes cannot be regarded as ordinary chemical reactions.

II. Law of Constant Proportions.—*A given chemical compound always contains the same elements united in the same proportions by weight.* For obvious reasons, this statement is sometimes called the law of definite proportions or of constant composition. Like the law of conservation of mass, this law is of fundamental importance to chemistry; it is based on the fact that the composition of a particular compound is definite, and is independent of the method, time or place of preparation. For example, cupric oxide may be obtained from copper in several ways; in every case, however, the product will be found to contain 79.9 per cent by weight of copper and 20.1 per cent of oxygen.

The existence of many elements in two or more isotopic forms, which will be considered further in § 7c, necessitates some modification in the statement of the law of constant proportions by weight. The isotopes of a given element may be regarded as having identical chemical properties, but equivalent units, i.e., the atoms, differ in weight. Consequently, a specimen of cupric oxide containing a predominating amount of one particular isotope of oxygen will have a composition by weight slightly different from a specimen which contains more of another isotope. As long as the proportions of the various isotopes remain constant, however, the composition by weight of any compound will be quite definite, in agreement with the law enunciated above. Unless deliberate efforts are made to vary the isotopic ratio, the actual value for a given compound, as it exists in nature or is prepared in the laboratory, is virtually constant; hence, in practice the law of constant proportions may be regarded as being obeyed. Nevertheless, it would probably be more satisfactory to modify the statement of the law in the following manner: *a given isotopic form of a chemical compound always contains the same isotopes of the constituent elements united in the same proportion by weight.*

III. Law of Multiple Proportions.—*If two elements* A *and* B *combine to form more than one compound, the different amounts of* A *that unite with a definite amount of* B *bear a simple ratio to one another.* Without going into details, it

will be evident that here, as in the case of the law of constant proportions, it is
supposed that the isotopic nature of the elements A and B is always the same.
The law of multiple proportions may be illustrated in a simple manner by
reference to three oxides of carbon, namely carbon dioxide, carbon monoxide
and carbon suboxide. The compositions by weight and the amounts of carbon
that combine with one part by weight of oxygen in each case are given below.

	Carbon	Oxygen	Carbon	Oxygen
Carbon dioxide	27.28%	72.72%	0.3752	1
Carbon monoxide	42.87	57.13	0.7505	1
Carbon suboxide	52.96	47.04	1.126	1

The amounts of carbon that combine with a fixed weight of oxygen are seen
to be in the simple ratio of 1 to 2 to 3, in agreement with the law of multiple
proportions.

It should be pointed out that the requirement of a "simple ratio," that is
to say, one that can be expressed in the form of small integers, can apply only
to simple compounds. Consider, for example, two members of the paraffin
series of hydrocarbons, viz., methane and triacontane. The amounts of hydrogen in these two substances that unite with a definite quantity of carbon are in
the ratio of 60 to 31; this can hardly be regarded as a ratio of small integers.
Although the ratio is approximately 2 to 1, it is nevertheless not this simple
ratio, but more exactly 1.9355 to 1. Actually the two substances under consideration do not provide an exception to the law of multiple proportions in its
fundamental significance. For reasons which will be evident shortly, it would
be better if the expression "simple ratio" were replaced by the words "an exact
integral ratio"; although the ratio of 60 to 31 is not simple, at least it does
involve exact integers.

IV. Law of Combining (or Reciprocal) Proportions.—*The proportions in
which any two elements unite with a third element are the proportions, or a simple
multiple (or submultiple) of the proportions, in which they combine with each other.*
For example, 64 grams of sulfur combine with 12 grams of carbon in carbon
disulfide, while this same weight of carbon is combined with 32 grams of oxygen
in carbon dioxide. Hence, when sulfur and oxygen unite they should do so in
the proportion of 2 parts by weight of the former to 1 part of the latter, or in
some simple multiple of this proportion. This is actually found to be the case,
for sulfur dioxide contains 1 part of sulfur to 1 part by weight of oxygen, and in
sulfur trioxide the corresponding proportions are 2 to 3. These are clearly
simple submultiples of the ratio of 2 to 1.

An important consequence of the law of combining proportions is the emer-
gence of the idea of **combining weight** or **equivalent weight**; with every element
there must be associated a definite weight, in simple multiples of which it takes
part in chemical combination. For the purpose of expressing these combining
weights numerically, it is necessary to fix upon a standard of reference; this is
taken as 8.000 parts by weight of the element oxygen. The equivalent weight
of any element is then defined as *the number of parts by weight of that element
which will combine chemically with, or will replace from chemical combination,*

8.000 parts by weight of oxygen. The equivalent weight, like all other properties depending upon weight, will vary with the isotopic composition of the element, but it is the invariable practice to state the result for the particular composition that occurs in nature. On this basis the equivalent weight of hydrogen is 1.0080, that of carbon (in carbon dioxide) is 3.0025, and that of chlorine (in chlorine monoxide) is 35.457. The equivalent weight of oxygen is always 8.000 by definition.

When a given element forms two or more compounds with oxygen, the equivalent weights will differ in the two cases, but the values will bear an integral ratio, generally a simple integral ratio, to one another. As seen above, there are three well known compounds of carbon and oxygen, and from the compositions recorded it can be readily calculated that the weights of carbon that unite with 8.000 parts of oxygen are 3.002 in carbon dioxide, 6.004 in carbon monoxide, and 9.008 in carbon suboxide. It is to be expected from the law of multiple proportions, of course, which these substances are known to obey, that the three equivalent weights will bear a simple ratio to each other.

In accordance with the law of combining proportions, the equivalent weights of different elements give the proportions in which, or in integral multiples of which, they combine with one another. Since the equivalent weights of hydrogen and chlorine are 1.008 and 35.46, respectively, a compound of these two elements would be expected to contain them in precisely this proportion; such is actually the case in hydrogen chloride. The equivalent weight of sulfur in its stable compounds is generally 16.03, and hence a compound containing 16.03 parts by weight of sulfur and 35.46 parts of chlorine is to be anticipated. This compound is known and is called sulfur dichloride; there is, however, another combination of the elements sulfur and chlorine, namely sulfur monochloride, in which there are 32.06 parts of sulfur to 35.46 of chlorine. Since 32.06 is exactly twice 16.03, this result is in complete agreement with expectation.

Attention should be drawn to the fact that the equivalent weight is essentially an experimental quantity. It was at one time defined in terms of combination or replacement of the element hydrogen, but since there are many elements, particularly metals, that do not form stable compounds with hydrogen, the basis of the definition was changed. Of course, there are some elements which do not form compounds with oxygen that are stable and easily purified, two primary requirements for the determination of equivalent weight. In order to maintain the experimental basis of this quantity, therefore, the definition is extended for practical purposes; the equivalent weight is thus taken as the quantity of an element which can combine with or replace 8.000 parts of oxygen, *or its equivalent*, e.g., 35.457 parts by weight of chlorine. Many elements form stable, easily purifiable chlorides, or other halides, and these have been employed for the experimental determination of equivalent weights.

2c. Dalton's Atomic Theory.—Now that the laws of chemical combination, which summarize the experimental facts, are known, it is desirable to see if a simple scheme can be proposed to account for the observed phenomena. Such a scheme, known as the **atomic theory,** was put forward by J. Dalton in 1803; this theory may be stated in the form of the following three postulates:

(i) *All matter is composed of small, definite and indestructible particles, called* **atoms,** *which are indivisible by ordinary chemical means.*

(ii) *Atoms of the same element are equal in weight and are alike in all respects, but atoms of different elements have different weights and properties.*

(iii) *Compounds are formed by the union of an integral number of atoms of one element with an integral number of atoms of one or more other elements.*

The theory summarized in the foregoing statements, representing the first step in the development of the modern idea of atoms, provides a satisfactory interpretation of the laws of chemical combination. In the first place, since the atoms are definite particles with a definite weight, there should be no change in mass as the result of a chemical reaction. Such a reaction involves merely the interchange of attachments between various atoms of different elements, and so the weight should remain constant. This is, of course, in harmony with the requirements of the law of conservation of mass. The postulate of definite and constant mass also leads directly to the law of constant proportions. If cupric oxide, for example, consists of a combination of an atom of copper with an atom of oxygen, as is very probable, then since each of these atoms has a perfectly definite and constant weight, the composition of the oxide will also be quite definite.

An explanation of the law of multiple proportions can be obtained by considering the chemical interaction of two elements A and B; according to the atomic theory, combination of an integral number of atoms of A will take place with an integral number of atoms of B. The formulae of some of the possible resulting compounds would thus be AB, AB_2 and A_2B_3, so that the amounts of B that unite with a constant quantity of A in these three substances are 2 to 4 to 3, respectively. These small integers bear a simple ratio to one another, as required by the law of multiple proportions. In the three compounds between A and B just suggested, the number of atoms involved is not large; although this is the case for many compounds, it is not necessarily always true. In some organic substances, for example, large numbers of atoms of different kinds may be joined together; thus, in the hydrocarbon triacontane, to which reference was made earlier, 30 atoms of carbon are united with 62 atoms of hydrogen. On the other hand, in the related paraffin hydrocarbon methane, there is one carbon atom to four hydrogen atoms. The amounts of hydrogen that are combined with a constant amount of carbon in these two compounds are thus in the proportion of 31 to 60, as stated in § 2b, III. This is not a simple ratio, but it is nevertheless in complete agreement with the atomic theory, since the theory postulates that chemical combination can occur only between whole numbers of atoms.

Consider the elements B and C, both of which can combine with the element A; according to the atomic theory, such compounds as AB, AB_2, A_2B_3, etc., and AC, AC_2, A_2C_3, etc., are to be expected. If the substance AB, on the one hand, is compared with AC_2, on the other hand, it is seen that one atom of B and two of C, respectively, combine with the same quantity, viz., one atom, of A. By the law of combining proportions, therefore, the elements B and C should unite in the atomic ratio of 1 to 2, that is, to yield the compound BC_2, or in some simple multiple of this ratio, which might result in such substances as BC or B_2C_3. Since these compounds all involve integral numbers of the atoms B and C, their existence would be in accord with the requirements of the atomic theory. This theory, therefore, provides a satisfactory basis for the law of combining proportions, as well as for the three other laws of chemical combination.

It may be noted that if all compounds formed between two elements contained only one atom of each, viz., AB, AC, BC, AD, BD, CD, etc., the ratio of the combining weights of the elements A, B, C, D, etc., would be identical with the ratio of the actual weights of these atoms. However, this is not always true and the ratio of the combining weights may differ from the ratio of the weights of the atoms; as is to be expected from the atomic theory, these ratios if not identical must be simple integral multiples of each other. It may be stated as a general rule that if two elements form a compound of the type AB, BC, CD, etc., the ratio of their equivalent or combining weights in that compound will be the same as the ratio of the weights of the atoms.

ATOMS AND MOLECULES

3a. Gay-Lussac's Law of Combination by Volume.—In addition to the laws of chemical combination considered in the preceding section, there is another important law, known as the **law of combination by volume,** discovered by J. L. Gay-Lussac (1808); this law cannot be explained in terms of the atomic theory alone. The law, which applies only to reactions involving gases, states that *when two gases combine chemically they do so in simple proportions by volume; further, the volume of the gaseous products also bears a simple ratio to that of the reacting gases.* It should be understood, of course, that the volumes are all measured under the same conditions of temperature and pressure.

In the formation of hydrogen chloride gas from hydrogen and chlorine, for example, it is found that

1 volume of hydrogen $+1$ volume of chlorine $=$ 2 volumes of hydrogen chloride.

The volumes of the two reacting gases and of the product are thus in the simple ratio of 1 to 1 to 2. Similarly, when hydrogen and oxygen react to form water vapor (steam),

2 volumes of hydrogen $+1$ volume of oxygen $=$ 2 volumes of steam;

here again, the ratios of the volumes are simple integers.

As in the case of the law of multiple proportions, the Gay-Lussac law of combination by volume holds strictly for relatively simple compounds; with more complex substances, there are apparent, although not real, exceptions. If the gas butane were completely burnt in oxygen, it would be found that 2 volumes of butane gas required 13 volumes of oxygen gas, and the products—carbon dioxide and water—would occupy 18 volumes in the gaseous state at the same temperature and pressure. These numbers, 2, 13 and 18, can hardly be said to bear a simple ratio to each other. The essential point here, however, as in other cases, is that the ratio of the volumes can be expressed in terms of integers.

3b. Atoms and Molecules.—The significance of Gay-Lussac's law of volumes was realized by A. Avogadro (1811), and it led him, in the first place, to distinguish between an atom and a **molecule.** Previously, the word "atom" had been used to describe the smallest conceivable particle of any substance, either element or compound, but Avogadro suggested that this term should be restricted to elements. In addition, he introduced the use of the term "molecule," which could be applied to both elements and compounds. The distinction between an atom and a molecule will be apparent from the following definitions:

An atom is the smallest particle of an element that can take part in chemical change.

A molecule is the smallest particle of an element or compound that can exist in the free state.

The smallest unit of a compound substance is thus seen to be the molecule; this can exist as such in the free state and it can also take part in chemical reaction. With an element, however, it is necessary to distinguish between the atom and the molecule, for the atom may not be capable of any prolonged existence in the free state. In some cases, for example, the inert gases of the atmosphere, i.e., helium, neon, etc., and the vapors of most metals, e.g., mercury, the smallest conceivable particle, which is the atom, is quite stable and is capable of a free and independent existence. For these elements the atom and the molecule are consequently identical. With the great majority of nonmetallic elements, however, the molecule contains two or more atoms, although the number may vary with the temperature.

As in many other instances, an attempt to give a precise definition of a molecule of an element involves some difficulties, for even when it is recognized that the atom and molecule are different, it is not strictly true to say that the atom does not exist in the free state. A hydrogen molecule, to take a simple illustration, normally contains two atoms; as the temperature is raised, the molecules split up into single atoms, and at sufficiently high temperatures hydrogen gas contains an appreciable proportion of atoms which can exist in the free state, alongside molecules containing two atoms. It would seem, therefore, that under these conditions both the atom and the molecule of hydrogen are capable of a free existence. Although this is true, in a sense, it would be more correct to say that at high temperatures there are two kinds of hydrogen molecules; one in which there are two atoms per molecule and the other with but one atom to the molecule. As the temperature is lowered the proportion of the latter type of molecule decreases, but even at ordinary temperatures there are undoubtedly a few that can exist in the free state. Since the number is so small that it can be neglected, hydrogen gas under normal conditions may be regarded as consisting entirely of molecules each of which contains two atoms. The possibility of the existence of different types of molecules of the same element, and even of a compound, must nevertheless always be borne in mind.

3c. Avogadro's Law.—After making the distinction between an atom and a molecule, Avogadro proposed a hypothesis which is now so universally accepted that it is regarded as one of the established laws of chemistry. According to **Avogadro's law,** *under the same conditions of temperature and pressure, equal volumes of different gases contain equal numbers of molecules.* If it may be supposed, as a consequence of the atomic theory, that when molecules react chemically they do so by simple whole numbers, then Gay-Lussac's law of volumes follows directly from the law of Avogadro. Suppose a small integral number a of molecules of the substance A interact with the integral number b of molecules of B, both being in the gaseous state; suppose further that, in accordance with Avogadro's law, a unit volume of each of these gases, or of any other gas, contains n molecules at the given temperature and pressure. It follows, therefore, that

$$\frac{a}{n} \text{ volumes of A combine with } \frac{b}{n} \text{ volumes of B,}$$

and hence the ratio of the volumes in which the gases A and B interact is equal to a to b. Since a and b are both small integers, this will be a simple ratio, as required by Gay-Lussac's law. The number of molecules c of the product (or products) resulting from the reaction must also be integral, since fractions of molecules cannot exist in the free state; hence, the volume of the gaseous products will bear a simple ratio to that of the reacting substances. It is now easy to understand why the ratio of the volumes of butane gas, oxygen gas, and the gaseous products of complete combustion are 2 to 13 to 18, as noted in § 3a. In the light of Avogadro's law, that equal volumes contain equal numbers of molecules, the explanation lies in the fact that the over-all reaction involves 2 molecules of butane, 13 molecules of oxygen and 18 molecules of products. Such a conclusion is quite in keeping with the atomic theory and its extension by the introduction of the idea of molecules.

There are many important consequences of Avogadro's law, some of which will be referred to here. As already seen, one volume of hydrogen and one of chlorine unite to produce two volumes of hydrogen chloride; consequently, supposing that there are n molecules per unit volume,

n molecules of hydrogen $+$ n molecules of chlorine

$$= 2n \text{ molecules of hydrogen chloride,}$$

or

1 molecule of hydrogen $+$ 1 molecule of chlorine

$$= 2 \text{ molecules of hydrogen chloride.}$$

A single molecule of hydrogen chloride, which is, of course, capable of free existence, thus contains one-half molecule of hydrogen and one-half molecule of chlorine. Since the atom is the smallest particle that can take part in chemical combination, it is evident that the one-half molecule of hydrogen and of chlorine must consist of a single atom *at least*. In other words, the molecule of hydrogen and the molecule of chlorine must each contain at least two atoms. There are good reasons for believing that, at ordinary temperatures and pressures, these molecules contain no more than two atoms; it follows, therefore, that it is possible to represent the reaction between hydrogen and chlorine gases as

2 atoms of hydrogen $+$ 2 atoms of chlorine $=$ 2 molecules of hydrogen chloride,

or

$$H_2 + Cl_2 = 2HCl,$$

so that the formula of hydrogen chloride gas must be HCl. Similar conclusions concerning the structures of other gaseous molecules can be reached in an analogous manner.

Before going on to consider other uses of Avogadro's law, brief reference may be made here to the limits of applicability of this law, and of the Gay-Lussac law of combination by volume. Strictly speaking, both of these laws refer to what are known as "ideal" or "perfect" gases, which will be considered more fully in Chapter IV. The nature and extent of the deviations from ideal or perfect behavior exhibited by actual gases will be discussed there, and it will be seen that allowance can be made for the small departures from Avogadro's law; for the present these deviations may be ignored. Incidentally, it should be noted that the conclusions reached above in connection with the hydrogen-chlorine reaction are independent of any failure of the gases to behave ideally; the small departures from Gay-Lussac's law balance those from Avogadro's law. Experiments of the highest precision would show that it is not exactly one volume of hydrogen that combines with one of chlorine to produce exactly two volumes of hydrogen chloride; the actual volumes would be very slightly different. Nevertheless, after allowing for the corresponding deviations from Avogadro's law, it would be found that precisely two atoms of hydrogen and two atoms of chlorine yield precisely two molecules of hydrogen chloride.

3d. Atomic and Molecular Weights.—One of the postulates of the atomic theory is that the atom of any given element has a definite and constant weight; since a molecule of an element or compound contains a definite integral number of atoms, it must also have a definite weight characteristic of the given molecule. These statements are, of course, based on the supposition that a particular isotopic form, or a certain isotopic composition of the element or compound, is under consideration. It should thus be possible to state the weight of an atom or molecule of any substance as a definite quantity. Because atoms and molecules are so small, their actual weights being of the order of 10^{-24} gram, it is more convenient in practice to state the weight of any atom or molecule in terms of that of a standard atom. The so-called atomic and molecular weights are thus really *relative* weights. At one time the hydrogen atom, the lightest known atom, was chosen as the standard of comparison, so that its atomic weight was taken as precisely unity. Since atomic weights are generally determined from the experimental equivalent weights and the latter, for reasons already given, are expressed in terms of the element oxygen as the standard, atomic weights are now given relative to that of the oxygen atom. The **atomic weight** of an element is thus defined as *the weight of an atom of the element relative to the weight of the oxygen atom taken as 16.0000.*

Oxygen exists in at least three isotopic forms with atoms of different weights; hence, the atomic weight of any element will depend on the isotopic composition of the oxygen employed as the standard of reference. If the value 16.0000 is taken as the mean atomic weight of oxygen having the same isotopic composition as in the atmosphere, the resulting figures for other elements are known as the **chemical atomic weights.*** On the other hand, if 16.0000 is assumed to be the atomic weight of the most abundant isotope, the **physical atomic weights** are obtained. From a study of the masses and relative proportions of the isotopes of oxygen (§ 7e), it is found that

$$\text{Chemical atomic weight} = \frac{\text{Physical atomic weight}}{1.00027}.$$

It is evident that the difference between the two sets of atomic weights is not large; nevertheless, it is necessary to distinguish between them. The chemical atomic weights are those employed by chemists in the quantitative study of reactions, but the physical atomic weights are often used in stating the weights of isotopes and in connection with atomic disintegration reactions (§ 8d). Unless a specific statement is made to the contrary, chemical atomic weights will be employed throughout this book.

It was noted earlier that the equivalent weight of oxygen, which is the standard of reference for equivalent weights, is taken as 8.000, whereas the atomic weight is 16.000. It is seen, therefore, that on the basis of the accepted scales, the atomic weight of oxygen is exactly twice the equivalent weight. According to the atomic theory, the weight of an atom of any element must always be a simple integral multiple of its combining weight; hence, it is possible to write the following general relationship:

$$\frac{\text{Atomic weight}}{\text{Equivalent weight}} = \text{a small integer.}$$

This integer, which is *the ratio of the atomic weight of an element to its equivalent weight,* is called the **valence** of the element in the particular compound employed in the determination of the equivalent weight; it is generally 1, 2, 3 or 4, although it is sometimes larger.

If the valence is known, it is possible to obtain the atomic weight from the accurately determined, experimental, equivalent weight; this is the principle most frequently employed in the evaluation of atomic weights. The valence of the element being studied is rarely in doubt, at the present time, but in the

* The familiar chemical atomic weights, like that of oxygen, are actually the mean of the values for the isotopic forms which may be present.

early development of chemistry the situation was frequently uncertain. Some of the methods that were applied to obtain the value of the integer by which the equivalent weight was to be multiplied in order to give the atomic weight will be considered below.

The **molecular weight** of a substance is also a relative quantity based on the same scale as is used for the chemical atomic weights. Several definitions of molecular weight, which are fundamentally identical, may be given; thus, *the molecular weight is the weight of a molecule of a given substance relative to the weight of the oxygen atom as 16.0000.* Since there are two atoms in the oxygen molecule, the molecular weight of any element or compound may be defined as *the weight of a molecule compared with that of the oxygen molecule as 32.0000.* Alternatively, the molecular weight may be regarded simply as *the sum of the atomic weights of all the constituent atoms of the molecule.* For example, a molecule of ordinary water contains two atoms of hydrogen (atomic weight 1.0080) and one atom of oxygen (atomic weight 16.0000); hence, the molecular weight of water is given by $(2 \times 1.0080) + 16.0000 = 18.0160$.

The atomic weight of an element expressed in grams is called the gram atomic weight or, more generally, a **gram atom;** thus 16.000 grams of oxygen, 12.01 grams of carbon, and 1.008 grams of hydrogen each constitute one gram atom of the corresponding element. Similarly, the molecular weight of any substance, element or compound, in grams is referred to as the gram molecular weight or, more frequently, as the **gram molecule;** it is the common practice, however, to speak of this quantity as a **mole** (sometimes spelled **mol**).

The values of atomic and molecular weights, as defined above, are, of course, proportional to the actual weights of the atoms and molecules, respectively. It follows then that 1 gram atom or 1 gram molecule of any substance always contains a definite, constant number of individual atoms or molecules. This constant is known as the **Avogadro number;** it is usually defined as *the number of individual molecules in one mole of any substance,* but it is also equal to the number of individual atoms in 1 gram atom or of ions in 1 gram ion. Several different methods, which will be described later, have been devised for determining the Avogadro number, and its accepted value is 6.023×10^{23}. The actual mass of a single atom or molecule of any species can be obtained upon dividing the ordinary atomic or molecular weight by this number. Since atomic and molecular weights, at least of simple molecules, lie between 1 and 300, it is evident that the actual weights of individual atoms and molecules are from about 1.7×10^{-24} to 5×10^{-22} gram.

3e. Molecular Weight and Gas Density.—The definition of molecular weight, based on the value of exactly 32.000 for oxygen, makes it possible to write

$$\frac{\text{Molecular weight}}{32.000} = \frac{\text{Wt. of 1 molecule of substance}}{\text{Wt. of 1 molecule of oxygen}} \tag{3.1}$$

$$= \frac{\text{Wt. of } n \text{ molecules of substance}}{\text{Wt. of } n \text{ molecules of oxygen}}.$$

If the substance under consideration is a gas, then the introduction of Avogadro's law leads to the result

$$\frac{\text{Molecular wt. of gas}}{32.000} = \frac{\text{Wt. of given volume of gas}}{\text{Wt. of equal volume of oxygen}},$$

$$\text{Molecular wt. of gas} = \frac{\text{Density of gas}}{\text{Density of oxygen}} \times 32.000, \qquad (3.2)$$

the two densities being determined at the same temperature and pressure. This result provides a direct experimental method for the evaluation of molecular weights of gaseous substances. Strictly, the relationship derived applies to ideal or perfect gases, for which Avogadro's law holds exactly; however, there are various methods available, as already indicated, for making the necessary corrections for departure from ideal behavior (§§ 14a, 14b).

Problem: The corrected density of carbon dioxide at 0° C. and 1 atm. pressure is 1.9635 grams per liter, and that of oxygen under the same conditions is 1.4277 grams per liter. Calculate the molecular weight of carbon dioxide.

$$\text{Molecular wt. of carbon dioxide} = \frac{1.9635}{1.4277} \times 32.000 = 44.010.$$

3f. Determination of Atomic Weights.—Up to about the middle of the nineteenth century there was considerable uncertainty in the matter of assigning atomic weights to many elements. Although the equivalent weights were known with moderate accuracy, there was no reliable method for the determination of the formulae of the molecules from which the valence of the elements under consideration could be derived. However, in 1858, S. Cannizzaro showed how the results of Avogadro's law could be applied to the problem of atomic weight determination. Since an atom is defined as the smallest particle of an element that can take part in chemical combination, *the atomic weight is the smallest weight in grams of the element that can be found in one gram molecular weight of any of its compounds.* This forms the basis for the procedure used by Cannizzaro for the assessment of atomic weights.

Volatile compounds of the given element were prepared and their molecular weights were determined from the densities of the vapors by means of equation (3.2). The various substances were then analyzed so as to find the weight of the element present in the gram molecular weight of the compound; the smallest weight found in this manner gives a maximum value, at least, for the atomic weight. If one or more of the compounds happens to contain only one atom of the given element per molecule, this maximum will be identical with the actual atomic weight. In any case, *the highest common divisor of the various weights of the element present in the gram molecular weight, i.e., a mole, of the different compounds will be equal to the atomic weight.* The method may be illustrated by reference to the results in Table I for a number of compounds containing chlorine; from the molecular weights and the percentages of chlorine

TABLE I. THE ATOMIC WEIGHT OF CHLORINE

Compound	Molecular Weight	Chlorine, per cent	Wt. of Chlorine, per mole
Hydrogen chloride	36.5	97.2	35.5
Thionyl chloride	119.0	59.7	71.0
Boron trichloride	117.3	90.8	106.5
Chloroform	119.5	89.1	106.5
Carbon tetrachloride	154.0	92.2	142.0

of the various substances, the results in the last column are obtained. The smallest weight of chlorine present in a mole of any of its compounds is 35.5, and this is accepted as the (approximate) atomic weight of chlorine. It may be noted that even if hydrogen chloride had not been included among the substances examined, the results in Table I would still have led to the value of 35.5 for the atomic weight of chlorine, since this is the largest common divisor of the figures in the last column.

The accuracy of the atomic weights obtained by the foregoing procedure is limited by the accuracy of the molecular weight determinations and the analyses; the latter are generally adequate, but the former are not satisfactory if they are derived from equation (3.2) without correction. By the use of accurate molecular weights, obtained as described in §§ 14a, 14b, it is possible to determine atomic weights with a considerable degree of precision.

As described above, the method requires the use of compounds that are volatile, so that their molecular weights can be determined from density measurements. It is possible, however, to obtain the molecular weights of non-volatile substances (§ 28b), and hence the procedure can be extended so as to include such compounds.

An approximate estimate of the atomic weight of a solid element, which is often sufficient for evaluating the integral ratio of the atomic weight to the equivalent weight, i.e., the valence, is based on the use of the **law of Dulong and Petit** (1818). According to this law *the atomic heat of a solid element is approximately 6.2 calories at ordinary temperatures;* the **atomic heat** is equal to the product of the atomic weight and the specific heat of the element. If the specific heat is known, an estimate of the atomic weight can thus be made, since the product is approximately 6.2 cal. per degree per gram atom., i.e., 6.2 cal. deg.$^{-1}$ g. atom^{-1}.

For certain light elements, e.g., carbon and boron, the atomic heats are considerably less than 6 cal. deg.$^{-1}$ g. atom^{-1}, but they approach this value at high temperatures (§ 21a).

Problem: The specific heat of lead is 0.031 cal. deg.$^{-1}$ g.$^{-1}$, and its equivalent weight, in lead chloride, is known, with a considerable degree of accuracy, to be 103.605. Calculate the accurate atomic weight of the element lead.

The approximate atomic weight of lead is obtained upon dividing 6 by the specific heat 0.031; this gives approximately 200. Since the atomic weight must be an exact integral multiple of the equivalent weight, this integer is 2; hence, the accurate atomic weight is 2 × 103.605 = 207.21.

The valence of an element in a particular compound can sometimes be estimated with the aid of Mitscherlich's **law of isomorphism** (§ 20a). The original form of the law is open to some objection, and so it is best stated in the following modified manner: *substances which are similar in crystalline form, i.e., isomorphous, and in chemical properties can usually be represented by similar formulae.* An example of the application of this law is provided by the element silver; the equivalent weight was known to be about 108, and the atomic weight, until 1837, was thought to be twice the equivalent weight, i.e., 216. On the basis of this atomic weight the formula of silver sulfide should be AgS. The fact that the latter substance is isomorphous with cuprous sulfide, Cu_2S, suggested that silver sulfide had the similar formula Ag_2S. If this is the case, the atomic weight of silver should be identical with its equivalent weight, and not double this quantity. The present accepted value of the atomic weight of silver is 107.880.

Problem: The green oxide of chromium was found to be isomorphous with ferric oxide (Fe_2O_3) and alumina (Al_2O_3). The accurate equivalent weight of chromium in the green oxide is 17.337; calculate the atomic weight of chromium.

In view of the isomorphism with Fe_2O_3 and Al_2O_3, the formula of the green oxide of chromium should be Cr_2O_3; the valence of chromium in this compound is thus 3, and the accurate atomic weight is $3 \times 17.337 = 52.01$.

A procedure for the accurate evaluation of atomic weights, which has assumed considerable importance in recent years, is based on the determination of the masses of the individual isotopes by a physical method. This will be described more fully in § 7e.

3g. The Periodic Table.—*When the elements are arranged in order of increasing atomic weight, a striking periodicity, or repetition, of physical and chemical properties becomes evident.* The existence of this periodic behavior was realized by J. A. R. Newlands (1864) and independently by D. I. Mendeléeff (1869) and L. Meyer (1870). It is to Mendeléeff, however, that the chief credit must be given for the development of the idea which has proved to be of fundamental chemical significance.

The element hydrogen, which has the smallest atomic weight, and the succeeding element helium fall into a category of their own; these are followed by eight elements, from lithium to neon, with steadily increasing atomic weight; thus,

Li   Be   B   C   N   O   F   Ne.

There next come a series of eight elements, from sodium to argon, viz.,

Na   Mg   Al   Si   P   S   Cl   A,

whose properties, both physical and chemical, resemble very closely the corresponding members of the preceding series of eight elements. In each case there is the same gradation of properties, particularly as regards valence and electropositive (metallic) or electronegative (nonmetallic) nature.

In the elements which follow argon, it is seen that the first two, namely potassium and calcium, resemble the first two members of the two preceding series. With the next element, however, i.e., scandium, some departure from strict periodicity is observed. This continues to be the case until the four elements arsenic, selenium, bromine and krypton are reached; these resemble very closely the last four members of the earlier series, e.g., phosphorus, sulfur, chlorine and argon. The two series, or periods, of eight elements are thus followed by a period of eighteen, from potassium to krypton. The next period, from rubidium to xenon, also contains eighteen elements whose properties bear marked analogies to those of the preceding series.

In the period which follows, a further anomaly is found after the second member; this is the occurrence of a group of fifteen elements, known as the **rare-earth elements,** with strikingly similar properties. However, when this group is completed, the elements which follow resemble closely those of the two preceding periods of eighteen elements. Because of the inclusion of fifteen elements in the place usually occupied by a single element, this period contains a total of thirty-two members. The final period, starting with an unstable alkali metal and ending with uranium, the element of highest atomic weight, is obviously incomplete. All the members are radioactive and unstable; beyond uranium the instability is presumably so great that the elements do not exist in nature.

The foregoing results may be summarized in the arrangement depicted in Table II, generally referred to as the **periodic table;** this is seen to be divided vertically into **groups,** and horizontally into **periods.** When the period contains more than eight elements, it is found convenient to divide the groups I to VIII into the subgroups A and B, and also to introduce a group VIII containing three elements in each period that have similar chemical and physical properties. It will be observed that the members of each A subgroup resemble one another, and so also do the elements of each B subgroup. There is some analogy between the members of the A and B subgroups in any main group, but this is usually not very marked. The first two elements in each group are sometimes referred to as the typical elements of the group. At the beginning and end of each period the properties resemble those of the typical elements, but in the middle this is not the case. An attempt is made to represent these general results by the positions of the symbols for the various elements in Table II.

3h. Features of the Periodic Table: Atomic Numbers.—An examination of the periodic table reveals many interesting features, which are treated in detail in most textbooks of general chemistry or inorganic chemistry. A few only of these matters will be referred to here. It will be observed, in the first place, that there are ninety-two elements, from hydrogen, the lightest atom, to uranium, the heaviest. Not all of these elements have yet been found in nature, although there is evidence of the formation of the elements occupying the positions 43, 61 (rare earth), 85 and 87 as the result of artificial disintegration processes (§§ 8a, 8b). The necessity for leaving gaps where these elements should be is evident from the fact that otherwise the periodicity would break down; there are also other reasons which will be referred to in § 4h.

TABLE II. THE PERIODIC TABLE

Period	Group I A	Group I B	Group II A	Group II B	Group III A	Group III B	Group IV A	Group IV B	Group V A	Group V B	Group VI A	Group VI B	Group VII A	Group VII B	Group VIII	Group 0
1	1 H 1.0080															2 He 4.003
2	3 Li 6.940		4 Be 9.02			5 B 10.82		6 C 12.010		7 N 14.008		8 O 16.0000		9 F 19.00		10 Ne 20.183
3	11 Na 22.997		12 Mg 24.32			13 Al 26.97		14 Si 28.06		15 P 30.98		16 S 32.06		17 Cl 35.457		18 A 39.944
4	19 K 39.096		20 Ca 40.08		21 Sc 45.10		22 Ti 47.90		23 V 50.95		24 Cr 52.01		25 Mn 54.93		26 Fe 55.85 27 Co 58.94 28 Ni 58.69	
4		29 Cu 63.57		30 Zn 65.38		31 Ga 69.72		32 Ge 72.60		33 As 74.91		34 Se 78.96		35 Br 79.916		36 Kr 83.7
5	37 Rb 85.48		38 Sr 87.63		39 Y 88.92		40 Zr 91.22		41 Cb 92.91		42 Mo 95.95		43 —		44 Ru 101.7 45 Rh 102.91 46 Pd 106.7	
5		47 Ag 107.880		48 Cd 112.41		49 In 114.76		50 Sn 118.70		51 Sb 121.76		52 Te 127.61		53 I 126.92		54 Xe 131.3
6	55 Cs 132.91		56 Ba 137.36		57–71 Rare earths		72 Hf 178.6		73 Ta 180.88		74 W 183.92		75 Re 186.31		76 Os 190.2 77 Ir 193.1 78 Pt 195.23	
6		79 Au 197.2		80 Hg 200.61		81 Tl 204.39		82 Pb 207.21		83 Bi 209.00		84 Po 210		85 —		86 Rn 222
7	87 —		88 Ra 226.05		89 Ac 227		90 Th 232.12		91 Pa 231		92 U 238.07					

Another point to be seen from Table II is that in three instances the order of the elements, required to give the proper periodic arrangement and the necessary gradation of properties, is not strictly in accordance with steadily increasing atomic weight. The three cases in which the positions of the elements have been transposed are argon and potassium, cobalt and nickel, and tellurium and iodine. Careful determinations of the atomic weights have proved beyond doubt that the values given are correct, and so the rule (or law) of Mendeléeff, that the properties of elements are periodic functions of their atomic weights, is not strictly true.

During the present century it has become evident that the important property of an element in determining the periodicity of behavior is not the atomic weight, but a quantity called the **atomic number** of the element. For the present this may be defined as *the ordinal number of the element in the periodic table*, due allowance being made for vacant spaces. The atomic numbers are, in fact, the numbers preceding the symbols of the various elements in Table II. In the majority of instances the atomic weight of an element increases with its atomic number, but in the three instances of inversion of order in the periodic table this is not the case. It will be seen in Chapter II that the atomic number has a fundamental significance in connection with the internal structure of atoms, and it is this which accounts for the periodic repetition of physical and chemical properties.

READING REFERENCES

1. **Nature and organization of scientific knowledge.** Wright, *Journal of Chemical Education*, **17**, 270 (1940).
2. **John Dalton.** Coward, *ibid.*, **4**, 23 (1927).
3. **The periodic system** (Historical). Weeks, *ibid.*, **9**, 1593, 1605 (1932).
4. **Discovery of the elements.** Weeks, reprinted from the *J. Chem. Ed.* in book form.

REVIEW QUESTIONS

1. Define the term "element." What factors render an exact definition difficult?
2. State and explain the law of conservation of mass. How must the law be modified in connection with energy changes?
3. State and explain the law of constant proportions. What limitations must be introduced as a result of the existence of isotopes?
4. State and illustrate the law of multiple proportions. How may the law be reconciled with the existence of compounds such as CH_4 and $C_{30}H_{62}$?
5. State the law of reciprocal proportions. Give examples of its application.
6. Define the term "equivalent weight." How does the concept of equivalent weights arise?
7. Why do some elements have more than one equivalent weight? How are the values related to one another?
8. State the postulates of Dalton's atomic theory. Show that the theory can account for the fundamental laws of chemical combination.
9. State and illustrate Gay-Lussac's law of combination by volume.
10. Define the terms "atom" and "molecule." Explain how the atom and molecule of an element may be identical.

11. State Avogadro's law. How does this law explain the law of combination by volume?

12. Two volumes of hydrogen and one of oxygen combine to form two volumes of water as steam; derive a chemical equation for the reaction.

13. Define "atomic weight" and "molecular weight." How is the molecular weight of a compound related to the atomic weights of its constituent elements?

14. Explain the relationship between equivalent weight and atomic weight.

15. What is the Avogadro number? How may it be used to determine the actual weight of an atom or molecule?

16. Explain the connection between the density of a gas and its molecular weight.

17. Describe the method of Cannizzaro for the determination of atomic weight.

18. How may (a) atomic heat, (b) the principle of isomorphism, be used to fix atomic weights?

19. Describe the fundamental basis of the periodic classification of elements.

20. What is meant by the "atomic number" of an element?

PROBLEMS

I

1. Sulfur and chlorine form three compounds containing 47.49, 31.12 and 18.43 per cent of sulfur, respectively. Show that these results are in agreement with the law of multiple proportions.

2. A compound of carbon and chlorine contains 7.81 per cent of carbon, and a compound of carbon and sulfur contains 15.77 per cent of carbon. Show that these results, together with those in problem 1, illustrate the law of reciprocal proportions.

3. The following results were obtained for the molecular weights and percentages of carbon in a number of compounds:

	Mol. Wt.	% C		Mol. Wt.	% C
Ethanol	46	52.2	Ethyl ether	74	64.8
Acetic acid	60	40.0	Butane	58	82.7
Acetone	58	62.0	Benzene	78	92.2

Determine the maximum atomic weight of carbon.

4. The (corrected) density of ammonia gas at $0°$ C and 1 atm. pressure is 0.7598 g. per liter; that of oxygen under the same conditions is 1.4277 g. per liter. What is the weight of a single molecule of ammonia?

5. The chloride of cerium was found to contain 43.152 per cent of chlorine. The specific heat of the element cerium is 0.042 cal. deg.$^{-1}$ g.$^{-1}$. What is the accurate atomic weight and valence of cerium?

6. A crystalline substance, isomorphous with potash alum $K_2SO_4 \cdot Al_2(SO_4)_3 \cdot 24H_2O$, was found to contain 23.41 per cent of a metal M and 4.75 per cent of aluminum. What is the atomic weight of the element M?

II

1. Nitrogen and oxygen form a number of compounds; three of these contain 46.69, 36.87 and 30.44 per cent of nitrogen, respectively. Show that these results are in agreement with the law of multiple proportions.

2. A compound of nitrogen and hydrogen contains 17.76 per cent of hydrogen, and a compound of oxygen and hydrogen contains 11.19 per cent of hydrogen. Show

that these results, together with those in problem 1, illustrate the law of reciprocal proportions.

3. The following results were obtained for the molecular weights and percentages of fluorine in three compounds:

	Mol. Wt.	% F
Calcium fluoride	78	48.7
Silicon fluoride	104	73.1
Boron fluoride	68	84.1

Determine the maximum atomic weight of fluorine.

4. The (corrected) density of nitrogen is 0.8755 times that of oxygen at the same temperature and pressure. What is the weight of a single molecule of nitrogen?

5. The bromide of tellurium contains 71.593 per cent of bromine. The specific heat of the element tellurium is 0.049 cal. deg.$^{-1}$ g.$^{-1}$. What is the accurate atomic weight and valence of tellurium?

6. Potassium selenate, which contains 35.77 per cent of selenium, is isomorphous with potassium sulfate K_2SO_4. What is the atomic weight of selenium?

CHAPTER II

THE STRUCTURE OF THE ATOM

THE FUNDAMENTAL PARTICLES OF MATTER

4a. Cathode Rays: The Electron.—In Chapter I the general nature of the results which led to the development of the concept of atoms and molecules was described; in Chapters II and III an account will be given of the information that has been obtained concerning the internal structures of atoms and the factors which determine the combination of atoms to form molecules. Several, apparently independent, lines of investigation have thrown light on these fundamental problems.

When an electrical discharge is passed through a gas at low pressure, e.g., 0.1 mm. of mercury or less, a variety of phenomena are observed. Among

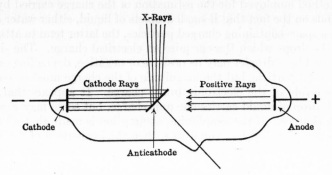

FIG. 1.   Rays in a discharge tube

these is the fact that a stream of rays, known as **cathode rays,** is emitted from the negative electrode or cathode (Fig. 1). These rays normally travel in straight lines perpendicular to the cathode, but they can be deflected by the application of an electric or a magnetic field. From various properties of the cathode rays it appears probable that they consist of a stream of negatively charged particles expelled from the cathode with high speed. The particles are called **electrons,** and the magnitude of the charge they carry is equal to the unit charge of electricity. In other words, all electrical charges are integral multiples of the charge carried by a single electron.

Electrons can be produced by several methods, in addition to the one described above. For example, the exposure of various materials, particularly

23

metals, to ultraviolet radiation, i.e., light of short wave length, results in the emission of electrons. This phenomenon is known as the **photoelectric effect.** High temperatures are frequently accompanied by the liberation of electrons, especially from certain oxides, such as calcium and barium oxides containing traces of cerium oxide. This is an illustration of the **thermionic effect** which is utilized in the production of electrons in vacuum (radio) tubes and similar devices.

By studying the deflection in electric and magnetic fields of a stream of electrons accelerated by moving through an electrical potential gradient, it is possible to calculate a quantity ϵ/m, which gives the ratio of the electronic (unit) charge ϵ (Greek, *epsilon*) to the mass m of a single electron. As a result of numerous experiments, the value of ϵ/m has been found to be 1.759×10^7 electromagnetic (e.m.) units, or 5.274×10^{17} electrostatic (e.s.) units per gram.* This result is the same, within the limits of experimental error, for all electrons, no matter what their origin, provided their speed of motion is not too great. This striking constancy of the ratio of charge to mass of electrons, produced under a variety of conditions and from various sources, leads to the important conclusion that *the electron is a definite and universal constituent of matter.*

4b. The Electronic Charge.—Since the charge to mass ratio ϵ/m of the electron is known, the mass can be evaluated if the charge is determined. One type of method employed for the estimation of the charge carried by an electron depends on the fact that if small droplets of liquid, either water or oil, are formed in a space containing charged particles, the latter tend to attach themselves to the drops which thus acquire an electrical charge. The sign of the charge carried by a droplet may be positive or negative, depending on the sign of the attached particle, but the magnitude of the charge must be equal to an integral multiple of the electronic (unit) charge. It appears that, in most cases, each drop of liquid carries one unit charge, but some may carry two or more such charges. If the simplifying assumption is made that all the drops have a charge of unity, i.e., equal to ϵ, then the evaluation of the electronic charge reduces to the determination of the quantity of electricity carried by a single droplet of the liquid.

Several procedures have been devised to achieve this end. In some of the earlier experiments, a cloud consisting of small drops of water, which had become electrically charged in the manner just described, was obtained by the sudden expansion of air saturated with water vapor. A cloud of this kind will fall with a constant speed under the influence of gravity; if the rate of descent u_1 is equal to the rate at which each single drop would fall, then it can be shown to be proportional to the gravitational force acting on each drop. If w is the mass of the drop and g is the acceleration due to gravity, i.e., 980.66 cm. per sec. per sec., then u_1 will be proportional to wg. Suppose now that an electric field of strength X is applied so as to increase the rate at which the drops descend; the force now acting on each drop is $X\epsilon + wg$, where ϵ is the

---

* To convert e.m. to e.s. units it is necessary to multiply by the velocity of light 2.998×10^{10} cm. per sec.

magnitude of the unit charge. The uniform rate of fall u_2 of the cloud under these conditions is thus proportional to $X\epsilon + wg$, and hence it follows that

$$\frac{u_1}{u_2} = \frac{wg}{X\epsilon + wg}. \qquad (4.1)$$

The values of u_1 and u_2 can be determined by observation of the cloud of droplets, and the field strength X is presumably known, as also is g; hence, the determination of the electronic charge by means of equation (4.1) requires only a knowledge of the mass w of a drop. For this purpose, use is made of Stokes's law (§ 17g), according to which the uniform velocity u of a spherical drop of radius r and density d, falling under the influence of gravity through a medium of viscosity η (Greek, *eta*), is given by

$$u = \frac{2gr^2d}{9\eta}. \qquad (4.2)$$

In this case, u of equation (4.2) is the same as u_1 of equation (4.1), that is, the rate of descent of the cloud under the influence of gravity alone. If the viscosity of the air and the density of the drop are known, the radius of the latter can thus be calculated. Since the droplets are supposed to be spherical, the volume of each is $\frac{4}{3}\pi r^3$, and hence the weight w of a single drop is equal to the product of this volume and the density; thus,

$$w = \tfrac{4}{3}\pi r^3 d. \qquad (4.3)$$

All the information is thus available for the evaluation of the electronic charge.

The results obtained by the foregoing procedure are approximate for a number of reasons, of which two may be mentioned; in the first place, the drops are not all the same size, and in the second place, they do not all necessarily carry just one single charge. These two, and other, sources of error were overcome by R. A. Millikan (1909, 1913), who made observations on a single drop of oil, instead of on a whole cloud. The rate of fall u_1 of the drop under the influence of gravity was determined by observing it in a telescope, and taking the time for the image to traverse the distance between two crosswires. An electric field of known strength X was now applied so as to make the droplet move *upwards*, and the rate u_2 was determined in the same manner. The ratio of the speeds u_1 and u_2 is now represented by

$$\frac{u_1}{u_2} = \frac{wg}{X\epsilon - wg}, \qquad (4.4)$$

the minus sign being used in the denominator, as compared with the plus sign in equation (4.1), because the force due to the electric field acts in a direction opposite to that of gravity. The radius of the drop, required for the calculation of its weight, was obtained, as before, by the use of Stokes's law; various corrections were applied, however, to allow for the fact that this law is not strictly applicable to small particles.

In the course of the experiments with the oil drop, it was found that although the rate of fall of the drop under the influence of gravity was always constant, the rate of rise, when the electric field was applied, was not necessarily the same on successive trips. The explanation of this observation was found to lie in the fact that the oil drop did not always carry the same charge. However, when the values of the charges were calculated from equation (4.4), they were always found to be an exact integral multiple of a definite quantity which was taken to be the unit electronic charge. Using the best available value for the viscosity of air in Stokes's equation (4.2), to determine the radius (and mass) of the oil drop, Millikan (1917) concluded that the electron carried a charge of 4.774×10^{-10} e.s. unit. Later, the viscosity datum was found to be incorrect, and a recalculation of the results gave 4.805×10^{-10} e.s. unit. A more recent repetition of the oil-drop method for the determination of the electronic charge has given an almost identical value.

It may be mentioned that the most accurate procedure for evaluating the charge of the electron depends on an entirely different principle; it involves a knowledge of two important constants, viz., the faraday (§ 44b) and the Avogadro number (§ 3d), both quantities having been determined with great accuracy. For the present, the faraday, which is equal to 2.893×10^{14} e.s. units,* may be regarded as the total charge on all the molecules in one mole if each carried a unit charge, and the Avogadro number, 6.023×10^{23}, is the number of individual molecules in one mole (§ 12k). It follows, therefore, that the electronic charge is equal to the value of the faraday divided by the Avogadro number; thus,

$$\epsilon = \frac{2.893 \times 10^{14}}{6.023 \times 10^{23}} = 4.803 \times 10^{-10} \text{ e.s. unit.}$$

4c. Mass and Radius of the Electron.—The apparent mass of an electron depends on the speed with which it travels; the value of ϵ/m of 5.274×10^{17} e.s. units, given previously, is for an electron moving with a small velocity, that is, one which is virtually at rest. The electronic mass m derived from this value of ϵ/m is consequently often referred to as the **rest mass**. Since ϵ is equal to 4.803×10^{-10} e.s. unit, it follows that

$$m = \frac{4.803 \times 10^{-10}}{5.274 \times 10^{17}} = 9.107 \times 10^{-28} \text{ gram.}$$

If the mass of the electron is regarded as being entirely electrical in origin, the radius of the electron can be calculated to be 2.8×10^{-13} cm.

Utilizing the magnitude of the Avogadro number given above, and taking the gram atom of hydrogen as 1.0080 gram, it can be readily shown that the mass m_H of a single hydrogen atom is

$$m_H = \frac{1.008}{6.023 \times 10^{23}} = 1.673 \times 10^{-24} \text{ gram.}$$

* The faraday is generally given as 96,500 coulombs; this value is converted into e.s. units upon multiplication by 2.998×10^9.

It follows, therefore, that the ratio of the mass of a hydrogen atom to that of an electron is given by

$$\frac{m_H}{m} = \frac{1.673 \times 10^{-24}}{9.107 \times 10^{-28}} = 1837.$$

The mass of an electron is consequently only 1/1837th part of the mass of a hydrogen atom, the lightest atom known. On the ordinary atomic weight scale, the mass of an electron, i.e., the weight of a "gram atom" of electrons, is 1.008/1837, i.e., 0.000548 gram.

4d. The Wave Nature of Electrons: Wave Mechanics.—In the foregoing discussion of the properties of electrons, the tacit assumption has been made that electrons are material particles of small mass. The discovery was made, however, by G. P. Thomson (1927) and by C. J. Davisson and L. H. Germer (1927), that when an electron stream passes through a thin film of metal or is reflected from the surface of a suitable crystal, it undergoes diffraction, just like a beam of light passing through a diffraction grating. In other words, the electrons have properties generally associated with *wave motion*. The fact that cathode rays, consisting of electrons, cast shadows and produce certain mechanical effects shows that moving *particles* are involved, and so it appears that *electrons have both wave and particle properties*. This apparent paradox occurs also with light, and radiations in general; it is probably a property of all material particles, but it becomes apparent only when their mass is small.

The simultaneous possession of wave and particle properties is one aspect of a fundamental postulate of modern physics, namely the *uncertainty principle*, put forward by W. Heisenberg (1927). According to this principle, *the simultaneous exact determination of the velocity (or energy) of a particle and its position is impossible*. When a particle, such as an electron, is exhibiting particle properties, its position can be known with some exactness, but there will be an uncertainty with regard to its velocity or momentum. On the other hand, when the wave properties are manifest, as in diffraction phenomena, the momentum of the electron can be specified accurately, but its position is uncertain.

The suggestion that an electron might exhibit the same wave-particle duality as does radiation was first made by L. de Broglie (1925), and this idea formed the basis of the new form of mechanics, known as the **wave mechanics,** developed by E. Schrödinger (1926). It is difficult to ascribe an exact significance to the theoretical treatment, but it may be thought of somewhat along the following lines. Since the position of an electron, or other particle, of definite energy cannot be known exactly, because of the uncertainty principle, it is only possible to state the *probability* of the particle being found at a given point. In the equations of wave mechanics *this probability is expressed by means of a relationship which is similar to that used for describing wave motion in general*. It should be clearly understood that there is no implication that an electron or other particle is actually associated with waves or wave motion. The situation, as far as it can be given a physical interpretation, is that the probability of finding a particle in a particular place is represented by an equation of the same form as that which describes the propagation of waves. Beyond this it is not possible to go at present.

4e. Positive Particles: The Proton and the Positron.—The discovery of the electron, the unit of negative electricity, naturally led to attempts to find the corresponding unit of positive charge. The discharge tubes, in which cathode rays are observed (Fig. 1), also contain **positive rays** consisting of a stream of positively charged particles moving in a direction opposite to that of the cathode rays. A determination of the charge to mass ratio of the particles constituting the positive rays shows, however, that they are very much heavier than electrons. In fact the lightest positively charged particle that has been detected in this manner has about the same mass as the hydrogen atom. This particle is probably *a hydrogen atom that has lost an electron, thus being left with a unit positive charge;* it is known as a **proton** in accordance with the proposal made by E. Rutherford (1922). The proton differs fundamentally from the electron because the latter is to be regarded as merely a charged particle free from matter in the ordinary sense, whereas the former is not; it is a hydrogen atom minus an electron.

Although the existence of positive electrons, as distinct from protons, was predicted theoretically, it was not until 1932 that their discovery was reported by C. D. Anderson. It was observed that positive electrons, now called **positrons,** are produced by the interaction of the cosmic rays, which originate in interstellar space, with matter. Strangely enough, in view of its apparently elusive nature, several other methods of positron production were found soon after the initial discovery of this unit particle of positive electricity free from matter. Experiments with positrons from different sources have shown that their charge and mass are practically identical with the corresponding properties of ordinary (negative) electrons. The two particles are thus to be regarded as the exact electrical opposites of each other. When a positive and a negative electron combine, the result is a neutralization of the charges accompanied by complete annihilation of both particles; in their place there appears an amount of energy, in the form of radiation, equivalent to the masses of the two electrons (§ 2b, I).

4f. The Neutron.—In 1920, E. Rutherford had suggested that there might exist a particle, which he called a **neutron,** *having no charge but with a mass about the same as that of a proton* (or a hydrogen atom). For several years, however, there was no direct evidence for the occurrence of such a particle, but in 1932, J. Chadwick showed that neutrons are formed when α-rays from radioactive substances (§ 5a) impinge on certain light elements, e.g., beryllium and boron. Neutrons can now be produced in various ways and they always have the same properties; they carry no resultant electrical charge, and their mass is very slightly greater than that of the proton. The mass of the neutron is 1.00866 compared with 1.00732 for the proton, on the chemical atomic weight scale.

4g. Characteristic X-Rays.—When the cathode rays from a discharge tube fall upon matter, new radiations, known as **X-rays,** are produced (W. C.

Röntgen, 1895). These rays differ from cathode rays in many respects; they have a greater penetrating power and are not deflected by electric and magnetic fields. From their properties it is evident that X-rays behave like electromagnetic waves, similar to light but having much shorter wave lengths. The rays constituting visible light have wave lengths of from 4×10^{-5} to 8×10^{-5} cm., but the wave lengths of X-rays are of the order of 10^{-8} cm.

The most convenient method for obtaining X-rays is to place a metal target, called an **anticathode,** in the path of the cathode rays in a discharge

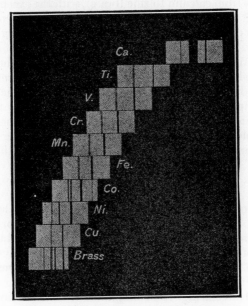

FIG. 2. Characteristic X-rays (Moseley)

tube (Fig. 1); the X-rays are then emitted from the anticathode. The wave lengths of the rays so obtained usually cover a fairly wide range, but there are always present certain wave lengths for which the intensity is much greater than that of the general background. The values of these wave lengths depend on the metal used as the anticathode, but they are quite definite for each particular element. The corresponding rays have thus been designated the **characteristic X-rays** of the given element. These characteristic X-rays have been found to fall into a number of groups or series which are represented by the letters K, L, M, N, etc.; the penetrating power, or "hardness," of the rays decreases in this order. For elements of low atomic weight, members of the K and L series only are generally observed, but with increasing atomic weight the characteristic X-rays of the M, N, and higher series can be detected. There are two or more characteristic radiations in each group, and these are distinguished by the use of Greek letters α, β, etc., as subscripts, e.g., K_α, K_β, L_α, etc.

Just as a ruled grating can be used to determine the wave length of visible light, so a crystal can act as a diffraction grating for evaluating the wave lengths of X-rays (§ 19c). With the object of studying the characteristic X-rays of various elements, H. G. J. Moseley (1913) used a crystal of potassium ferrocyanide as a grating, and allowed the resulting rays to fall on a photographic plate. The position of the line produced on the plate in this manner is then related to the wave length of the characteristic X-radiation of the particular element present in the anticathode. The results obtained for a series of elements from calcium to zinc (brass), with the exception of scandium, are shown in Fig. 2. It is at once evident that the wave lengths of the characteristic X-rays change in a regular manner with increasing atomic weight of the element.

4h. Characteristic X-Rays and Atomic Number.—Although there is no obvious relationship between the wave length or the frequency, i.e., the velocity of light divided by the wave length, and the atomic weight, Moseley found a very simple connection between the frequencies of the characteristic X-rays and the *atomic numbers* (§ 3h) of the respective elements. If ν (Greek, *nu*) is the frequency of the characteristic radiation belonging to any particular series, and Z is the atomic number of the element producing that radiation, then

$$\sqrt{\nu} = a(Z - b), \qquad (4.5)$$

where a is a proportionality constant and b has a definite value for all the lines in a given series. For the K_α rays the value of b is 1.0, and for the L_α radiations it is 7.4. According to equation (4.5), a straight line should be obtained when the square root of the frequencies of the characteristic X-rays of a given series are plotted against the atomic numbers of the corresponding elements. This expectation is fulfilled with fair accuracy for the K lines of all elements which could be studied conveniently from aluminum ($Z = 13$) to silver ($Z = 47$), and for the L series from zirconium ($Z = 40$) to gold ($Z = 79$). Although some discrepancies, which actually have an important theoretical interpretation, have been observed for certain elements, the broad relationship between the frequency of the characteristic X-rays and the atomic number, as indicated by equation (4.5), is generally maintained. It may be concluded, therefore, that *the atomic number of an element is a property of fundamental significance;* the exact nature of this significance will be evident shortly.

Since the frequency of the characteristic X-ray in a given series is definitely related to the atomic number of the element, it is clearly possible to determine the latter, by using the appropriate form of equation (4.5), if the former is measured. If this method is applied to the three pairs of elements, viz., argon and potassium, cobalt and nickel, and tellurium and iodine, which are inverted in the periodic table (§ 3h), the transposition is found to be justified. This may be seen, for example, in Fig. 2; although nickel has a somewhat smaller atomic weight than cobalt, it is apparent that as far as the atomic number, that is, the position in the periodic table, is concerned, cobalt must precede nickel.

Another use of characteristic X-rays in connection with the periodic table is to indicate the presence of gaps; for example, the atomic numbers of molybdenum and of ruthenium were found to be 42 and 44, respectively, and so there must be an element between them. In this particular instance, it was evident from the chemical properties of molybdenum and ruthenium that they could not occupy immediately successive positions in the table. With the rare-earth elements, however, the characteristic X-rays provided information which could not have been deduced from chemical considerations. Although it can be stated that the rare-earth group lies between barium and hafnium, the properties of the elements in the group are so similar that there would be no way of knowing how many such elements are to be expected. From the frequencies of the characteristic X-rays, it is known that the atomic number of barium is 56, whereas that of hafnium is 72; hence, there must be a total number of fifteen rare-earth elements. Of this total, fourteen are known definitely, but there is some uncertainty concerning the one with atomic number 61. It is of interest to note that the element hafnium was first definitely identified by its characteristic X-rays; its association with zirconium, rather than with the rare-earth minerals, showed that it did not belong to the latter group of elements.

RADIOACTIVITY

5a. Radioactive Radiations.—It was discovered by H. Becquerel (1895) that compounds of uranium are capable of spontaneously emitting radiations which are able to affect a photographic plate and which produce charged particles (gaseous ions) in their passage through air. This property, which appeared to be associated with the uranium atom, irrespective of its state of combination, was called **radioactivity.** It was found to be unaffected by temperature or by the previous history of the uranium compound. In the course of an examination of the uranium mineral *pitchblende*, P. and M. Curie (1898) discovered the element radium, which was even more radioactive than uranium itself. Shortly afterward, M. Curie and G. C. Schmidt (1898) found that thorium compounds were also active, and since that time over forty radioactive elements, frequently referred to as **radioelements,** have been identified as existing in nature. The remarkable manner in which these elements are accommodated within the limits of a few spaces in the periodic table is considered in § 7b.

The radiations emitted from radioactive substances are of three types, identified by the Greek letters, α (alpha), β (beta) and γ (gamma). By deflection of α-**rays** in electric and magnetic fields it has been shown that they consist of *positively charged particles having a mass of 4* on the conventional atomic weight scale. They are, in fact, identical with helium atoms that have lost two electrons (negative charges) and have thus acquired a *positive charge of two units.* The α-particles move with high velocity, about 1.4×10^9 to 2.0×10^9 cm. per sec., the actual value depending on the source of the radiations. Because of their relatively large mass and high speed, α-particles have considerable penetrating power.

The behavior of the β-**rays** in electric and magnetic fields shows them to consist of *negatively charged particles that are identical with electrons.* Due to their high velocity, which approaches that of light, β-particles are able to penetrate matter, but on account of their small mass they are easily deflected from their course. Consequently, while α-particles move considerable distances in straight lines, β-rays follow tortuous paths in their passage through matter.

Finally, the γ-**rays** do not consist of charged particles; like X-rays, they are not deflected in electric and magnetic fields. They are *electromagnetic radiations of very short wave length,* between 10^{-8} and 10^{-11} cm., and high energy. Most radioelements emit either α- or β-rays, and each of these is nearly always, if not always, accompanied by γ-rays, although they may not be actually detected. The difference between α-, β-, and γ-rays is represented diagrammatically in Fig. 3, in which it is supposed that a radioactive material is placed in the cavity shown and an electric field is applied. The α-rays are deflected to a small extent in one direction, the β-rays, consisting of lighter particles, are deflected to a greater extent in the opposite direction; the γ-rays, however, remain undeflected.

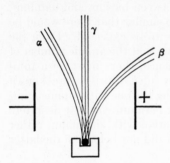

FIG. 3.   Radioactive material in an electric field

5b. Radioactive Disintegration.—It was observed by H. Becquerel (1901) that when a solution of a uranium salt is treated with ammonium hydroxide, a precipitate is obtained which possesses almost the whole of the original radioactivity; the uranium remaining in solution is practically inactive. It appears, therefore, that most of the observed activity of compounds of uranium is not due to this element but to another, separable from it, to which the name uranium-*X* was given. On standing for some weeks, however, the uranium solution gradually regains its initial activity, but that of the precipitate falls off at about the same rate, so that the total activity remains virtually constant. This process of separating the active uranium-*X*, followed by its regeneration in the solution and decay in the precipitate, can apparently be repeated indefinitely.

These and other remarkable phenomena led E. Rutherford and F. Soddy (1903) to propose the revolutionary theory of **radioactive disintegration.** It was suggested that, unlike those of stable elements, *an atom of a radioelement undergoes spontaneous disintegration with the emission of an α- or a β-particle and the formation of an atom of a new element.* This new element, which is quite different physically and chemically from its parent, may in turn also be unstable and emit a particle with the production of still another element. There may, in fact, be a succession of radioactive transformations, each accompanied by its characteristic rays.

The results described above in connection with the addition of ammonium hydroxide to a uranium solution can now be readily explained. The solution contains the feebly active parent element uranium and the highly active product uranium-X, which is actually a mixture of two or three elements; upon the addition of ammonia, the uranium-X is precipitated, giving an active precipitate and an inactive filtrate. In the course of time, the uranium-X in the precipitate disintegrates further, the product being less active; hence, there is a gradual decay of its radioactivity. The uranium in solution, however, also continues to disintegrate, and in doing so produces more uranium-X; the activity consequently increases until a certain equilibrium amount, equal to that initially present, is attained. The disintegration stages may thus be represented (approximately) by the following scheme:

$$\text{Uranium} \rightarrow \text{Uranium-}X \rightarrow \text{Products.}$$
(feeble activity)　(strong activity)　(feeble activity)

5c. Radioactive Series.—The atomic weight and other properties of the element produced in a particular radioactive disintegration depend on the nature of the particle (α or β) that is emitted. Since an α-particle has a mass of 4 units, the emission of such a particle in a radioactive change will mean that the atomic weight of the product is 4 units less than that of the parent. For example, an atom of the element radium, of atomic weight 226.05, gives off an α-particle, and hence the product should be an element of atomic weight 222; thus,

$$\text{Radium} \rightarrow \alpha\text{-particle} + \text{Product (Radon).}$$
226　　　　4　　　　222.

It has been found that this product is actually a gas, now known as **radon**; its density has been determined, and from this it has been verified that its atomic weight is close to 222, as expected. The gas radon is itself radioactive; it disintegrates further to give an α-particle and a product which is a solid that is also active.

The mass of a β-particle, i.e., an electron, is negligible (§ 4c), and hence when a radioactive change is accompanied by the emission of a β-particle, the resulting atom has an atomic weight almost identical with that of its parent. In spite of the similarity of atomic weight, the chemical and physical properties of the product, which may possess either α- or β-activity, are quite different from those of the parent element.

Every natural radioelement must belong to a particular series, and three such series, known by the names of prominent members, have been identified; they are the uranium, thorium and actinium series. The first members, or **parents,** are the elements uranium, thorium and actinouranium, respectively. After a number of successive radioactive changes, each involving the emission of an α- or a β-particle, there is finally obtained a nonradioactive **end product.** It is seen, therefore, that each of the radioactive series is complete, with a definite number of stages from parent to end product. It may be mentioned that occasionally—it occurs at least once in each series—a radioelement undergoes **branched disintegration;** the element then disintegrates simultaneously in two alternative ways, one leading to the emission of an α-particle and the other of a β-particle. Part of the uranium series of radioelements, including the branched disintegration of radium C, is shown in Table III.

TABLE III. THE URANIUM SERIES OF RADIOELEMENTS

Element	Particle Emitted	Atomic Wt.
Uranium		238
↓ (5 stages)	$(3\alpha + 2\beta)$	
↓ Radium	α	226
↓ Radon (gas)	α	222
↓ Radium A	α	218
↓ Radium B	β	214
↓ Radium C	β or α	214
Radium C′	α	214
Radium C″	β	210
↓ Radium D	β	210
↓ Radium E	β	210
↓ Radium F	α	210
↓ Radium G (end product)	none	206

THE STRUCTURE OF THE ATOM

6a. The Nuclear Theory of the Atom.—When α-particles from a radioactive source pass through matter, such as a thin metallic film, most of them travel in a straight line and suffer no appreciable deflection. A small proportion of the α-particles, however, are deflected through large angles. For example, with a gold foil 0.0004 mm. in thickness, one α-particle in 20,000 was found to be deflected through 90° or more. This **scattering** of α-particles, as the phenomenon is called, must be due to encounters of these particles with the atoms of the metal, and E. Rutherford (1911) showed that the experimental results provided a satisfactory basis for a theory of atomic structure, known as the **nuclear theory.**

It was seen in § 4a that the electron is probably a universal constituent of matter, but since matter is normally electrically neutral, there must be positively charged particles to balance exactly the negative charges of the electrons. It was suggested by Rutherford that the whole of the positive charge associated with any atom was concentrated at a very small center or **nucleus.**

This positively charged atomic nucleus would then be surrounded, at relatively large distances, by electrons equal in number to the number of unit positive charges carried by the nucleus, thus giving an electrically neutral atom. Calculations show that the radius of an atomic nucleus is about 10^{-13} to 10^{-12} cm., which is of the same order as that of an electron. The radii of atoms are, however, in the vicinity of 10^{-8} cm., which is nearly 100,000 times as great, and so it is evident that the atom must have a relatively "empty" structure. It has been estimated, in fact, that the actual volume of the electrons and nuclei constituting matter is no more than about 10^{-12} of the total effective, or observed, volume.

The theory of atomic structure just outlined, which forms the basis of the views accepted at the present day, permits of a ready interpretation of the observations on α-ray scattering. Because of the large amount of "vacant space" in an atom, the great majority of α-particles will pass clear through without any appreciable change of path. It is true that a number of α-particles will encounter electrons, but on account of the small charge and mass of the latter the deflecting effect will be almost negligible. However, an occasional α-particle, which carries two positive charges, as already seen, will enter the powerful electric field in the vicinity of the small positively charged nucleus of the scattering atom; the result will, of course, be a violent deflection of the α-particle from its original path. It is obvious that encounters of this type will be rare, and so a small proportion only of the α-particles will undergo marked scattering.

6b. The Nuclear Charge.—If the atom is to be regarded as consisting of a small positively charged nucleus surrounded, at relatively large distances, by electrons, so as to produce an electrically neutral system, the next point in the development of a theory of atomic structure is to obtain information concerning the number of unit positive charges carried by the nucleus. This will not only give the number of surrounding electrons, which must of course be equal to the number of positive charges, but since the masses of the atom and of an electron are known, the mass of the nucleus can be calculated.

According to the suggestion made by A. van den Broek (1913), *the number of charges on the nucleus of an atom is equal to its atomic number.* In view of the importance of the atomic number, that is, the ordinal number of an element in the periodic table, in determining the physical and chemical properties of an element, and also in view of its direct relationship to the frequencies of the characteristic X-rays, as shown by Moseley, the suggestion appears to be eminently reasonable. Direct experimental proof for it has been obtained in a few cases from quantitative measurements of the scattering of α-particles. By assuming Coulomb's inverse square law of electrical interaction (§ 17k) to apply to the repulsion between the nucleus of an atom and the positively charged α-particle, it is possible to derive an equation relating the charge on the nucleus with the extent of scattering at different angles. The accurate determination of the actual scattering is not easy, but the difficulties were largely overcome by J. Chadwick (1920). From his experimental results he calculated, with the aid of the equation just mentioned, the nuclear charges of copper, silver and platinum; they were found to be 29.3, 46.3 and 77.4 units, respectively, which may be compared with the atomic numbers 29, 47 and 78. Bearing in mind the uncertainties in the measurement of α-particle scattering, the experiments may be regarded as providing confirmation of the idea that the number of unit positive charges carried by the nucleus of any atom is equal to its atomic number.

6c. Constitution of the Nucleus.—Since the positive charges on the nucleus must be balanced by the negative charges of the electrons, the number of the latter that surround the nucleus must also be equal to the atomic number. The highest atomic number for elements that occur in nature is 92, for uranium; hence, no atom has more than 92 electrons. Since the mass of an electron is 0.000548 on the standard atomic weight scale (§ 4c), it is obvious that the electrons do not contribute any appreciable proportion of the mass of the atom, even for elements of high atomic number; the contribution for uranium (atomic weight 238.07) is only 0.05, and for other elements it will be less. It is evident, therefore, that virtually the whole of the mass of an atom is concentrated upon its nucleus. From this fact it follows that the nucleus must be made up of relatively massive positively charged particles.

At one time it was supposed that the nucleus consisted of protons, each having a mass of approximately unity and carrying a single positive charge (§ 4e), and electrons, the number of the former being greater than that of the latter, so as to give a resultant positive charge. This view has now been discarded and it is generally accepted that *the nuclei of atoms are built up of protons and neutrons*. The latter, like protons, have roughly unit mass, but carry no electrical charge; hence, it can be seen, that *the total number of protons and neutrons is equal to the atomic weight of the element, while the number of protons is equal to the atomic number*. Thus, if an element of atomic weight A has an atomic number Z, its nucleus will consist of Z protons, giving a positive charge of Z units, and $A - Z$ neutrons. The mass of the Z protons and of the $A - Z$ neutrons will, of course, add up to the total mass of the nucleus, and hence to that of the atom. To take a specific case, the atomic weight of sodium is 23.0 and its atomic number is 11; the sodium nucleus thus consists of 11 protons and 12 neutrons.

The atomic number of hydrogen is unity, and so the normal atom possesses just one electron; if this becomes detached, the resulting particle, having a mass of unity and carrying a unit positive charge, thus consists of a nucleus only. Since the proton has a unit positive charge and a mass of unity, it is evidently identical with a bare hydrogen nucleus, and might be represented as H^+ (§ 4e). The next element, helium, has an atomic number of two, and if the atom lost two electrons, the resulting nucleus would have a mass of four units, since the atomic weight of helium is 4.00, and a positive charge of two units. These are the characteristic properties of the α-particle as obtained from radioactive sources; hence, the α-particle may be regarded as identical with the bare helium nucleus, He^{++}.

For the helium atom, the atomic weight A is 4 and the atomic number Z is 2; consequently, the helium nucleus, or α-particle, should consist of two protons and two neutrons. There are reasons for believing that this system constitutes an exceptionally stable grouping, so that the α-particle is regarded as forming a secondary unit of nuclear structure. In this event, atomic nuclei will presumably be made up of α-particles, protons and neutrons. There is no obvious way of determining how many of each are present in a given nucleus, but the exceptional stability of the nuclei of the atoms of helium, carbon and oxygen, whose masses are 1×4, 3×4 and 4×4, respectively, has led to the suggestion that these nuclei consist of α-particles only.

6d. Nuclear Structure and Radioactivity.—As the atomic number of the element increases, the nucleus probably contains increasing numbers of α-particles, and also some protons and neutrons. When the atomic numbers are high, the complexity of the nuclear structure leads to instability; under these conditions the nucleus may spontaneously eject an α-particle. This may be taken as the basis of α-ray emission in radioactivity. It might be imagined that types of activity leading to the liberation of neutrons and protons should be observed, but such is not the case. It appears that when a nucleus contains too many neutrons, one of these changes into a proton plus an electron, with a total mass of unity and a net charge of zero. The proton is then retained by the nucleus, while the electron is expelled in the form of β-ray activity. If there are too many protons for stability of the nucleus, a proton is converted into a neutron and a positron; again, the former remains in the nucleus and the latter is emitted.

For all the naturally occurring radioelements, the number of neutrons, i.e., $A - Z$, is greatly in excess of the number of protons, e.g., 132 and 82, respectively, for radium B. Hence, the possibility of the nucleus containing too many protons for stability does not arise, and no natural positron activity has been detected or is to be expected. On the other hand, a number of light, unstable nuclei, with more protons than neutrons, have been obtained by artificial means. Such nuclei, e.g., a form of silicon made up of 14 protons and 13 neutrons, spontaneously emit positrons (§ 8b).

It may be noted that the positron, unlike the electron, does not appear to play any direct part in atomic structure. It is formed only when, for one reason or another, a proton changes into a neutron and a positron. The life of the positron is in any case very short, for it is removed when it encounters an electron; since the latter are common, the probability of such encounters, which are accompanied by the destruction of positrons, is very considerable.

ISOTOPES

7a. The Group Displacement Law.—When a radioactive element emits an α-particle, with mass 4 and charge $+2$, the positive charge on the nucleus of the product must be two units less than that of its parent. In other words, the atomic number of the element produced in an α-ray disintegration stage is two less than that of the element from which it originates. Since the atomic number gives the ordinal position of the element in the periodic table, it follows that when a particular radioelement emits an α-particle, the product occupies a position in the periodic table that is two places to the left of the original element. On the other hand, the expulsion of a β-particle is accompanied by a gain of one proton by the nucleus; the nuclear charge, i.e., the atomic number, of the product is thus one greater than that of the parent. The former thus occupies a position in the periodic table that is one place to the right of the latter. These conclusions provide the basis of the **group displacement law** of radioactivity; this law, which was proposed independently by K. Fajans, A. S. Russell and F. Soddy (1913), before the development of the modern ideas concerning nuclear structure, has been put in the following form. *When an α-particle is emitted in a radioactive change, the product is displaced two places (or groups) to the left in the periodic table; the emission of a β-particle results in a displacement of one place (or group) to the right.*

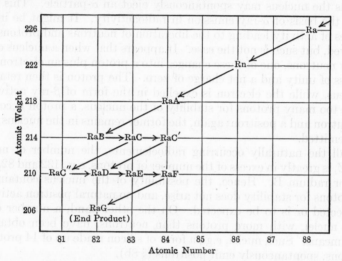

FIG. 4.   Radioactive disintegration in the uranium series

7b. Radioactive Isotopes.—The results of applying the group displacement law to part of the uranium disintegration series are shown in Fig. 4, in which the atomic weights are plotted as ordinates and the atomic numbers as abscissae. An α-particle disintegration is represented by a line sloping downward and to the left, since the change is accompanied by a decrease of four units in the atomic weight and two units in the atomic number. A β-particle change is indicated by a horizontal line pointing to the right, because the atomic weight remains constant while the atomic number increases by unity.

An examination of Fig. 4 shows that the three elements radium A, radium C′ and radium F, which have different atomic weights and different radioactive properties, have the same atomic number, viz., 84, and hence must occupy the same position in the periodic table. A similar conclusion is reached for the pair of elements radium C and radium E, atomic number 83, and for the trio, radium B, radium D and radium G, atomic number 82. *Such elements, possess-*

ing the same atomic number and requiring to be placed in the same position in the periodic table, are called **isotopes** (Greek: *same place*).

In addition to the isotopes in the uranium series, others have been found to occur in the thorium and actinium series. It can be easily deduced from the group displacement law, that *whenever there are three successive stages involving one α-particle and two β-particle emissions, the resulting element will be isotopic with the first element.* Further, isotopic elements are not restricted to one radioactive series; for instance, the following seven elements, three belonging to the uranium series and two to each of the other two series, all have the atomic number 84 and hence are isotopic:

Radium A, C′ and F; Thorium A and C′; Actinium A and C′.

The atomic weights of these elements range from 210 to 218.

Although the radioactive properties of isotopes are different, they have the important property of being inseparable by chemical methods; this is not strictly true, as will be seen later, but for the present it may be supposed that isotopic elements have identical chemical properties. Since such properties are determined essentially by the atomic number of the element, this result is not surprising, in spite of the differences in radioactive behavior.

7c. Nonradioactive Isotopes.—One of the most remarkable conclusions to be drawn from the group displacement law is in connection with the nonradioactive end products of the uranium and thorium disintegration series. It was found that these substances should, in each case, possess an atomic number of 82 (Fig. 4), which happens also to be that of the nonradioactive element lead. The end products should thus be isotopic with ordinary lead; further, since, like the latter, they are not radioactive, they should be identical with ordinary lead. Nevertheless, there should be one important although somewhat astonishing difference: the end product of the uranium series should have an atomic weight of 206 (see Table III and Fig. 4), whereas that of the end product of the thorium series should be 208, compared with 207.2 for the atomic weight of ordinary lead. Uranium and thorium minerals in nature are almost invariably associated with lead, and if some, at least, of this element were of radioactive origin, having been formed by the gradual disintegration from its parent over a long period of time, the atomic weight should differ from that of lead obtained from a nonradioactive source. This expectation has been confirmed, for lead derived from a number of uranium minerals has been found to have an atomic weight of 206.01 to 206.08, whereas that extracted from thorium minerals has an atomic weight of 207.8 to 207.9. It may be regarded as established, therefore, that the lead associated with radioactive minerals can exist in two isotopic forms, at least, with atomic weights of approximately 206 and 208. Ordinary lead, from nonradioactive sources, with an atomic weight of 207.2, is either a mixture of these two isotopes, or it consists of a third isotope of mass 207; actually it contains all three, together with a small amount of a fourth isotope of mass 204.

The occurrence of nonradioactive lead in isotopic forms not only provides strong support for the theories of radioactivity, it also proves the possibility of the existence of isotopic forms of a nonradioactive element; the isotopes differ in atomic weight, but they have the same nuclear charge and hence occupy the same position in the periodic table. As a consequence of this identity of atomic number, the isotopes have identical, or virtually identical, chemical properties.

7d. The Mass Spectrograph.—The discovery of the isotopes of nonradioactive lead stimulated the search for isotopic forms of other elements, and in this connection the most valuable results have come from a study of the positive rays in discharge tubes (§ 4e). These rays are made up of atoms and molecules, present in the tube or derived from the anode material, that have lost an electron (or occasionally two or three electrons), and so have acquired a positive charge. By applying electric and magnetic fields, at right angles to

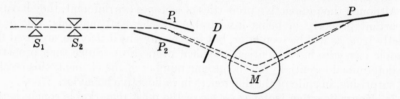

FIG. 5.   Aston's mass spectrograph

one another, to a stream of positive rays, it is possible to sort them into groups, each made up of particles having the same ratio of charge to mass. Since most of the particles carry the same charge, it is apparent that *by means of the electric and magnetic fields the positive rays are divided into groups of particles of equal mass;* in other words, a sort of **mass spectrum** is produced. Since isotopic forms of the same element have different masses, they can evidently be separated from each other by the use of positive rays; in this way, their presence can be detected.

The first application of positive rays to the study of isotopes was made by J. J. Thomson (1913), and the procedure was developed and improved by F. W. Aston, from 1919 onward, and by others in more recent years. The principle of the instrument, known as a **mass spectrograph,** used by Aston (1927), is shown in Fig. 5. The positive rays from a discharge tube containing the element under investigation, either in the pure state or as a compound, first pass through two narrow slits S_1 and S_2, and the resulting fine beam is spread out by means of an electric field applied across the plates P_1 and P_2. A section of the beam emerges through a small aperture in D, and then passes between the pole pieces M of a large electromagnet. The magnetic field is so arranged as to bend the rays in the opposite direction to, although in the same plane as, the electric field. The rays are thus brought to a focus on the photographic plate P, and on this a sharp line is produced for each type of particle of different mass present in the positive ray beam. Examples of such mass spectra, obtained by A. J. Dempster (1935), with an improved instrument, are shown in Fig. 6.

In order to determine the values of the masses corresponding to the various lines in the mass spectrum, the most abundant isotope of oxygen is taken to have a mass of 16.0000. With this standard, it is possible to extend the scale to both higher and lower masses, secondary standards, which have been compared with oxygen, being introduced at various points. With modern forms of the mass spectrograph, it is possible to determine the masses of isotopes with an error of less than one part in 10,000; this is better than can be achieved in most chemical determinations. Each line in the mass spectrum represents an isotopic form of the element under consideration; hence, the use of the mass spectrograph permits the direct investigation of the existence of isotopes and

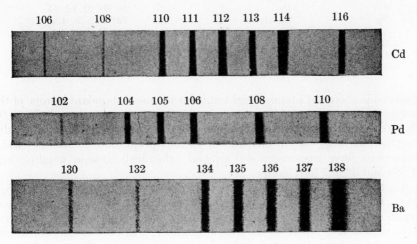

FIG. 6. Mass spectra of cadmium, palladium and barium (Dempster)

of the determination of their masses. Further, by measuring the intensities of the lines in the mass spectrum, the relative proportions, or **abundance ratio,** of the various isotopes may be evaluated. In some types of mass spectrograph the abundance of the isotopes can be derived directly from the strength of an electric current, or ion current, due to the flow of the positively charged particles (ions).

7e. Mass Numbers and Atomic Weights.—All the definitely known elements have now been subjected to mass spectroscopic study, and it has been found that there are only twenty elements which are simple and have no stable isotopes. Some elements have many isotopes—tin, for example, has ten—while others may have two, three or more isotopic forms. The isotopic compositions of a few common elements are recorded in Table IV.

It will be noted that the atomic weight figures in Table IV are given as whole numbers; these are called the **mass numbers** of the isotopes, and are the integers nearest to the actual atomic weights. Although the latter are not exactly integral, the differences from whole numbers throughout the whole series of isotopes is so small as to be remarkable. The largest discrepancy

TABLE IV.   STABLE ISOTOPES OF COMMON NONRADIOACTIVE ELEMENTS

Element	Mass Numbers of Isotopes	Element	Mass Numbers of Isotopes
H	1, 2	P	31
He	3, 4	S	32, 33, 34
Li	6, 7	Cl	35, 37
Be	9	A	36, 38, 40
B	10, 11	K	39, 40, 41
C	12, 13	Ca	40, 42, 43, 44
N	14, 15	Fe	54, 56, 57, 58
O	16, 17, 18	Co	57, 59
F	19	Ni	58, 60, 61, 62, 64
Ne	20, 21, 22	Te	120, 122–26, 128, 130
Na	23	I	127
Mg	24, 25, 26	Hg	196, 198, 199–202, 204
Al	27	Pb	204, 206, 207, 208
Si	28, 29, 30	Bi	209

observed is about 0.1 atomic weight unit for the most abundant isotope of tin; its (physical) atomic weight, as determined by the mass spectrograph, is 119.91. The occurrence of fractional atomic weights, e.g., 35.457 for chlorine, is readily explained as being due to mixtures in various proportions of isotopes which themselves have approximately integral (chemical) atomic weights, viz., 34.989 and 36.987 for chlorine.

On the basis of the view that atomic nuclei consist of protons and neutrons (§ 6c), the essential difference between the isotopic forms of the same element should lie in the number of neutrons in the respective nuclei. The number of protons, which is equal to the atomic number, will be constant for all the isotopes of a given element, but the number of neutrons will vary. The sum of the protons and neutrons is equal to the mass number in each case. The atomic number of chlorine, for instance, is 17: hence, the nucleus of the isotope of mass number 35 will consist of 17 protons and 18 neutrons, while that of the isotope of mass number 37 will contain 17 protons and 20 neutrons. The nuclear structures of the isotopes of other elements can be derived in a similar manner.

The actual atomic weights and the abundance ratios of the various isotopes of a given element can be determined with great accuracy by means of the mass spectroscope; hence, it should be possible to calculate the mean atomic weight of the element and compare it with the accepted value. In doing this, it must be remembered, of course, that since mass-spectroscopic atomic weights are based on the value of 16.0000 for the most abundant isotope of oxygen, they represent the physical atomic weights (§ 3d); to obtain the atomic weights generally employed by the chemist, it is necessary to divide the result by 1.00027. It is of interest to see how this ratio of physical to chemical atomic weights is obtained. Atmospheric oxygen consists of 0.9976 parts of the isotope of mass 16.0000, 0.0004 parts of mass 17.0045, and 0.0020 parts of mass 18.0037; the weighted mean of these values is 16.0044 on the physical scale.

The mean atomic weight of oxygen on the chemical scale is 16.0000, by convention, and so the ratio of the two scales is

$$\frac{\text{Physical atomic weight}}{\text{Chemical atomic weight}} = \frac{16.0044}{16.0000} = 1.00027,$$

as recorded previously.

The mean atomic weight derived from measurements with the mass spectrograph are in excellent agreement with those obtained by chemical methods. In two instances at least, however, the chemical atomic weights have been corrected as a consequence of the determination of the isotopic weights and abundance ratios; with boron and antimony the chemical data were found to be in error. The present accepted value for the atomic weight of hydrogen, i.e., 1.0080, is derived from the mass-spectroscopic results, in the following manner. Ordinary hydrogen consists of two isotopes, whose masses are 1.00813 and 2.01473, respectively, as determined by the mass spectrograph. The amounts of these forms present in ordinary hydrogen are in the ratio of 6400 to 1, and so the mean atomic weight of hydrogen on the chemical scale is given by

$$\frac{(1.00813 \times 6400) + (2.01473 \times 1)}{(6400 + 1) \times 1.00027} = 1.0080.$$

7f. The Packing Fraction.—The fact that all isotopes have masses that are very nearly integral is in harmony with the view expressed in § 6c that the nuclei of atoms are made up of protons and neutrons, of unit mass. However the masses of both the proton and the neutron are slightly greater than unity on the physical atomic weight scale, viz., 1.00759 and 1.00893, respectively, and so the isotopic masses of all elements should be somewhat in excess of integral values. Actually, the large majority, except for the lightest atoms, are less than whole numbers. The probable explanation of this discrepancy is that in the formation of the heavier nuclei from protons and neutrons, some of the mass has been transformed into energy (§ 2b, I). If the loss of mass in the (hypothetical) formation of a particular nucleus is large, then considerable energy is liberated in the process; consequently, a large amount of energy would have to be supplied to disintegrate the nucleus. Such a nucleus would thus be exceptionally stable. On the other hand, if the loss of mass is small, or there is an actual increase of mass, the nucleus should be unstable.

The difference between the atomic weight of an isotope, on the physical scale, and the corresponding integral value has been expressed by F. W. Aston (1927) in the form of the **packing fraction,** defined by

$$\text{Packing fraction} = \frac{\text{Isotopic atomic weight} - \text{Mass number}}{\text{Mass number}} \times 10^4.$$

When the packing fractions of the elements are plotted against the corresponding atomic weights, the values are found to fall on, or close to, the curve shown in Fig. 7; only helium (mass number = 4), carbon (mass number = 12) and oxygen (mass number = 16) show any considerable departure from the general behavior. In accordance with the arguments of the preceding paragraph, a negative packing fraction implies nuclear stability, whereas a positive value means relative instability. The latter part of this statement is not strictly correct for elements of low atomic weight, for it is really the difference between the isotopic weight and the appropriate multiple of about 1.008,* and not of unity, which should determine nuclear stability. If the atomic weight is high, the packing fraction is not seriously affected, but for light atoms the conventional packing fraction, as defined above, is misleading. For example, boron

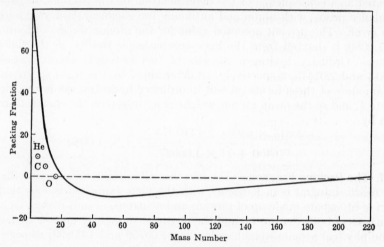

Fig. 7. Packing fractions (Aston)

has an isotope of mass number 10 and physical atomic weight 10.0161; the packing fraction is thus +16.1, suggesting a not too stable nucleus. However, if allowance is made for the actual masses of the protons and neutrons, the packing fraction is found to be about −65.

Taking this matter into consideration, it is evident that the nuclei of helium 4, carbon 12, and oxygen 16 are exceptionally stable, as already noted. The lowest packing fractions, implying considerable nuclear stability, are observed for the transition elements between chromium and zinc. With increasing atomic number the packing fraction increases, and for mass numbers exceeding 200 it becomes positive, indicating growing instability. This agrees with the occurrence of spontaneous disintegration, i.e., radioactivity, among such elements; the nuclei are then relatively unstable, and so they break down in a series of stages until a lighter, more stable, nucleus results.

7g. The Separation of Isotopes.—The earliest successes in connection with the separation of isotopes was achieved by making use of the different rates of diffusion of gaseous isotopic molecules. The rate of diffusion of a gas is in-

* This is approximately the mean mass of a proton and a neutron (see above).

versely proportional to the square root of its density (§ 11h), and hence also to the square root of its molecular weight [equation (3.2)]. The lighter isotopic form of a given substance will thus diffuse more rapidly than the heavier form, and a partial separation should be possible. By using a number of diffusion units in series, striking successes have been achieved in the separation of the isotopes of the lighter elements (G. Hertz, 1932).* Other procedures for separating isotopes, which make use of properties that are appreciably dependent upon mass, involve evaporation, distillation, and thermal diffusion, i.e., a combination of diffusion and convection.

One of the most striking achievements in relation to the separation of isotopes of an element is in connection with hydrogen. The first partial separation was achieved by the fractional distillation of liquid hydrogen (H. C. Urey, 1931), but better results were subsequently obtained in an alternative manner. It is well known that when an electric current is passed through a dilute aqueous solution of an acid or an alkali, hydrogen gas is evolved at the negative electrode (cathode). It was noted that this gas contained a higher proportion of the lighter isotope, of mass number 1, than did the original water. Prolonged electrolysis, therefore, resulted in the accumulation of the heavier isotope, of mass number 2, in the residual solution; it was thus possible to obtain appreciable quantities of water in which more than 99 per cent of the hydrogen was the heavier isotopic form. Such water has been called **heavy water,** its density being actually over 10 per cent greater than that of ordinary water. Because the atomic weights of the two isotopes of hydrogen are in the approximate ratio of 2 to 1, which is greatly in excess of that for any other element, the differences in properties between the isotopes are quite marked. For this reason it has been found convenient to devise a special name for the heavier isotope; it has been called **heavy hydrogen,** but the name **deuterium** (Greek: *the second*) and the corresponding symbol D are now generally adopted. The nucleus of the deuterium atom, made up of a proton and a neutron, is called a **deuteron,** by analogy with the proton.

The differences in the physical properties of the isotopic forms of hydrogen are very apparent; for example, the boiling point of liquid deuterium is more than 3° higher than that of liquid hydrogen. The molar heats of vaporization are 303.1 and 217.7 cal. per mole, respectively, while the molar volumes are 23.17 and 26.15 cc. per mole. Analogous differences occur between the physical properties of light and heavy water, i.e., H_2O and D_2O, as may be seen from the data in Table V.

TABLE V.   PHYSICAL PROPERTIES OF ISOTOPIC FORMS OF WATER

Property	H_2O	D_2O
Relative density at 25°	1.0000	1.1079
Boiling point	100.00°	101.42°
Freezing point	0.00°	3.82°
Maximum density at	4.0°	11.6°
Surface tension at 20°	72.75	67.8 dynes cm.$^{-1}$

* A remarkable achievement has been the partial separation, by diffusion of UF_6 vapor of the 235 isotope of uranium for the atomic bomb.

7h. Chemical Separation of Isotopes.—Until the discovery of deuterium, it had been generally assumed that isotopes had identical chemical properties; it is now known that this is not strictly correct. It is true that isotopic forms of a given element or compound undergo the same reactions, but the rates, or extents, of the reactions are different. For the heavier atoms the ratio of the isotopic atomic weights is very close to unity, but with the lighter elements, particularly with hydrogen, this ratio differs appreciably from unity, and the differences in chemical reactivity, as well as in physical properties, become noticeable. The small, but important, differences in reactivity have been utilized to achieve the partial separation of the isotopes of a number of elements, e.g., carbon, nitrogen and sulfur (H. C. Urey, 1936).

In certain cases, one isotope of an element in a particular state of combination will exchange with a second isotope of the same element in another compound. For example, if oxygen gas is passed continuously through water, the lighter isotopic atom, designated by the symbol ^{16}O, in the gas exchanges with the heavier isotopic atom ^{18}O in the liquid water; this exchange may be represented by the equation

$$\tfrac{1}{2}{}^{16}O_2 \text{ (gas)} + H_2{}^{18}O \text{ (liquid)} = \tfrac{1}{2}{}^{18}O_2 \text{ (gas)} + H_2{}^{16}O \text{ (liquid)}.$$

When a state of equilibrium is attained, the isotopic distribution is not the same in the oxygen gas and in the water, as would have been the case if the two isotopes of oxygen had identical chemical reactivities. Because of a slight difference in this respect, the oxygen gas phase is found to contain relatively more of the heavier isotope than does the liquid water. The isotopic exchange reaction between molecular oxygen gas and liquid water thus makes possible a partial separation of the isotopes of oxygen. An interesting consequence of this exchange is that the atomic weight of atmospheric oxygen is very slightly greater than that of oxygen derived from lake water.

In general, whenever an isotopic atom in a gaseous substance can exchange with another isotope of the same element in a liquid or in a solution, the gas will have a different isotopic composition from the liquid when equilibrium is attained. If the exchange process is carried out continuously with fresh portions of the gas, there will eventually be an appreciable difference in the relative amounts of the isotopes. This is the basis of the chemical method for the partial separation of isotopes which has been used to obtain the heavier isotopes of nitrogen and carbon. In the former case, isotopic exchange occurs between the nitrogen atom in ammonia gas and that in an ammonium salt in solution, whereas in the latter case, the carbon atom, or rather the CN group in hydrogen cyanide, exchanges with that of a metallic cyanide in aqueous solution. The isotopes ^{13}C and ^{15}N have been concentrated in this manner.

7i. Isotopes as Indicators.—Since isotopic elements have virtually, if not quite, identical chemical properties, but are distinguishable because of differences in mass or radioactivity, they have been employed as **indicators** or **tracers** in connection with many different phenomena. The use of radioactive isotopes, both those occurring in nature and others that have been prepared by special methods (§ 8b), is particularly advantageous, because they can be detected and estimated in amounts that are so small as to be beyond the limits of chemical analysis.

The behavior of such elements as hydrogen, carbon, nitrogen, phosphorus or sulfur in various biological processes, for instance, can be followed by employing compounds having a small quantity of one or other of these elements in isotopic forms that differ from those normally present. By employing the mass spectroscope or an instrument for detecting radioactivity, e.g., a Geiger-Müller counter, to trace the fate of these isotopes, it is possible to obtain valuable data concerning the processes in which their compounds are involved. For example, when carbon dioxide, containing a small proportion of a radioactive isotope of the element carbon, was used in photosynthesis, the activity was found, within a very short time, to be concentrated in a solid substance having a molecular weight of about 1000 and possessing a carboxyl group. It follows, therefore, that one of the early stages in the process of photosynthesis in the green plant is the formation of a compound with these properties. Further, by means of isotopic forms of sodium, potassium, chlorine, bromine, etc., it has been possible to follow salt absorption in plant and animal organisms.

By the use of deuterium or a radioactive isotope of hydrogen of mass 3, or by employing radioactive halogens, interesting information can be obtained relating to the mechanisms of chemical changes. As an illustration, reference may be made to the familiar Friedel-Crafts reaction in which aluminum chloride acts as a catalyst for the interaction of an aromatic hydrocarbon and an acyl chloride, e.g.,

$$C_6H_6 + CH_3COCl = C_6H_5COCH_3 + HCl.$$

When the aluminum chloride catalyst contained some radioactive chlorine, the hydrogen chloride gas evolved was found to possess the same activity as the chloride remaining in the solution. It is evident that the chlorine in the hydrogen chloride could not have come from the CH_3COCl, as implied by the equation given above, since this was not radioactive. It appears, therefore, that the chlorine atom is first removed from the latter and becomes attached to the aluminum chloride, forming $(CH_3CO)(AlCl_4)$. The particular atom of chlorine which is then removed from the $AlCl_4$ grouping, as hydrogen chloride, depends upon chance; hence, the proportion of radioactive chlorine present in the evolved gas will be the same as that in the liquid, as found experimentally.

Radioactive substances have been used to determine the solubilities of sparingly soluble salts of isotopic elements. A trace of radium D, isotopic with lead, and of known activity, is mixed with a definite amount of an ordinary, nonradioactive, lead salt. This gives the proportion of radium D to lead in the mixture, and because of the virtual identity of properties this remains unchanged in the course of the subsequent treatment. The mixture is converted into the sulfate, or other sparingly soluble salt, and a saturated solution is prepared; a known volume is then evaporated to dryness and its radioactivity measured to determine the amount of radium D present. Since the proportion of this isotope in the system is known, the quantity of lead, and hence the solubility of the lead sulfate, can be calculated.

ARTIFICIAL DISINTEGRATION AND RADIOACTIVITY

8a. Atomic Disintegration.—It was observed by E. Rutherford in 1919 that when α-particles of high velocity, and hence of high energy, are passed through nitrogen gas, protons of long range are produced. It is believed that the process which occurs involves, in the first place, the fusion of the nitrogen nucleus with the α-particle (helium nucleus) to form an unstable system which immediately ejects a proton in the effort to attain stability. The change may be written in the form of the equation

$$^{14}_{7}N + {}^{4}_{2}He = {}^{17}_{8}O + {}^{1}_{1}H,$$

where each symbol represents the nucleus of the corresponding element, the upper prefix giving the mass number, and the lower the nuclear charge, i.e., the atomic number; the mass numbers and the atomic numbers must balance on the two sides of the equation. It is evident from the equation just given that the interaction of an α-particle with a nitrogen nucleus must yield an oxygen nucleus of mass number 17, in addition to the proton ($^{1}_{1}H$). This is consequently an example of the **artificial transmutation** or **artificial disintegration** of atoms. Many other elements, besides nitrogen, undergo this type of change under the influence of α-particles, with the notable exceptions of ^{4}He, ^{12}C and ^{16}O. In order to achieve the disintegration of relatively heavy atoms, it is necessary to use α-particles (helium nuclei) of very high energy; these are not obtained from radioactive sources, but by the use of such instruments as the **cyclotron** of E. O. Lawrence (1933) or the **electrostatic generator** of R. J. Van de Graaff (1936).

In addition to the disintegration just described, there is another type in which neutrons are produced by the action of α-particles; this is, in fact, the process which resulted in the discovery of the neutron (§ 4f). For example, with beryllium the disintegration which occurs may be represented by

$$^{9}_{4}Be + {}^{4}_{2}He = {}^{12}_{6}C + {}^{1}_{0}n,$$

where the symbol $^{1}_{0}n$, indicating a mass of unity and a charge of zero, is used for the neutron. The other product in this case is a normal carbon atom.

Similar disintegrations and transmutations can be brought about by using neutrons or specially accelerated (high energy) protons or deuterons as projectiles, in place of α-particles. In a few instances γ-rays have proved capable of disintegrating the nuclei of light atoms. Neutrons are especially effective because they carry no electrical charge and are consequently not repelled by the nuclei of the atoms which they are approaching. Many types of disintegration have been observed with the different projectiles; neutrons, protons, deuterons, α-particles or γ-rays, i.e., energy, may be emitted, according to the isotopic nature of the bombarded nucleus and the particle employed as projectile. A few examples of nuclear processes of different types are given below.

Projectiles: *neutrons*

$$^{27}_{13}Al + ^{1}_{0}n = ^{27}_{12}Mg + ^{1}_{1}H$$

$$^{23}_{11}Na + ^{1}_{0}n = ^{24}_{11}Na + \gamma\text{-ray.}$$

Projectiles: *protons*

$$^{9}_{4}Be + ^{1}_{1}H = ^{6}_{3}Li + ^{4}_{2}He$$

$$^{44}_{20}Ca + ^{1}_{1}H = ^{44}_{21}Sc + ^{1}_{0}n.$$

Projectiles: *deuterons*

$$^{27}_{13}Al + ^{2}_{1}D = ^{25}_{12}Mg + ^{4}_{2}He$$

$$^{209}_{83}Bi + ^{2}_{1}D = ^{210}_{83}Bi + ^{1}_{1}H.$$

8b. Unstable Nuclei.—While studying the effect of α-particles on boron, magnesium and aluminum, I. Curie and F. Joliot (1934) noted that positrons were emitted, in addition to neutrons. When the source of α-particles was removed, the emission of neutrons ceased, but the positrons continued to be evolved for some time, the intensity falling off gradually. The explanation suggested for this phenomenon is that the α-particle is first taken up by the bombarded nucleus to form a complex nucleus, which disintegrates instantaneously with the emission of a neutron; thus, with magnesium the process would be

$$^{24}_{12}Mg + ^{4}_{2}He = ^{27}_{14}Si + ^{1}_{0}n.$$

The product $^{27}_{14}Si$, known as radiosilicon, is not a stable isotope of silicon, but it is not so unstable that it is incapable of existence for any appreciable time. Actually, it disintegrates at a definite rate like a radioactive element, although positrons are emitted instead of α- or β-particles; thus,

$$^{27}_{14}Si = ^{27}_{13}Al + ^{0}_{1}e^{+},$$

the symbol $^{0}_{1}e^{+}$ being used for the positive electron, i.e., the positron. The final product of the transmutation process is the familiar stable isotope of aluminum.

The results described above show that when certain elements are bombarded by α-particles, artificial radioelements are produced; this phenomenon is known as **induced radioactivity** or **artificial radioactivity**. Further investigation has shown that many such artificial radioelements can be obtained by the bombardment of stable elements with protons, deuterons, neutrons, or α-particles. In all, over four hundred different unstable isotopes of all the familiar elements, from hydrogen to uranium, with very few exceptions, have been identified. Although the earliest artificial radioelements to be discovered possessed positron activity, because they contained too many protons (§ 6d), the majority, particularly those of high atomic number, emit β-particles, i.e., ordinary electrons. A few instances of the formation and disintegration of artificial radioelements are appended; in each case, the first equation gives the process of formation and the second indicates the mode of disintegration.

$$^{25}_{12}Mg + ^{4}_{2}He = ^{1}_{1}H + ^{28}_{13}Al, \qquad ^{28}_{13}Al = ^{28}_{14}Si + _{-1}^{0}e.$$

$$^{32}_{16}S + ^{2}_{1}D = ^{4}_{2}He + ^{30}_{15}P, \qquad ^{30}_{15}P = ^{30}_{14}Si + ^{0}_{1}e^{+}.$$

$$^{19}_{9}F + ^{1}_{1}H = ^{1}_{0}n + ^{19}_{10}Ne, \qquad ^{19}_{10}Ne = ^{19}_{9}F + ^{0}_{1}e^{+}.$$

$$^{27}_{13}Al + ^{1}_{0}n = ^{4}_{2}He + ^{24}_{11}Na, \qquad ^{24}_{11}Na = ^{24}_{12}Mg + _{-1}^{0}e.$$

The same radioelement can often be produced in several different ways; for example, the $^{24}_{11}Na$ isotope of sodium can also be obtained by bombardment of ordinary sodium or of magnesium by deuterons or neutrons. Its activity and other properties are always the same, irrespective of its origin.

An artificial radioelement of particular interest, and which is likely to find many important applications in connection with the use of isotopes as tracers (§ 7i), is radiohydrogen or **tritium** (Greek: *the third*); this ($^{3}_{1}T$) is obtained by the action of deuterons on deuterium, viz.,

$$^{2}_{1}D + ^{2}_{1}D = ^{3}_{1}T + ^{1}_{1}H,$$

and by the bombardment of beryllium by deuterons, viz.,

$$^{9}_{4}Be + ^{2}_{1}D = ^{3}_{1}T + ^{8}_{4}Be.$$

The radioactive disintegration of tritium is represented by

$$^{3}_{1}T = ^{3}_{2}He + _{-1}^{0}e,$$

the emitted particle being an electron; the residue is a stable isotope of helium.

8c. Fission of Uranium Atoms.—An entirely new type of atomic disintegration was discovered as a result of the bombardment of uranium compounds by neutrons. The products, which possessed a complex artificial radioactivity, were found to consist of radioactive elements, whose atomic numbers lie between 35 (bromine) and 57 (lanthanum). It appears, therefore, that after the uranium atom takes up a neutron, the resulting nucleus is so unstable that it breaks up immediately into two nuclei of somewhat the same size. There is consequently a complete splitting or **fission** of the uranium nucleus. The particular isotope of uranium that is split up in this manner is one with a mass number of 235, present in ordinary uranium to the extent of less than 1 per cent. Apart from the fact that it leads to a splitting of the nucleus, the fission of uranium is of particular interest as it is accompanied by the emission of an enormous amount of energy.*

8d. Conservation of Mass and Energy in Atomic Transformations.—An examination of the mass and energy changes involved in the disintegration processes has frequently been used to confirm the nature of the transformation. This subject is of importance as it brings out clearly the equivalence of mass and energy. As previously noted (§ 2b, I), in ordinary chemical reac-

---

* The energy liberated in fission, due to a loss of mass (§ 2b, I), is utilized in the atomic bomb.

tions the mass equivalent of the energy change is so small as to be undetectable, but this is not the case for nuclear reactions. For example, in the process

$$^{14}N + {}^{2}D = {}^{12}C + {}^{4}He,$$

in which a nitrogen nucleus is bombarded by a deuteron, to produce a normal carbon nucleus and an α-particle, the masses of the substances concerned, on the physical atomic weight scale, are as follows:

$^{14}N = 14.00750$	$^{12}C = 12.00398$
$^{2}D = 2.01473$	$^{4}He = 4.00389$
16.02223	16.00787

There is consequently a decrease in mass of 0.01436 unit, which is equivalent to 3.08×10^{11} cal. or 12.85×10^{18} ergs per gram atom, according to equation (2.2). If the transmutation process depicted above actually takes place, this amount of energy should be set free; the value found experimentally is 3.08×10^{11} cal. This energy appears largely as the kinetic energy of the helium nucleus (α-particle) which is emitted with high velocity.

A remarkable result of the study of mass and energy changes in atomic disintegration processes was the discovery that the mass-spectroscopic atomic weights of the lighter elements in use prior to 1935 were in error. In a number of instances there appeared to be a discrepancy between the energy change calculated from the decrease of mass, using the accepted atomic weights, and the observed value. The bold suggestion was therefore made that the atomic weights were incorrect, and careful observation with the mass spectroscope confirmed this view. With the newer atomic weight values the discrepancies disappeared.

READING REFERENCES

1. **What is light?** Compton, *Journal of Chemical Education*, **7**, 2769 (1930).
2. **Quantum theory and wave mechanics.** Dushman, *ibid.*, **8**, 1074 (1931).
3. **Atomic weights and isotopes.** Wildman, *ibid.*, **10**, 238 (1933).
4. **Radio elements as indicators.** Rosenblum, *ibid.*, **11**, 622 (1934).
5. **Nuclear chemistry.** Darrow, *ibid.*, **12**, 76 (1935).
6. **Heavy hydrogen as indicator.** James, *ibid.*, **13**, 458 (1936).
7. **The neutron.** Shadduck, *ibid.*, **13**, 303 (1936).
8. **Nuclear phenomena.** Croup and Goldblatt, *ibid.*, **14**, 210 (1937).
9. **Electron diffraction.** Clark and Wolthuis, *ibid.*, **15**, 64 (1938).
10. **Atomic weight of hydrogen.** Brescia and Rosenthal, *ibid.*, **16**, 494 (1939).
11. **Essential postulates of atomic structure.** Goldblatt and Croup, *ibid.*, **17**, 238 (1940).
12. **Isotopes as indicators.** Rosenblum, *ibid.*, **17**, 567 (1940).
13. **Electron microscope.** Alyea, *ibid.*, **18**, 236 (1941).
14. **Isotopes in study of plant growth.** Brewer, *ibid.*, **18**, 217 (1941).
15. **Electron diffraction of gases.** Spurr and Pauling, *ibid.*, **18**, 458 (1941).
16. **Heavy water.** Selwood, *ibid.*, **18**, 515 (1941).
17. **Photosynthesis and radioelements.** Spoehr, *ibid.*, **19**, 20 (1942).
18. **Putting tagged atoms to work.** Timm, *ibid.*, **20**, 54 (1943).

1. Describe three methods for the production of electrons.

2. Explain how the charge and mass of the electron have been determined.

3. What is the accepted value of the electronic charge? How does the mass compare with that of a hydrogen atom?

4. State the uncertainty principle. How can it be used to reconcile the wave and particle properties of electrons?

5. Explain the difference between the cathode and positive rays obtained in a discharge tube.

6. What is a proton? Explain the difference between the proton, the positron and the electron.

7. Outline the discovery and properties of the neutron.

8. How are X-rays obtained? Explain the notation used to describe various types of X-rays.

9. What is meant by characteristic X-rays of an element? How are their frequencies related to the atomic number?

10. Explain the importance of characteristic X-rays in relation to the periodic table.

11. Describe briefly the properties of α, β and γ rays.

12. State and explain the theory of radioactive disintegration in relation to a radioactive series.

13. Describe the nuclear theory of the atom. Show how it accounts for the observed scattering of α-rays.

14. Explain the relation between the nuclear charge and atomic number.

15. Describe the constitution of the atomic nucleus in relation to the atomic number and atomic weight.

16. Explain the changes in the nucleus accompanying α and β particle emission in radioactivity.

17. What is the group displacement law in radioactivity? How does it lead to the idea of radioactive isotopes?

18. Explain how the existence of nonradioactive isotopes of lead were discovered.

19. Explain the difference in the nuclear structure of two isotopes of a given element.

20. Describe the mass spectroscope. How is it used to detect isotopes?

21. How is the accepted value of 1.008 for the atomic weight of hydrogen derived?

22. What is meant by the packing fraction? What information does it provide concerning nuclear stability?

23. What are heavy hydrogen and heavy water? How are they obtained? Describe some of their properties relative to those of ordinary hydrogen and water.

24. What methods have been used for the separation of isotopes?

25. Describe some uses of isotopes as indicators.

26. Give some instances of the artificial disintegration brought about by protons, neutrons, deutrons and α-particles.

27. What is meant by induced (or artificial) radioactivity? Explain how artificial radioelements are obtained.

28. How is it possible to explain the difference in mass between the two sides of an atomic (nuclear) transformation?

PROBLEMS

I

1 The wave lengths of the K_α characteristic X-rays of iron and copper are 1.931×10^{-8} and 1.541×10^{-8} cm., respectively. What is the atomic number and name of the element for which the characteristic K_α wave length is 2.289×10^{-8} cm? (The frequency is equal to the velocity of light, 3×10^{10} cm. sec.$^{-1}$, divided by the wave length).

2. The atomic weight of thorium is 232.12 and its atomic number is 90; in the course of its radioactive disintegration six α and four β particles are emitted. What is the atomic weight and atomic number of the end product?

3. The chemical atomic weight of chlorine is 35.457. The physical atomic weights of the two isotopes are 34.980 and 36.978, as determined by the mass spectrograph. What is the isotopic composition of ordinary chlorine?

4. Calculate the packing fractions for the two isotopes of chlorine, using the data in problem 3.

5. The mass of the helium atom is 4.00389, while that of the proton is 1.00759 and that of the neutron 1.00893, all on the physical atomic weight scale. Calculate the energy in ergs liberated when 1 gram atom of helium nuclei are formed from protons and neutrons.

6. The following artificial radioelements have been prepared. State in each case whether electron or positron activity is to be expected, and explain the nature of the remaining nucleus: ^{12}B, ^{14}C, ^{13}N, ^{17}F, ^{23}Ne, ^{24}Na, ^{35}A, ^{42}K.

7. Complete the following nuclear disintegration equations: $^{27}Al + He \rightarrow n + ?$; $^{15}N + H \rightarrow He + ?$; $^{23}Na + D \rightarrow H + ?$; $^{39}K + n \rightarrow 2n + ?$

II

1. The wave lengths of the K_α characteristic X-rays of potassium and iron are 3.737×10^{-8} and 1.931×10^{-8} cm., respectively. What is the expected value for the element calcium? (See note to problem I, 1).

2. The radioelement actinium (atomic weight 227, atomic number 90) undergoes a series of disintegrations leading to the formation of an isotope of lead of atomic weight 207. How many α and β particle emissions are involved?

3. The element boron was found to consist of two isotopes, viz., 18.4 per cent of physical atomic weight 10.161 and 81.6 per cent of physical atomic weight 11.013. Calculate the chemical atomic weight of ordinary boron.

4. The physical atomic weights of the isotopes of magnesium are 23.9924, 24.9938 and 25.9898. Calculate the packing fraction in each case.

5. In the disintegration process $^{14}_{7}N + ^{4}_{2}He \rightarrow ^{1}_{1}H + ^{17}_{8}O$ there is an absorption of 12.47×10^{17} ergs per gram atom, as shown by the difference in the energies of the colliding nuclei and the products. The masses of the nitrogen, helium and hydrogen atoms are 14.0075, 4.0039 and 1.0081; calculate the mass of the ^{17}O oxygen isotope on the same (physical atomic weight) scale.

6. The following artificial radioelements have been prepared. State in each case whether electron or positron activity is to be expected, and explain the nature of the remaining nucleus: ^{11}C, ^{16}N, ^{15}O, ^{19}O, ^{19}Ne, ^{20}F, ^{28}Al, ^{38}Cl.

7. Complete the following nuclear disintegration equations: $^{24}Mg + He \rightarrow n + ?$; $^{16}O + n \rightarrow He + ?$; $^{9}Be + H \rightarrow D + ?$; $^{27}Al + D \rightarrow n + ?$.

CHAPTER III

ELECTRONIC STRUCTURES OF ATOMS AND MOLECULES

THE ELECTRONIC CONFIGURATIONS OF ATOMS

9a. Atomic Spectra.—When a solid is heated or a discharge of electricity is passed through a gas, there is an emission of light; an examination of this light by means of a spectroscope often reveals a series of lines occupying positions in the spectrum corresponding to definite wave lengths or frequencies. These **line spectra** are produced by atoms, and so they are often referred to as **atomic spectra,** as distinct from the so-called band spectra that are characteristic of molecules (§ 62d). From a study of atomic spectra much information has been obtained concerning the arrangements of the electrons surrounding the nuclei of atoms.

In spectroscopic work it is the general practice to express the vibration frequencies of the radiations producing spectral lines in terms of **wave numbers,** that is, in terms of the number of wave lengths per cm. If the frequency of a given line is represented by $\bar{\nu}$ cm.$^{-1}$, in wave numbers, and λ cm. is the corresponding wave length, then by definition

$$\bar{\nu} = \frac{1}{\lambda} \text{ cm.}^{-1} \tag{9.1}$$

The corresponding frequency ν in vibrations per second, i.e., in sec.$^{-1}$ units, is given by

$$\nu = \frac{c}{\lambda} \text{ sec.}^{-1}, \tag{9.2}$$

where c is the velocity of light, viz., 3×10^{10} cm. per sec. It follows, therefore, from equations (9.1) and (9.2) that

$$\bar{\nu} = \frac{\nu}{c}, \tag{9.3}$$

which relates the frequency in wave numbers (cm.$^{-1}$) to the true frequency (sec.$^{-1}$).

It has been known for some time that *the frequency of any line in a particular spectral series of a given atom can be represented as a difference of two terms,* one of which is constant and the other variable throughout the series. This is the **combination principle** enunciated by W. Ritz (1908) as a generalization of an earlier rule, applicable to the spectrum of atomic hydrogen, proposed by J. J.

Balmer (1885). According to the Ritz principle, the frequency $\bar{\nu}$ of any line in a given spectral series is given by the general expression

$$\nu = R\left(\frac{1}{x^2} - \frac{1}{y^2}\right),$$ (9.4)

where R is virtually a universal constant, especially for heavier atoms, known as the **Rydberg constant.** For a particular series, the quantity represented by x^2 remains constant, but y^2 varies regularly from one line to another.

For hydrogen atoms, and for certain positively charged atoms (ions) which, like hydrogen, possess but one electron, both x and y in equation (9.4) are integers for all the observed spectral lines. Thus, the frequencies of the lines in the Balmer series of atomic hydrogen, first observed in the visible spectrum of the sun, can be expressed with great accuracy by the equation

$$\nu = R_{\mathrm{H}}\left(\frac{1}{2^2} - \frac{1}{n^2}\right),$$ (9.5)

where n is 3, 4, 5, 6, etc., for successive lines; the value of R_{H}, the Rydberg constant for hydrogen, is 109,677.76 cm.$^{-1}$. A similar equation, with 1^2 in place of 2^2, gives the frequencies of the lines in the Lyman (ultraviolet) series, while the frequencies of the Paschen (infrared) series of lines in the spectrum of atomic hydrogen can be expressed by replacing 2^2 by 3^2, with n equal to 4, 5, 6, etc.

9b. The Quantum Theory.—An interpretation of the significance of the Ritz combination principle was given by N. Bohr (1913), making use of the **quantum theory** of radiation, as postulated by M. Planck (1900) and extended by A. Einstein (1905). According to this theory, a body cannot emit or absorb energy, in the form of radiation, in a continuous manner; *the energy can only be taken up or given out as integral multiples of a definite amount, known as a* **quantum.** If E is the energy of the quantum for a particular radiation of frequency ν sec.$^{-1}$, then by the quantum theory

$$E = h\nu,$$ (9.6)

where h is a universal constant, called **Planck's constant.** Since E is an energy quantity and ν is expressed in time^{-1} units, it follows that h has the dimensions of energy $\times$ time; this product is sometimes referred to as "action," so that h is the **action constant.** As a result of a variety of measurements the value of h has been found to be 6.624×10^{-27} erg sec., the energy being in ergs and the time in seconds. Making use of equation (9.3), it is possible to represent the magnitude of the quantum in terms of the frequency $\bar{\nu}$ in wave numbers; thus,

$$E = hc\bar{\nu},$$

and hence

$$\nu = \frac{E}{hc},$$ (9.7)

so that the wave number corresponding to the quantum of energy E is obtained upon dividing E by hc, that is, by the product of the Planck constant and the velocity of light.

9c. Energy Levels: Quantum Numbers.—In order to account for the observed frequencies of the lines in the spectra of atoms, Bohr suggested that the electrons belonging to an atom move in definite stable orbits which surround the nucleus, a number of such orbits, corresponding to different energy values, being possible. By assuming the angular momentum of an electron moving in its orbit to be "quantized," that is to say, the angular momentum was supposed to be an exact integral multiple of a definite amount, or quantum, Bohr was able to derive an expression for the frequencies of the spectral lines of hydrogen which was in almost precise agreement with the experimental values. An important weakness of the Bohr theory is that it implies a precise knowledge of the position (orbit) and momentum of an electron; such a knowledge is ruled out, however, by the uncertainty principle (§ 4d).

The modern attitude is to discard the idea of definite orbits, and to replace it by the postulate that an electron in an atom possesses a number of different **energy levels.** The position of an electron, when it occupies a given level, is not precisely defined, although it can be expressed in terms of a probability by means of the equations of wave mechanics. As long as the electron remains in a particular energy level, there should be no absorption or emission of radiation. However, if an electron passes from one level to another, there will be a change in the energy of the atom, and a line will be produced in the atomic spectrum. If E' is the energy of the level or state from which the electron starts, and E'' is the energy of the level to which it passes, then according to equation (9.7) of the quantum theory, the frequency of the corresponding spectral line should be given by

$$\bar{\nu} = \frac{E' - E''}{hc} \text{ cm.}^{-1} \tag{9.8}$$

since $E' - E''$ is equal to the energy absorbed or emitted by the atom. Each particular transition from one energy level to another should thus result in the formation of a spectral line with a definite frequency. If the atom acquires energy, so that the electron passes from a lower to a higher level, the line will appear in the **absorption spectrum,** but if the transition is from a higher to a lower level, so that energy is evolved, the line will be part of an **emission spectrum.**

It is evident that equation (9.8) can be written in the form

$$\bar{\nu} = \frac{E'}{hc} - \frac{E''}{hc}, \tag{9.9}$$

and if this is compared with the Ritz equation (9.4), it follows that the energy E of a given level may be represented by

$$E = \frac{Rhc}{n^2}. \tag{9.10}$$

Since R, h and c may be regarded as constant, the energy of an electron in any particular level is apparently determined by the quantity n^2, where n is an integer for the hydrogen atom, or for hydrogen-like atoms with a single electron. By the use of the methods of quantum mechanics, it is possible to derive equation (9.10) for the energy in a given level, even to the extent of obtaining the correct value for R, the Rydberg constant, as given by

$$R = \frac{2\pi^2 \epsilon^4 m}{h^3 c},$$ (9.11)

where ϵ is the charge and m the mass of an electron. The integer n in equation (9.10) is referred to as a **quantum number,** each value referring to a particular energy level. As n increases there is a greater probability of the electron being further from the nucleus; the binding energy of the electron in the atom decreases correspondingly. It may be mentioned that equations (9.10) and (9.11) were also derived by Bohr on the basis of his theory of orbits, but the number of assumptions or postulates that had to be made were greater than those required by the quantum mechanical treatment.

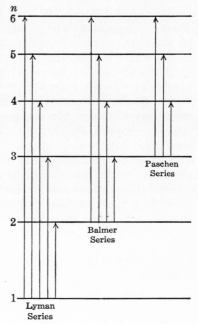

FIG. 8. Energy levels of hydrogen atom and origin of spectra

The concept of energy levels permits of a ready explanation of atomic spectra; thus, the levels of the hydrogen atom for various values of n are indicated in Fig. 8. As depicted in the diagram, the Lyman (absorption) lines result from electronic transitions for which the quantum number n is 1 in the initial state in each case. The energy E' of the $n = 1$ level is given by equation (9.10) as $Rhc/1^2$, and E'' for any of the final levels is Rhc/n^2, where n is seen to be 2, 3, 4, etc.; hence, by equation (9.9), the frequencies of the lines in the Lyman series will be represented by

$$\bar{\nu} = R\left(\frac{1}{1^2} - \frac{1}{n^2}\right),$$

in agreement with observation. For the Balmer series, the initial state for every transition is the level for which n is 2, so that E' is $Rhc/2^2$ in each case; since E'' is Rhc/n^2, where n is 3, 4, 5, etc., it is evident that the frequencies of the lines are given by an expression equivalent to equation (9.5). The lines of the Paschen and other spectral series of atomic hydrogen can be accounted for in a similar manner.

Although the calculations of the actual energy values in different levels has been possible for the simplest atoms only, the general conclusions are of wide applicability and they provide an explanation of the Ritz combination principle. The energy of an electronic level is given by $E' = Rhc/x^2$, where x may be different from an integer when the atom has several electrons. If a series of transitions take place from this level to a number of other levels in which the energy E'' is Rhc/p^2, Rhc/q^2, Rhc/r^2, etc., then by equation (9.9) the general expression for the frequencies of the corresponding series of lines will be

$$\bar{\nu} = \frac{R}{x^2} - \frac{R}{y^2} = R\left(\frac{1}{x^2} - \frac{1}{y^2}\right),$$

where x^2 is a constant, and y^2 takes on a series of values p^2, q^2, etc., as required, by the Ritz principle [equation (9.4)]. The significance of the combination principle is, therefore, that the spectral lines in any given (absorption) series are due to electronic transitions from one and the same initial energy level to a number of different, successive, final levels.

9d. Quantum Numbers and the Pauli Principle.—In the development of the theory of atomic spectra, both from the older (classical) and the newer (wave mechanical) standpoints, it has been found that one quantum number is insufficient to provide a complete description of an electron in an atom; four such quantum numbers are actually necessary. The energy is determined primarily by the **principal quantum number** n, referred to in the preceding section; this can have any integral value, but not zero. A secondary effect is exerted by the **azimuthal quantum number** l, which, according to classical theory, determines the angular momentum of the electron in its motion around the nucleus. It has been established theoretically that for any particular value of the principal quantum number n, the values of l may be $n - 1$, $n - 2, \cdots$, 0; that is to say, l may have any integral value from $n - 1$ to zero. For example, if n is 4, then l can be 3, 2, 1 and 0. In order to specify the angular momentum completely, it is necessary to state the magnitude of its component along a particular direction; this is given by the **magnetic quantum number** m, representing the possible components of the angular momentum vector in the direction of a magnetic field. For a given l, the values of m may be $\pm l$, $\pm(l - 1)$, $\pm(l - 2), \cdots$, 0, giving a total of $2l + 1$ possible values. If l is 3, for example, then m can be ± 3, ± 2, ± 1 and 0, a total of seven possibilities. Finally, to complete the specification of the electron, it is necessary to give its **spin quantum number** s; this can have but two possible values, viz., $+\frac{1}{2}$ or $-\frac{1}{2}$, according as the so-called spin angular momentum is in one direction or in the opposite direction.

The distribution of quantum numbers among the electrons in a given atom is restricted by the **exclusion principle,** enunciated by W. Pauli (1925). This principle has, as yet, no theoretical explanation, but it is in agreement with many known facts; it states that *it is impossible for any two electrons in the same atom to have their four quantum numbers identical.* By means of this rule the number of electrons that can occur in any quantum group can be derived in a simple manner. If n is 1, for example, l can only be zero, and m must also be zero; s may then be either $+\frac{1}{2}$ or $-\frac{1}{2}$ without infringing the Pauli principle that the four quantum numbers must not be the same for two electrons. The values of n, l, m and s for these two electrons are then as follows:

$$(1) \quad n = 1 \quad l = 0 \quad m = 0 \quad s = +\tfrac{1}{2}$$

$$(2) \quad n = 1 \quad l = 0 \quad m = 0 \quad s = -\tfrac{1}{2}.$$

It is thus seen that in the first ($n = 1$) quantum group there may be up to two, and no more, electrons.

For the second ($n = 2$) group, l may be 1 or 0; if l is 0, then two electrons are possible, as in the previous case. If l is 1, then there are three possibilities for m, namely -1, 0 and $+1$; in each case the spin s may be $+\frac{1}{2}$ or $-\frac{1}{2}$, so that for $l = 1$ there can be six electrons in the atom. The total number of electrons in the second quantum group is thus $2 + 6$, i.e., 8, and their specifications are given below.

n	2	2	2	2	2	2	2	2
l	0	0	1	1	1	1	1	1
m	0	0	-1	-1	0	0	$+1$	$+1$
s	$+\frac{1}{2}$	$-\frac{1}{2}$	$+\frac{1}{2}$	$-\frac{1}{2}$	$+\frac{1}{2}$	$-\frac{1}{2}$	$+\frac{1}{2}$	$-\frac{1}{2}$

It is seen that no two electrons have their four quantum numbers identical.

Working in this manner, the results shown in Table VI may be derived for the maximum numbers of electrons corresponding to various n and the possible l values.

TABLE VI.   DISTRIBUTION OF ELECTRONS IN QUANTUM GROUPS

	$l = 0$	1	2	3	4
	Maximum Numbers of Electrons				
$n = 1$	2	—	—	—	—
2	2	6	—	—	—
3	2	6	10	—	—
4	2	6	10	14	—
5	2	6	10	14	18

9e. Electronic Arrangements in Atoms.—By means of the data in Table VI many of the general features of the periodic table can be interpreted; if, in addition, information derived from atomic spectra and from the characteristic X-rays is utilized, it is possible to deduce the details of the arrangement of the electrons in the atoms of most elements. The complete arguments are somewhat complicated, and so a broad outline only will be given here. The procedure adopted is to imagine the electrons, equal in number to the positive nuclear charge, to be added to the system one at a time until the complete atom is built up. It is then necessary to find in which group each successive electron is accommodated. In order to simplify the treatment, the assumption is made that the main inner structure of any atom is the same as that of the preceding one in order of atomic number. All that is necessary, then, is to determine the position occupied by the additional electron which distinguishes the two atoms. Suppose, for example, the electronic arrangement in the sodium atom has been worked out; in order to find that of the next element, magnesium, it is required merely to discover where the one extra electron must be placed. The structure of the magnesium atom now being known, it is possible to go on to derive that of the aluminum atom, and so on, throughout the periodic table. There are a few cases in which the foregoing assumption requires slight modification, but these do not cause any serious difficulty.

Starting with hydrogen, which has one electron, it is evident that this will be in the $n = 1$, $l = 0$ group; similarly, the two electrons of helium will be in this group. It is seen from Table VI that the $n = 1$, $l = 0$ group can contain only two electrons, and so with the helium atom the group is completed. In the next atom, lithium, the extra electron must go into the $n = 2$, $l = 0$ subgroup; this is completed with the following atom, beryllium. Proceeding in this manner, with increasing atomic number, the electrons in the succeeding atoms enter the $n = 2$, $l = 1$ subgroup, which is capable of containing six electrons (Table VI). With the element neon, atomic number 10, the first

TABLE VII.   ELECTRONIC ARRANGEMENTS IN GROUPS I AND II

Quantum Numbers

| | $n = 1$ | $n = 2$ | |
Atom	$l = 0$	$l = 0$	$l = 1$
Hydrogen	1	—	—
Helium	2	—	—
Lithium	2	1	—
Beryllium	2	2	—
Boron	2	2	1
Carbon	2	2	2
Nitrogen	2	2	3
Oxygen	2	2	4
Fluorine	2	2	5
Neon	2	2	6

two electron groups or shells, $n = 1$ and $n = 2$, are completed, the distribution of the electrons in the first two groups of the periodic table being shown in Table VII. Since the numbers of electrons in the first two shells are 2 and $2 + 6$, i.e., 8, respectively, the configuration of neon may be represented as 2, 8.

At sodium, which is the next element, the process of filling up the subgroups, starting with the $n = 3$, $l = 0$ subgroup, begins to repeat itself; this element has the electronic arrangement 2, 8, 1. As before, the $l = 0$ subgroup is first completed, and then the electrons enter the $l = 1$ subgroup, which is just filled when the element argon, atomic number 18, is reached; the electronic configuration is 2, 8, 8.

At this point the next electron can either enter the $n = 3$, $l = 2$ subgroup, for a subgroup with $l = 2$ is now possible for the first time (cf. Table VI), or it can start a new main group with $n = 4$. All the evidence points to the latter alternative for the potassium atom, which thus has the electronic grouping

2, 8, 8, 1. Similarly, for the next atom, calcium, the configuration is 2, 8, 8, 2. However, with the following element, scandium, a more stable system apparently results when the additional electron enters the still vacant $n = 3, l = 2$ subgroup, giving the structure 2, 8, 9, 2. In the succeeding atoms, this subgroup, which is capable of holding ten electrons, is gradually filled up; it is the introduction of the $l = 2$ subgroup which accounts for the fact that the fourth period of the periodic table contains eighteen elements, as compared with eight in the two preceding periods. The $n = 3, l = 2$ subgroup is completed at zinc, with the arrangement 2, 8, 18, 2, and the next element, gallium, has the structure 2, 8, 18, 3, and so on. These configurations are now somewhat analogous to those of the corresponding elements in the two short periods; it can be understood, therefore, why the elements at the end of the long period begin to resemble the typical elements once more (see Table II).

When krypton, atomic number 36, is reached, the configuration is 2, 8, 18, 8; with the succeeding atom, rubidium, a new $(n = 5)$ group is started, thus 2, 8, 18, 8, 1. As in the previous case, the next electron enters the same subgroup, i.e., strontium is 2, 8, 18, 8, 2, but with yttrium, the hitherto vacant $n = 4, l = 2$ subgroup begins to be occupied. The subsequent behavior follows closely that of the preceding period of the periodic table, giving a series of eighteen elements; the fifth period ends with the inert gas xenon, atomic number 54, having the electronic arrangement 2, 8, 18, 18, 8.

The situation now becomes somewhat more complicated, for although the first three electron shells, with $n = 1, 2$ and 3, are filled, the fourth and fifth shells are still incomplete. An examination of Table VI, for example, shows that the $n = 4$ group is capable of holding a total of 32 electrons, so that there are still 14 places, in the $l = 3$ subgroup, to be filled. In addition, there are three vacant subgroups in the $n = 5$ shell. There is no doubt that in the first two elements of the sixth period, cesium and barium, which succeed xenon, a new $(n = 6)$ group is started, so that the structures are analogous to those of the first two members of the four preceding series, viz., 2, 8, 18, 18, 8, 1 and 2, 8, 18, 18, 8, 2 respectively. As in the fourth and fifth periods, with the next element, lanthanum, the electron enters an inner subgroup, viz., $n = 5, l = 2$, so that the structure is 2, 8, 18, 18, 9, 2. Following this, however, there is an entirely novel development, for the $n = 4, l = 3$ subgroup, capable of containing 14 electrons, as seen above, begins to be occupied with the element cerium, i.e., 2, 8, 18, 19, 9, 2. Apparently, the introduction of an electron in such an inner group has little effect on the chemical properties, so that cerium and lanthanum are similar chemically. These two elements are, in fact, the first of the rare-earth series. With the succeeding thirteen elements the $n = 4$, $l = 3$ subgroup is increasingly occupied, and with lutecium, 2, 8, 18, 32, 9, 2 it is completed. This element, atomic number 71, is the last of the rare-earth group, and hence the occurrence of fifteen elements in this group can be explained.

Following the completion of the rare-earth series of elements, the electrons steadily fill the $l = 2$ subgroup of the $n = 5$ shell, the $l = 0$ and $l = 1$ subgroups being already fully occupied. Subsequently the electrons proceed to complete the $n = 6$, $l = 1$ subgroup, so that finally the configuration 2, 8, 18, 32, 18, 8 is obtained. The corresponding atomic number is 86, which is that of the inert radioactive gas radon. The total number of elements in the sixth period of the periodic table is thus $86 - 54 = 32$; this is 14 more than the number in the two preceding periods, because of the inclusion of the $n = 4$, $l = 3$ subgroup.

For the elements which follow radon, there are clearly many possibilities, since the fifth and sixth ($n = 5$ and $n = 6$) shells are still incomplete; in the former the $l = 3$ and $l = 4$ subgroups are vacant, while in the latter the $l = 0$ and $l = 1$ subgroups only are occupied. It is probable, nevertheless, that with the two elements of atomic number 87 and 88, the latter being radium, the $n = 7$ shell is begun. Unfortunately, no elements beyond uranium, atomic number 92, exist in nature, for it would have been of great interest to know how the still vacant inner electron subgroups are filled.*

THE ELECTRONIC THEORY OF VALENCE

10a. The Electron Octet.—With the information already obtained in connection with the electronic structures of atoms, it is possible to proceed to the consideration of molecular structure. The combination of atoms to form molecules involves what have been called valence forces, and there is no doubt that the "valence bonds" which hold the atoms together in a molecule are related to the electronic configurations of the atoms concerned. This is the fundamental basis of the **electronic theory of valence.**

An examination of the results of § 9e shows that the inert gases, in group 0 of the periodic table, have the following electronic configurations:

Helium	2
Neon	2, 8
Argon	2, 8, 8
Krypton	2, 8, 18, 8
Xenon	2, 8, 18, 18, 8
Radon	2, 8, 18, 32, 18, 8

In each of these atoms, with the exception of helium, *the outermost shell contains eight electrons*, irrespective of whether the inner shells have been completely filled or not. Since the inert gases are extremely unreactive, it may be concluded that an outer group of eight electrons, known as an **electron octet,** is an exceptionally stable arrangement. One of the postulates of the electronic theory of valence is, therefore, that, in general, *when atoms combine they do so in such a manner as to lead to the formation of complete electron octets, as far as possible.*

10b. Electrovalence.—One way in which complete octet formation can be achieved is as follows: suppose a particular atom has electrons in excess of the octet while another has a deficit; both atoms could then acquire complete octets if the extra electrons of the former atom were transferred to the latter

---

* The elements 93 (neptunium) and 94 (plutonium) have been obtained artificially (§ 8a); the latter, which undergoes neutron fission (§ 8c), has been used in the atomic bomb. Both elements resemble uranium chemically.

(W. Kossel, 1916). Each of the alkali metals, namely, lithium, sodium, potassium, rubidium and cesium, immediately follows an inert gas in the periodic table; consequently, the atoms of these elements all have one electron in excess of that required for a stable configuration. On the other hand, the halogen atoms, viz., fluorine, chlorine, bromine and iodine, each precede an inert gas, and so these atoms require an additional electron to complete the octet. It follows, therefore, that if the extra electron possessed by an alkali metal atom were transferred to a halogen atom, both would have their octets complete; the resulting system, which would represent an alkali halide, would be a stable one.

The electron transfer just described may be represented pictorially in the manner shown in Fig. 9; this type of diagram must not be interpreted too

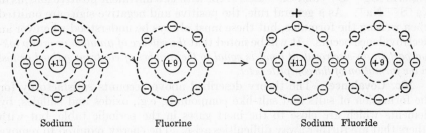

| Sodium | Fluorine | Sodium Fluoride |

FIG. 9.   Formation of electrovalence in sodium fluoride

literally, especially as regards the positions of the electrons (see § 4d). On the left-hand side are depicted sodium and fluorine atoms; in each case the number of electrons on the atom is equal to the nuclear charge. The right-hand side represents sodium fluoride, in which the two atoms now have completed octets. It will be noted, however, that the sodium has eleven positive charges on the nucleus but only ten negative electrons; it must consequently have a resultant positive charge. In other words, the sodium is now in the form of a singly charged, or univalent, **positive ion.** Similarly, it is apparent that the fluorine has an excess negative charge, and so it is a univalent **negative ion.** *The two oppositely charged ions will be held together by electrostatic attraction,* and this is the basis of the "valence bond" in sodium fluoride. The same type of union, which has been called **electrovalence** by I. Langmuir (1919), is supposed to exist in all simple salts; such salts are, therefore, said to be **electrovalent compounds.** In each case, the solid salt consists of positive and negative ions—each with a complete electron octet—held together by electrostatic forces. It may be remarked that support for this interpretation of the valence bonds in simple salts has been obtained from a study of the internal structures of the crystals (§ 19b) and from the properties of their solutions (§ 46d).

The metals of group II A of the periodic table, viz., magnesium, calcium, strontium, barium, and radium, each have two electrons per atom in excess of the octet number; by transferring the two electrons to two halogen atoms, salt formation, involving a bivalent positive (metal) ion and two univalent negative (halogen) ions, is possible by the operation of electrovalence. The process may be depicted in the following manner:

$$\overset{\bullet\bullet}{\underset{\bullet\bullet}{:}}Ca\overset{\bullet\bullet}{:}: \, + \, 2:\overset{\bullet\bullet}{\underset{\bullet\bullet}{Cl}}\cdot \; = \; :\overset{\bullet\bullet}{\underset{\bullet\bullet}{Cl}}: \overset{++}{\underset{\bullet\bullet}{:Ca:}} :\overset{\bullet\bullet}{\underset{\bullet\bullet}{Cl}}:$$

in which the symbol of an element is used to represent the atomic nucleus and the inner electron shells; the additional electrons are indicated by dots.

If an atom, e.g., oxygen or sulfur, or a group of atoms, e.g., SO_4, requires two electrons to complete its octet (or octets), it can become a bivalent negative ion, and form an electrovalent compound with a single bivalent positive ion, as in $Mg^{++}O^{--}$ and $Ca^{++}SO_4^{--}$, or with two univalent positive ions, as in $Na^+S^{--}Na^+$. As a general rule, the positive and negative signs are omitted when writing the formulae, but these must always be understood wherever an electrovalence occurs. It will be noted that *the valence of an atom or group taking part in an electrovalent bond is equal to the number of electrons gained or lost in the formation of the complete octet.*

10c. Covalence.—The theory described above accounts satisfactorily for the formation of salts and salt-like compounds, e.g., oxides and sulfides, by elements which are close to the inert gases in the periodic table, but with others that are further away difficulties arise. The energy required to remove an electron from an atom increases with the number of electrons removed; it is for this reason that trivalent positive ions are uncommon and quadrivalent ions are very rare. Similarly, simple negative ions carrying three charges are unknown, although complex ions with a valence of three or four can exist. Because of the difficulty in removing three or more electrons from, or adding such numbers to, an atom, the ions B^{+++}, C^{++++}, C^{----} or N^{---} are unlikely to be involved in chemical combination. Atoms like boron, carbon, nitrogen, etc., cannot therefore take direct part in electrovalent bond formation, and they must combine in another way.

A second manner whereby two atoms with incomplete electron octets can complete these octets is by sharing electrons, as suggested by G. N. Lewis (1916); this leads to another type of valence, known as **covalence.** According to Lewis, the sharing involves pairs of electrons, or **electron duplets,** *each shared duplet being equivalent to one conventional valence bond.* It is of interest to note that Lewis was led to this suggestion by the fact that all stable compounds, with very few exceptions, contain an even number of electrons. In recent years, however, the electron-pair bond has acquired something of a theoretical significance. By means of wave mechanics, W. Heitler and F. London (1927) showed that two hydrogen atoms can come together in two ways, one leading to the formation of a stable hydrogen molecule, whereas the other leads to an unstable system. In order to obtain the stable molecule it is necessary for the two hydrogen atoms to have the spins of their electrons in opposite directions. If the two spins are in the same direction, a stable molecule cannot be formed. From this result it has been inferred that covalent bond formation, in general, involves the pairing of electrons with opposite spins, not only in hydrogen but in all other molecules. If this is the case, the postulate that electron sharing occurs in pairs can be readily understood.

The formation of covalent bonds may be illustrated by considering the combination of carbon and four chlorine atoms; the former has four electrons in its outer shell and the latter require one electron each to complete their octets. If the carbon atom contributes one electron to each of four pairs, the other electron coming from a chlorine atom, an arrangement is possible in which all five atoms have completed their octets; the resulting compound is clearly carbon tetrachloride. The formation of this compound from the atoms may be depicted in the following manner; as before, the symbol of an element is supposed to represent the nucleus and the inner electron shells.

$$4 \; :\!\overset{\cdot\cdot}{\underset{\cdot\cdot}{Cl}}\!\cdot \;\; + \;\; \cdot\overset{\cdot}{\underset{\cdot}{C}}\cdot \;\; = \;\; :\!\overset{\cdot\cdot}{Cl}\!:\!\overset{:\overset{\cdot\cdot}{Cl}:}{\underset{:\overset{\cdot\cdot}{Cl}:}{C}}\!:\!\overset{\cdot\cdot}{Cl}\!: \quad \text{or} \quad \overset{\textstyle Cl}{\underset{\textstyle Cl}{Cl - C - Cl}}$$

The conventional formula of carbon tetrachloride is given at the right; the four bonds are seen to be covalent in nature, each involving the sharing of a pair of electrons between a chlorine atom and the central carbon atom.

It will be understood, of course, that the hydrogen atom is, to some extent, exceptional, because it cannot form an octet; in this case the stable electronic configuration consists of only two electrons, as in helium. In the formation of covalent bonds, therefore, the hydrogen atom is associated with but two electrons; the electronic arrangements of a number of simple hydrides, together with their usual chemical structural formulae, are shown below.

$$H:\overset{\cdot\cdot}{\underset{\cdot\cdot}{Cl}}: \qquad H:\overset{\cdot\cdot}{\underset{\cdot\cdot}{O}}:H \qquad H:\overset{H}{\underset{\cdot\cdot}{N}}:H \qquad H:\overset{H}{\underset{H}{C}}:H$$

$$H-Cl \qquad H-O-H \qquad H-\overset{H}{\underset{}{N}}-H \qquad H-\overset{H}{\underset{H}{C}}-H$$

When there are an insufficient number of electrons to complete all the octets (or duplets, in the case of hydrogen) by the sharing of electron pairs, it is possible for two atoms to share two pairs; this is consequently the equivalent of a double bond. Similarly, a triple bond implies the sharing of three duplets between two atoms. The formation of carbon dioxide and of acetylene is thus to be represented in the following manner.

$$\overset{..}{\underset{..}{\text{C}}} + 2\overset{..}{\underset{..}{\text{O}}} = \overset{..}{\underset{..}{\text{O}}}::\text{C}::\overset{..}{\underset{..}{\text{O}}} \quad \text{or} \quad \text{O} = \text{C} = \text{O}$$

$$2\overset{.}{\text{C}} + 2\text{H}\cdot = \text{H}:\text{C}:::\text{C}:\text{H} \quad \text{or} \quad \text{H} - \text{C} \equiv \text{C} - \text{H}$$

In each case the octet (or duplet) of every atom is completed by the device of sharing more than one pair of electrons.

It should be mentioned that although the octet rule is a useful general guide to the problems of bond formation, it is probably not strictly applicable in all cases; it appears that in certain instances groups of more than eight electrons are possible. For example, in SF_6 the six fluorine atoms share electron pairs with the sulfur atom, and so the latter probably has an external group of twelve electrons; similarly, in PCl_5 the phosphorus atom has apparently ten electrons in its outer shell. On the other hand, there are a few cases, particularly the boron halides, e.g., BF_3 and BCl_3, in which the central atom, i.e., boron, has only six electrons. In this case, however, there is a strong tendency for the octet to be completed, as will be seen in § 10e.

10d. Properties of Electrovalent and Covalent Compounds.—Although it is not always possible to differentiate strictly between electrovalent and covalent compounds, there are some generalizations which are useful, even if they are not always exact. According to the electronic theory of valence, electrovalent compounds, such as simple salts, consist of positive and negative ions held together by electrostatic attraction. These ions presumably exist in the solid, but owing to the restrictive forces in the crystal, they are not free to move under the influence of an applied electric field. However, if the solid is melted, or dissolved in a suitable liquid, the ions acquire mobility and can be directed by an electrical potential. In other words, the molten solid and the solution are capable of conducting an electric current. One characteristic of an electrovalent compound is, therefore, that *it is an electrical conductor in the liquid state, either when pure or dissolved in a suitable solvent*. A pure covalent compound, on the other hand, does not conduct an electric current. Sometimes a mixture of two covalent substances produces a conducting system, e.g., hydrogen chloride and water; this is the result of a chemical action which leads to the formation of ions (§ 53a).

It will be seen later (§ 19b) that in an electrovalent solid, the molecule, e.g., sodium chloride, does not exist as a definite entity; instead there are interlocking arrangements of ions, e.g., sodium ions and chlorine ions. Each positive ion is surrounded by a number, often six or eight, of negative ions, while each negative ion is surrounded by positive ions. The result of this type of structure is that very powerful forces hold the crystal together. It is not surprising, therefore, to find that *electrovalent compounds have high melting points and high boiling points.* Covalent compounds, however, generally exist as single molecules in the solid state. The forces of attraction between the molecules is not large, and so *covalent substances melt and boil at relatively low temperatures.* It is only necessary to make a few comparisons, e.g., sodium chloride and silicon tetrachloride, calcium oxide and carbon dioxide, and sodium sulfide and hydrogen sulfide, to appreciate the approximate truth, at least, of these generalizations. The low boiling point of aluminum chloride (182° C) shows that this substance is a covalent compound. It is true that it forms a conducting solution in water, but this is due to ions formed by chemical reaction.

Electrovalent compounds are generally soluble in liquids such as water, alcohol and liquid ammonia, which are "polar" compounds (see § 10f), but are insoluble in "nonpolar" solvents, such as hydrocarbons and carbon tetrachloride. With covalent substances the reverse is often true, unless compound formation with the solvent occurs. Many covalent compounds, e.g., alcohol, acetic acid, etc., are soluble in polar liquids, because the former are themselves polar, but there are few cases of electrovalent compounds being soluble in nonpolar liquids.

As in many other aspects of science, it is not really possible to make a sharp distinction between electrovalent and covalent compounds. According to modern ideas, based on wave mechanics, all bonds partake both of electrovalent and covalent character. Generally one of these predominates greatly over the other: for example, in sodium chloride the electrovalent character is dominant, while in carbon tetrachloride the covalent character is all important. In some cases, however, both are present to a somewhat similar extent; the properties are then intermediate between those of covalent and electrovalent compounds. It has been found that an electrovalence tends to pass over into a covalence when the positive ion is small and the negative ion is large. This may be illustrated by lithium iodide, consisting of a small lithium ion and a large iodine ion; this salt has a relatively low melting point, and it is soluble in a number of organic liquids in which most salts are insoluble.

10e. Coordinate Covalence.—In the covalent compounds considered previously, each atom taking part in the formation of a particular bond contributed one electron toward the duplet; in certain circumstances, however, *both electrons are supplied by one of the atoms.* The resultant covalent bond is then called a **coordinate bond** or a **coordinate link.** Certain atoms, particularly those of oxygen, nitrogen, sulfur, phosphorus, and of other bivalent or trivalent elements, in their normal compounds, possess one or two pairs of electrons which are not shared with other atoms. This is seen to be the case in the electronic formulae given above for water and ammonia; the oxygen atom has two unshared pairs of electrons, sometimes known as **lone pairs,** while the nitrogen atom has one such pair. Under suitable conditions a lone pair of electrons on one atom may be shared with another atom or ion, thus producing a coordinate covalence. The ammonium and hydrogen (hydronium) ions, for example, are obtained in this manner. In the former case the lone pair of electrons of the nitrogen atom in ammonia is shared with a hydrogen nucleus, or proton; thus,

$$
\text{H} : \overset{\text{H}}{\underset{..}{\overset{..}{\text{N}}}} : \text{H} \; + \; \text{H}^{+} \; = \; \left[\; \text{H} : \overset{\text{H}}{\underset{\text{H}}{\overset{..}{\text{N}}}} : \text{H} \; \right]^{+} .
$$

The positive charge, which was originally associated with the hydrogen nucleus, is treated as ultimately belonging to the ammonium ion as a whole, although there is a possibility that it may be on the nitrogen atom. The formation of the hydronium ion, H_3O^+ (§ 53a), takes place in an analogous manner, one of the lone electron pairs of the oxygen atom being shared with a positively charged hydrogen nucleus (proton); thus,

$$
\text{H} : \overset{..}{\underset{..}{\text{O}}} : \text{H} \; + \; \text{H}^{+} \; = \; \left[\; \text{H} : \overset{\text{H}}{\underset{..}{\overset{..}{\text{O}}}} : \text{H} \; \right]^{+}
$$

An interesting type of coordinate bond formation involves trivalent boron compounds; as mentioned previously, the boron atom in many of its compounds has only six electrons, in place of the more usual octet. The boron atom is thus capable of accepting a lone pair of electrons from another atom or ion, so as to complete the group of eight electrons. For example, the lone pair of electrons on the nitrogen atom of ammonia may be shared with the boron atom of boron trichloride in the following manner:

$$
\begin{array}{ccccc}
: \overset{..}{\text{Cl}} : & & \text{H} & & \text{Cl} \quad \text{N} \\
: \overset{..}{\underset{..}{\text{Cl}}} : \text{B} & + & : \overset{..}{\text{N}} : \text{H} & = & : \overset{..}{\underset{..}{\text{Cl}}} : \text{B} : \overset{..}{\text{N}} : \text{H} \\
: \overset{..}{\underset{..}{\text{Cl}}} : & & \text{H} & & : \overset{..}{\underset{..}{\text{Cl}}} : \text{H}
\end{array}
$$

In the resulting "molecular compound," viz., $BCl_3 \cdot NH_3$, the boron, nitrogen and chlorine atoms all have completed their electron octets. The BF_4^- ion is formed in an analogous manner from a molecule of boron trifluoride and a fluoride ion; thus,

$$
\begin{array}{ccccc}
: \overset{..}{\underset{..}{\text{F}}} : & & & & : \overset{..}{\underset{..}{\text{F}}} : \\
: \overset{..}{\underset{..}{\text{F}}} : \text{B} & + & \left[: \overset{..}{\underset{..}{\text{F}}} : \right]^{-} & = & : \overset{..}{\underset{..}{\text{F}}} : \text{B} : \overset{..}{\underset{..}{\text{F}}} : \\
: \overset{..}{\underset{..}{\text{F}}} : & & & & : \overset{..}{\underset{..}{\text{F}}} :
\end{array}^{\large -}
$$

The compounds of ammonia with metallic salts, frequently known as metallic ammines, e.g., cobaltammines, many salt hydrates and complex cyanides, such as those of the transition elements iron, platinum, etc., involve coordinate bond formation between the central metal atom and the molecules of ammonia or water, or the cyanide ion. In each case, a lone pair belonging to the molecule or ion is shared with the metal atom. It is, in fact, because this type of linkage is concerned in the so-called "coordination compounds" of Werner, that it has been referred to as a coordinate bond.

10f. Polar and Nonpolar Molecules.—When two atoms share a pair of electrons, it is generally true, unless the atoms are identical, that the electrons will be drawn more closely to one of the atoms than to the other. The result of this is that the electrical center of the negative charges (electrons) will not correspond with that of the positive charges (nuclei). In other words, the positive and negative charges associated with the covalent bond may be regarded as being displaced relative to one another, so as to form a **dipole.** In general, therefore, every covalent bond between two atoms will be associated with a **dipole moment;** the value of this moment is equal to the product of the electronic charge and the relative displacement of the positive and negative electrical centers. The magnitude of the dipole moment, or the **polarity** of the bond, to use a general term, depends primarily on the relative electron-attracting tendencies of the two atoms concerned. This property, sometimes known as the **electronegativity** of the atoms, varies from one element to another; two examples of series of elements of increasing electronegativity are the following:

$$H < C \ll N < O < F \quad \text{and} \quad I < Br < Cl < F,$$

and similarly for other periods and groups of the periodic table.

Dipole moments of bonds are to be regarded as vectorial in character, that is to say, they have magnitude and direction, the latter being along the direction of the bond. The dipole moment of a molecule as a whole may be regarded as equal to the vector sum of the individual bond moments. Perfectly symmetrical molecules, such as carbon tetrachloride, benzene and other hydrocarbons, have dipole moments of zero; they are consequently called **nonpolar** molecules. Unsymmetrical molecules, however, are almost invariably **polar** in character; such substances possess resultant dipole moments which may be quite large (§ 17l). Compounds containing the groups —OH, —CN, —COOH and —NO$_2$, which are examples of **polar groups,** are generally highly polar in character, unless they happen to be completely symmetrical. *Nonpolar substances are usually readily volatile and are soluble in other nonpolar compounds.* Polar molecules, having an appreciable electrostatic field because of the resultant dipoles, will attract each other; consequently, *polar liquids have relatively high boiling points.* Further, *such liquids are generally soluble in one another, but do not dissolve so readily in nonpolar solvents.* Although these rules may be regarded as useful generalizations, they are approximate only, for other factors, besides polarity, influence volatility and mutual solubilities.

10g. Resonance.—One of the most interesting consequences of the application of wave mechanics to the problems of valence and molecular structure is the development of the concept of **resonance.** *If the electronic structure of a molecule can be depicted in two or more ways, in which the positions of the atomic nuclei remain unchanged, and the energies of the various configurations do not* *differ appreciably from each other, then the actual state of the molecule has a greater stability than any of the individual structures.* In other words, the actual strengths of the bonds in the molecule are greater than would be expected from any of the possible individual electronic configurations; at the same time there is a shortening of the distances between the atoms forming the bonds. A simple illustration of resonance is found in the molecule of carbon dioxide; there are three possible electronic structures in which the positions of the nuclei are unaltered and the energies do not differ greatly, viz.,

:Ö : C ::: O :   :Ö :: C :: Ö :   : O ::: C :Ö :

The middle structure is the one based on the conventional chemical formula, $O{=}C{=}O$, whereas the other two represent possible alternative arrangements of the same number of electrons. Since these three structures correspond to approximately equal energies—the two outer structures, of course, have identical energies—the phenomenon of resonance is possible. The effect of this resonance is to give an actual structure for carbon dioxide which is more stable than any of the three shown above. The distances between the nuclei are, at the same time, less than is to be expected from the ordinary double-bonded structure.

A particularly important instance of resonance is that in the benzene molecule; five different electronic arrangements, of approximately the same energy, are possible, viz.,

I   II   III   IV   V

Of these I and II are alternative Kekulé structures, and the others, III, IV and V, are similar to the Dewar formula for benzene. It is the occurrence of resonance among these structures that accounts for the exceptional stability of the benzene ring. One of the results of the resonance is that the distinction between single and double carbon-carbon bonds no longer exists; all these bonds in the benzene molecule become identical in character. This is shown by the fact that the distances between adjacent carbon atoms in benzene are all 1.40×10^{-8} cm.; this may be compared with 1.54×10^{-8} cm. for a single bond and 1.35×10^{-8} cm. for a double bond.

10h. The Hydrogen Bond.—An unusual type of bonding, which may be partly due to resonance, is exhibited by hydrogen in certain circumstances. Although the hydrogen atom possesses but one electron, and is as a consequence normally univalent, it is capable of forming a bond or bridge between two atoms, provided these are small and fairly strongly electronegative in character, e.g., F, O, N (§ 10f). An outstanding example of the formation of such a **hydrogen bond** or **hydrogen bridge**, as it is called, is provided by the familiar acid fluoride ion, HF_2^-, as in the salt KHF_2. There is little doubt that the structure of this ion is to be represented as $(FHF)^-$, with the hydrogen atom acting as a link between the two fluorines. In this instance, because of the very strongly electronegative nature of fluorine, it is probable that the electron of the hydrogen atom has passed completely to the fluorine, so that the HF_2^- ion consists essentially of a proton (H^+) holding two fluoride ions, viz., $F^-H^+F^-$, by electrostatic forces. This is admittedly an extreme case, and in most instances the hydrogen bond formation does not involve complete electron transfer.

It is well known that the simple hydrogen compounds of nitrogen, oxygen and fluorine, i.e., NH_3, H_2O and HF, differ markedly in physical properties from their homologous compounds in the periodic table. A particular instance is the fact that water is a liquid boiling at 100° C, whereas the analogous compounds of sulfur, selenium and tellurium, viz., H_2S, H_2Se and H_2Te, are gases liquefying at temperatures of about $-62°$, $-42°$ and $0°$ C, respectively. If water behaved normally in this series, it should be a gas which would condense to a liquid only if cooled below about $-80°$ C at ordinary pressures. Similar discrepancies exist for ammonia and hydrogen fluoride, but the corresponding hydride of carbon, viz., CH_4 (methane), is quite normal in this respect. The explanation of these facts lies in hydrogen bond formation. The hydrogen atom in a molecule of hydrogen fluoride is able to form a bridge between two fluorine atoms, so that chains of the type $\cdots H—F\cdots H—F\cdots H—F\cdots H—F$ are possible. There is evidence that such structures, which are zigzag rather than linear, with the $H—F\cdots H$ angle about 140°, are present in the liquid, and even in the gas. In the homologue, hydrogen chloride, there is little, if any, hydrogen bonding, because of the decreased electronegativity and larger size of the chlorine atom as compared with that of fluorine. It is seen, therefore, that hydrogen fluoride is "associated" (cf. § 14f), and exists as $(HF)_n$ molecules, where n is an indefinite, possibly large, number; hydrogen chloride, on the other hand, exists essentially as single HCl molecules, as do the other homologues, HBr and HI.

Similar hydrogen bond formation accounts for the abnormal properties of water and of liquid ammonia. In the former instance, since there are two hydrogen atoms joined to each oxygen atom, and each of these has two lone pairs of electrons where hydrogen bonds may become attached, it is possible for each molecule of water to be surrounded by four others connected with the central one through hydrogen bonds. This structure actually exists in ice, every crystal of which consists virtually of one large molecule, since every H_2O unit is attached to four others. Upon melting, the same structure persists to a large extent in liquid water in the vicinity of 0° C, but as the temperature is raised there is some breaking of the hydrogen bonds. Nevertheless, at ordinary temperatures there is still considerable complexity in liquid water, for at any instant each H_2O unit is attached by hydrogen bonds to two or three others. Although there is probably a continual interchange of partners in the liquid, it is evident that structures involving large, but indefinite, numbers of molecules will be present in water. Because oxygen is less electronegative than fluorine, water vapor consists of single molecules, with no hydrogen bonding; the same appears to be true for ammonia gas. In methane (CH_4) there is no tendency for hydrogen bonds to occur, since the carbon atom has no lone pairs of electrons and its electronegativity is small. Consequently, there is no association in solid or liquid methane, and its physical properties are not abnormal when compared with those of its homologues.

The alcohols and phenols, which have the general formula ROH, behave like water in respect to hydrogen bond formation. The extent is less marked, however, since the former substances have only one hydrogen atom in the molecule, whereas water has two such atoms. There is evidence that in the crystals of alcohols each ROH unit is attached by hydrogen bonds to two others, in the manner indicated below, and this structure persists to an appreciable extent even in the liquid.

As with water, however, the vapors consist essentially of single molecules.

In alcohols, phenols and water there is no obvious limit to the total number of molecules that can be held together by hydrogen bonds (see § 31a), although thermal agitation does set an approximate limit at each temperature. With carboxylic acids, which also possess an —OH group, permitting hydrogen bonding, the union is definitely restricted to a pair of molecules, as represented below.

Carboxylic acids, such as formic acid, acetic acid, benzoic acid, etc., would thus be expected to form double molecules very readily. There is ample evidence that such molecules exist in the pure liquid and in solution, and also in the vapor at not too high temperatures (§ 14f).

The formation of hydrogen bridges is not restricted to identical molecules, as in the cases cited above; it is possible for a hydrogen bond to hold together two different molecules, or even to link up two parts of the same molecule. However, there is one essential restriction, namely, that a hydrogen atom can form a bridge only between electronegative atoms, the most important being nitrogen, oxygen and fluorine; the two atoms joined by the bridge may be the same or different. It may be mentioned that hydrogen bonds are very much weaker than ordinary bonds, and so the former are readily broken as the temperature is raised. Finally, there is evidence that in most cases the hydrogen atom forming the bridge is closer to one atom than the other; this fact, together with its weakness, justifies the use of a dotted line, as above, to indicate the presence of a hydrogen bond.

READING REFERENCES

1. **Structure of atoms.** Urey, *Journal of Chemical Education*, **8,** 1114 (1931).
2. **Concept of polar molecules.** French, *ibid.*, **13,** 122 (1936).
3. **Magnetism and chemical constitution.** Robey and Dix, *ibid.*, **14,** 414 (1937).
4. **Magnetism and molecular structure.** Selwood, *ibid.*, **18,** 181 (1941).
5. **Structure of water molecule.** Forbes, *ibid.*, **18,** 18 (1941).
6. **Quantum numbers and periodic table.** Hazlehurst, *ibid.*, **18,** 580 (1941).
7. **Electron configuration and periodic table.** Luder, *ibid.*, **20,** 21 (1943).
8. **Coordination and valence.** Blanchard, *ibid.*, **20,** 454 (1943).

REVIEW QUESTIONS

1. What is meant by the combination principle in atomic spectra?

2. Explain the basis of the quantum theory. What is the connection between the energy of a quantum and the frequency of the radiation (a) in sec.$^{-1}$, (b) in wave numbers (cm.$^{-1}$).

3. Show how the concept of energy levels may be used to explain the frequencies of the lines in the spectra of atomic hydrogen.

4. What are the four quantum numbers required to specify completely an electron in an atom?

5. State the Pauli exclusion principle, and illustrate its application to cases in which the principal quantum number is 1 and 2, respectively.

6. Explain the general principle used in determining the arrangement of electrons in atoms; illustrate by reference to a number of elements.

7. How is it possible to account for the occurrence of the rare-earth group of elements in the periodic table?

8. State the common characteristic of the electronic structures of the inert gases of group 0. Explain the importance of the result in connection with the electronic theory of valence.

9. Explain, with examples, the meaning of electrovalence.

10. Explain, with examples, the meaning of covalence.

11. What is the relation between electrons and valence bonds? Write the conventional and electronic structures of the molecules HCl, H_2O, NH_3, CCl_4, CO_2, C_2H_2, N_2.

12. Describe the main difference in the physical properties between covalent and electrovalent compounds.

13. Explain, with examples, the meaning of coordinate covalence.

14. What is meant by polar and nonpolar covalent compounds? How do they differ in properties?

15. What is the meaning of resonance? Explain by reference to carbon dioxide and benzene.

16. Explain the occurrence of the hydrogen bond in (a) water, (b) alcohols and phenols, (c) carboxylic acids.

PROBLEMS

I

1. Using the value of the Rydberg constant in § 9a, calculate the frequencies in wave numbers of the first four lines of the Balmer spectrum of atomic hydrogen. Evaluate the corresponding energy changes, in ergs, according to the quantum theory.

2. Give the detailed quantum numbers (n, l, m and s) of the eighteen electrons in the third ($n = 3$) quantum group (see Table VI).

3. Write out the arrangement of electrons among the various subgroups (as in Table VII) of the elements from sodium to argon.

4. Represent the structures of the following molecules in terms of the electronic theory of valence: Cl_2O, CaO, $MgCl_2$, BCl_3, ClO_4^-, Cl_2, C_2H_6.

5. Which of the following pairs of bonds has the larger dipole moment? H—O, H—N; C—N, C—F; C—Br, C—F.   Give reasons.

II

1. Show that the frequencies of successive lines in the Lyman series of atomic hydrogen tend toward a limiting value equal to R cm.$^{-1}$.   The corresponding energy change represents the amount necessary to remove an electron completely from a normal hydrogen atom; what is the value of this (ionization) energy in ergs?

2. Give the values of the quantum numbers m and s of the fourteen electrons for which n is 4 and l is 3 (see Table VI).

3. Write out the distribution of electrons among the main quantum groups of the alkali metals and the halogen elements.

4. Give the electronic structures of C_2H_4, NCl_3, H_2, $LiCl$, CH_2Cl_2, SiO_2, HCl.

5. Which compound of each of the following pairs might be expected to be more polar in character? HI and HF; NH_3 and PH_3; H_2O and H_2S.   Give reasons.

CHAPTER IV

THE PROPERTIES OF GASES

THE GAS LAWS

11a. The States of Matter.—As a general rule, the chemist or physicist is unable to study the properties of individual molecules, but he deals rather with the aggregates of molecules as they occur in nature. It is the aggregations of molecules which come within the scope of human experience that constitute what is known as **matter.** The various kinds of substances that make up matter can be divided roughly into three catagories, namely, gases, liquids and solids; these are often referred to as the three **states of matter.**

The gaseous state is characterized by a marked sensitivity of the volume to changes of temperature and pressure, and also by the fact that a gas normally has no bounding surface and so it tends to fill completely any available space. A liquid, like a gas, has no definite shape, and so it takes the shape of the vessel in which it is placed. There is, however, an important difference between a gas and a liquid; while the former has no surface at all, the latter has a surface which places a limit on the extent of space or volume it can occupy. It is this surface, as will be seen in Chapter V, which is responsible for many of the characteristic properties of liquids. As a general rule, liquids are more dense, that is, they have a greater density, than gases, but there are certain conditions (§ 15b) under which the densities become similar in value. Solids differ markedly from liquids and gases in the respect that they have a definite shape; like liquids, however, their volumes do not alter greatly when subjected to changes of temperature and pressure. From their general behavior, it may be concluded that the properties of liquids are intermediate between those of gases and solids; the order of increasing complexity of the states of matter is thus: gas, liquid, solid. The gaseous state will, therefore, be treated first, and the other states will be considered in later chapters.

11b. Boyle's Law.—When the pressure on a gas is increased, at constant temperature, the volume decreases; a simple relationship between the volume and the pressure was discovered by R. Boyle (1662). He found, within the limits of error of his somewhat crude experiments, that *at constant temperature the volume of a definite mass of gas is inversely proportional to the pressure.* In other words, *the product of the pressure and volume of a given mass of gas is constant at a fixed temperature.* These are alternative statements of **Boyle's law,** which may also be written in the form of the equation

$$PV = \text{constant,} \qquad (11.1)$$

where P is the pressure and V is the volume of a definite mass of gas at a constant temperature. The magnitude of the constant depends on the tempera-

ture and mass of the gas, and also upon its nature. The facts implied by
equation (11.1) may be expressed in still another manner; thus, if V_1 is the
volume of a given mass of gas when the pressure is P_1, and V_2 is the volume of
the same mass of gas when the pressure is changed to P_2, at the same temperature, then

$$P_1 V_1 = P_2 V_2. \tag{11.2}$$

The value of Boyle's law lies in its usefulness for calculating the volume of a
gas at any required pressure, if the volume at another pressure is known.

Problem: A given mass of gas occupies a volume of 240 milliliters (ml.) at a pressure of 1.25 atmospheres (atm.); by how much would the volume change if the pressure
were altered to 0.75 atm. at the same temperature? What would be the volume of
double the given mass of gas at the latter pressure?

Let V ml. be the volume at 0.75 atm.; then by Boyle's law, e.g., equation (11.2),

$$1.25 \times 240 = 0.75 \times V$$

$$V = \frac{1.25 \times 240}{0.75} = 400 \text{ ml.}$$

The volume has therefore increased by $400 - 240 = 160$ ml. as a result of the pressure change.

At a definite temperature and pressure, the volume of a gas is directly proportional
to its mass; hence, doubling the mass would double the volume. The volume of
double the given mass of gas at 0.75 atm. would thus be $2 \times 400 = 800$ ml.

The result of Boyle's law may be represented graphically by plotting the
pressures as ordinates and the corresponding volumes, at constant temperature, as abscissae, as in Fig. 10. The
curve drawn through the resulting points
will then be a rectangular hyperbola, as
shown, if Boyle's law is obeyed. The
general term **isothermal** or **isotherm** is
used to describe a curve, such as that
in Fig. 10, which gives the variation of
volume with pressure of a gas at constant temperature. According to Boyle's
law, then, the isotherm for a definite
mass of a given gas should be a rectangular hyperbola; for each temperature a
different hyperbola would be obtained.

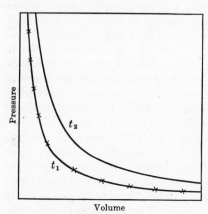

Volume

FIG. 10.   Boyle's law isothermals

**11c. Gay-Lussac's Law: Absolute
Temperatures.**—The variation of the
volume of a gas with temperature, at
constant pressure, is expressed by the
generalization often called **Gay-Lussac's law** (J. L. Gay-Lussac, 1802); it is
sometimes referred to as **Charles's law,** because similar results were obtained
by J. A. C. Charles in 1787, although they were not published at that time.
In its simplest form, the law states that *at constant pressure, the volume of a*

fixed mass of any gas increases by $\frac{1}{273}$ of its volume at $0°$ C for every degree its temperature is raised. If V_0 is the volume of a definite mass of gas at $0°$ C, then the volume V_t at the temperature $t°$ C will be given by

$$V_t = V_0 + t\left(\frac{V_0}{273}\right) \tag{11.3}$$

according to Gay-Lussac's law. An important alternative form of the law may be derived from equation (11.3), by considering the volumes V_1 and V_2 of the same mass of gas at the two temperatures t_1 and t_2, respectively; it follows from equation (11.3) that

$$V_1 = V_0 + t_1\left(\frac{V_0}{273}\right) = V_0\left(1 + \frac{t_1}{273}\right) \tag{11.4}$$

$$V_2 = V_0 + t_2\left(\frac{V_0}{273}\right) = V_0\left(1 + \frac{t_2}{273}\right). \tag{11.5}$$

Upon dividing equation (11.4) by (11.5), the result is readily seen to be

$$\frac{V_1}{V_2} = \frac{273 + t_1}{273 + t_2}. \tag{11.6}$$

Suppose a new scale of temperature is devised in which the degree has the same size as the Centigrade degree, but the zero is $273°$ below the zero on the Centigrade scale; that is to say, the zero on the new scale is at $-273°$ C. Temperatures T on the new scale are then obtained by adding $273°$ to the Centigrade temperature t, viz.,

$$T = 273 + t.$$

The temperatures on the new scale, which is defined more exactly below, are called **absolute temperatures,** because there are reasons for believing that the zero on this scale is the lowest conceivable temperature. The symbol $°K$, that is, "degrees Kelvin," is most frequently employed to represent absolute temperatures, in honor of Lord Kelvin (William Thomson) who derived an exactly equivalent scale from considerations of thermodynamics (§ 25i).

Making use of the definition of absolute temperature, equation (11.6) becomes

$$\frac{V_1}{V_2} = \frac{T_1}{T_2} \tag{11.7}$$

or

$$\frac{V_1}{T_1} = \frac{V_2}{T_2} \tag{11.8}$$

or

$$\frac{V}{T} = \text{constant.} \tag{11.9}$$

These are alternative expressions of Gay-Lussac's law, and their significance may be stated in words in the form of the following statement of the law: *the volume of a given mass of gas at a definite pressure is directly proportional to the absolute temperature.* It may be noted that according to the Gay-Lussac law, the volume of a gas should be zero at the absolute zero, i.e., at −273° C; however, apart from the fact that the gas will have liquefied and solidified before this temperature can be attained, it will be seen shortly that Gay-Lussac's law fails to hold at low temperatures.

Problem: The volume of a given mass of gas is 360 ml. at 15° C; at what temperature will the volume be 480 ml., assuming constant pressure?

The absolute temperature corresponding to 15° C is 273 + 15 = 288° K; the volume is then 360 ml. Let T be the absolute temperature at which the volume is 480 ml.; then according to Gay-Lussac's law, e.g., equation (11.8),

$$\frac{360}{288} = \frac{480}{T}$$

$$T = \frac{480 \times 288}{360} = 384° \text{ K.}$$

The corresponding Centigrade temperature is thus 384 − 273 = 111° C.

11d. Equation of State.—The results of the laws of Boyle and of Gay-Lussac may be combined in an expression which represents the relationship between the pressure, volume and temperature of a given mass of gas; such an expression is described as an **equation of state.** Suppose the gas has initially a volume V_1 at the pressure P_1 and temperature T_1; then when the pressure is changed to P_2 and the temperature to T_2, the volume will be V_2. The relationship between these quantities may be derived in the following manner. Suppose the temperature is maintained at T_1 while the pressure is changed from P_1 to P_2; if the accompanying volume change is from V_1 to V'_1, then Boyle's law, equation (11.2), which is applicable since the temperature is constant, gives

$$P_1 V_1 = P_2 V'_1$$

$$V'_1 = \frac{P_1 V_1}{P_2}. \tag{11.10}$$

The pressure is now kept constant at P_2, and the temperature is altered from T_1 to T_2; the volume will then change from V'_1 to the final value of V_2. Applying Gay-Lussac's law [equation (11.8)], at constant pressure, it follows that

$$\frac{V'_1}{T_1} = \frac{V_2}{T_2},$$

and upon introducing the value of V'_1 from equation (11.10), it is seen that

$$\frac{P_1 V_1}{T_1} = \frac{P_2 V_2}{T_2}. \tag{11.11}$$

An exactly similar result will be obtained for the volume V_3 at pressure P_3 and temperature T_3, and so on; hence,

$$\frac{P_1 V_1}{T_1} = \frac{P_2 V_2}{T_2} = \frac{P_3 V_3}{T_3} = \cdots,$$

or, in general,

$$\frac{PV}{T} = \text{constant}, \qquad (11.12)$$

for a given mass of gas. The equation (11.12) is thus a form of the equation of state for a gas which obeys Boyle's law and Gay-Lussac's law; it implies that, for a definite mass of gas, *any change of temperature and pressure will be accompanied by an adjustment of volume so that the quantity PV/T remains unaltered.*

Problem: A given mass of gas occupies a volume of 250 ml. at 21° C and a pressure of 1.4 atm. At what pressure will the volume be 300 ml. when the temperature is raised to 49° C?

For this problem it is convenient to use equation (11.11); then

$P_1 = 1.4$ atm. $V_1 = 250$ ml. $T_1 = 273 + 21 = 294°$ K

$P_2 = ?$ $V_2 = 300$ ml. $T_2 = 273 + 49 = 322°$ K

Consequently,

$$\frac{1.4 \times 250}{294} = \frac{P_2 \times 300}{322}$$

$$P_2 = \frac{1.4 \times 250 \times 322}{294 \times 300} = 1.28 \text{ atm.}$$

11e. The Ideal Gas Equation.—The value of the constant in equation (11.12) depends upon the mass and nature of the gas, but the introduction of Avogadro's law permits of a remarkable simplification. According to this law, equal numbers of molecules of different gases will occupy the same volume, at a given temperature and pressure. In other words, provided equal numbers of molecules are concerned, and P and T are the same, V will be the same for different gases; the constant in equation (11.12) will then obviously be independent of the nature of the gas. As seen in § 3d, one mole, i.e., one gram molecular weight, of any substance always contains the same number of molecules; hence, *provided one mole of gas is under consideration, PV/T will be equal to a universal constant R, known as the* **gas constant,** *which has the same value for all gases.* The general equation of state for any gas would then be

$$\frac{PV}{T} = R$$

or

$$PV = RT, \qquad (11.13)$$

where V is the volume occupied by 1 mole, i.e., the **molar volume,** at the pressure P and the temperature T. At the same pressure and temperature, the

volume of n *moles* would be n times as great as for 1 mole; if v is this volume,*
then
$$Pv = nRT. \tag{11.14}$$

So far it has been tacitly assumed that gases do actually obey the laws of Boyle and Gay-Lussac; however, for real gases these laws can only be regarded as approximations applicable at relatively low gas pressures and moderately high temperatures. It will be seen later (§ 13a) that actual gases exhibit deviations from the gas laws, such deviations being greater the nearer the temperatures and pressures are to the conditions under which the gas can be condensed to a liquid. It appears, therefore, that equations (11.13) and (11.14), and all other equations based on Boyle's law and Gay-Lussac's law, as given in previous sections, cannot be regarded as correct for real gases. It is, nevertheless, very useful to postulate a hypothetical or imaginary **ideal gas**, or **perfect gas**, defined as a gas to which the laws of Boyle and Gay-Lussac are strictly applicable. For such a gas, too, the Avogadro law, from which actual gases show deviations, holds precisely, and so equations (11.13) and (11.14) are exact; these are consequently forms of the equation of state for an ideal gas. The equation (11.13) is thus frequently referred to as the **ideal gas equation** or the **ideal gas law equation** for one mole.

Since equations (11.13) and (11.14) do not apply to real gases, there immediately arises the problem of the evaluation of the ideal gas constant R, for it is only for ideal gases that R would be an exact constant. If the pressure P and volume V of 1 mole of an ideal gas were known at a definite temperature T, it would be a simple matter to evaluate R from equation (11.13), but as no gas behaves ideally, this procedure would appear to be ruled out. Fortunately, it is an experimental fact that all gases *approach* ideal behavior as the pressure is decreased. Hence, by making pressure, volume and temperature measurements on a real gas at a number of pressures, and extrapolating the results to zero pressure, it is possible to derive the properties of an ideal gas.

The data obtained in this manner, after extrapolation, should be independent of the actual gas employed for the experiments, and this expectation has been confirmed. From measurements of the effect of temperature on the volume of a gas at constant pressure, the limiting (extrapolated) value of the coefficient of expansion at zero pressure is found to be 0.0036609, in place of the approximate figure $\frac{1}{273}$ given in § 11c. The absolute zero of temperature for an ideal gas on the Centigrade scale is then

$$0°\,K = -\frac{1}{0.0036609} = -273.16°\,C.$$

Strictly speaking, therefore, it is necessary to add 273.16 to the Centigrade temperature to obtain that on the absolute (Kelvin) scale. For many purposes, however, it is sufficient to use the approximate value of $-273°$ C for the absolute zero.

* The convention which will be employed subsequently, as far as possible, is to use capital V for the volume of 1 mole, and a small v when the given volume contains the general number n moles.

By measuring the volumes of gases at different pressures and constant temperature, and making allowance for the departure from ideal behavior, in the manner to be described in § 14a, the volume occupied by 1 mole of an ideal gas at standard temperature and pressure (S.T.P.), defined as 0° C, i.e., 273.16° K, and 1 atm., i.e., 76.0 cm. of mercury, respectively, is 22.414 liters.

11f. Evaluation of the Gas Constant.—All the data are now available for calculating the ideal gas constant R, but before doing so it is necessary to consider the matter of the proper **units** to employ. The question of units is one that is of fundamental importance in many aspects of physical chemistry, and the evaluation of the gas constant will serve to illustrate some of the points involved.

The most general definition of R is given by equation (11.14) as

$$R = \frac{Pv}{Tn}, \tag{11.15}$$

and so the gas constant has the dimensions of pressure × volume divided by number of moles × temperature. The dimensions of pressure are force × (area)$^{-1}$, i.e., pressure is force per unit area, and area is (length)^2; hence,

$$\text{pressure} = \text{force} \times (\text{length})^{-2}. \tag{11.16}$$

Since volume has the dimensions of (length)^3, and temperature is expressed in degrees, it follows from equation (11.15) that

$$R = \frac{\text{force} \times (\text{length})^{-2} \times (\text{length})^3}{\text{degrees} \times \text{no. of moles}}.$$

The product of force and length is energy, and so

$$R = \frac{\text{energy}}{\text{degrees} \times \text{no. of moles}}. \tag{11.17}$$

It is thus seen that *the proper dimensions for the expression of R are energy per degree per mole*, i.e., energy degree^{-1} mole^{-1}. It may be noted, incidentally, by comparing equations (11.15) and (11.17), that the product of pressure and volume has the dimensions of energy.

The temperature employed in the evaluation of the gas constant is invariably the absolute temperature, based on the Centigrade degree, but the energy may be stated in various ways, of which three are most commonly used; these are (i) liter-atmospheres, (ii) ergs, and (iii) calories, which will be considered in turn.

I. Energy in Liter-Atmospheres.—For this purpose, the volume of the gas is expressed in liters and the pressure in atmospheres; the energy is then in liter-atmospheres. As seen above, 1 mole, i.e., $n = 1$, of an ideal gas occupies 22.414 liters at 1 atm. pressure and a temperature of 273.16° K; hence,

$$R = \frac{PV}{T} = \frac{1 \times 22.414}{273.16}$$
$$= 0.082054 \text{ liter-atm. degree}^{-1} \text{ mole}^{-1}.$$

II. Energy in Ergs.—The pressure must now be stated in cm. gram sec. (c.g.s.) units, i.e., dynes per sq. cm., and the volume in cubic centimeters. Since 1 atm. is equivalent to 76.0 cm. of mercury, the density of which is 13.595 at 0° C, it follows that

$$1 \text{ atm.} = 76.0 \times 13.595 \times 980.66 \text{ dynes cm.}^{-2},$$

where 980.66 cm. per sec. per sec. is the acceleration due to gravity. Upon multiplying out, it is found that

$$1 \text{ atm.} = 1.0132 \times 10^6 \text{ dynes cm.}^{-2}$$

The volume of 1 mole of ideal gas at S.T.P. is 22,414 ml. and since 1 ml. is actually 1.000027 cc., this volume is 22,414.6 cc. The value of R is then given by

$$R = \frac{PV}{T} = \frac{1.0132 \times 10^6 \times 22,414.6}{273.16}$$

$$= 8.314 \times 10^7 \text{ ergs degree}^{-1} \text{ mole}^{-1}.$$

III. Energy in Calories.—The evaluation of the gas constant with the energy in calories is most readily made by utilizing the fact that a calorie is equivalent to 4.184×10^7 ergs (§ 23a). It follows then that

$$R = \frac{8.314 \times 10^7}{4.184 \times 10^7} = 1.987 \text{ cal. degree}^{-1} \text{ mole}^{-1}.$$

It is seen that the gas constant is very close to 2 cal. degree^{-1} mole^{-1}, i.e., 2 cal. per degree per mole. This approximate value is frequently employed in calculations, but it must be clearly understood that this can only be done if the energy, i.e., the pressure-volume product, is expressed in calories. The necessity for exercising great care in the matter of the use of the proper units cannot be stressed too strongly; examples will be given from time to time illustrating the correct choice of units.

Problem: How many moles of oxygen are contained in 10.0 liters of the gas at a pressure of 75.0 cm. of mercury and a temperature of 27° C, assuming ideal behavior?

A pressure of 75.0 cm. of mercury is equal to 75.0/76.0 atm., and since the volume is given in liters, it is convenient to express R in liter-atm., i.e., 0.082. The temperature T is $273 + 27 = 300°$ K, and hence rearrangement of equation (11.14) gives

$$n = \frac{Pv}{RT} = \frac{(75/76) \times 10.0}{0.082 \times 300} = 0.401 \text{ mole.}$$

11g. Mixtures of Gases: Dalton's Law of Partial Pressures.—The connection between the total pressure of a mixture of gases and the pressures of the individual gases was expressed by J. Dalton (1801) in the form of the **law of partial pressures.** The **partial pressure** of each gas in a mixture is defined as *the pressure the gas would exert if it alone occupied the whole volume of the mixture at the same temperature.* According to Dalton's law of partial pressures, *the* *total pressure of a mixture of gases is equal to the sum of the partial pressures of the constituent gases.*

Consider a vessel of volume v containing three gases, the amounts being n_1, n_2 and n_3 moles, respectively. Suppose that if the vessel were occupied exclusively by the n_1 moles of the first gas, the pressure would be p_1; if it contained the n_2 moles of the second gas only, the pressure would be p_2; and if the n_3 moles of the third gas were the sole occupants of the vessel the pressure would be p_3, all at a definite temperature. If the total pressure when the three gases are present in the vessel is P, then by the law of partial pressures

$$P = p_1 + p_2 + p_3, \tag{11.18}$$

and so on, for any mixture of gases. For reasons which will appear shortly, the law of partial pressures suffers from the same limitations as do the other gas laws. The equation (11.18) is strictly applicable, therefore, to a mixture of ideal gases, although the deviations exhibited by actual gases are not large unless the conditions approach those under which liquefaction is possible.

If each of the gases present in the mixture behaves ideally, it is possible to write for each of the gases separately occupying the vessel of volume v,

$$p_1 v = n_1 RT \tag{11.19a}$$

$$p_2 v = n_2 RT \tag{11.19b}$$

$$p_3 v = n_3 RT, \text{etc.,} \tag{11.19c}$$

and hence,

$$(p_1 + p_2 + p_3 + \cdots)v = (n_1 + n_2 + n_3 + \cdots)RT. \tag{11.20}$$

According to the law of partial pressures, represented by equation (11.18), the sum of the partial pressures p_1, p_2, p_3, etc., may be replaced by the total pressure P; consequently equation (11.20) becomes

$$Pv = (n_1 + n_2 + \cdots)RT = nRT, \tag{11.21}$$

where n, equal to $n_1 + n_2 + n_3 + \cdots$, is the total number of moles in the gas mixture. By combining equation (11.19a) with (11.21), it is seen that

$$p_1 = \frac{n_1}{n} P. \tag{11.22a}$$

Similarly, from equations (11.19b) and (11.21),

$$p_2 = \frac{n_2}{n} P, \tag{11.22b}$$

and so on. The fractions n_1/n, n_2/n, etc., are called the **mole fractions** of the respective gases. The mole fraction of a constituent of any mixture—gaseous, liquid or solid—is defined as *the number of moles (or molecules) of that constituent divided by the total number of moles (or molecules) in the mixture.* If the symbol

x is used to represent the mole fraction, it is seen that the equations (11.22) may be written as

$$p_1 = x_1 P, \quad p_2 = x_2 P, \text{ etc.} \tag{11.23}$$

This result is an important consequence of Dalton's law, for it enables the partial pressure of any constituent of a mixture of ideal gases to be calculated from the total pressure, at the same temperature, if the mole fraction is known.

There are many useful applications of the law of partial pressures in physical chemistry; some of these are illustrated by the following problems.

Problem: A gas collected over water at 25° C becomes saturated with water vapor; the measured volume is 190 ml. at a total pressure of 740 mm. of mercury. The partial pressure of the water vapor in the mixture, equal to the vapor pressure of water at 25°, is 23.8 mm. Calculate the volume the dry gas would occupy at a pressure of 760 mm., assuming the gas and the water vapor to behave ideally.

The partial pressure p of the dry gas is equal to the total pressure, i.e., 740 mm., minus the partial pressure of the water vapor, i.e., 23.8 mm.; hence,

$$p = 740 - 23.8 = 716.2 \text{ mm.}$$

This is the pressure of the dry gas when it occupies the whole volume of 190 ml.; the volume v of the dry gas at a pressure of 760 mm. is then given by Boyle's law as

$$716.2 \times 190 = 760 \times v$$

$$v = \frac{716.2 \times 190}{760} = 179.0 \text{ ml.}$$

Problem: A mixture consists of 0.495 gram of gas A of molecular weight 66.0, and 0.182 gram of a gas B of molecular weight 45.5; the total pressure is 76.2 cm. of mercury. Calculate the partial pressures of the two gases.

$$\text{Number of moles of gas A is } \frac{0.495}{66.0} = 0.0075$$

$$\text{Number of moles of gas B is } \frac{0.182}{45.5} = 0.0040$$

$$\text{Total number of moles} = 0.0075 + 0.0040 = 0.0115.$$

The mole fraction of A is thus 0.0075/0.0115, and hence by equation (11.23),

$$\text{Partial pressure of A} = \frac{0.0075}{0.0115} \times 76.2 = 49.7 \text{ cm. of mercury,}$$

and

$$\text{Partial pressure of B} = \frac{0.0040}{0.0115} \times 76.2 = 26.5 \text{ cm. of mercury.}$$

Alternatively, the latter quantity can be obtained by subtracting 49.7 cm. from the total pressure 76.2 cm.

Problem: A volume of 125 ml. of gas A measured at 0.60 atm., and 150 ml. of a gas B at a pressure of 0.80 atm., are passed into a vessel whose capacity is 500 ml. What is the total pressure of the mixture in the vessel at the same temperature?

The partial pressure p_A of A is the pressure the gas would exert if it alone occupied the 500 ml. vessel; since its pressure is 0.60 atm. when it occupies 125 ml., it follows from Boyle's law that

$$p_A \times 500 = 0.60 \times 125,$$

$$p_A = \frac{0.60 \times 125}{500} = 0.15 \text{ atm.}$$

Similarly, the partial pressure p_B of B will be given by

$$p_B \times 500 = 0.80 \times 150,$$

$$p_B = \frac{0.80 \times 150}{500} = 0.24 \text{ atm.}$$

The total pressure, which is the sum of the two partial pressures, is then $0.15 + 0.24 = 0.39$ atm.

11h. Diffusion of Gases: Graham's Law.—The phenomenon of **diffusion** may be described as *the tendency for any substance to spread uniformly throughout the space available to it.* Diffusion is exhibited by gases, liquids and even by solids, but it is most rapid with gases. If a wide-mouthed jar of hydrogen is placed mouth to mouth with a jar of oxygen, it will be found, after a short time, that the two gases will spread uniformly throughout the two jars. This will happen irrespective of whether the lighter gas is in the top or the bottom jar. It is true that gravity has some effect on the distribution of the gases, but this is quite negligible unless a long column of gas is under consideration, as in the earth's atmosphere.

The term diffusion is frequently applied, also, to the movement of gases through porous media, such as porous earthenware. If a porous pot, filled with hydrogen, for example, is left in air, the hydrogen will diffuse out of the interior and the air will diffuse in from the outside. A phenomenon that is probably related to this passage of gases through fine pores, is that which has been called **effusion**; this is the streaming of a gas through a small hole.

The rate at which a gas diffuses, or effuses, is dependent upon its density, and the connection is given by Graham's **law of diffusion** (T. Graham, 1829). According to this law, which, like the other gas laws, is approximate only, *the rate of diffusion (or effusion) of a gas is inversely proportional to the square root of its density.* If D_1 and D_2 represent the rates of diffusion of two gases whose densities under the given conditions are d_1 and d_2, respectively, then

$$\frac{D_1}{D_2} = \sqrt{\frac{d_2}{d_1}}. \tag{11.24}$$

As seen in § 3e, the density of a gas is directly proportional to its molecular weight; hence, equation (11.24) may be written as

$$\frac{D_1}{D_2} = \sqrt{\frac{M_2}{M_1}}, \tag{11.25}$$

where M_1 and M_2 are the molecular weights of the two gases.

It follows from Graham's law of diffusion that a light gas will diffuse more rapidly than a heavy one. This fact was utilized in the earliest attempts to separate the isotopes of neon (F. W. Aston, 1913), and diffusion methods have frequently been used for isotopic separations in more recent times (§ 7g). The greatest success has been achieved in connection with the separation of the isotopes of hydrogen, because of the relatively large ratio of the densities. The ratio of the density of hydrogen to that of deuterium is approximately 1 to 2, and hence the rates of diffusion are in the ratio of $\sqrt{2}$ to 1.

The results of Graham's law of diffusion have been used to determine gas densities by measuring the time required for a definite volume of the gas to effuse through a small hole in a thin metal plate. The experiment is then repeated, under precisely the same conditions, with a gas of known density. The time required for the volume of gas to pass through the hole is inversely proportional to its rate of diffusion (or effusion); if the times for the two gases are t_1 and t_2, then by equations (11.24) and (11.25),

$$\frac{t_2}{t_1} = \sqrt{\frac{d_2}{d_1}} = \sqrt{\frac{M_2}{M_1}}. \tag{11.26}$$

Hence, either the density or the molecular weight of the unknown gas can be determined, approximately, provided a comparison gas, of known density or molecular weight, is available. The effusion method was used by A. Debierne (1910) to obtain the molecular weight, and hence the atomic weight, of the radioactive gas radon.

Problem: The time taken for a certain volume of gas to stream through a small hole was 1.44 min.; under exactly the same conditions an equal volume of oxygen took 1.80 min. to pass through. Calculate the approximate density of the gas relative to hydrogen.

The molecular weight of oxygen is 32, and hence its density d_1 relative to that of hydrogen (molecular weight = 2) is 16; the time t_1 of diffusion of oxygen is 1.80 min., while that, t_2, for the other gas is 1.44 min. If the density of the latter is d_2, then, by equation (11.26),

$$\frac{1.44}{1.80} = \sqrt{\frac{d_2}{16}}$$

$$d_2 = \left(\frac{1.44}{1.80}\right)^2 \times 16 = 10.2.$$

THE KINETIC THEORY OF GASES

12a. The Fundamentals of the Kinetic Theory.—Now that the general properties of gases, particularly ideal gases, have been described, it is of interest to develop a theory which permits the various laws of gaseous behavior to be coordinated. Such a theory is the **kinetic theory of gases**. The essential postulate of this theory is that *a gas consists of a large number of very small, perfectly elastic particles, which may be identified with the chemical molecules,* *moving about in all directions.* As a result of this continual movement, the molecules will frequently collide with each other and with the walls of the containing vessel; it is these elastic impacts on the walls of the vessel that are supposed to be responsible for the pressure exerted by the gas. Increase of temperature will result in a more vigorous movement of the molecules, so that if the volume is kept constant the pressure will increase. Further, if the molecules are made to occupy a smaller volume, they will strike the walls of the vessel more frequently, and so there will be an increase of pressure. These qualitative conclusions, drawn from the kinetic theory of gases, are, of course, in agreement with observation; it is more important, however, to see if the theory can predict quantitatively the behavior of gases.

For the present, the treatment will be restricted to an ideal gas; for such a substance, it is postulated that *the molecules are so small that their actual volume is negligible in comparison with the total volume of the gas.* Further, it is supposed that *the molecules exert no attraction upon one another.* With these simple assumptions, it is possible to develop an expression for the pressure of an ideal gas.

12b. Pressure of an Ideal Gas.—Several methods have been proposed for the calculation of gas pressure from the kinetic theory; the most rigid are somewhat complicated, and so a simple, although approximate, derivation which leads to the correct result will be given here. Imagine a cube of l cm. edge, containing n molecules, each having an actual mass of m gram. These molecules are moving at random in all directions, but since no direction will be preferred over any other, the molecules may be regarded as divided up into three equal sets, each containing $\frac{1}{3}n$ molecules, moving parallel to each of the three axes of the cube. Thus, one third of the molecules are supposed to be moving right and left; another third are regarded as moving up and down; and the last third are imagined to be moving back and forth in the cubic vessel.

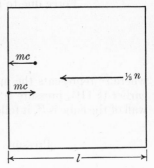

Fig. 11. Impacts of perfectly elastic molecules on wall of vessel

Consider the group of $\frac{1}{3}n$ molecules moving right and left; they will be travelling in a direction perpendicular to the right and left walls of the cube, as indicated in Fig. 11. The velocities of all the molecules will not be the same, and so one particular molecule, having a velocity of c cm. per sec., will be considered. This molecule will strike the wall with a momentum equal to the product of its mass and velocity, i.e., mc gram cm. per sec. Since the molecule is supposed to be perfectly elastic, it will rebound with exactly the same velocity, and momentum, *in the opposite direction*, as shown in Fig. 11. The change in momentum per impact is thus $2mc$ gram cm. per sec. Before the molecule can return to strike the same wall again, it must travel twice across the cube, that is, a distance of $2l$ cm.; since the speed is c cm. per sec., the number of impacts per second on the given wall will be $c/2l$. The change of momentum per second due to impacts of the molecule is thus equal to the product of $2mc$ and $c/2l$, i.e., mc^2/l; hence,

Rate of change of momentum for a single molecule $= \dfrac{mc^2}{l}$ gram cm. sec.$^{-2}$

According to Newton's laws of motion, the rate of change of momentum is equal to the force acting; consequently,

$$\text{Force due to impacts of a single molecule} = \frac{mc^2}{l} \text{ dynes.}$$

It may be noted that force expressed in dynes is equivalent to gram cm. per sec. per sec., i.e., gram cm. sec.$^{-2}$, units.

Each of the $\frac{1}{3}n$ molecules moving in the same direction as the single molecule just considered will strike the wall with a force of similar value, but since the velocities of the molecules are not all equal, it is seen that

$$\text{Force due to impacts of } \tfrac{1}{3}n \text{ molecules} = \frac{m\overline{c^2}}{l} \times \frac{n}{3}$$

$$= \frac{nm\overline{c^2}}{3l} \text{ dynes,}$$

where $\overline{c^2}$ represents the mean square velocity of all the molecules.* As seen earlier (§ 11f), pressure is defined as force per unit area; since the area of the wall of the cube is l^2, it follows that the pressure exerted on this wall is given by

$$\text{Pressure} = \frac{nm\overline{c^2}}{3l} \times \frac{1}{l^2} = \frac{nm\overline{c^2}}{3l^3} \text{ dynes cm.}^{-2}$$

The quantity l^3 is obviously equal to the volume v of the cube, and if the pressure is represented by P, it follows that

$$P = \frac{nm\overline{c^2}}{3v} \text{ dynes cm.}^{-2} \tag{12.1}$$

Although this result has been obtained for the pressure exerted by the $\frac{1}{3}n$ molecules on one particular face of the cube, it is obvious that an exactly similar pressure can be calculated for the molecules striking the other faces. This must therefore represent the actual pressure of the gas in the containing vessel. An expression has thus been derived from the kinetic theory which relates the gas pressure to the volume of the vessel and to certain properties of the molecules.

---

* This quantity $\overline{c^2}$ is equivalent to finding the squares of the velocities of all the molecules, adding these squares together, and taking the average. It must not be confused with the square of the mean velocity, i.e., $\bar{c}^2$, which would be obtained by evaluating the mean velocity of all the molecules and then squaring the result. The square root of the mean square velocity, i.e., $\sqrt{\overline{c^2}}$, is thus not equal to the mean velocity $\bar{c}$; it can be shown that the latter is equal to $\sqrt{8/3\pi}$, i.e., 0.921, times the former.

12c. Derivations from the Kinetic Theory.—The speeds of the molecules of a gas will increase with increasing temperature, and it is possible to define temperature, on the basis of the kinetic theory, as being proportional to the mean kinetic energy $\frac{1}{2}m\overline{c^2}$ per molecule. This definition is in harmony with the theoretical deduction of J. Clerk Maxwell (1860) that *the mean kinetic energies of the molecules of all gases are the same at constant temperature.* It will be seen shortly that the temperature scale based on the mean kinetic energy is actually identical with the familiar absolute scale of temperature. In the meantime, however, use will be made of the conclusion, which follows from the definition, that at constant temperature the kinetic energy $\frac{1}{2}m\overline{c^2}$ is constant for a given gas. If a definite mass of gas is under consideration, the total number of molecules n will evidently remain unchanged; hence, for a given mass of gas at constant temperature, the quantity $\frac{1}{2}nm\overline{c^2}$ will be constant. If, now, equation (12.1) is rewritten in the form

$$Pv = \tfrac{1}{3}nm\overline{c^2}, \tag{12.2}$$

it is apparent that, for a definite mass of gas at constant temperature, the right-hand side of equation (12.2) will remain constant; hence,

$$Pv = \text{constant},$$

in agreement with Boyle's law. The kinetic theory of gases, as applied to an ideal gas, thus provides a satisfactory basis for this law.

For any two gases, indicated by the suffixes 1 and 2, it is possible to write, in accordance with equation (12.2),

$$P_1 v_1 = \tfrac{1}{3} n_1 m_1 \overline{c_1^2} \quad \text{and} \quad P_2 v_2 = \tfrac{1}{3} n_2 m_2 \overline{c_2^2}. \tag{12.3}$$

If the two gases have the same pressure, i.e., $P_1 = P_2$, and occupy the same volume, i.e., $v_1 = v_2$, it follows from the equations (12.3) that

$$\tfrac{1}{3} n_1 m_1 \overline{c_1^2} = \tfrac{1}{3} n_2 m_2 \overline{c_2^2}. \tag{12.4}$$

If the gases are also at the same temperature, the mean kinetic energies of the molecules will be the same, as mentioned above; that is,

$$\tfrac{1}{2} m_1 \overline{c_1^2} = \tfrac{1}{2} m_2 \overline{c_2^2}. \tag{12.5}$$

Combination of equations (12.4) and (12.5) then immediately leads to the result

$$n_1 = n_2.$$

In other words, it is seen that for two gases at the same pressure and temperature, equal volumes should contain equal numbers of molecules; this is, of course, Avogadro's law, which has thus been derived from the kinetic theory for an ideal gas.

12d. Kinetic Energy and Temperature.—As a result of introducing the postulate that the temperature T of the gas is proportional to the mean kinetic energy $\frac{1}{2}m\overline{c^2}$ of the molecules, it follows from equation (12.2) that

$$Pv = nkT, \tag{12.6}$$

where k is a proportionality constant that is the same for all gases. (The conclusion that k is a universal constant follows from Maxwell's proof that at a given temperature the mean kinetic energy is independent of the nature of the gas.) If the pressure P of a given mass of gas is maintained constant, it is evident from equation (12.6) that v will be proportional to T, since P, n and k are all constant; hence,

$$\frac{v}{T} = \text{constant.}$$

This result is identical with equation (11.9) which expresses the experimental facts of Gay-Lussac's law. It is seen, therefore, that the temperature scale defined in terms of the mean kinetic energy of the molecules is the same as the absolute scale derived from the expansion of an ideal gas (§ 11c).

For 1 mole of gas, the number n of molecules in the given volume, now represented by V, is equal to the Avogadro number N(§ 3d); equation (12.6) may then be written as

$$PV = NkT. \tag{12.7}$$

Further, since both N and k are universal constants, their product will have a constant value for 1 mole of any ideal gas; representing this by R, equation (12.7) becomes

$$PV = RT,$$

which is the same as the familiar equation of state for 1 mole of an ideal gas, R being the gas constant.

It may be noted, incidentally, that since k is equal to R/N, it may be regarded as the *gas constant per single molecule;* this quantity is known as the **Boltzmann constant.** It is usually expressed in ergs deg.$^{-1}$; thus, since R is 8.314×10^7 ergs deg.$^{-1}$ mole^{-1} (§ 11f, II), and N is 6.023×10^{23}, it follows that the value of the Boltzmann constant is 1.380×10^{-16} erg deg.$^{-1}$ molecule^{-1}.

Since $\frac{1}{2}m\overline{c^2}$ is the mean kinetic energy per molecule, $\frac{1}{2}Nm\overline{c^2}$ will be equal to the total kinetic energy of all the molecules in 1 mole of gas; if this is represented by E_K, then

$$E_K = \frac{1}{2}Nm\overline{c^2}.$$

For 1 mole of gas, containing N molecules, equation (12.2) may be expressed as

$$Pv = \frac{1}{3}Nm\overline{c^2}, \tag{12.8}$$

and hence,

$$Pv = \frac{2}{3}E_K. \tag{12.9}$$

Further, since Pv is equal to RT for 1 mole,

$$E_K = \frac{3}{2}RT. \tag{12.10}$$

The total kinetic energy of the molecules in 1 mole of an ideal gas is thus equal to $\frac{3}{2}RT$.

12e. The Law of Partial Pressures.—If n_1 molecules of a gas 1, each having a mass m_1 and a mean square velocity $\overline{c_1^2}$, occupied a volume v, the pressure p_1 exerted by these molecules would be given by the kinetic theory [equation (12.1)] as

$$p_1 = \frac{n_1 m_1 \overline{c_1^2}}{3v}. \tag{12.11}$$

Similarly, if n_2 molecules of gas 2 occupied the same volume v, to the exclusion of the other molecules, the pressure would be

$$p_2 = \frac{n_2 m_2 \overline{c_2^2}}{3v}, \tag{12.12}$$

where m_2 is the mass and $\overline{c_2^2}$ is the mean square velocity of these molecules. Analogous expressions can, of course, be derived for the pressures p_3, p_4, etc., for any molecular (gaseous) species occupying the same volume.

If all the gases 1, 2, 3, etc., were present in the vessel of volume v at the same time, then, provided the various molecules do not interact with one another, and they all behave ideally, the kinetic theory treatment would lead to the result

$$P = \frac{n_1 m_1 \overline{c_1^2}}{3v} + \frac{n_2 m_2 \overline{c_2^2}}{3v} + \frac{n_3 m_3 \overline{c_3^2}}{3v} + \cdots \tag{12.12}$$

for the total pressure P due to all the molecules. Upon introducing the results of equations (12.11), (12.12), etc., which give the values of the partial pressures of the constituents of the mixture, it is seen that

$$P = p_1 + p_2 + p_3 + \cdots,$$

which is Dalton's law of partial pressures [equation (11.18)]. This law, like the other laws applicable to ideal gases, may therefore be correlated with the simple kinetic theory of gases.

12f. Molecular Velocities: Diffusion.—For 1 mole of gas, the gas law equation (11.13) and equation (12.8) yield the result

$$PV = RT = \tfrac{1}{3} N m \overline{c^2},$$

and since the product of the Avogadro number N and the weight m of a single molecule is equal to the molecular weight M, it follows that

$$RT = \tfrac{1}{3} M \overline{c^2},$$

and consequently,

$$\sqrt{\overline{c^2}} = \sqrt{\frac{3RT}{M}}. \tag{12.14}$$

This equation shows that the velocity of a molecule or, more exactly, *the square root of the mean square velocity of the molecules, is directly proportional to the square root of the absolute temperature and inversely to the square root of the molecular weight of the gas.* If the latter is known, the molecular velocity can be calculated at any desired temperature, making use of the experimental value of R derived in § 11f.

Problem: Calculate the approximate mean velocity of oxygen molecules at 25° C.

If the velocity is to be expressed in cm. per sec., i.e., in c.g.s. units, the value of R must be in the same units, i.e., ergs deg.$^{-1}$ mole^{-1}, that is, 8.31×10^7. The absolute temperature T is $273 + 25 = 298°$ K, and the molecular weight M of oxygen is 32; hence, by equation (12.14),

$$c \approx \sqrt{\overline{c^2}} = \sqrt{\frac{3 \times 8.31 \times 10^7 \times 298}{32}} = 4.82 \times 10^4 \text{ cm. sec.}^{-1}$$

The average velocity of an oxygen molecule at 25° C is about 482 meters per sec., which is approximately the same as the velocity of sound in the gas at the same temperature. For a substance of higher molecular weight the average speed of the molecules would be less; for higher temperatures the velocities would be greater. Although the direct experimental determination of the speeds with which molecules travel is not an easy matter, a number of methods have been devised that make this possible. The results are not exact, but they are nevertheless in very satisfactory agreement with those calculated from the kinetic theory of gases.

Because of frequent collisions with one another, the molecules of a gas do not travel very far in a direct line; however, the resultant rate of progress in a particular direction may be expected to be dependent on the molecular velocity. If this is the case, the rate at which a gas diffuses should be proportional to the speeds of the molecules; thus, for two gases whose rates of diffusion are D_1 and D_2, it is reasonable to write

$$\frac{D_1}{D_2} = \frac{c_1}{c_2}, \tag{12.15}$$

where c_1 and c_2 are the mean velocities of the molecules of the two gases. Assuming, as is actually the case (see footnote, page 88), that the mean velocity of the molecules of a gas is proportional to, if not equal to, the square root of the mean square velocity, it follows from equations (12.14) and (12.15) that

$$\frac{D_1}{D_2} = \sqrt{\frac{M_2}{M_1}}$$

at constant temperature. Comparison with equation (11.25) shows that this is a form of Graham's diffusion law, which has thus been derived from the kinetic theory.

The rate of the true process of effusion, that is, the passage of gas through a small hole in a thin plate, depends on the number of molecules that strike the area occupied by the hole, in a given time. The conditions are then such that every molecule striking this area passes through the hole. It is possible to calculate from the kinetic theory the rate of effusion of a gas on this basis, and it is found to be inversely proportional to the square root of the molecular weight (or density), as is found experimentally.

12g. Distribution of Molecular Velocities.—The molecules of a gas do not all move with the same speed; because of the frequent collisions, there is a continual interchange of momentum between the molecules, and hence their velocities will vary. Even if all the molecules in a vessel were started off moving in parallel lines with the same velocity, the slightest disturbance of a single molecule, due to gravitational or other forces, would result in collisions and ultimately in the chaotic molecular movement that is believed to occur in a gas. The manner in which the molecules of a gas are distributed over the possible velocities, from zero to very high values, was first worked out by

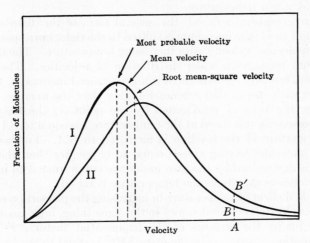

FIG. 12.   Maxwell's law of the distribution of molecular velocities

J. C. Maxwell (1860), using the theory of probability. The results are expressed as the **law of distribution of molecular velocities,** one form of which is

$$\frac{1}{n} \cdot \frac{dn}{dc} = 4\pi \left(\frac{M}{2\pi RT}\right)^{3/2} e^{-Mc^2/2RT} c^2. \tag{12.16}$$

In this expression, the left-hand side is virtually (although not exactly) the fraction of the total number of molecules (n) having a particular velocity c. This fraction can be readily calculated, for all the quantities on the right-hand side of equation (12.16) are known; thus, M is the molecular weight of the gas, R is the gas constant, which must be expressed in ergs deg.$^{-1}$ mole^{-1}, if the velocity c is in cm. per sec.; T is the absolute temperature and e is the base of natural logarithms. By deciding on any given gas of molecular weight M, at any desired temperature T, the fraction of the molecules having a particular velocity c can be determined.

The consequences of Maxwell's law are conveniently represented graphically, as in curve I in Fig. 12; the ordinates give the fraction of the molecules having velocities indicated by the abscissae. The actual curve will depend on the molecular weight of the gas and the temperature, but the general form is always the same. The maximum of the curve indicates the **most probable velocity,** which is the velocity possessed by more molecules than is any other velocity. The relationship of this is to the mean velocity, $\bar{c}$, and to the square root of the mean square velocity, $\sqrt{\bar{c^2}}$, is shown; the values are seen to be close together but not identical. It is evident from the shape of the curve that the majority of the molecules of the gas have speeds that are in the vicinity of the average or most probable velocities. Nevertheless, there are always some molecules that have very low and some that have very high speeds at any given temperature.

As the temperature is raised, the general form of the distribution curve changes from I to II; the maximum is shifted to the right, corresponding to the increase of molecular velocity with increasing temperature. The flattening of the maximum indicates a wider distribution of velocities. The important point to note, however, is that there is a pronounced increase in the number of molecules with speeds that are much higher than the average. Consider, for example, the velocity represented by the point A; the fraction of the molecules possessing this speed at the temperature I is equal to BA, but at the higher temperature II the fraction is increased to $B'A$. Further, the total number of molecules having speeds equal to or greater than the particular value at A is determined by the area under the curve from A to infinity; this obviously increases rapidly as the temperature is raised..

The marked effect of temperature in increasing the proportion of molecules having high velocities or, what comes to the same thing, high kinetic energies, is provided for by the presence of the exponential factor $e^{-Mc^2/2RT}$ in the Maxwell equation (12.16). The quantity $\frac{1}{2}Mc^2$ is equal to the kinetic energy of 1 mole of molecules each of which has the same velocity c; this may be replaced by E, representing the kinetic energy of these molecules, so that the exponential factor may be written as $e^{-E/RT}$. A factor of this type appears in other expressions for the distribution of various forms of energy, such as rotational, vibrational and electronic, and in related equations (see § 38c); it is frequently referred to as the **Boltzmann factor.** Because of the presence of the temperature T in the denominator of the negative exponent, this factor increases markedly with increasing temperature. The greater the value of E, the more rapid is the *relative* increase of the Boltzmann factor. This result is of particular importance in connection with the theory of reaction rates (Chapter XVIII).

12h. Mean Free Path and Viscosity.—*The average distance a molecule travels between two successive collisions* is called the **mean free path.** Its value is determined essentially by the number of molecules present in a given volume of gas, and by a property of the molecules known as the **collision diameter.** When two molecules approach one another a point is reached at which mutual repulsion becomes so great as to cause a reversal of direction of motion. *The distance between the centers of the molecules at this point of closest approach* is the collision diameter (Fig. 13), represented by the symbol σ (Greek, *sigma*). Even if the molecules are infinitesimally small, as has been postulated for an ideal gas (§ 12a), they would still have an effective collision diameter, because of their mutual repulsion. By means of the kinetic theory of gases, it can be shown that the mean free path l of the molecules of a gas is given by

$$l = \frac{1}{\sqrt{2}\pi n\sigma^2},\qquad (12.17)$$

where σ is the collision diameter and n is the number of molecules in unit volume of the gas.

Various relationships exist between the mean free path and other properties of a gas; one of these properties is the **viscosity.** Consider two layers of gas, one of which is streaming over the other; because of their continual movement, there will be an interchange of molecules between the two layers, with the result that some of the momentum of the streaming layer will be transferred to the stationary layer. The net effect will be a decrease of the relative rate of movement of one layer with respect to the other. *This retarding influence of a stationary layer of gas on a moving one* is the property referred to as viscosity; it may be described in simple terms as an internal friction or an internal resistance to motion. The

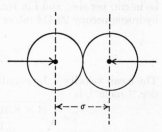

Fig. 13. Collision diameter of molecules

coefficient of viscosity or, in brief, the **viscosity,** is defined as *the force in dynes that must be exerted between two parallel layers, 1 sq. cm. in area and 1 cm. apart, in order to maintain a velocity of streaming of 1 cm. per sec. of one layer past the other.* In terms of these quantities (c.g.s. units) the viscosity is expressed in dynes cm.$^{-2}$ sec. units; this unit is called a **poise,** in honor of J. L. M. Poiseuille. In 1844, the latter derived the fundamental equation of viscosity, namely

$$\eta = \frac{\pi r^4 t p}{8vL},\qquad (12.18)$$

relating the coefficient of viscosity η (Greek, *eta*) to the volume v cc. of gas (or liquid) which will flow through a narrow tube of length L cm. and radius r cm. in the time t sec., when under the influence of a driving pressure of p dynes per sq. cm. The experimental methods for the determination of viscosity are based on the Poiseuille equation.

Since gaseous viscosity may be ascribed to the interchange of molecules between two adjacent layers of gases, some connection between the coefficient of viscosity and the mean free path of the molecules is to be expected. For an ideal gas, the relationship

$$\eta = \tfrac{1}{3}d\bar{c}l,\qquad (12.19)$$

where d is the density of the gas, $\bar{c}$ is the mean velocity of the molecules, and l is the mean free path, has been derived from the kinetic theory. The viscosity and density of a gas can be determined, and the mean velocity is given by

$$\bar{c} = \sqrt{\frac{8RT}{\pi M}} \; ; \qquad (12.20)$$

hence, it should be possible to calculate the value of the mean free path of the molecules under the given conditions.

Problem: The viscosity of hydrogen gas at 0° C is 8.41×10^{-5} poise; determine the mean free path of the molecules at this temperature and 1 atm. pressure.

If η in equation (12.19) is in poises, the density d must be in grams per cc.; $\bar{c}$ must be in cm. per sec., and l in cm. At 0° C and 1 atm. pressure, 2.0 grams (1 mole) of hydrogen occupy 22,414 ml. or cc., and hence

$$d = \frac{2}{22,414} = 8.9 \times 10^{-5} \text{ gram cc.}^{-1}$$

The mean velocity $\bar{c}$, by equation (12.20), with R in c.g.s. units, i.e., 8.31×10^7 ergs deg.$^{-1}$ mole^{-1}, is

$$\bar{c} = \sqrt{\frac{8 \times 8.31 \times 10^7 \times 273}{3.14 \times 2.0}} = 1.70 \times 10^5 \text{ cm. sec.}^{-1}$$

From equation (12.19), therefore

$$8.41 \times 10^{-5} = \tfrac{1}{3} \times 8.9 \times 10^{-5} \times 1.70 \times 10^5 \times l$$

$$l = 1.67 \times 10^{-5} \text{ cm.}$$

The mean free paths of most gases at atmospheric pressure and room temperatures are of the order of 10^{-5} cm.; the reason for this approximate constancy may be seen from equation (12.17). At definite temperature and pressure, the number of molecules n in unit volume is constant, by Avogadro's law, and since nearly all molecules that are gaseous at ordinary temperatures and pressures have collision diameters of about 2×10^{-8} to 4×10^{-8} cm. (see Table VIII), it follows that the mean free path will not vary greatly from one gas to another.

The effects of temperature and pressure may also be derived from equation (12.17); it is seen from this equation that the product of n and l should be constant, provided the collision diameter does not change. At constant pressure, the number of molecules n in unit volume is inversely proportional to the absolute temperature, and so the mean free path l will be directly proportional to this temperature. On the other hand, at constant temperature, n is directly proportional to the pressure, and hence l will be inversely proportional to the latter; thus,

$$\frac{l}{T} = \text{constant, at constant pressure}$$

and

$$l \times P = \text{constant, at constant temperature.}$$

Since the value of l is about 10^{-5} cm. at ordinary temperature and 1 atm. pressure, it follows that it would be necessary to decrease the pressure to about 10^{-5} atm. in order to make the mean free path about 1 cm.

12i. Collision Numbers.—In accordance with the definition of the mean free path, a gas molecule travels the very small distance of about 10^{-5} cm. between collisions at 1 atm. pressure and normal temperatures; the total number of such collisions between molecules in unit time must therefore be very large. This number Z, for unit volume per second, is given by the kinetic theory as

$$Z = 2n^2\sigma^2 \sqrt{\frac{\pi RT}{M}}, \qquad (12.21)$$

where all the symbols have the same significance as before. In order to utilize this equation to calculate the number of collisions, it is necessary to know n and σ; the former can be obtained from the Avogadro number, and the latter is most simply derived from the viscosity. By combining equations (12.17) and (12.19), so as to eliminate l, the result is

$$\sigma^2 = \frac{d\bar{c}}{3\sqrt{2}\pi\eta n}. \qquad (12.22)$$

It is not actually necessary to evaluate σ^2, for introduction of equation (12.22) into (12.21), and making use of equation (12.20) to give the value of $\bar{c}$, it follows that

$$Z = \frac{4nd}{3\pi\eta} \cdot \frac{RT}{M}. \qquad (12.23)$$

Problem: Utilizing the data of the preceding problem, calculate the number of collisions taking place in 1 sec. between hydrogen molecules in 1 cc. of gas at 0° C and 1 atm. pressure.

To obtain the number of collisions per sec. in 1 cc., i.e., collisions sec.$^{-1}$ cc.$^{-1}$, all the data must be expressed in c.g.s. units. The values of d and of η are given in the previous problem, viz., 8.9×10^{-5} g. cc.$^{-1}$ and 8.41×10^{-5} poise, respectively; R is 8.31×10^{7} ergs deg.$^{-1}$ mole^{-1}, T is 273° K and M is 2.0; only n remains to be estimated. At 0° C and 1 atm., 1 mole of gas occupies 22,414 ml. or cc., and since 1 mole of any substance contains 6.02×10^{23}, i.e., the Avogadro number (§ 12k), individual molecules, the number n of molecules per cc. is $6.02 \times 10^{23}/22,414 = 2.69 \times 10^{19}$. Hence, from equation (12.23)

$$Z = \frac{4 \times 2.69 \times 10^{19} \times 8.9 \times 10^{-5}}{3 \times 3.14 \times 8.41 \times 10^{-5}} \times \frac{8.31 \times 10^{7} \times 273}{2.0}$$

$$= 13.7 \times 10^{28} \text{ molecular collisions sec.}^{-1} \text{ cc.}^{-1}$$

The number of collisions between molecules at ordinary temperatures and pressures is of the enormous order of 10^{28} per second in 1 ml. (or 1 cc.) of gas. That the value does not vary greatly with the molecular weight may be seen from equation (12.21), since an increase of M is usually accompanied by a compensating increase of σ. Further, at constant pressure, temperature has a relatively small effect, since it is the square root of the absolute temperature that appears in equation (12.21); in any event, there is some compensation due to the decrease in the value of n. The number of collisions is, however, seen to be proportional to the square of the number of molecules in unit volume, i.e., to n^2, by equation (12.21); it is thus proportional to the square of the pressure, at constant temperature. Increase of pressure thus has a marked effect in increasing the number of collisions.

In a mixture of gases A and B, the number of collisions $Z_{A,B}$, each involving an A molecule and a B molecule, taking place per second in 1 cc., may be calculated from the equation

$$Z_{A,B} = n_A n_B \sigma_{A,B}^2 \left(8\pi RT \frac{M_A + M_B}{M_A M_B} \right)^{\frac{1}{2}}, \qquad (12.24)$$

where n_A and n_B are the respective numbers of molecules in unit volume, and M_A and $M_B^{\P}$ are the molecular weights of the two gases. The mean collision diameter $\sigma_{A,B}$ is equal to $\frac{1}{2}(\sigma_A + \sigma_B)$. This equation reduces to equation (12.21) when A and B are the same, provided the result is divided by 2, to avoid counting each collision twice; otherwise, each molecule would be treated as colliding with itself, as well as with other molecules.

12j. Collision Diameters.—Although the concept of collision diameters has been used in the foregoing sections, there has been no necessity to calculate the values of these diameters. The results are nevertheless of interest, because they give a measure of the effective dimensions of molecules, at least in collisions. One way of determining the collision diameter is to utilize equation (12.22), after inserting the expression for $\bar{c}$ [equation (12.20)]; thus,

$$\sigma^2 = \frac{2d}{3\pi\eta n} \sqrt{\frac{RT}{\pi M}}, \qquad (12.25)$$

so that the collision diameter σ can be evaluated if the viscosity η of the gas is known.

Problem: Calculate the collision diameter of hydrogen, using the viscosity and other data from the two preceding problems.

Again, c.g.s. units must be used throughout to obtain σ in cm.; thus, d is 8.9×10^{-5} gram cc.$^{-1}$, n is 2.7×10^{19} molecules cc.$^{-1}$, η is 8.41×10^{-5} poise and R is 8.31×10^7 ergs deg.$^{-1}$ mole^{-1}; hence

$$\sigma^2 = \frac{2 \times 8.9 \times 10^{-5}}{3 \times 3.14 \times 8.41 \times 10^{-5} \times 2.7 \times 10^{19}} \sqrt{\frac{8.31 \times 10^7 \times 273}{3.14 \times 2.0}}$$

$$= 5.0 \times 10^{-16} \text{ cm.}^2$$

$$\sigma = 2.24 \times 10^{-8} \text{ cm.}$$

The collision diameters of most gaseous molecules are found to lie in the range of 2×10^{-8} to 4×10^{-8} cm. Since distances of the order of 10^{-8} cm. appear frequently in chemistry, e.g., molecular and atomic dimensions, and in physics, e.g., wave lengths of X-rays, the term **Ångström unit** and the symbol Å are used to represent a length of 10^{-8} cm. Consequently, it may be stated that the collision diameters are generally from 2 Å to 4 Å for molecules of gaseous substances. Some actual results, obtained from viscosity measurements, after applying certain corrections for nonideal behavior, are given in Table VIII. Similar values have been derived from other physical properties

TABLE VIII. COLLISION DIAMETERS FROM VISCOSITY MEASUREMENTS

Substance	σ	Substance	σ
Hydrogen	2.45 Å	Hydrogen chloride	2.86 Å
Helium	2.18	Hydrogen bromide	3.16
Nitrogen	3.50	Hydrogen iodide	3.50
Oxygen	3.40	Carbon dioxide	4.20
Chlorine	4.50	Ammonia	3.05

of gases, such as heat conductivity and diffusion, which also depend on the mean free path of the molecules and hence on the collision diameter. It may be mentioned that the collision diameters do not differ greatly from the actual diameters obtained in other ways not depending on the kinetic theory of gases; as a general rule, the former are larger than the latter by about 1 Å, so that molecular dimensions are of the order of 10^{-8} cm. (see Chapter VI).

12k. The Real Existence of Molecules: The Avogadro Number.—The general agreement between the experimental facts and the conclusions drawn from the kinetic theory provides strong support for this theory, but it would obviously be important if more direct evidence were available for the real existence of molecules. Such evidence was obtained by J. Perrin (1908) from a study of the phenomenon known as the **Brownian movement**. In 1827, the botanist R. Brown noticed that pollen grains when suspended in water exhibited continual and haphazard motion in all directions. This Brownian movement has been observed with small particles of all kinds; it is quite independent of the nature of the particles or of the medium in which they are suspended. It is generally accepted that *the movement is caused by the continual bombardment of the suspended particles by the molecules of the medium.* The increasing and erratic motion of the particles is thus a direct result of the movements of the molecules surrounding them; in fact, the Brownian movement may be regarded as providing a magnified picture of the motion of the molecules themselves.

Because of the influence of gravity, the molecules in a column of gas are not distributed uniformly; there are more molecules at lower than at higher levels. This fact is illustrated by the decrease of atmospheric pressure at increasing elevations. If n_1 molecules are present in unit volume at a height h_1, and n_2 at a height h_2, then according to the kinetic theory

$$\ln \frac{n_1}{n_2} = \frac{3Nmg(h_2 - h_1)}{2E_K}, \tag{12.26}$$

when "ln," sometimes written "$\log_e$," is the symbol for natural logarithms. *

* The relationship between natural and common logarithms, i.e., to the base of 10, is given by the expressions

$$\ln x = 2.303 \log x \quad \text{or} \quad 0.4343 \ln x = \log x.$$

In this equation N is the Avogadro number, i.e., the actual number of molecules in 1 mole, m is the weight of a single molecule, g is the acceleration due to gravity, and E_K is the kinetic energy of all the gas molecules in 1 mole; by equation (12.10), the latter quantity is seen to be equal to $\frac{3}{2}RT$.

In his treatment of the Brownian movement, Perrin made two assumptions which are in complete accord with the views expressed above concerning the origin of this movement. In the first place, it was supposed that the distribution of the particles suspended in a liquid under the influence of gravity would be given by an equation exactly analogous to equation (12.26). The only modification necessary is the introduction of the factor $(1 - d'/d)$ on the right-hand side to allow for the buoyancy of the particles of density d suspended in a liquid of density d'. The second assumption was that the kinetic energy of motion of a suspended particle was the same as that of a gas molecule at the same temperature. This is to be expected if the Brownian movement is due to the impacts of the surrounding molecules. Consequently, when E_K in equation (12.26) is replaced by its value for a gas, i.e., $\frac{3}{2}RT$, the result should also be applicable to a suspension. Making the necessary adjustments, therefore, the equation for the number of particles n_1 and n_2 at heights h_1 and h_2, respectively, in a suspension is given by

$$\ln \frac{n_1}{n_2} = \frac{Nmg(h_2 - h_1)}{RT}\left(1 - \frac{d'}{d}\right), \tag{12.27}$$

where m is now the mass of a suspended particle. If the latter is spherical, then m is equal to $\frac{4}{3}\pi r^3 d$, where r is the radius of the particle and d is its density. Making this substitution for m in equation (12.27), and rearranging, the result is

$$\frac{RT}{N}\ln\frac{n_1}{n_2} = \frac{4}{3}\pi r^3 g(h_2 - h_1)(d - d'). \tag{12.28}$$

By working with suspensions of gamboge and mastic in water, the particles of which were visible in the microscope, Perrin was able, by the use of very ingenious methods, to determine the numbers of particles n_1 and n_2 at different levels, and also their radius r and density d. In this way all the information necessary to calculate the Avogadro number N by means of equation (12.28) was obtained. As the result of many experiments made under a wide variety of conditions, Perrin found the value of N to be about 6×10^{23}, and a similar figure was obtained from other measurements with suspended particles.

In addition to the methods which depend directly or indirectly on the kinetic theory of gases, several procedures are available for the calculation of the Avogadro number which are quite independent of the kinetic theory. Two examples of such methods may be given here (see also § 19c). The volume of helium gas, measured at S.T.P., liberated from radium in its disintegration is 0.043 ml. per gram of radium per year; the number of α-particles emitted in the same time by the same amount of radium, calculated from direct observations, is 11.6×10^{17}. Each α-particle should yield one atom or one molecule of helium, since for this element the atom and molecule are identical; it follows, therefore, that 0.043 ml. should contain 11.6×10^{17} individual molecules. One mole of gas occupies 22,414 ml., and consequently the number of molecules in 1 mole, which is the Avogadro number, is given by

$$N = \frac{11.6 \times 10^{17} \times 22,414}{0.043} = 6.05 \times 10^{23}.$$

The second method depends on a knowledge of the charge carried by an electron. It was seen at the end of § 4b that the electronic charge could be calculated from a knowledge of the values of the faraday and the Avogadro number. This procedure can, of course, be reversed so as to determine the latter quantity. Both the electronic charge and the faraday can be determined by direct experiment, the values being 4.803×10^{-10} and 2.893×10^{14} e.s.u., respectively; the ratio of these quantities gives the Avogadro number, i.e.,

$$N = \frac{2.893 \times 10^{14}}{4.803 \times 10^{-10}} = 6.023 \times 10^{23}.$$

The remarkable agreement between these results and those derived from a study of the Brownian movement, on the basis of the kinetic theory of gases, provides very strong evidence for the real existence of molecules. As stated in § 3d, the accepted value of the Avogadro number is 6.023×10^{23}.

121. Heat Capacity and the Kinetic Theory.—The **heat capacity** of any system is *the quantity of heat required to raise the temperature of the system by one degree.* If the weight of the material is 1 gram, the heat capacity is then called the **specific heat** of the substance. In physical chemistry, the quantity considered is frequently 1 mole, and so the heat capacity is referred to as the **molar heat capacity,** or sometimes as the **molecular heat.** Heat capacities are generally expressed in **calories,** where the "15° calorie" is the amount of heat required to raise the temperature of 1 gram of water from 14.5° to 15.5° C. Because of the uncertainty in the isotopic composition of water, it has been recommended that the calorie be defined as 4.1833 international joules; * this value is only very slightly different from that of the 15° calorie.

For all substances, and particularly for gases, the heat capacity depends on whether both the pressure and volume are allowed to vary or not. In order to obtain definite results, therefore, it is necessary to specify the conditions; two such conditions are in general use. First, it can be specified that the volume is maintained constant while the temperature is being raised, and the pressure is consequently allowed to increase; this is the **heat capacity at constant volume.** Second, the pressure may be maintained constant, and the volume permitted to change, thus giving the **heat capacity at constant pressure.** The specific heats at constant volume and constant pressure are designated c_V and c_P, respectively, while the molar heat capacities are repre-

---

* An international joule is equivalent to 1.0002×10^7 ergs, so that 1 defined calorie is equivalent to 4.184×10^7 ergs (§ 23a).

sented by C_V and C_P, respectively. The latter symbols are also frequently used for heat capacities in general, where the amount of the substance, or substances, concerned is not stated explicitly.

Suppose the molecules of a gas possess one kind of energy only, namely kinetic energy of translation, sometimes called **translational energy**; this is the energy whose value has been already calculated by means of the kinetic theory of gases. If the temperature of the gas is raised, *at constant volume*, the heat supplied goes merely to increase the kinetic energy of the molecules. This fact makes it immediately possible to calculate the heat capacity of such a gas from the kinetic theory. From equation (12.10), the kinetic energy of the molecules in 1 mole of ideal gas is equal to $\frac{3}{2}RT$ at the temperature T. If the temperature is raised by 1° to $T + 1$, the kinetic energy becomes $\frac{3}{2}R(T + 1)$, so that

$$\text{Increase of kinetic energy per degree} = \tfrac{3}{2}R(T + 1) - \tfrac{3}{2}RT$$

$$= \tfrac{3}{2}R.$$

Since, as postulated above, the heat supplied to the gas at constant volume is used up entirely for increasing the translational kinetic energy, it follows that the heat capacity per mole, which is the heat required to raise the temperature by 1°, is given by

$$C_V = \tfrac{3}{2}R. \tag{12.29}$$

The value of R is 1.987 cal. deg.$^{-1}$ mole^{-1} (§ 11f); hence, the molar heat capacity at constant volume of a gas possessing translational energy only should be 2.98 cal. deg.$^{-1}$ mole^{-1}. It is of interest to note that results close to 3 cal. deg.$^{-1}$ mole^{-1} have been recorded for helium, neon and other gases of group 0 of the periodic table, and also for the vapors of mercury, potassium and other metals. There are many reasons for believing that in all these substances the molecules are *monatomic*, i.e., the molecule contains but one atom. Such molecules would be expected to possess translational energy as the only, or essential, form of energy. At very low temperatures the value of C_V of hydrogen, which is not monatomic, also approaches 3 cal. deg.$^{-1}$ mole^{-1}. However, whereas for helium, neon, etc., the heat capacity remains almost constant, that for hydrogen increases rapidly as the temperature is raised. The reason for this, as will be seen below, is that the hydrogen molecules can possess other forms of energy, in addition to translational, and these become apparent with increasing temperature.

When a gas, or in fact any substance, expands it has to do work against the external pressure, generally the pressure of the atmosphere. Consequently, when the temperature of a gas is raised at constant pressure, and the volume increases, heat must be supplied to perform the external work, in addition to that required to increase the kinetic energy of the molecules. The value of the work done by the gas when it expands against a constant external pressure may be obtained in the following manner. Consider a gas, *or in fact any substance*, contained in a cylinder of cross section a sq. cm., fitted with a piston upon which is exerted a constant pressure of P dynes per sq. cm. The total force acting on the piston is equal to the pressure multiplied by the area, i.e., to Pa dynes. Suppose the substance in the cylinder expands, *the external pressure remaining constant;* the piston is raised through a height h cm. (Fig. 14). The work done against the external pressure is equal to the product of the force acting and the displacement of the point of application; it follows, therefore, that

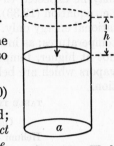

External work done in expansion of gas $= Pa \times h$ ergs.

The quantity $a \times h$ represents the increase in volume during expansion, and this may be replaced by ΔV, so that

External work done in expansion of gas $= P\Delta V$.   (12.30)

This result holds for any system, gaseous, liquid or solid; hence, *the external work done is always equal to the product of the (constant) external pressure and the change of volume.*

Fig. 14. Work done in expansion against an external pressure

For 1 mole of an ideal gas at a temperature T,

$$PV = RT,$$

and if the temperature is raised by 1° at constant pressure, the volume increases by ΔV to $V + \Delta V$, so that

$$P(V + \Delta V) = R(T + 1).$$

Upon subtraction of these two equations, it is seen that

$$P\Delta V = R.$$

It follows, therefore, that when the temperature of 1 mole of an ideal gas is raised by 1° at constant pressure, the work done on account of expansion is equal to the value of the gas constant R. This gives the contribution to the molar heat capacity due to the external work, and if it is added to the heat required to increase the kinetic energy of the molecules, i.e., $C_V = \frac{3}{2}R$, the total is the molar heat capacity of the gas at constant pressure; thus,

$$C_P = C_V + R = \tfrac{3}{2}R + R$$

$$= \tfrac{5}{2}R. \qquad (12.31)$$

There are two important consequences of the foregoing arguments; first, *the difference between the molar heat capacities of a gas at constant volume and at constant pressure should be equal to R;* thus,

$$C_P - C_V = R = 1.987 \text{ cal. deg.}^{-1} \text{ mole}^{-1}, \qquad (12.32)$$

i.e., approximately 2 cal. deg.$^{-1}$ mole^{-1}. Second, *the ratio of the two heat capacities for any ideal gas possessing translational energy only should be $\frac{5}{3}$,* i.e.,

1.667; thus, representing this ratio by the symbol γ, it follows from equations (12.29) and (12.31) that

$$\gamma = \frac{C_P}{C_V} = \frac{\frac{5}{2}R}{\frac{3}{2}R} = 1.667. \tag{12.33}$$

It may be noted that the former of these conclusions, i.e., equation (12.32) may be expected to hold, *at least approximately*, for any gas, but the latter, i.e., equation (12.33), will be applicable to a gas whose molecules possess translational energy only. This is particularly the case for monatomic gases, at all temperatures; as indicated above, hydrogen gas has this property at low, but not at higher, temperatures. The results in Table IX, for some gases and vapors which are believed to be monatomic, are in agreement with expectation.

TABLE IX. MOLAR HEAT CAPACITIES OF MONATOMIC GASES

Gas	C_P	C_V	γ
Helium	5.00	3.02	1.66
Argon	4.98	2.99	1.67
Mercury	4.97	2.98	1.67
Iodine (atomic)	5.0	3.0	1.67

12m. Heat Capacities of Polyatomic Molecules.—If the heat capacities of gases which contain two or more atoms in the molecule, that is, of polyatomic gases, are studied, it is found that although $C_P - C_V$ is approximately equal to 2 cal. per deg. per mole, the actual values of the heat capacities are usually greater than $\frac{5}{2}R$ and $\frac{3}{2}R$ for C_P and C_V, respectively; for polyatomic molecules, therefore,

$$\gamma = \frac{C_P}{C_V} = \frac{\frac{5}{2}R + c}{\frac{3}{2}R + c} < 1.667,$$

so that the ratio of the heat capacities is less than 1.667. The cause of this discrepancy lies in the fact that when it contains more than one atom, the molecule possesses other forms of energy, in addition to translational, which can increase as the temperature is raised and thus contribute to the heat capacity. These forms of energy are **rotational energy** and **vibrational energy.** The rotational energy is due to the rotation of the molecule as a whole about three axes at right angles to one another, while the vibrational energy is associated with the oscillations of the atoms within the molecule. According to calculations based on classical mechanics, known as the **principle of the equipartition of energy,** each type of rotation should contribute an amount $\frac{1}{2}R$, while each mode of vibration should contribute R, to the molar heat capacity of a gaseous substance.

A diatomic molecule has two types of rotation that vary with temperature; the third type, about the line joining the nuclei, does not affect the heat capacity. In addition there is one kind of oscillation or vibration of the two atoms with respect to each other. The total molar heat capacity at constant volume should thus be $\frac{3}{2}R$ for kinetic energy, $2 \times \frac{1}{2}R$ for the two rotations and R for the vibration, making a total of $\frac{7}{2}R$, i.e., about 7 cal. deg.$^{-1}$ mole^{-1}. At ordinary temperatures, most diatomic molecules, e.g., hydrogen, oxygen, nitrogen, carbon monoxide, hydrogen chloride, etc., have values of C_V of about 5 cal. deg.$^{-1}$ mole^{-1}, but there is a definite increase with increasing temperature. This is most marked with chlorine, the molecule of which is also diatomic; at 0° C the molar heat capacity at constant volume is 5.95 and it reaches a value of about 7 cal. deg.$^{-1}$ mole^{-1} at 700° C, there being little change above this temperature.

Although the classical theory of energy is inadequate to interpret these results, the quantum theory provides the explanation. It appears that both the rotational and vibrational energies are quantized; that is to say, the molecule does not take up its rotational and vibrational energy in a continuous manner, but only in the form of definite amounts or quanta (§ 9b). The rotational quanta are small, and so at ordinary temperatures virtually all the molecules possess appreciable amounts of rotational energy; the behavior then approaches that required by classical theory, the contribution to the heat capacity being $\frac{1}{2}R$ for each type of rotation. The vibrational quanta, on the other hand, are much larger, and at ordinary temperatures the vibrational energy of most simple molecules is insufficient to raise them above the lowest quantum level.* In this event, the vibrational energy does not affect the heat capacity, as is actually the case for the majority of diatomic molecules. The molar heat capacity at constant volume is then the sum of $\frac{3}{2}R$ for the kinetic energy and $2 \times \frac{1}{2}R$ for the rotational energy, making a total of $\frac{5}{2}R$, i.e., 5 cal. deg.$^{-1}$ mole^{-1}, in agreement with experiment.

As the temperature is raised, increasing numbers of molecules acquire various quanta of vibrational energy, with the result that the contribution to the heat capacity increases toward the classical value of R for each mode of vibration. This explains why the C_V values of diatomic gases increase steadily to about 7 cal. deg.$^{-1}$ mole^{-1} as the temperature is raised (Table X). With

TABLE X. MOLAR HEAT CAPACITIES OF DIATOMIC GASES AT CONSTANT VOLUME

Gas	0°	100°	200°	500°	1200°	2000° C
H_2	4.87	4.93	5.05	5.16	5.67	6.28
N_2, O_2, CO	4.99	5.05	5.15	5.26	5.75	6.3
HCl	5.00	5.09	5.27	5.46	6.13	6.9
Cl_2	5.95	6.3	6.7	6.9	7.1	7.2

chlorine, the vibrational energy quanta are not too large, and so an appreciable number of molecules have such quanta even at ordinary temperatures; hence, the molar heat capacity of chlorine at constant volume already exceeds $\frac{5}{2}R$ at 0° C.

* It is of interest to mention that even in its lowest vibrational energy state a molecule still possesses some energy of vibration; this is known as the **zero-point energy**, and is $\frac{1}{2}h\nu$ per molecule for each mode of vibration, h being the Planck constant and ν the frequency of vibration (cf. § 9b). The presence of zero-point energy, even at the absolute zero, is of fundamental importance in certain aspects of the chemistry and physics of molecules.

If the foregoing arguments are correct, it is to be expected that at sufficiently low temperatures the rotational contribution to the heat capacity should fall off to zero. This condition has been realized with ordinary hydrogen gas, for at a temperature of 50° K, i.e., −223° C, its heat capacity has decreased to 3 cal. deg.$^{-1}$ mole^{-1}, which is the value for a monatomic gas. At these low temperatures, translational energy only, and no rotational energy, contributes to the heat capacity, as stated earlier. For other gases, liquefaction has occurred before the temperature is reached at which the rotational contribution ceases.

As a general rule, a diatomic molecule or a *linear* polyatomic molecule, i.e., one containing more than two atoms that lie in a straight line, has $3n - 5$ modes of vibration, where n is the number of atoms in the molecule; there are in addition two types of rotation. The maximum (limiting) heat capacity at constant volume of a diatomic or a linear polyatomic gas thus consists of $(3n - 5)R$ for vibration, R for rotation and $\frac{3}{2}R$ for translation, making a total of $(3n - \frac{5}{2})R$. This is the value which will be approached as the temperature is raised. A *nonlinear* polyatomic molecule has $3n - 6$ modes of vibration and three types of rotation; the maximum (limiting) heat capacity C_V is thus made up of $(3n - 6)R$ for vibration, $\frac{3}{2}R$ for rotation and $\frac{3}{2}R$ for translation, so that the total is $(3n - 3)R$. The heat capacity at constant pressure is greater by R, approximately, in each case.

Problem: Calculate the maximum high temperature molar heat capacity at constant volume to be expected for (i) acetylene (C_2H_2), which is a linear molecule, and (ii) ammonia, which is nonlinear.

(i) For acetylene, n is 4, so that there are $3n - 5 = (3 \times 4) - 5 = 7$ modes of vibration; these can contribute up to $7R$ to the heat capacity. There are 2 types of rotation, and these can contribute $2 \times \frac{1}{2}R$, i.e., R. Translation contributes $\frac{3}{2}R$, and so the total maximum C_V is $9\frac{1}{2}R$, i.e., 19 cal. deg.$^{-1}$ mole^{-1}.

(ii) For ammonia, n is 4, but as the molecule is nonlinear, there are $3n - 6 = (3 \times 4) - 6 = 6$ modes of vibration, contributing a maximum of $6R$; the 3 types of rotation add $3 \times \frac{1}{2}R$, i.e., $\frac{3}{2}R$, and translation a further $\frac{3}{2}R$, making a total maximum C_V of $9R$, i.e., 18 cal. deg.$^{-1}$ mole^{-1}. (The actual value is 6.6 cal. at 0° C increasing to 11.4 at 1200°; it is seen therefore that at 0° the rotational and translational contributions account for most of the heat capacity. Because of decomposition at high temperatures the limiting heat capacity has not been observed.)

Real Gases

13a. Deviations from Ideal Behavior.—As already indicated (§ 11e), real gases do not obey the ideal gas laws exactly. At low pressures and moderately high temperatures the laws of Boyle, Gay-Lussac and Avogadro, as expressed in the form of the equation $PV = RT$ for 1 mole of gas, are obeyed approximately, but as the pressure is increased or the temperature decreased, marked departure from ideal behavior becomes apparent. The magnitude and nature of these deviations from Boyle's law may be seen from an examination of the product of pressure and volume for various pressures, at constant temperature;

if Boyle's law were obeyed the values would be constant. The data for hydrogen and nitrogen at 0° C, and for carbon dioxide at 40° C, are given in Table XI and are plotted in Fig. 15; the value of PV at 1 atm. pressure is taken as

TABLE XI. VARIATION OF THE PRESSURE-VOLUME PRODUCT WITH PRESSURE

Pressure	Hydrogen	Nitrogen	Carbon Dioxide
1 atm.	1.000	1.000	1.000
50	1.033	0.985	0.741
100	1.064	0.985	0.270
200	1.134	1.037	0.409
400	1.277	1.256	0.718
800	1.566	1.796	1.299

unity in each case. For an ideal gas, obeying Boyle's law, the effect of pressure on the pressure-volume product would be represented by a horizontal

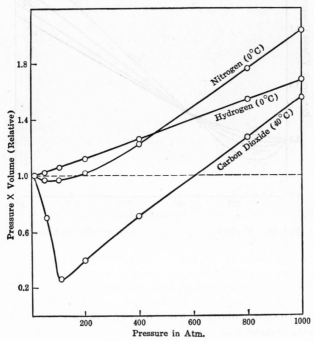

FIG. 15. Variation of pressure-volume product with pressure

straight line in Fig. 15. It is obvious from this figure, as well as from the results in Table XI, that real gases show considerable deviations from ideal behavior, especially at high pressures. At pressures of the order of 1 atm., or less, the departure from Boyle's law is usually small.

An examination of Fig. 15 reveals the fact that whereas the value of PV for hydrogen increases continuously as the pressure is increased, with the other gases there is at first a decrease, followed by an increase. Helium and neon are similar to hydrogen in their behavior at ordinary temperatures. However, if the temperature is lowered, the shape of the curve changes, and in each case it eventually becomes like that for nitrogen or carbon dioxide in Fig. 15. On the other hand, at sufficiently high temperatures, the pressure-volume product curves of these and other gases become like those for hydrogen, helium and neon at ordinary temperatures. The curves in Fig. 16 show the relative values of PV for nitrogen plotted against the pressure for a number of temperatures;

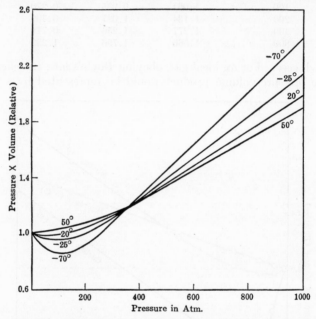

FIG. 16.   Variation of pressure-volume product of nitrogen

the change in the shape of the curves with increasing temperature is clearly seen. It appears, therefore, that the general nature of the deviations from ideal behavior does not depend on the gas, but rather on the temperature. Actually, the determining factor is the temperature relative to the point of liquefaction of the particular gas; when near this point the PV curves are like that for carbon dioxide, but when far away the curves are like that for hydrogen in Fig. 15.

In addition to the deviations from Boyle's law, real gases exhibit departures from Gay-Lussac's law; this is apparent from the fact that the shape of the PV curves, e.g., in Fig. 16, changes with temperature. In general, the discrepancies are greater the higher the pressure and the closer the temperature is to that at which liquefaction is possible.

The accuracy of Avogadro's law may be tested by determining the volume occupied by 1 mole of a gas at 0° C and 1 atm. pressure; the molecular weight required for this purpose is determined from the sum of the atomic weights of the constituent atoms. If the law were strictly true, the volume would be independent of the nature of the gas, but the results in Table XII show that this is

TABLE XII. TEST OF AVOGADRO'S LAW

Gas	Molecular Weight	Volume of 1 Mole at 0° and 1 Atm.
Hydrogen	2.016	22.427 liters
Nitrogen	28.02	22.405
Oxygen	32.00	22.394
Carbon dioxide	44.01	22.264
Ammonia	17.03	22.084
Ethyl chloride	50.49	21.879

not the case. As before, the largest deviations are shown by the most easily liquefiable gases, e.g., ammonia and ethyl chloride; the departure from ideal behavior increases with decreasing temperature and increasing pressure. By measuring the volume occupied by 1 mole of gas at 0° C and various pressures, and extrapolating the pressure-volume product to zero pressure, the volume of 1 mole of an ideal gas at 0° and 1 atm. has been found to be 22.414 liters, as mentioned earlier.

Provided the pressure is of the order of 1 atm. or less, and the temperature is not too near the point of liquefaction, the deviations from the ideal gas laws are not more than a few per cent. Under these conditions, therefore, the equation $PV = RT$, and related expressions, may be used for approximate calculations, at least. The lower the pressure and the higher the temperature, the more reliable are the results obtained in this manner.

13b. Causes of Deviations from Ideal Gas Law.—The ideal gas laws were derived from the kinetic theory on the basis of two important assumptions; these were that the volume of the molecules is negligible in comparison with the total volume of the gas, and that the molecules exert no attraction upon one another (§ 12a). It is because neither of these assumptions can be regarded as applicable to real gases that the latter show departure from ideal behavior. The fact that even the simple kinetic theory leads to the necessity for postulating a collision diameter, representing the distance of closest approach of two molecules in a collision, shows the molecule must possess an *effective volume*. Further, the volume of a gas can be reduced by increasing the pressure and cooling until liquefaction and eventually solidification occur. In the solid state, however, there is a considerable resistance to any further attempt at compression. It is apparent, therefore, that the molecules of a gas must have an appreciable volume, which is probably of the same order as the volume occupied by the same molecules in the solid state.

If the molecules of a gas did not attract one another, it is doubtful whether gases could ever be liquefied; actually, any gas can be converted into a liquid by the use of low temperatures and high pressures (§ 15a). One of the essential properties of a liquid is that of cohesion, and this is attributed to the molecular attraction in the gas, as well as in the liquid. More direct evidence for the existence of this attractive force was obtained by J. P. Joule and W. Thomson (Lord Kelvin) in the course of experiments carried out between 1852 and 1862. A stream of gas at constant pressure was passed through a tube into which was fixed a porous plug of absorbent cotton or silk; the gas emerging from the plug was found to be, in general, appreciably cooler than the entering gas. The change of temperature, known as the **Joule-Thomson effect,** is due to a decrease of the speed, and hence of the kinetic energy, of the molecules; this occurs because energy must be supplied in order to overcome the molecular attractive forces when the gas expands in passing through the porous plug.

In addition to attracting each other, it can be shown that there must be forces of repulsion exerted between molecules. This is evident from the existence of a more or less definite collision diameter; the latter represents the distance at which the repulsive force becomes so great that the direction of motion of the molecules is reversed, i.e., from toward one another to away from one another. However, the forces of repulsion fall off extremely rapidly with increasing distance of separation of the molecules, much more rapidly than do the forces of attraction. As a result there is a net attraction between a pair of molecules when they are an appreciable distance apart, and a net repulsion when they are very close together. When two molecules approach one another the attractive forces at first increase to some extent, until a certain point when the repulsive forces begin to be detectable. The *net* attraction then diminishes as the intermolecular distance becomes smaller, and eventually the repulsive forces become dominant. The distance between the molecules when the rapidly increasing repulsion just counterbalances the more slowly increasing attraction represents the so-called collision diameter.

13c. The van der Waals Equation.—In order to adapt the ideal gas law equation to the behavior of real gases allowance should be made for the attractive and repulsive forces between molecules. One of the simplest and most useful attempts in this direction was made by J. D. van der Waals (1873) somewhat along the following lines. Consider a molecule in the interior of a gas; it is surrounded by other molecules equally distributed in all directions (Fig. 17, A), so that they exert no *resultant* attractive force on the molecule under consideration. As the latter approaches the wall of the containing vessel, however, the uniform average distribution of the molecules changes to one in which gas molecules are present on one side only (Fig. 17, B), so that a force is exerted tending to pull the molecule inwards. It appears, therefore, that at the instant any molecule is about to strike the containing vessel, and thus contribute its share toward the total gas pressure, the molecules in the bulk of the gas exert a force having the effect of pulling the molecule away from the wall. The measured pressure P is thus less than the ideal pressure required by the simple kinetic theory. It is conse-

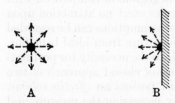

FIG. 17. Molecular attractions: (A) in the interior of gas, (B) at the wall

quently necessary to *add* a correction term to the observed pressure in order to obtain the ideal pressure, that is, the pressure an ideal gas would exert under the same conditions.

The attractive force exerted on a single molecule about to strike the wall is proportional to the number n of molecules per unit volume in the bulk of the gas. Further, the number of molecules striking the walls is also proportional to this number, so that the total attractive force, which is related to the correction term to be added to the measured pressure, is proportional to n^2. If V is the volume occupied by 1 mole of gas, then n is inversely proportional to V, and hence the attractive force will vary as $1/V^2$. The correction term may then be represented by a/V^2, where a is a constant; thus,

$$\text{Corrected (ideal) pressure} = P + \frac{a}{V^2},$$

where P is the actual (observed) gas pressure.

The effect of combined repulsive and attractive forces is to give the molecules an appreciable size, and hence the space available for their movement is less than the actual measured volume V of the gas. In order to obtain the ideal volume, therefore, it is necessary to *subtract* an appropriate correction term from the total volume. This correction term, which has been shown in various ways to be equal to four times the actual volume of the molecules, is given the symbol b, and is called the **covolume.** It is seen, consequently, that

$$\text{Corrected (ideal) volume} = V - b.$$

The product of the ideal pressure and ideal volume derived in this manner may be expected to be equal to RT, as for an ideal gas; hence, it is reasonable to write

$$\left(P + \frac{a}{V^2}\right)(V - b) = RT \tag{13.1}$$

for 1 mole of an actual (real) gas. This is the **van der Waals equation,** one of the best known and simplest of the equations of state proposed for real gases.

The values of the van der Waals constants a and b, the former giving a measure of the molecular attraction and the latter of the volume of the molecules, may be obtained in several ways. The one generally used is based on the critical temperature, pressure and volume of the gas (§ 15c). Actually, the so-called constants vary to some extent with temperature, and this shows that the van der Waals equation is not a complete solution of the problem of real gases. Nevertheless, it is possible to ascribe values to the van der Waals constants a and b which provide a useful, if not exact, means for correcting for departure from ideal behavior. The values of a and b depend on the units employed for expressing P and V; the results in Table XIII are based on V in liters and P in atm. per mole of gas. It is seen that a is largest for the most easily liquefiable gases, such as those on the right-hand side of the table; this is to be expected if this constant is a measure of the attractive forces between the molecules of a gas.

TABLE XIII. VAN DER WAALS CONSTANTS

Gas	a	b	Gas	a	b
Hydrogen	0.245	2.67×10^{-2}	Hydrogen chloride	3.8	4.1×10^{-2}
Helium	0.034	2.36	Ammonia	4.0	3.6
Nitrogen	1.38	3.94	Acetylene	4.4	5.1
Oxygen	1.32	3.12	Ethylene	4.5	5.6
Carbon monoxide	1.49	4.00	Chlorine	5.5	4.9
Carbon dioxide	3.60	4.28	Sulfur dioxide	6.7	5.6

Problem: One mole of carbon dioxide was found to occupy a volume of 1.32 liters at 48° C and a pressure of 18.40 atm. Calculate the pressure that would have been expected (i) from the ideal gas equation, (ii) from the van der Waals equation.

(i) Making use of the ideal gas equation, for 1 mole, in the form $P = RT/V$, with V in liters and P in atm., then R is 0.0820 liter-atm. deg.$^{-1}$ mole^{-1}, and T is $273 + 48 = 321°$ K; hence, since V is 1.32 liters,

$$P = \frac{0.0820 \times 321}{1.32} = 19.9 \text{ atm.}$$

(ii) For this purpose the van der Waals equation may be written

$$P = \frac{RT}{V - b} - \frac{a}{V^2},$$

and since $a = 3.60$ and $b = 4.28 \times 10^{-2}$ (Table XIII), it follows that

$$P = \frac{0.0820 \times 321}{1.32 - 0.043} - \frac{3.60}{(1.32)^2} = 18.5 \text{ atm.}$$

13d. Applicability of the van der Waals Equation.—As indicated above, the van der Waals equation does not reproduce the exact behavior of real gases, but it is certainly a great improvement on the ideal gas equation. That it is in agreement with the general properties of gases, as represented by Fig. 15, may be seen in the following manner. At low pressures, the volume V in so large that b may be neglected in comparison; hence, the van der Waals equation (13.1) may then be simplified to

$$\left(P + \frac{a}{V^2}\right) V = RT,$$

$$PV = RT - \frac{a}{V}. \tag{13.2}$$

Under these conditions, therefore, PV should be less than RT, the difference, which is equal to a/V, increasing as V decreases, that is, as the pressure increases. The dip in the plot of PV against P in Fig. 15, for nitrogen and carbon dioxide, can thus be correlated with the effect of the a/V^2, i.e., molecular attraction, term of the van der Waals equation. This is in agreement with the statement made earlier that when the molecules are relatively far apart, as at low pressures, the attractive predominate over the repulsive forces.

At fairly high pressures, the a/V^2 term in equation (13.1) may be neglected in comparison with P; the b term is, however, retained since V is now fairly small, so that the van der Waals equation becomes

$$P(V - b) = RT,$$

$$PV = RT + Pb. \tag{13.3}$$

It is seen that PV is now greater than RT, and that it increases in a linear manner with the pressure; this accounts for the rising part of the three curves in Fig. 15, which is evidently due to the influence of the b term, i.e., the volume of the molecules or the repulsive forces. For most gases, *at ordinary temperatures*, the effect of the a/V^2 term is dominant at low pressures, while that of b is most important at high pressures. With hydrogen, helium and neon, however, the values of a, i.e., the molecular attractions, are so small (see Table XIII) that the b, i.e., volume of molecules, effect predominates even at low pressures. It is for this reason that the PV curve for hydrogen shows no dip, at ordinary temperatures (Fig. 15).

At extremely low pressures, when V is very large, both a/V^2 and b are small in comparison with P and V, respectively; the van der Waals equation then reduces to the ideal gas equation, $PV = RT$. Under these conditions, therefore, all real gases should obey the ideal gas laws, and consequently these laws may be regarded as representing the limiting behavior of gases at infinitesimally small pressures, as implied in previous sections. The physical basis of this result is that at small pressures there are so few molecules in unit volume that the attractive force between them may be ignored; further, the volume of the gas is then so large that the actual volume of the molecules is negligible in comparison. The real gas consequently behaves as if it consisted of point molecules which do not attract one another, that is, as an ideal gas.

13e. Other Equations of State.—Something like one hundred different equations of state for gases have been proposed from time to time. The majority of these depend on the same principles as does the van der Waals equation, corrections being applied to the ideal gas equation to allow for the volume of the molecules and their mutual attraction. In the **Dieterici equation** (1899), for example, allowance for the effect on the pressure, due to the attraction of the molecules, is made by means of an exponential factor $e^{\alpha/RTV}$; thus,

$$Pe^{\alpha/RTV}(V - b) = RT,$$

or

$$P = \frac{RT}{V - b} e^{-\alpha/RTV}. \tag{13.4}$$

At moderately low pressures, this expression becomes identical with the van der Waals equation, but at higher pressures it gives somewhat better agreement with experiment. Because the Dieterici equation is more difficult to handle mathematically than is the van der Waals equation, it has not taken the place of the latter for general use.

Most equations of state achieve an improvement by the introduction, in addition to a and b, of further empirical constants derived from experimental data. Such equations contribute little to the underlying theory of the behavior of real gases, but they are useful as a means of expressing the observed pressure-volume-temperature relationships of a gas in the form of an equation. The chief function of these equations is for the interpolation or extrapolation of experimental data. Mention may be made in this connection of two modifications of the van der Waals equation which have at least a partial theoretical basis; these are the **Keyes equation** (1917) and the **Beattie and Bridgeman equation** (1927). The former has four empirical constants, in addition to R, while the latter has five such constants.

In recent years increasing use has been made of the **virial equation** (virial: Greek, *force*) of H. K. Onnes (1901); this is a very general equation of the form

$$PV = RT\left(1 + \frac{B}{V} + \frac{C}{V^2} + \cdots\right), \tag{13.5}$$

where the coefficients B, C, etc., which vary with temperature, are called the second, third, etc., **virial coefficients.** An equation of this type is useful for extrapolation purposes, the values of the coefficients B, C, etc., being calculated from the experimental pressure-volume-temperature measurements. The virial equation is, however, more than a mere empirical expression, for theoretical methods are being developed for calculating the virial coefficients from the forces of intermolecular attraction and repulsion. Ultimately this is likely to provide the most complete approach to the problem of real gases.

13f. Origin of Molecular Attraction and Repulsion.—The existence of forces of repulsion between molecules can be readily understood. They probably arise from the interaction of the electron cloud or field of one molecule with that of another, when they are close together. The explanation of the origin of the physical forces of molecular attraction, generally known as **van der Waals forces,** however, presented a difficulty for many years. For polar molecules, that is, those possessing resultant or permanent dipole moments (§ 10f), it might be possible to account for the molecular forces by the electrical interaction of the dipoles. However, van der Waals forces occur between nonpolar molecules, such as hydrogen, oxygen, nitrogen, etc., and even between monatomic molecules, such as helium, neon, etc. It was suggested by F. London (1930) that in molecules (and atoms) of all kinds, the positively charged nuclei and the negatively charged electrons must be regarded as undergoing some kind of oscillations with respect to each other; as a result of this displacement of positive and negative charges, every molecule behaves as an **oscillating dipole.** It is the electrostatic attraction between these dipoles and corresponding dipoles induced in adjacent molecules that is the cause of molecular attraction. The forces due to these oscillating dipole interactions are called **dispersion forces,** because the dispersion of light is also related to these dipoles. For nonpolar molecules, the dispersion forces constitute the whole of the van der Waals attractive forces, but for polar molecules, possessing permanent dipole moments, in addition to those due to the oscillating dipoles, other electrostatic forces contribute to the total molecular attraction.

GAS DENSITIES AND MOLECULAR WEIGHTS

14a. Limiting Densities.—The equation of state for an ideal gas system containing n moles in a volume v is given by equation (11.14), viz.,

$$Pv = nRT. \tag{14.1}$$

If w is the weight of the gas and M is its molecular weight, the number of moles n is equal to w/M; hence, equation (14.1) may be written as

$$Pv = \frac{w}{M} RT, \tag{14.2}$$

$$M = \frac{wRT}{Pv} = \frac{w}{v} \cdot \frac{RT}{P}. \tag{14.3}$$

The quantity w/v is equal to the density d of the gas, generally expressed in grams per liter, at the temperature T and pressure P; equation (14.3) for an ideal gas then becomes

$$M = \frac{d}{P} RT. \tag{14.4}$$

It is evident from this equation that if the density of the gas is measured at a series of pressures, at constant temperature, the ratio d/P should be constant, since M, R and T are constant.

Experiments have shown that for a real gas this ratio is not constant but varies with the pressure; however, if the values of d/P for various pressures are extrapolated to zero pressure, the limiting value, designated by $(d/P)_0$, should correspond to that to be expected if the gas behaved ideally. It is possible, therefore, to write equation (14.4), for an actual gas, in the form

$$M = \left(\frac{d}{P}\right)_0 RT. \tag{14.5}$$

Since R is known, e.g., from similar experiments with oxygen whose molecular weight is taken to be 32.0000, the molecular weight of a gas can be determined from density measurements with the aid of equation (14.5). This is known as the **method of limiting densities.**

The extrapolation of d/P to zero pressure is, of course, a device for correcting for departure from ideal behavior, and this correction has been applied in various ways. The simplest is based on the actual plot of d/P against P, as shown in Fig. 18 for ammonia gas at 0° C. At pressures below 1 atm. this plot is very close to a straight line for most gases, and so accurate extrapolation to zero pressure is possible without the necessity of making measurements at very low pressures. From Fig. 18 it is found that $(d/P)_0$ for ammonia at 0° C is 0.75988 gram liter^{-1} atm.$^{-1}$, the volume being expressed in liters and the pressure in atm.; hence, with R equal to 0.082054 liter-atm. deg.$^{-1}$ mole^{-1}, it follows from equation (14.5) that

$$M = 0.75988 \times 0.082054 \times 273.16 = 17.034.$$

The accurate molecular weights of gases determined by the method of limiting densities have been used for the evaluation of atomic weights, particularly of nonmetallic elements, such as carbon, nitrogen, fluorine, etc., that do not form easily analyzable compounds, and of the inert gases of group 0

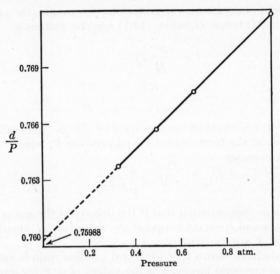

Fig. 18.   Extrapolation of gas densities

that form no stable compounds at all.   From the results given above, the molecular weight of ammonia (NH_3) is found to be 17.034, and since the atomic weight of hydrogen is 1.0080, it follows that

Atomic weight of nitrogen = $17.034 - 3 \times 1.0080 = 14.010$.

The accepted value of the atomic weight of nitrogen at the present time is 14.008.

14b. Limiting Pressures.—A modification of the method of limiting densities, for use in connection with the buoyancy balance (see § 14c), is known as the **method of limiting pressures.**   Consider two gases, of molecular weights M_1 and M_2; by means of the buoyancy balance, these gases are found to have exactly the same density d at the pressures P_1 and P_2, respectively, at a given temperature.   It follows then from equation (14.4) that

$$\frac{M_2}{M_1} = \frac{P_1}{P_2}. \tag{14.6}$$

For actual gases this equation is not strictly correct, but if the experimental ratio P_1/P_2 of the two pressures, for a series of densities, is plotted against one of the pressures, e.g., P_1, and the plot is extrapolated to zero pressure, the limiting pressure ratio $(P_1/P_2)_0$ corresponds to the ideal gas value; hence, for real gases

$$\frac{M_2}{M_1} = \left(\frac{P_1}{P_2}\right)_0. \tag{14.7}$$

If the molecular weight M_1 of one of the gases, e.g., oxygen, is known, the molecular weight M_2 of the other can thus be determined.

14c. Determination of Gas Densities.—Three chief methods have been used for the experimental determination or comparison of gas densities. In the **Regnault method,** a glass globe or bulb of about 500 ml. capacity is dried, evacuated and weighed; it is then filled with the gas to be studied at a known pressure and reweighed. The difference between the two weights gives the weight of the gas filling the bulb at the particular temperature and pressure. The volume of the bulb is then found by filling it with water and weighing again. Various corrections must be applied to obtain accurate results.

In the **volumeter method,** the gas is liberated from a suitable generating apparatus, and its weight is determined by the change in weight of the apparatus. The gas is collected in a globe, or globes, of known volume at a definite temperature, and the pressure is measured by a manometer. In this way the mass, volume, pressure and temperature of the gas are found, thus providing all the data necessary for the evaluation of the density at the particular temperature and pressure. In a modification of this method, the weight of the gas is obtained by pumping it out of the globes and absorbing it in a convenient reagent.

Instead of actually measuring the density at a given pressure, in the **buoyancy method** the pressure is determined at which the density has a particular value. The buoyancy balance consists of a small evacuated bulb suspended by a fine quartz fiber from one end of a beam, the other end having a suitable counterweight attached. The balance, which is quite small in size, is enclosed in a tube of 2 to 3 cm. diameter and 8 to 10 cm. in length. The tube is evacuated and the first gas is gradually admitted; the suspended bulb rises, because of its buoyancy, and the pressure is measured when a pointer attached to the counterweight reaches a certain level. The gas is then pumped out, and the observation is repeated with the second gas. The two pressures measured are those at which the two gases have precisely the same density at the temperature of the experiment. By replacing the suspended bulb by one having a different weight, the measurements may be carried out at a series of pressures, as required for the application of the method of limiting densities described above.

14d. Vapor Densities and Molecular Weights.—The vapors of volatile substances which are solid or liquid at ordinary temperatures deviate so considerably from ideal behavior that no great accuracy could be expected from the molecular weights obtained from density measurements. It is useful, nevertheless, to have methods whereby approximate molecular weights of such substances can be determined with fair rapidity; these are generally referred to as **vapor density methods,** because they involve measurement of the weight and volume of the vapor, at a known temperature and pressure. The approximation is made of supposing the ideal gas laws to be applicable, and then the approximate molecular weight of the vapor is given by equation (14.3); thus,

$$M = \frac{wRT}{Pv}.$$
(14.8)

The various experimental procedures that have been used involve different means for the determination of the weight w, the volume v, and the pressure P of the vapor; three of the more important of these methods will be described briefly.

In the **Dumas method** (1826), the substance to be studied, usually a liquid, is introduced into a weighed glass bulb, about 250 ml. capacity, having a narrow outlet tube that can either be sealed off or closed by a stopcock. The bulb is heated in a constant temperature bath, about 20° above the boiling point of the experimental liquid. The heating is continued until the whole of the liquid has been converted into vapor and the air is completely expelled from the bulb. The latter is thus filled with the vapor at atmospheric pressure P and the temperature T of the heating bath. The bulb is now closed off, cooled and weighed; the difference between this weight and the weight of the "empty" bulb, after allowing for the air contained in the latter, gives the weight w of the vapor. The volume v of the bulb may be obtained in the familiar manner by filling with water and weighing.

Problem: Calculate the molecular weight of chloroform from the following data obtained with the Dumas method: weight of bulb with air = 52.30 g.; weight of bulb filled with vapor = 52.96 g.; weight of bulb filled with water at 20° C = 302 g.; temperature of heating bath, 100° C; atmospheric pressure, 752 mm. of mercury. (The density of air at ordinary temperatures and pressures may be taken as 1.29 g. per liter.)

The weight of water filling the bulb is 302 − 52.3 = 250 g., and taking the density as approximately unity, the volume v is 250 ml. The density of air is 1.29 g. per liter, and so this volume of air will weigh 0.32 g.; hence, the weight w of the vapor is 52.96 − (52.30 − 0.32) = 0.98 g. Expressing v in liters, i.e., 0.25 l., the pressure P in atm., i.e., 752/760 atm., and R in liter-atm. deg.$^{-1}$ mole^{-1} units, i.e., 0.082, with $T = 273 + 100 = 373°$, it follows from equation (14.8) that

$$M = \frac{wRT}{Pv} = \frac{0.98 \times 0.082 \times 373}{(752/760) \times 0.25} = 121.$$

The **Hofmann method** (1868) utilizes a graduated barometer tube containing mercury, surrounded by a jacket for maintaining a suitable constant temperature by means of the vapor of a boiling liquid. A weighed quantity, e.g., 0.1 to 0.3 gram, of the experimental substance is enclosed in a tiny stoppered (Hofmann) bottle and introduced into the apparatus by allowing it to rise through the mercury. The liquid vaporizes into the space above the mercury so that the level of the latter falls; this lowering gives the pressure P of the vapor, and its volume v is read off from the graduations on the tube. Since the temperature of the heating jacket is known, all the information is available for the determination of the approximate molecular weight. The chief advantage of the Hofmann method is that vaporization occurs under reduced pressure in the space above the mercury in the barometer tube. This means that the temperature can be well below the normal boiling point (see § 16b), and so it is possible to work with materials which may decompose on heating.

The most familiar of the vapor density methods is the **Victor Meyer method** (1878). The apparatus consists of a long vertical tube widening out into an elongated bulb at its lower end, and having a side-tube near the top. The side-tube is connected to a gas buret containing water or mercury, or to any convenient device for measuring the volume of air expelled from the apparatus. The vertical tube and bulb are surrounded by a jacket kept at a constant temperature, about 20° or 30° above the boiling point of the material being studied, by vapor from a boiling liquid. A weighed quantity of the experimental substance, contained in a small (Hofmann) bottle, is dropped into the apparatus; vaporization occurs immediately and an equal volume of air at the temperature of the bulb is expelled. This is cooled to room temperature, however, in the measuring apparatus, and the volume recorded is that which the vapor would occupy at atmospheric pressure if determined at the temperature of the gas buret. The assumption made here is that the air and the vapor have the same coefficient of expansion, as would be the case if they both behaved as ideal gases. Since the Victor Meyer method is an approximate one, in any case, the error is not serious. As the weight of the material is known, and the volume of its vapor, at the atmospheric temperature and pressure, have been measured, the molecular weight can be calculated. One advantage of the method is that the volume is obtained at atmospheric temperature, and so the temperature of the heating bath need not be known.

Problem: In a Victor Meyer experiment, 0.241 gram of chloroform expelled 47.9 ml. of air, collected over mercury, measured at 23° C, and 764 mm. pressure. Calculate the approximate molecular weight of chloroform.

It is again convenient to express v in liters, i.e., 0.0479, and P in atm., i.e., 764/760, so that R is 0.082 liter-atm. deg.$^{-1}$ mole^{-1}; T is $273 + 23 = 296°$; w is 0.241 g. Hence,

$$M = \frac{wRT}{Pv} = \frac{0.241 \times 0.082 \times 296}{(764/760) \times 0.0479} = 121.$$

If the displaced air is collected over water, it will become saturated with water vapor. If the air in the Victor Meyer tube was originally dry, or almost dry, it is necessary to correct for the presence of the water vapor. This is done by making use of Dalton's law of partial pressures (see § 11g); the actual pressure of the dry air is equal to the total (atmospheric) pressure minus the pressure of the water vapor at the temperature of the gas-collecting device.

A modification of the Victor Meyer apparatus, employing a small bulb made of porcelain or iridium, has been used for determinations of molecular weights at temperatures up to 2000° C.

14e. Molecular Weights of Elements.—Molecular weight determinations based on density methods, i.e., on pressure, volume and temperature measurements of a given mass of gas or vapor, have given results that are generally in agreement with those expected from ordinary chemical considerations. In addition a number of facts of special interest and importance have come to light. For example, it has been found that in the vapor state the molecular weights of many metals, e.g., sodium, zinc, cadmium, mercury, thallium and lead, are almost the same as the atomic weights. This means that the molecules of the metal vapors are mainly monatomic, the atom and the molecule being identical.

At moderate temperatures the gaseous nonmetals, such as hydrogen, nitrogen, oxygen and the halogens have molecular weights which are twice the respective atomic weights; these substances are consequently diatomic. There is evidence, however, that at elevated temperatures the diatomic molecules, particularly those of the heavier halogens, break up to some extent and that free atoms, i.e., monatomic molecules, can exist. Provided the temperatures are not too high, the molecules of phosphorus, arsenic and antimony each contain four atoms in the vapor state, i.e., P_4, As_4 and Sb_4, while sulfur and selenium vapors consist largely of molecules containing eight atoms, i.e., S_8 and Se_8. In every case, however, increase of temperature results in a simplification of the molecules, so that at very high temperatures a considerable proportion are monatomic.

14f. Molecular Association.—It has been observed that a number of compounds have molecular weights in the vapor state that are appreciably higher than those to be anticipated from simple valence considerations. Structural organic chemistry leads to the view that the formula of acetic acid is CH_3COOH, so that the molecular weight should be 60.0; nevertheless, actual measurements made just above the boiling point at atmospheric pressure give a value of about 100. The result varies with the temperature and pressure of the vapor; the observed molecular weight approaches a limiting value of 120, i.e., twice the theoretical molecular weight, as the temperature is lowered. It appears, therefore, that acetic acid vapor contains a large number of double molecules, i.e., $(CH_3COOH)_2$; these molecules split up into single molecules as the temperature is raised or the pressure lowered. Similar results have been obtained with formic acid and with other carboxylic acids.

Substances which have molecular weights that are larger than those expected for the simple molecules are said to be **associated,** and to exhibit the phenomenon of molecular **association.** Acetic acid and other carboxylic acids are thus associated in the vapor state; this is in agreement with the resonance structures for such compounds suggested in § 10h. It is probable that carboxylic acids are almost completely associated to form double molecules in the liquid state, and are also associated to some extent in solution (§ 31a) as well as in the vapor. It should be noted, however, that other hydroxylic substances, such as water, alcohols and phenols, which undoubtedly form associated molecules in the liquid state and in certain solutions, are not associated in the vapor state. Vapor density determinations show that the vapors of these compounds consist of single molecules. This difference between the behavior of carboxylic acids, on the one hand, and water, alcohols and phenols, on the other hand, is in accord with the different types of hydrogen bonds in the two cases; with the former the resulting molecular association is of a specific character, leading to the production of double molecules, but with the latter the association is more general in nature. Thus, with the carboxylic acids the double molecules exist as units in the liquid and vaporize as such; with water, etc., only single molecules, which break away from their general attachment with other molecules, escape into the vapor under normal conditions.

14g. Thermal Dissociation.—In contrast to the behavior just described, certain substances give molecular weights that are less than expected, the value decreasing towards a limit as the temperature is raised. This is undoubtedly due to the splitting up of a relatively complex molecule into simpler molecules when the substance is heated and vaporized. The phenomenon is known as **thermal dissociation,** and it may be described as *the decomposition of a molecule into simpler parts on heating, these parts recombining to form the original molecule on cooling.* The vapors of ammonium chloride, and of other ammonium salts, and of phosphorus pentachloride, for example, exhibit molecular weights that approach one-half the chemical values as the temperature is raised; in these cases there is chemical evidence for the dissociations

$$NH_4Cl = NH_3 + HCl \qquad \text{and} \qquad PCl_5 = PCl_3 + Cl_2.$$

Since each molecule of the original substance can split up into two molecules of product, when the dissociation is complete, the actual number of molecules present in the vapor will be about twice as great as the value that would have been observed if there had been no dissociation. As a result the volume is doubled, and hence the density and the approximate molecular weight will be about one-half the theoretical value. The occurrence of dissociation upon vaporization is thus able to account for the observed molecular weight being lower than would otherwise have been anticipated.

The extent to which a particular substance dissociates in the vapor state depends on the temperature and pressure (see Chapter X), and it is possible to derive a simple expression relating the experimental observations to the proportion of the molecules which have dissociated. Consider a perfectly general case in which one molecule of the substance under examination dissociates into m molecules of product when completely dissociated. If α is the fraction of the material that has dissociated, at the experimental temperature and pressure, then for every molecule of original substance, $1 - \alpha$ will remain undissociated while $m\alpha$ molecules of products are formed; the total number of moles in the vapor will thus be $1 - \alpha + m\alpha$ for every 1 mole expected theoretically if there were no dissociation. If w grams of a substance of molecular weight M_0 occupies a volume v_0, at a temperature T and pressure P, when no dissociation occurs, then by equation (14.2), assuming ideal behavior,

$$Pv_0 = \frac{w}{M_0} RT. \qquad (14.9)$$

As a result of dissociation, however, the number of moles, i.e., w/M_0, is increased by a factor of $1 - \alpha + m\alpha$, as shown above; the volume v occupied by the dissociated vapor is then determined by

$$Pv = \frac{w}{M_0} (1 - \alpha + m\alpha)RT. \tag{14.10}$$

From this equation it is possible to calculate the fraction of dissociation α at any temperature and pressure from a knowledge of the volume v occupied by a known weight w of the substance as vapor; M_0 is the theoretical molecular weight.

Problem: In a vapor density experiment, 1.35 gram of nitrogen tetroxide (N_2O_4) was found to occupy a volume of 0.501 liter at 45° C and a pressure of 795 mm. Calculate the fraction of N_2O_4 dissociated into NO_2 molecules under these conditions.

The dissociation reaction is $N_2O_4 = 2NO_2$, and since 1 molecule of N_2O_4 dissociates into 2 molecules of NO_2, the value of m is 2; equation (14.10) therefore becomes

$$Pv = \frac{w}{M_0} (1 + \alpha)RT.$$

The simplest units to employ are P in atm. and v in liters, so that R is 0.082 liter-atm. deg.$^{-1}$ mole^{-1}; P is then 795/760 atm., v is 0.501 liter, T is $273 + 45 = 318°$ K, w is 1.35 g. and M_0, for N_2O_4, is 92. Substitution in the above equation gives

$$\frac{795}{760} \times 0.501 = \frac{1.35}{92} (1 + \alpha) \times 0.082 \times 318$$

$$\alpha = 0.370.$$

The results just described are sometimes expressed in alternative forms; thus, if equation (14.10) is divided by (14.9), it is seen that

$$\frac{v}{v_0} = 1 - \alpha + m\alpha. \tag{14.11}$$

The density of the gas, i.e., the mass per unit volume, is inversely proportional to the volume, and the apparent, i.e., observed, molecular weight is directly proportional to the experimental density [equation (3.2)]; hence, it is possible to derive from equation (14.11),

$$\frac{d_0}{d} = \frac{M_0}{M} = 1 - \alpha + m\alpha,$$

$$\alpha = \frac{d_0 - d}{d(m - 1)} = \frac{M_0 - M}{M(m - 1)}, \tag{14.12}$$

where d and M are the observed density of the dissociated vapor and its apparent molecular weight, respectively, while d_0 and M_0 are the theoretical values to be expected for the given substance if there had been no dissociation. The densities d and d_0 refer, of course, to the same temperature and pressure

From equation (14.12) the value of α may be calculated from the density or from the apparent molecular weight.

It is important to point out that whereas a low vapor density or molecular weight implies dissociation, the process of dissociation is not always accompanied by a decrease of density. Such a decrease is observed only when there is an increase in the number of molecules as a result of the dissociation. If there is no change in the number of molecules as, for example, when gaseous hydrogen iodide dissociates to form hydrogen gas and iodine vapor, i.e.,

$$2HI = H_2 + I_2,$$

the volume, density and molecular weight are unaffected. It is then not possible to calculate the fraction of dissociation from pressure-volume, i.e., density, measurements. The same conclusion may be reached by putting m equal to unity in any of the equations of this section.

READING REFERENCES

1. **Modified Victor Meyer apparatus.** Blank, *Journal of Chemical Education*, **8**, 546 (1931); **10**, 505 (1933).
2. **Apparatus for Graham's law of effusion.** Wenaas, *ibid.*, **8**, 2257 (1931).
3. **Micro Victor Meyer apparatus.** Blank and Willard, *ibid.*, **9**, 1819 (1932).
4. **Equation of state of perfect gas** (historical). Roseman and Katzoff, *ibid.*, **11**, 350 (1934).
5. **Equations of state.** Woolsey, *ibid.*, **16**, 60, 498 (1939).
6. **Kinetic theory of gases.** Pease, *ibid.*, **16**, 242, 366 (1939).
7. **Improved Victor Meyer apparatus.** Hendel and Ochsenreiter, *ibid.*, **17**, 533 (1940).
8. **Molecular state of acetic acid vapor.** Wright, *ibid.*, **20**, 179 (1943).
9. **Study of gas laws.** Steinbach and Conery, *ibid.*, **21**, 216 (1944).
10. **Properties of gases.** Martin, *ibid.*, **21**, 383 (1944).
11. **Gas law demonstrations.** Hickey, *ibid.*, **21**, 491 (1944).

REVIEW QUESTIONS

1. Compare the properties of the three states of matter.
2. State Boyle's law in words, in the form of an equation and graphically.
3. State Gay-Lussac's law in words and in the form of an equation.
4. Explain the meaning of the absolute temperature. How does the volume of a gas depend on the absolute temperature?
5. What is an equation of state? Derive the equation of state for a gas obeying the laws of Boyle and Gay-Lussac.
6. What is an ideal gas? Derive the equation of state (a) for n moles, (b) for w grams, of an ideal gas.
7. How is the accurate value of the absolute zero of temperature derived?
8. Derive the correct dimensions for the gas constant R.
9. Determine the value of the gas constant in the three units generally employed.
10. What is the meaning of partial pressure? State Dalton's law of partial pressures. Derive an expression relating the partial pressure of a gas in a mixture to the total pressure.

11. What is the meaning of the mole fraction? A mixture consists of n_A moles of A and n_B moles of B; write the expressions for the mole fractions of A and B. What is their sum?

12. State Graham's law of gaseous diffusion in words and in the form of an equation.

13. What is effusion? What law is applicable to the rate of effusion? Explain how effusion may be used to calculate the density or molecular weight of a gas.

14. Outline the fundamental basis of the kinetic theory of gases. What restrictions are applicable to an ideal gas?

15. Derive an expression for the pressure of a gas by means of the kinetic theory.

16. Derive Boyle's law and Avogadro's law from the kinetic theory of gases. What is postulated concerning the absolute temperature?

17. Derive a relationship between the kinetic energy of all the molecules in 1 mole of a gas and the absolute temperature.

18. Show that Dalton's law of partial pressures can be derived from the kinetic theory of gases.

19. Derive the laws of diffusion and effusion from the kinetic theory.

20. Represent diagrammatically the result of Maxwell's law of the distribution of molecular velocities, and show the effect of increasing temperature.

21. What is the Boltzmann factor? Explain its significance.

22. Define the mean free path. How is it related to (a) the collision diameter, (b) viscosity?

23. How can the number of collisions per sec. in a given volume of gas or a mixture of gases be calculated?

24. How is the Avogadro number determined from measurements on small suspended particles? What other methods have been used? What conclusions can be drawn from the agreement of the results?

25. Explain the difference between heat capacities at constant pressure and constant volume.

26. Calculate the molar heat capacity of a monatomic gas at constant pressure and constant volume. Why is the difference always (approximately) equal to R?

27. Explain why the heat capacities of a polyatomic gas are different from the results derived by the kinetic theory. Why do the values vary with temperature?

28. Describe, with the aid of a figure, the deviations of a real gas from the ideal behavior of the laws of Boyle, Gay-Lussac and Avogadro.

29. What are believed to be the chief causes of the deviation of gases from ideal behavior? How are they allowed for in the van der Waals equation?

30. What conclusions may be drawn from the van der Waals equation concerning the behavior of gases at low and high pressures? Do they agree with experiment?

31. Describe briefly some other equations of state for nonideal gases.

32. What theory has been proposed to account for molecular attractions?

33. How are accurate molecular weights determined by the method of (a) limiting densities, (b) limiting pressures?

34. Outline the three chief methods for determining accurate gas densities.

35. Outline three methods for determining molecular weights from vapor density measurements.

36. Define and explain, with examples, what is meant by molecular association.

37. Define and illustrate the meaning of thermal dissociation.

38. How can the extent of dissociation be determined from pressure-volume (density) measurements? When is this not possible?

I

1. At a pressure of 752 mm.* a mass of 0.324 g. of an ideal gas occupies 280 ml. at 23° C. At what temperature will 1.00 g. of the same gas occupy exactly 1 liter at 1 atm. pressure?

2. Assuming ideal behavior, calculate the weight of oxygen in 1.40 liters at a temperature of 0° C and a pressure of 10 mm. How many individual molecules are present?

3. Calculate the density, in g. per liter, of carbon monoxide gas at 15° C and a pressure of 740 mm., assuming ideal behavior.

4. A mixture consisting of 0.150 g. hydrogen, 0.700 g. nitrogen and 0.340 gram ammonia has a total pressure of 1 atm. at 27° C. Calculate (a) the mole fraction, (b) the partial pressure of each gas, (c) the total volume.

5. Calculate (a) the root mean square velocity, (b) the average speed, of the molecules of carbon monoxide at 15° C.

6. A large volume of electrolytic gas, i.e., containing 2 vols. of hydrogen to 1 vol. of oxygen is allowed to diffuse through a porous partition; what will be the composition of the initial gas diffusing through?

7. The viscosity of carbon monoxide at 15° C is 1.72×10^{-4} poise. Calculate (a) the mean free path, (b) the collision diameter, (c) the number of collisions per sec. in 1 cc. at 15° C and 740 mm. (The results of problems 3 and 5 may be used.)

8. Calculate the Avogadro number from the following data on the distribution of gamboge particles, of radius 2.12×10^{-5} cm., under the influence of gravity at 15° C. At two depths 6×10^{-3} cm. apart, the ratio of the numbers of particles was 4.43. The density of the particles was 1.205, while that of the medium (water) may be taken as 0.999.

9. Determine the high temperature (limiting) value of γ, the ratio of the heat capacities at constant pressure and volume, for (a) CO_2 (linear), (b) H_2O (nonlinear). What are the probable values at normal temperatures?

10. Calculate the pressure exerted by 1 mole of nitrogen when it occupies a volume of 70.3 ml. at 0° C by means of (a) the ideal gas equation, (b) the van der Waals ,equation. (The actual value is about 400 atm.)

11. The following results have been recorded for the density of carbon dioxide, in grams per liter, at several pressures at 0° C.

P	1	$\frac{2}{3}$	$\frac{1}{2}$	$\frac{1}{3}$ atm.
d	1.97676	1.31485	0.98505	0.65596

Determine the molecular weight of carbon dioxide, and hence the atomic weight of carbon, by the method of limiting densities.

12. At 250° C, and 765 mm. pressure phosphorus pentachloride vapor is dissociated to the extent of 81 per cent into phosphorus trichloride and chlorine, i.e., $PCl_5 = PCl_3 + Cl_2$. What is the volume of the vessel in which 1.24 g. of the pentachloride is vaporized at specified temperature and pressure?

II

1. A quantity of an ideal gas weighing 3.062 g. occupies a volume of 1.224 liters at 10° C and 2 atm. pressure. At what pressure, in cm. of mercury, will 0.436 g. of the same gas occupy a volume of 300 ml. at 25° C?

* Unless otherwise stated, pressures in cm. or mm. always refer to cm. or mm. of mercury.

2. Calculate (a) the number of moles, (b) the number of individual molecules contained in 0.476 liter of an ideal gas at 120° C and 87.3 cm. pressure.

3. Calculate the density, in g. per liter, of oxygen gas at 25° and 770 mm. pressure, assuming ideal behavior.

4. When phosphorus pentachloride is heated at 200° C and 1.22 atm. pressure its vapor is dissociated, to the extent of 0.42, into the trichloride and chlorine. What is (a) the mole fraction, (b) the partial pressure, of PCl_5, PCl_3 and Cl_2?

5. Calculate (a) the root mean square velocity, (b) the average speed, of the molecules of oxygen at 25° C.

6. The time taken for a definite volume of oxygen to effuse through an orifice was found to be 135 sec. Under exactly the same conditions, another gas took 236 sec. to pass through; what is the molecular weight of the gas?

7. The viscosity of oxygen at 25° C is 2.01×10^{-4} poise. Calculate (a) the mean free path, (b) the collision diameter, (c) the number of collisions per sec. in 1 cc. at 25° C and 770 mm. (The results of problems 3 and 5 may be used.)

8. The following data were obtained for the distribution under gravity of very small gold particles, of radius 2.1×10^{-6} cm., suspended in water at 20° C; utilize them to calculate the Avogadro number. At two depths 0.080 cm. apart the ratio of the numbers of particles was 5.83. The density of the gold particles may be taken as 19.3, and that of the water as 1.0.

9. The ratio of the heat capacities at constant pressure and constant volume of hydrogen gas is 1.32 at 2000° C. Calculate the molar heat capacity (a) at constant pressure, (b) at constant volume. What is the combined vibrational and rotational contribution to the heat capacity at 2000° C?

10. One mole of ether occupies 741 ml. at 300° C and a particular pressure; calculate the pressure (a) assuming ideal behavior, (b) from the van der Waals equation, taking a as 17.4 and b as 13.4×10^{-2} in liter and atm. units. (The experimental pressure is 48.4 atm.)

11. The following values were obtained for the density of phosphine in grams per liter, at several pressures at 0° C.

P	1	$\frac{3}{4}$	$\frac{1}{2}$	$\frac{1}{4}$ atm.
d	1.5307	1.1454	0.76190	0.38012

Determine the molecular weight of phosphine, and hence the atomic weight of phosphorus, by the method of limiting densities.

12. The volume occupied by 0.492 g. of nitrogen tetroxide at a pressure of 753 mm. was 241 ml. at 65° C. Calculate the apparent molecular weight, and the fraction of dissociation according to the reaction $N_2O_4 = 2NO_2$.

CHAPTER V

LIQUEFACTION AND THE PROPERTIES OF LIQUIDS

The Liquefaction of Gases

15a. The Critical State.—During the early part of the nineteenth century, a number of gases, such as carbon dioxide, sulfur dioxide, hydrogen sulfide, ammonia, etc., were liquefied by the simultaneous use of high pressure and low temperature. Further, by allowing compressed liquid carbon dioxide to evaporate, the temperature was lowered sufficiently for the solid to be obtained. The same principle is used at the present time in the manufacture of "dry ice," as solid carbon dioxide is called. By mixing solid carbon dioxide with ether, M. Thilorier (1835) was able to obtain temperatures as low as $-110°$ C, and this permitted the liquefaction of such gases as ethylene, phosphine and silicon tetrafluoride. In spite of numerous attempts, however, involving the use of pressures up to 3000 atm., the gases hydrogen, oxygen, nitrogen and carbon monoxide could not be liquefied. The general opinion in the middle of the last century was, therefore, that certain gases, called "permanent gases," could not be converted into liquids under any circumstances; this conclusion was shortly to be proved incorrect.

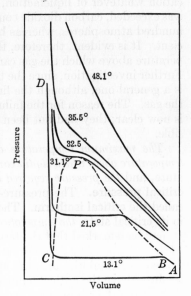

Fig. 19.   Pressure-volume isothermals of carbon dioxide

The essential conditions for the liquefaction of gases were discovered by T. Andrews (1869) as the result of a study of the pressure-volume-temperature relationships of carbon dioxide. A definite amount of the gas was enclosed in a glass tube kept at a constant temperature, and the volumes at different pressures were measured; the results for a series of temperatures were plotted in the form of isothermals (§ 11b), as shown in Fig. 19.

At the lowest temperature employed by Andrews, 13.1° C, the carbon dioxide is entirely gaseous at low pressures, as at *A;* upon increasing the pressure the volume decreases, as indicated by the curve *AB*, approximately in accordance with Boyle's law. At the pressure *B*, however, liquefaction com-

127

mences, and the volume decreases rapidly as the gas is converted to liquid with a much higher density. At C the carbon dioxide has been completely liquefied, and the steepness of the curve CD is evidence of the fact that the liquid is not easily compressed. It should be noted that the portion AB of the isothermal represents *gas only*, and CD represents *liquid only;* along BC, however, *gas and liquid can coexist.* Since BC is parallel to the volume axis, it follows that the pressure remains constant while gas and liquid are present together, irrespective of the relative amounts of the two forms. The constant pressure represented by BC is the vapor pressure of the liquid at the temperature of the isotherm; this property of liquids will be considered in § 16a.

The pressure-volume curve at 21.5° C is similar to that for the lower temperature, except that the horizontal portion, over which liquefaction occurs, is shorter. In fact, as the temperature is raised, this section of the isotherm becomes less and less, as indicated by the dashed "boundary curve" in Fig. 19; finally, at 31.1° C it is reduced to a mere point. Above 31.1° there is no indication whatever of liquefaction, and Andrews found that if this temperature was exceeded, carbon dioxide could not be liquefied even at pressures of several hundred atmospheres, whereas below 31.1° C, a pressure of 75 atm. was sufficient. It is evident, therefore, that for carbon dioxide there is a limit of temperature above which the gas cannot be liquefied no matter what the pressure. Further investigation, since the time of Andrews, has shown that this property is a general one, although the limiting temperature depends on the nature of the gas. The reason for the failure to liquefy the so-called "permanent gases" is now clear; they had not been cooled sufficiently for liquefaction to be possible.

The maximum temperature at which a gas can be liquefied, that is, *the temperature above which liquid cannot exist,* is referred to as the **critical temperature,** and *the pressure required to cause liquefaction at this temperature* is the **critical pressure.** The pressure-volume curve for the critical temperature is called the **critical isotherm.** The point P in Fig. 19 represents carbon dioxide in its **critical state,** *the temperature, pressure and volume being the critical values.* It may be remarked that the term **vapor** is used to describe *a gaseous substance when its temperature is below the critical value;* a vapor can, therefore, be condensed to a liquid by pressure alone.

Just above the critical temperature the P-V isotherms show marked deviations from the rectangular hyperbola to be expected for an ideal gas, e.g., the 32.5° and 35.5° C isotherms in Fig. 19. This corresponds to the marked dip in the plot of PV against P for carbon dioxide at 40° C in Fig. 15. At higher temperatures, e.g., 48.1° C, the deviation from ideal behavior is evidently very much less, the isotherm in Fig. 19 approximating to that expected for an ideal gas.

15b. Determination of Critical Constants: The Law of the Rectilinear Diameter.—The obvious method for the determination of the critical constants of a gas is to use the procedure of Andrews, and to plot the P-V isotherms for a number of temperatures. Other methods, which are much simpler, are, however, available; the essential principle involved is based on the fact that at the critical temperature the densities of liquid and vapor become identical, and the surface of separation—the meniscus—between them disappears. The experimental substance is placed in the bulb A which is attached to a mercury manometer B, as in Fig. 20; the bulb is cooled if necessary, so that the surface between the liquid and vapor is apparent. The temperature is raised gradually until the meniscus just disappears; this gives the critical temperature, and the critical pressure can be obtained from the mercury level in the manometer. It may be mentioned that more modern theoretical and experimental studies indicate that there is a sort of critical region, rather than a definite temperature; the liquid-vapor surface apparently disappears a few degrees below the temperature at which the liquid ceases to exist.

The critical volume, and the critical temperature also, can be obtained with the aid of the rule of L. Cailletet and E. Mathias (1886), known as the **law of the rectilinear diameter.** According to this law, *the mean value of the densities of any substance in the states of liquid and of saturated vapor at the same temperature*, e.g., as represented by the points B and C in Fig. 19, *is a linear function of the temperature.* The densities of the liquid (d_l) and of the saturated vapor (d_v) in equilibrium with it, are known as the **orthobaric densities,** and by the law of Cailletet and Mathias,

$$\tfrac{1}{2}(d_l + d_v) = a + bt, \tag{15.1}$$

where a and b are constants, and t is the temperature. The orthobaric densities of the hydrocarbon n-pentane are plotted in Fig. 21; the points on AC give the densities of the saturated vapor and on BC are those of the liquid at various temperatures. The maximum C of the curve is the critical temperature. The mean densities are plotted along CD, and the close approximation to a straight line, as required by equation (15.1), is evident. This line must cut the curve ACB at C, which gives the critical temperature and density; from the latter, the critical volume per mole is readily obtained. It is evident from Fig. 21 that the density of liquid and saturated vapor become identical at the critical temperature, as stated above.

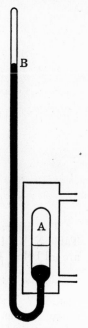

Fig. 20. Observation of critical phenomena

In order to evaluate the critical volume and temperature, the orthobaric densities are plotted, as in Fig. 21, and a curve is drawn through the points. The mean densities are also plotted, and the point where the resulting straight line cuts the curve, corresponding to C in Fig. 21, gives the required information. To determine the orthobaric densities, a known mass m of liquid is sealed in a graduated tube and is heated to a particular temperature; the volumes v_l and v_v of liquid and vapor, respectively, are then read off from the graduations. Since the densities are d_l and d_v, respectively, it follows that

$$m = v_l d_l + v_v d_v. \tag{15.2}$$

The experiment is repeated at the same temperature with a different mass of substance, and from the two equations, of the form of (15.2), the two unknowns d_l and d_v can be calculated.

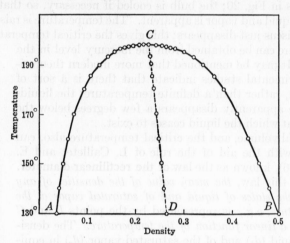

FIG. 21.   Orthobaric densities and rectilinear diameter of n-pentane

The critical constants for a number of common substances are given in Table XIV. It is seen that the critical temperatures of the "permanent gases" are all below 154° K, i.e., about −120° C. Since the lowest temperature at-

TABLE XIV.   CRITICAL CONSTANTS

Sub-stance	Temp.	Press.	Molar Vol.	Sub-stance	Temp.	Press.	Molar Vol.
He	5.2° K	2.26 atm.	60 ml.	H_2S	373.5° K	89.0 atm.	127 ml.
H_2	33.2°	12.8	68	NH_3	406.0°	112.3	72
N_2	126.0°	33.5	90	Cl_2	417.1°	76.1	124
CO	133.6°	35.5	90	SO_2	430.3°	77.6	125
O_2	154.3°	49.7	74	CCl_4	556.2°	45.0	275
CO_2	304.2°	73.0	95	C_6H_6	561.6°	47.9	256
HCl	324.1°	81.5	89	H_2O	647.3°	217.7	57

tainable in the middle of the nineteenth century was about −110° C, it can now be readily understood why these gases resisted all attempts at liquefaction.

15c. The van der Waals Equation and the Critical State.—The van der Waals equation

$$\left(P + \frac{a}{V^2}\right)(V - b) = RT$$

can be multiplied out and rearranged so as to give the cubic equation

$$V^3 - \left(b + \frac{RT}{P}\right)V^2 + \frac{a}{P}V - \frac{ab}{P} = 0. \qquad (15.3)$$

Such an equation will have three roots, that is, there will be three values of V for given values of P and T; the three roots may be real, or one may be real and the others imaginary. If the values of V are plotted against P, for a constant T, then equation (15.3) should, from purely mathematical considerations, give a curve similar to I in Fig. 22. It is evident from this curve that, within a certain range of P values, there will be three real solutions for V, as, for example, the three points B, F and C. As T is increased, the curve is raised along the P axis, e.g., curve II; it will be observed that at the same time the three possible values of V for a given P are much closer together. At a certain value of T, for which the P-V curve is represented by III, the three solutions for V become identical at the point X. If T is raised still further, there is only one real value of V, the other two being imaginary, as is indicated by curve IV.

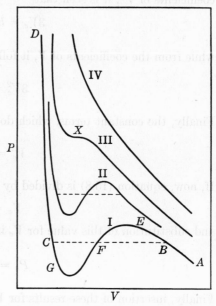

FIG. 22.   Isothermal curves according to the van der Waals equation

A comparison of Fig. 22, which has been derived from purely mathematical consideration of the van der Waals equation in the form of (15.3), with the experimental facts for carbon dioxide represented in Fig. 19, shows a striking resemblance. The only essential difference is that the horizontal lines in Fig. 19, where liquefaction occurs, are replaced by ᔋ-shaped (sigmoid) curves in Fig. 22. It is of interest to mention that portions of the curves corresponding to BE and CG in the latter figure have been realized under the abnormal conditions of "supersaturated vapors" and "superheated liquids," respectively.

The curve III in Fig. 22, for which the three real values of V become identical, corresponds to the isothermal in Fig. 19 on which the horizontal line representing liquefaction is just a single point, i.e., the critical isotherm; this correspondence can be utilized to express the critical constants of a gas in terms of the van der Waals constants. At the critical point X, the three values of V are all equal to the critical volume V_c, and this condition may be represented by the equation

$$(V - V_c)^3 = 0,$$

which upon multiplying out becomes

$$V^3 - 3V_cV^2 + 3V_c^2V - V_c^3 = 0. \qquad (15.4)$$

Further, at the critical temperature and pressure, equation (15.3) may be written as

$$V^3 - \left(b + \frac{RT_c}{P_c}\right) V^2 + \frac{a}{P_c} V - \frac{ab}{P_c} = 0, \qquad (15.5)$$

and according to the arguments presented above, this should be completely identical with equation (15.4). It follows, therefore, that the coefficients of the various terms in the two equations must be identical; thus, comparing the coefficients of V^2, it is seen that

$$3V_c = b + \frac{RT_c}{P_c} \qquad (15.6)$$

while from the coefficients of V, it follows that

$$3V_c^2 = \frac{a}{P_c}. \qquad (15.7)$$

Finally, the constant terms, which do not contain V. must be equal, so that

$$V_c^3 = \frac{ab}{P_c}. \qquad (15.8)$$

If, now, equation (15.8) is divided by (15.7), the result is

$$V_c = 3b,$$

and substitution of this value for V_c in equation (15.7) gives

$$P_c = \frac{a}{27b^2}.$$

Finally, insertion of these results for V_c and P_c in equation (15.6) yields

$$T_c = \frac{8a}{27Rb}.$$

There have thus been obtained, from the van der Waals equation, the expressions

(i) $V_c = 3b$,   (ii) $P_c = \dfrac{a}{27b^2}$,   and   (iii) $T_c = \dfrac{8a}{27Rb}$ (15.9)

relating the critical constants to a, b and R, for the given gas.

These equations may be tested by determining the van der Waals constants a and b from P-V-T measurements, and seeing how closely the experimental critical data can be reproduced. The results obtained in this manner are, however, not too satisfactory, one reason being that a and b vary with temperature, as mentioned earlier. If the van der Waals constants are derived from P-V-T data obtained not too far from the critical point, then the agreement between calculated and observed critical constants is moderately good, but otherwise there are appreciable differences. As stated in § 13c, it is the general practice to reverse the procedure and to determine the van der Waals constants from the experimental critical data, utilizing the relationships derived above. It is evident, however, that the results can be satisfactory only if the conditions are not too far removed from the critical state.

A further consequence of the van der Waals equation is obtained by combining the three equations (15.9); the result is

$$\frac{RT_c}{P_cV_c} = \frac{8}{3} = 2.67,$$

so that RT_c/P_cV_c should be a constant, irrespective of the nature of the substance, equal to 2.67 for 1 mole. The data in Table XV show, however,

TABLE XV. VALUES OF RT_c/P_cV_c

Substance	RT_c/P_cV_c	Substance	RT_c/P_cV_c
Hydrogen	3.28	Chlorine	3.63
Helium	3.18	Sulfur dioxide	3.64
Nitrogen	3.42	Carbon tetrachloride	3.68
Oxygen	3.42	Benzene	3.75
Carbon dioxide	3.68	Ethyl ether	3.81
Hydrogen chloride	3.66	Stannic chloride	3.75

that although RT_c/P_cV_c is approximately constant for a number of elements and compounds, it is appreciably greater than 2.67. Substances containing hydroxyl groups, and which are associated in the liquid state, because of hydrogen bonding (§ 10h), give still higher values for RT_c/P_cV_c, e.g., 4.4 for water, 4.0 for ethanol and 5.0 for acetic acid. Other equations of state, e.g., the Dieterici equation (13.4), lead to somewhat better agreement with experiment than does the van der Waals equation in this connection, but they are more difficult to manipulate and so are used for special purposes only.

For 1 mole of an ideal gas, RT is equal to PV; the fact that RT_c/P_cV_c is about 3.7 for many substances shows, therefore, that the pressure-volume product at the critical point is less than the ideal gas value in the ratio of 1 to 3.7. This is in harmony with the marked dip in the curve showing the variation of PV with P which becomes evident as the critical temperature is approached (see Figs. 15 and 16).

15d. The Law of Corresponding States.—A striking consequence of his equation was pointed out by van der Waals in 1881. If the pressure, volume and temperature of a gas are expressed in terms of the critical pressure, volume and temperature, respectively, thus,

$$P = \pi P_c, \qquad V = \phi V_c \qquad \text{and} \qquad T = \theta T_c, \qquad (15.10)$$

the van der Waals equation becomes

$$\left(\pi P_c + \frac{a}{\phi^2 V_c^2} \right) (\phi V_c - b) = R\theta T_c.$$

If the values for P_c, V_c and T_c, as given by the equation (15.9), are now introduced, the result is

$$\left(\frac{-a}{27b^2} + \frac{a}{9\phi^2 b^2} \right) (3\phi b - b) = \frac{8a\theta}{27b}$$

or

$$\left(\pi + \frac{3}{\phi^2} \right) (3\phi - 1) = 8\theta. \tag{15.11}$$

The quantities π, ϕ (Greek, *phi*) and θ (Greek, *theta*) are called the **reduced pressure, volume** and **temperature,** respectively, and equation (15.11) is the **reduced equation of state.** The important point to note about this equation is that it is perfectly general, and does not involve either R or the specific a and b values for any gas; it should thus be applicable to all substances.

According to equation (15.11), *if any two or more substances have the same reduced pressure π, that is to say, their pressures are the same fraction or multiple π of their respective critical pressures, and are at equal reduced temperatures θ, their temperatures being the same fraction or multiple θ of their respective critical temperatures, then their reduced volumes ϕ should be equal, i.e., V/V_c should be the same in each case.* Substances under these conditions are said to be in **corresponding•states,** and the foregoing statement may be taken as an expression of the **law of corresponding states.** Although the law has been derived here from the van der Waals equation, it is important to point out that any equation of state involving two arbitrary constants in addition to R, e.g., the Dieterici equation, can be converted into an equation containing only the reduced quantities π, ϕ and θ. The generalized form of the law of corresponding states given above will then follow directly. The difference between the various equations of the form of (15.11), as derived from different equations of state, is that they do not give the same numerical relationship between π, ϕ and θ.

The accuracy of the law of corresponding states in its general form has been verified for a number of substances, both in the liquid and gaseous states. The van der Waals equation represents, qualitatively at least, the behavior of liquid, e.g., curve CD in Fig. 22, as well as that of gas; hence, the law of corresponding states should apply to both conditions. It has been found experimentally that when the pressure is such that π, that is P/P_c, is 0.08846, and the temperature is such that θ, that is T/T_c, is 0.74, the reduced volume ϕ, i.e., V/V_c, lies between 0.400 and 0.408 for the liquid, and between 27.2 and 29.3 for the saturated vapor, for a number of substances. These results show that the law of corresponding states is obeyed, as a first approximation. However, as in connection with other physical properties, although the van der Waals equation does represent the general nature of the results, the quantitative agreement is not good; this may be seen by inserting the values of π and θ given above into equation (15.11) and comparing the calculated ϕ with that observed.

15e. The Liquefaction of Gases.—As a consequence of the discovery that a gas had to be cooled below a certain temperature before it could be liquefied, attention was concentrated on the problem of obtaining low temperatures. One of the earliest methods, which was used to solidify carbon dioxide and was utilized by R. P. Pictet (1877) for the liquefaction of oxygen, depended on the cooling accompanying vaporization of a readily liquefied gas. For example, by rapid evaporation of liquid sulfur dioxide a temperature of $-65°$ C was obtained; at this low temperature carbon dioxide was readily liquefied, and by vaporization of this liquid under reduced pressure the temperature fell to $-130°$ C. This was sufficient to bring about the liquefaction of compressed oxygen. The cooling associated with evaporation is due to the heat of vaporization which must be supplied to the liquid (§ 16a); if this does not come from an outside source, it will be obtained from the liquid itself, the temperature of which consequently falls. The method of cooling by evaporation is still employed in the production of "dry ice," as already noted, and it is also utilized in commercial and domestic refrigeration. It finds little or no application, however, in the liquefaction of gases at the present day.

Two principles are most widely used to liquefy gases on the large scale. The first, developed by W. Hampson (1895) and by C. von Linde (1895), makes use of the cooling due to the **Joule-Thomson effect** (§ 13b). The gas, at an initial pressure of about 250 atm., is allowed to stream through a throttle, as a result of which the pressure falls. The gas is thus cooled because of the energy required to overcome the attraction of the molecules during the expansion that accompanies the decrease in pressure. The drop in temperature may not be sufficient to cause liquefaction, but the cooled gas is used to lower the temperature of the incoming gas; after passage through the throttle the latter is generally cooled to a sufficient extent for liquefaction to occur.

The second principle, known as cooling due to **adiabatic expansion** (see § 23g), was employed by G. Claude (1900) for the commercial liquefaction of air. The gas is compressed to about 200 atm., and is then allowed to expand in an engine where it does mechanical work. As a result, kinetic energy is removed from the gas molecules and the temperature falls. The incoming gas is divided into two streams; one goes to the compression-expansion engine where it is cooled, as just described, while the other, after being cooled by the gas leaving the engine, passes through a throttle and so has its temperature lowered further by the Joule-Thomson effect. The advantage of the Claude method lies in the fact that the Joule-Thomson cooling is greater the lower the temperature, at moderate pressures.

At ordinary temperatures, hydrogen and helium exhibit an unusual Joule-Thomson effect; the temperature increases, instead of falling, when these gases are streamed through a throttle. At low temperatures, however, both hydrogen and helium behave in a normal manner and undergo cooling in the Joule-Thomson expansion. Such behavior is in accord with the change in the shape of the PV against P curve described in § 13a. As may be expected, all gases become warmer in a Joule-Thomson expansion above an appropriate temperature, known as the **inversion temperature.** The point of immediate interest, however, is to note that, starting from ordinary temperatures, hydrogen and helium could not possibly be liquefied by the Joule-Thomson effect alone. If the gases are first cooled below their respective inversion points, either by the method of adiabatic expansion or by utilizing another liquefied gas, subsequent cooling and liquefaction as a result of the Joule-Thomson effect are possible.

The liquefaction of gases is of industrial importance, and the liquids also find application in many laboratory studies requiring the use of low temperatures. Oxygen, argon and neon are obtained in commercial quantities by the fractional distillation of liquid air, while helium is extracted from natural gases by removing the hydrocarbons by liquefaction. Liquid carbon dioxide is employed in the manufacture of "dry ice," and other liquefied gases, such as sulfur dioxide, ammonia, as well as certain patented compounds of the "Freon" type, e.g., difluoro-dichloromethane, are used in refrigeration.

VAPOR PRESSURE AND VAPORIZATION

16a. The Vapor Pressure of Liquids.—In the preceding sections the relationship between gas and liquid has been treated mainly from the standpoint of the gas; it will now be considered with special reference to the liquid. It has been seen that if a gas is compressed when below its critical temperature, liquefaction commences at a certain pressure; this pressure remains constant, at each temperature, as long as liquid and vapor are present together (cf. *BC* in Fig. 19). This pressure, under which liquid and vapor can coexist at equilibrium, is the **saturation vapor pressure** or, in brief, the **vapor pressure** of the liquid (§ 15a). It is seen from Fig. 19 that this pressure increases as the temperature is raised, although a limit is set by the critical point. The critical pressure may thus be described as *the highest possible, or limiting, vapor pressure of a liquid.*

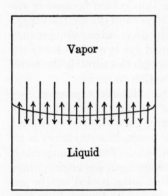

FIG. 23.   Equilibrium between liquid and vapor in a closed space

Suppose a quantity of liquid is sealed into a vessel, leaving a free space not filled by the liquid (Fig. 23); the molecules of the latter, like those of a gas, may be supposed to be in continual motion, and since the liquid has an open surface, some of the molecules will escape into the space above it. Since this space is limited, by the closed vessel, the molecules will steadily accumulate in it, and some of them will return to the liquid, the rate of return becoming greater as their number increases. A condition of equilibrium will ultimately be attained at each temperature, when the number of molecules leaving the liquid to enter the space above it is equal to the number returning to the liquid in a given time. The space above the liquid is now said to be **saturated** with vapor, and the pressure it exerts is the quantity which has been referred to above as the vapor pressure of the liquid at the given temperature. This pressure is independent of the amounts of liquid and vapor, provided they are in equilibrium at the specified temperature. Increase of temperature increases the kinetic energy of the molecules, with the result that there is a greater number per unit volume of vapor, and hence the latter has a greater pressure when equilibrium is attained.

In order for molecules to leave the surface of a liquid and become vapor, they have to overcome the forces of attraction of the other molecules in the liquid. Such forces are relatively large because the molecules are much closer together in the liquid than in the vapor state, provided the temperature is well below the critical point. In order to overcome these attractive forces, energy must be supplied to the liquid in the form of heat; this is the (latent) **heat of vaporization** of the liquid. It is the heat absorbed when a definite quantity, e.g., 1 gram or 1 mole, of the liquid is vaporized; if the quantity is 1 mole, then the expression **molar heat of vaporization** is employed.

16b. Vapor Pressure and Boiling Point.—If the pressure above the liquid is adjusted to a definite value, say 1 atm., it is possible to raise the temperature of the liquid until its vapor pressure is equal to the arbitrary external pressure. At this point the liquid can evaporate freely, and bubbles of vapor are seen to form within it and to escape from the surface. This is, of course, the **boiling point** of the liquid, which can consequently be defined as *the temperature at which the vapor pressure is equal to the external pressure.* If the latter is 1 atm., the temperature is the normal boiling point. A lowering of the external pressure will mean that the boiling point is decreased, as in distillation under reduced pressure, but an increase of pressure will result in a rise of the boiling point of a liquid. It is evident from these considerations that a plot of the variation of vapor pressure with temperature, will also give the variation of boiling point with the external pressure.

16c. The Determination of Vapor Pressure.—The methods most frequently used for measuring vapor pressure fall into three categories, viz., static, dynamic and gas saturation methods. In the simplest form of the **static method** two barometer tubes are used, one of which is for purposes of comparison. The liquid under investigation is introduced into the other, until the space above the mercury is saturated with vapor, as shown by a small quantity of liquid remaining on the surface of the mercury. The difference in the levels of the mercury in the two tubes gives the vapor pressure of the liquid at the experimental temperature. The measurements can be made at a series of temperatures by surrounding the barometer tubes with a heating jacket.

In the **dynamic method** the external pressure is fixed, and the temperature at which the liquid boils is then measured. In accordance with the definition of boiling point, given above, this represents the temperature at which the liquid has a vapor pressure equal to the external pressure. Because of the possibility of the liquid becoming superheated, the thermometer is placed in the vapor when the boiling point of a pure substance is being measured. The pressure in the apparatus is then equal to the vapor pressure of the liquid at the temperature recorded on the thermometer.

In the **gas saturation (transpiration) method,** dry air, or other gas, is bubbled through the liquid at constant temperature; the gas becomes saturated with the vapor of the liquid, and the partial pressure of the vapor in the result-ing mixture is equal to the vapor pressure of the liquid. Assuming that Dal-ton's law of partial pressures (§ 11g) holds, then according to the equations (11.22),

$$p = \frac{n_1}{n_1 + n_2} P, \qquad (16.1)$$

where p is the vapor (partial) pressure, P is the total pressure of the air and the vapor, i.e., the external atmospheric pressure, n_1 is the number of moles of vapor and n_2 the number of moles of air in the gas leaving the saturator. If the air may be supposed to obey the ideal gas law, then

$$Pv = n_2 RT,$$

where v is the volume of the n_2 moles of dry air, before entering the saturator, measured at the atmospheric pressure P. Hence, Pv/RT may be substituted for n_2 in equation (16.1), and n_1 may be replaced by w/M, where w is the weight of the vapor taken up by the volume v of air, and M is the molecular weight of the vapor; equation (16.1) thus becomes

$$p = \frac{\dfrac{w}{M} P}{\dfrac{w}{M} + \dfrac{Pv}{RT}}. \qquad (16.2)$$

The value of w is obtained by determining the loss in weight of the saturator, or the gain in weight of a suitable absorbing agent, resulting from the passage of the volume v of air, measured at the temperature T and pressure P; thus all the information is available for calculating the vapor pressure. If the latter is low, no serious error will be incurred if w/M in the denominator of equation (16.2) is neglected in comparison with Pv/RT; the equation can then be written in the simple, but more approximate, form

$$p = \frac{w}{M} \cdot \frac{RT}{v}. \qquad (16.3)$$

Problem: The passage of 10 liters of dry air, measured at 22° C and at the atmos-pheric pressure of 752 mm., through a saturator containing ethanol at 28° C, resulted in the vaporization of 1.947 gram of the liquid. Calculate the vapor pressure of ethanol, in mm. of mercury, at the given temperature. Compare the results given by equations (16.2) and (16.3).

The units of p will be the same as those of P in the numerator of equation (16.2); hence, the latter may be expressed in mm., i.e., 752 mm. In the denominator, it is more convenient to use P in atm., v in liters, and R in liter-atm. deg.$^{-1}$ mole^{-1}, i.e., 752/760 atm., 10.0 liters and 0.0820, respectively. The value of T to be employed is that at which the volume of air was measured, i.e., $273 + 22 = 295°$ K. The molecular weight M of ethanol is 46; it follows then from equation (16.2) that

$$p = \frac{\dfrac{1.947}{46.0} \times 752}{\dfrac{1.947}{46.0} + \dfrac{(752/760) \times 10}{0.082 \times 295}} = 70.5 \text{ mm.}$$

To obtain the vapor pressure according to equation (16.3), the first term in the denominator of the foregoing expression is omitted; hence,

$$p = \frac{\dfrac{1.947}{46.0} \times 752}{\dfrac{(752/760) \times 10}{0.082 \times 295}} = 78 \text{ mm.}$$

The same result is obtained directly from equation (16.3) in the following manner. If R is in liter-atm. deg.$^{-1}$ mole^{-1} units and v in liters, p will be given in atm.; the result must then be multiplied by 760 to obtain p in mm. Thus,

$$p = \frac{1.947}{46.0} \times \frac{0.082 \times 295}{10} \times 760 = 78 \text{ mm.}$$

(The vapor pressure is too large for the use of equation (16.3) to be justified here.)

The vapor pressures of a number of familiar liquids at a series of temperatures between 0° and 100° C are collected in Table XVI.

TABLE XVI.   VAPOR PRESSURES IN MM. OF MERCURY

Temp.	Water	Ethanol	Acetic acid	Ethyl acetate	Acetone	Benzene	Aniline
0° C	4.58	12.2	—	24.2	67.3	26.5	—
10°	9.21	23.6	—	42.8	115.6	45.4	—
20°	17.53	43.9	11.7	72.8	184.8	74.7	—
30°	31.82	78.8	20.6	118.7	282.7	119.6	—
40°	55.32	135.3	34.8	186.3	421.5	182.7	—
50°	92.51	222.2	56.6	282.3	612.6	271.3	2.4
60°	149.4	352.7	88.9	415.3	860.6	391.7	5.7
70°	233.7	542.5	136.0	596.3	—	551.0	10.6
80°	355.1	812.6	202.3	832.8	—	757.6	18.0
90°	525.8	—	293.7	—	—	1016.1	29.2
100°	760.0	—	417.1	—	—	—	45.7

16d. The Clapeyron Equation.—The vapor pressures of all substances increase with increasing temperature, and the variation is always represented by a curve of the type shown in Fig. 24. The highest temperature at which vapor pressure can be measured is, of course, the critical point, since liquid cannot exist above this temperature; provided supercooling does not occur, the lower limit is the freezing point of the liquid. In view of the significance of the boiling point, it is apparent that the same curve represents the influence of pressure on the boiling point, as already mentioned.

The variation of vapor pressure with temperature is best considered in connection with an equation, first derived by means of thermodynamics (§ 26c) by B. P. E. Clapeyron (1834) and later developed by R. Clausius (1850). For present purposes the **Clapeyron equation** may be written in the form

$$\frac{dp}{dT} = \frac{L_v}{T(V_v - V_l)}, \tag{16.4}$$

where dp/dT represents the rate of change of vapor pressure with temperature, that is, the slope of the plot of vapor pressure against the temperature, as in Fig. 24; L_v is the molar heat of vaporization of the liquid, and V_v and V_l are

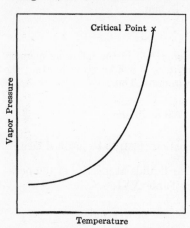

the molar volumes of vapor and liquid, respectively, at the absolute temperature T, at which dp/dT is determined. Since the molar heat of vaporization L_v is equal to $M \times v$, where M is the molecular weight and l_v is the heat of vaporization per gram of the liquid, and the molar volumes V_v and V_l are equal to M times the specific volumes, v_v and v_l, i.e., the volumes per gram of vapor and liquid, respectively, equation (16.4) may be written as

$$\frac{dp}{dT} = \frac{l_v}{T(v_v - v_l)}. \tag{16.5}$$

Fig. 24.   Vapor pressure-temperature curve

The Clapeyron equation is of value in a number of connections; for example, if the rate of change of the vapor pressure with temperature is known, it is possible to calculate the heat of vaporization of the liquid at that temperature. Alternatively, if the latent heat is known, the rate of change of vapor pressure with temperature or, in other words, the change of boiling point with pressure can be determined.

Problem: The vapor pressure of water changes by 27.17 mm. from 99.5° to 100.5°; the specific volumes of water vapor and liquid water at 100° are 1674 and 1.04 cc. per gram, respectively. Calculate the heat of vaporization of water, in calories per gram, at 100° C.

In the use of the Clapeyron equation care must be exercised in the matter of units; the best procedure is to use c.g.s. units, so that the heat is obtained in ergs, which can be converted into calories (see § 23a).

The vapor pressure changes by 27.17 mm. of mercury, i.e., 2.717 cm., per degree, and this may be taken as the value of dp/dT at 100° C. To convert to c.g.s. units, i.e., dynes per sq. cm. per degree, it is necessary to multiply the cm. of mercury by the density of the latter (13.595) and by the acceleration due to gravity (980.7), so that

$$\frac{dp}{dT} = 2.717 \times 13.595 \times 980.7 \text{ dynes cm.}^{-2} \text{ deg.}^{-1}$$

Since v_v and v_l are 1674 and 1.04 cc., respectively, $v_v - v_l = 1673$, the 0.04 being ignored, since the use of more than four significant figures is not justified. Substitution of these figures in equation (16.5), with $T = 273.2 + 100 = 373.2°$, gives l_v in ergs per degree; to convert ergs into calories it is necessary to divide by 4.184×10^7, so that

$$l_v = T\,(v_v - v_l)\,\frac{dp}{dT}$$

$$= \frac{373.2 \times 1673 \times 2.717 \times 13.595 \times 980.7}{4.184 \times 10^7} = 540.5 \text{ cal. g.}^{-1}$$

(The directly determined experimental value is 539.9 cal. g.$^{-1}$)

Problem: The heat of vaporization of water at 100° C is 539.9 cal. per gram. Utilizing the values of v_l and v_v given above, calculate the temperature at which water will boil at a pressure of 770 mm.

This is the reverse of the preceding problem; it is required to calculate dp/dT, or rather dT/dp, to find how the boiling point changes with pressure. By equation (16.5),

$$\frac{dT}{dp} = \frac{T(v_v - v_l)}{l_v} = \frac{373.2 \times 1673}{539.9 \times 4.184 \times 10^7} \text{ deg. cm.}^2 \text{ dyne}^{-1}.$$

To convert into degree per cm. of mercury units, this should be multiplied by 13.595×980.7; the result is found to be $0.368°$ per cm. of mercury. The boiling point of water is thus raised by $0.368°$ for 1 cm. of mercury increase in the pressure. Since the boiling point of water at 760 mm. is 100°, the value at 770 mm. should thus be 100.37° C.

16e. Vapor Pressure Equations.—If the temperature is not near the critical point, the molar volume V_l of the liquid will be small and can be neglected in comparison with V_v, the molar volume of the vapor; equation (16.4) will then become

$$\frac{dp}{dT} = \frac{L_v}{TV_v}. \tag{16.6}$$

Further, in regions below the critical temperature, the vapor pressure is relatively small and the vapor may be supposed to obey the ideal gas laws, so that pV_v is equal to RT, or $V_v = RT/p$; making this substitution in equation (16.6), the result is

$$\frac{dp}{dT} = \frac{L_v p}{RT^2}. \tag{16.7}$$

Using the mathematical identity,

$$\frac{d \ln p}{dT} = \frac{1}{p} \cdot \frac{dp}{dT},$$

it follows from equation (16.7) that

$$\frac{d \ln p}{dT} = \frac{L_v}{RT^2}. \tag{16.8}$$

This result, first obtained by R. Clausius (1850), is frequently referred to as the **Clapeyron-Clausius equation,** although the same name is sometimes applied to a more general form of equation (16.4). This is one form of an important equation which finds wide application in many aspects of physical chemistry (§ 36a). It should be remembered that equations (16.7) and (16.8) are approximate only, because they are based on the ideal gas law; nevertheless, they have many uses.

Problem: Given that dp/dT is 2.72 cm. of mercury per degree for water at 100° C, calculate the approximate heat of vaporization in cal. per gram, at this temperature.

The calculation is made very easily by equation (16.7), the question of units being quite simple, as may be seen by writing this equation in the form

$$\frac{1}{p} \cdot \frac{dp}{dT} = \frac{L_v}{RT^2}.$$

Since dp/dT is in cm. deg.$^{-1}$, p may be expressed in cm.; further, as L_v is required in calories, R may be taken as 2 cal. deg.$^{-1}$ mole^{-1}; hence, since the vapor pressure p of water is 76 cm. at 100° C, i.e., 373° K,

$$L_v = \frac{RT^2}{p} \cdot \frac{dp}{dT} = \frac{2 \times (373)^2}{76} \times 2.72 \text{ cal. mole}^{-1}.$$

To obtain the heat of vaporization per gram, this is divided by 18, the molecular weight of water; the result is 553 cal. g.$^{-1}$, which is just over 2 per cent higher than the experimental value.

If the heat of vaporization can be regarded as constant, equation (16.8) may be readily integrated; thus, after rearrangement,

$$\int d \ln p = \frac{L_v}{R} \int \frac{dT}{T^2},$$

$$\ln p = -\frac{L_v}{RT} + c, \tag{16.9}$$

where c is the integration constant. Upon converting the natural logarithm (i.e., ln) to the base of 10 (i.e., log), equation (16.9) becomes

$$\log p = -\frac{L_v}{2.303RT} + C, \tag{16.10}$$

where C is also a constant. Since the heat of vaporization L_v is assumed to be constant, this equation may be written as

$$\log p = -\frac{A}{T} + C, \tag{16.11}$$

where the constant A is given by

$$A = \frac{1}{2.303R} L_v. \tag{16.12}$$

According to equation (16.11), if the logarithm of the vapor pressure, i.e., log p, is plotted against the reciprocal of the absolute temperature, i.e., $1/T$, the result should be a straight line; the slope of this line, i.e., $-A$, will be related to the molar heat of vaporization by equation (16.12).

That this linear relationship is, at least approximately, true is shown in Fig. 25; the full line is drawn straight, and the experimental results are indicated by the points. Exact agreement with equation (16.11) is not to be expected for two reasons; first, the ideal gas laws have been assumed in deriv·ing equation (16.8), upon which (16.11) is based, and second, the heat of vaporization is not constant over an appreciable temperature range.

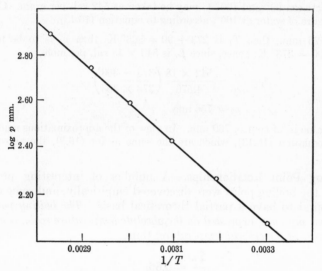

Fig. 25. Plot of logarithm of vapor pressure of ethyl acetate against reciprocal of the absolute temperature

For many purposes it is more convenient to utilize a different form of the equations given above; thus, if p_1 is the vapor pressure at the temperature T_1, and p_2 is that at T_2, then from equation (16.10),

$$\log p_1 = -\frac{L_v}{2.303RT_1} + C$$

and

$$\log p_2 = -\frac{L_v}{2.303RT_2} + C.$$

Subtracting one from the other gives

$$\log \frac{p_2}{p_1} = \frac{L_v}{2.303R}\left(\frac{1}{T_1} - \frac{1}{T_2}\right) = \frac{L_v}{2.303R}\left(\frac{T_2 - T_1}{T_1 T_2}\right).$$

If L_v is in calories per mole, then R is 1.987, and this expression becomes

$$\log \frac{p_2}{p_1} = \frac{L_v}{4.576}\left(\frac{T_2 - T_1}{T_1 T_2}\right). \tag{16.13} *$$

By means of equation (16.13) it is possible to calculate the heat of vaporization if the vapor pressures of the liquid at two temperatures are known; alternatively, the vapor pressure at one temperature can be determined from that at another temperature, together with the heat of vaporization. Since the equation involves a ratio of two pressures, any convenient units may be used.

Problem: The vapor pressure of water at 90° C is 526 mm., and the mean heat of vapori.'ation between 90° and 100° C may be taken as 542 cal. per gram. Calculate the vap. r pressure of water at 100°, according to equation (16.13).

Let $p_1 = 526$ mm., then T_1 is $273 + 90 = 363°$ K; then p_2 is to be found at $T_2 = 273 + 100 = 373°$ K; hence, since L_v is 540×18 cal. per mole,

$$\log \frac{p_2}{526} = \frac{542 \times 18}{4.576}\left(\frac{373 - 363}{373 \times 363}\right),$$

$$p_2 = 756 \text{ mm.}$$

(The correct value is, of course, 760 mm. In view of the approximations made in the derivation of equation (16.13), which are the same as for (16.8), the agreement is good.)

16f. Eoiling Point Relationships.—A number of interesting properties applicable at the boiling point were discovered empirically, and some of them have been found to have a partial theoretical basis. *The boiling point of a 'iquid at 1 atm. pressure, expressed on the absolute temperature scale, is approximately twc -thirds of the critical temperature;* thus,

$$\frac{T_b}{T_c} \approx 0.66, \tag{16.14}$$

where T_b and T_c are the normal boiling point and critical temperature, respectively. The data in Table XVII (below), for a variety of liquids, provide support for this relationship; helium is an outstanding exception, but in the liquid state this substance is abnormal in other respects. Since the boiling point is approximately a constant fraction of the critical temperature for most liquids, the former may be regarded as a corresponding temperature, in the sense defined in § 15d.

Another property of liquids at the boiling point is known as **Trouton's rule**; according to this, *the molar heat of vaporization in calories divided by the normal boiling point on the absolute scale has the approximately constant value of 21,* i.e.,

$$\frac{L_v}{T_b} \approx 21, \tag{16.15}$$

* This equation can, of course, be obtained by definite integration of equation (16.8) between the limits of T_1 and T_2 (for T) and p_1 and p_2 (for p).

as may be seen from the few results in Table XVII. For reasons which will be apparent later (§ 25f), this quantity is called the "entropy of vaporization." It is evident that the Trouton rule is approximate only; it holds more closely for nonassociated substances of molecular weight about 100, and of not too high boiling point. For substances of low boiling point, e.g., hydrogen and helium, the ratio L_v/T_b is much less than 21. On the other hand, for associated liquids, such as water and alcohol, it is greater than the usual value; the reason for this is not difficult to understand. The hydrogen bonds which exist in these liquids are usually absent in the vapor, and so extra energy, over and above the normal heat of vaporization, must be supplied in order to break

TABLE XVII.   PROPERTIES OF THE LIQUID AT THE BOILING POINT

Substance	T_b	T_c	T_b/T_c	L_v	L_v/T_b
Helium	4.2° K	5.2° K	0.81	22 cal./mole	5.2
Hydrogen	20.3°	33.2°	0.61	216	10.6
Oxygen	90.2°	154.3°	0.58	1610	17.9
Ammonia	239.7°	405.5°	0.59	5560	23.2
Carbon tetrachloride	350°	556°	0.63	7140	20.4
Ethanol	351°	516°	0.68	9450	26.9
Benzene	353°	562°	0.63	7500	21.2
Water	373°	647°	0.58	9700	26.0
Acetic acid	391°	594°	0.66	5810	14.9

these bonds. The actual value of the molar heat of vaporization is thus relatively larger than for analogous nonassociated liquids. It is true that the boiling points are also raised, but this is not sufficient to compensate for the increase in the heat of vaporization, so that L_v/T_b is greater than 21. It is of interest to mention that the apparent value of the Trouton ratio for acetic acid is 14.9. However, this substance is appreciably associated even in the vapor state (§ 14f), and if allowance is made for the fact that the average molecular weight is about 100, instead of the value for single molecules, L_v/T_b is found to be about 24.

Various attempts have been made to improve the Trouton equation (16.15) so as to make it more widely applicable. One of the most successful of these was proposed by J. H. Hildebrand (1915) who compared the values of L_v/T for different substances under such conditions that the number of molecules per unit volume of vapor was the same in every case, instead of the pressure as in the Trouton rule. For most substances L_v/T obtained in this way is approximately constant, although associated liquids and helium still behave in an exceptional manner.

Boiling points of liquids are usually recorded at 1 atm., i.e., 760 mm. pressure, but this exact pressure is rarely obtained under ordinary experimental conditions. A simple equation for correcting boiling points to the standard pressure would thus be useful; such an expression, which can be derived from a combination of equation (16.7) with Trouton's law, was proposed by J. M. Crafts (1887), viz.,

$$\Delta t = cT_b(760 - p), \qquad (16.16)$$

where Δt is the amount which must be added to the boiling point measured at a pressure of p mm. to correct it to 760 mm. For associated liquids, the constant factor c is 0.00010 and for liquids of very low boiling points it is 0.00014; for most ordinary liquids, the value 0.00012 may be used.

Problem: The boiling point of water at 770 mm. is 100.37° C; calculate the value at 1 atm. by means of Craft's rule.

In this case the liquid is associated, and so c may be taken as 0.00010; T_b is 273 + 100 = 373°, with sufficient accuracy; and $760 - p$ is $760 - 770 = -10$; hence,

$$\Delta t = -0.0001 \times 373 \times 10 = -0.37.$$

The correct boiling point is thus $100.37 - 0.37 = 100.00°$ C.

16g. Molar Volumes at the Boiling Point.—An additive property of a molecule is *one which is the sum of the corresponding properties of the constituent atoms*. Strictly speaking, molecular weight is the only exactly additive property, but certain other properties of liquids are at least approximately additive in nature. One of these, as was discovered by H. Kopp (1855), is the molar volume at the boiling point. Although Kopp's choice of the boiling points of liquids as the temperatures for comparison of molar volumes was empirical, it evidently has some theoretical basis, for the boiling points are corresponding temperatures, as seen above. The molar volume is equal to the product of the molecular weight M and the specific volume v, i.e., the volume per gram; the latter is equal to the reciprocal of the density d, and so it follows that

$$\text{Molar volume} = Mv = \frac{M}{d}.$$

If the molar volumes of isomeric compounds of similar constitution, e.g., propyl formate, ethyl acetate and methyl propionate, are compared at their respective boiling points, the values are found to be almost identical. Further, in any particular homologous series of organic compounds, a constant difference of about 22.2 cc. is found in the molar volume at the boiling points for each CH_2 group. These facts suggest that the molar volume might be largely an additive property, and this has been confirmed by evaluating the volume equivalents of various elements in the following manner. Paraffins have the general formula C_nH_{2n+2}, and if from the molar volume of a particular paraffin is subtracted the contribution of the nCH_2 groups, i.e., $n \times 22.2$ cc., the result may be taken as the volume equivalent of the two remaining hydrogen atoms. From an examination of a number of liquid paraffins, this mean difference was found by G. Le Bas (1912) to be 7.4, i.e., 3.7 cc. per hydrogen atom. Since a CH_2 group contributes 22.2 cc. to the molar volume at the boiling point, the volume equivalent of a carbon atom is $22.2 - 7.4$, i.e., 14.8 cc. Now that the equivalents for carbon and hydrogen atoms are known, it is a relatively simple matter to derive those for other elements, e.g., oxygen from the molar volume of an alcohol, ether, aldehyde, ketone, etc., and halogen from the molar volume of an alkyl halide.

From such determinations it has become evident that the molar volume at the boiling point is not entirely additive in character; for example, the oxygen atom in alcohols and ethers, represented by —O—, contributes 7.4 cc., while in a carbonyl group, indicated by =O, the contribution is 12.0 cc. Further, in benzene derivatives there is apparently a *contraction* of 15.0 cc. It follows, therefore, that the molar volume is partly a **constitutive property,** for it depends to some extent upon the arrangement of the atoms within the molecule.

The volume equivalents of a number of atoms and for the benzene ring are given in Table XVIII; their application may be illustrated by calculating the

TABLE XVIII.   VOLUME EQUIVALENTS AT THE BOILING POINT

Hydrogen	3.7 cc.	Iodine	37.0 cc.
Carbon	14.8	Oxygen (—O—)	7.4
Chlorine	22.1	Oxygen (=O)	12.0
Bromine	27.0	Benzene ring	−15.0

molar volume of a liquid at its boiling point and comparing it with the experimental value. Consider, for example, ethyl benzoate, $C_6H_5COOC_2H_5$; this contains nine carbon atoms, ten hydrogen atoms, two oxygen atoms (one —O— and one =O), and a benzene ring. The contributions are as follows:

$$
\begin{aligned}
9C &= 9 \times 14.8 = 133.2 \\
10H &= 10 \times 3.7 = 37.0 \\
\text{—O—} &= 1 \times 7.4 = 7.4 \\
\text{=O} &= 1 \times 12.0 = 12.0 \\
\text{Benzene ring} &= -15.0 \\
\hline
& 174.6 \text{ cc.}
\end{aligned}
$$

This result, 174.6 cc., agrees exactly with the observed molar volume of ethyl benzoate at its boiling point. The molar volume is thus seen to be mainly an additive, and partly a constitutive, property. By utilizing the known volume equivalents, it is possible to calculate the molar volume, and hence the density, of a liquid at its boiling point.

Other physical properties which have been correlated with the structure and constitution of molecules are the parachor (§ 17f), molar refraction (§ 17j), dielectric constant (§ 17k), and dipole moments (§ 17l).

PHYSICAL PROPERTIES OF LIQUIDS

17a. Surface Tension.—A molecule in the interior of a liquid is completely surrounded by other molecules, and so, on the average, it is attracted equally in all directions. On a molecule in the surface, however, there is a resultant attraction inwards, because the number of molecules per unit volume is greater in the liquid than in the vapor. As a consequence of this inward pull, the surface of the liquid always tends to contract to the smallest possible area; it is for this reason that drops of liquid and bubbles of gas become spherical, as far as is feasible, for the surface area is then a minimum for the given volume. As a result of the tendency to contract, a surface behaves as if it were in a state of tension, rather like a stretched sheet of rubber. It is possible to ascribe a definite value to the **surface tension** of a liquid, which is defined as *the force in dynes acting in the surface at right angles to any line of 1 cm. length.* The surface tension, in dynes per cm., is represented by the symbol γ; the value is the same at every point and in all directions along the surface of the liquid.

FIG. 26. Forces inside spherical bubble

One of the consequences of the existence of surface tension is that the pressure on the concave side of a surface is greater than that on the convex side. To illustrate this statement, consider a spherical gas bubble in a liquid; suppose this to be cut by an imaginary plane into two hemispheres (Fig. 26). If P dynes per sq. cm. is the excess pressure inside the sphere, there will be a tendency for the two halves to be driven apart by a force F, equal to the product of the pressure and the area of the circle where the hemispheres meet. The area of this circle, indicated by the dotted line, is πr^2, where r cm. is the radius of the sphere; hence,

$$F = P \times \pi r^2 \text{ dynes.}$$

The force is counteracted by the surface tension γ dynes per cm., acting along the circumference $2\pi r$ of the same circle, which tends to draw the hemispheres together; the surface tension force F is thus given by

$$F = \gamma \times 2\pi r \text{ dynes.}$$

At equilibrium the two forces must be equal, and by equating the two quantities, it is seen that

$$P = \frac{2\gamma}{r} \text{ dynes per sq. cm.} \tag{17.1}$$

The excess pressure inside the spherical bubble, that is, on the concave side, is thus inversely related to the radius of the bubble. It may be noted that if there were no excess pressure on the concave side, the bubble could not exist, for it would collapse as a result of the force due to surface tension.

The fact that the pressures inside small bubbles are large accounts for the phenomena of "superheating" and "bumping" that are frequently observed when a pure liquid is heated in a perfectly clean, smooth vessel. In the absence of rough places, excrescences, etc., where bubbles can grow, the bubbles are almost molecular in size, and the pressures required to form them are very high. The temperature thus tends to rise above the normal boiling point of the liquid, so as to increase the pressure of the vapor sufficiently to produce the very small bubbles. As the bubbles grow, however, the pressure is larger than necessary; rapid expansion of the vapor, leading to "bumping," then occurs.

17b. Capillary Action.—Because of the forces acting between the molecules of a liquid themselves, and between these molecules and those of the solid material, e.g., glass, with which it is in contact, the surface of a liquid in a tube, that is, the **meniscus** (Greek: *small moon*), is always curved. The nature of the curvature depends on whether the liquid and the solid attract one another strongly or not; in the former case the liquid "wets" the solid and the meniscus is concave upward, as in Fig. 27A, but in the latter case the solid is not wetted, and the meniscus is concave downward as in Fig. 27B. These two types of behavior are well illustrated by water and mercury, respectively, in contact with glass.

If a liquid is placed in a capillary tube, the radius of curvature of the meniscus will be small; as a result [see equation (17.1)], there will be a considerable difference of pressure on the two sides of the meniscus, and this has significant consequences. Consider the case of a liquid which wets the surface of glass, and suppose a capillary tube is placed vertically in a large vessel of the liquid, in which the surface is almost flat. Since the liquid wets the glass, the meniscus in the tube will be concave upward, as indicated in Fig. 28A. At the point X, just below the surface in the capillary tube, i.e., on the convex side, the pressure will be less than that in the vapor space just above the surface by the amount $2\gamma/a$, where a is the radius of curvature of the surface and γ is the surface tension of the liquid. On the other hand, at the point Y, where the surface is virtually flat and the radius of curvature is very large, there will be little difference of pressure between the two sides of the surface. Since the pressure in the vapor space above X must be the same as that above Y, it follows that the pressure under the surface of the liquid at Y will be greater by the amount $2\gamma/a$ dynes per sq. cm. than it is under the surface at X.

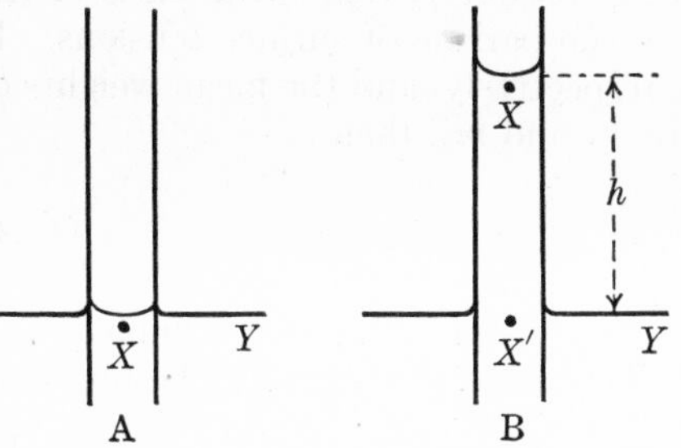

FIG. 27. Curvature of liquid surface (meniscus) in a tube

The result of the greater pressure at Y than at X is that the liquid is forced up the capillary tube, and equilibrium is attained only when the surface of the liquid in the tube is h cm. above that outside, as in Fig. 28B. The pressure at the point X' is now the same as at Y because of the column of liquid above the former. The hydrostatic pressure of the column of h cm. of liquid, i.e., hgd dynes per cm., where g is the acceleration due to gravity, and d is the density of the liquid, is then equal to the pressure difference $2\gamma/a$ between X and Y; that is,

FIG. 28. Capillary rise and surface tension

$$hgd = \frac{2\gamma}{a},$$

$$(17.2)$$

$$\gamma = \tfrac{1}{2}hgda.$$

As a first approximation, the radius of curvature of the meniscus will be equal to the radius r of the capillary tube,* so that equation (17.2) becomes

$$\gamma = \tfrac{1}{2}hgdr. \tag{17.3}$$

It is seen, therefore, that as a result of the existence of surface tension, a liquid must rise in a capillary tube, provided it wets the surface of the tube.

A liquid which does not wet glass, e.g., mercury, forms a surface which is convex upward; the pressure just below the meniscus in the capillary tube will thus be *greater* than at a plane surface. The level of the mercury in a glass capillary tube will consequently be forced down below that of the surrounding liquid. Equation (17.3) will be approximately applicable to this case also, where h is the distance of the meniscus in the capillary tube below the flat surface.

The rise or fall of liquid in capillary tubes is seen to be related to the surface tension of the liquid; phenomena associated with surface tension are thus frequently considered under the general headings of **capillarity** or **capillary action.** These terms are sometimes used even though capillary tubes may not actually be involved.

17c. Measurement of Surface Tension.—The best known method for determining surface tension, and one which is capable of considerable accuracy, depends on the measurement of the rise of the liquid surface in a capillary tube. If the height h to which the liquid ascends is ascertained, and the radius r of the tube is known, the surface tension can be calculated by means of equation (17.3). For accurate work, however, a number of corrections must be applied.

The weight m of a drop of liquid falling from a narrow vertical tube is approximately proportional to the surface tension γ; this is the basis of the **drop weight method,** used mainly for the comparison of surface tensions. If the values for two liquids are γ_1 and γ_2, respectively, and the mean weights of the drops falling from the same tube are m_1 and m_2, then

$$\frac{\gamma_1}{\gamma_2} = \frac{m_1}{m_2}. \tag{17.4}$$

If one of the liquids is water or benzene, whose surface tension is known from capillary rise measurements, the surface tension of the other can be obtained by utilizing equation (17.4).

A number of other methods for the determination of surface tension have been employed. Among these mention may be made of one which depends on the pressure required to produce gas bubbles at the end of a tube of known radius inserted in the liquid, and of another which involves measurement of the force necessary to detach a platinum wire ring from the surface of the liquid. An apparatus for the rapid determination of surface tensions, based on the latter principle, is available; it is called the du Noüy tensiometer.

* The radius of curvature of the meniscus will be exactly equal to the radius of the tube if the angle of contact between the glass and the liquid at the meniscus is zero. This will only be the case if the meniscus is hemispherical in shape.

The value of the surface tension is affected to some extent by the nature of the gas above the surface; substances which are able to dissolve in, or to react with, the liquid produce the most marked effects. The results are also dependent on whether the space above the meniscus consists only of the saturated vapor of the liquid or whether it is open to the air. The surface tension values for a number of liquids recorded in Table XIX were obtained with the surface in contact with air.

TABLE XIX.   SURFACE TENSIONS OF LIQUIDS AT 20° C

Water	72.8 dynes cm.$^{-1}$	Carbon tetrachloride	26.9 dynes cm.$^{-1}$
Nitrobenzene	41.8	Acetone	23.7
Carbon disulfide	33.5	Methanol	22.6
Benzene	28.9	Ethanol	22.3
Toluene	28.4	Diethyl ether	16.9

17d. Interfacial Tension.—The force, equivalent to surface tension, that is operative at the surface of separation between two insoluble, or sparingly soluble, liquids is called the **interfacial tension**. The value of the interfacial tension is generally less than that of the larger of the two surface tensions; this is because the attraction across the interface, between the molecules of one liquid and those of the other, tends to reduce the inward pull of the molecules in the surface by those of the same kind. The greater the molecular attraction between the two liquids the lower is the interfacial tension. For example, the interfacial tensions between the long-chain aliphatic alcohols and acids, on the one hand, and water, on the other hand, are about 10 to 15 dynes per cm.; with liquid paraffins and water, however, the values are between 50 and 60 dynes per cm. The polar alcohols and acids, containing OH groups, are attracted by the polar water molecules (see § 56f), but the latter are virtually indifferent to the nonpolar hydrocarbon molecules.

Both capillary rise and drop weight methods have been adapted to the measurement of interfacial tensions, the latter being frequently employed for the purpose. The average weight, or volume, of a drop of one liquid forming in the other is determined. The usual procedure is to fill a pipet with one liquid, e.g., the heavier, and to immerse the tip in the other liquid; drops are allowed to fall from the end of the pipet, and by counting their number the average volume v of a drop can be calculated. The effective mass of the drop, equal to $v(d_1 - d_2)$, where d_1 and d_2 are the densities of the two liquids, is proportional to the interfacial tension.

The subject of interfacial tension is of considerable importance in connection with the properties of emulsions (§ 57n), and also in certain physiological problems.

17e. Surface Tension and Temperature.—*Surface tensions almost invariably decrease with increasing temperature*, and R. von Eötvös (1886) proposed a relationship between the molar surface energy and the temperature. If v is the specific volume of a liquid, i.e., the reciprocal of the density, and M is the molecular weight, Mv is the molar volume, as already seen. If this volume is considered to be spherical, which is the stable form, the area of the sphere will be proportional to $(Mv)^{2/3}$; the product of this molar surface area and the surface tension gives the molar surface energy, i.e., $\gamma(Mv)^{2/3}$. According to Eötvös, this quantity varies in a linear manner with the temperature, so that a form of the **Eötvös equation** is

$$\gamma(Mv)^{2/3} = a - kt, \qquad (17.5)$$

where a and k are constants, and t is the temperature. The value of a may be derived by utilizing the fact that at the critical temperature t_c, when the surface of separation between a liquid and its saturated vapor disappears (§ 15b), the surface tension should be zero. It is thus readily seen from equation (17.5) that a should be equal to kt_c, so that this equation can be written as

$$\gamma(Mv)^{2/3} = k(t_c - t), \qquad (17.6)$$

where t_c is the critical temperature.

A study of the Eötvös equation was made by W. Ramsay and J. Shields (1893), who found that the experimental results for a number of liquids could be better expressed by the relationship

$$\gamma(Mv)^{2/3} = k(t_c - 6 - t). \qquad (17.7)$$

This implies that the surface tension becomes zero at a temperature 6° below the critical point, a fact which may be of significance in connection with the observation, referred to in § 15b, that the meniscus of a liquid disappears at a temperature a few degrees below the point at which the liquid ceases to exist.

The constant k in equations (17.5), (17.6) and (17.7) is the slope of the linear plot of $\gamma(Mv)^{2/3}$ against the temperature t; it is, consequently, the temperature coefficient of the molar surface energy. According to Ramsay and Shields, this coefficient has the same value, namely 2.12, for all normal, non-associated liquids. For certain substances, e.g., water, alcohols and carboxylic acids, all of which contain hydroxyl groups, the temperature coefficient is not only less than 2.12, but it varies with temperature. The abnormal behavior was attributed to the fact that these substances form associated molecules in the liquid state (see § 10h), and attempts were made to calculate the extent of association by determining the value of M which must be used in order to make k in equation (17.5) equal to 2.12. The ratio of this value of M to that for the simple molecules was believed to give a measure of the association factor. More recent work, however, has shown that although associated liquids give temperature coefficients that are lower than 2.1 and that vary with temperature, the so-called factors of association calculated from the results have no exact significance. Further, many substances which are apparently not associated, e.g., succinic nitrile, give very low values of k, viz., 0.56, whereas others, glyceryl tristearate, have very high values, viz., 6.0.

Theoretical considerations suggest that in addition to association, the temperature coefficient of the molar surface energy will be affected by the shape and orientation of the molecules in the surface of the liquid, and also by their mutual attraction. A *marked* increase of the Eötvös coefficient k with increasing temperature, as observed with hydroxylic compounds, is probably a satisfactory indication that the liquid is associated, but the values certainly have no simple quantitative meaning.

17f. The Parachor.—It was observed by D. B. Macleod (1923) that the surface tension γ of a liquid was related to the orthobaric densities d_l and d_v, of liquid and saturated vapor (§ 15b), at the same temperature, by the expression

$$\frac{\gamma^{\frac{1}{4}}}{d_l - d_v} = C, \tag{17.8}$$

where C is a constant over a considerable range of temperature; the value of C depends on the nature of the liquid. If both sides of the Macleod equation (17.8) are multiplied by M, the molecular weight of the substance, the result is

$$\frac{M\gamma^{\frac{1}{4}}}{d_l - d_v} = \text{constant}, [P]. \tag{17.9}$$

The constant $[P]$ has been called the **parachor** (S. Sugden, 1924), a name which implies that it is a comparative or relative volume.

If the density d_v of the saturated vapor is neglected in comparison with that of the liquid, as is justifiable provided the temperature is not too near the critical point, equation (17.9) may be written as

$$\frac{M}{d_l} \gamma^{\frac{1}{4}} = [P]. \tag{17.10}$$

The quantity M/d_l is the molar volume of the liquid, as already defined; hence, if the temperature is such that the surface tension γ is unity, the molar volume is equal to the parachor, according to equation (17.10). It follows, therefore, that the parachor may be regarded as the molar volume of a liquid when its surface tension is unity. A comparison of the parachors of different substances is thus equivalent to a comparison of molar volumes under conditions of equal (unit) surface tension. Since the molecular attractions would then be approximately equal, it is to be expected that the parachor may provide a better basis for the comparison of molar volumes than the measurements at the boiling point (§ 16g).

From an examination of the data for isomeric substances and of members of homologous series, the parachor has been found to be primarily an additive, and partly a constitutive, property. By the procedure described in § 16g for molar volumes, the parachor equivalents have been determined for a number of elements and also for certain structural factors; some of the results are recorded in Table XX.

TABLE XX. PARACHOR EQUIVALENTS

Carbon	7.2	Sulfur	48.5	Nitrogen	12.5
Hydrogen	16.2	Chlorine	53.8	Double bond	23.2
Oxygen	20.0	Bromine	68.0	Triple bond	46.6
O_2 in esters	60.0	Iodine	90.0	6-membered ring	6.1

Problem: The density of acetone is 0.7910 at 20° C; utilize the additivity of the parachor to calculate the surface tension of acetone.

Acetone, CH_3COCH_3, contains three carbon atoms, six hydrogen atoms, one oxygen atom, and one double bond; the parachor calculated from the equivalents in Table XX is thus:

$$(3 \times 7.2) + (6 \times 16.2) + 20.0 + 23.2 = 162.0$$

The molecular weight of acetone is 58.08 and the density at 20° is 0.7910; hence, by equation (17.10)

$$\frac{58.08}{0.7910} \times \gamma^{\frac{1}{4}} = 162.0$$

$$\gamma = 23.7 \text{ dynes cm.}^{-1}$$

(The experimental value is also 23.7 dynes cm.$^{-1}$)

In view of the appreciable contributions made by structural factors, such as double and triple bonds, and by ring formation, it is evident that the parachor might be used in certain cases to decide between alternative possible configurations. One example of this type will be cited here. Acetaldehyde forms a liquid polymer, known as *paraldehyde,* having the formula $(C_2H_4O)_3$; its parachor, determined from surface tension and density measurements, is 298.7. Two reasonable formulae for paraldehyde have been favored, one involving a ring (I) and the other a straight chain (II); these, together with the corresponding calculated parachors are represented below.

I	II

```
          O
        /   \
    CH3CH    CHCH3
      |       |
      O       O
        \   /
        CHCH3
```

$CH_3CH(OH)CH_2CH(OH)CH_2CHO$

6C = 6 × 7.2 = 43.2	6C = 6 × 7.2 = 43.2
12H = 12 × 16.2 = 194.4	12H = 12 × 16.2 = 194.4
3O = 3 × 20.0 = 60.0	3O = 3 × 20.0 = 60.0
6-membered ring = 6.1	Double bond = 23.2
303.7	320.8

The observed parachor of 298.7 thus favors formula I. Unfortunately there are some limitations to the strict additivity of parachor equivalents, and so the conclusions cannot always be accepted unequivocally.

17g. Viscosity and Fluidity.—Liquids, like gases, exhibit the resistance to flow known as viscosity (§ 12h). In general, it is the property which opposes the relative motion of adjacent layers of the liquid, and so it may be regarded as an internal friction. As with gases, the **coefficient of viscosity** η in poises, i.e., dynes cm.$^{-2}$ sec. units, is defined as the force per unit area, in dynes per sq. cm., required to maintain a difference of velocity of 1 cm. per sec. between two parallel layers of liquid, 1 cm. apart. The relationship between the coefficient of viscosity and the rate of flow of the liquid through a tube is also given by the Poiseuille equation (12.18), which may here be written in the form

$$\eta = \frac{\pi r^4 t p}{8vL}, \tag{17.11}$$

where v cc. is the volume of liquid flowing in t sec. through a *narrow* tube of radius r cm. and length L cm., under a driving pressure of p dynes per sq. cm. If a liquid has a low coefficient of viscosity it is said to be "mobile," but if the coefficient is high, the liquid is "viscous" and does not flow easily. The reciprocal of the viscosity is frequently employed; it is called the **fluidity,** and is given the symbol ϕ (Greek, *phi*), that is, ϕ is equal to $1/\eta$. The fluidity is a measure of the ease with which a liquid can flow.

If a solid body is falling through a liquid, the effect of viscosity is to exert a drag on the falling body. Instead of a continued increase in its rate of fall, the body acquires a constant velocity, when the gravitational pull downwards just balances the upward drag due to viscosity. For a falling sphere of radius r this steady velocity u is related to the viscosity η by the **Stokes's law** equation

$$u = \frac{2gr^2(d' - d)}{9\eta}, \tag{17.12}$$

where g is the gravitational acceleration, d' is the density of the sphere and d is that of the liquid. If d is small in comparison with d', equation (17.12) reduces to the simple form given in § 4b [equation (4.2)]; this is particularly applicable when the medium is a gas instead of a liquid.

17h. Measurement of Viscosity.—The direct measurement of viscosity is based on the Poiseuille equation (17.11), the rate of flow of the liquid, under a definite pressure, through a capillary tube being determined. For general laboratory work, however, a comparative method, using an instrument known as a **viscometer,** is employed. A simple form of viscometer, due to W. Ostwald, is shown in Fig. 29. A definite volume of liquid is introduced into the bulb C and is then sucked into $A;$ the time t is observed for the liquid to flow through the capillary tube B, between the marks x and y. The measurement is then repeated with another liquid whose viscosity is known. Referring to equation (17.11), it is seen that, since the same viscometer is used for the two liquids, the radius r and length L of the capillary tube, and the volume v of the bulb A, are the same in both cases. The pressure p depends on the head of liquid and its density; the former is constant, but the latter varies for the two liquids. With these facts in mind, it can be readily shown from equation (17.11) that

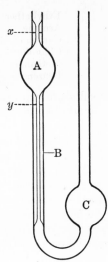

FIG. 29.   Ostwald viscometer

if η_1 and η_2 are the viscosities of two liquids of density d_1 and d_2, respectively, and t_1 and t_2 are the times of flow in the given viscometer, then

$$\frac{\eta_1}{\eta_2} = \frac{d_1 t_1}{d_2 t_2}.$$ (17.13)

If the viscosity coefficient η_2 and density d_2 of one-liquid are known, the viscosity of the other can be calculated from its density and the times of flow.

For viscous liquids, such as hydrocarbon oils, the **falling sphere method,** which is based on the Stokes equation (17.12), is frequently employed for the determination of viscosity. A small steel sphere is introduced below the surface of the liquid in a tall cylinder, and the time taken for it to fall between two marks is noted. The observation is then repeated with the same sphere and another liquid of known viscosity. The distance fallen is the same in each case, and so the rate of fall u is inversely proportional to the time of fall t; it follows, therefore, from equation (17.12), since g and r are constant, that

$$\frac{\eta_1}{\eta_2} = \frac{t_1(d' - d_1)}{t_2(d' - d_2)},$$

where d' is the density of the steel ball, and d_1 and d_2 are the densities of the two liquids. Since the viscosity of one liquid is known that of the other can be determined from observations on the falling sphere.

The viscosities of a number of liquids at 20° C are given in Table XXI; the

TABLE XXI.   VISCOSITIES AT 20° C IN MILLIPOISES

Ethyl ether	2.33	Chlorobenzene	8.00
Acetone	3.29	Carbon tetrachloride	9.68
Carbon disulfide	3.68	Water	10.09
Chloroform	5.63	Ethanol	12.0
Methanol	5.93	Acetic acid	12.2
Benzene	6.47	Nitrobenzene	20.1

results are expressed in terms of the **millipoise,** equal to 0.001 poise (§ 12h). Liquids like glycol and glycerol, which have two or more hydroxyl groups, generally have high viscosities. The reason is that a network of hydrogen bonds is formed between the molecules; this network extends throughout the liquid, thus making flow difficult.

17i. Viscosity and Temperature.—The effect of temperature on the viscosity of a liquid is strikingly different from the behavior with a gas; while in the latter case the viscosity coefficient increases with temperature, *the viscosity of a liquid decreases markedly as the temperature is raised.* The variation of the viscosity of a liquid with temperature is best expressed by means of an exponential or logarithmic equation, viz.,

$$\eta = A e^{E/RT}$$ (17.14)

or

$$\log \eta = \frac{B}{T} + C,$$ (17.15)

where A and E, or B and C, are constants for the given liquid. According to equation (17.15), the plot of log η against the reciprocal of the absolute temperature, i.e., $1/T$, should yield a straight line; this has been verified for a large number of liquids.

The entirely different effects of temperature on the viscosities of liquids and gases implies that the fundamental cause of the viscosity is different in the two cases. It has been suggested that before a molecule can take part in liquid flow it must acquire sufficient energy to push aside the molecules which surround it. As the temperature increases the number of such molecules *increases* in proportion to the Boltzmann factor $e^{-E/RT}$ (see § 12g), and hence the resistance to flow, that is, the viscosity, may be expected to *decrease* in a reciprocal manner, i.e., according to the factor $e^{E/RT}$, as in equation (17.14).

An empirical relationship, which probably has important theoretical significance, was discovered by A. J. Batschinski (1913); if η is the viscosity and v is the specific volume of a liquid, at the same temperature, then

$$\eta = \frac{c}{v - b}, \qquad (17.16)$$

where b and c are constants for each liquid. A rearrangement of equation (17.16), and introduction of the fluidity ϕ in place of $1/\eta$, gives

$$v = b + c\phi, \qquad (17.17)$$

so that over a range of temperature the fluidity should be a linear function of the specific volume. This relationship has been found to hold with an accuracy of better than 1 per cent for over sixty non-associated liquids. It may be mentioned that the value of b is almost identical with that of the van der Waals constant b for each substance.

17j. Molar Refraction.—The property of molar refraction is characteristic of both gaseous and liquid states, but as it is usually measured on the liquid, it is convenient to consider it in the present chapter. It is well known that when light passes from one medium to another, it almost invariably suffers **refraction**, that is, *a change of direction.* If a beam of light travels, as shown in Fig. 30, from air (or vacuum) into a more dense medium, e.g., a liquid, then i is called the angle of incidence and r is the angle of refraction; the **refractive index** n of the medium is then defined by

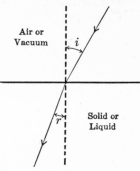

FIG. 30. Refraction of light

$$n = \frac{\sin i}{\sin r}. \qquad (17.18)$$

By measuring the angles of incidence and refraction in a suitable manner, the refractive index n can be determined. The value of this quantity depends on the wave length of the light, and for most purposes either the familiar D-line of sodium or the α-, β- or γ-lines of the hydrogen (Balmer) spectrum are employed. A subscript to the letter n, e.g., n_D, n_α, etc., indicates the particular type of light used for the measurement of the refractive index.

The theoretical work of H. A. Lorentz (1880) and L. V. Lorenz (1880) indicated that the **molar refraction** of a compound, defined by the expression

$$[M.R.] = \frac{n^2 - 1}{n^2 + 2} \cdot \frac{M}{d}, \tag{17.19}$$

where M is the molecular weight and d the density, was a characteristic property of a substance independent of the temperature. The value is almost the same in both gaseous and liquid states. The presence of the factor M/d shows that the molar refraction is a type of molar volume; if the refractive index were the value for light of very long wave length, the molar refraction should, according to theory, be equal to the actual volume of the molecules present in 1 mole of the substance.

Like other forms of molar volume considered earlier, the molar refraction is an additive and constitutive property. The refraction equivalents, based on refractive indices measured with the D-line of sodium, and which have been derived in the usual manner (§ 16g), are recorded in Table XXII.

TABLE XXII.   REFRACTION EQUIVALENTS FOR THE D-LINE

Carbon	2.42 cc.	Chlorine	5.97 cc.
Hydrogen	1.10	Bromine	8.87
Oxygen (in CO group)	2.21	Iodine	13.90
Oxygen (in ethers)	1.64	Double bond	1.73
Oxygen (in OH group)	1.53	Triple bond	2.40

Problem: The refractive index n_D of acetone is 1.3591 and the density is 0.7910 at 20°. Calculate the molar refraction of this substance, and compare it with the value obtained from the refraction equivalents in Table XXII.

The molecular weight of acetone, CH_3COCH_3, is 58.08; hence, by equation (17.19)

$$[M.R.] = \frac{(1.3591)^2 - 1}{(1.3591)^2 + 2} \cdot \frac{58.08}{0.7910} = 16.17 \text{ cc.}$$

The calculated value is 3×2.42 (for 3 C atoms) $+ 6 \times 1.10$ (for 6 H atoms) $+ 2.21$ (for O in CO) $= 16.07$ cc.

It is evident from the data in Table XXII that the molar refraction is decidedly a constitutive property; for example, the refraction equivalent of the oxygen atom depends on whether it is present in a hydroxyl, carbonyl or ether grouping. Similar variations have been found for the nitrogen atom. In addition to the normal contribution of the double bond, the presence of conjugated double bonds in a straight chain molecule, e.g., CH_3—CH═CH—CH═CH—CH_3, results in a further increase of the molar refraction. Because of these marked constitutive influences, molar refractions have been used to decide between alternative structures of some organic compounds; the particular formula is accepted as the correct one which gives a calculated molar refraction in best agreement with the experimental value.

17k. Dielectric Constant: Molar Polarization.—The magnitude of the force acting between two given electric charges placed at a definite distance apart in a uniform medium is determined by a property of the latter known as the **dielectric constant.** All forms of matter, gaseous, liquid and solid, possess definite dielectric constants; the dielectric properties of gases are important, but the subject will not be treated here, although it may be mentioned that the dielectric constants are very close to that for a vacuum, which is taken as unity. If e_1 and e_2 are the values of two electric charges placed at a distance r apart in a uniform medium, then the force F acting between them is given by Coulomb's law as

$$F = \frac{e_1 e_2}{Dr^2},$$ (17.20)

where D is the dielectric constant of the medium. If the two charges have opposite signs, the force is one of attraction, and it is seen that the higher the dielectric constant the smaller is the force of attraction between the charges; this fact is of importance in connection with the electrical properties of salts in solvents of different dielectric constants.

The dielectric constant of a substance is usually measured by determining the electrostatic capacity C of a condenser containing the given material between the plates; if C_0 is the value for the same condenser when completely evacuated, then

$$D = \frac{C}{C_0}.$$ (17.21)

In actual practice dielectric constants are usually obtained by comparing the capacity of the condenser when filled with a given liquid with that for the same condenser containing a standard liquid, e.g., benzene, whose dielectric constant is known from precise measurements based on equation (17.21). If D_1 and D_2 are the dielectric constants of the experimental and standard liquids, respectively, and C_1 and C_2 are the electrostatic capacities of a condenser when filled alternately with these liquids, then

$$\frac{D_1}{D_2} = \frac{C_1}{C_2}.$$

Since C_1 and C_2 can be measured, and D_2 is known, the value of D_1 can be calculated. The results for a number of liquids at 25° are given in Table XXIII; it will be noted that nonpolar substances, e.g., benzene and other hydrocar-

TABLE XXIII. DIELECTRIC CONSTANTS OF LIQUIDS AT 25° C

Hexane	1.90	Chloroform	4.80
Cyclohexane	2.03	Acetone	21.2
Carbon tetrachloride	2.24	Ethanol	24.3
Benzene	2.28	Nitrobenzene	34.8
Diethyl ether	4.30	Water	78.5

bons, and carbon tetrachloride, have low dielectric constants, but polar liquids, e.g., water, nitrobenzene and ethanol, have higher dielectric constants.

The molar polarization $[M.P.]$ of a substance is a property related to the dielectric constant by the expression, derived by O. F. Mosotti (1850) and R. Clausius (1879),

$$[M.P.] = \frac{D-1}{D+2} \cdot \frac{M}{d}, \qquad (17.22)$$

where, as before, M and d are the molecular weight and density of the substance; this result is often referred to as the **Mosotti-Clausius equation.** The molar polarization, like the molar refraction, is evidently a form of molar volume. By the electromagnetic theory of light, the dielectric constant should be equal to the square of the refractive index n_∞ for light of infinite, i.e., very long, wave length. Actually the relationship holds only for *nonpolar* molecules, and for such substances equation (17.22) becomes

$$[M.P.] = \frac{n_\infty^2 - 1}{n_\infty^2 + 2} \cdot \frac{M}{d}, \qquad (17.23)$$

which is identical with the expression for the molar refraction [equation (17.19)] for light of very long wave length. The refractive index of a nonpolar material does not vary greatly with wave length, and so it is possible to state that *the molar polarization and the molar refraction are approximately equal for nonpolar substances.*

Problem: The dielectric constant of cyclohexane is 2.033 at 20°, and its density is 0.7784 at this temperature; calculate the molar polarization of cyclohexane and compare it with the molar refraction derived from the equivalents in Table XXII.

The formula of cyclohexane is C_6H_{12}, and so the molecular weight is 84.16; hence

$$[M.P.] = \frac{2.033 - 1}{2.033 + 2} \cdot \frac{84.16}{0.7784} = 27.69 \text{ cc.}$$

From Table XXII, the refraction contribution of six C atoms is 6×2.42, and that of twelve H atoms is 12×1.10; the total is 27.72 for the molar refraction for the D-line.

171. Dipole Moments.—For polar molecules, that is, molecules possessing resultant **dipole moments** (§ 10f), the molar polarization and refraction are quite different. For water, for example, the former is about 18 cc., while the latter is 3.7 cc.; similar discrepancies have been observed in other cases. A more complete theoretical treatment by P. Debye (1912) has shown that, provided there is no restriction to the movement of the molecular dipoles in an electric field,

$$[M.P.] = \frac{D-1}{D+2} \cdot \frac{M}{d} = [M.R.]_\infty + \frac{4\pi N}{9kT} \mu^2, \qquad (17.24)$$

where μ (Greek, *mu*) is the magnitude of the dipole moment of the substance of dielectric constant D; in this expression N is the Avogadro number (§ 3d), T is the absolute temperature, and k is the Boltzmann constant (§ 12d), i.e., the gas constant per single molecule. The quantity $[M.R.]_\infty$ is the molar refraction for light of long wave length, as defined by the right-hand side of equation (17.23). For a nonpolar material, the dipole moment μ is zero, and then equation (17.24) leads to the result obtained in the previous section, that the molar polarization $[M.P.]$ is equal to the molar refraction for long wave lengths. If the substance is polar, however, and μ is not zero, this equality will not be expected to hold; according to equation (17.24) the difference will depend on the magnitude of the dipole moment.

As mentioned above, the Debye equation (17.24) is applicable only if the dipoles are free to rotate in an electric field; this is not strictly the case for pure liquids, because of the interaction of adjacent molecules. Consequently, equation (17.24) should be applied to gases and vapors, where the molecules are relatively far apart; it can also be used, with appropriate modification, for measurements on dilute solutions of a polar substance in a nonpolar liquid solvent. For gases and dilute solutions it is thus possible to utilize equation (17.24) to evaluate dipole moments. One method is to obtain the molar polarization from dielectric constant measurements, and the molar refraction from the refractive index, or from Table XXII; the difference is then equal to $4\pi N\mu^2/9kT$, from which the dipole moment μ can be calculated. A second method, which can be used for gases and vapors, requires the determination of the molar polarization at two or more temperatures; the results are then plotted against $1/T$, i.e., the reciprocal of the absolute temperature. It can be seen from equation (17.24), since $[M.R.]_\infty$ is a constant, that the plot should be a straight line whose slope is $4\pi N\mu^2/9k$. The dipole moment can thus be evaluated from the experimental slope. Alternatively, if any two of the values of the molar polarization are inserted in equation (17.24) it can be solved for μ.

For the calculation of dipole moments the Boltzmann constant k is expressed in ergs per molecule per degree, i.e., 1.38×10^{-16}; the value of μ is then in electrostatic-cm. units. The observed moments of polar substances are of the order of 10^{-18} in these units,* and consequently it is the general practice to express the results in **Debye units,** where one such unit is equal to 10^{-18} electrostatic-cm. units. The dipole moments of a number of polar compounds are recorded in Table XXIV. In addition to the data in the table, it

TABLE XXIV.   DIPOLE MOMENTS IN DEBYE UNITS

Water	1.84	Chloroform	1.15	Chlorobenzene	1.73
Ammonia	1.46	Diethyl ether	1.29	Aniline	1.56
Sulfur dioxide	1.62	Ethanol	1.70	Diphenyl ether	1.15
Hydrogen chloride	1.03	Methyl chloride	1.86	Benzonitrile	4.37
Hydrogen bromide	0.74	Acetone	2.72	Nitrobenzene	4.23

may be noted that hydrogen, nitrogen, carbon dioxide, carbon disulfide, carbon tetrachloride, stannic chloride, boron trichloride, paraffins, cyclohexane

* The dipole moment is the product of an electrical charge and a distance; the electronic charge is of the order of 10^{-10} e.s. unit, and molecular distances are of the order of 10^{-8} cm. The product is consequently of the order of 10^{-18}, as found experimentally.

and benzene have zero moments. In fact all molecules possessing a center of symmetry are nonpolar; the explanation of this fact is important. It was seen in § 10f that the dipole moment is really a property of every bond between two different atoms; *the observed dipole moment of a molecule is the vector sum of all the individual bond moments,* the term "vector sum" implying that the *direction and magnitude* are taken into account in the summation. In carbon tetrachloride, for example, each C—Cl bond possesses a dipole moment, but since the molecule is symmetrical the four bond moments cancel each other exactly to give a resultant dipole moment of zero. The same is true for stannic chloride and for the hydrocarbons.

The zero dipole moment of carbon dioxide indicates that the molecule is symmetrical and linear, but the association of a definite moment with the water molecule and with sulfur dioxide suggests that these latter substances have angular structures, as indicated below. The arrows, which point from the positive to the negative end of the dipoles, indicate the directions of the various bond moments.

$$O \leftarrow\!\!+\ C \ +\!\!\rightarrow O$$

Carbon Dioxide	Water	Sulfur Dioxide

In carbon dioxide the two C—O bond moments cancel each other exactly, but the vector sums of the O—H moments in water, and of the S—O moments in sulfur dioxide, are not zero, since the molecules are not linear.

Numerous applications, similar to those just described, have been made of dipole moments in the elucidation of the structures of inorganic and organic molecules; a few illustrations only will be given here. The fact that boron trichloride has a zero moment while phosphorus trichloride, and analogous compounds of other elements of group V, have appreciable moments, suggests that the BCl_3 molecule is flat and symmetrical, but the molecules of PCl_3, $AsCl_3$, NH_3, etc., are not. The latter are probably in the form of triangular pyramids with the phosphorus or similar atom at the apex. Measurements of dipole moments of benzene derivatives have confirmed that the benzene ring is a planar, regular hexagon, for only upon this basis is it possible to explain quantitatively the observed moments of ortho-, meta- and para-compounds.

17m. The Structure of Liquids.—It was seen earlier that at the critical point the gaseous and liquid forms of a substance become indistinguishable. On the other hand, the small volume change accompanying fusion suggests that there is some similarity between the arrangement of the molecules in the liquid and solid states near the melting point. In a gas the molecules are distributed in a purely random manner, whereas in the solid there is complete regularity of structure (Chapter VI). It appears, therefore, that as the temperature of a liquid is raised the internal structure should change gradually from some sort of order near the melting (or freezing) point to complete disorder at the critical temperature. This conclusion is supported by observations made by means of X-rays. Since these can best be understood after a study of the structure of solids, further data concerning liquid structure will be deferred to § 19f.

READING REFERENCES

1. **Surface tension by ring method.** Macy, *Journal of Chemical Education*, **12**, 573 (1935).
2. **Correcting boiling points to standard pressure.** Hass, *ibid.*, **13**, 490 (1936).
3. **Surface tension by maximum bubble pressure.** Haendler and McGuire, *ibid.*, **14**, 591 (1937).
4. **Vapor pressure demonstration.** Smith and Ridgely, *ibid.*, **15**, 145 (1938).
5. **Structure of liquids.** Hirschfelder, *ibid.*, **16**, 540 (1939).
6. **Measurement of dielectric constant.** Hudson and Hobbs, *ibid.*, **17**, 366 (1940).
7. **Surface tension by capillary rise.** Hazlehurst, *ibid.*, **19**, 61 (1942).
8. **Surface and interfacial tensions.** Steinbach, *ibid.*, **21**, 582 (1944).

REVIEW QUESTIONS

1. What experimental conditions are necessary for the liquefaction of a gas?

2. Draw and explain the Andrews pressure-volume-temperature diagram for carbon dioxide.

3. Define the critical temperature, pressure and volume of a gas.

4. Explain how the critical constants of a gas can be determined.

5. State and illustrate the law of the rectilinear diameter.

6. Show that the van der Waals equation is able to account for the existence of the critical state.

7. Derive the relationships between the critical constants and the van der Waals constants.

8. How can the law of corresponding states be derived from the van der Waals equation? Explain the significance of this law.

9. What are the principles employed in obtaining low temperatures for the liquefaction of gases?

10. What is meant by the vapor pressure of a liquid? Explain the existence of a saturation vapor pressure.

11. Explain the relationship between vapor pressure and boiling point.

12. Outline three methods for determining vapor pressures.

13. State the Clapeyron equation and describe some of its uses.

14. Show how the Clapeyron equation may be reduced to a simple form (the Clausius-Clapeyron equation) for the vaporization of a liquid.

15. Derive an expression for the variation of vapor pressure with temperature.

16. State and explain some important relationships involving the boiling point.

17. Explain what is meant by an additive property; illustrate by reference to the molar volume at the boiling point.

18. What is meant by the surface tension of a liquid? How can the shape of a (a) water, (b) mercury, surface in a glass tube be explained?

19. Describe three methods for the measurement of surface tension.

20. What is meant by interfacial tension? How is it determined?

21. Describe the influence of temperature on the surface tension of a liquid, with special reference to the Eötvös equation.

22. What is the parachor? Describe some of its properties and uses.

23. Explain what is meant by the viscosity of a liquid. How is the viscosity determined?

24. State and explain some relationships between viscosity, temperature and volume.

25. Define molar refraction and explain its additive character.

26. What is the dielectric constant? How is it measured?

27. Define molar polarization. What is its relationship to the molar refraction of a nonpolar substance?

28. How is the dipole moment of a polar molecule determined from the molar polarization?

29. Outline the application of bond moments and dipole moments to the determination of molecular structure.

PROBLEMS

I

1. When 1.064 g. of ethanol was heated at 230° C in a closed tube, it was found to consist of 1.25 ml. of liquid and 4.36 ml. of vapor. In another experiment at the same temperature, 1.503 g. consisted of 2.42 ml. of liquid and 3.54 ml. of vapor. Calculate the orthobaric densities of ethanol liquid and vapor at 230° C.

2. The orthobaric densities of ethyl ether ($C_4H_{10}O$) at several temperatures are as follows:

	160°	170°	180°	190° C
d_l	0.4947	0.4658	0.4268	0.3663 g. per ml.
d_v	0.06911	0.08731	0.1135	0.1620

Plot the results and determine the critical temperature and volume of ethyl ether from the graph. Estimate the critical pressure.

3. The critical temperature and pressure of hydrogen are −239.9° C and 12.8 atm., respectively. Determine the van der Waals constants a and b.

4. When 7.40 liters of dry air, measured at 25° C and an atmospheric pressure of 76.8 cm., were passed through a saturator containing a liquid of molecular weight 45.2, 0.7642 g. of the latter was vaporized. Calculate the vapor pressure of the liquid.

5. The heat of vaporization of carbon tetrachloride (CCl_4) at its boiling point 76.75° C is 46.4 cal. per g. The densities of the liquid and vapor at the boiling point are 1.4833 and 0.0054 g. per ml. Calculate, by exact and approximate methods, the rate of change of vapor pressure with temperature in cm. deg.$^{-1}$ units. Estimate the boiling point at 745 mm. atmospheric pressure.

6. Utilize the data in Table XVI to calculate the mean (approximate) heat of vaporization of acetic acid in the range from 20° to 30° C.

7. Using the volume equivalents in Table XVIII, calculate the densities at their respective boiling points of (a) carbon tetrachloride, (b) diethyl ether, (c) toluene.

8. Liquid ethanol (C_2H_5OH) of density 0.7893 at 20° C rises to a height of 5.38 cm. in a capillary tube of 0.0107 cm. diameter. Calculate the parachor of the ethanol, and compare it with the value derived by summing the parachor equivalents.

9. A viscometer was standardized by means of benzene, whose viscosity coefficient is 6.47×10^{-3} poise and density 0.8794 at 20° C. The time of flow was found to be 183 sec. The time of flow for ethanol, density 0.7893 at 20° C, was 378 sec.; what is the viscosity of ethanol?

10. The index of refraction, for the sodium D-line, of ethyl acetate is 1.3701, and its density is 0.9015 at 20° C. Calculate the molar refraction and compare it with the value obtained by the summation of the refraction equivalents.

11. The nonpolar liquid carbon tetrachloride has a refractive index (D-line) of 1.4573 and a density of 1.595 g. per ml. Calculate the approximate dielectric constant at 0° C when the density is 1.632 g. per ml.

12. The molar polarization of ethyl ether in cyclohexane solution, extrapolated to infinite dilution, is found to be 58.5 ml. at 20° C. The refractive index of the ether is 1.350 and its density is 0.7135 g. per ml. at this temperature. Calculate the dipole moment of ethyl ether.

II

1. When 1.731 g. of methanol was heated at 230° C in a closed tube, it was found to consist of 2.38 ml. of liquid and 5.76 ml. of vapor. In another experiment at the same temperature, 2.391 g. consisted of 4.42 ml. of liquid and 3.72 ml. of vapor. Calculate the orthobaric densities of methanol liquid and vapor at 230° C.

2. The orthobaric densities of methyl ether (C_2H_6O) at several temperatures are as follows:

	100°	110°	115°	120°	125°
d_l	0.4950	0.4575	0.4350	0.4040	0.3510 g. per ml.
d_v	0.0810	0.1060	0.1222	0.1465	0.1930

Plot the results and determine the critical temperature and volume of methyl ether from the graph. Estimate the critical pressure.

3. The critical temperature and pressure of oxygen are $-118.8°$ C and 49.7 atm., respectively. Evaluate the van der Waals constants a and b.

4. A volume of 5 liters of inert gas, measured at 20° C and an atmospheric pressure of 74.8 cm., was passed through a saturator containing water at 25.2° C, at which temperature the vapor pressure of water is 24.04 mm. How much water was vaporized?

5. The rate of change of vapor pressure of benzene in the vicinity of its boiling point 80.2° C is 23.3 mm. per degree; the density of the liquid at the boiling point is 0.8154 and that of the vapor 0.0026 g. per ml. Calculate by approximate and exact methods the latent heat of vaporization of benzene in cal. per g.

6. The normal boiling point of chloroform is 61.5° C and its heat of vaporization is 59.0 cal. per g. Calculate the approximate pressure at which the liquid will boil at 50.0° C.

7. A liquid having the formula $C_2H_4O_2$ was found to have a density of 0.9380 at its boiling point. Making use of the volume equivalents at the boiling point, what conclusions can be drawn concerning the nature of the two oxygen atoms?

8. The density of chloroform is 1.490 and that of diethyl ether is 0.7135 at 20° C. Calculate the parachor of each substance from the equivalents in Table XX, and compare the weights of the drops of these liquids falling from the same capillary tube.

9. Utilizing the viscosity data in Table XXI and the densities in problem 8, calculate the ratio of the times required for equal volumes of chloroform and diethyl ether to flow through the same viscometer at 20° C.

10. A hydrocarbon of formula $C_{10}H_{16}$ has a density of 0.855 and a refractive index (D-line) of 1.4823 at 20° C. Utilizing the data in Table XXII, determine the number of double bonds in the molecule.

11. The dielectric constant of the nonpolar liquid dioxane ($C_4H_8O_2$) is 2.229 and its density is 1.0335 at 20°. Calculate its molar refraction and refractive index.

12. The molar polarization of gaseous hydrogen chloride is 30.59 ml. at 21.0° C and 23.19 ml. at 160.7° C. Determine the dipole moment of this substance.

CHAPTER VI

THE SOLID STATE

CRYSTAL STRUCTURE

18a. The Study of Crystals.—The solid state is characterized by a rigidity of form and a tendency to maintain a definite shape; further, the volume of a solid changes only slightly with temperature and pressure. The true solid state is probably always associated with a definite crystalline form; that is to say, there is a complete regularity in the arrangement of the atoms or molecules of which the substance is constituted. Amorphous solids, such as glass and pitch, are really intermediate between solids and liquids; in these substances there may be some regularity of internal structure, but it is only partial, at best (§ 19f). Crystals, or true solids, can be distinguished from amorphous solids in many ways; for example, the former possess a sharp melting point, whereas the latter do not. Another important difference is to be found in the regularity of the external form, as well as in the internal arrangement, of crystals.

Except for those belonging to the cubic or regular system (see below), all crystals have certain properties that vary with the direction; such substances are said to be **anisotropic,** to distinguish them from cubic crystals and amorphous materials which are **isotropic,** having identical characteristics in all directions. The velocity of light is one property that depends on the direction in which it is measured; the result is that when a ray of light enters an anisotropic crystal, it is split into two separate components which travel with different velocities and follow different paths. This phenomenon, known as **double refraction,** is shown by all solids, except crystals of the cubic system and those, e.g., glass, which are amorphous in nature. The marked double refraction exhibited by Iceland spar (calcium carbonate) is made use of in the Nicol prism for the production and examination of polarized light.

The shape of a crystal of a given compound or element may vary with the conditions under which crystallization occurs, but *the angles between the faces are always constant.* The external shape or **habit** depends on the relative development of the different faces, but the interfacial angles remain unchanged, as shown by the two-dimensional representation in Fig. 31. The measurement of the angles of a crystal is thus an important part of the study of crystals, known as **crystallography;** the instrument used for the purpose is the **goniometer** (Greek: *angle measurer*).

In addition to the angles, another important property of crystals is their **symmetry.** Several types of symmetry are possible, but only three of the simplest will be described here for purposes of illustration. A crystal is said to have a **plane of symmetry** *when it can be divided by an imaginary plane into two parts, such that one is the exact mirror image of the other.* An **axis of symmetry** *is a line about which the crystal may be rotated so that it presents exactly the same appearance more than once in the course of a complete revolution.* If the original aspect appears again after a rotation through 180°, the axis is said to be one of two-fold (diad) symmetry. Other possibilities are repetition of the original appearance every 120° (three-fold or triad axis), 90° (four-fold or tetrad axis), and 60° (six-fold or hexad axis). In addition, a crystal may have a **center of symmetry**; this is *a point such that any line drawn through it will intersect the surface of the crystal at equal distances in both directions.* A crystal can have one or more planes, and one or more axes of symmetry, but never more than one center of symmetry. In fact, many crystals are not centro-symmetric, for they develop differently at opposite ends. The total number of **elements of symmetry**, as the various possible types of symmetry are called, depends on the nature of the crystal; a simple cubic crystal, such as one of

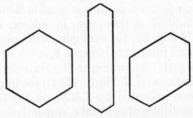

FIG. 31.   Crystal habit

sodium chloride, may possess as many as twenty-three elements of symmetry, but a crystal of copper sulfate pentahydrate is highly unsymmetric and may have no elements of symmetry.

From considerations of geometry and symmetry, it has been found that there are thirty-two different classes of crystal symmetry, and these fall conveniently into seven **crystal systems.** These systems are characterized by the number of geometric axes (three or four), the angles between them, and the intercepts along them, in terms of which every face of the crystal can be defined. From the measurement of the interfacial angles with a goniometer, the crystallographer is able to identify the particular system to which a given crystal belongs. The essential properties of the various crystallographic systems are as follows.

I. *The Cubic (or Regular) System:* Three axes at right angles with all intercepts equal; e.g., diamond, gold, silver, calcium fluoride, sodium chloride, zinc sulfide.

II. *The Tetragonal System:* Three axes at right angles with two intercepts equal; e.g., tin dioxide, titanium dioxide (rutile), lead tungstate ($PbWO_4$).

III. *The Orthorhombic (or Rhombic) System:* Three axes at right angles with all intercepts different, e.g., sulfur, potassium nitrate, barium sulfate, potassium sulfate.

IV. *The Monoclinic System:* Three axes, two pairs, e.g., OX and OY, and OX and OZ, at right angles, the other pair, OY and OZ, not; all intercepts different; e.g., sulfur, calcium sulfate dihydrate (gypsum), cryolite, borax.

V. *The Triclinic (or Anorthic) System:* Three axes, but none at right angles to each other; all intercepts different; e.g., copper sulfate pentahydrate, potassium dichromate.

VI. *The Hexagonal System:* Four axes, three being coplanar at angles of 60°, and the fourth at right angles to the plane; the intercepts on the planar axes are equal, but that on the fourth axis is different; e.g., zinc, cadmium, magnesium, cinnabar, quartz.

VII. *The Rhombohedral (or Trigonal) System:** Three axes equally inclined but not at right angles, with all intercepts equal; e.g., arsenic, antimony, bismuth, calcium carbonate (calcite), magnesium carbonate (magnesite), sodium nitrate.

18b. Law of Rational Indices: Miller Indices.—*The intercepts of any face of a crystal along the crystallographic axes, which determine the crystal system, are found to be always equal to the unit intercepts* (a, b, c) *or some simple integral multiple of them*, e.g., la, mb, nc, where l, m and n are small whole numbers. In Fig. 32, for example, ABC represents a **standard plane** or **unit plane**, the unit intercepts being a, b, c; for a cubic crystal these three intercepts would be equal. According to the statement made above, which is the **law of rational indices** (R. J. Haüy, 1784), the intercepts of any face of the crystal, such as the one indicated by LMN, on the three axes OX, OY and OZ, will be simple multiples of a, b and c, respectively; in the figure these multiples are 2, 2 and 3.

In order to represent any particular face of a crystal, use is made of the reciprocals of the multiples; thus, for the LMN plane in Fig. 32, the reciprocals are $\frac{1}{2}$, $\frac{1}{2}$ and $\frac{1}{3}$, which are in the integral ratio of 3 : 3 : 2. These numbers constitute the **Miller indices** (W. H. Miller, 1839) of the face LMN, and the latter is designated a (332) face. The Miller indices are thus inversely proportional to the intercepts of a given crystal face on the chosen axes. For the unit or standard plane ABC, the Miller indices are (111), since the multiples of a, b and c are all unity in this case. When a face cuts only two of the axes, e.g., OX and OY, and is parallel to the third, OZ, the intercept on the latter is then infinite and the corresponding Miller index is 0. If the face is parallel to one of the planes containing two of the axes, so that it has a finite intercept on one plane only, the symbol 00 is employed in the Miller index.

18c. The Space Lattice.—One of the consequences of the regularity of crystal structure is the development of the idea of the **space lattice**; the concept can be explained most simply by reference to a particular case. Consider, for example, a crystal of sodium chloride; this will consist of a perfectly regular arrangement of sodium atoms (or ions) and chlorine atoms (or ions). If the position of each sodium unit in the crystal is represented by a point, the result will be a regular three-dimensional network of points; this is the space lattice of the sodium atoms (or ions) in the crystal of sodium chloride. Similarly, there will be a space lattice for the chlorine units, and the space lattice of sodium chloride is made up of the interpenetration of the sodium and chlorine lattices. The symmetry of the combined lattice determines the symmetry of the crystal as a whole. In some cases, the lattices of the constituent units are identical, as is apparently true for sodium chloride, but in other instances,

---

* Some crystallographers include the rhombohedral in the hexagonal system; crystals of the former type have a three-fold axis of symmetry, while truly hexagonal crystals have a six-fold axis of symmetry.

e.g., calcium fluoride, there are reasons for believing that the space lattices of the constituents, viz., calcium and fluorine, are different.

No matter how complicated the combined space lattice for all the atoms or ions of a crystal, there is always one essential property of the lattice: *each point in the lattice has exactly the same environment as any other point representing the same atom or ion.* For example, in the space lattice of calcium carbonate, every point representing a calcium atom (or ion) will have exactly the same environment of carbon, oxygen, and other calcium atoms. For this

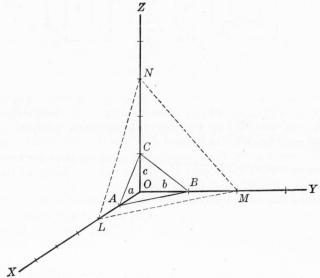

FIG. 32.   Crystallographic axes and law of rational indices

reason the three-dimensional space lattice of a crystal has been likened to a patterned wall-paper in two dimensions. Further, just as the pattern on the paper may be regarded as made up of a single pattern which is continuously repeated, so the space lattice of the crystal may be considered as built up of a three-dimensional basic pattern; this is called the **unit cell** and the external appearance of the crystal is determined by the shape and dimensions of the unit cell.

By means of arguments based on geometry, it has been proved that only fourteen different kinds of simple space lattice, for single atoms or ions, are possible; in other words, there are only fourteen ways in which similar points can be arranged in a regular three-dimensional order. The symmetry of these lattices corresponds to the seven crystallographic systems described in § 18a; each system is associated with certain definite types of lattice. For example, all crystals in the cubic or regular system are made up of one or more of three kinds of lattice; these are (i) the simple cube, (ii) the face-centered cube, and (iii) the body-centered cube. The unit cells corresponding to these space lattices are shown in Fig. 33; the actual lattice consists of a repetition of these unit cells in three dimensions. The simple cubic lattice has points only at the corners of each unit cube; in the face-centered lattice there are, in addition, points at the center of each of the six faces, while the body-centered lattice has a point in the center of each cube as well as those at the corners. By taking combinations of the various lattices that are possible for each crystallographic

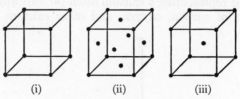

(i)   (ii)   (iii)

FIG. 33.   Cubic lattices

system, there have been built up 230 different arrangements known as **space groups.** Every crystal, depending upon its symmetry elements and crystallographic system, must belong to one or other of these groups.

Attention may be called to the fact that it is the *points* that constitute the space lattice, and not the lines joining them. Such lines are frequently inserted as a convenience to indicate the shape and dimensions of the unit cell, but they are not actually part of the lattice.

18d. Lattice Planes and Dimensions.—The points in a space lattice can be arranged in a number of ways as a series of parallel and equidistant planes; these are known as the **lattice planes.**

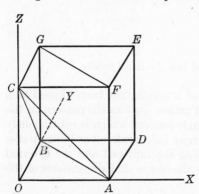

FIG. 34.   Important planes in cubic lattice

The external faces of the complete crystal are parallel to these planes; the most frequently occurring types of faces are those corresponding to planes containing the largest number of points. The lattice planes, like the faces of a crystal, are identified by Miller indices; these are inversely proportional to the intercepts made by a particular lattice plane on three convenient axes. For a cubic crystal these axes are at right angles to each other. The identification of the most important planes of the cubic lattice may be explained with reference to Fig. 34, which shows a unit cube and the three axes OX, OY and OZ. The plane $ADEF$, which cuts the OX axis at the point A, but does not intersect either of the other axes, is a (100) plane; all faces of the cube, in fact, represent planes of this same type. Planes such as $ABGF$ and $ACGD$, which cut the cube diagonally, are seen to make equal intercepts on two of the axes, but to be parallel to the third; hence, these are (110) planes. Finally, the planes ABC and DFG make equal intercepts on all three axes, and so they are both (111) planes. The (100), (110) and (111) planes are the most important planes for a simple cubic lattice, and it is of interest to note that the corresponding (100), (110) and (111) faces are those most frequently observed in crystals belonging to the cubic system. All the faces in a regular octahedron, which is the form generally taken by the alums, for example, are of the (111) type.

In connection with certain aspects of the internal structure of crystals, to be considered shortly, it is desirable to know the distances between successive lattice planes of the same type. This information may be readily obtained by simple geometrical methods, and the general nature of the results can be

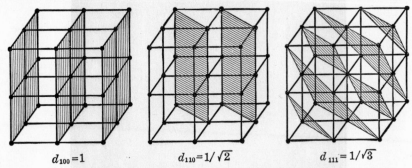

$$d_{100} = 1 \qquad d_{110} = 1/\sqrt{2} \qquad d_{111} = 1/\sqrt{3}$$

FIG. 35. Distances between planes in simple cubic lattice

indicated by means of Fig. 35, for a simple cubic lattice. In order to make the situation clear a portion of the lattice consisting of eight unit cubes is shown in each case, and the successive planes of the same type are shaded. If the distance between planes of a particular type is represented by using the Miller indices as a subscript, viz., d_{100}, d_{110} and d_{111}, then the following results are obtained for the ratios of these three distances.

Lattice Type	d_{100} : d_{110} : d_{111}
Simple cubic	$1 \ : \ \dfrac{1}{\sqrt{2}} \ : \ \dfrac{1}{\sqrt{3}}$
Face-centered cubic	$1 \ : \ \dfrac{1}{\sqrt{2}} \ : \ \dfrac{2}{\sqrt{3}}$
Body-centered cubic	$1 \ : \ \sqrt{2} \ : \ \dfrac{1}{\sqrt{3}}$

It will be observed that the spacing of similar lattice planes, e.g., d_{110} planes, depends on the type of lattice. The reason for this can be readily seen by means of diagrams similar to those of Fig. 33; the presence of extra points, which do not appear in the simple cubic lattice, results in the introduction of additional planes in the face-centered and body-centered cubic lattices.

X-Rays and Crystal Structure

19a. Diffraction of X-Rays.—A new and significant field of investigation was opened up by the discovery that X-rays could be used to study the interior structure of crystals. The fact that the wave lengths of X-rays are of the same order, viz., 10^{-8} cm., as the distance between atoms in a crystal, indicated to W. von Laue (1912) the possibility that a crystal might be used as a diffraction grating for X-rays. At his suggestion, W. Friedrich and P. Knipping (1912) passed a beam of inhomogeneous X-rays, that is, a beam consisting

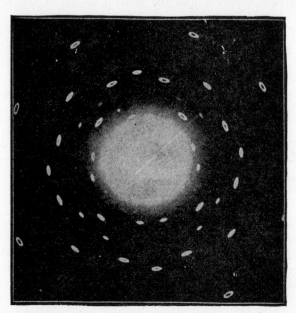

Fig. 36.   Laue photograph of magnesium oxide

of X-rays of many different wave lengths, through a crystal of zinc blende; when the resulting radiation fell on a photographic plate a definite diffraction pattern was obtained. A pattern of this type, given by a crystal of magnesium oxide, is depicted in Fig. 36; it is generally referred to as a **Laue photograph** or **Laue pattern.** The important fact that a crystal could behave as a three-dimensional diffraction grating, led W. L. Bragg (1913) to the use of X-rays for the purpose of studying crystal structure. The Laue patterns have been used to a considerable extent for such studies in recent years, but the interpretation of the results is not easy, although special mathematical and geometrical methods have been developed for this purpose.

The principle involved in the procedure devised by W. H. Bragg and W. L. Bragg, in which the crystal is used as a reflection grating for homogeneous X-rays, i.e., of uniform wave length, is much simpler to understand. Every atom is able to scatter X-rays to an extent dependent upon the number of its electrons, and every atom-bearing plane in a crystal, that is, every lattice plane, can cause reflection of the rays. Consider, for illustrative purposes, a number of identical lattice planes, represented in section by the lines AA, BB, CC, etc., in Fig. 37; each of these planes really consists of a regular arrangement of points indicating the positions of the atoms in the crystal. A parallel beam of uniform X-rays impinges on the crystal so that the **glancing angle** is θ, as shown. Part of the beam, i.e., LM, will be reflected at M along MN; on the other hand, some of the rays, i.e., PQ, will penetrate the crystal and be reflected along QN by the atoms in the lattice plane BB. If the length of the

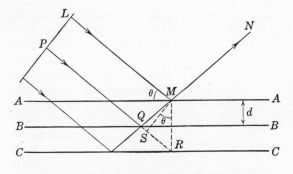

Fig. 37. X-ray reflection from equidistant planes

path LMN differs from that of PQN by a whole number of wave lengths, then the two beams, from L and P, reinforce one another after reflection, and a strong beam will result.

The condition for the reinforcement to occur can be derived in the following manner. From M draw MR perpendicular to the reflecting (lattice) planes, and MS perpendicular to QR. The difference in the paths LMN and PQN is obviously equal to $QM - QS$, and since $QM = QR$, it is equal to SR. As the angle SMR is the same as the glancing angle θ, it is seen that SR is equal to $2d$ sin θ, where d is the distance between the successive lattice planes. For a reflection of maximum intensity this quantity must be a whole number n of wave lengths λ, as stated above; hence, the condition for maximum reflection is

$$n\lambda = 2d \sin \theta. \qquad (19.1)$$

This result, known as the **Bragg equation,** is also applicable to reflection from other planes, e.g., CC in Fig. 37.

For a given set of lattice planes, e.g., (100) planes, d is fixed; further, for homogeneous X-rays the wave length λ has a definite value. The possibility of obtaining maximum reflection will thus depend on θ, the glancing angle. As θ is increased gradually, a series of positions are found, corresponding to n equal to 1, 2, 3, 4, etc., at which the reflection is a maximum. These are separated by regions in which the reflected X-ray beams from successive lattice planes differ in length by a fractional number of wave lengths; the rays are then not "in phase," and so cancel each other to a great extent, thus resulting in a decrease of intensity. By means of a crystal it is thus possible to obtain an X-ray "spectrum," consisting of a number of fairly strong reflections separated by regions of low intensity. The successive maxima are called first, second, third, etc., order reflections, according as the value of n in equation (19.1) is 1, 2, 3, etc.; their intensity falls off as n increases, and reflections of the fifth or higher order are generally too feeble to be detected.

19b. The Determination of Crystal Structure.—It will be evident from equation (19.1) that if the glancing angles θ are measured for various orders n

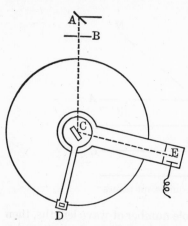

FIG. 38.   X-ray spectrometer (Bragg)

of maximum reflection, the distance d between successive lattice planes of a given type in the crystal can be calculated, provided the wave length of the X-rays is known. Even if this wave length is not known, it should still be possible to calculate the *ratio* of the separations for planes of different types. In order to determine the positions of maximum reflection intensity, use can be made of the Bragg **X-ray spectrometer,** shown diagrammatically in Fig. 38. A beam of X-rays of definite wave length, coming from the anticathode A of an X-ray tube, passes through a slit B and then falls upon a known face of the crystal C mounted on a rotating table, the position of which can be read on the scale D. The rays reflected from the crystal pass through another slit and into the ionization chamber E containing an easily ionizable gas, such as ethyl bromide vapor. In the chamber are electrodes raised to a high voltage, and connected through an electrometer. The entry of X-rays into E causes the gas to ionize, and a flow of current is registered on the electrometer; the strength of this current is a measure of the intensity of the entering X-rays.

Starting with a small glancing angle between incident X-rays and the crystal face, the value is increased in stages by rotating the table. The apparatus is so designed that the reflected ray always enters the ionization chamber, and the intensities of the reflected X-rays for the various angles are determined from the corresponding electrometer current. The glancing angles θ for which the strongest reflections are obtained are those which satisfy the Bragg equation (19.1). The procedure just described is repeated for all the important planes of the crystal; if necessary, artificial faces, parallel to some lattice planes, must be cut. For example, the faces of a perfect cube are all (100), and so it would be necessary to cut artificial (110) and (111) faces, to study reflections from the (110) and (1Ī1) lattice planes, respectively, which are parallel to these faces.

The practical application of the X-ray spectrometer may be illustrated by reference to some simple cases. The (100) face of a sodium chloride crystal, belonging to the cubic system, was found to give reflection maxima, for the K_α X-rays from a palladium anticathode, at glancing angles of 5.9°, 11.85° and 18.15°. If these angles represent first, second and third order reflections, respectively, then according to equation (19.1) their sines should be in the ratio of 1, 2 and 3, since λ and d are constant. The actual values of the sines are 0.103, 0.205 and 0.312, and these are very close to the expected ratios.

The first order reflection from the (100) planes of sodium chloride thus occurs at a glancing angle of 5.9°; the values for the (110) and (111) planes, with the same X-rays, were found to be 8.4° and 5.2°, respectively. The Bragg equation (19.1) may be written in the form

$$d = \frac{n\lambda}{2} \cdot \frac{1}{\sin \theta}, \tag{19.2}$$

and since n and λ are the same in the three cases, for the first order ($n = 1$) reflections, it follows that the distance d between successive planes is inversely proportional to the sine of the glancing angle; hence, the ratio of the spacings for the three principal lattice planes of sodium chloride is given by the following relationships:

$$d_{100} : d_{110} : d_{111} = \frac{1}{\sin 5.9°} : \frac{1}{\sin 8.4°} : \frac{1}{\sin 5.2°}$$

$$= 9.731 \quad : 6.844 \quad : 11.04$$

$$= 1.000 \quad : 0.704 \quad : 1.136.$$

This ratio is almost identical with $1 : 1/\sqrt{2} : 2/\sqrt{3}$, i.e., $1 : 0.707 : 1.155$, which gives the relative spacings for the unit cell of a face-centered cubic lattice (§ 18d). It appears, therefore, that this type of lattice forms the basis of the internal structure of the sodium chloride crystal.

By means of the foregoing information, in conjunction with evidence derived from the relative intensities of the successive X-ray maxima, the space lattice of sodium chloride can be shown to consist of a face-centered lattice of sodium units interlocked with a similar lattice of chlorine units. A portion of this combined lattice is depicted in Fig. 39; it should be understood, of course, that the lattice extends throughout the whole crystal, but in the figure only one unit cell is shown. The black circles represent sodium atoms or ions, and the white circles indicate chlorine atoms or ions.* It can be seen that each chlorine unit is surrounded by six sodium units, and each sodium by six chlorine units. It will be noted that there are no sodium chloride *molecules* as structural units in the lattice. This fact, which is in harmony with the electronic theory of valence (§ 10b), suggests that the units of structure in the sodium chloride crystal are sodium and chloride *ions*, and not the

* Since the sodium and chlorine lattices are the same. the black circles might equally well represent chlorine, and the white circles sodium.

atoms. All truly electrovalent compounds, such as sodium chloride and similar salts, possess **ionic lattices** of this type.

It should be recalled, as noted above, that in depicting a space lattice, the position of an atom or ion is represented by a point, or a small circle. The size of the point or circle provides no information concerning the size of the atom or ion, and this important fact must always be remembered. Actually, there are reasons for believing that *the atoms or ions in a crystal practically touch one another*, with little or no "free space" between them.

It is to be expected from general considerations that sodium and potassium chlorides should have similar structures. An examination of the first

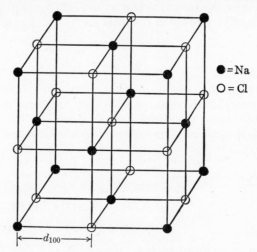

$$\bullet = Na$$
$$O = Cl$$

$$\vdash\!\!-d_{100}\!-\!\!\dashv$$

FIG. 39.   Sodium chloride lattice

order spectra from the (100), (110) and (111) planes of potassium chloride shows, however, that the ratio of the spacings is represented by

$$d_{100} : d_{110} : d_{111} = 1 : \frac{1}{\sqrt{2}} : \frac{1}{\sqrt{3}},$$

which is that required for a *simple* cubic lattice (§ 18d). This apparent discrepancy is readily explained when it is realized that the X-ray scattering intensity of an atom or ion is dependent on the number of electrons associated with that atom or ion. The ions of potassium and chlorine actually possess equal numbers of electrons, viz., 18, and so their scattering powers will evidently be virtually identical. If the space lattice of potassium chloride is the same as that of sodium chloride, as is probable, it is evident from Fig. 39 that if all the lattice points had equal scattering effects, the whole system should behave to X-rays just as if it consisted of a lattice of simple cubes. In sodium chloride the scattering effects of the sodium and chloride ions are different, and so the true structure, as two interpenetrating face-centered lattices, is apparent.

Problem: Sodium and potassium chlorides form similar cubic crystals; the first order X-ray reflections from the (100) planes are at glancing angles of 5.9° and 5.3°, respectively. Calculate the ratio of the molar volumes of the two crystalline chlorides.

Since the interplanar distance d is inversely proportional to sin θ, it follows that

$$\frac{d_{100}(\text{KCl})}{d_{100}(\text{NaCl})} = \frac{\sin 5.9°}{\sin 5.3°} = \frac{0.1028}{0.0924} = 1.11.$$

The volume of a small lattice cube is equal to $(d_{100})^3$, and so the ratio of the volumes of potassium and sodium chlorides containing equal numbers of ions (or molecules) will be $(1.11)^3$, i.e., 1.37. (The direct experimental value is 1.39, thus providing confirmation of the similarity of the two lattices.)

19c. Lattice Dimensions: The Avogadro Number.—In Fig. 39 the unit cell of the space lattice of sodium chloride is seen to consist of fourteen points representing sodium ions, and thirteen points for chloride ions. Of the former, there is one at each of the eight corners, and one in the middle of each of the six faces. The eight sodium points at the corners are shared equally by eight cubes meeting at each corner, so that there is effectively only one per unit cell; similarly, the sodium points on the six faces are each shared by two cubes, giving an average of three for each unit cell. There are thus an average of four sodium ions associated with the unit cell shown. Of the thirteen chlorine points, the one in the center belongs exclusively to the unit cell, but the other twelve are each shared between four cubes meeting at each of the edges. There are thus four chloride ions that belong to the unit cell. Four "molecules" of sodium chloride, i.e., four sodium ions and four chloride ions, are consequently associated exclusively with the unit cell in Fig. 39. If M is the molecular weight of sodium chloride and N is the Avogadro number, the average mass per unit cube must be $4M/N$. Further, if the specific volume, i.e., the volume of unit mass, is v, then the mean volume of the unit cube will be $4Mv/N$. It can be seen from Fig. 39 that each edge of the unit cube has a length of $2d_{100}$, and so the volume of this cube must be $(2d_{100})^3$; equating this result to the one just given, it follows that

$$(2d_{100})^3 = \frac{4Mv}{N},$$

$$d_{100} = \sqrt[3]{\frac{Mv}{2N}}. \tag{19.3}$$

For sodium chloride, M is 58.454, v is 0.4621 at 20° C and the Avogadro number is 6.023×10^{23}; it follows, therefore, that d_{100} is 2.82×10^{-8} cm., i.e., 2.82 Å.

From this result for the distance between successive (100) planes in the sodium chloride crystal, it is possible to calculate the wave length of the X-rays. The first order diffraction maximum of the K_α rays of palladium, reflected from the (100) planes of sodium chloride occurs at a glancing angle of 5.9°; hence, n is 1 and sin θ is 0.103. Making use of equation (19.1), in conjunction with the value of d_{100}, i.e., 2.82×10^{-8} cm., obtained above, it follows that λ is 0.581 × 10⁻⁸ cm., i.e., 0.581 Å. It is thus seen, as mentioned at the beginning of § 19a, that atomic (or ionic) distances and the wave lengths of X-rays are of the order of 10^{-8} cm.

If the wave length of the X-rays can be determined in another way, not dependent on crystal structure, e.g., by using an ordinary line grating and very small glancing angles, it is possible to reverse the foregoing calculations and thus to determine the Avogadro number. It is generally agreed that one of the most accurate procedures for determining this constant is based on observations of the diffraction of X-rays by calcite crystals.

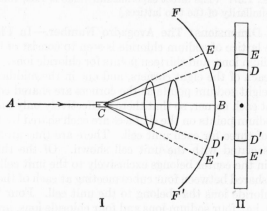

FIG. 40. Principle of the powder method

19d. Other Methods of X-Ray Investigation.—The X-ray spectrometer method of studying crystal structure requires the use of a relatively large crystal with well defined faces, and since reflections of several orders must be examined for a number of faces, the total labor involved is large. This is compensated for, however, by the comparatively simple interpretation of the results. As already stated, the study of crystals based on the use of the Laue patterns is possible, but the evaluation of the results is complicated. At the present time the Laue method is used mainly to determine the symmetry class of the crystal space lattice.

For certain substances belonging to the cubic or hexagonal systems, as do most metals and their alloys, the **powder method** of X-ray crystallography, devised independently by P. Debye and P. Scherrer (1916) and A. W. Hull (1917), has many advantages. A narrow beam AB of uniform X-rays (Fig. 40) is allowed to fall on the finely powdered substance C to be examined, and the diffracted rays impinge upon a strip of photographic film FF'. In the fine powder the crystals are oriented in all directions, and so a large number will have their lattice planes in the correct positions for maximum X-ray reflection to occur. All crystalline particles whose (100) planes make the proper angle with the incident beam of X-rays will produce first order maxima in directions lying on a circular cone, as shown by DCD' in Fig. 40, I. Similarly, some crystals will be oriented in such a manner as to produce a circular cone ECE', as the second order reflection from the (100) planes, and so on for other planes and for higher orders. The strip of film FF' cuts the cones in such a way as to produce two arcs (Fig. 40, II); each pair gives the position of a reflection of a definite order from a particular plane. From these positions the information necessary for the elucidation of the structure of the crystalline material can be obtained. As mentioned earlier, the powder method is most suitable for cubic crystals and for many metals (hexagonal system); the association of the various lines with the possible planes and orders of reflection is then not too difficult.

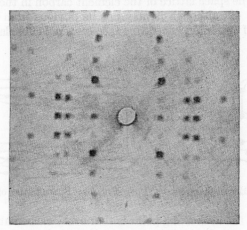

FIG. 41. X-ray rotation photograph of benzil

The powder method has been employed particularly in the study of metals and alloys, for which single crystals are not easily obtained. It has also been used for analytical and identification purposes, as the X-ray powder photograph of a given crystalline substance is characteristic of that substance.

The most modern, and widely applicable, procedure for the X-ray investigation of crystal structure is the **rotating crystal method** or a modification, the **oscillating crystal method.** A moderately small crystal is rotated or oscillated about an axis parallel to one of the crystal axes, and is exposed to a beam of homogenous X-rays from a direction at right angles. As the crystal rotates, various planes come successively into positions for diffraction to occur, and corresponding spots are produced on a photographic plate. A typical rotation photograph is shown in Fig. 41. Three such photographs are taken with crystal rotating about each of the three principal axes, and from the results the lattice spacings and size of the unit cell can be deduced. If, in addition, the intensities of the various spots are measured it is possible to determine the exact positions of the atoms, or ions, in the crystal. For this purpose the detailed information obtained by oscillating the crystal through an angle of about 15° at a time, while the photographic plate (or film) is moved in a synchronized manner, is particularly useful, especially for complex molecules.

19e. Results of X-Ray Studies of Crystals.—A very large number of crystalline substances have been examined by X-ray methods, and many of the results are of considerable interest and importance to chemistry. A few only of the conclusions will be described here under several headings.

I. Elements: Nonmetals.—The crystals of nonmetals are characterized by the fact that each atom is joined by definite covalent bonds to one or more adjoining atoms, the actual number being equal to the usual valence of the element. It follows, therefore, that the crystal of a nonmetallic element is constructed in such a manner as to allow every atom to complete its electron octet (§ 10a). The space lattice of the element carbon in the form of diamond is shown in Fig. 42; although it may not be obvious from the diagram, the lattice consists of two interpenetrating face-centered cubic lattices. From the

 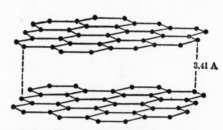

3.41 Å

FIG. 42.   Space lattice of diamond   FIG. 43.   Space lattice of graphite

chemical aspect, the interesting point is that every carbon atom in diamond is surrounded by four others at the corners of a regular tetrahedron. The distance between two adjoining atoms is 1.54 Å, which corresponds very closely to the distance between two carbon atoms attached to each other by a single covalent bond, as in aliphatic organic compounds. This agreement, together with the fact that each carbon atom in the diamond has four others situated around it at the corners of a regular tetrahedron, suggests that every atom in the crystal is joined to four others by covalent linkages. A diamond is thus to be regarded as one large carbon molecule, a type of structure for which the term **macromolecule** has been proposed. It is probable that the hardness of diamond is to be attributed to this particular structure.

The allotropic form of carbon known as graphite crystallizes in the hexagonal system, and its space lattice is represented in Fig. 43. The carbon atoms are seen to be arranged in flat sheets parallel to one another, 3.41 Å apart; this distance is too large to correspond to a chemical bond, and so each carbon atom is attached to three others, instead of four as in diamond. In each layer the carbon atoms form flat hexagons, the distance between centers of adjacent atoms being 1.42 Å; the arrangement of the atoms in each hexagon corresponds almost exactly to that in the six-membered rings of benzene, naphthalene, etc., and their derivatives.

Crystals consisting of sheets of atoms, not necessarily all in one plane, extending throughout the whole crystal, and separated from one another by a distance too large for chemical bonding, are said to be **layer lattices.** They generally have the property of forming flakes, because cleavage occurs readily between the sheets of atoms. The use of graphite as a lubricant depends upon the ability of one plane of atoms to slide easily over another. Among more complex substances that have layer lattices, and hence form flaky crystals, mention may be made of the minerals mica and talc.

The tendency for every atom to complete its octet, and to exhibit its normal valence in the crystal, results in the other nonmetallic elements of group IV of the periodic table, viz., silicon, germanium and gray tin, having crystal lattices similar to that of diamond. In group V, however, the atoms are tervalent, having five electrons in the outermost shell and requiring only three additional electrons to complete their octets; hence, it is found that each atom in the crystal is attached by covalent bonds to three others. This leads to an arrangement of puckered six-membered rings in the rhombohedral crystals of arsenic, antimony and bismuth.

The elements of group VI have six outer electrons and are bivalent; they thus tend to form chains in which each atom is joined to two others. The crystals of selenium and tellurium are, in fact, made up of a series of such spiral chains held parallel to each other by relatively weak (van der Waals) forces. In rhombic sulfur the inclination to form chains still exists, but instead of being continuous, the ends join to form puckered eight-membered rings. This result, arrived at from X-ray studies of the crystal, is of special interest in view of the fact that the vapor of sulfur just above its boiling point is known to contain S_8 molecules. Plastic sulfur, on the other hand, evidently consists of long chains of atoms.

Iodine is the only halogen atom (group VII) whose crystal structure has been determined; in the crystal a simple I_2 molecule is situated at each lattice point. In this case, therefore, the unit of crystal structure is the normal chemical molecule; iodine thus provides an example of a simple **molecular crystal.** Each iodine atom can be attached to only one other iodine atom; since the atoms are univalent, combination in pairs is the sole type of union that is reasonably possible. *The formation of covalent bonds between adjoining atoms in the crystal thus accounts for the transition from macromolecules, through layers and chains (or rings, as in rhombic sulfur), to single diatomic molecules, as the number of electrons in the outermost shell of the atom increases from four in carbon, silicon, etc., to seven in iodine.*

II. Elements: Metals.—The great majority of metallic elements crystallize in one of three forms, viz., face-centered cubic, close-packed hexagonal, or body-centered cubic lattices. The first two classes are of special interest, as they represent the most efficient packing of spherical units. Suppose a number of spheres are laid close together, as shown by the full circles in Fig. 44A and B, and then others are placed above them in the hollows formed where the spheres meet in the lower layer, as indicated by the dotted circles. This is seen to form a close-packed arrangement. A third layer of the same type may be built up in two different ways; either the spheres may be placed in the hollows marked A, in which case the spheres in this (third) layer will be exactly over those in the first, or they may be placed in the hollows marked B, and then the *fourth* layer will correspond with the first. The former type of structure is that of a close-packed hexagonal lattice, while the latter is a face-centered cubic lattice. Since a large proportion of the metallic elements have such crystal lattices, it is apparent that in the solid state most metals consist of approximately spherical atoms packed together as closely as possible. The body-centered cubic lattice structure possessed by some metals, e.g., the alkali metals, is a less compact arrangement; this probably accounts for the unusual softness of the alkali metals.

In both the face-centered cubic and close-packed hexagonal lattices, each atom is in contact with twelve others, and even in the body-centered cubic

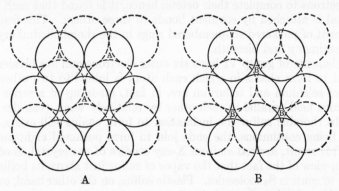

Fig. 44. Packing of atoms in metals: (A) closed-packed hexagonal, (B) face-centered cubic

lattice the number of adjacent atoms is as high as eight. In nonmetallic elements, as seen above, no atom is attached to more than four others; this is the maximum, observed with elements of group IV, while for other elements the number is less. It is evident, therefore, that the atoms in a metal cannot be held together by ordinary covalent bonds resulting from the pairing of electrons, since the number of electrons available is quite insufficient for the purpose. It has been suggested, therefore, that the atoms in a metal are held together by a special type of bond, known as a **metallic bond.** It is possible that the metallic atoms lose some of their electrons and so become positive ions; the electrons then form a more or less mobile arrangement which binds the ions together. The high electrical conductance of metals is apparently due to these mobile electrons.

III. Simple Inorganic Compounds.—A study, by means of X-rays, of the lattice structures of many simple inorganic compounds of the type AX and AX$_2$ has brought to light some important generalizations. It appears that the structure of a crystal of a given type of compound, e.g., AX or AX$_2$, is determined essentially by the ratio of the radii of the atoms (or ions), and also by the tendency of an electrovalence to pass over into a covalent bond (see § 10d).

Although the majority of alkali halides have face-centered cubic lattices of the sodium chloride (NaCl) type, as in Fig. 39, cesium chloride, bromide and iodide crystallize with body-centered cubic lattices, as shown in Fig. 45. A comparison of the two types of structure shows that in the former case each ion is surrounded by six others of opposite sign, while in the latter there are eight ions around each oppositely charged ion. The explanation of this difference lies in the larger size of the cesium ion as compared with that of the other alkali metal ions. Because of the relative radii of the ions, it is possible to pack eight halogen ions closely about a cesium ion, but this cannot be done with the ions of lithium, sodium, potassium or rubidium. Around these latter positive ions, however, a group of six halogen ions can be arranged, thus giving rise to the face-centered (NaCl) type of cubic lattice. It may be mentioned that because of the small size of the fluoride ion, a configuration of eight of these ions around potassium and rubidium, as well as cesium, ions is theoretically possible. Nevertheless, these three fluorides have the NaCl-type of lattice. The strongly electronegative character of the fluoride ion presumably resists the tendency toward close packing.

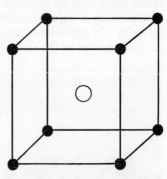

FIG. 45. Body-centered cubic lattice of cesium chloride

With changing ionic size it may become impossible to arrange as many as six ions about a central ion; in this event the compound AX will generally possess either a zinc oxide or a zinc sulfide (zinc blende) type of lattice. In these lattices each ion is surrounded by four others of opposite sign; the zinc blende lattice is, in fact, similar to that of diamond. This type of lattice is favored by substances in which there is a tendency, as in zinc sulfide, for the electrovalence to pass over into a covalent bond. Cuprous bromide, silver iodide, cadmium telluride (CdTe) and the completely covalent silicon carbide (SiC) crystallize in the zinc blende type of lattice.

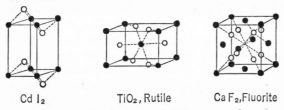

Cd I₂   TiO₂, Rutile   Ca F₂, Fluorite

FIG. 46. Lattice types of AX₂ compounds

Similar transitions in lattice type have been observed with changing ionic (or atomic) radii in compounds of formula AX_2 (Fig. 46). When the negative ion is small in comparison with the positive ion, the calcium fluoride (fluorite) type of lattice is found, but this passes into the titanium dioxide (rutile) structure with increasing size of the negative ion or decreasing size of the positive ion. If there is a tendency for the formation of covalent bonds, the cadmium iodide type of lattice, which is a layer lattice, is observed, as in cadmium iodide itself, as well as in the disulfides and diselenides of quadrivalent tin, palladium, titanium, zirconium, etc.

IV. Organic Compounds.—The crystals of organic compounds have been shown by X-ray analysis to consist of molecular lattices (§ 19e, I); that is to say, the structural unit in these compounds is the molecule itself. The various atoms are joined by covalent bonds, and it is the arrangement of the complete molecules in a regular pattern that determines the interior structure of the crystals. In aliphatic compounds the carbon atom is found to be tetrahedral in character, as in the diamond; the distance between the centers of two such atoms joined by a single bond is 1.54 Å. For double-bonded atoms the corresponding distance is 1.32 Å.

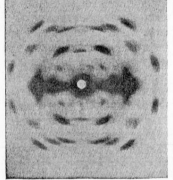

In aromatic compounds, such as benzene and its derivatives, the C—C distance in the ring is always 1.40 ± 0.01 Å. The benzene ring is itself found to be a regular hexagon with all the adjacent interatomic distances equal. All the carbon-carbon linkages in benzene thus partake of both single bonded and double bonded character, as is to be expected from the resonance type of structure (§ 10g).

Although fibrous substances, such as cellulose, silk, wool and hair are not strictly crystalline in nature, they give characteristic X-ray patterns (Fig. 47), which are somewhat similar to rotation photographs (see Fig. 41).

FIG. 47.   X-ray diffraction pattern of ramie fiber

From these patterns it has been shown that natural fibers consist mainly of numbers of long, thin pseudo-crystals, or **crystallites,** arranged with their long axes approximately parallel to the length of the fiber. It is this particular arrangement of the crystallites, which are themselves made up of long molecular chains, which is responsible for the essential properties of a fibrous material. Stretched rubber gives a fiber-like X-ray diffraction pattern, indicating a partial orientation of long hydrocarbon chains. In the unstretched form, however, the chains are apparently distributed in a random manner, for the X-ray pattern consists of diffuse rings like those obtained with a liquid.

V. Miscellaneous Crystalline Substances.—Mention only will be made of a number of other fields of investigation in which the examination of crystals by means of X-rays has provided results of importance; among these are the study of metallic alloys, the structure of silicates, coordination compounds, water of crystallization, and hydrogen bonds in crystals.

19f. The Structure of Liquids and Glasses.—A form of the X-ray method has been used to throw light on the problem of the internal structure of liquids. It appears, in many cases, that provided the temperature is not too far from the melting point, the distances between atoms in the liquid are not greatly different from those in the solid, e.g., for water, 2.90 Å between oxygen atoms in the liquid and 2.76 Å in the solid; for aluminum, 2.96 Å in the liquid and 2.86 Å in the solid. Further, the average number of nearest neighbors to any given atom is usually approximately the same as in the solid. This similarity between liquid and solid, especially near the melting point, is not unexpected. As a general rule, the atoms (or molecules) in the solid are packed as efficiently as possible, and since the density of the liquid is not very different from that of the solid, the packing in the former must be similar to that in the latter. However, the resemblance between liquid and solid becomes less marked as the distance from a given atom increases beyond its immediate neighbors. It appears, therefore, that there is some sort of regularity of structure, i.e., "order," in a liquid, but it is of the "short range" variety, extending for a short distance only from any given atom or other unit. A solid possesses both long range and short range order, for the regularity of structure extends throughout the whole crystal; the long range order in a liquid is, however, negligible. Even the short range order in the liquid is not as regular as in the solid, for the order may be regarded as being somewhat "blurred" in the liquid; this is probably due to the larger available volume and hence greater freedom of movement in the liquid state. As the temperature is raised this blurring increases; the distance between nearest neighbors increases, and the number of these neighbors decreases, so that eventually there is a virtually random arrangement of molecules in the liquid, just as in a gas.

When certain liquids are cooled fairly rapidly there is no formation of crystals at a definite temperature, such as occurs on slow cooling. The viscosity of the liquid increases steadily, and eventually a "glass" is obtained. This property of forming glasses is possessed particularly by silica and boron trioxide, and by their mixtures with oxides of the alkali or alkaline-earth metals. It has been shown by means of X-ray diffraction studies that the unit of structure in silica glass, i.e., vitreous silica, is the same as in the crystalline form. Each silicon atom is surrounded by four oxygen atoms, and each of the latter is shared between two silicon atoms, giving the resultant formula $(SiO_2)_n$. In the crystal these units are built up in a completely regular manner, whereas in the glass their arrangement is almost random. The short range order in the glass is virtually perfect, but there is no definite long range order. A glass is thus intermediate in structure between a liquid, as described above, and a solid. Glasses owe their stability to a number of factors; among these may be mentioned their high viscosity which prevents rearrangement of the atoms into the completely regular structure of the crystalline form.

Isomorphism and Polymorphism

20a. Isomorphism.—The term **isomorphism** (Greek: *same shape*) is used to indicate *the occurrence of different chemical compounds in the same crystalline form;* such substances are said to be **isomorphous** with one another. As mentioned in § 3f, isomorphous compounds which have similar chemical properties can usually be represented by similar formulae; however, the reverse of this statement is not necessarily true, for substances with similar formulae and chemical properties are frequently not isomorphous, e.g., sodium and potassium nitrates, and magnesium and strontium carbonates. The explanation of this discrepancy is similar to that given above to account for the change of lattice type in the AX and AX_2 compounds. For example, in passing from the magnesium ion to the strontium ion, the most efficient arrangement of carbonate ions around the central positive ion changes, so that the lattice types and crystal forms are different. It is of interest to record in this connection that calcium carbonate exists in two crystalline forms, one of which, i.e., calcite, is isomorphous with magnesium carbonate, whereas the other, i.e., aragonite, is isomorphous with strontium carbonate. Since the radius of the calcium ion is intermediate between that of the magnesium and strontium ions, both types of packing of the carbonate ions are evidently more or less equally possible.

In order that two salts may be isomorphous, with the same crystal form and approximately equal interfacial angles and axial ratios, three conditions must be satisfied. First, *the two substances must have the same formula type,* although it is not necessary that they should be chemically similar; thus $KMnO_4$ and $BaSO_4$; $KClO_4$ and KBF_4; $NaNO_3$ and $CaCO_3$; and K_2SO_4, K_2BeO_4 and $K_2P(O_3F)$ are isomorphous groups of compounds having the same formula type, but with entirely different chemical properties. In addition to having the same formula type the ionic groups must have the same stereochemical form. Sodium chlorate ($NaClO_3$), for example, is not isomorphous with $NaNO_3$ or $CaCO_3$; the primary reason is that the ClO_3^- ion has a pyramidal structure while the NO_3^- and CO_3^{--} ions are flat, as shown by X-ray studies. The second condition for isomorphism is that *the relative sizes of the structural units, atoms or ions, should be approximately equal,* so as to ensure the same type of packing in each case. It should be noted that the actual sizes of the units are not important; it is the relative size which determines the most efficient packing. Third, *the electrovalent and covalent characteristics of the bonds should be similar in the two molecules;* as in the case of the simple AX and AX_2 compounds, the tendency for an electrovalence to pass over into a covalent bond may result in a change of lattice type.

If a solution containing two isomorphous salts is allowed to crystallize, the solid that separates out is homogeneous in nature, but it contains both substances, the proportions depending on the composition of the solution. Homogeneous solids of this kind, containing two, or more, isomorphous compounds are sometimes called **mixed crystals** or, better, **mix-crystals.** Since the solid is quite homogeneous, it is similar to a solution, and so the term **solid solution** is frequently employed; this avoids the implication that it is a mere mixture of two or more substances. *The formation of a solid solution upon crystallization is a characteristic property of isomorphous substances. Another criterion of isomorphism is the ability of a crystal of one compound to continue to grow when placed in a saturated solution of another;* this phenomenon is known as the formation of **overgrowths.** The second substance is deposited on the crystal of the first, without change of form.

In some cases where the formation of solid solutions and overgrowths is to be expected, because of isomorphism, these do not actually occur; in other instances solid solutions are formed over a limited range of compositions only. From X-ray diffraction studies of substances having the same crystalline form, it has been concluded that solid solutions and overgrowths can occur only if the dimensions of the unit cells in the crystal lattices do not differ by more than about 10 per cent. If this is exceeded, the entry of one substance into the space lattice of the other, which is what occurs in the formation of solid solutions, would cause so much distortion as to make the crystal unstable.

20b.—Polymorphism.—*The occurrence of a given substance in more than one crystalline form* is known as **polymorphism.** Polymorphism has been observed among substances of various types, elements and compounds, inorganic and organic. With elements it is generally referred to as **allotropy,** the allotropic forms of carbon, sulfur and phosphorus being well known.

The particular crystal form adopted by a polymorphic substance depends on the conditions of crystallization, e.g., upon temperature and pressure. Frequently there is a definite temperature at each pressure, known as the **transition point,** at which one form changes reversibly into the other. For example, the stable form of sulfur at ordinary temperatures belongs to the rhombic system, but if heated to 95.6° C, i.e., the transition point at 1 atm. pressure, the rhombic crystals change to the monoclinic form. On cooling from above 95.6°, the monoclinic crystals change back to rhombic at this temperature. Similar reversible transitions are shown by ammonium nitrate, mercuric iodide, and certain forms of silica. *Crystalline forms that can undergo reversible changes of this type at the transition temperature* are said to be **enantiotropic,** the phenomenon being referred to as **enantiotropy** (Greek: *opposite change*). The transition point is then somewhat similar to a melting point, as will be seen in a later treatment (§ 22f).

In certain instances of polymorphism *the change from one form to another does not take place in both directions;* for example, yellow phosphorus can be readily changed into the violet form, but the reverse transition is not possible in a direct manner. Similarly, diamond can be converted directly into graphite, but the reverse change cannot be carried out. Substances of this type are said to be **monotropic,** and the phenomenon is called **monotropy** (Greek: *one change*). To put the matter in very simple terms, it may be stated that monotropic substances have an imaginary transition point lying above the melting points of both solid forms; on heating, therefore, each solid will melt before the transition point is reached. The reversible transition observed with enantiotropic substances is thus not possible.

HEAT CAPACITIES OF SOLIDS

21a. Atomic Heat Capacity.—It was seen in § 3f that according to the law of Dulong and Petit, the product of the specific heat and atomic weight, i.e., the atomic heat, of solid elements has the almost constant value of 6.2 cal. per deg. per gram atom at ordinary temperatures. The specific heat of a solid is generally measured at constant (atmospheric) pressure, but, as with gases

(§ 121), this includes an allowance for the work done in expansion when the temperature is raised. It would appear, therefore, that atomic heat capacities should be compared at constant volume, rather than at constant pressure. Such a comparison was made by G. N. Lewis (1907), who found that, with the exception of the alkali metals, the atomic heats of seventeen solid elements are close to 5.9 cal. per deg. per gram atom, as may be seen from Table XXV. The

TABLE XXV. ATOMIC HEATS AT CONSTANT VOLUME AT $25°$ C IN CAL. DEG.$^{-1}$ G. ATOM^{-1}

Al	5.7 cal.	Au	5.9 cal.	Pt	5.9 cal.
Sb	5.9	Fe	5.9	Ag	5.8
Bi	6.2	Pb	5.9	Tl	6.1
Cd	5.9	Ni	5.9	Sn	6.1
Cu	5.6	Pd	5.9	Zn	5.6

deviations from constancy are appreciably less than for the atomic heat capacities at constant pressure.

The earliest explanation of the constant heat capacity of solid elements was based on the principle of the equipartition of energy (§ 12m). A monatomic solid element, such as a metal, could be regarded as consisting of a space lattice of independent atomic, or ionic, units vibrating about their respective equilibrium positions. Since there will be no preferred direction of vibration, the actual atomic vibrations may be regarded as taking place in three independent directions. As already seen, each mode of vibration makes a contribution of R to the molar heat capacity at constant volume; hence, the three types of vibration in the monatomic solid will give a molar (or atomic) heat capacity of $3R$, i.e., 5.96 cal. deg.$^{-1}$ g. atom^{-1}, in general agreement with experiment.

According to this simple argument the atomic heat capacity of a solid element should be independent of the temperature. However, all heat capacities increase with temperature, the effect being most marked with the light elements, such as beryllium, carbon and boron, whose atomic heats are exceptionally low at ordinary temperatures. Even the heat capacities of those elements which are usually about 6 cal. diminish at low temperatures, and so it is partly a matter of chance that they behave in an apparently normal manner. An important advance in the calculation of atomic heat capacities was made by A. Einstein (1907) by application of the quantum theory. In Einstein's treatment it was supposed that all the atoms vibrate with the same frequency, but with different amplitudes, that is, with different amounts (quanta) of vibrational energy. At very low temperatures the great majority of the atoms will have small or zero energy, and the contribution to the heat capacity will be small. As the temperature is raised, the vibrational energy of the atoms increases, and the heat capacity should increase toward the classical value of $3R$.

21b. Debye Theory of Atomic Heat Capacities of Solids.—Although the Einstein theory of the specific heat of elementary solids represented an improvement on the older theory, it predicted a falling off of the atomic heat with temperature that was greater that the observed rate. By introducing the postulate that the vibration frequencies of the atoms are not constant, but vary throughout the solid from zero to a certain maximum value which depends on the nature of the solid, P. Debye (1912) was able to derive an equation for the dependence of atomic heat capacity at constant volume upon the temperature. The essential conclusion drawn from the Debye equation, which is somewhat complicated, is that the heat capacity of an element at any temperature is determined by a quantity θ, called the **characteristic temperature,** defined by

$$\theta = \frac{h\nu_m}{k},\qquad(21.1)$$

where h is the Planck constant (§ 9b), k is the Boltzmann constant (§ 12d), and ν_m is the maximum vibration frequency of the atoms in the given solid.

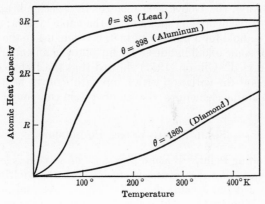

FIG. 48. Variation of atomic heat of elements with temperature

If the characteristic temperature θ is small, as it is for all the heavier elements, the heat capacity C_V should rise rapidly, at first, with increasing temperature, and then more slowly toward the limiting (classical) value of $3R$, as shown in Fig. 48. On the other hand, if θ is large, as it evidently is for carbon, boron and beryllium, the heat capacity increases slowly, but should attain the same limit of $3R$, as the temperature is raised. By ascribing an appropriate characteristic temperature to each element, it is possible to reproduce closely the actual variation of the heat capacity with temperature, over a considerable range, by means of the Debye equation. At very high temperatures the heat capacities of many metals exceed $3R$; this is attributed to the contribution of the mobile electrons (cf. § 19e, II) which increases as the temperature is raised.

An examination of Fig. 48 reveals the fortuitous nature of the Dulong and Petit law; it is because most solid elements have values of θ less than 400 that the atomic heat capacity has almost reached its limit of $3R$, i.e., 5.96 cal. deg.$^{-1}$ g. atom^{-1}, at ordinary temperatures, viz., about 300° K. If it had happened that the characteristic temperatures of most elements had been more than 400, the ordinary form of the Dulong and Petit law would not have held. However, an equivalent law would have been obeyed at higher temperatures when the heat capacities reached their (approximate) limiting values.

At very low temperatures the Debye equation for the atomic heat capacity reduces to the simple form

$$C_V = 464.5 \left(\frac{T}{\theta}\right)^3 \text{ cal. deg.}^{-1} \text{ g. atom}^{-1}. \tag{21.2}$$

Since the characteristic temperature θ is a constant for each substance, it follows from this result that at low temperatures the atomic heat capacity of a solid should be directly proportional to T^3, that is, to the cube of the absolute temperature. Further, as the temperature approaches the absolute zero, the heat capacity should tend toward zero. Both these expectations have been verified by experiment.

Strictly speaking, the Debye treatment of the specific heats of solids was meant to apply to elements crystallizing in the cubic system; nevertheless, it has been found to hold for a number of metals belonging to the hexagonal system, and also for some alkali halides. By introducing an empirical correction, G. N. Lewis and G. E. Gibson (1917) showed that the Debye equation could be used to represent the variation with temperature of the heat capacities of a number of nonmetallic elements and even of certain compounds.

Solid-Liquid-Vapor Equilibria

22a. The Melting Point.—*When a pure crystalline solid is heated it changes sharply into a liquid at a certain temperature*; this is the **melting point** of the solid, which has a definite value depending on the external pressure. If the liquid is cooled solidification will occur at the same temperature, which is the **freezing point,** for the given pressure; hence, for a pure substance the melting and freezing points are identical. The melting or freezing points that are usually quoted in tables are those for a pressure of one atmosphere, that is, 76 cm. of mercury.

The variation of the melting point with pressure was represented by R. Clausius (1850) by an expression analogous to the Clapeyron equation (§ 16d); as applied to the phenomenon of melting or **fusion,** as it is frequently called, the equation is written in the inverted form, thus

$$\frac{dT}{dP} = \frac{T(V_l - V_s)}{L_f}, \tag{22.1*}$$

where the fraction dT/dP represents the rate of variation with the external pressure P of the melting point T on the absolute scale. The quantities V_l and V_s are the molar volumes of liquid and solid, respectively; L_f is the **molar heat of fusion,** that is, the (latent) heat taken up by 1 mole of the solid

---

*A capital P is used here to represent the external pressure, whereas in § 16d the lower case p was employed for vapor pressure; see also, equations (22.4) and (22.5), below.

when it melts. Instead of using the molar volumes and molar heat of fusion, equation (22.1) may be written in the alternative form

$$\frac{dT}{dP} = \frac{T(v_l - v_s)}{l_f}, \tag{22.2}$$

where v_l and v_s are the specific volumes and l_f is the heat of fusion per gram. It is important to note that since the specific volumes of solid and liquid at the melting point are not very different, it is not permissible to neglect one in comparison with the other. The simplification (§ 16e) that was possible with equation (16.4), as applied to vaporization, cannot therefore be made here.

Problem: The specific volumes of liquid water and of ice are 1.0001 and 1.0907 cc. per gram, respectively, at the normal freezing point, 0° C; the heat of fusion is 79.8 cal. per gram. Calculate the change in melting point of ice for an increase of 1 atm. in the external pressure.

Since v_l is 1.0001 and v_s is 1.0907, it follows that $v_l - v_s$ is -0.0906 cc. g.$^{-1}$; the value of l_f is 79.8 cal. g.$^{-1}$, i.e., $79.8 \times 4.184 \times 10^7$ ergs g.$^{-1}$. If these results were inserted in equation (22.2) it would give the change of melting point for an increase of 1 c.g.s. unit, i.e., 1 dyne cm.$^{-2}$, in the pressure. Since the change is required for an increase of 1 atm., i.e., $76.0 \times 13.595 \times 980.7 = 1.013 \times 10^6$ dynes cm.$^{-2}$, it is necessary to multiply by the latter figure. Thus, since the freezing point of water is 0° C, the value of T is 273.2° K, and hence,

$$\frac{dT}{dP} = \frac{273.2 \times (-0.0906) \times 1.013 \times 10^6}{79.8 \times 4.184 \times 10^7} = -0.0075° \text{ per atm.}$$

The negative sign implies that an increase of 1 atm. in the pressure, in the vicinity of 0° C, *lowers* the melting point of ice by 0.0075°.

Increase of pressure results in a small decrease in the melting point of ice; the reason why there is a decrease, rather than an increase, is because $v_l - v_s$ in equation (22.2) is negative, that is, because the specific volume of the solid (ice) is greater than that of the liquid (water) at the freezing point. In other words, the melting point decreases with increasing pressure because the density of the solid is less than that of the liquid. Water is one of the few substances exhibiting this unusual behavior of expansion on freezing. *For most substances the solid has a larger density than the liquid, and hence increase of pressure brings about an increase in the melting point.* Because the densities, and hence the specific volumes, of the solid and liquid are never very different at the melting point, $v_l - v_s$ is always small numerically; the effect of pressure on the melting point is consequently also small.

In addition to water, the elements bismuth and antimony expand when they solidify; it is this property which makes the latter an important constituent of "type metal." For both of these elements the melting point decreases as the external pressure is increased, as is to be expected.

22b. Vapor Pressures of Solids: Sublimation.—A solid, like a liquid, has a definite vapor pressure at each temperature; with increasing temperature the vapor pressure increases, and the variation can be represented by a curve similar to that for a liquid (see Fig. 24). Such a curve is called a **sublimation**

curve, the term **sublimation** being used to indicate direct conversion of solid to vapor without the intervention of liquid. Similarly, under suitable conditions, a vapor may be condensed directly to a solid; this occurs, in general, upon cooling the vapor provided its pressure is less than the vapor pressure of the solid at its melting point. For example, the vapor pressure of ice at 0° C is about 4.6 mm. of mercury, and if the partial pressure of water vapor is less than this value, sudden cooling will result in the direct deposition of solid from the vapor. It is in this manner that the formation of frost occurs in nature. If the partial pressure of the water vapor exceeds 4.6 mm., then liquid will first be formed when the temperature is lowered.

The purification of such substances as iodine, sulfur, naphthalene and benzoic acid by sublimation is rendered feasible by the fact that the vapor pressures of these solids have quite high values. If a cold surface is placed in the vapor, the partial pressure of the latter at the surface is maintained below that at the melting point, and condensation occurs directly from the vapor to the solid. Further, because of the high vapor pressure, the rate at which the solid sublimes is sufficiently great to make the sublimation process a practical one.

A particularly interesting case of sublimation is that of carbon dioxide. At the melting point ($-56.5°$ C) the equilibrium vapor pressure of the solid is 5 atm.; this means that solid carbon dioxide cannot be converted into liquid unless the pressure exceeds this value. At ordinary atmospheric pressures, therefore, solid carbon dioxide passes directly into gas, at all temperatures, without the intermediate formation of liquid. It is this fact which represents one of the advantages of "dry ice" as a refrigerant, and accounts for the use of the adjective "dry."

The change from solid to vapor, like that from liquid to vapor, or from solid to liquid, is accompanied by an absorption of heat; this is the (latent) **heat of sublimation**, L_s. It is related to the heats of vaporization (L_v) and of fusion (L_f) in the following manner

$$L_s = L_f + L_v, \qquad (22.3)$$

where the three values must refer to the same temperature. In other words, the same quantity of heat (L_s) must be supplied to convert 1 mole of solid directly to vapor as would be required first to melt the solid (L_f) and then to vaporize it (L_v). This result is in accord with the law of conservation of energy (§ 23b).

The influence of temperature on the vapor pressure of a solid is given by a form of the Clapeyron equation which is exactly equivalent to (16.4); thus, the rate of variation of the vapor pressure with temperature, i.e., dp/dT, is expressed by

$$\frac{dp}{dT} = \frac{L_s}{T(V_v - V_s)} = \frac{l_s}{T(v_v - v_s)}, \qquad (22.4)$$

where V_v and V_s are the molar volumes, and v_v and v_s are the specific volumes, of vapor and solid, respectively, at the temperature T; l_s is the heat of sublimation per gram. As in § 16e, it is permissible here to neglect V_s in comparison with V_v, since the density of the vapor is very much less than that of the solid; hence, equation (22.4) may be converted into a form analogous to the Clapeyron-Clausius equation (16.8), viz.,

$$\frac{d \ln p}{dT} = \frac{L_s}{RT^2}. \tag{22.5}$$

This expression may be integrated in the manner already described. The chief use of equations (22.4), (22.5), and those obtained by integration, is that they permit the value of the heat of sublimation of the solid to be calculated at any temperature from a knowledge of the sublimation vapor pressures in the vicinity of that temperature.

22c. The Triple Point.—The sublimation curve for the solid form of a substance and the vapor pressure curve for the liquid may be combined in one diagram, as represented in Fig. 49. In this figure OA indicates the variation of the vapor pressure of the liquid with temperature, while OB, the sublimation curve, shows the change in the vapor pressure of the solid form. As seen in § 16a, OA extends only as far as the critical temperature; on the other hand, OB can continue down to the absolute zero, although it may change in direction if there is a change in the crystalline form of the solid. The vapor pressure curve OA indicates the conditions, as given by the temperature and pressure, for a system of liquid and vapor to be in equilibrium (see § 16a); similarly, the sublimation curve OB gives the conditions under which the solid and vapor are in equilibrium with one another. The two curves meet at O, and hence at this point, known as the **triple point,** the three physical states of the substance, viz., solid, liquid and vapor, must be able to coexist. It will be seen shortly that the term triple point is used, in general, for *the temperature and pressure at which any three states (phases) of a given substance are in equilibrium.*

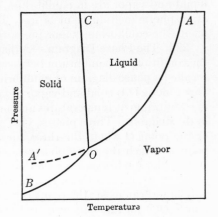

Fig. 49.   Phase equilibrium diagram

The conditions of equilibrium of solid and liquid, which is simply another way of referring to the variation of the melting point with pressure, are represented by the third curve, viz., OC, in Fig. 49. This must obviously pass through the triple point O, where solid, liquid and vapor are in equilibrium. The direction of the slope of the line OC depends on whether increase of pressure raises or lowers the melting point; in Fig. 49 the curve slopes to the left, implying that the melting point is lowered by an increase of pressure, e.g., water, bismuth or antimony. For other substances, e.g., sulfur, to be considered below, the curve slopes to the right. In any case, because of the small variation of the melting point with pressure, the line OC is always almost vertical; its slope has been exaggerated in Fig. 49 for the sake of clarity.

Since solid and liquid are in equilibrium at the triple point, this is obviously a melting point. It is not, however, the normal melting point of the solid at 1 atm. pressure, but *the melting point at the pressure of the vapor which is in equilibrium with the solid and liquid*. For example, the normal freezing point of water at 1 atm. pressure is 0° C, and hence the triple point must be somewhere in this vicinity; the vapor pressure of water, or of ice, is then about 4.6 mm. The triple point of water is thus the melting point of ice, or the freezing point of water, at a pressure of 4.6 mm., rather than at 760 mm., i.e., 1 atm.; the pressure is thus 755.4 mm. *less* than atmospheric. It was seen above that increase of pressure by 1 atm. lowers the melting point of ice by 0.0075°; hence, a decrease of 755.4 mm., which is very nearly 1 atm., must raise the melting point by 0.0075°. The triple point of water, at which solid, liquid and vapor are in equilibrium, should thus be 0.0075° *above* the normal atmospheric melting point of ice. This result has been confirmed by experiment, the equilibrium vapor pressure being then 4.58 mm. of mercury.*

22d. The Phase Diagram.—A diagram, such as that in Fig. 49, which gives the conditions of equilibrium between various forms, or phases, of a substance is called a **phase diagram** or **equilibrium diagram.** Two phases, viz., liquid and vapor along OA, solid and vapor along OB, and solid and liquid along OC, are in equilibrium at temperatures and pressures represented by each of the curves in the diagram. Three phases, viz., solid, liquid and vapor, are in equilibrium at the point O where the three curves meet; there is consequently only one point at which the three phases can coexist. In the areas lying between the curves, the conditions are such that there can be but one phase, either solid or liquid or vapor. In the region between the curves OA and OC, for instance, only liquid can exist; the temperatures are seen to be above the melting point (curve OC) for any pressure, and the pressures are greater than the equilibrium vapor pressure of the liquid (curve OA) for any temperature. Similarly, the region to the left of the curves OB and OC represents temperatures and pressures at which solid only exists, while in the area below OB and OA the conditions are such that the only possible phase is the vapor. The phase diagram for a single substance, such as water, thus consists of three regions in each of which only one phase can occur; these regions meet at three lines, along which two phases can be in equilibrium, and the three lines intersect at a single point where all three phases can coexist.

If a liquid, free from dust particles, is cooled in a clean, smooth vessel, the temperature can frequently be brought below the normal freezing point without solid appearing; the liquid is then said to be **supercooled.** At each

* The temperature of 0.0000° C is defined as the freezing point of water, *saturated with air*, at 1 atm. pressure; this is actually 0.0024° below the freezing point of pure water, free from dissolved air, at 1 atm. The melting point of ice is thus strictly +0.0024° C at 1 atm. pressure; the triple point temperature of water is consequently +0.0024 + 0.0075 = +0.0099° C.

temperature the supercooled liquid will have a definite vapor pressure, and the vapor pressure curve is actually a continuation, without a break, of the curve for the liquid. For example, the curve OA' in Fig. 49 represents the variation with temperature of the vapor pressure of the supercooled liquid. The liquid-vapor system along OA' is said to be in a condition of **metastable equilibrium.** The term "metastable" is used to describe *a definite equilibrium which is, nevertheless, not the most stable equilibrium at the given temperature;* the change from metastable to stable equilibrium frequently occurs either spontaneously or upon addition of the stable phase. Thus, the introduction of a small amount of solid to the supercooled liquid along OA' will usually result in immediate separation of solid from the liquid; the temperature and pressure will change to a point on the stable curve OB. In any event, the realizable portion of the metastable curve OA' is generally short, because a point is soon reached at which the supercooled liquid undergoes spontaneous change to the stable, i.e., solid, state. It may be remarked that although a liquid can be supercooled, the corresponding metastable extension of the curve BO, to indicate the superheating of a solid without melting, has been observed only in a few special instances.

22e. The Phase Rule.—The general conditions of equilibrium for one, two and three phases, as derived from the experimental results represented in Fig. 49, as well as many other cases of equilibrium, can be conveniently summarized in the form of a simple generalization known as the **phase rule.** This rule was deduced theoretically by J. Willard Gibbs (1876), but its application to physical chemistry may be attributed to H. W. B. Roozeboom (1884 *et seq.*). Before the rule can be stated it will be necessary to define and explain the terms involved, viz., phase, component and degrees of freedom (or variance).

A **phase** is defined as *any homogeneous and physically distinct part of a system which is separated from other parts of the system by definite bounding surfaces.* Ice, liquid water and water vapor, for example, are three phases, as has been already implied; each is physically distinct and homogeneous, and there are definite boundaries between them. In general, every solid constitutes a separate phase, although a solid solution (§ 20a) is a single phase no matter how many individual substances it may contain. In the same way, one liquid layer constitutes one phase, whether it is a pure substance or a mixture. Two liquid layers in contact represent two phases, for there is a definite surface of separation between them. A gas or a mixture of gases always constitutes one phase, for the system is homogeneous, and there is obviously no bounding surface between the different gases that may be present.

The number of **components** is *the smallest number of independent chemical constituents by means of which the composition of every possible phase can be expressed.* The water system, for example, consists of one component; the composition of each of the three phases, viz., solid, liquid and vapor, can be expressed in terms of the component H_2O. Any system consisting of a single chemical individual is always a one-component system. The treatment in the present chapter will be restricted to such systems; those involving two or more components will be considered in Chapter XII. A salt and water, to quote a simple case, form a familiar type of two-component system. For example, copper sulfate and water can yield solid $CuSO_4 \cdot 5H_2O$, $CuSO_4 \cdot 3H_2O$, $CuSO_4 \cdot H_2O$ and $CuSO_4$ anhydrous, ice, solution and vapor as separate phases, but the composition of each phase can be expressed in terms of two independent components, such as $CuSO_4$ and H_2O. One component would be insufficient to express *every possible* composition, e.g., that of a solution, and three would be more than necessary.

Another type of system is that represented by the equilibrium

$$CaCO_3 \rightleftharpoons CaO + CO_2,$$

solid   solid   gas

in which there are three phases, viz., solid $CaCO_3$, solid CaO, and gaseous CO_2. It might appear, at first sight, that there are three components, viz., $CaCO_3$, CaO and CO_2, but it is evident that these substances are *not independent*, as required by the definition of component, given above; thus, $CaCO_3$ is really equivalent to $CaO + CO_2$. The two components may consequently be taken as CaO and CO_2, so that the composition of the calcium carbonate phase can be represented as $x\ CaO + x\ CO_2$, that of the calcium oxide as $y\ CaO + 0\ CO_2$, while that of the carbon dioxide gas phase is $0\ CaO + z\ CO_2$. The two components might equally have been chosen as $CaCO_3$ and CaO, when the composition of the gas phase would be given by $z\ CaCO_3 - z\ CaO$. As in the previous example, one component, e.g., $CaCO_3$, would be insufficient, for it would not then be possible to express the composition of every phase, e.g., the gas phase. The actual nature of the components is not important; it is their number that is significant, and this should always be the same for a given system if the components are chosen properly.

The number of **degrees of freedom** or **variance** of a system is *the number of variable factors, such as temperature, pressure and concentration, which need to be fixed in order that the condition of a system at equilibrium may be completely defined.* Systems possessing one, two, three, etc., degrees of freedom are said to be univariant, bivariant, trivariant, etc., respectively. The significance of the number of degrees of freedom may be readily explained by means of Fig. 49. A system consisting of *one phase only*, e.g., solid, liquid or vapor, is represented by an area in the diagram; in order to define such a system completely, it is obviously necessary to state both the temperature and pressure of the phase. The temperature or pressure alone is insufficient to define the condition of the system, for two coordinates, i.e., temperature and pressure, are required to specify precisely any point lying in a particular region of Fig. 49. A system of a single phase thus has two degrees of freedom; that is to say, it is a bivariant (one-component) system.

When two phases are in equilibrium, however, the conditions must correspond to a point on one of the lines OA, OB or OC in Fig. 49; in order to define such a system completely, it is sufficient to state either the temperature or the pressure. The fact that the system must be represented by a point situated on a definite curve makes it unnecessary to state both temperature and pressure; by arbitrarily fixing one of these variables, the other is automatically determined by the appropriate curve OA, OB or OC. The one-component system of two phases in equilibrium is thus univariant, having one degree of freedom. Finally, since three phases can coexist only at the triple point, the system will then have no degrees of freedom, that is, it will be invariant; the fact that the three given phases are in equilibrium means that the system must be at the triple point, and it is consequently unnecessary to prescribe either the temperature or pressure.

Provided the equilibrium between the phases is not influenced by gravity, by electrical or magnetic forces, or by surface action, and only by temperature, pressure and concentration, then the number of degrees of freedom (F) of the system is related to the number of components (C) and of phases (P) present at equilibrium by the phase rule

$$F = C - P + 2. \tag{22.6}$$

For a one-component system, such as that of water, C is 1, and so the phase rule takes the form

$$F = 3 - P \qquad \text{or} \qquad F + P = 3.$$

That is to say, the sum of the number of phases and of the degrees of freedom should always be equal to 3, if the system is in equilibrium. This conclusion is in agreement with the results just derived from Fig. 49. It was seen that for a system consisting of one phase only (P = 1) there are two degrees of freedom (F = 2); when two phases are in equilibrium (P = 2), the number of degrees of freedom is reduced to one (F = 1); finally, at the triple point, where three phases are in equilibrium (P = 3), there are no degrees of freedom (F = 0). It is evident that the sum of P and F is equal to 3 in each case, as required by the phase rule.

22f. Phase Equilibria in the Sulfur System.—An interesting, but somewhat more complicated illustration of a one-component system is provided by the element sulfur. As seen in § 20b, this substance exists in two different crystalline forms, and its behavior may be taken as typical of an enantiotropic system. Below the transition temperature of 95.6° C, at ordinary pressures, the rhombic form of sulfur is stable, while above it the stable modification belongs to the monoclinic system. The complete phase diagram, representing the temperature and pressure conditions of equilibrium between the various possible phases of sulfur, is shown schematically in Fig. 50; AB is the vapor pressure curve of the rhombic crystals, and BC is that of the monoclinic form. The point B is the transition temperature under a pressure equal to the vapor pressure at that temperature. The melting points of the two forms are at E (113°) and C (119°), respectively; the former can be realized only if sulfur is heated rapidly, so that the transition to the monoclinic form does not occur at B. The curves BF and CF show the effect of pressure on the transition point and on the melting point of the monoclinic solid, respectively; in other words, they give the conditions of equilibrium of the rhombic and monoclinic forms (along BF), and of the monoclinic solid and liquid (along CF). It will be observed that both curves slope to the right so that the transition point and the melting point of monoclinic sulfur increase with increasing pressure. However, because the former happens to change more rapidly than the latter the two curves meet at the point F.

The dashed curves BE, EC and EF represent metastable equilibria; BE is the metastable vapor pressure curve for the rhombic system which can be realized if this substance is heated rapidly past the transition point. The system then continues along ABE, without a break, instead of passing on to the stable curve BC. At E, the metastable melting point, the sulfur liquefies,

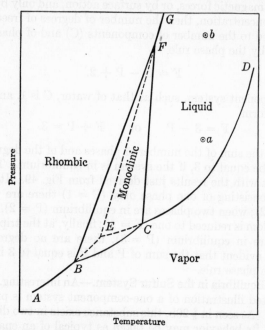

Fig. 50.   Phase equilibrium diagram of sulfur (schematic)

and EC is the metastable vapor pressure curve of the liquid; this is continuous with the stable vapor pressure curve CD for the liquid form. The influence of pressure on the melting point of the rhombic solid is indicated by EFG, and the portion EF gives the conditions of the metastable equilibrium between rhombic sulfur and the liquid form. The curve FG, which is a continuation of EF, represents stable equilibrium between these two phases of sulfur.

An examination of Fig. 50 shows that the sulfur system has four observable triple points at each of which three phases are in equilibrium; the four points and the corresponding phases are as follows:

B Rhombic, monoclinic, vapor
C Monoclinic, liquid, vapor
E Rhombic, liquid, vapor
F Rhombic, monoclinic, liquid

These are all invariant points, with no degrees of freedom, since the very fact of the three particular phases being in equilibrium automatically fixes both the temperature and pressure of the system.

The diagram also shows six curves representing the conditions of equilibrium of two phases; these are:

$AB(E)$	Rhombic, vapor
BC	Monoclinic, vapor
$(E)CD$	Liquid, vapor
BF	Rhombic, monoclinic
$(E)FG$	Rhombic, liquid
CF	Monoclinic, liquid.

There are thus six kinds of univariant system that are possible; in each case there is one degree of freedom only. By specifying the nature of the two phases that are in equilibrium, and the temperature *or* the pressure, the state of the system will be completely defined. The nature of the phases indicates which of the six curves is applicable, and one coordinate, i.e., temperature or pressure, will then exactly identify the particular point representing the system that is being described.

The four single phases of sulfur, namely rhombic solid, monoclinic solid, liquid and vapor, each occupy a region of the equilibrium diagram, as indicated in Fig. 50. A single phase is thus a bivariant system, that is, one with two degrees of freedom, since both temperature and pressure must be given if the exact state of the system is to be defined.

It will be observed from Fig. 50 that if rhomic sulfur is heated rapidly, so that the transition to the monoclinic form does not occur, the phase diagram consists of but three lines, AE, ED and EG, meeting at the triple point E. Such a diagram is then, as it should be, of the same form as Fig. 49, for a one-component system with a single solid phase.

Attention may be called to the triple point F, at 151° C and 1290 atm.; it owes its existence to the fact that the slopes of the curves BF and CF are such that they intersect, as mentioned previously. The result is that the region of stability of monoclinic sulfur is definitely bounded by the lines BF, CF and BC, and this form of solid sulfur cannot exist at temperatures and pressures lying outside the triangular region BCF. Above F, therefore, solid sulfur can be obtained in one solid modification only, namely rhombic crystals. If liquid sulfur represented by a point such as a in Fig. 50 is cooled at approximately constant pressure, monoclinic solid will separate out when the conditions fall on the curve FC. On the other hand, if the initial temperature and pressure of the liquid are given by a point such as b, then upon cooling, at constant pressure, rhombic crystals must form along FG. It is believed that the large crystals of rhombic sulfur found in nature were obtained by direct crystallization from the liquid under these conditions, that is, at temperatures above 151° C and pressures in excess of 1290 atm.

22g. Application of Phase Rule to the Sulfur System.—It is of interest to turn now to the phase rule to see if it correctly summarizes the experimental facts given above. Four phases of sulfur are possible, but the phase rule shows that they cannot all coexist in stable equilibrium; thus, since C = 1, for a one-component system, if P = 4, the value of F would be given by C − P + 2 = 1 − 4 + 2, i.e., −1, which is impossible. This result means that one factor too many has been specified, and this is the fourth phase. Three phases of a one-component system should thus be the maximum number that can be in equilibrium at one time, as is actually found to be the case. For three phases in equilibrium P is 3, and since C is 1, it follows from the phase rule that

$$F = 1 - 3 + 2 = 0.$$

Systems consisting of three phases must therefore be invariant, and should be represented by definite individual points on the pressure-temperature diagram. It can consequently be deduced, without knowing anything further about the experimental behavior, that there should be four such definite points, i.e., triple points, on the phase diagram of sulfur, since there are four ways of combining four different objects three at a time. Writing R for rhombic solid, M for monoclinic solid, L for liquid and V for the vapor of sulfur, these combinations are (i) R-M-V, (ii) M-L-V, (iii) R-L-V, and (iv) R-M-L, corresponding with the four observed triple points, B, C, E and F, respectively, in Fig. 50.

For systems involving two phases in equilibrium, P is 2, and since C is 1, it is seen that

$$F = 1 - 2 + 2 = 1,$$

so that such systems are univariant and hence will be represented by lines (or curves) on the pressure-temperature phase diagram. For sulfur there should be six such curves, for there are six different ways of combining two out of four phases; thus, (i) R-V, (ii) M-V, (iii) L-V, (iv) R-M, (v) R-L, and (vi) M-L. This is also in accord with the experimental results already described.

According to the phase rule, one phase alone, i.e., P = 1 and C = 1, will be a bivariant system, with two degrees of freedom, i.e., temperature and pressure. A single phase should thus occupy an area on the equilibrium diagram, and for sulfur there should be four such areas corresponding to the four possible phases. The predictions of the phase rule are consequently here also in agreement with observation (Fig. 50). The phase rule thus defines correctly, although only qualitatively, the conditions of equilibrium between the possible phases in one-component systems, such as those of water and sulfur.

It should be pointed out that the phase rule is unable to distinguish between a metastable system, e.g., the point E, and a stable system, for the former still represents an equilibrium, even if not the most stable. Further, the phase rule predicts the *possible* equilibria, but it cannot tell whether they are observable or not. For example, the triple point F in the sulfur system can be observed because the lines BF and CF happen to slope toward one another with increasing temperature. If the slopes had been in the opposite direction, the lines would have intersected at some very low pressure, in the region where vapor alone is stable. The triple point would then be possible theoretically, as predicted by the phase rule, but it could not be realized experimentally.

READING REFERENCES

1. **Principles of X-ray analysis.** Reinmuth, *Journal of Chemical Education*, **7**, 138, 860, 1373 (1930).
2. **X-Rays in science and industry.** Clark, *ibid.*, **8**, 625 (1931).
3. **Crystal Chemistry.** Stillwell, *ibid.*, **10**, 590, 667 (1933); **11**, 159 (1934). More advanced series, *ibid.*, **13**, 415, 469, 521, 566 (1936); **14**, 34, 131, (1937).
4. **Nature of the metallic state.** Fernelius and Robey, *ibid.*, **12**, 53 (1935).
5. **Crystal structure research.** Huggins, *ibid.*, **13**, 560 (1936).
6. **Construction of crystal models.** Scattergood, *ibid.*, **14**, 140 (1937); Seymour, *ibid.*, **15**, 192 (1938); Hauser, *ibid.*, **18**, 164 (1941).
7. **Introduction to the phase rule.** Deming, *ibid.*, **16**, 215 (1939).
8. **Structure of long chain polymers.** Fuller and Baker, *ibid.*, **20**, 3 (1943).

REVIEW QUESTIONS

1. Describe the characteristic properties of the crystalline form.
2. Explain the seven crystal systems.
3. State and explain the law of rational indices. What are the Miller indices of a crystal face?
4. What is meant by the space lattice of a crystal? Draw a unit cell for space lattices of the following types: (*a*) simple cubic, (*b*) face-centered cubic, (*c*) body-centered cubic.
5. What are the lattice planes of a crystal? What is meant by the (100), (110) and (111) planes of a cubic lattice? How do the spacings of these three planes differ?
6. Derive the Bragg equation for the diffraction of X-rays by reflection from a crystal.
7. Explain the principles involved in the use of X-rays to study crystal structure.
8. Describe the use of X-rays to determine the crystal lattice of sodium chloride. Draw a portion of the lattice.
9. How has X-ray diffraction of crystals been used to determine (*a*) the wave length of X-rays, (*b*) the Avogadro number?
10. Outline the powder and rotating crystal methods for the study of crystals by X-rays.
11. Draw the space lattices for diamond and graphite. How do they account for some of the physical properties of these forms of carbon?
12. Explain what is meant by (*a*) a macromolecule, (*b*) a layer lattice.
13. Show how the tendency to complete the electron octet accounts for the difference in the structures of the elements from groups IV to VII in the periodic table.
14. Explain the essential characteristics of the structure of metals. What is meant by the metallic bond?
15. How do the relative dimensions of the atoms (or ions) account for the structures of compounds of AX and AX$_2$ types?
16. State some of the results obtained by the X-ray study of organic compounds.
17. Describe the internal structure of (*a*) a liquid, (*b*) a glass.
18. What is meant by isomorphism? Explain the requirements of the tests for isomorphous substances.
19. What is polymorphism? Describe and name the two chief types of polymorphism.
20. State the theoretical reason why the atomic heats of elements at constant volume are approximately constant. What modifications have been made by Einstein and Debye?

21. How do the heat capacities of solid elements depend on temperature? What special relationship holds at low temperatures?

22. State the form of the Clapeyron equation as applied by Clausius to fusion, and illustrate some of its uses.

23. What is meant by sublimation? How do the Clapeyron and Clapeyron-Clausius equations apply?

24. What is a triple point? Illustrate with reference to water.

25. Explain the difference between stable and metastable equilibrium by reference to the vapor pressure curves of liquid water and ice.

26. Define and explain the meanings of phase, component, and degree of freedom.

27. State the phase rule and apply it to account for the conditions of equilibrium of the phases of water.

28. Draw and explain the equilibrium phase diagram of sulfur.

29. Show how the phase rule is able to account for the phase diagram of the sulfur system.

PROBLEMS

I

1. The second order X-ray reflections from the (100), (110) and (111) lattice planes of sodium chloride occur at angles of 11.85°, 17.0° and 10.5°, respectively. Show that these results are in agreement with a face-centered crystal lattice.

2. The first order reflection for the (100) plane of potassium chloride was observed at a glancing angle of 5.3°. Calculate the glancing angles for the second order reflections from the (100), (110) and (111) planes.

3. Using the K_α rays of palladium, wave length 0.58×10^{-8} cm., the glancing angle for the first order X-ray reflection from the (100) face of potassium chloride, which has the same structure as sodium chloride, is 5.3°. The density of potassium chloride is 1.98 g. per cc. Calculate the Avogadro number.

4. The specific heat of copper at $-253°$ C is 0.0031 cal. deg.$^{-1}$ g.$^{-1}$. Calculate the specific heat at 10° K. What is the Debye characteristic temperature?

5. The melting point of acetic acid at 1 atm. pressure is 16.6° C, and the heat of fusion is 43.2 cal. per g. The specific volumes of liquid and solid at the melting point are 0.9315 and 0.7720 cc. per g., respectively. Estimate the melting point of acetic acid at a pressure of 5 atm.

6. The vapor pressure of ice is 4.579 mm. at 0° C and 4.217 mm. at $-1°$ C. The specific volume of vapor may be derived from the ideal gas law, while that of the solid may be neglected. Calculate the heat of sublimation of ice. Using the accepted value of the heat of fusion, 79.8 cal. per g., determine the heat of vaporization of water at 0° C.

II

1. The glancing angle for the first order X-ray reflection from a given lattice plane is 9.8°. Calculate the glancing angles for the second and third order reflections from the same plane.

2. The density of rubidium chloride, which has a NaCl-type of lattice, is 2.76, while that of sodium chloride is 2.17 g. per cc. The first order reflection from the (110) plane of the latter, with given X-rays, occurs at 8.4°; calculate the glancing angles for first order reflections from the (100), (110) and (111) planes of rubidium chloride.

3. Magnesium oxide has a face-centered cubic lattice of the NaCl-type, and its density is 3.66 g. per cc. The first order reflection of X-rays from the (100) plane occurred at an angle of 8.0°; calculate the wave length of the X-rays.

4. The Debye characteristic temperature of silver is 214; determine the specific heat of this element at 10° and 15° K in cal. deg.$^{-1}$ g.$^{-1}$.

5. The melting point of bismuth, which is 271° C at 1 atm. pressure, decreases at the rate of 3.55° per 1000 atm. increase of pressure. The heat of fusion is 12.6 cal. per g. Calculate the difference between the specific volume of liquid and solid bismuth at its melting point, and state which is the larger.

6. The vapor pressure of solid iodine at 20° C is 0.202 mm. while at 30° C it is 0.471 mm. Evaluate the approximate heat of sublimation in cal. per g. in the given temperature range.

CHAPTER VII

THERMODYNAMICS AND THERMOCHEMISTRY

The First Law of Thermodynamics

23a. Thermodynamics and Energy.—The **energy** of a body may be defined broadly as its capacity for doing work. This energy may take various forms, such as kinetic energy of a body in motion, potential energy due to position, heat energy as measured by the temperature, electrical energy, chemical energy, etc. Chemical and physical processes are almost invariably accompanied by energy changes, and results of considerable importance have been obtained by studying the laws underlying these changes. It is this study of energy transformation which constitutes the subject matter of **thermodynamics.** Although thermodynamics may appear to be somewhat theoretical in nature, the two laws have led to results of fundamental importance to chemistry, as well as to physics and engineering.

All forms of energy have the dimensions of mass $\times$ (length)^2 $\times$ (time)$^{-2}$ and they can be expressed in terms of the same units, viz., ergs, joules or calories. The unit of energy in the c.g.s. system is the **erg**; it is equal to the work done when a force of 1 dyne acts through a distance of 1 cm., the dyne being the force which acting on a mass of 1 gram gives it an acceleration of 1 cm. per sec. per sec. Since the erg is so small, a subsidiary unit, the **absolute joule,** is defined as 10^7 ergs. The **international joule,** which is based on electrical measurements (§ 48a), differs slightly from the absolute joule; it is equivalent to 1.0002×10^7 ergs.

There is a natural tendency for other forms of energy ultimately to change into heat, e.g., chemical energy may change into heat as the result of a chemical reaction, electrical energy is converted into heat when an electric current is passed through a resistance, mechanical energy is transformed into heat by friction, and so on. It is, therefore, convenient to express the values of other forms of energy in terms of the unit of heat energy, that is, in terms of calories (§ 12l). Careful experiments initiated by J. P. Joule, between 1848 and 1873, have shown that *when a definite amount of any form of energy, particularly mechanical and electrical energy, is converted into heat, a perfectly definite number of calories of heat is always produced.* There is thus an exact relationship between heat and other forms of energy; this is known as the **mechanical equivalent of heat.** At the present time the calorie is defined in terms of its equivalent in mechanical work; thus, *1 calorie is taken as equal to 4.184 $\times$ 10^7 ergs*, or 4.1833 international joules.

Problem: Calculate the energy in calories required to increase the volume of a substance by 1 cc. against a pressure of 1 atm.

As seen in § 12l, the work done in the expansion is equal to $P\Delta V$, where ΔV is the increase of volume. In the present case, the values of both pressure and the volume change should first be expressed in c.g.s. units; 1 atm. pressure is equivalent to 1.013×10^6 dynes cm.$^{-2}$ (§ 11f, II), and since ΔV is 1 cc., it follows that

$$\text{Work done} = 1.013 \times 10^6 \times 1 = 1.013 \times 10^6 \text{ dynes cm., i.e., ergs.}$$

To convert into calories, this is divided by 4.184×10^7 ergs; the result is 0.0242 cal.

Three forms of energy, in particular, are frequently encountered in chemical thermodynamics; these are heat energy, mechanical work due to a volume change, and electrical energy. In each case the magnitude of the energy is obtained as a product of two factors, viz., an **intensity factor** and a **capacity factor.** In the case of heat energy the intensity factor is the temperature in degrees, while the capacity factor is the heat capacity, usually expressed in calories per degree, for a given mass; the product of these two quantities gives the heat energy in calories. For mechanical work accompanying expansion or contraction, the two factors are the pressure and the volume change, respectively, in agreement with the results arrived at in § 12l. If the pressure is in dynes per sq. cm., and the volume change is in cc., the work will be in ergs, which can be readily converted into calories if desired, as shown in the problem given above. The intensity factor for electrical energy is the electrical pressure or electromotive force, and the capacity factor is the quantity of electricity, i.e., the product of the strength of the electric current and the time for which it is passed (§ 44b). If the electromotive force is in volts, the current strength in amperes and the time in seconds, so that the quantity of electricity is in coulombs, the electrical energy is given in volt-coulomb units. The (absolute) volt and the (absolute) ampere are so defined that the volt-coulomb is equal to 10^7 ergs, i.e., 1 absolute joule.

23b. Conservation of Energy: The First Law of Thermodynamics.—Many attempts have been made from time to time to realize "perpetual motion," that is, the continuous production of mechanical work without supplying an equivalent amount of energy from another source. The failure of all such efforts has led to the universal acceptance of the **principle of conservation of energy.** This principle has been stated in many forms, but essentially they amount to the fact that *although energy can be converted from one form to another, it cannot be created or destroyed* or, alternatively, *whenever a quantity of one kind of energy is produced, an exactly equivalent amount of other kinds must disappear.* It is evident that perpetual motion, in the generally accepted sense of the term, would be contrary to this principle, for it would involve the creation of energy. Further, the exact equivalence of mechanical or electrical work and heat, as found by Joule and others, is a necessary consequence of the same principle.

The law of conservation of energy is purely the result of experience, no exception to it having as yet been found. The assumption that it is of universal applicability is the basis of the **first law of thermodynamics.** This law can be stated in any of the ways given above for the principle of the conservation of energy, or else it may be put in the following form. *The total energy of a system * and its surroundings must remain constant, although it may be changed from one form to another.*

Attention may be called to the equivalence of mass and energy referred to in § 2b, I; this introduces something of a limitation upon the principle of the conservation of energy, for energy can be produced by the destruction of mass. Strictly speaking the laws of conservation of mass and of conservation of energy are part of a comprehensive law, according to which the combined mass and energy of an isolated system remains constant. One form of energy may be changed into another form, and mass may be converted into energy, or vice versa, but the total mass and energy must be unchanged. In the problems treated by thermodynamics there is no conversion of mass into energy, and so the simple forms of the principle of conservation of energy may be regarded as adequate.

23c. Internal Energy.—Consider any system—gas, liquid or solid—represented by the state A in Fig. 51, where the coordinates are the factors, e.g.,

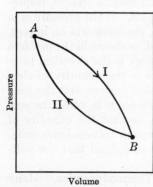

Fig. 51. Energy change independent of path

pressure and volume, upon which the energy of the system depends.† Suppose the conditions are now altered so that the system moves to B by the path I, and is then brought back again to the state A by a different path II. It is a direct consequence of the first law of thermodynamics that the total energy change in path I must be identical with that in path II; if it were not, perpetual motion would be possible. Imagine, for instance, that the increase in energy involved in path I were greater than the decrease in returning by II; then by carrying out the process $A \rightarrow B$ by path I and $B \rightarrow A$ by path II, the system would be brought back to its original state, but there would be a net gain of energy. In other words, energy would have been created without the disappearance of an equivalent amount of another kind. Since this is contrary to all human experience, it must be concluded that the resultant energy in passing from the state A to the state B depends only on the initial and final conditions, and is independent of the path followed in going from A to B.

According to the foregoing arguments, it is possible to ascribe a definite amount of energy to any given state of a system, which is determined only by

* The term "system" refers to a specified portion of matter containing a definite amount (or amounts) of the substance (or substances) under consideration.

† The state of a system depends upon its pressure, volume and temperature; these three quantities are related, in principle, by an equation of state, so that for a given pressure and volume the temperature of a definite mass is automatically fixed.

the state itself, and not by its previous history. If E_A represents the energy in the state A and E_B that in the state B, then the increase in energy ΔE in passing from A to B is given by

$$\Delta E = E_B - E_A, \qquad (23.1)$$

and is independent of the path taken. The same conclusion is sometimes expressed in mathematical language by stating that in an infinitesimal process the small change dE is a **complete** or **exact differential**. The quantity E, which depends on pressure, volume and temperature, is generally called the **internal energy** or, in brief, the energy of the system; it includes all forms of energy, other than those resulting from the position of the system in space, for this is assumed to remain constant. The *actual* value of the internal energy is generally not known, but this is of no significance, for thermodynamics is concerned primarily with *changes* in energy, and these are measurable quantities.

The internal energy is an example of an **extensive property**, for it is determined not only by the state of the system but also by the amount (or amounts) of the substance (or substances) concerned. If the quantity of material in the system is changed, the extensive property is changed in a proportionate manner. Volume is perhaps one of the simplest illustrations of such a property. Extensive properties may be distinguished from **intensive properties**, such as density, surface tension, refractive index, viscosity, vapor pressure, etc., for these are independent of the quantity of material concerned.

23d. Internal Energy, Work and Heat Changes.—When a system changes from one state to another, it may perform some kind of external work, such as mechanical work of expansion, electrical work, etc.; this work is represented by the symbol w. If work is done *by* the system, e.g., as in the expansion of a gas, the value of w is positive, but if work is done *on* the system, e.g., as in compression of a gas, the value is negative. Further, the system may absorb or evolve heat in the course of the change, and this quantity of heat is indicated by q. If the system *absorbs* heat q is positive, but if heat is *evolved* the value is negative. It is seen, therefore, that when a system changes from the state A to the state B, its internal energy increases by ΔE, while at the same time the system does work w and absorbs heat q.

According to the first law of thermodynamics the *total* energy of system and surroundings must remain unaltered as the system changes from A to B; hence the increase ΔE in the internal energy of the system must be exactly equivalent to the energy q absorbed from the surroundings in the form of heat, less the energy w lost to the surroundings in the form of external work done by the system; thus,

$$\Delta E = q - w. \qquad (23.2)$$

For an infinitesimal stage in a change which the system is undergoing, equation (23.2) may be written in the form

$$dE = dq - dw, \qquad (23.3)$$

where dE represents the small increase in the internal energy, dq is the small quantity of heat absorbed, and dw is the small amount of external work done at the same time by the system.

It was seen above that dE is a complete or exact differential, for the change in E depends only on the final and initial states of the system and is independent of the path taken between them; however, dq and dw are not exact differentials, for their values generally depend on the nature of the path. This fact may be conveniently represented by writing δw and δq in place of dw and dq, so that equation (23.3) becomes

$$dE = \delta q - \delta w. \tag{23.4}$$

Although δq and δw are not exact differentials, their difference must nevertheless be an exact differential.

Although the work w and heat q are both forms of energy, there are good reasons for considering them separately, as in the foregoing treatment. While all forms of work can be converted completely into one another and into heat, it is not possible to convert heat completely into work. This experimental fact forms the basis of the second law of thermodynamics (Chapter VIII).

23e. Reversible Processes: Maximum Work.—A system can be changed from a particular state A to another state B under a great variety of conditions. In every case the energy change is definite, but the heat and work changes may or may not be so. From the thermodynamic standpoint one of the most important of such conditions is that *the change be carried out infinitesimally slowly, so that the system is always in temperature and pressure equilibrium with its surroundings.* A process carried out in this manner is said to be **thermodynamically reversible,*** for all changes that occur in any part of the process are exactly reversed when the process is carried out in the reverse manner. It may be remarked that a reversible process is to be regarded as a hypothetical or imaginary ideal process, for in actual practice complete thermodynamic reversibility cannot be realized. Nevertheless, in spite of its hypothetical nature, the concept is of great value.

As a simple illustration of a reversible process, imagine a liquid in equilibrium with its vapor in a vessel closed by a frictionless piston and placed in a constant temperature bath. The pressure on the piston will then be equal to the vapor pressure of the liquid at the given temperature. If the external pressure is increased by an infinitesimally small amount the vapor will condense, but the condensation will occur so slowly that the heat evolved will be taken up by the bath; the temperature of the system will not rise and the pressure above the liquid will remain constant. Although condensation of the vapor is taking place, the system at every instant is in a state of equilibrium. Similarly, if the external pressure is made just smaller than the vapor pressure, the liquid will vaporize at a very slow rate, and again the temperature and pressure will remain constant. Although the system is changing, since evapo-

---

* The term "reversible" as applied to a thermodynamic process must not be confused with the use of the same adjective in connection with the so-called reversible chemical reactions which take place simultaneously in both directions (see Chapter X).

ration is occurring, the changes may be regarded as a series of equilibrium states. Rapid evaporation or condensation, resulting from rapid expansion or compression, will lead to temperature changes and to considerable disturbance of equilibrium; such processes are not thermodynamically reversible.

The work done in reversible vaporization or condensation is a definite quantity which can be readily calculated. It was seen in § 12l that the work done by a system in expansion is equal to the product of the external pressure and the increase of volume. In the case under consideration the pressure is p, the vapor pressure of the liquid at the given temperature, and this remains constant throughout the process. If ΔV is the increase of volume in the course of the reversible evaporation, then the work done by the system is equal to $p\Delta V$. For the corresponding condensation, the same amount of work would be done by the system. Since ΔE and w have definite values, it follows that q must also be definite for reversible evaporation or condensation; this is actually equal to the heat of vaporization at the specified temperature.

An important characteristic of infinitesimally slow or reversible processes is that if they take place at constant temperature, i.e., if they are **isothermal,** such as is the case for reversible evaporation, the work obtainable from the system not only has a definite value, it is also the **maximum work** possible for the given change. If, for example, in the evaporation process just considered, the external pressure had been released suddenly, instead of extremely slowly, the work done by the system would have been less than $p\Delta V$, since the pressure against which the expansion occurred would be smaller than the vapor pressure p. This coincidence of the conditions for maximum work and for reversibility, at constant temperature, is of importance to thermodynamics.

23f. Maximum Work in Isothermal Expansion of a Gas.—In the course of the reversible evaporation process considered in the preceding section, the pressure of the vapor remained constant because it was always in equilibrium with the liquid. When a gas expands at constant temperature the pressure must decrease during the course of the expansion. In order to carry out such a process as expansion or compression in a reversible manner, it must be supposed that *the external pressure continuously adjusts itself so as to be always less than the pressure of the gas by an infinitesimally small amount.* Under these ideal conditions the expansion takes place infinitesimally slowly, and the work done by the gas is the reversible work of expansion for the given process.

If P is the pressure of the gas at any stage in the expansion, the external pressure will then be $P - dP$, where dP is a very small quantity. The work δw done, when the gas increases its volume by an extremely small amount dV, is then equal to the product of the external pressure $P - dP$ by this volume change; thus,

$$\delta w = (P - dP)dV.$$

Neglecting the very small product $dPdV$, it follows that

$$\delta w = PdV. \tag{23.5}$$

The total work w done in the expansion will be the sum of a continuous series of PdV terms, with the value of P decreasing steadily, and the volume increasing, from the initial state to that in the final state. The result may be expressed mathematically by means of the integral

$$w = \int_{V_1}^{V_2} PdV, \tag{23.6}$$

where V_1 is the initial volume of the gas and V_2 is the final volume after expansion; this is the general equation for the reversible work of expansion.

The reversible work integral in equation (23.6) may be evaluated if the relationship between pressure and volume is known. For example, if the system consists of *1 mole of an ideal gas*, then $PV = RT$, and P is equal to RT/V; hence, if the expansion is isothermal, i.e., the temperature remains constant, insertion of this result in equation (23.6) gives

$$w = RT \int_{V_1}^{V_2} \frac{dV}{V} = RT \ln \frac{V_2}{V_1}. \tag{23.7}$$

Since the *isothermal, reversible work* is also the maximum work it is a simple matter to calculate the maximum work done by 1 mole of an ideal gas in expanding between two prescribed volumes. It is obvious from equation (23.7) that the result depends only on the final and initial volumes, apart from the constant temperature, and is independent of the path, provided it is a reversible one.

Problem: Calculate the maximum work in ergs for the expansion of 1 mole of an ideal gas from a volume of 10 liters to 20 liters (exactly) at 25° C.

Since V_2/V_1 in equation (23.7) is a ratio it is independent of the units of volume; the value of w is then given in the same units as R (strictly RT). The maximum work is required in ergs mole^{-1}, and so R is taken as 8.314×10^7 ergs deg.$^{-1}$ mole^{-1}. The absolute temperature T is $273.2 + 25.0 = 298.2°$ K, and hence,

$$w = 8.314 \times 10^7 \times 298.2 \ln \tfrac{2}{1}$$

$$= 8.314 \times 10^7 \times 298.2 \times 2.303 \log 2 = 1.719 \times 10^{10} \text{ ergs mole}^{-1}.$$

An alternative form of equation (23.7) is often convenient; since the gas is supposed to be ideal, $P_1V_1 = P_2V_2$ at constant temperature, and so V_2/V_1 is equal to P_1/P_2. If the appropriate substitution is made in equation (23.7), the maximum work of isothermal expansion for 1 mole of an ideal gas is given by

$$w = RT \ln \frac{P_1}{P_2}. \tag{23.8}$$

An ideal gas possesses an important property which may be considered here. Experiments with actual gases show that as a gas approaches ideal behavior the Joule-Thomson effect (§ 13b) becomes less marked, and it is possible to state that an ideal gas will show no Joule-Thomson effect at any temperature. This is to be expected, since the molecules of an ideal gas are supposed not to attract one another or to have appreciable volume. Since the Joule-Thomson effect is zero, there is no absorption or liberation of heat, i.e., $q = 0$, when an ideal gas is allowed to expand into a vacuum.* At the same time, no work is done, i.e., $w = 0$, since the external pressure, in the vacuum, is zero. It follows, therefore, from the first law equation (23.2), that ΔE will then also be zero. In other words, the expansion of an ideal gas, at constant temperature, is accompanied by no change in the internal energy. This result can be generalized in the statement that, *at any constant temperature, the internal energy of a given quantity of an ideal gas is independent of its volume.*

For an ideal gas, therefore, ΔE *is zero for any isothermal expansion or compression*, irrespective of whether it takes place into a vacuum or in any other way; hence it follows from equation (23.2) that for such processes

$$q = w, \tag{23.9}$$

so that the heat absorbed is equal to the work done by the ideal gas. Combination of equation (23.9) with equations (23.7) and (23.8) thus gives

$$q = RT \ln \frac{V_2}{V_1} = RT \ln \frac{P_1}{P_2} \tag{23.10}$$

for the heat absorbed in the isothermal, reversible expansion of 1 mole of an ideal gas from the state 1 to the state 2.

23g. Adiabatic Changes.—A special type of process which can be carried out reversibly is that known as an **adiabatic change** (Greek: *not passing through*); such a change is *one in which no heat enters or leaves the system*. In the adiabatic expansion or compression of a gas, for example, the temperature and volume are supposed to adjust themselves automatically to the proper equilibrium values as the pressure is changed; the process is then thermodynamically reversible. The essential difference between isothermal and adiabatic processes is that in the former case the temperature remains constant and the system exchanges heat with its surroundings, while in the latter case there must be no heat exchange and so the temperature will be altered. In an adiabatic expansion of a gas the system does external work, and since no heat can be taken up, the necessary energy comes from the kinetic energy of the molecules; the decrease in the value of the latter means that there is a fall in the temperature. Similarly, in an adiabatic compression the temperature of the gas will rise.

In mathematical terms, the characteristic of an adiabatic change is that q, the heat absorbed, is zero; hence, by equation (23.2),

$$\Delta E = -w. \tag{23.11}$$

---

* This experiment, with an actual gas, was carried out by J. L. Gay-Lussac (1807) and by J. P. Joule (1845), who observed no detectable temperature change. A small change should have been detected, however, if the apparatus had been sensitive enough, since a real gas (not an ideal one) was used.

The work $-w$ done *on* the system in an adiabatic process is thus equal to the increase of internal energy, and hence it is a definite quantity that is independent of the path, provided it is adiabatic in nature.

It can be shown by means of the first law of thermodynamics that if the pressure and volume of an ideal gas is changed adiabatically from P_1 and V_1 to P_2 and V_2, then

$$P_1V_1^{\gamma} = P_2V_2^{\gamma}, \tag{23.12}$$

where γ is the ratio of the heat capacities of the gas at constant pressure and constant volume (§ 121). If the initial temperature is T_1 and the final temperature is T_2, then for 1 mole of the gas,

$$P_1V_1 = RT_1 \quad \text{and} \quad P_2V_2 = RT_2,$$

and using these expressions to eliminate V_1 and V_2 from equation (23.12), it is found that

$$\left(\frac{T_2}{T_1}\right)^{\gamma} = \left(\frac{P_2}{P_1}\right)^{\gamma-1}$$

or

$$\gamma \log \frac{T_2}{T_1} = (\gamma - 1) \log \frac{P_2}{P_1}. \tag{23.13}$$

By means of this equation the change of temperature in an adiabatic expansion or compression, from pressure P_1 to pressure P_2, can be readily calculated.

23h. Heat Changes at Constant Pressure and Constant Volume.—There are certain simple conditions under which the heat absorbed in a particular process becomes a definite quantity, depending only on the initial and final states. Writing equation (23.2) in the form

$$q = \Delta E + w,$$

it will be supposed, as in the case of most thermodynamic changes which do not involve electrical processes, that the work w is only mechanical work of expansion or contraction. It is then possible to replace w in general by $P\Delta V$, where P is the constant external pressure and ΔV is the increase of volume, so that

$$q = \Delta E + P\Delta V. \tag{23.14}$$

For a process occurring at constant volume ΔV is zero, and then equation (23.14) becomes

$$q_V = \Delta E, \tag{23.15}$$

so that the heat absorbed in a constant volume process is equal to the increase of internal energy in that process. Since the latter depends only on the initial and final states of the system, the same must apply to the heat change at constant volume.

At constant pressure, equation (23.14) is written as

$$q_P = \Delta E + P\Delta V. \tag{23.16}$$

The increase of internal energy ΔE is equal to $E_2 - E_1$, where the subscripts 1 and 2 are used, as before, to indicate initial and final states, respectively; similarly, the volume increase ΔV may be replaced by $V_2 - V_1$, so that

$$q_P = (E_2 - E_1) + P(V_2 - V_1)$$
$$= (E_2 + PV_2) - (E_1 + PV_1). \qquad (23.17)$$

Since P and V are properties of state of the system, it follows that the quantity $E + PV$, like the internal energy E, is dependent only on the state of the system, and not on its previous history. This extensive property is called the **heat content** and is represented by the symbol H, i.e.,

$$H = E + PV,$$

so that equation (23.17) for constant pressure P can be put in the form

$$q_P = H_2 - H_1 = \Delta H. \qquad (23.18)$$

The increase ΔH in the heat content of the system at constant pressure is thus equal to the heat absorbed under these conditions; the latter quantity, like ΔH, will consequently depend on the initial and final states of the system, and not on the path taken in the process.

A useful thermodynamic equation is obtained by combining equations (23.16) and (23.18); the result is

$$\Delta H = \Delta E + P\Delta V, \qquad (23.19)$$

and since ΔH at constant pressure is equal to q_P, while ΔE at constant volume is equal to q_V, it follows that

$$q_P = q_V + P\Delta V. \qquad (23.20)$$

It is seen from this equation that the heat absorbed in a process occurring at constant pressure exceeds that for the same process taking place at constant volume by the amount $P\Delta V$, where P is the constant pressure and ΔV is the accompanying increase of volume. The reason for this difference lies in the fact that when the volume is constant the system does no external mechanical work of expansion or compression; the heat absorbed q_V is then merely equal to the increase ΔE in the internal energy of the system. If the pressure is kept constant, however, there may be a volume change and external work may be done; in this event the heat absorbed q_P will not only go to increase the internal energy but an additional amount, equivalent to the work done, i.e., $P\Delta V$, will be required.

It should be noted that equations (23.19) and (23.20), like other thermodynamic equations, automatically include proper allowance for the signs of the various quantities involved. For example, if the process at constant pressure is accompanied by a *decrease* of volume, ΔV will be negative and ΔH (or q_P) will then be less than ΔE (or q_V). Because of the contraction in volume at constant pressure work is done *on* the system, which thus gains energy; hence, a smaller amount of heat q_P will be required from an outside source at constant pressure than the amount q_V required at constant volume. As will be seen shortly, in some processes there is no volume change even when they are carried out at constant pressure; in such cases $P\Delta V$ is zero, and ΔE and ΔH, that is, q_V and q_P, are then identical. The foregoing considerations apply to processes of all kinds, both physical and chemical, provided the external work is only mechanical work due to a volume change.

23i. Heat Capacities at Constant Pressure and Constant Volume.—It was seen in § 12l that the heat capacity of a system is defined as the heat required to raise the temperature of the system by one degree. Since the heat capacity C may vary with temperature, it is preferable to define it in the differential form, viz.,

$$C = \frac{\delta q}{dT},$$

where δq may be regarded as the heat absorbed when the temperature is raised by dT degrees. Since δq, as already seen, is not in general an exact differential, the heat capacity will be an indefinite quantity unless certain conditions, particularly constant volume or constant pressure, are specified. The heat capacity at constant volume is then given by

$$C_V = \frac{\delta q_V}{dT}, \tag{23.21}$$

while for constant pressure,

$$C_P = \frac{\delta q_P}{dT}. \tag{23.22}$$

According to equation (23.15), the heat q_V absorbed at constant volume is equal to the increase ΔE in the internal energy under the same conditions; for a small change the corresponding quantities are δq_V and dE_V, and so the heat capacity at constant volume, defined by equation (23.21), may be written as

$$C_V = \left(\frac{dE}{dT}\right)_V. \tag{23.23}$$

The internal energy E, as seen in § 23c, is a function of both pressure and volume, and so the subscript V is used to indicate that in this case the volume is maintained constant. The heat capacity at constant volume is consequently equal to the rate of increase of the internal energy with temperature, also at constant volume.

In an exactly similar manner, utilizing the fact that q_P, the heat absorbed, is equal to ΔH at constant pressure, by equation (23.18), and utilizing equation (23.22) for the heat capacity, it can be shown that

$$C_P = \left(\frac{dH}{dT}\right)_P. \tag{23.24}$$

The heat capacity of a system at constant pressure is consequently represented by the rate of increase of the heat content with temperature at constant pressure.

THERMOCHEMISTRY

24a. Heat Changes in Chemical Reactions.—The subject of **thermochemistry** *deals with the heat changes accompanying chemical reactions.* As will be seen shortly, the laws of thermochemistry are based largely on the principle of the conservation of energy or the first law of thermodynamics. Different substances have different amounts of internal (chemical) energy, and so the total energy of the products of a reaction is generally different from that of the reactants; hence, the chemical change will be accompanied by the liberation or absorption of energy, which may appear in the form of heat. If heat is liberated in the reaction the process is said to be **exothermic,** but if heat is absorbed it is described as **endothermic.** The majority of, although not all, chemical reactions which go to virtual completion at ordinary temperatures are exothermic in character, since they are accompanied by an evolution of heat.

If a chemical reaction is associated with a volume change, as is particularly the case for many processes involving the combination of gases, the magnitude of the heat change will depend on whether the reaction is carried out at constant pressure or at constant volume, as seen in § 23h. Since many reactions normally occur at constant (atmospheric) pressure it is the usual practice to record heat changes by quoting the value of q_P, the heat absorbed at constant pressure; this may, of course, be identified with ΔH, the increase of heat content under the same conditions. This quantity is often referred to as the **heat of reaction;** it represents *the difference in the heat contents of the reaction products and of the reactants, at constant pressure, and at a definite temperature, with every substance in a definite physical state.* From the value of q_P (or ΔH) the value of q_V (or ΔE) can be readily determined if the volume change ΔV at the constant pressure P is known, as will be seen below.

The heat change accompanying a reaction, for example, that between solid carbon (graphite) and gaseous oxygen to yield carbon dioxide gas, is represented in the form of a thermochemical equation, as follows:

$$C(s) + O_2(g) = CO_2(g) \qquad \Delta H = -94.00 \text{ kcal.}$$

This means that when 12.01 grams of solid carbon (graphite) and 32 grams of gaseous oxygen react completely to yield 44.01 grams of gaseous carbon dioxide, at constant pressure, there is a *decrease* in heat content, since ΔH is negative, of 94.00 kilocalories (kcal.), i.e., 94,000 calories. It is the general practice in modern thermochemical work to express results in kilocalories because the statement of heat changes in calories implies an accuracy greater than is usually attainable experimentally. It should be noted, incidentally, that the ΔH (or ΔE) values always refer to *completed* reactions, appropriate allowance having been made, if necessary, if the process does not normally go to completion. Further, the results are for the reaction taking place with all the reactants and products *at a definite temperature,* which should be specified (see § 24h). The symbols *g*, *l* and *s*, placed in parentheses after the formula, indicate whether the substance taking part in the reaction is gas, liquid or solid.   Reactions taking place in aqueous solution are indicated by the symbol *aq;* thus,

$$HCl(aq) + NaOH(aq) = NaCl(aq) + H_2O \qquad \Delta H = -13.70 \text{ kcal.}$$

Strictly speaking the use of *aq* implies that the reaction is occurring in such dilute solution that the addition of further water causes no detectable heat change.

A negative value of ΔH, as in the two instances quoted above, means that the reaction is accompanied by a decrease in heat content; that is to say, the heat content of the products is less than that of the reactants, at a specified temperature.   In other words, the reaction, at the given temperature, is associated with an evolution of heat.   It follows, therefore, that when ΔH is negative the reaction is exothermic; similarly, if ΔH is positive the process is endothermic.   The same conclusions can be reached directly, of course, from the fact that q_P, which is equal to ΔH, is the *heat absorbed* in the reaction; hence, when ΔH is negative heat is actually evolved.

24b. Heats of Reaction at Constant Pressure and Constant Volume.— The relationship between heats of reaction at constant pressure and at constant volume is given by equations (23.19) or (23.20); thus,

$$\Delta H = \Delta E + P\Delta V, \qquad (24.1)$$

where ΔV is the increase of volume when the reaction occurs at the constant pressure P.   As explained previously, $P\Delta V$ represents the external work done by the system when the reaction is carried out at constant pressure.   For a process involving solids or liquids only, the volume change ΔV is generally so small that it can be neglected, and ΔH and ΔE may be taken as being equal, within the limits of experimental error.   If gases are concerned, however, the change in volume may be quite large; in this case the difference between ΔH and ΔE may be readily calculated with sufficient accuracy in the following manner.   If n_A is the number of moles of gaseous reactants, i.e., in the initial state of the reaction, and n_B is the number of moles of gaseous products, i.e., in the final state, the process is accompanied by an increase of $n_B - n_A = \Delta n$ moles of gas.   If V is the volume of 1 mole of any gas, at the given temperature and pressure, then the increase of volume ΔV in the reaction will be equal to $V\Delta n;$ equation (24.1) may therefore be written as

$$\Delta H = \Delta E + PV\Delta n.$$

If the gases are assumed to behave ideally, PV is equal to RT, and hence

$$\Delta H = \Delta E + RT\Delta n. \qquad (24.2)$$

From this expression the difference between ΔH and ΔE can be obtained without difficulty.

Problem: When 1 mole of liquid benzene is completely burnt in oxygen to form liquid water and carbon dioxide gas, ΔH is -783.4 kcal. at $18°$ C.   Calculate the heat of this reaction at constant volume at the same temperature.

For this reaction,

$$C_6H_6(l) + 7\tfrac{1}{2}O_2(g) = 3H_2O(l) + 6CO_2(g) \qquad \Delta H = -783.4 \text{ kcal.}$$

The number of moles n_A of gaseous reactants is 7.5, while the number of moles n_B of gaseous products is 6, so that $\Delta n = n_B - n_A = -1.5$. The temperature T is $273 + 18 = 291°$ K, and R may be taken as 2 cal, or 2×10^{-3} kcal., deg.$^{-1}$ mole^{-1}; hence,

$$\Delta H = \Delta E - (2 \times 10^{-3} \times 291 \times 1.5)$$

$$-783.4 = \Delta E - 0.87$$

$$\Delta E = -782.5 \text{ kcal.}$$

This is the heat (absorbed) of reaction at constant volume. (Combustion reactions, such as that of benzene, are generally studied at constant volume; the calculation given above is then reversed so as to derive ΔH from ΔE.)

For reactions involving solids or liquids only, such as

$$Al(s) + Fe_2O_3(s) = Al_2O_3(s) + 2Fe(s)$$

$$Na(s) + \tfrac{1}{2}Br_2(l) = NaBr(s),$$

and for reactions in which the same number of gaseous molecules occur on both sides of the equation, e.g.,

$$C(s) + O_2(g) = CO_2(g)$$

$$H_2(g) + Cl_2(g) = 2HCl(g),$$

the change of volume is negligible, and hence the heats of reaction at constant pressure and constant volume may be taken as identical.

24c. Heat of Formation.—The **heat of formation** of a compound is usually defined as *the increase of heat content* (ΔH) *when 1 mole of the substance is formed from its elements.* It is generally postulated that the elements are in their so-called **standard states,** that is, in their stable forms at ordinary temperature and 1 atm. pressure. From the data already given for the reaction between carbon and oxygen to form carbon dioxide, it is evident that the heat of formation of this gas is -94.00 kcal. It may be noted in this connection that graphite is the stable form of carbon, and hence it represents the standard state of this element. The heat of formation of gaseous hydrogen iodide may be obtained from the thermochemical equation

$$H_2(g) + I_2(s) = 2HI(g) \qquad\qquad \Delta H = 11.90 \text{ kcal.}$$

Since two moles of hydrogen iodide are formed, the heat of formation is 5.95 kcal. The heats of formation of a number of compounds at 18° C are recorded in Table XXVI.*

The heats of formation of the compounds taking part in a chemical reaction have an important connection with the heat of reaction. For purposes of

---

* In the most recent work, it has become the practice to record the values at 25° C; the difference from those at 18° C is often insignificant.

TABLE XXVI. HEATS OF FORMATION IN KCAL. AT $18°$ C

Substance	ΔH	Substance	ΔH
$H_2O(l)$	−68.4 kcal.	$C_2H_4(g)$	+11.0 kcal.
$HCl(g)$	−22.0	$C_2H_6(g)$	−20.5
$HBr(g)$	−8.6	$C_2H_2(g)$	+53.9
$HI(g)$	+6.0	$CH_3OH(l)$	−50.9
$CO(g)$	−26.4	$C_2H_5OH(l)$	−66.2
$CO_2(g)$	−94.0	$CH_3COOH(l)$	−117.0
$NH_3(g)$	−11.0	$C_6H_6(l)$	+12.3
$NO(g)$	+21.6	$PbO(s)$	−52.5
$H_2S(g)$	−5.2	$HgO(s)$	−21.6
$SO_2(g)$	−70.9	$AgCl(s)$	−30.3
$CH_4(g)$	−17.9	$NaCl(s)$	−98.3

calculation the following convention is adopted: *The heat contents of all elements in their standard states are arbitrarily taken to be zero at all temperatures.*[*] *The heat content of a compound is then equal to the heat of formation ΔH*, as may be seen by considering a simple case. The heat of formation of hydrogen chloride from its elements is represented by

$$H_2(g) + Cl_2(g) = 2HCl(g) \qquad \Delta H = -44.0 \text{ kcal.}$$

or, dividing through by two,

$$\tfrac{1}{2}H_2(g) + \tfrac{1}{2}Cl_2(g) = HCl(g) \qquad \Delta H = -22.0 \text{ kcal.}$$

There is here a decrease of 22.0 kcal. in the heat content of the system when 1 mole of hydrogen chloride is formed from its elements. If the heat contents of the latter are taken as zero, in accordance with the convention, the heat content of hydrogen chloride must obviously be −22.0 kcal., in agreement with the statement made above.

By means of the two rules, viz., the heat content of an element is zero and that of a compound is equal to its heat of formation, the heat change in a reaction can be readily calculated. Considering the chemical change

$$CH_4(g) + 2O_2(g) = CO_2(g) + 2H_2O(l),$$
$$-17.9 \qquad 0 \qquad -94.0 \qquad -2 \times 68.4$$

and writing the heat content of each species below its formula, it is seen that the total heat content of the products is $-94.0 - (2 \times 68.4)$, and that of the reactants is $-17.9 + 0$; the increase ΔH of the heat content in the reaction is thus given by the difference between these two quantities, viz.,

$$\Delta H = \{-94.0 - (2 \times 68.4)\} - (-17.9 + 0) = -212.9 \text{ kcal.}$$

Instead of using the heats of formation to calculate the heat of reaction, the procedure may be reversed; the heat of formation of a compound taking part

[*] It should be clearly understood that since thermochemical quantities are always *differences* in heat content, i.e., ΔH, it is quite immaterial what basis of reference is chosen for calculation purposes, *provided it is always the same.* The one given above has the great merit of simplicity and convenience, but *it does not imply that the heat contents of elements are actually zero.*

in a reaction can be calculated, provided the values for all the other compounds and the heat of reaction are known.

Problem: The heat change of the reaction

$$Al_2Cl_6(s) + 6Na(s) = 2Al(s) + 6NaCl(s)$$

is -256.2 kcal. The heat of formation of solid NaCl is -98.3 kcal.; calculate the heat of formation of solid Al_2Cl_6.

The heat contents of the reactants and products may be written as follows:

$$Al_2Cl_6 + 6Na = 2Al + 6NaCl$$
$$x \qquad\quad 0 \qquad 0 \qquad -6 \times 98.3$$

where x is the heat content, and hence the heat of formation, of Al_2Cl_6. For the whole reaction ΔH is -256.2 kcal.; consequently,

$$-256.2 = \{0 + (-6 \times 98.3)\} - (x + 0)$$

$$x = -333.6 \text{ kcal.}$$

24d. Heat of Combustion.—Organic compounds containing carbon, hydrogen and oxygen can be burnt in oxygen to give carbon dioxide and water as the sole products; *the heat change accompanying the complete combustion of 1 mole of a compound* is called the **heat of combustion.** From data given in preceding sections, it will be seen that the heat of combustion of benzene is -783.4 kcal., and that of methane is -212.9 kcal. The values for a number of familiar compounds are quoted in Table XXVII; the products are gaseous carbon dioxide and liquid water in each case.

TABLE XXVII.   HEATS OF COMBUSTION PER MOLE IN KCAL. AT $18°$ C

Substance	ΔH	Substance	ΔH
Methane (g)	-212.8 kcal.	Acetic acid (l)	-207.0 kcal.
Ethylene(g)	-337.0	Ethyl acetate (l)	-538.0
Ethane (g)	-373.0	Benzene (l)	-783.4
Acetylene (g)	-310.5	Benzoic acid (s)	-771.8
Methanol (l)	-173.7	Naphthalene (s)	-1231.0
Ethanol (l)	-327.0	Sucrose (s)	-1350.0

The heats of combustion of both liquid and gaseous hydrocarbons are important from the industrial standpoint, and the term **calorific value** is frequently used for the heat of combustion of a substance used as a fuel. The heats of combustion of fat, carbohydrate and protein, which are the essential energy constituents of food, are of significance in nutritional studies.

The heat of combustion of a compound may be used to calculate its heat of formation, utilizing the procedure described in § 24c; this fact is of particular value, for the heats of formation of many organic compounds cannot be determined by direct experiment.

Problem: The heat of combustion ΔH of liquid ethanol is -327.0 kcal. at $18°$ C; calculate its heat of formation from the elements in their standard states at this temperature.

The equation for the combustion may be written out, and the conventional heat contents of oxygen, gaseous carbon dioxide and liquid water may be inserted in the usual manner; thus,

$$C_2H_5OH(l) + 3O_2(g) = 2CO_2(g) + 3H_2O(l)$$
$$x \qquad 0 \qquad -2 \times 94.0 \quad -3 \times 68.4$$

For the over-all reaction, ΔH is -327.0 kcal.; hence,

$$-327.0 = \{(-2 \times 94.0) + (-3 \times 68.4)\} - (x + 0)$$

$$x = -66.2 \text{ kcal.}$$

Thus,

$$2C(s) + 3H_2(g) + \tfrac{1}{2}O_2(g) = C_2H_5OH(l) \qquad \Delta H = -66.2 \text{ kcal.}$$

24e. Thermochemical Laws.—The calculation of heats of reaction and of heats of formation given above have all been tacitly based on the principle of conservation of energy, and hence on the first law of thermodynamics. Two important thermochemical laws are based on the same fundamental principle. According to the observations of A. L. Lavoisier and P. S. Laplace (1780), *the quantity of heat which must be supplied to decompose a compound into its elements is equal to the heat evolved when that compound is formed from its elements.* In other words, the heat of decomposition of a compound is numerically equal to its heat of formation but of opposite sign. This experimental result is, of course, in direct agreement with the first law of thermodynamics, for otherwise it would be possible to create heat energy by making a compound from its elements and then decomposing it, or vice versa. An important consequence of the law of Lavoisier and Laplace is that thermochemical equations can be reversed, provided the sign of the heat term is changed, its numerical value remaining the same. This rule applies not only to reactions involving a compound and its constituent elements, e.g.,

$$S(s) + O_2(g) = SO_2(g) \qquad\qquad \Delta H = -70.9 \text{ kcal.}$$
$$SO_2(g) = S(s) + O_2(g) \qquad\qquad \Delta H = 70.9 \text{ kcal.,}$$

it can be extended to reactions of all types, thus

$$CO_2(g) + H_2(g) = CO(g) + H_2O(g) \qquad \Delta H = -11.2 \text{ kcal.}$$
$$H_2O(g) + CO(g) = CO_2(g) + H_2(g) \qquad \Delta H = 11.2 \text{ kcal.}$$

The second important law of thermochemistry was discovered experimentally by G. H. Hess (1840); it is known as **Hess's law** or **the law of constant heat summation.** This law states that *the resultant heat change in a chemical reaction is the same whether it takes place in one or several stages.* This means that the *net* heat of reaction, *at constant pressure or constant volume*, depends only on the initial and final states, and not on the intermediate states through which the system may pass. The law of Hess is thus a direct consequence of the first law of thermodynamics. It has been seen that according to this law the quantities ΔE and ΔH, which are equal to the heats of reaction at constant volume and constant pressure, respectively, are dependent only on the initial and final states of the system, and are independent of the path connecting them.

The great practical value of Hess's law lies in the fact that, as a consequence of this law, thermochemical equations can be added and subtracted like algebraic equations; as a result heats of reaction which cannot be determined by direct experiment can be calculated from other thermochemical data. The heat of formation of hydrogen bromide gas was determined from the measured heats of the following seven reactions; the data are for constant pressure throughout.

$$\Delta H$$

(i)	$KBr(aq) + \frac{1}{2}Cl_2(g) = KCl(aq) + \frac{1}{2}Br_2(aq)$	-11.5 kcal.
(ii)	$\frac{1}{2}H_2(g) + \frac{1}{2}Cl_2(g) = HCl(g)$	-22.0
(iii)	$HCl(g) + aq = HCl(aq)$	-17.5
(iv)	$KOH(aq) + HCl(aq) = KCl(aq) + H_2O$	-13.7
(v)	$KOH(aq) + HBr(aq) = KBr(aq) + H_2O$	-13.7
(vi)	$\frac{1}{2}Br_2(g) + aq = \frac{1}{2}Br_2(aq)$	-0.5
(vii)	$HBr(g) + aq = HBr(aq)$	-19.9

[It will be noted that processes (iii), (vi) and (vii) represent the addition of large amounts of water to hydrogen chloride, bromine and hydrogen bromide, respectively; the corresponding heat changes are the **heats of solution** of the respective substances (see § 24g).] If the thermochemical equations (ii), (iii), (iv) and (vi) are added together, and from the total the sum of (i), (v) and (vii) is subtracted, the result is

$$\frac{1}{2}H_2(g) + \frac{1}{2}Br_2(g) = HBr(g) \qquad \Delta H = -8.6 \text{ kcal.}$$

The heat of formation of hydrogen bromide, from gaseous hydrogen and bromine, is thus -8.6 kcal. per mole.

Since all thermochemical calculations are based on the first law of thermodynamics, the law of constant heat summation may be used as an alternative to the procedure described in § 24c and § 24d for calculating heats of formation. For example, to calculate the heat of formation of liquid ethanol, use is made of the three thermochemical equations:

(i)	$C_2H_5OH(l) + 3O_2(g) = 2CO_2(g) + 3H_2O(l)$	$\Delta H = -327.0$ kcal.
(ii)	$C(s) + O_2(g) = CO_2(g)$	$\Delta H = -94.0$
(iii)	$H_2(g) + \frac{1}{2}O_2(g) = H_2O(l)$	$\Delta H = -68.4$

Equation (ii) is multiplied by 2, and (iii) multiplied by 3 is added; equation (i) is then subtracted, and the result is

$$2C(s) + 3H_2(g) + \frac{1}{2}O_2(g) = C_2H_5OH(l) \qquad \Delta H = -66.2 \text{ kcal.,}$$

as before. This method of calculating the heat of formation of ethanol utilizes the same data as that given in the problem in § 24d; the difference in procedure is purely formal.

Another application of Hess's law is to determine the heat of a reaction from a knowledge of the heats of combustion of all the reactants and products; suppose it is required to find the heat of the reaction

$$C_2H_4(g) + H_2(g) = C_2H_6(g),$$

the heats of combustion of ethylene (C_2H_4), hydrogen (H_2), and ethane (C_2H_6) being -337.0, -68.4 and -373.0 kcal., respectively, at $18°$ C. The three thermochemical equations are then written:

(i) $\qquad C_2H_4(g) + 3O_2(g) = 2CO_2(g) + 2H_2O(l) \qquad \Delta H = -337.0$ kcal.

(ii) $\qquad H_2(g) + \frac{1}{2}O_2(g) = H_2O(l) \qquad \Delta H = -68.4$

(iii) $\qquad C_2H_6(g) + 3\frac{1}{2}O_2(g) = 2CO_2(g) + 3H_2O(l) \qquad \Delta H = -373.0$

If (i) and (ii) are added together and (iii) is subtracted, the result is

$$C_2H_4(g) + H_2(g) = C_2H_6(g) \qquad \Delta H = -32.4 \text{ kcal.}$$

All that is necessary, therefore, is to add the heats of combustion of the re- actants and to subtract from this the sum of the heats of combustion of the products; the result will then be equal to the heat change of the reaction un- der consideration.

24f. Influence of Physical State.—The change in heat content in a reaction must depend on the physical state, i.e., solid, liquid or gaseous, of the sub- stances involved. An illustration of this fact is provided by reactions in which water is concerned; for example, the thermochemical equation for the forma- tion of *liquid* water from its elements at $18°$ C is

$$H_2(g) + \frac{1}{2}O_2(g) = H_2O(l) \qquad \Delta H = -68.40 \text{ kcal.}$$

If, however, water *vapor* is the product, the heat of reaction is obtained by adding the molar heat of vaporization, at constant pressure, at the particular temperature; thus, at $18°$,

$$H_2O(l) = H_2O(g) \qquad \Delta H = 10.55 \text{ kcal.,}$$

and hence, by addition of the two equations,

$$H_2(g) + \frac{1}{2}O_2(g) = H_2O(g) \qquad \Delta H = -57.85 \text{ kcal.}$$

The heat of formation of 1 mole of water vapor at $18°$ C is thus -57.85 kcal.

Different heat changes are generally involved for different allotropic modi- fications of an element or for different crystalline forms of a compound. If the data are available for a given reaction in which the two separate forms take part, it is possible to evaluate the heat of transition of one form to the other. For example, the heats of combustion of the two allotropic forms of carbon, namely diamond and graphite, are -94.5 and -94.0 kcal., respectively; thus,

$$C(\text{diamond}) + O_2(g) = CO_2(g) \qquad \Delta H = -94.5 \text{ kcal.}$$

$$C(\text{graphite}) + O_2(g) = CO_2(g) \qquad \Delta H = -94.0 \text{ kcal.,}$$

and hence by subtraction it follows that

$$C(\text{diamond}) = C(\text{graphite}) \qquad \Delta H = -0.5 \text{ kcal.}$$

Consequently, when 12.01 grams of diamond are converted into graphite, there is a decrease in heat content of 0.5 kcal., that is to say, 0.5 kcal. of heat is evolved.

24g. Heats of Solution and Dilution.—When a solute is dissolved in a solvent to form a solution, there is frequently an evolution or absorption of heat. The heat change per mole of solute dissolved is not constant, however, but usually varies with the concentration of the solution. If the total change of heat content ΔH observed when m moles of solute are added to a definite quantity, e.g., 1000 grams, of solvent is plotted against m, for various values of the latter, the type of curve obtained is shown in Fig. 52. The curve reaches a limit at the point S when the solution is saturated at the experimental temperature; the solution then contains m_s moles of solute to 1000 grams of solvent. The height of the ordinate ΔH_x at any point, e.g., X, divided by the corresponding number of moles m_x of solute dissolved, i.e., $\Delta H_x/m_x$, represents *the increase of heat content per mole of solute when it dissolves to form a solution of a particular concentration;* this quantity is called the **integral heat of solution** at the given concentration. It is evident from Fig. 52 that the integral heat of solution is, in general, approximately constant in dilute solution, but becomes smaller with increasing concentration.

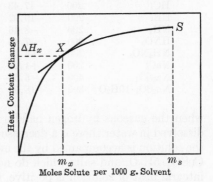

Moles Solute per 1000 g. Solvent

Fig. 52.   Heat of solution

The increase of heat content when 1 mole of solute is dissolved in such a large volume of solvent, at a particular concentration, that there is no appreciable change in the concentration, is the **differential heat of solution** at the specified concentration. This property is given by the slope of the curve in Fig. 52 or, expressed mathematically, by $d(\Delta H)/dm$, at the point corresponding to the given concentration. As in the case of the integral heat of solution, it is seen from the shape of the curve that the differential heat of solution is almost constant in the very dilute solutions; however, it generally decreases as the concentration increases.

When recording integral heats of dilution it is the general practice to state the number of moles of solvent in which 1 mole of solute is dissolved; thus,

$$HCl(g) + 50H_2O(l) = HCl(50H_2O) \qquad \Delta H = -17.21 \text{ kcal.,}$$

indicates that when 1 mole of hydrogen chloride gas is dissolved in 50 moles of water there is an evolution of 17.21 kcal. of heat energy. For infinite dilution, that is, when the solution is so dilute that further dilution causes no detectable heat change, the corresponding thermochemical equation for the integral heat of solution would be written

$$HCl(g) + aq = HCl(aq) \qquad \Delta H = -17.54 \text{ kcal.}$$

If the integral heats of solution for a given solute are known at a series of concentrations, it is of course possible to derive the differential heat of solution graphically by means of a plot of the type shown in Fig. 52.

The integral heats of solution of a number of substances in water, at the specified concentrations, are given in Table XXVIII. It will be observed that

TABLE XXVIII.   INTEGRAL HEATS OF SOLUTION IN KCAL. IN WATER AT 18° C

Substance	H_2O moles	ΔH kcal.	Substance	H_2O moles	ΔH kcal.
HCl	200	−17.43	KCl	200	+4.44
HBr	200	−19.92	KOH	200	−13.29
NH_3	200	−8.46	KNO_3	200	+8.46
HNO_3	200	−7.45	K_2SO_4	400	+6.55
NH_4NO_3	200	+6.34	$CaCl_2$	400	−18.00
NaCl	200	+1.28	$CaCl_2 \cdot 6H_2O$	394	+4.56
Na_2SO_4	400	−5.50	$CuSO_4$	800	−15.89
$Na_2SO_4 \cdot 10H_2O$	390	+18.90	$CuSO_4 \cdot 5H_2O$	795	+2.80

when the gaseous hydrogen halides and ammonia, and in fact all gases, are dissolved in water there is a decrease in the total heat content; in other words, the solution is accompanied by the evolution of heat. For hydrated salts, e.g., $CuSO_4 \cdot 5H_2O$, and salts which do not form stable hydrates, e.g., KNO_3, the integral heat of solution is positive, so that heat is absorbed when these substances dissolve. When a salt which is capable of existing in a hydrated form dissolves in the anhydrous form, e.g., $CuSO_4$, there is almost invariably a liberation of heat energy, i.e., the integral ΔH value is negative. The difference in behavior of the hydrated and anhydrous forms of a given salt is due to the change in heat content associated with the hydration reaction; there is usually an evolution of heat in these processes, i.e., ΔH of hydration is negative. The value of this heat change can be readily calculated from the integral heats of solution; thus, using the data for copper sulfate in Table XXVIII, it is seen that

$$CuSO_4(s) + 800H_2O(l) = CuSO_4(800H_2O) \quad \Delta H = -15.89 \text{ kcal.}$$

$$CuSO_4 \cdot 5H_2O(s) + 795H_2O(l) = CuSO_4(800H_2O) \quad \Delta H = +2.80$$

and hence, by subtraction,

$$CuSO_4(s) + 5H_2O(l) = CuSO_4 \cdot 5H_2O(s) \quad \Delta H = -18.69 \text{ kcal.}$$

The hydration of 1 mole of solid anhydrous copper sulfate to form solid pentahydrate, by the addition of 5 moles of liquid water, is thus accompanied by the evolution of 18.69 kcal. of heat energy at 18° C. The heat of hydration by water vapor at the same temperature would, of course, be different.

Problem: Calculate the heat of hydration of 1 mole of $CuSO_4$ by 5 moles of water vapor at 18° C. The heat of vaporization of water at 18° is 10.55 kcal. mole^{-1}.

The required thermochemical equations are

$$5H_2O(l) = 5H_2O(g) \qquad \Delta H = 5 \times 10.55 \text{ kcal.}$$

$$CuSO_4(s) + 5H_2O(l) = CuSO_4 \cdot 5H_2O(s) \qquad \Delta H = -18.69$$

and hence, by subtraction,

$$CuSO_4(s) + 5H_2O(g) = CuSO_4 \cdot 5H_2O(s) \qquad \Delta H = -71.44 \text{ kcal.}$$

The fact that the heat of solution of a solute varies with its concentration implies that there must be a change of heat content when a solution is diluted by the addition of solvent. The **integral heat of dilution** is *the change in heat content when a solution containing 1 mole of solute is diluted from one concentration to another;* it can be readily seen from Hess's law that it is equal to the difference between the integral heats of solution at the two concentrations. The integral heat of dilution of hydrogen chloride from a solution containing 1 mole of solute in 50 moles of water to one at infinite dilution is obtained by subtracting the thermochemical equations given previously for the two heats of solution; the result is

$$HCl(50H_2O) + aq = HCl(aq) \qquad \Delta H = -0.33 \text{ kcal.}$$

Of theoretical interest is the **differential heat of dilution,** which may be defined as *the heat change when 1 mole of solvent is added to a large volume of the solution at the specified concentration.* This can be obtained by plotting the ΔH of solution at various concentrations against the number of moles of *solvent* associated with a definite quantity of solute, and finding the slope of the curve at the point corresponding to any particular concentration. Because of the approximate constancy of the integral heat of solution at small concentrations, such a curve flattens out at high dilutions, and the differential heat of dilution then approaches zero.

24h. Effect of Temperature on Heat of Reaction: Kirchhoff's Equation.— The heat change associated with any process, physical or chemical, usually varies with temperature; the relationship of this variation to other properties of the system can be readily determined by means of the first law of thermodynamics. Consider any process represented by

$$A \rightarrow B,$$

where A is the initial state, i.e., the reactants, and B is the final state, i.e., the products. The heat of reaction at constant pressure, i.e., ΔH, is equal to the difference between the heat contents H_B and H_A of the final and initial states, respectively; thus,

$$\Delta H = H_B - H_A.$$

In order to determine the variation of ΔH with temperature, this expression is differentiated with respect to temperature at constant pressure; the result is simply

$$\left(\frac{d(\Delta H)}{dT} \right)_P = \left(\frac{dH_B}{dT} \right)_P - \left(\frac{dH_A}{dT} \right)_P. \qquad (24.1)$$

According to equation (23.24), the quantity $(dH/dT)_P$ is equal to C_P, the heat capacity at constant pressure; hence, equation (24.1) may be written as

$$\left(\frac{d(\Delta H)}{dT}\right)_P = C_{P(B)} - C_{P(A)} = \Delta C_P, \qquad (24.2)$$

where ΔC_P, equal to $C_{P(B)} - C_{P(A)}$, is the difference in the heat capacities at constant pressure of the final and initial states, e.g., products and reactants in a chemical change. This expression was derived by G. R. Kirchhoff (1858), and is generally referred to as the **Kirchhoff equation.**

It is seen that equation (24.2) gives the rate of change of the heat of reaction ΔH with the temperature in terms of the heat capacities of the substances involved. In order to make practical use of this expression it is integrated between the temperature limits of T_1 and T_2, with the result

$$\Delta H_2 - \Delta H_1 = \int_{T_1}^{T_2} \Delta C_P dT, \qquad (24.3)$$

where ΔH_1 and ΔH_2 are the heats of reaction, at constant pressure, at the temperatures T_1 and T_2, respectively. In order to proceed further, it is necessary to know how the heat capacities of A and B, and hence ΔC_P, vary with temperature. In the simplest case the assumption may be made that ΔC_P is constant and independent of temperature, over a limited range; equation (24.3) then becomes

$$\Delta H_2 - \Delta H_1 = \Delta C_P(T_2 - T_1). \qquad (24.4)$$

If $T_2 - T_1$ represents an appreciable temperature range, ΔC_P may be taken preferably as equal to $\overline{C}_{P(B)} - \overline{C}_{P(A)}$, where $\overline{C}_P$ is the *mean* heat capacity of the indicated state (or substances) for the particular temperature range concerned.

Problem: The heat of formation of liquid water is -68.4 kcal. at 25° C; calculate the value at 100°, taking the mean molar heat capacities at constant pressure, in the given temperature range, of $H_2(g)$, $O_2(g)$ and $H_2O(l)$ to be 6.89, 6.97 and 18.0 cal. deg.$^{-1}$ mole^{-1}, respectively.

Writing the equation for the reaction, with the mean heat capacity $\overline{C}_P$ below each substance,

$$H_2(g) + \tfrac{1}{2}O_2(g) = H_2O(l)$$
$$\overline{C}_P \quad 6.89 \quad \tfrac{1}{2} \times 6.97 \quad 18.0 \quad \text{cal. deg.}^{-1}$$

it is seen that

$$\Delta C_P = 18.0 - \{6.89 + (\tfrac{1}{2} \times 6.97)\} = 7.63 \text{ cal. deg.}^{-1}$$

$$= 7.63 \times 10^{-3} \text{ kcal. deg.}^{-1}$$

Let T_1 be 25° C and T_2 be 100° C, so that $T_2 - T_1$ is 75°; the heat of reaction ΔH_1 at T_1 is thus -68.4 kcal., and hence ΔH_2 at 100° C is given by equation (24.4) as

$$\Delta H_2 + 68.4 = 7.63 \times 10^{-3} \times 75,$$

$$\Delta H_2 = -67.8 \text{ kcal.}$$

For the purpose of more accurate calculations, however, it is necessary to express the heat capacities of products and reactants as functions of the temperature; in this way a complete expression for ΔC_P can be obtained. This can then be inserted in equation (24.3) and the complete integration carried out, as shown in the following problem.

Problem: For the reaction $N_2(g) + 3H_2(g) = 2NH_3(g)$, the value of ΔH is -22.10 kcal. at $25°$ C. The molar heat capacities at constant pressure of nitrogen, hydrogen and ammonia can be expressed as functions of the absolute temperature in the following manner:

$$C_{N_2} = 6.5 + 1.0 \times 10^{-3}T \text{ cal. deg.}^{-1}$$

$$C_{H_2} = 6.5 + 0.9 \times 10^{-3}T$$

$$C_{NH_3} = 8.04 + 0.7 \times 10^{-3}T + 5.1 \times 10^{-6}T^2.$$

Calculate the heat of reaction at $125°$ C.

The value of ΔC_P is given by

$$\Delta C_P = 2C_{NH_3} - (C_{N_2} + 3C_{H_2})$$

$$= -9.92 - 2.3 \times 10^{-3}T + 10.2 \times 10^{-6}T^2 \text{ cal. deg.}^{-1}$$

Hence,

$$\int_{T_1}^{T_2} \Delta C_P dT = \left[-9.92T - 2.3 \times 10^{-3}\frac{T^2}{2} + 10.2 \times 10^{-6}\frac{T^3}{3} \right]_{T_1}^{T_2}$$

$$= -9.92(T_2 - T_1) - 1.15 \times 10^{-3}(T_2^2 - T_1^2) + 3.4 \times 10^{-6}(T_2^3 - T_1^3)$$

and this is equal to $\Delta H_2 - \Delta H_1$ by equation (24.3). The temperature T_1 is $25°$ C, i.e., $273 + 25 = 298°$ K, and T_2 is $273 + 125 = 398°$ K; consequently,

$$\Delta H_2 - \Delta H_1 = -9.92(398 - 298) - 1.15 \times 10^{-3}\{(398)^2 - (298)^2\}$$

$$+ 3.4 \times 10^{-6}\{(398)^3 - (298)^3\}$$

$$= -948 \text{ cal.} = -0.95 \text{ kcal.}$$

Since ΔH_1 (at $25°$ C) is -22.10 kcal., it follows that

$$\Delta H_2 = -22.10 - 0.95 = -23.05 \text{ kcal.}$$

It will be evident from either equation (24.3) or (24.4) that the variation of the heat of reaction with temperature depends on the magnitude and sign of ΔC_P. The larger this difference in the heat capacities of the products and the reactants the greater will be the variation of the heat of reaction with temperature. If ΔC_P is positive, that is to say, if the total heat capacity of the products is greater than that of the reactants, ΔH will increase with increasing temperature. On the other hand, if ΔC_P is negative, so that the reactants have the greater heat capacity, the value of ΔH will diminish as the temperature is raised. If ΔC_P is zero, or very small, the heat of reaction will be independent of temperature.

An alternative integrated form of the Kirchhoff equation is frequently used; thus, the general integration of equation (24.3) gives

$$\Delta H = \Delta H_0 + \int \Delta C_P dT, \tag{24.5}$$

where ΔH_0, equivalent to the hypothetical heat of reaction at the absolute zero, is the integration constant. Since heat capacities can be represented as functions of successive powers of the absolute temperature, as seen in the problem given above, it is possible to write

$$\Delta C_P = a + bT + cT^2 + \cdots, \tag{24.6}$$

where a, b, c, etc., are constants determined by the nature of the reactants and products. Upon inserting this result in equation (24.5), it is seen that

$$\Delta H = \Delta H_0 + \int (a + bT + cT^2 + \cdots)dT$$

$$= \Delta H_0 + aT + \tfrac{1}{2}bT^2 + \tfrac{1}{3}cT^3 + \cdots. \tag{24.7}$$

In this manner the heat of reaction ΔH is expressed in terms of the temperature T, and the constants ΔH_0, a, b, c, etc., which are characteristic of the reaction. The values of a, b, c, etc., are derived from the measured heat capacities, while ΔH_0 is calculated from equation (24.7), utilizing the known heat of reaction ΔH at one particular temperature.

Problem: Use the data in the preceding problem to express the heat of the reaction $N_2(g) + 3H_2(g) = 2NH_3(g)$ in the form of equation (24.7).

It was found in the preceding problem that for this reaction

$$\Delta C_P = -9.92 - 2.3 \times 10^{-3}T + 10.2 \times 10^{-6}T^2 \text{ cal. deg.}^{-1}$$

and comparison with equation (24.6) shows that

$$a = -9.92, \quad b = -2.3 \times 10^{-3} \quad \text{and} \quad c = 10.2 \times 10^{-6}.$$

Hence, by equation (24.7)

$$\Delta H = \Delta H_0 - 9.92T - 1.15 \times 10^{-3}T^2 + 3.4 \times 10^{-6}T^3 \text{ cal.}$$

At 25° C, i.e., 298° K, the value of ΔH is given as -22.10 kcal., i.e., $-22,100$ cal.; hence,

$$-22,100 = \Delta H_0 - 9.92 \times 298 - 1.15 \times 10^{-3} \times (298)^2 + 3.4 \times 10^{-6} \times (298)^3 \text{ cal.}$$

$$\Delta H_0 = -19,130 \text{ cal.},$$

and consequently, converting into kilocalories,

$$\Delta H = -19.13 - 9.92 \times 10^{-3}T - 1.15 \times 10^{-6}T^2 + 3.4 \times 10^{-9}T^3 \text{ kcal.}$$

24i. Calorimetric Measurements.—The heat changes involved in chemical reactions are measured by carrying out the process in a suitable vessel surrounded by a definite amount of water; the whole apparatus is known as a **calorimeter.** If heat is liberated in the reaction the temperature of the water rises, but if heat is absorbed the temperature falls. The product of the rise or fall of temperature and the heat capacity of the water and other parts of the calorimeter gives the heat change of the reaction. The heat capacity of the calorimeter and its contents may be determined from the weights and specific heats of the various parts. An alternative method is to place a heating coil in the calorimeter and to generate a definite amount of heat by the passage of an electric current. From the corresponding rise in temperature of the water in the calorimeter the heat capacity can be evaluated.

One of the great difficulties encountered in carrying out accurate thermo-chemical measurements is the avoidance of heat losses due to radiation. Two chief procedures have been used to overcome this source of error. In one, the calorimeter vessel containing the water is surrounded by various jackets or, better, it is placed inside a Dewar vacuum vessel, so as to minimize the loss of heat by radiation. In the other method, which employs what is called the **adiabatic calorimeter,** the temperature of an outer jacket, generally containing water, is continuously adjusted during the course of the reaction so as to differ by not more than 0.1° from that of the reaction vessel itself. In this case the amount of heat radiating from or to the latter is quite negligible.

In carrying out a thermochemical measurement it is desirable that the reaction should take place as rapidly and as completely as possible. For this reason, reactions between gases are sometimes accelerated by means of a catalyst placed in a tube contained in the calorimeter reaction vessel. Heats of combustion of organic solids and liquids, including fuels and food materials, are measured by means of an explosion or combustion "bomb." This is a cylindrical vessel, of 400 to 500 cc. capacity, made of strong steel or other alloy. A known weight of the material to be studied is placed in the bomb which is then filled with oxygen at a pressure of 25 to 30 atm. The apparatus is inserted in a calorimeter, and the organic compound is ignited by the passage of a small electric current through a fine iron wire sealed into the bomb. Rapid combustion occurs in the oxygen under pressure, and the heat liberated is determined from the rise in temperature of the calorimetric liquid. Various corrections must be applied in order to obtain accurate results.

Problem: The combustion of 1.247 gram of benzoic acid at 18° in a bomb contained in a calorimeter of total heat capacity 2745 cal. deg.$^{-1}$ was accompanied by a rise of temperature of 2.870°. Neglecting corrections, calculate the molar heat of combustion of benzoic acid.

The heat evolved in the combustion is the product of the heat capacity of the calorimeter and the rise of temperature, i.e., 2745 × 2.870 cal. or 2.745 × 2.870 kcal. This is produced by 1.247 gram of benzoic acid, and since the molecular weight of benzoic acid is 122.12, the molar heat of combustion is

$$\frac{2.745 \times 2.870 \times 122.12}{1.247} = 771.5 \text{ kcal. mole}^{-1}.$$

READING REFERENCES

1. **The Person-Kirchhoff law.** Gucker, *Journal of Chemical Education*, **8**, 2391 (1931).

2. **Kinetic theory of heat.** Timm, *ibid.*, **12**, 31 (1935).

3. **Fundamentals of thermodynamics.** Roseveare, *ibid.*, **15**, 214 (1938).

4. **Simple calorimeter.** Livingston and Horvitz, *ibid.*, **16**, 287 (1939).

5. **Calorimetry experiments.** Cameron and Wright, *ibid.*, **18**, 510 (1941).

6. **Calorimeter studies.** Pattison, Miller and Lucasse, *ibid.*, **20**, 319 (1943).

REVIEW QUESTIONS

1. State the dimensions of energy. Define the erg and joule; state the value of the calorie in terms of these quantities.

2. What are the two factors involved in all forms of energy? Give examples.

3. Upon what principle is the first law of thermodynamics based? State the principle and the law in different forms.

4. What is meant by a complete or exact differential? Explain why the change dE in the internal energy is always a complete differential.

5. Distinguish, with examples, between extensive and intensive properties.

6. Derive an expression relating the change of internal energy to the heat absorbed and the work done in any process.

7. Explain what is meant by a thermodynamically reversible process. Illustrate by reference to vaporization of a liquid and expansion of a gas.

8. Calculate the reversible, isothermal work done in the expansion of one mole of an ideal gas from volume V_A to volume V_B. How is this related to the heat absorbed?

9. What is meant by an adiabatic change? Write the characteristic pressure-volume equation for an adiabatic change, and derive from it an equation relating the temperatures and pressures in such a change.

10. Explain why heat changes at constant pressure and constant volume have definite values. How are these quantities related to certain thermodynamic properties?

11. How is it possible to define the heat capacities of a gas at constant pressure and constant volume in terms of thermodynamic quantities?

12. Explain the terms exothermic, endothermic and heat of reaction. Write out two thermochemical equations of different types and explain their meaning.

13. State how heats of reaction at constant pressure and constant volume are related for a system involving ideal gases.

14. Define the heat of formation of a compound. How is it related to the conventional heat content? What is the use of heat content data?

15. Explain the meaning and applications of heats of combustion.

16. State the two laws of thermochemistry, and show how they are based on the first law of thermodynamics. Illustrate the use of these laws.

17. How does the physical state of a substance, e.g., solid, liquid or crystalline form, affect the heat of reaction?

18. Define integral and differential heats of solution, and illustrate graphically. How do the heats of solution of hydrated and anhydrous salts differ?

19. Define integral and differential heats of dilution. How is the former related to the heat of solution?

20. Derive an expression for the influence of temperature on heat of reaction.

Show how it may be used to calculate the value at one temperature if that at another is known.

21. Outline the methods used for the measurement of heats of reaction and heats of combustion.

PROBLEMS

I

1. Calculate the work done in calories when one mole of water is vaporized reversibly at the boiling point at 1 atm. pressure. The specific volume of water vapor at 100° C is 1670 cc. per g.; the decrease in volume of the liquid may be neglected.

2. Calculate the maximum work in ergs for the isothermal expansion of 2.5 moles of an ideal gas from a pressure of 10 atm. to 1 atm. at 25° C.

3. Oxygen gas at 25° C was expanded adiabatically from a pressure of 100 atm. to 10 atm. Calculate the final temperature. (The heat capacity of oxygen at constant pressure may be taken as 7 cal. deg.$^{-1}$ mole^{-1}.)

4. Calculate the difference, in calories, in the heat changes at constant pressure (ΔH) and constant volume (ΔE) for the following reactions:

$$C_2H_5OH(l) + 3O_2(g) = 2CO_2(g) + 3H_2O(g) \text{ at } 0° C$$

$$C_2H_5OH(g) + 3O_2(g) = 2CO_2(g) + 3H_2O(l) \text{ at } 25° C.$$

State whether ΔE or ΔH is larger in each case.

5. Use the data in Table XXVI and in § 24f to calculate ΔH for the following reactions:

$$C_2H_4(g) + H_2(g) = C_2H_6(g)$$

$$PbO(s) + H_2(g) = Pb(s) + H_2O(l)$$

$$CO(g) + \tfrac{1}{2}O_2(g) = CO_2(g)$$

$$2H_2S(g) + SO_2(g) = 3S(s) + 2H_2O(g).$$

6. Using data in Table XXVI, calculate the heat of formation of solid lead chloride, given that for the following reaction

$$Ag(s) + PbCl_2(s) = 2AgCl(s) + Pb(s)$$

ΔH is + 25.1 kcal. at 18° C.

7. Utilize the data in Tables XXVI and XXVII to calculate the heat of formation from its elements of liquid benzene (C_6H_6).

8. Calculate the heat of formation of solid sodium hydroxide from the following data:

$$Na(s) + H_2O(l) + aq = NaOH(aq) + \tfrac{1}{2}H_2(g) \qquad \Delta H = -43.8 \text{ kcal.}$$

$$H_2(g) + \tfrac{1}{2}O_2(g) = H_2O(l) \qquad\qquad\qquad -68.4$$

$$NaOH(s) + aq = NaOH(aq) \qquad\qquad\qquad -10.3$$

9. Compare the heats of hydration of one mole of calcium chloride by six moles of (a) liquid water, (b) water vapor, at 18° C. The heat of vaporization of water is 586 cal. per g. at 18° C. The data in Table XXVIII should be employed.

10. Calculate the heat of formation of lead monoxide (PbO) at 200° C from the value for 18° C in Table XXVI. The mean specific heat of lead is 0.032, of oxygen 0.222, and of lead monoxide 0.052 cal. deg.$^{-1}$ g.$^{-1}$ at constant pressure.

11. The molar heat capacities at constant pressure of carbon, carbon monoxide and carbon dioxide are as follows:

Carbon $\qquad$ $2.67 + 0.0026T$ cal. deg.$^{-1}$

Carbon monoxide $6.60 + 0.0012T$

Carbon dioxide $\qquad$ $7.70 + 0.0053T$.

Derive an expression for the variation with temperature of ΔH for the reaction

$$C(s) + CO_2(g) = 2CO(g).$$

II

1. Calculate the work done, in calories, when one mole of iodine is vaporized reversibly from the solid at the triple point (114.15° C) when the vapor pressure is 90.1 mm. (The assumption may be made that the vapor behaves as an ideal gas; the change in volume of the solid may be neglected.)

2. The reversible compression of five moles of an ideal gas at a temperature of 30° C from 20 liters to a smaller volume results in the liberation of 5.82×10^{11} ergs of heat energy. What is the smaller volume?

3. An adiabatic expansion of helium gas results in the fall of temperature from 0° to $-230°$ C; what is the ratio of the initial to the final pressure? (The molar heat capacity of helium is 5 cal. deg.$^{-1}$ at constant pressure and 3 cal. deg.$^{-1}$ at constant volume.)

4. Calculate the difference, in calories, in the heat changes at constant pressure (ΔH) and constant volume (ΔE) for the following reactions:

$$2H_2S(g) + SO_2(g) = 3S(s) + 2H_2O(l) \text{ at } 100° C$$

$$Al(s) + 3HCl(aq) = AlCl_3(aq) + \tfrac{3}{2}H_2(g) \text{ at } 20° C.$$

State whether ΔE or ΔH is the larger in each case.

5. Use the data in Table XXVI to calculate ΔH for the following reactions:

$$AgCl(s) + \tfrac{1}{2}H_2(g) = Ag(s) + HCl(g)$$

$$C(s) + CO_2(g) = 2CO(g)$$

$$C_2H_2(g) + \tfrac{5}{2}O_2(g) = H_2O(l) + 2CO_2(g)$$

$$3C_2H_2(g) = C_6H_6(l)$$

6. Using data in Table XXVI, calculate the heat of formation of solid silver iodide, given that for the following reaction

$$2AgCl(s) + I_2(s) = 2AgI(s) + Cl_2(g)$$

ΔH is $+30.8$ kcal. at 18° C.

7. From the heat of formation of liquid ethanol in Table XXVI, calculate the heat of combustion at 18° C.

8. Calculate the heat of formation of solid aluminum chloride (Al_2Cl_6) from the following data:

$Al(s) + 3HCl(aq) = AlCl_3(aq) + \tfrac{3}{2}H_2(g)$	$\Delta H = -127.0$ kcal.
$H_2(g) + Cl_2(g) = 2HCl(g)$	-44.0
$HCl(g) + aq = HCl(aq)$	-17.5
$Al_2Cl_6(s) + aq = 2AlCl_3(aq)$	-155.8

9. Employing the data in Table XXVIII, compare the heats of hydration of one mole of sodium sulfate by ten moles of (a) liquid water, (b) water vapor, at 18° C. The heat of vaporization of water is 586 cal. per g. at 18° C.

10. Calculate the heat of formation of hydrogen bromide gas at 250° C from the value for 18° C in Table XXVI. The mean specific heats of hydrogen, bromine and hydrogen bromide at constant pressure are 3.41, 0.055 and 0.086 cal. deg.$^{-1}$ g.$^{-1}$, respectively.

11. The molar heat capacities at constant pressure of hydrogen and water (in the gaseous state) are as follows:

Hydrogen $\quad$ $6.85 + 0.00028T$ cal. deg.$^{-1}$
Water vapor $8.22 + 0.00015T$.

Use these data, together with those in problem I, 11, to derive an expression for the variation with temperature of ΔH for the reaction

$$H_2O(g) + CO(g) = CO_2(g) + H_2(g).$$

CHAPTER VIII

THE SECOND LAW OF THERMODYNAMICS

ENTROPY

25a. Spontaneous Processes.—The second law of thermodynamics has led to results which are of considerable importance to chemistry, physics and engineering, but to the chemist its greatest value probably lies in the fact that it provides a means of foretelling whether a particular reaction can occur, and if so to what extent. However, thermodynamics can only indicate if the reaction is possible or not; other considerations, which lie outside thermodynamics, are necessary, as will be seen in Chapter XVIII, to determine whether the process will take place slowly or rapidly. Even with this limitation in mind, it must be admitted that information concerning the fundamental possibility of a reaction, apart from its speed, would be of great interest to the chemist. At one time it was believed that chemical changes always occurred spontaneously in the direction of heat evolution, that is, in the direction leading to a decrease in the heat content. This conclusion is, however, manifestly incorrect, as is evident from the fact that many reactions which take place spontaneously are known to involve an absorption of heat.

The question being considered resolves itself into the problem of understanding the conditions under which spontaneous processes, in general, take place. It is convenient in this connection to examine some physical processes that are of spontaneous occurrence; the conclusions drawn are found to be applicable to all changes that tend to take place without external influence. Consider, for example, a bar of metal that is hot at one end and cold at the other; heat will be conducted spontaneously along the bar from the hot end to the cold end until the temperature is uniform. It is important to note, however, that *this process is not found to reverse itself spontaneously;* it has not been observed that a metal bar of uniform temperature spontaneously becomes hotter at one end and colder at the other. Nevertheless, the process could be reversed somewhat in the following manner: heat is allowed to pass from one end of the uniform bar to a machine where it is converted into work; by means of friction the work is reconverted into an equivalent amount of heat which is now transferred to the other end of the bar. In this way the bar at uniform temperature might be restored to its original state.

25b. The Second Law of Thermodynamics.—Although there is nothing in the procedure just described, for reversing the spontaneous process of conduction of heat along a bar, that is contrary to the first law of thermodynamics, it is a matter of actual experience that a complete reversal is impossible. The difficulty lies in the fact that *heat cannot be completely converted into an*

234

equivalent amount of work without leaving changes in some parts of the system. This conclusion, drawn from actual experience, is one way of stating the **second law of thermodynamics.** In order for a machine to convert heat continuously into work, without producing changes in other parts of the system, it is necessary that the machine take up heat from a "source" at a higher temperature, convert *part* of it into an equivalent amount of work, and then give up the remainder to a "sink" at a lower temperature. The fraction of the heat absorbed at the higher temperature that is converted into work is called the **efficiency** of the machine, and *no machine has yet been made that has an efficiency of unity*, or 100 per cent. This is another way of formulating the second law of thermodynamics.

It will be recalled that at the end of § 23f it was stated that in the isothermal, reversible expansion of an ideal gas the work done by the gas was exactly equal to the heat absorbed. In other words, in this process the heat is completely converted into work. However, it is important to note that this result is not contrary to the second law of thermodynamics, for according to this law *it is impossible to carry out this conversion of heat into work continuously without producing changes in some part of the system.* In the case of the isothermal expansion, for example, the volume of the gas is changed, because it is greater at the end of the process than at the beginning. If the gas is restored to its original state by compression, an amount of work exactly equal to that obtained in the expansion will have to be done on the gas, and an equivalent quantity of heat will be evolved. The net result of restoring the system to its original state will be that no heat is absorbed and no work is done. The study of numerous cases of this type has established the reliability of the second law of thermodynamics.

Returning now to the bar of metal which has spontaneously attained a uniform temperature, after being initially hot at one end and cold at the other, it will be apparent that the original state can be restored, without leaving changes elsewhere, only if heat can be completely converted into work. Since this is known to be impossible, in accordance with experience, i.e., the second law of thermodynamics, it is evident that the spontaneous process cannot be reversed. A partial reversal is possible, since a portion of the heat could be transformed into the equivalent amount of work, and then back again to heat; the complete reversal would, however, be contrary to experience.

The general conclusions drawn above, in connection with the heated bar, will be found applicable to other spontaneous physical processes, such as expansion of a gas from a region of high pressure to one of low pressure, diffusion of one gas into another, the diffusion of a concentrated solution into water, the conversion of electrical energy into heat, the production of heat by friction, and so on. The conclusions must apply also to spontaneous chemical processes, as may be seen from a consideration of a simple example. A piece of zinc will dissolve spontaneously in an aqueous solution of copper sulfate, according to the reaction

$$Zn + CuSO_4 = ZnSO_4 + Cu,$$

with the evolution of a definite amount of heat. This reaction could be reversed by passing an electric current between the metallic copper and the solution of zinc sulfate in an appropriate manner, thus regenerating the zinc metal and copper sulfate. In order for the reversal to be complete, the heat evolved in the original reaction would need to be completely converted into electrical energy, without leaving changes in any other parts of the system. This again is contrary to experience, and so the spontaneous chemical process cannot be reversed, in the thermodynamic sense (see footnote, p. 208). It is possible to state, therefore, in the most general terms that *all natural or spontaneous processes, i.e., processes occurring without external interference, are irreversible in character;* this is still another way of expressing the second law of thermodynamics. Incidentally, the fact that a process is spontaneous means that it is taking place at a finite rate; it is consequently to be expected that it is irreversible, since thermodynamically reversible processes are required to occur infinitesimally slowly (§ 23e).

Before passing on, it is of interest to call attention to the contrast between the first and second laws of thermodynamics; the first law merely states that when one form of energy is converted into another the amounts involved of the two forms must be exactly equivalent, but it says nothing concerning the possibility or extent of such conversion. The second law, however, indicates that heat energy is exceptional in nature; while, in principle, other forms of energy can be converted into heat, the complete conversion of heat into other forms of energy, without leaving changes in the system, is not possible.

25c. Entropy.—It having been established that spontaneous processes are thermodynamically irreversible, the next stage in the development of the criteria of processes of this kind is to define certain thermodynamic properties or **thermodynamic functions.** One of these, of great importance, is known as the **entropy** (Greek: *change*) and is represented by the letter S; like the function E, i.e., the internal energy, it is a property that depends only on the state of a substance or system, and not on its previous history, as will be seen shortly. The actual entropy of a system is not easily defined, and it is more convenient, in the first place, to define the *change* of entropy. Thus, *the increase of entropy dS in the course of an infinitesimal process is equal to δq, the heat absorbed when the process is carried out in a reversible manner, divided by the absolute temperature T;* thus, by definition

$$dS = \frac{\delta q}{T}.$$
(25.1)

Although δq is not an exact differential, it has a definite value for a reversible, isothermal process, and it can be shown that dS as defined by equation (25.1) is an *exact differential*. The entropy S of a system is thus a definite property of the system, depending only on its condition or state, as mentioned above.

In order to express the entropy increase ΔS corresponding to a finite change in the system, it is necessary to integrate equation (25.1) between the limits of the initial state 1 and the final state 2; thus,

$$\Delta S = S_2 - S_1 = \int_{T_1}^{T_2} \frac{\delta q}{T} , \qquad (25.2)$$

where S_1 is the actual entropy value in the initial state and S_2 is that in the final state of the process. In view of the conclusion stated above, the value of ΔS should depend only on the initial and final states of the system, and not on the nature of the connecting path; hence, the entropy change ΔS, which is equal to $S_2 - S_1$, should be the same *irrespective of whether the path from initial to final state is thermodynamically reversible or not*. However, if it is required to calculate the actual magnitude of ΔS by means of equation (25.2), the value of δq must be that accompanying a *reversible* change at constant temperature; when the change is carried out irreversibly the heat absorbed is an indefinite and uncertain quantity which cannot be used for the determination of the entropy increase.

Since entropy is equal to a quantity of heat divided by the absolute temperature, the dimensions are energy $\times$ temperature^{-1}. It is the general practice to express the energy in calories, so that entropy is given in the units of calories per degree, i.e., cal. deg.$^{-1}$. This is sometimes referred to as an "entropy unit," and is represented by the symbol E. U. The entropy is an extensive property, in the sense defined in § 23c, and so its value depends upon the quantity of substance concerned; for this reason the amount of substance, usually 1 mole, should be stated.

In an adiabatic process no heat enters or leaves the system (§ 23g) so that δq is zero. It follows, therefore, from equation (25.1) that the corresponding entropy change dS must be zero. The interesting result is thus obtained that *an adiabatic process is associated with no change in the entropy;* for this reason such processes have been referred to as **isentropic.**

25d. Entropy Changes for an Ideal Gas.—For an ideal gas the integral in equation (25.2) can be evaluated and relatively simple expressions for ΔS can be obtained. For an infinitesimal stage of any process, equation (23.4) may be written

$$\delta q = dE + \delta w, \qquad (25.3)$$

and if the external work is restricted to that associated with a volume change, i.e., work of expansion, δw may be replaced by PdV, so that

$$\delta q = dE + PdV. \qquad (25.4)$$

According to equation (23.23) the heat capacity C_V at constant volume is given by

$$C_V = \left(\frac{dE}{dT}\right)_V ,$$

but for *an ideal gas* the internal energy is independent of the volume, as indicated in § 23f, and so it is possible to write this expression in the simpler form

$$C_V = \frac{dE}{dT},$$

$$dE = C_V dT. \tag{25.5}$$

Insertion of this result in equation (25.4) then gives

$$\delta q = C_V dT + PdV. \tag{25.6}$$

For *one mole* of an ideal gas P is equal to RT/V, so that

$$\delta q = C_V dT + RT \frac{dV}{V}. \tag{25.7}$$

It follows, therefore, from equation (25.2), assuming C_V to be independent of temperature for an ideal gas, that for 1 mole of gas

$$\Delta S = S_2 - S_1 = C_V \int_{T_1}^{T_2} \frac{dT}{T} + R \int_{V_1}^{V_2} \frac{dV}{V}$$

$$= C_V \ln \frac{T_2}{T_1} + R \ln \frac{V_2}{V_1}. \tag{25.8}$$

The entropy change for a process involving an ideal gas thus depends on the initial and final temperatures and volumes.

Since $P_1 V_1 = RT_1$ for the initial state and $P_2 V_2 = RT_2$ for the final state, it follows that V_2/V_1 is equal to $T_2 P_1/T_1 P_2$, and making this substitution in equation (25.8) leads to

$$\Delta S = S_2 - S_1 = C_V \ln \frac{T_2}{T_1} + R \ln \frac{T_2}{T_1} - R \ln \frac{P_2}{P_1}. \tag{25.9}$$

According to equation (12.32), $C_V + R$ is equal to C_P, and hence

$$\Delta S = S_2 - S_1 = C_P \ln \frac{T_2}{T_1} - R \ln \frac{P_2}{P_1}. \tag{25.10}$$

Two special cases are of particular interest. For an *isothermal process* there is no change of temperature, and hence T_1 is equal to T_2; equations (25.8) and (25.10) are then simplified to give

$$\Delta S_T = R \ln \frac{V_2}{V_1} = -R \ln \frac{P_2}{P_1}, \tag{25.11}$$

the subscript T in ΔS_T being used to indicate constant temperature. If V_2 is greater than V_1, that is, in an expansion process, ΔS_T will be positive, by equation (25.11); the isothermal expansion of an ideal gas is thus accompanied by an increase of entropy of the gas. Similarly, the isothermal compression of an ideal gas is associated with an entropy decrease.

The second case of interest is for a change occurring *at constant pressure;* in this event, P_1 and P_2, are equal, so that equation (25.10) reduces to

$$\Delta S_P = C_P \ln \frac{T_2}{T_1}. \tag{25.12}$$

Increase of temperature at constant pressure is thus associated with a gain of entropy of the ideal gas.

25e. Entropy Changes at Constant Pressure or Constant Volume.—From equations (23.21) and (23.22), it is seen that

$$\delta q_P = C_P dT \qquad \text{and} \qquad \delta q_V = C_V dT,$$

where δq_P and δq_V have definite values, representing the heat absorbed in infinitesimal processes at constant pressure and constant volume, respectively. The entropy change under these specified conditions is therefore given by

$$dS_P = \frac{\delta q_P}{T} = C_P \frac{dT}{T} \tag{25.13}$$

and

$$dS_V = \frac{\delta q_V}{T} = C_V \frac{dT}{T}. \tag{25.14}$$

For an appreciable change of temperature from T_1 to T_2, *at constant pressure,* the corresponding entropy change is given by integration of equation (25.13) between the temperature limits; thus,

$$\Delta S_P = \int_{T_1}^{T_2} C_P \frac{dT}{T} = \int_{T_1}^{T_2} C_P d \ln T. \tag{25.15}$$

A similar expression, involving C_V, can be obtained for a temperature change occurring at constant volume by integration of equation (25.14). *These equations are of general applicability; they are independent of whether the system under consideration consists of solid, liquid or gas,* for no assumption concerning its nature has been made in deriving equation (25.15) or its analogue for constant volume.

The exact evaluation of the integral in equation (25.15) is possible either if C_P is independent of temperature, or if its variation with temperature is known; in these cases it is a relatively simple matter to determine the entropy increase for a temperature change. The former condition holds for an ideal (monatomic) gas, and then equation (25.15) reduces to the same form as (25.12), viz.,

$$\Delta S_P = C_P \ln \frac{T_2}{T_1}. \tag{25.16}$$

If the heat capacity can be expressed as a function of the absolute temperature (§ 24h), the integration can be carried out in the usual manner. An alternative, approximate, possibility is to take a mean value of C_P in the temperature range T_1 to T_2 and to assume that this remains constant; the entropy change of the gas may then be obtained from equation (25.16).

Problem: The molar heat capacity at constant pressure of ammonia gas is expressed by $C_P = 8.04 + 7.0 \times 10^{-4}T + 5.1 \times 10^{-6}T^2$ cal. deg.$^{-1}$ mole^{-1}. Calculate the increase of entropy when 1 mole of ammonia is heated from 25° to 125° C at constant pressure. Compare the result with that obtained by taking a mean value of 8.92 cal. deg.$^{-1}$ mole^{-1} for the heat capacity in the given temperature range.

Insertion of the value for C_P in equation (25.15), with T_1 equal to $273 + 25 = 298°$ K, and $T_2 = 273 + 125 = 398°$ K, gives

$$\Delta S_P = \int_{298}^{398} \left(\frac{8.04}{T} + 7.0 \times 10^{-4} + 5.1 \times 10^{-6}T \right) dT$$

$$= 8.04 \ln \tfrac{398}{298} + 7.0 \times 10^{-4}(398 - 298) + 2.55 \times 10^{-6}\{(398)^2 - (298)^2\}$$

$$= 2.57 \text{ cal. deg.}^{-1} \text{ mole}^{-1}.$$

Alternatively, assuming a constant heat capacity of 8.92 cal. deg.$^{-1}$ mole^{-1}, i.e., the mean value in the range from 298° to 398° K, then by equation (25.16),

$$\Delta S_P = 8.92 \ln \tfrac{398}{298} = 8.92 \times 2.303 \log \tfrac{398}{298}$$

$$= 2.58 \text{ cal. deg.}^{-1} \text{ mole}^{-1}.$$

The change of entropy with temperature at constant pressure can be determined by graphical integration; this method is particularly useful for

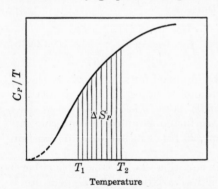

F$_{IG}$. 53. Determination of entropy change

solids and liquids, because the variation of the heat capacity cannot be expressed as a simple function of the temperature, especially at low temperatures. The experimental values of C_P/T for a number of temperatures are plotted against T, as in Fig. 53, or, alternatively, C_P is plotted against $\ln T$; then, according to equation (25.15), the area under the curve between the temperature ordinates from T_1 to T_2 (or $\ln T_1$ to $\ln T_2$) gives the entropy increase ΔS_P of the given substance at constant pressure accompanying the temperature change.

25f. Entropy Change Accompanying Change of Phase.—When a substance undergoes a change of phase, e.g., solid to liquid or liquid to vapor, there is an absorption of heat and consequently a change of entropy. Both fusion and vaporization may be carried out reversibly (§ 23e) and the heat taken up, at constant pressure, is equal to the normal heat of fusion or vaporization at the given temperature. The corresponding entropy changes are then obtained by dividing the heat absorbed by the (constant) temperature at which the change of phase occurs. For most purposes the values are required at the melting point and boiling point at atmospheric pressure, and hence the molar entropy of fusion is given by

$$\Delta S_f = \frac{L_f}{T_f}, \tag{25.17}$$

where L_f is the molar heat of fusion, and T_f is the freezing (or melting) point on the absolute scale. Similarly, the molar entropy of vaporization is represented by

$$\Delta S_v = \frac{L_v}{T_b}, \tag{25.18}$$

where L_v is the molar heat of vaporization and T_b is the normal boiling point. Comparison of equation (25.18) with that given in § 16f for the Trouton constant shows that the latter is really the molar entropy of vaporization of a liquid at 1 atm. pressure. Since heat is absorbed in both fusion and vaporization, that is to say, since both L_f and L_v are positive, these processes are accompanied by an increase of entropy. The entropy of a liquid is therefore greater than that of the solid with which it is in equilibrium at the melting point, and that of the vapor is greater than for the liquid at the boiling point.

Transition from one crystalline form to another is also associated with a reversible heat change, and hence with a change of entropy. The entropy of transition is equal to the heat of transition L_t divided by the transition temperature T_t on the absolute scale, i.e., $\Delta S_t = L_t/T_t$.

If, as a result of changing the temperature, there is an alteration in the phase or crystalline form of the substance whose entropy is being studied, due allowance must be made in the calculations for the entropy of fusion, vaporization or transition, as the case may be.

Problem: Calculate the increase of entropy when 1 mole of ice at 0° C is heated until it forms steam at 100° C at a constant pressure of 1 atm. The molar heat of fusion of ice at 0° is 1436 cal. and the heat of vaporization of water at 100° is 9720 cal. The mean specific heat of liquid water may be taken as 1.0 cal. deg.$^{-1}$ g.$^{-1}$

The entropy of fusion ΔS_f at 0°, i.e., 273° K, is $1436/273 = 5.26$ cal. deg.$^{-1}$ mole^{-1}. The increase of entropy accompanying the increase in the temperature of the water from 0° to 100° C, i.e., from 273° to 373° K, is given by equation (25.16); since the specific heat of water is 1.0, the molar heat capacity is 18.0,

$$\Delta S = 18.0 \ln \tfrac{373}{273} = 18.0 \times 2.303 \log \tfrac{373}{273}$$

$$= 5.62 \text{ cal. deg.}^{-1} \text{ mole}^{-1}.$$

Finally, there must be added the entropy of vaporization at 100° C, i.e., 373° K; this is $9720/373 = 26.06$ cal. deg.$^{-1}$ mole^{-1}. The total entropy increase is thus

$$5.26 + 5.62 + 26.06 = 36.94 \text{ cal. deg.}^{-1} \text{ mole}^{-1}.$$

25g. Entropy Change in Spontaneous (Irreversible) Processes.—The problem of immediate interest is to determine the nature of the entropy change for a spontaneous, i.e., thermodynamically irreversible, process. For this purpose a simple case will be considered, namely, a system consisting of an ideal gas. This is allowed to expand *spontaneously* into a vacuum at constant temperature; as stated in § 23f, no heat is evolved or absorbed in this process. Consequently no heat is supplied to or removed from the surroundings, and hence the entropy of the latter remains unchanged. However, the entropy of the system, i.e., the gas, increases, because its volume has increased, e.g., from V_1 to V_2, in the expansion. It has been stated previously that the entropy depends only on the temperature and pressure (or volume) of the system, and not on its previous history. The fact that the volume of the ideal gas has increased from V_1 to V_2, at the temperature T, means that the entropy has increased by an amount given by equation (25.11), viz.,

$$\Delta S = R \ln \frac{V_2}{V_1}. \tag{25.19}$$

The total increase of entropy of the *system and its surroundings* is thus equal to ΔS, as represented by equation (25.19), since the entropy change of the surroundings is zero in this case. Since V_2 is greater than V_1, it follows that ΔS is positive, and hence *the spontaneous (irreversible) isothermal expansion of the gas is accompanied by an increase of entropy of the system and its surroundings.*

The isothermal expansion of the gas from V_1 to V_2 could have been carried out infinitesimally slowly and reversibly by allowing it to push back a frictionless piston, the external pressure being adjusted so as to be always less than that of the gas by an extremely small amount (§ 23f). In this case the gas does external work and so a quantity of heat q is absorbed from the surroundings. Since this is taken up reversibly the gain of entropy of the system is equal to q/T. The heat lost by the surroundings, also at the temperature T, is equal to q, and hence the decrease of entropy of the surroundings is q/T. *The total entropy change of the system and surroundings in the reversible process is thus zero.* The results derived above for the expansion of an ideal gas can be shown to be completely general; *a spontaneous, i.e., irreversible, process is always accompanied by an increase of entropy of the system and its surroundings, but for a reversible process the entropy remains unchanged.*

Consider a system subjected to an irreversible process at constant temperature T; let $q_{\text{irr.}}$ represent the heat absorbed by the system from the surroundings in the course of this process. The increase of entropy of the system, represented by ΔS, is the same, irrespective of whether the process is carried out reversibly or not, for, as mentioned above, the entropy depends on the state of the system and not on how that state is attained. The entropy change of the surroundings may be determined by supposing them to be restored reversibly to their original state; this can be achieved by supplying the quantity of heat $q_{\text{irr.}}$ *in a reversible manner* at the temperature T, i.e., by increasing the entropy by $q_{\text{irr.}}/T$. The entropy of the surroundings is thus changed by $-q_{\text{irr.}}/T$ in the process under consideration. As the process is irreversible, there must be a net increase in the entropy of the system and its surroundings, so that

$$\Delta S - \frac{q_{\text{irr.}}}{T} > 0,$$

$$T\Delta S > q_{\text{irr.}}. \qquad (25.20)$$

For an irreversible process at constant temperature, therefore, *the heat absorbed by the system is less than the product of the temperature and the entropy increase.* For a reversible process the two quantities would, of course, be equal, i.e., $q_{\text{rev.}} = T\Delta S$. When considering an infinitesimal stage of a process, the foregoing results may be generalized in the expression

$$TdS \geq \delta q \qquad (25.21)$$

where the "greater than" sign refers to an irreversible (spontaneous) process, and the "equal to" sign applies to a thermodynamically reversible (equilibrium) one. This conclusion is of the greatest importance, as will be seen later (§ 26b); by the use of equation (25.21) it is possible to derive relatively simple rules for determining whether a given process can occur spontaneously or not.

25h. The Physical Significance of Entropy.—Although a precise physical interpretation of entropy cannot be given easily, it is nevertheless possible to obtain an indication of its significance in a relatively simple manner. A characteristic of spontaneous processes is that they are accompanied by an increase in the "disorder" or "chaos" of the system. In the metal bar which is hot at one end and cold at the other, there is some sort of order, in so far as most of the high energy (hot) molecules are segregated at one end, while the low energy (colder) molecules are largely at the other end of the bar. As a result of the spontaneous conduction of heat, there is a uniform distribution of energy throughout. The state of partial order has spontaneously become one of greater disorder. The same type of change, from order to disorder, occurs when one gas diffuses into another, when a concentrated solution diffuses into pure water, when a gas expands into a vacuum, and so on for other spontaneous processes. It was proved in the preceding section that such processes are accompanied by an increase of entropy, and hence it is possible to regard the entropy as a measure of the disorder or chaos of a system.

It has been seen, for example, that fusion and evaporation are both associated with an increase of entropy of the substance concerned; in each instance there is a decrease of order. In the solid the atoms, ions or molecules are arranged in a regular manner in the crystal lattice; upon melting most of the order is destroyed, and vaporization results in a further increase of disorder. Increase of temperature of a gas at constant pressure and increase of volume at constant temperature are both processes for which the entropy of the gas is increased; in each case the molecular chaos is increased. Lowering the temperature of a solid results in a decrease of entropy as the molecules or atoms become more and more ordered in their space lattices. In fact, it appears, as will be seen in Chapter XI, that at the absolute zero of temperature, when the order is probably perfect, the entropy of most pure solids is actually zero. The correlation of increase of entropy with increase of disorder is not restricted to physical processes; it is applicable also to chemical changes, although it is not always immediately obvious in such cases.

Since spontaneous processes lead to increasing disorder, it is evident that a disordered state is more probable than one of partial or complete order, for a spontaneous change will obviously occur from a less probable to a more probable state. It is to be expected, therefore, that there might be a connection between entropy, which increases in a spontaneous process, and the probability of the state, which increases at the same time. Considerations of this kind led L. Boltzmann (1896) to put forward the equation

$$S = k \ln W + \text{constant}, \tag{25.22}$$

relating the *actual entropy* S of a system to its **thermodynamic probability** W, where k is the Boltzmann constant, i.e., the gas constant per single molecule. The thermodynamic probability of a system was defined as the ratio of the probability of the actual state to that in which there is complete order, for the same energy and volume. In 1912, M. Planck suggested that the undetermined constant in equation (25.22) should be zero, so that

$$S = k \ln W. \tag{25.23}$$

In a completely ordered arrangement, as might exist in a solid at the absolute zero, W would be unity and S would be zero; this is apparently the case for most crystalline solids (§ 38a). It may be mentioned that in modern quantum mechanics, equation (25.23) is retained in form, but the symbol W takes on a somewhat modified significance; it is regarded as the number of possible quantum states of the system corresponding to approximately the same energy.

25i. Efficiency of Reversible Cycle.—Before proceeding to the development of new thermodynamic properties, the idea of entropy will be used to derive an expression for the maximum efficiency of a machine for the conversion of heat into work. In order that such a machine may function continuously, it must operate in **cycles,** *a cycle or cyclic process being a succession of changes as a result of which the system returns to its original state.* The internal energy change ΔE in a complete cycle is evidently equal to zero, and hence the resultant work done in the cycle must be equal to the net heat absorbed. Since maximum work can be obtained from an isothermal process when it is carried out reversibly, it is apparent that the maximum efficiency for the conversion of heat into work is obtainable from a reversible cycle. It can be shown by means of the second law of thermodynamics that *all reversible cycles operating between the same two temperatures must have identical efficiencies.* Consequently, any convenient thermodynamically reversible cycle can be chosen and its efficiency calculated; the result will then be applicable to all other reversible cycles.

A convenient form of cycle for purposes of calculation is that known as the **Carnot cycle,** named after its originator S. Carnot (1824); the system is an ideal gas, and it is subjected to a series of reversible changes in the following manner.

I. The gas is expanded isothermally and reversibly at the higher temperature T_2; this is accompanied by an absorption of heat q_2 from the "source," so that the entropy change of the gas is q_2/T_2.

II. The next stage is an adiabatic (reversible) expansion which results in a fall of temperature from T_2 to that of the "sink," viz., T_1. Since the change is adiabatic the entropy remains constant (§ 25c).

III. The gas is now compressed isothermally and reversibly at the lower temperature T_1; there is a liberation of heat q_1 to the "sink." (The value of q_1 here is purely numerical and does not include the sign of the heat change.) The entropy change of the gas in this stage is q_1/T_1.

IV. By suitable adjustment of the isothermal compression in stage III, a final adiabatic compression results in a return of the gas to its original state. The entropy change in this process is again zero.

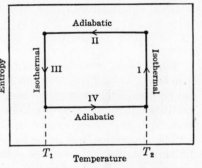

FIG. 54. The Carnot cycle

As a result of these four reversible stages the cycle has been completed, as shown diagrammatically in Fig. 54. Since the heat q_2 was taken up by the working substances at the higher temperature, while q_1 was evolved at the lower temperature, the net heat absorbed is $q_2 - q_1$, and this must represent the work w done in the reversible cycle. The efficiency of the machine is the fraction of the heat taken in at the higher temperature that is converted into work; that is,

$$\text{Efficiency} = \frac{w}{q_2} = \frac{q_2 - q_1}{q_2}. \tag{25.24}$$

It will be evident from Fig. 54 that the entropy changes in stages I and III are equal numerically, so that

$$\frac{q_2}{T_2} = \frac{q_1}{T_1},$$

and hence from equation (25.24),

$$\text{Efficiency} = \frac{q_2 - q_1}{q_2} = \frac{T_2 - T_1}{T_2}. \tag{25.25}$$

The efficiency of a reversible machine, which is the maximum possible efficiency, is thus determined by the temperatures of both the "source" and the "sink"; the greater the difference between these temperatures the greater is the efficiency of the cycle. This is one of the reasons why "superheated" steam, at high pressure, is frequently employed in the steam engine. It will be noted, incidentally, from equation (25.25) that for the complete conversion of heat into work, that is, for the efficiency to be unity, it would be necessary for the temperature T_1 of the "sink" to be the absolute zero.

Problem: Compare the maximum efficiencies of reversible engines in which the working substances are (i) water, (ii) mercury, the temperatures of the sources being the respective boiling points at 1 atm. pressure, viz., 100° C and 357° C. The temperature of the sink is 25° C in each case.

(i) For the engine using water vapor, T_1 is $273 + 100 = 373°$ K, and T_2 is $273 + 25 = 298°$ K; hence,

$$\text{Efficiency} = \frac{T_2 - T_1}{T_2} = \frac{373 - 298}{373} = 0.201.$$

(ii) For the mercury engine, T_2 is $273 + 357 = 630°$ K, and T_1 is $298°$ K; hence,

$$\text{Efficiency} = \frac{T_2 - T_1}{T_2} = \frac{630 - 298}{630} = 0.527.$$

For a cycle involving an irreversible stage or stages the efficiency is less than that given by equation (25.25). In actual practice, of course, no machine can be completely reversible; for one thing, the processes are not carried out infinitesimally slowly, as would be necessary, and for another, irreversible effects, such as friction, cannot be eliminated.

The suggestion was made by W. Thomson (Lord Kelvin) that a thermodynamic temperature scale be defined in such a manner that the actual temperature is proportional to the quantity of heat taken up or given out by the working substance in the isothermal stages of a reversible cycle. Provided the degree is taken as equal to the Centigrade degree, the thermodynamic scale is identical with the usual absolute temperature scale based on the volume of an ideal gas (§ 11c). It is for this reason that absolute temperatures are now generally referred to as "degrees Kelvin" and are represented by the symbol °K.

FREE ENERGY

26a. Free Energy and Maximum Work Functions.—Although the entropy is a fundamental thermodynamic property having important significance, it is more convenient for practical purposes to define certain other functions which may be used, in place of entropy, to express the conditions for spontaneous processes. These functions are represented by A and F, and although they have definite physical meanings, as will be seen shortly, they may be expressed, for the present, by the equations

$$A = E - TS \qquad (26.1)$$

$$F = H - TS, \qquad (26.2)$$

where, as before, E is the internal energy, and H, equal to $E + PV$ (§ 23h), is the heat content. Since E, H and S are extensive properties which depend only on the state of the system and the amounts of its constituents, it is evident that the functions A and F have the same characteristics.

Let A_1, E_1 and S_1 represent the values of these three functions in a particular state at the temperature T; then, from equation (26.1),

$$A_1 = E_1 - TS_1. \qquad (26.3)$$

Suppose an appreciable change takes place, so that the new values of the functions are A_2, E_2 and S_2, at the same temperature T; then,

$$A_2 = E_2 - TS_2, \qquad (26.4)$$

and subtraction of equation (26.3) from (26.4) gives

$$A_2 - A_1 = E_2 - E_1 - T(S_2 - S_1)$$

or

$$\Delta A = \Delta E - T\Delta S, \qquad (26.5)$$

where ΔA is the increase in the function A, ΔE is the increase of internal energy, and ΔS is the increase of entropy in the given change at constant temperature.

It can be shown, in exactly the same manner, from equation (26.2) that

$$\Delta F = \Delta H - T\Delta S. \qquad (26.6)$$

It was seen in § 23h that at constant pressure,

$$\Delta H = \Delta E + P\Delta V, \qquad (26.7)$$

and hence, from equations (26.5), (26.6) and (26.7),

$$\Delta F = \Delta A + P\Delta V, \qquad (26.8)$$

for an appreciable change at constant pressure.

The equations (26.5) and (26.6) express the changes in A and F in terms of the quantities ΔE, ΔH and ΔS whose significance has been already considered; it will now be shown that ΔA and ΔF have themselves a simple physical interpretation. For a *reversible process* taking place at the *constant temperature* T, the increase of entropy is given by

$$\Delta S = \frac{q}{T},$$

where q is the heat absorbed; consequently, q is equal to $T\Delta S$, as seen earlier (§ 25g), and if this is substituted in equation (26.5), the result is

$$\Delta A = \Delta E - q. \qquad (26.9)$$

By the first law of thermodynamics [equation (23.2)],

$$-w = \Delta E - q,$$

and comparison with equation (26.9) shows immediately that

$$w = -\Delta A. \qquad (26.10)$$

Since a reversible, isothermal process has been postulated, w is the maximum work that can be obtained from the system in the given change; hence, $-\Delta A$, i.e., the decrease in the A function, is equal to the maximum work obtainable. For this reason the property A is called the **maximum work function** or, briefly, the **work function.**

The function F, which is much more important from the standpoint of chemistry, is generally known as the **free energy,** although other descriptions have been used. If ΔA in equation (26.8) is replaced by its equivalent, $-w$, it is seen that *at constant temperature and pressure*

$$-\Delta F = w - P\Delta V. \tag{26.11}$$

The quantity $P\Delta V$ is the work of expansion done against the external pressure, and so $-\Delta F$ represents *the maximum work at constant temperature and pressure other than that due to a volume change.* The quantity $w - P\Delta V$ is thus sometimes called the **net work,** and so the decrease $-\Delta F$ in the free energy of a system is equal to the net work obtainable (at constant temperature and pressure) from the system under reversible conditions. An important form of net work, since it does not involve external work due to a volume change, is electrical work; consequently a valuable method for determining the free energy change of a process is to carry it out electrically, in a reversible manner, at constant temperature and pressure (§ 48a).

An expression that is frequently used for the free energy change in an isothermal and reversible process, not occurring at constant pressure, is obtained in the following manner. Since H is equal to $E + PV$, by definition, equation (26.2) may be written

$$F = E + PV - TS, \tag{26.12}$$

and upon differentiation it is seen that

$$dF = dE + PdV + VdP - TdS - SdT. \tag{26.13}$$

By the first law of thermodynamics, $\delta q = dE + \delta w$; if the restriction is applied of assuming that the work δw is due only to work of expansion against the external pressure, then

$$\delta q = dE + PdV.$$

Further, $\delta q/T$ is equal to dS, so that δq may be replaced by TdS, giving

$$TdS = dE + PdV. \tag{26.14}$$

Combination of equations (26.13) and (26.14) then yields the result

$$dF = VdP - SdT. \tag{26.15}$$

Two special conditions may be applied to equation (26.15); first, *at constant pressure,* dP is zero, so that

$$dF = -SdT \tag{26.16}$$

or, alternatively,

$$\left(\frac{dF}{dT}\right)_P = -S. \tag{26.17}$$

Second, *at constant temperature*, dT is zero, and hence from equation (26.15),

$$dF = VdP, \qquad (26.18)$$

that is,

$$\left(\frac{dF}{dP}\right)_T = V. \qquad (26.19)$$

For an appreciable process taking place at constant temperature, integration of equation (26.18) or (26.19), between the initial pressure P_1 and the final pressure P_2, gives

$$F_2 - F_1 = \Delta F = \int_{P_1}^{P_2} VdP. \qquad (26.20)$$

Since the free energy of a system depends only on its state, the value of ΔF given by equation (26.20) will hold for any change of pressure from P_1 to P_2, irrespective of whether it is reversible or not. The only conditions are that the temperature is constant and that all the work done is due to the volume change accompanying the change of pressure.

In order to evaluate the integral in equation (26.20), the volume may be expressed as a function of the pressure; a particularly simple case is that of an ideal gas, for which V is equal to RT/P per mole. In this instance equation (26.20) becomes

$$\Delta F = RT \int_{P_1}^{P_2} \frac{dP}{P}, \qquad (26.21)$$

since R and T are constant. It follows, therefore, that for 1 mole of an ideal gas undergoing a change of pressure at constant temperature,

$$\Delta F = RT \ln \frac{P_2}{P_1}. \qquad (26.22)$$

For n moles of ideal gas the free energy change would be n times as great as given by equation (26.22).

Problem: Calculate the free energy change in calories accompanying the expansion of 1 mole of water vapor in equilibrium with liquid water at 25° C to a pressure of 1 atm., at the same temperature, assuming the vapor to behave like an ideal gas. The vapor pressure of water at 25° C is 23.76 mm. of mercury.

In this case the initial pressure P_1 is 23.76 mm. while the final pressure P_2 is 1 atm.; the same units must be used for P_1 and P_2, and so the latter may be taken as 760 mm. It can be seen from equation (26.21) that ΔF will be obtained in the same units as R (more correctly RT); since ΔF is required in calories, R is taken as 1.987 cal. deg.$^{-1}$ mole^{-1}. The temperature T is $273.2 + 25 = 298.2°$ K, and so by equation (26.22),

$$\Delta F = 1.987 \times 298.2 \ln \frac{760}{23.76}$$

$$= 1.987 \times 298.2 \times 2.303 \log \frac{760}{23.76} = 2054 \text{ cal. mole}^{-1}.$$

26b. Conditions of Spontaneous Change and Equilibrium.—By combining the result of (§ 25g), as expressed by equation (25.21), i.e., $TdS \geq \delta q$, with the first law relationship, $\delta q = dE + PdV$, when the work δw is external work due to a volume change, i.e., PdV, it follows that

$$TdS \geq dE + PdV, \tag{26.23}$$

where, as before, the "greater than" sign applies to an irreversible (spontaneous) process and the "equal to" sign refers to a reversible process, i.e., an equilibrium state. If equation (26.23) is now introduced into (26.13), it is seen that

$$dF \leq VdP - SdT. \tag{26.24}$$

Hence, at constant temperature and pressure, i.e., when dT and dP are both zero, it follows from equation (26.24) that

$$(dF)_{T,P} \leq 0, \tag{26.25}$$

where the "less than" sign now refers to the spontaneous process. For an appreciable process, equation (26.25) may be written in the form

$$(\Delta F)_{T,P} \leq 0. \tag{26.26}$$

It is seen from equation (26.26) that for any process, physical or chemical, to take place spontaneously, at a definite temperature and pressure, the increase of free energy must be less than zero, that is to say, it must be negative. In other words, *a spontaneous process at constant temperature and pressure is accompanied by a decrease of free energy of the system*, provided the work involved is only work of expansion. For a thermodynamically reversible process taking place under the same conditions there is no change in the free energy. From the aspect of practical chemistry, the foregoing conclusions represent some of the most important results derived from the second law of thermodynamics; they provide the most useful solution to the problem presented at the beginning of this chapter, namely that of foretelling the conditions under which a reaction will occur spontaneously.

As long as the physical conditions are not altered, a system in equilibrium is never observed spontaneously to depart from equilibrium; *the free energy of the system must then be a minimum, at the given temperature and pressure*, for it is apparently unable to decrease further. In accordance with the mathematical properties of a minimum, *a small change in the equilibrium system, at constant temperature and pressure, should leave the free energy unaltered*, i.e., for such a change ΔF is zero. This is in agreement with equation (26.26) that for a thermodynamically reversible process, which is actually a succession of equilibrium states, ΔF is zero.

26c. Phases in Equilibrium: The Clapeyron Equation.—The chemical applications of the results given above will be considered more fully in Chapter XI, but it is of interest here to show how they may be utilized to derive the Clapeyron equation, which has already been used on several occasions. Consider any two phases of the same substance, e.g., liquid and vapor, or solid and liquid, in equilibrium with one another at a temperature T and pressure P. By supplying or withdrawing heat very slowly from the system, it is possible to change one phase reversibly into another, e.g., liquid into vapor, the system remaining at equilibrium all the time. In accordance with equation (26.26), since the only work done will be due to a possible change of volume, the free energy change ΔF will be zero, in spite of the change from one phase to another. It follows, therefore, that *equal amounts of a given substance must have exactly the same free energy in two phases at equilibrium.** If F_A and F_B are the free energies per mole of the substance in the two phases, indicated by A and B, respectively, at the equilibrium temperature and pressure, then

$$F_A = F_B. \tag{26.27}$$

As shown in § 22e, a system consisting of two phases of one component in equilibrium has one degree of freedom; consequently, if the temperature is changed, the pressure must be altered correspondingly if the system is to stay in equilibrium. Suppose the original temperature T is raised to $T + dT$; the equilibrium pressure will then be increased from P to $P + dP$. At the same time the free energy per mole of phase A will become $F_A + dF_A$, while that of phase B will be $F_B + dF_B$. Since the system is in equilibrium at the new temperature and pressure, the free energies per mole of each phase must still be equal; hence,

$$F_A + dF_A = F_B + dF_B. \tag{26.28}$$

It follows, therefore, from equations (26.27) and (26.28) that

$$dF_A = dF_B. \tag{26.29}$$

For an infinitesimal change occurring under such conditions that the only work is due to a volume change, as is true for the type of process under consideration, equation (26.15) is applicable. It is thus possible to write

$$dF_A = V_A dP - S_A dT$$

and

$$dF_B = V_B dP - S_B dT,$$

where V_A and V_B are the molar volumes, and S_A and S_B are the molar entropies of the two phases. Since dF_A is equal to dF_B, by equation (26.29), it follows that

$$V_A dP - S_A dT = V_B dP - S_B dT,$$

and hence,

$$\frac{dP}{dT} = \frac{S_B - S_A}{V_B - V_A}. \tag{26.30}$$

* This important result can be extended to a system of several phases consisting of more than one substance; the (partial) molar free energy of each substance is the same in all the phases at equilibrium.

The quantity $S_B - S_A$ is the entropy change accompanying the change of phase; if B is the phase which tends to be formed as the temperature is raised, then in accordance with the results in § 25f,

$$S_B - S_A = \frac{L}{T},$$ (26.31)

where L is the molar heat absorbed in the phase change, e.g., the molar heat of vaporization, fusion, sublimation or transition. Substitution of equation (26.31) in (26.30) then gives the general form of the Clapeyron (Clausius) equation

$$\frac{dP}{dT} = \frac{L}{T(V_B - V_A)}.$$ (26.32)

In accordance with its deduction, equation (26.32) is applicable to the equilibrium between two phases of any substance, e.g., liquid and vapor, solid and liquid, solid and vapor, or two crystalline forms of a solid. In each case V_B is the molar volume of the phase which tends to be formed as the temperature is raised, and V_A is the value for the phase that exists at low temperatures; L is the heat absorbed when 1 mole of the latter is converted into the former at the temperature T. If the equilibrium pressure is the vapor pressure, P in equation (26.32) is replaced by p, thus giving expressions of the form of (16.4) and (22.4). On the other hand, if the system is in equilibrium with the external pressure, P is used as in equation (22.1).

26d. The Gibbs-Helmholtz Equation.—Apart from questions relating to the criteria of equilibria and of spontaneous processes, a number of valuable results can be derived from the second law of thermodynamics. One of these is the Gibbs-Helmholtz equation, which is applicable to any physical or chemical change. Suppose F_1 is the free energy of a system in its initial state at the temperature T, and let $F_1 + dF_1$ be the value at the temperature $T + dT$. Similarly, suppose the free energy of the final state, after the change has occurred, is F_2 at the temperature T, and $F_2 + dF_2$ at the temperature $T + dT$. For a change taking place at constant pressure, equation (26.16) is applicable, so that

$$dF_1 = -S_1 dT \quad \text{and} \quad dF_2 = -S_2 dT,$$

where S_1 and S_2 are the entropies of the system in the initial and final states of the process. Subtraction of dF_1 from dF_2 then gives

$$d(F_2 - F_1) = -(S_2 - S_1)dT,$$

and writing ΔF for $F_2 - F_1$, the increase of free energy accompanying the process, and ΔS for $S_2 - S_1$, the corresponding entropy increase, it follows that

$$d(\Delta F) = -\Delta S dT.$$

Since constant pressure has been assumed, this result can be written as

$$\left(\frac{d(\Delta F)}{dT}\right)_P = -\Delta S,$$ (26.33)

with the subscript P to indicate constant pressure. If this expression for ΔS is substituted in equation (26.6) the result is

$$\Delta F = \Delta H + T\left(\frac{d(\Delta F)}{dT}\right)_P,$$ (26.34)

which is a form of the important **Gibbs-Helmholtz equation,** deduced by J. Willard Gibbs (1875) and by H. von Helmholtz (1882). The value of this equation lies in the fact that it can be used to calculate the heat change ΔH in a reaction from a knowledge of the free energy change ΔF, and its variation with temperature at constant pressure. Some practical applications of the Gibbs-Helmholtz equation will be considered in § 48a.

READING REFERENCES

1. **Second law of thermodynamics.** Hazelhurst, *Journal of Chemical Education,* **8,** 498 (1931); **9,** 1087 (1932).
2. **Second law of thermodynamics.** Cantelo, *ibid.,* **8,** 2198 (1931); **10,** 45, 306 (1933).
3. **Kinetic theory of heat.** Timm, *ibid.,* **12,** 31 (1935).
4. **Free energy.** Davis, *ibid.,* **13,** 376 (1936).
5. **Fundamentals of thermodynamics.** Roseveare, *ibid.,* **15,** 214 (1938).
6. **Second law of thermodynamics.** Wright, *ibid.,* **18,** 263 (1941).
7. **Thermodynamic functions.** Becher, *ibid.,* **19,** 237 (1942).
8. **Thermodynamic functions.** Wood, *ibid.,* **20,** 80 (1943).
9. **Entropy and free energy.** Luder, *ibid.,* **21,** 265 (1944).
10. **Second law of thermodynamics.** Luder, *ibid.,* **21,** 600 (1944).

REVIEW QUESTIONS

1. State the second law of thermodynamics in several forms, and explain why they are identical in significance.
2. Explain, with illustrations, the essential character of spontaneous processes.
3. Define the entropy change and show that it is a complete differential. Upon what does the entropy of a substance depend?
4. Derive an expression for the change of entropy accompanying the change of state of one mole of an ideal gas. What special forms apply (a) at constant pressure, (b) at constant temperature?
5. Derive the general equation for the change of entropy accompanying a change of temperature at constant pressure applicable to any substance. How is this used to evaluate actual entropy changes?
6. Explain how the molar entropies of fusion, vaporization and transition can be calculated. Why are these quantities important?
7. Show that the spontaneous isothermal expansion of a gas is accompanied by an increase in entropy of a system and its surroundings, whereas in a reversible isothermal expansion the entropy remains unchanged. State these conclusions in their most general form.
8. Give some indication of the physical significance of entropy. How is this used to derive an expression for the entropy of a substance?
9. Derive an expression for the efficiency of a machine for converting heat into work which operates in a completely reversible manner.

10. Define the work content, free energy, and changes in these quantities. How are the latter related to one another?

11. Show that there is justification for referring to ΔA and ΔF as the maximum work and net work, respectively.

12. Derive a general equation for the change of free energy accompanying a change of pressure at constant temperature. Convert this into the form applicable to one mole of an ideal gas.

13. Develop the conditions for reversible and irreversible processes in terms of the free energy changes. Explain the importance of these results in connection with (a) spontaneous processes, (b) equilibrium.

14. Derive the condition concerning the molar free energies of a substance in two phases at equilibrium.

15. Derive the general form of the Clapeyron equation.

16. Derive the Gibbs-Helmholtz equation.

PROBLEMS

I

1. Calculate the entropy change of one mole of an ideal monatomic gas when transferred from an initial state of 0° C and 1 atm. pressure to a final state of 100° C and 2.50 atm. pressure.

2. The molar heat capacity at constant pressure of carbon dioxide is expressed by

$$C_P = 7.70 + 5.3 \times 10^{-3}T - 0.83 \times 10^{-6}T^2 \text{ cal. deg.}^{-1}.$$

Calculate the entropy change when one mole of carbon dioxide is cooled from 100° C to 0° C at constant pressure.

3. Utilize the result for the entropy change in problem 2 to calculate the mean molar heat capacity of carbon dioxide in the range from 0° to 100° C.

4. The heat of fusion of acetic acid at its normal freezing point, i.e., 16.6° C, is 43.2 cal. per g.; the heat of vaporization at its normal boiling point, i.e., 118.3° C, is 96.8 cal. per g. The mean specific heat of liquid acetic acid is 0.460 cal. deg.$^{-1}$ g.$^{-1}$. Calculate the entropy change of the acetic acid when one mole is condensed from the vapor at the boiling point to form solid at the freezing point, at 1 atm. pressure.

5. At a pressure of 22.8 atm. water boils at 220° C. Calculate the maximum fraction of the heat absorbed at the higher temperature that can be converted into work by a steam engine operating with a boiler at 22.8 atm. and a condenser (sink) at 45° C.

6. Calculate the free energy change ΔF in calories, including the sign, when a quantity of an ideal gas occupying 1.12 liters at 760 mm. pressure is compressed at a constant temperature of 0° C until its volume is 0.20 liters.

7. In the formation of silver chloride from its elements under normal conditions, ΔF is -26.3 kcal. and ΔH is -30.3 kcal. per mole at 18° C. What is the corresponding entropy change? Calculate the change in free energy for a 10° rise of temperature, assuming the rate of change of ΔF with temperature, i.e., $d(\Delta F)/dT$, to remain constant.

II

1. The temperature of an ideal monatomic gas is raised from 25° C to 250° C. What must be the accompanying pressure change in order that the entropy of the gas may be unaffected by the complete process?

2. The mean molar heat capacity of oxygen gas from 0° to 100° C is 6.98 cal. deg.$^{-1}$ mole^{-1} at constant pressure. Starting at 0° C, to what temperature must one mole of oxygen be raised at constant volume in order to increase the entropy by 1 cal. deg.$^{-1}$ mole^{-1}?

3. The molar heat capacity of hydrogen at constant pressure may be expressed by

$$C_P = 6.85 + 0.28 \times 10^{-3}T + 0.22 \times 10^{-6}T^2 \text{ cal. deg.}^{-1}.$$

Calculate the change of entropy when one mole of hydrogen is heated from 0° to 120° C.

4. One mole of solid iodine at 20° C is heated at a constant pressure of 1 atm. to form liquid at 150° C. Calculate the change of entropy accompanying this process. The mean specific heat of solid iodine is 0.055 cal. deg.$^{-1}$ g.$^{-1}$, and that of the liquid is 0.108 cal. deg.$^{-1}$ g.$^{-1}$. The melting point of iodine at 1 atm. is 114° C and the heat of fusion is 11.7 cal. per g.

5. A refrigerating machine may be regarded as a heat engine working in the opposite direction, heat being absorbed at the lower temperature and given up at the higher temperature while work is done on the machine. What is the least amount of work in ergs which would be required to withdraw 1 cal. from a vessel at 0° C, the upper temperature being 25° C?

6. The vapor pressure of liquid mercury at 160° C is 4.19 mm. Calculate the free energy change in ergs accompanying the expansion of one mole of mercury vapor in equilibrium with liquid at 160° C to a pressure of 1 atm. at the same temperature, assuming the vapor to behave like an ideal monatomic gas.

7. The free energy change ΔF accompanying a given process is -20.5 kcal. per mole at 25° C, while at 35° C it is -20.0 kcal. per mole. Calculate the approximate entropy change ΔS and the change in heat content ΔH for the process at a temperature of 30° C.

CHAPTER IX

DILUTE SOLUTIONS

LOWERING OF VAPOR PRESSURE

27a. Raoult's Law.—A solution may be described as a homogeneous mixture of two (or more) substances; it consists of a single phase, in the sense defined in § 22e. A solution may be gaseous, liquid or solid; in the present chapter the treatment will refer particularly to solutions which are liquid, although the dissolved substance may be a solid. It will be seen in Chapter XII that there is no fundamental difference between the components of a solution, but for certain purposes it is convenient to distinguish between them. The component which constitutes the largest proportion of the solution is called the **solvent,** while the other, the dissolved substance, is referred to as the **solute.** If the concentration of solute, i.e., the amount in a given volume of solution, is small the solution is said to be dilute; the treatment in this and subsequent sections will deal essentially with such solutions.

It has been known for many years that when a solute is dissolved in a liquid the vapor pressure of the latter is lowered. The quantitative connection between the lowering of the vapor pressure and the composition of the solution was discovered by F. M. Raoult (1887) as the result of a large number of experiments with a variety of solutions. If p^0 is the vapor pressure of the pure solvent at a particular temperature, and p is the vapor pressure of the solution at the same temperature, the difference $p^0 - p$ is the lowering of the vapor pressure; if this is divided by p^0 the result, that is $(p^0 - p)/p^0$, is known as the **relative lowering of the vapor pressure** for the given solution. According to one form of **Raoult's law,** *the relative lowering of the vapor pressure is equal to the mole fraction of the solute in the solution.* If n_1 and n_2 are the numbers of moles of solvent and solute,[*] respectively, then in accordance with the definition of mole fraction given in § 11g, the mole fraction x_2 of the solute is

$$x_2 = \frac{n_2}{n_1 + n_2}, \qquad (27.1)$$

and hence, by Raoult's law,

$$\frac{p^0 - p}{p^0} = x_2 = \frac{n_2}{n_1 + n_2}. \qquad (27.2)$$

The results in Table XXIX, taken from the work of Raoult, show that the law is obeyed, at least approximately, for a number of solutes in ether solution;

---

[*] It is a widely used convention for dilute solutions to indicate the solvent by the subscript 1 and the solute by 2.

TABLE XXIX.   TEST OF RAOULT'S LAW IN ETHER SOLUTION

Solute	Mole Fraction of Solute	Relative Lowering of Vapor Pressure	Ratio
Nitrobenzene	0.060	0.055	0.92
Methyl salicylate	0.092	0.086	0.93
Ethyl benzoate	0.096	0.091	0.95
Benzaldehyde	0.130	0.132	1.02
Aniline	0.077	0.081	1.05

if the law were exact, the ratio in the last column would have been unity in each case. There are theoretical reasons for believing that Raoult's law could only be expected to hold for solutions having a heat of dilution of zero, and for which there is no volume change upon mixing the components in the liquid state. Such solutions, which should obey Raoult's law exactly at all concentrations and all temperatures, are called **ideal solutions.** Actually very few solutions behave ideally (§ 40a) and some deviation from Raoult's law is always to be anticipated; however, for dilute solutions these deviations are small and can usually be ignored.

An alternative form of Raoult's law, which will be used later, is obtained by subtracting unity from both sides of equation (27.2); the result is

$$\frac{p}{p^0} = 1 - x_2. \tag{27.3}$$

The sum of the mole fractions of solvent and solute must always equal unity; hence, if x_1 is the mole fraction of the solvent, and x_2 is that of the solute, as given above, it follows that

$$x_1 + x_2 = 1, \tag{27.4}$$

and hence equation (27.3) can be reduced to

$$p = x_1 p^0. \tag{27.5}$$

In words, therefore, *the vapor pressure of the solvent in a solution is directly proportional to the mole fraction of the solvent,* if Raoult's law is obeyed. It will be observed that the proportionality constant is p^0, the vapor pressure of the pure solvent.

27b. Determination of Molecular Weights.—It is possible, by means of Raoult's law, to determine the molecular weight of a dissolved substance. If the solution consists of w_1 grams of solvent of molecular weight M_1, and w_2 grams of solute of molecular weight M_2, the respective numbers of moles are given by

$$n_1 = \frac{w_1}{M_1} \quad \text{and} \quad n_2 = \frac{w_2}{M_2},$$

and, consequently, from equations (27.1) and (27.2),

$$\frac{p^0 - p}{p^0} = \frac{w_2/M_2}{(w_1/M_1) + (w_2/M_2)}. \tag{27.6}$$

For dilute solutions, the small number of moles n_2 of the solute may be neglected in comparison with that of the solvent, i.e., n_1; under these conditions equation (27.2) becomes

$$\frac{p^0 - p}{p^0} \approx \frac{n_2}{n_1} = \frac{w_2}{M_2} \cdot \frac{M_1}{w_1}. \tag{27.7}$$

By making up a solution containing known weights of solvent (w_1) and of solute (w_2), it is possible to determine the molecular weight M_2 of the latter, if the vapor pressure of the solvent (p^0) and solution (p) can be measured. The molecular weight M_1 of the solvent is assumed to be known.

Problem: When 18.04 g. of the sugar alcohol mannitol were dissolved in 100 g. of water, the vapor pressure of the latter at 20° C was lowered from 17.535 mm. to 17.226 mm. of mercury. Calculate the molecular weight of mannitol.

In this case, w_1 is 100 g. and M_1, the molecular weight of water, is 18.02; w_2 is 18.04 g. The values of p^0 and p are 17.535 and 17.226 mm., respectively. The *relative lowering* of the vapor pressure is obviously independent of the units used for the vapor pressures, provided p^0 and p are expressed in the same units. Hence, by equation (27.6),

$$\frac{17.535 - 17.226}{17.535} = \frac{18.04/M_2}{(100/18.02) + (18.04/M_2)},$$

$$M_2 = 181.$$

Although the solution is not particularly dilute, the use of the approximate equation (27.7) gives $M_2 = 184$. The correct value is 182.

27c. Measurement of Vapor Pressure Lowering.—Since the actual lowering of vapor pressure is small, the obvious procedure, of measuring the vapor pressure of the solvent and the solution separately by the methods described in § 16c and subtracting the two values, is not often used. The vapor pressure of the solvent is determined in the usual manner, and then the lowering $p^0 - p$ is measured directly by some type of differential manometer. This procedure has been used to obtain very accurate results.

The gas saturation or transpiration method (§ 16c) has been adapted for the determination of the relative lowering of vapor pressure. The same volume of dry gas, e.g., air, is passed through saturators containing the solvent and solution, respectively, with a suitable absorber in between. From the losses in weight of the saturators, the relative lowering can be calculated, without actually evaluating the separate vapor pressures of solvent and solution.

Another procedure, known as the **isopiestic method,** has attracted attention in recent years. If two vessels containing solutions of different solutes in the same solvent are placed side by side in a closed space at constant temperature, vapor will pass from the solution of higher to that of lower vapor pressure until both solutions have the same vapor pressure. The two solutions are then said to be **isopiestic** (Greek: *equal pressure*), and they are analyzed to determine their concentrations. If one of the solutes is a substance, e.g., potassium chloride, for which the vapor pressures of its solutions at various concentra-

ions are known, the vapor pressure of the isopiestic solution of the other
solute, at the measured concentration, is immediately available.

ELEVATION OF THE BOILING POINT

28a. Vapor Pressure and Boiling Point.—A direct consequence of the reduction of the vapor pressure by a *nonvolatile* solute is that the boiling point of
the solution, i.e., the temperature at which its vapor pressure becomes equal
to 1 atm., must be higher than for the
pure solvent. This can be readily seen
from the curves in Fig. 55, which represent the variation of vapor pressure
with temperature of pure solvent and a
solution; the latter is, of course, always
below the former. The boiling point of
the solvent is T_0 and that of the solution is T; the boiling point is thus raised
by the amount $T - T_0 = \Delta T$. This
quantity is known as the **boiling point
elevation,** and it is represented by the
distance AB in the diagram. The point
A gives the vapor pressure p^0 of the
solvent, i.e., 1 atm., while C is that of
the solution, at the temperature T_0;
hence, the distance AC is equivalent to
$p^0 - p$. Since p^0 is a constant quan-

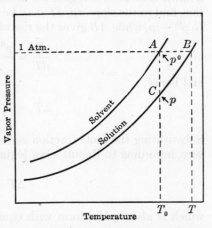

FIG. 55.   Rise of boiling point of solution

tity, namely 1 atm., it follows that AC proportional to the relative lowering
of vapor pressure, i.e., $(p^0 - p)/p^0$.

If the vapor pressure curves for a series of solutions are almost parallel in
the region of the boiling point, as is probably true for dilute solutions, the
ratio of the distances AB to AC will be constant for these solutions. In other
words, the boiling point elevation AB will be proportional to the relative lowering of the vapor pressure AC. Further, since the relative lowering is equal
to x_2, the mole fraction of the solute, by Raoult's law, it follows that

$$\Delta T = k_b x_2, \tag{28.1}$$

where k_b is the proportionality constant.

The result of equation (28.1) may be derived in a more precise manner
which gives the value of the constant k_b in terms of properties of the solvent.
Although the exact derivation is not very difficult, it will be sufficient to give
an approximate modification that is particularly applicable to dilute solutions.
For the variation of the vapor pressure of a liquid with temperature, the
Clapeyron-Clausius equation may be written in the form of equation (16.7),
viz.,

$$\frac{dp}{dT} = \frac{L_v p}{RT^2}. \tag{28.2}$$

This expression will represent the slope of the vapor pressure curve of the solution, but near the boiling point p and T may be replaced by p^0 and T_0, respectively, if the solution is dilute; hence, the relationship

$$\frac{dp}{dT} = \frac{L_v p^0}{RT_0^2} \qquad (28.3)$$

may be used to give the slope of the vapor pressure curve of the solution. For a dilute solution the region BC of this curve (Fig. 55) will be almost a straight line, and so the slope dp/dT may be represented by AC/AB; since AC is equal to $p^0 - p$, while AB gives the rise of boiling point ΔT, it follows that

$$\frac{dp}{dT} = \frac{p^0 - p}{\Delta T} = \frac{L_v p^0}{RT_0^2}, \qquad (28.4)$$

and hence,

$$\Delta T = \frac{RT_0^2}{L_v} \cdot \frac{p^0 - p}{p^0}. \qquad (28.5)$$

Substituting the mole fraction x_2 for the relative lowering of the vapor pressure, according to Raoult's law [equation (27.2)], it follows that

$$\Delta T = \frac{RT_0^2}{L_v} x_2, \qquad (28.6)$$

which is identical in form with equation (28.1), since R, T_0 and L_v are constants.

The most important application of these equations is for the determination of molecular weights of dissolved substances, and for this purpose an alternative form is more useful. Since the solutions are dilute, the mole fraction x_2 may be replaced by n_2/n_1, that is, by $w_2 M_1 / M_2 w_1$, as in equation (27.7); hence, (28.6) becomes

$$\Delta T = \frac{RT_0^2}{L_v} \cdot \frac{w_2 M_1}{M_2 w_1}$$

$$= \frac{RT_0^2}{l_v} \cdot \frac{w_2}{M_2 w_1}, \qquad (28.7)$$

where l_v, equal to L_v/M_1, is the heat of vaporization *per gram* of solvent.

In the study of dilute solutions, it has been found convenient to express the concentration of a solution in terms of its **molality**; * this is *the number of moles of solute dissolved in 1000 grams of solvent*. In the solution under consideration w_2/M_2 moles of solute are dissolved in w_1 grams of solvent, and so the molality m is given by

$$m = \frac{w_2}{M_2 w_1} \times 1000. \qquad (28.8)$$

---

* The term "molality" should not be confused with "molarity"; the latter is the number of moles of solute *per liter of solution*. For dilute *aqueous* solutions the molality and molarity are approximately equal.

Substitution of this result into equation (28.7) leads to

$$\Delta T = \frac{RT_0^2}{1000 l_v} m$$

$$= K_b m, \tag{28.9}$$

where K_b is a constant for each solvent, defined by

$$K_b = \frac{RT_0^2}{1000 l_v}, \tag{28.10}$$

which depends on its boiling point and heat of vaporization. According to equation (28.9), therefore, *the elevation of the boiling point of a solution is proportional to its molality*, provided it is dilute and obeys Raoult's law. This theoretical deduction has been confirmed experimentally for a number of solvents and solutes. Strict proportionality between the molality and boiling point elevation holds only in extremely dilute solutions, but there is an approximate proportionality even in solutions of moderate concentration. Such deviations as are observed are due partly to the solutions not being dilute enough for the approximations made in the derivation of equation (28.9) to be justifiable, and partly because of deviations from Raoult's law due to nonideal behavior.

The constant K_b is called the **molal elevation constant;** it can be seen from equation (28.9) that it is physically equivalent to the rise of boiling point for a solution of unit molality, i.e., $m = 1$. Actually, a solution with a molality of unity would not be sufficiently dilute for equation (28.9) to be valid, and so K_b may be regarded as the boiling point elevation for a unit molal solution, if the value were proportional to that for a dilute solution.

28b. Molecular Weight from Boiling Point Elevation.—Since the molality of a solution is related to the molecular weight M_2 of the solute, according to equation (28.8), measurements of the boiling point elevation can be used to determine molecular weights of dissolved substances. For this purpose, combination of equation (28.8) with (28.9) gives

$$\Delta T = K_b \frac{1000 w_2}{M_2 w_1},$$

$$M_2 = K_b \frac{1000 w_2}{\Delta T w_1}. \tag{28.11}$$

In order to apply this result it is necessary to know the value of K_b; this may be obtained in two ways. First, from the boiling point and heat of vaporization of the solvent, by means of equation (28.10), and second, by measuring the boiling point elevation ΔT experimentally for a solution containing a solute of known molecular weight M_2 and applying equation (28.11). The results obtained by the two methods are generally in excellent agreement, provided

the solutions are dilute, thus supplying confirmation of the theoretical argu‑
ments presented above.

Problem: Calculate the experimental molal elevation constant of water from the
fact that a solution containing 0.450 g. of urea (molecular weight 60.06) in 22.5 g. o
water gave a boiling point elevation of 0.170°. Compare the result with the valu
derived from the heat of vaporization of 539.9 cal. g.$^{-1}$ at the boiling point.

To obtain K_b from the experimental data, equation (28.11) is written in the form

$$K_b = \Delta T \frac{M_2 w_1}{1000 w_2} = 0.170 \times \frac{60.06 \times 22.5}{1000 \times 0.450}$$

$$= 0.510.$$

To obtain K_b from the heat of vaporization, use is made of equation (28.10), where
l_v is 539.9 cal. g.$^{-1}$. The energy units for R must be the same as those for l_v; hence R
is 1.987 cal. deg.$^{-1}$ mole^{-1}. The boiling point of water is 100° C, and hence T_0 is
$273.2 + 100.0 = 373.2°$ K; consequently

$$K_b = \frac{1.987 \times (373.2)^2}{1000 \times 539.9} = 0.513.$$

The molal elevation constants for a number of common solvents are quoted
in Table XXX, and these may be used for the determination of the molecular

TABLE XXX.   MOLAL ELEVATION CONSTANTS

Solvent	K_b	Solvent	K_b
Water	0.513	Benzene	2.63
Methanol	0.83	Acetic acid	3.14
Ethanol	1.20	Chloroform	3.85
Acetone	1.72	Carbon tetrachloride	5.02

weights of a variety of solutes by means of equation (28.11). The principle of
the method used is to take a definite weight w_2 of solute, whose molecular
weight is to be found, and to dissolve it in a known weight w_1 of solvent;
the elevation ΔT of the boiling point is then measured. Since the molal eleva‑
tion constant is known, the molecular weight M_2 of the solute can be calcu‑
lated.

28c. Determination of Boiling Point Elevation.—When observing the
boiling point of a solution it is necessary that the thermometer be placed in the
liquid, and not in the vapor; as a result there is a possibility of serious error due
to superheating. Various devices have been described from time to time
whose purpose is to overcome this difficulty. In the procedure employed by
W. Landsberger (1898), superheating is avoided by using the vapor of the
boiling solvent to raise the solution to its boiling point. As the vapor con‑
denses it gives up its heat of vaporization to raise the temperature of the solu‑
tion, but this cannot, theoretically, exceed the boiling point of the latter. A
disadvantage of this method is that the condensation of the vapor changes the
concentration of the solution which is being studied; the boiling point, there‑
fore, does not remain constant. Nevertheless, for approximate purposes the
Landsberger procedure is quite satisfactory.

More accurate results may be obtained by the method of F. G. Cottrell (1919); the thermometer is placed above the surface of the liquid, and the boiling solution is made to pump itself continuously over the bulb. The latter is thus covered with a thin layer of boiling solution, and so the temperature recorded should be the true boiling point. In precision work the boiling points of solvent and solution should be determined simultaneously, so as to avoid the error due to possible changes in the atmospheric pressure. Since it is only the elevation of the boiling point that is required, and not the actual boiling points themselves, differential methods have been used to measure the difference in temperature between the solvent and solution boiling side by side.

DEPRESSION OF THE FREEZING POINT

29a. Vapor Pressure and Freezing Point.—Another consequence of the lowering of the vapor pressure of the solvent in a solution is that the freezing point of the solution is lower than that of the pure solvent. It has been long known that a dissolved substance depresses the freezing point of water, and the familiar use of common salt to melt snow is based on this fact. The relationship between the freezing point of the pure solvent and that of a solution may be seen with the aid of the vapor pressure curves in Fig. 56; these curves show the temperature variation of the vapor pressure of the solvent over the pure solvent (e.g., water), the solution, and the solid solvent (e.g., ice), respectively. Comparison with Fig. 49 shows that A is the freezing point of the solvent, temperature T_0; similarly, B, temperature T, is the freezing point of the solution, where the latter is in equilibrium with ice.

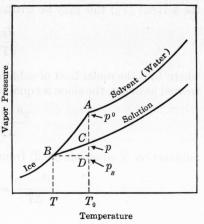

FIG. 56. Lowering of freezing point of solution

The freezing point of the solution is obviously lower than that of the solvent, and the **freezing point depression** ΔT is equal to $T_0 - T$. The distance AC is equivalent to $p^0 - p$ at the freezing point of the solvent, and since p^0 at this temperature is a constant, it follows, as in § 28a, that AC is proportional to the relative lowering of the vapor pressure. If, as before, the vapor pressure curves for a number of dilute solutions are almost parallel straight lines in the vicinity of the freezing point, the ratio AC/BC will be constant. For such solutions, therefore, the depression of the freezing point ΔT will be proportional to the relative vapor pressure lowering, and hence to the mole fraction x_2 of the solute. It follows, therefore, as for the boiling point elevation, that

$$\Delta T = k_f x_2. \tag{29.1}$$

The more complete derivation of this expression is again based on the Clapeyron-Clausius equation. The slope of the vapor pressure curve for the dilute solution in the vicinity of the freezing point is given by equation (28.3), viz.,

$$\frac{dp}{dT} = \frac{L_v p^0}{RT_0^2},$$

where T_0 is now the freezing point of the solvent. If BC in Fig. 56 is taken to be a straight line, the slope dp/dT may be replaced by CD/BD, i.e., by $(p - p_s)/\Delta T$, so that

$$\frac{p - p_s}{\Delta T} = \frac{L_v p^0}{RT_0^2}. \tag{29.2}$$

The slope of the vapor pressure curve of the solid solvent (e.g., ice) is also given by a form of the Clapeyron-Clausius equation, derived from equation (22.5), which is analogous to (28.3); at the temperature of the freezing point of the solvent (T_0) this may be written as

$$\frac{dp}{dT} = \frac{L_s p^0}{RT_0^2}, \tag{29.3}$$

where L_s is the molar heat of sublimation of the solid solvent. Again, if AB is treated as linear, the slope is equal to AD/BD; hence, equation (29.3) becomes

$$\frac{p^0 - p_s}{\Delta T} = \frac{L_s p^0}{RT_0^2}. \tag{29.4}$$

Subtraction of equation (29.2) from (29.4) then gives

$$\frac{p^0 - p}{\Delta T} = \frac{(L_s - L_v)p^0}{RT_0^2}$$

$$\Delta T = \frac{RT_0^2}{L_f} \cdot \frac{p^0 - p}{p^0}, \tag{29.5}$$

where L_f, equal to $L_s - L_v$ [equation (22.3)], is the molar heat of fusion of the solid solvent. If Raoult's law is obeyed, the relative lowering of the vapor pressure in equation (29.5) may be replaced by x_2, the mole fraction of solute, so that

$$\Delta T = \frac{RT_0^2}{L_f} x_2. \tag{29.6}$$

This equation is seen to be equivalent to (29.1) and exactly analogous to equation (28.6), except that the molar heat of fusion now replaces the heat of vaporization. By using arguments exactly similar to those employed previously, it is found that for dilute solutions

$$\Delta T = K_f m, \tag{29.7}$$

where the **molal depression constant** K_f is defined by

$$K_f = \frac{RT_0^2}{1000l_f}, \qquad (29.8)$$

l_f being the heat of fusion per gram, and T_0 is the freezing point of the solvent. *The depression of the freezing point is thus proportional to the molality of the solution;* as before, the essential condition is that the solution should be dilute. Experimental determinations of freezing point depressions are in general agreement with this conclusion; with relatively concentrated solutions deviations from equation (29.7) are observed, as is to be expected.

29b. Molecular Weight from Freezing Point Depression.—The molal depression constant must first be determined, and this is obtained either by calculation, from equation (29.8), or by direct measurement of the freezing point depression with a solute of known molecular weight. The results obtained by the two methods are in excellent agreement; the values for some familiar solvents are given in Table XXXI. If the depression constant is

TABLE XXXI. MOLAL DEPRESSION CONSTANTS

Solvent	K_f	Solvent	K_f
Water	1.86	Naphthalene	7.0
Acetic acid	3.90	Bromoform	14.3
Benzene	5.12	Cyclohexane	20.2
Nitrobenzene	6.90	Camphor	40.0

known, the molecular weight of the dissolved substance can then be derived from the expression

$$M_2 = K_f \frac{1000w_2}{\Delta T w_1}, \qquad (29.9)$$

which is exactly analogous to equation (28.11).

Problem: For a solution of 0.911 gram of carbon tetrachloride in 50.00 grams of benzene, the freezing point depression was found to be 0.603°. Calculate the molecular weight of the carbon tetrachloride.

According to equation (29.9), using $K_f = 5.12$ from Table XXXI,

$$M_2 = \frac{5.12 \times 1000 \times 0.911}{0.603 \times 50.00} = 155.$$

Attention should be called to the fact that the foregoing treatment will hold only if the solid which separates on freezing the solution is pure solvent, e.g., pure ice. Sometimes a solid solution (§ 20a), i.e., a homogeneous solid containing both solute and solvent, will separate; in this event, the equations given above are no longer applicable.

29c. Determination of Freezing Point Depression.—For general purposes, freezing point determinations may be made by placing the solvent in a tube surrounded by an air jacket and a suitable freezing bath. The tube containing the solvent is fitted with a stirrer and a thermometer graduated in hundredths of a degree. By gradually lowering the temperature of the liquid, and stirring at the same time to avoid supercooling, the freezing point, at which the temperature remains stationary, can be observed. A known weight of solute is then dissolved in a definite quantity of solvent, and the freezing point is determined. The difference in the two readings gives the lowering of the freezing point for the solution of known composition. This is the principle used by E. Beckmann (1888) in the first accurate measurements of freezing point depressions.

The method just described has a number of inherent difficulties which have been overcome in what is called the **equilibrium method.** If water is the solvent, the solution is very thoroughly stirred with cracked ice in a vacuum-jacketed vessel until equilibrium is attained. The temperature, which is the true freezing point of the solution, is then recorded; some of the liquid is removed by means of a pipet and analyzed so as to determine its composition. The same procedure, without the necessity for analysis, is carried out with pure water in order to give the freezing point of the solvent. The difference is the required depression of the freezing point. For precision measurements, two similar vessels are used, one containing the solvent (water) and the other the solution, together with crushed ice; when equilibrium is reached the difference in temperature of the two vessels is measured. This gives the freezing point depression directly. Results of a very high order of accuracy have been obtained in this manner.

It will be noted from Table XXXI that camphor has an exceptionally high molal depression constant; this fact is utilized in a simple, although approximate, method for determining molecular weights of organic compounds that are soluble in camphor. An intimate mixture of the solute with about ten times its weight of camphor is made, and its melting point is determined in a small tube, in the manner commonly used in the organic chemical laboratory. The depression of the freezing point from that of pure camphor, measured in the same manner, is of the order of 10° or more, and so may be read with sufficient accuracy on a thermometer graduated in degrees.

OSMOSIS AND OSMOTIC PRESSURE

30a. Semipermeable Membranes.—An important property of solutions, related to those already considered in this chapter, is that of **osmosis** (Greek: *push*); this term is used to describe *the spontaneous flow of solvent into a solution, or from a more dilute to a more concentrated solution, when the two liquids are separated from each other by a suitable membrane.* Osmosis strictly refers to the flow of *solvent only;* if there is a movement of solute, in the opposite direction, the behavior is then called diffusion. The essential property of a membrane which permits osmosis to occur is that it allows free passage of the solvent, e.g., water, but not of the dissolved substance, e.g., sugar. Membranes possessing this property are said to be **semipermeable.**

The phenomenon of osmosis may be illustrated in a simple manner by tying an animal membrane, e.g., bladder, over the end of an inverted thistle tube

(Fig. 57), which is then partly filled with a concentrated solution of sucrose (cane sugar) and dipped into a beaker of water, as shown in the figure. The level of the liquid will rise in the tube until the excess hydrostatic pressure causes the water to flow outward at the same rate as the inward flow due to osmosis. This particular arrangement, however, does not lend itself to the quantitative study of osmosis, because the animal membrane is not completely semipermeable. The sugar from inside the thistle tube thus tends to diffuse out into the water, and as a result the level of the liquid in the tube falls slowly. Incidentally, the solution becomes considerably diluted by the entry of the water, and this also affects the results.

For the measurement of osmotic effects it is necessary to have a membrane that is as near as possible to being perfectly semipermeable. In 1864, M. Traube suggested the use of artificial membranes made of copper ferrocyanide, $Cu_2Fe(CN)_6$, and this is still regarded as the best material for the purpose. Many improvements have since been made in the method of supporting the membrane but no better substance has yet been found.

30b. Osmotic Pressure and its Measurement.— Following upon Traube's discovery of the semipermeable property of a copper ferrocyanide membrane, quantitative measurements of osmosis were made by W. F. P. Pfeffer (1877). A porous pot, made of fine-grained, unglazed porcelain, was thoroughly soaked in a solution of copper sulfate. The pot was then filled with a solution of potassium ferrocyanide and immersed in one of copper sulfate. The two substances diffusing into the walls of the vessel reacted there to form a precipitate of insoluble copper ferrocyanide which filled the pores. A satisfactory membrane prepared in this manner appeared as a fine reddish-brown line in the white material of the porcelain vessel. After suitable washing, the osmosis cell prepared as just described was attached to a wide T-tube and a sealed manometer (Fig. 58). The cell was then filled with an experimental solution of known concentration, and closed with a rubber stopper; a glass tube passing through the latter was sealed off in such a way as to leave no air in the cell. The whole apparatus was then immersed in pure water at a constant temperature.

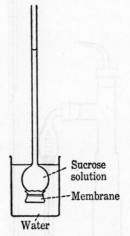

Sucrose solution

Membrane

Water

FIG. 57. Osmosis through animal membrane

As a result of osmosis, there was a tendency for water to pass into the cell from the outside. The cell was completely sealed, however, and so the amount of water that entered was extremely small; instead, a steady pressure was ultimately developed inside the cell, the magnitude of which could be read on the manometer. This pressure is called the **osmotic pressure** of the solution; it is best defined as *the excess pressure which must be applied to a solution to prevent the passage into it of solvent when separated from the latter by a perfectly semipermeable membrane.* There has been some tendency to think of osmotic pressure as a pressure produced by the solution, but this point of view is misleading. It is more satisfactory to consider the osmotic pressure as being brought into existence only when the solution is separated from the solvent by a semipermeable membrane. The resulting osmosis, or tendency for osmosis to occur, then produces an excess pressure in the solution, as in the work of Pfeffer just described. When this excess pressure attains the value of the osmotic pressure, the tendency for solvent to enter the solution is exactly counterbalanced by the reverse tendency, and a condition of equilibrium results.

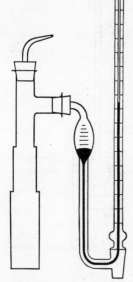

The definition of osmotic pressure given above may be well illustrated by the method employed by the Earl of Berkeley and E. G. J. Hartley (1906–09) in their accurate measurements. A gradually increasing pressure was applied by means of a pump to the solution, separated from the solvent by a semipermeable membrane deposited in a porous cylinder. The pressure which had to be exerted in order just to prevent the entry of the solvent was taken as the osmotic pressure of the solution. The results obtained in this manner were almost identical with those given by an improved form of Pfeffer's method, in which the solvent was allowed to produce the excess pressure in the solution.

Important advances in the measurement of osmotic pressure were made by H. N. Morse and J. C. W. Frazer, and their collaborators (1901–23). Great improvements were made in the production of cells containing strong semipermeable membranes capable of withstanding pressures up to 270 atm. without leakage. The actual determination of the osmotic pressure was based on observation of the pressure produced in the solution by the tendency of the solvent to enter it through the semipermeable membrane.

FIG. 58. Measurement of osmotic pressure (Pfeffer)

30c. Comparison of Osmotic Pressures: Isotonic Solutions.—Plant and animal cells usually contain solutions of salts, sugars, etc., enclosed in membranes that are largely, although not completely, semipermeable in character. In a normal, healthy plant cell water has entered through the membrane and has set up an excess pressure in the interior; this causes the cell material to be pressed against the walls, producing the phenomenon known as "turgidity." If such a cell is placed in water or in a solution of osmotic pressure less than that of the solution in the cell, there will be a tendency for water to enter, but owing to the rigidity of the outer cellulose walls little change is observed. On the other hand, if the cell is immersed in a solution having a higher osmotic pressure, water will pass out from the interior of the cell through the membrane. The material of the cell will thus shrink and will detach itself from the walls; this effect is referred to as **plasmolysis**.

\ By taking a number of solutions of a given substance at different concentrations and observing the change in the plant cells, it is possible to find the solution which just fails to bring about plasmolysis. *This solution has then the same osmotic pressure as the cell solution,* and is said to be **isotonic** (Greek: *same tension*) with it.* Working in the same manner with a variety of solutes, and a given type of cell, it is possible to prepare a series of isotonic solutions of different substances; such solutions have approximately the same osmotic pressure. If the osmotic pressure of one of these solutions is known by direct measurement, the value gives the approximate osmotic pressure of all the other solutions. The results are not exact, however, because the cell membranes are not perfectly semipermeable.

30d. Results of Osmotic Pressure Measurements.—Although Pfeffer made measurements on solutions of sucrose, dextrose, potassium nitrate and other substances, his results with sucrose have become of historical importance. Some of the data on the influence of concentration on osmotic pressure are recorded in Table XXXII; they were obtained at a temperature of about

TABLE XXXII. OSMOTIC PRESSURES OF SUCROSE SOLUTIONS

Concentration	Osmotic Pressure	Ratio
1 per cent	535 mm.	535
2	1016	508
4	2082	521
6	3075	513

15° C. The approximate constancy of the ratio of the osmotic pressure to the concentration, as shown by the figures in the last column, indicates that at constant temperature the osmotic pressure of a solution is almost directly proportional to its concentration.

The effect of temperature is demonstrated by the results in Table XXXIII,

TABLE XXXIII. INFLUENCE OF TEMPERATURE ON OSMOTIC PRESSURE

Temperature		Osmotic Pressure	Ratio
6.8° C	280.0° K	505	1.80
13.7°	286.9°	525	1.83
22.0°	295.2°	548	1.85
32.0°	305.2°	544	1.79
36.0°	309.2°	567	1.83

which Pfeffer obtained with a 1 per cent sucrose solution. It is evident that the osmotic pressure increases with temperature, and the approximate constancy of the ratio of the osmotic pressure to the absolute temperature shows the close proportionality between these quantities.

It was shown by J. H. van't Hoff (1887) that Pfeffer's measurements of osmotic pressure indicated a parallelism between the properties of solutions and of gases. If c is the concentration of a solution, expressed in moles per

---

* Isotonic solutions are also isopiestic (§ 27c), for they have the same vapor pressure (cf. § 30e).

unit volume of solution, and V is the volume of the solution, in the same units, containing 1 mole, then c is equal to $1/V$. As seen above, the osmotic pressure divided by the concentration is constant at a given temperature; even though the concentration units in Table XXXII are not the same as defined here, the values are roughly proportional, and so it is possible to write

$$\frac{\Pi}{c} = \text{constant},$$

where Π is the osmotic pressure, and replacing c by $1/V$, it follows that

$$\Pi V = \text{constant}, \tag{30.1}$$

at constant temperature. This result is seen to be the analogue of Boyle's law, with the osmotic pressure of the solution substituted for the pressure of the gas.

Further, the proportionality between osmotic pressure and the absolute temperature, at a given concentration (Table XXXIII), shows that a law equivalent to Gay-Lussac's law for gases applies to solutions; thus,

$$\frac{\Pi}{T} = \text{constant}, \tag{30.2}$$

for a solution of a definite concentration. Combination of equations (30.1) and (30.2), as is the case with gases, leads to the result

$$\Pi V = RT, \tag{30.3}$$

where R is a constant. By inserting actual values of the osmotic pressure for a solution of known concentration at a definite temperature, the interesting fact has emerged that the constant R in equation (30.3) is almost identical with the familiar gas constant. The equation (30.3), frequently referred to as the **van't Hoff equation** for dilute solutions, is thus seen to be exactly analogous to the ideal gas equation.

For convenience in evaluating R from osmotic pressure data, equation (30.3) may be written as

$$\Pi = RTc, \tag{30.4}$$

since the concentration c is equal to $1/V$. According to Pfeffer's results in Table XXXIII, a solution of 1 gram of sucrose in 100 grams of water gave an osmotic pressure of 505 mm. of mercury at 6.8° C. Suppose R is to be expressed in liter-atm. per degree per mole, the dimensions generally used in osmotic pressure calculations, Π must be in atm., and c in moles per liter. The volume of the solution containing 1 gram of sucrose was 100.6 ml., and since the molecular weight of sucrose is 342, it follows that

$$c = \frac{1.0}{342} \times \frac{1000}{100.6} = 0.0291 \text{ mole per liter.}$$

The osmotic pressure Π is $505/760$ atm., and the absolute temperature is $273.2 + 6.8$, i.e., $280°$ K; hence, from equation (30.4),

$$R = \frac{\Pi}{Tc} = \frac{505}{760} \times \frac{1}{280 \times 0.0291} = 0.0816 \text{ liter-atm. deg.}^{-1} \text{ mole}^{-1}.$$

This may be compared with the value of 0.0820 in the same units, for the ideal gas constant.

The constant R in equations (30.3) and (30.4) may thus be taken as being equal to the gas constant, and these equations may consequently be used for the purpose of calculating approximate osmotic pressures. Alternatively, if the osmotic pressure is known the molal concentration of the solution can be evaluated. This result can be utilized to determine the molecular weight of the solute, provided the weight concentration is known. The measurement of osmotic pressure has actually been used to obtain the molecular weights of complex molecules, such as proteins, carbohydrates and various polymers.

Problem: A solution containing 4.0 g. of a polyvinyl chloride polymer in 1 liter of dioxane was found to have an osmotic pressure of 6.4×10^{-4} atm. at $27°$ C. Calculate the approximate molecular weight of the polymer.

The concentration of the solution is $4.0/M$ mole liter^{-1}, where M is the required molecular weight; since the osmotic pressure is given in atm., R is expressed in liter-atm. deg.$^{-1}$ mole^{-1}, i.e., 0.082, and hence, by equation (30.4),

$$6.4 \times 10^{-4} = 0.082 \times 300 \times 4.0/M$$

$$M = 1.5 \times 10^5.$$

The more accurate measurements of osmotic pressure made in recent years have shown that the van't Hoff equation (30.3) or (30.4) is applicable only in very dilute solution. As the concentration increases the deviations become more and more marked, the observed osmotic pressures being greater than the calculated values. Better agreement with experiment is obtained by using the modified equation proposed by H. N. Morse (1905) in which V, the volume of the solution, in equation (30.3), is replaced by V', *the volume of the solvent associated with 1 mole of solute*; thus,

$$\Pi V' = RT. \tag{30.5}$$

In dilute solutions, the difference between the volumes of solvent (V') and of solution (V) is negligible, and so equation (30.3) may be used. However, as the concentration is increased, V' becomes increasingly less than V, and hence the osmotic pressures calculated from equation (30.5) become increasingly greater than those given by (30.3), in agreement with the experimental results.

To some extent the deviations from equation (30.3) exhibited by solutions, with increasing concentration, are comparable with the deviations from ideal behavior shown by real gases as the pressure is increased (§ 13a), but the situations are not quite similar. It will be shown in § 30f that even if a solution behaved ideally, it would not be expected to obey the van't Hoff equation except at very high dilutions. At appreciable concentrations deviations are to be anticipated for ideal, as well as nonideal, solutions. This fact is very important, for it calls attention to the danger of carrying too far the apparent analogy between gases and solutions.

30e. Mechanism of the Semipermeable Membrane and of Osmotic Pressure.—It can be shown theoretically that the magnitude of the osmotic pressure developed when a solution and solvent are separated by a semipermeable membrane should be independent of the actual nature of the membrane. Differences have sometimes been observed with different membranes, but this is due to the fact that certain membranes are not completely semipermeable. Such membranes, which allow the passage of solute molecules, even to a small extent, will give low osmotic pressures. These are, however, not true osmotic pressures, for the latter are developed only if the membrane is perfectly semipermeable.

Numerous attempts have been made to explain the property of semipermeability possessed by certain materials, but the problem cannot yet be regarded as solved. Some indication of the action of semipermeable membranes may be obtained from the following experiment, using an apparatus similar to that shown in Fig. 57. The animal membrane is first thoroughly soaked in water, and then the thistle tube is filled with a mixture of ether and benzene. If the thistle tube is now immersed in a beaker containing moist ether, the level of the liquid in the tube will be seen to rise, just as in the experiment described in § 30a to illustrate osmosis. The animal membrane saturated with water behaves just like a semipermeable membrane, permitting the passage of ether molecules through it from the outside, while not allowing benzene molecules to pass in the opposite direction. The explanation of this result is to be found in the solubility of ether in the water with which the membrane is saturated; ether molecules can thus move through the membrane with ease. On the other hand, benzene is insoluble in water and its passage is consequently prevented.

It appears from this and similar experiments that semipermeability, in connection with osmosis, might be explained by supposing the solvent to be soluble in the membrane whereas the solute is insoluble. It is not easy to see exactly what is meant by "soluble" and "insoluble" in a semipermeable material like copper ferrocyanide. One view, which has found wide acceptance, is that the solvent, e.g., water, molecules are attracted by the membrane surface, that is to say, they are "adsorbed" (§ 56a). As a result, there is a continuous connection between the solvent molecules on both sides of the membrane; these molecules can therefore pass through without difficulty. The molecules of solute, however, are unable to penetrate the complex network of pores that constitutes the semipermeable membrane, since there is no direct connection from one side to the other.

Another suggestion which has received some support is that the semipermeable material consists of a large number of fine capillaries that are not wetted by the liquid; direct passage of liquid through the capillaries is thus not possible. Molecules of the vapor are nevertheless able to diffuse into the pores, so that when pure solvent is placed on one side of the membrane and solution on the other side, distillation occurs through the capillaries from the region of high vapor pressure, i.e., the solvent, to that of lower vapor pressure, i.e., the solution, and hence osmosis results. This mechanism does not account so well as the one given above for the behavior of different membranes towards different solvents. For example, copper ferrocyanide acts as a semipermeable membrane when water is the solvent, but for certain nonaqueous solvents other membranes must be used, e.g., vulcanized rubber for pyridine and acetone. If the function of the semipermeable membrane is merely to act as a structure of nonwettable capillaries, this result would not have been expected, for pyridine is likely to wet rubber while water is not. The adsorption theory, however, is in better agreement with the facts, for rubber would adsorb the molecules of the organic solvent, but copper ferrocyanide would adsorb water molecules.

Various mechanisms have also been proposed to account for osmotic pressure; as a result of the apparent analogy between solutions and gases, attempts were made to explain osmotic pressure as being due to bombardment by the molecules of solute. As mentioned earlier, the so-called analogy may be misleading, and in any case the bombardment theory encounters many difficulties. Another view of osmotic pressure is based on the bombardment of the semipermeable membrane by the molecules of solvent, rather than of solute. Since there are relatively more solvent molecules in the pure solvent than in the solution, there should be a resultant pressure tending to drive solvent molecules into the solution, as is actually the case. The theory that a semipermeable membrane consists of dry capillaries through which the molecules of vapor distil from solvent to solution, as mentioned in the preceding paragraph, provides another interpretation of osmosis. As the external (osmotic) pressure on the solution increases so its vapor pressure increases (§ 30f); when the latter becomes equal to that of the solvent, the distillation, i.e., the flow of solvent, ceases. The external pressure at which this occurs would be the osmotic pressure of the solution.

In recent years there has been a growing opinion, first voiced by van't Hoff himself in 1892, that the actual mechanism of osmotic pressure is not important; both solvent and solute molecules will undoubtedly bombard the semipermeable membrane, and distillation may also occur at the same time through the pores. All this is, however, immaterial; in the study of osmotic pressure the essential point is that, for some reason connected with the presence of solute molecules, the "escaping tendency" or "activity" of the solvent molecules is less in a solution than it is in the pure liquid. This decrease of escaping tendency or activity is immediately evident in the fact that the vapor pressure of the solution is less than that of the solvent. One result of this difference in escaping tendency is that molecules of solvent will always tend to pass from the solvent to the solution. Expressed in more precise thermodynamic terms, it may be said that the free energy of 1 mole of solvent molecules in the solution is less than in the pure solvent. The transfer of these molecules from pure solvent to solution will thus be accompanied by a decrease of free energy; consequently such a transfer will tend to occur spontaneously, in accordance with the conclusions reached in § 26b.

If solvent and solution are placed in two vessels side by side, in an enclosed space, the difference in free energy, escaping tendency or activity of the solvent molecules will manifest itself by distillation from the solvent to the solution. If two solutions of different concentrations are used the process will continue until they have the same vapor pressure; this principle has been employed in the isopiestic method for studying vapor pressures of solutions (§ 27c). Similarly, when solvent and solution are separated by a semipermeable membrane, the difference in free energy, etc., must result in the passage of solvent molecules into the solution until equilibrium is attained by the building up of an excess pressure, the osmotic pressure. It follows, therefore, that the setting up of an osmotic pressure is the inevitable result of the introduction of a semipermeable membrane between the solvent and solution, since the escaping tendencies of the solvent molecules are different on the two sides of the membrane. When a state of equilibrium is reached under the influence of the external (osmotic) pressure acting on the solution, the escaping tendency (vapor pressure) of the solvent molecules in the solution must, of necessity, become equal to the value in the pure solvent.

30f. Osmotic Pressure Relationships.—From the foregoing statements it is clear that there should be a relationship between the osmotic pressure of a solution and its vapor pressure as compared with that of the pure solvent. Such a connection can be derived from thermodynamics, and is quite independent of the mechanism of osmotic pressure. Suppose that under the influence of an external pressure P_0, e.g., 1 atm., the vapor pressure of a pure solvent is p^0, while that of a solution at the same temperature is p. The vapor pressure of the solution is increased by increasing the external pressure, and when this is raised to P, the vapor pressure increases to p^0, the value for the pure solvent at the pressure P_0. It follows, therefore, that the excess pressure $P - P_0$, which must be applied to the solution in order to bring it into equilibrium with the solvent, is equal to the osmotic pressure Π. The problem now is to derive a relationship between P_0 and P, on the one hand, and p^0 and p, on the other hand.

Consider a solution under an external pressure P, in equilibrium with vapor of the solvent at pressure p; in accordance with the results in § 26c, the free energy per mole of solvent will be the same in both liquid and vapor phases. If the external pressure on the solution is altered, the vapor pressure will change, so as to maintain the equality of the molar free energy. Suppose the external pressure is increased by a small amount from P to $P + dP$, and the equilibrium vapor pressure is consequently changed by dp to $p + dp$, the corresponding free energy changes at constant temperature are given by equation (26.18) as

$$dF_l = V_l dP \quad \text{and} \quad dF_v = V_v dp,$$

where the subscript l refers to the liquid (solution) phase and v to the vapor. The quantity V_l is the volume occupied by 1 mole of solvent in the given solution * at the pressure P, and V_v is the molar volume of the vapor at the pressure p. As just noted, these free energy changes must be equal if the system is to remain in equilibrium; hence, at a given temperature,

$$V_l dP = V_v dp.$$

At low vapor pressures the vapor may be supposed to obey the ideal gas laws, so that V_v may be replaced by RT/p; hence,

$$V_l dP = RT \frac{dp}{p}. \tag{30.6}$$

As seen above, when the external pressure is changed from P_0 to P, where $P - P_0$ is equal to the osmotic pressure of the solution, the vapor pressure is increased from p to p^0; consequently, the left-hand side of equation (30.6) may be integrated between the limits of P_0 to P, and the right-hand side from p to p^0, viz.,

$$\int_{P_0}^{P} V_l dP = RT \int_{p}^{p^0} \frac{dp}{p}.$$

If the solution is virtually incompressible, the volume V_l will be almost independent of the pressure; replacing this by V_1 and assuming it to be constant, the indicated integrations are readily carried out, with the result

$$V_1(P - P_0) = RT \ln \frac{p^0}{p}.$$

Since $P - P_0$ is equal to Π, osmotic pressure of the solution, it follows that

$$\Pi V_1 = RT \ln \frac{p^0}{p}. \tag{30.7}$$

This relationship between osmotic pressure and vapor pressure can be obtained thermodynamically in several different ways; it is independent of any theory or mechanism of osmotic pressure. It is exact, provided the vapor behaves as an ideal gas and the solution is incompressible; these are the only approximations made in the treatment so far. The agreement between equation (30.7) and actual experiment will be shown below.

If the solution under consideration behaves ideally, in the sense that Raoult's law is obeyed, then by equation (27.3),

$$\frac{p}{p^0} = 1 - x_2$$

and so, for an ideal solution, equation (30.7) becomes

$$\Pi V_1 = -RT \ln (1 - x_2).$$

---

* Strictly speaking, V_l is the "partial" molar volume of the solvent in the solution; this is the change in volume resulting from the addition to or removal of 1 mole of solvent from a large quantity of the solution at the given concentration.

For a dilute solution the mole fraction x_2 of solute is small, and hence

$$\ln (1 - x_2) \approx -x_2,$$

so that

$$\Pi V_1 = RTx_2. \tag{30.8}$$

It has been already seen that for a dilute solution x_2 may be replaced by n_2/n_1, where n_1 and n_2 are the numbers of moles of solvent and solute, respectively, in the solution; equation (30.8) may therefore be written as

$$\Pi V_1 \frac{n_1}{n_2} = RT. \tag{30.9}$$

For an ideal solution, such as has been postulated, there is no volume change on mixing the liquid solvent and solute (§ 40a); hence V_1, the molar volume of the solvent in the given solution, becomes identical with the ordinary molar volume of the solvent. The product $V_1 n_1$ is then the total volume of solvent in the solution, and $V_1 n_1/n_2$ is the volume of solvent per mole of solute. This quantity has previously (§ 30d) been represented by the symbol V'; hence, equation (30.9) becomes

$$\Pi V' = RT, \tag{30.10}$$

which is identical with the empirical Morse equation (30.5). It is obvious, from the foregoing deduction, that this expression can be expected to hold only for a moderately dilute solution, provided Raoult's law is obeyed.

For an extremely dilute solution the volume V' of the solvent may be replaced by the volume V of the solution containing 1 mole of solute; under these conditions

$$\Pi V = RT, \tag{30.11}$$

which is the van't Hoff equation. Since the solvent in a dilute solution almost invariably satisfies Raoult's law, it follows that the necessary condition for equation (30.11) is a very low molar concentration of solute.

It is of interest to compare the osmotic pressures calculated from the various equations derived above and those obtained by experiment. A number of results of measurements on sucrose solutions at 30° C are given in Table XXXIV, together with the osmotic pressure values calculated from equation

TABLE XXXIV. OSMOTIC PRESSURES OF SUCROSE SOLUTIONS AT 30° C

Molality of Solution	Observed Osmotic Pressure	Calculated Osmotic Pressure		
		Eq. (30.7)	Eq. (30.10)	Eq. (30.11)
0.1	2.47 atm.	2.47	2.47	2.40 atm.
1.0	27.22	27.0	24.7	20.4
2.0	58.37	58.5	49.4	35.1
3.0	95.16	96.2	74.2	45.5
4.0	138.96	138.5	98.9	55.7
5.0	187.3	183.0	123.6	64.5

(30.7), the Morse equation (30.10) and the van't Hoff equation (30.11). It is seen that the theoretical equation (30.7), which involves measured vapor pressures, is in good agreement with experiment at all the concentrations; the van't Hoff equation fails in all but the most dilute solutions, but the Morse equation is somewhat of an improvement.

The relationship between the osmotic pressure and vapor pressure of a solution is given by equation (30.7), but since the vapor pressure is also related to the lowering of the freezing point and the elevation of the boiling point, a quantitative connection between these properties of a solution and its osmotic pressure is also to be expected. The simplest way of deriving this connection for dilute solutions is to combine equation (28.6), or the exactly analogous (29.6), with equation (30.8); the result, for both cases, may be put in the form

$$\Pi = \frac{LT}{V_1 T_0^2} \Delta T, \tag{30.12}$$

where L, T_0 and ΔT represent the molar heat of vaporization, boiling point of the solvent, and rise of the boiling point, respectively, or the molar heat of fusion, freezing point of the solvent and depression of the freezing point, respectively; T is the temperature at which the osmotic pressure is measured, and V_1 may be taken, approximately at least, to be the molar volume of the solvent at this temperature. The quantities L, T_0 and V_1 are virtually constant for a given solvent, and hence it is seen from equation (30.12) that, at constant temperature, *the osmotic pressure of a dilute solution is directly proportional to the elevation of the boiling point or the depression of the freezing point.*

Problem: The osmotic pressure of a 0.1 molal aqueous solution of sucrose at 30° C is 2.47 atm.; the molar volume of water at this temperature is 18.10 cc. Calculate the elevation of boiling point of this solution, and compare it with the value to be expected from the known molal elevation constant of water.

In this problem particular care must be exercised in the matter of units; the best plan is to express Π, L and V_1 in c.g.s. units; thus, Π is converted into dynes cm.$^{-2}$, L into ergs mole^{-1} and V_1 into cc. Hence,

$\Pi = 2.47$ atm. $= 2.47 \times 1.013 \times 10^6$ dynes cm.$^{-2}$

$L = 539.9 \times 18.02$ cal. mole^{-1} $= 539.9 \times 18.02 \times 4.184 \times 10^7$ ergs mole^{-1}

$V_1 = 18.10$ cc.

The temperature T at which the osmotic pressure was measured is $273.2 + 30 = 303.2°$ K, and T_0, the boiling point of water, is $373.2°$ K; consequently, by equation (30.12),

$$\Delta T = \frac{V_1 T_0^2}{LT} \Pi = \frac{18.10 \times (373.2)^2 \times 2.47 \times 1.013 \times 10^6}{539.9 \times 18.02 \times 4.184 \times 10^7 \times 303.2}$$

$$= 0.0511°$$

From Table XXX the molal elevation of the boiling point of water is 0.513°, and hence for a 0.1 molal solution the rise of boiling point should be 0.0513°.

The lowering of vapor pressure, the rise of boiling point, the depression of the freezing point and the osmotic pressure of a solution are all properties which depend, as a first approximation, on the *molecular concentration of the solute in the solution, and not on the nature of the solute.* Thus a 0.1 molal solution of any substance in a given solvent should produce the same lowering of vapor pressure, rise of boiling point, and so on.* Properties of this type, which are determined mainly by the number, and not by the nature, of the molecules, are called **colligative properties.**

IDEAL AND NONIDEAL SOLUTIONS

31a. Molecular Weights and Ideal Behavior.—In view of the direct connection with the molar concentration, any of the four colligative properties referred to above could be used for the determination of molecular weights of dissolved substances. Except for the special case of compounds of high molecular weight, mentioned earlier, the elevation of boiling point and depression of freezing point methods are most generally employed for this purpose. As a rule, the molecular weights obtained are in good agreement with the values to be expected, so that the broad accuracy of the equations derived in the preceding sections may be accepted. In certain cases, however, marked deviations have been observed, even in moderately dilute solutions; these may be attributed, in general terms, to departure of the solutions from ideal behavior.

The essential postulate made in the deduction of the various equations for the elevation of boiling point, depression of the freezing point and osmotic pressure is that Raoult's law is applicable to the solvent. For solutions obeying this law, therefore, the equations should be satisfactory. Strictly speaking, an ideal solution is defined as one obeying Raoult's law *at all concentrations,* but it is frequently observed that the law applies to the solvent, to a good approximation, for dilute solutions, although deviations occur at higher concentrations (§ 40b). These solutions are not completely ideal, but they may be treated as ideal, for present purposes, in the dilute range in which Raoult's law is approximately obeyed by the solvent. The equations derived in this chapter will then apply to these dilute solutions in the same region as they behave as ideal. Theoretical considerations (§ 40a) have shown that the condition for Raoult's law to hold is that the solute should not affect the forces acting between the molecules of solvent. This will be the case if the solvent and solute have similar characteristics, e.g., both are nonpolar or both are related polar substances. As a very rough generalization, it may be stated, therefore, that Raoult's law and hence such equations as (27.6), (28.9), (29.7) and (30.8), will hold moderately well for solutions of appreciable concentration, e.g., up to about 0.1 molal, if these conditions are satisfied. On the other hand, the presence of a polar solute in a nonpolar solvent, or vice versa, will so affect the forces between the molecules of solvent that Raoult's law would not be expected to hold with any degree of accuracy in solutions of appreciable concentrations. Under these conditions the equations generally used for cal-

---

* Electrolytes are apparently exceptional in this respect (cf. § 31b).

culating molecular weights from the boiling point elevation or the freezing point depression will fail, except for very dilute solutions.

This conclusion may be illustrated by reference to the determination of the molecular weight of nitrobenzene in benzene as solvent; the molecules of the former are highly polar (see Table XXIV) while those of the latter are nonpolar. Deviations from ideal behavior are thus to be anticipated in all solutions except the most dilute. The molecular weight of nitrobenzene, $C_6H_5NO_2$, is 123, and the observed value, derived from the depression of the freezing point of benzene, was found to be 126.7 in a 0.12 molar solution; at 0.5 molar the apparent molecular weight was 137, and at 1.0 molar it was about 150. With solutions of nitrobenzene in cyclohexane even greater discrepancies, mainly due to departure from the ideal Raoult's law, have been noted.

Apart from deviations due to changes in the intermolecular forces, there is another important type due, mainly, to the fact that the solute does not exist in solution in a simple molecular form; that is to say, the solute forms associated molecules (§ 14f). The number of moles, or the mole fraction, of the solute is then not equal to that derived from the ordinary molecular weight; hence, Raoult's law *appears* to fail for such solutions. For example, the molecular weights of acetic acid, benzoic acid, and other carboxylic acids, as determined from measurements on benzene solutions, are almost exactly twice the expected values in all but the most dilute solutions. This result is attributed to the actual formation of double molecules, in agreement with the conclusions reached from molecular weight determinations made with the vapors of carboxylic acids (§ 14f). If proper allowance were made for the fact that these substances have molecular weights which are double the values calculated for the simple molecular formulae, the solutions of carboxylic acids in benzene, etc., would exhibit relatively little departure from ideal behavior.

Other hydroxylic compounds, such as alcohols and phenols, have molecular weights in benzene and other nonhydroxylic solvents that increase steadily with increasing concentration. This result, as in the case of nitrobenzene in benzene, is partly due to the difference in polarity of solute and solvent, but there is probably also some association of the molecules of the hydroxylic solute. Whereas the association of carboxylic acids leads to the formation of definite double molecules, with alcohols and phenols the character of the association is much less well defined (§§ 10h, 14f). For this reason the apparent molecular weight does not have a value which is a definite multiple of that of the simple molecules, but increases steadily with concentration, as the general extent of the association increases.

In studying the effect of the solvent on the molecular weight of associated substances, it has been found that in hydroxylic solvents, such as water and alcohols, the results are almost what might be expected for simple molecules. Such solvents have been described as **dissociating solvents,** for they tend to split up or dissociate the double molecules into single molecules. In contrast to the behavior of these hydroxylic solvents, the nonpolar solvents, such as benzene, have been referred to as "associating solvents." It is doubtful, however, if this description can be justified, for the solutes are already associated, both in the vapor and liquid states, and the solvent does not increase the extent of association as the name would imply.

31b. Dissociation in Electrolytic Solutions.—An entirely different type of departure from ideal behavior, which is of great chemical significance, has been observed with aqueous solutions of strong acids and bases, of salts, and, in general, with solutions capable of conducting an electric current. For these solutes, particularly in water as solvent, the molecular weights are found to be considerably less than those anticipated; the values become smaller, approaching a limiting value, with decreasing concentration, that is, with increasing dilution, of the solution. Without offering any explanation of this discrepancy, van't Hoff represented the ratio of the theoretical molecular weight M_0 to the apparent (experimental) value M in the solution, i.e., M_0/M, by the letter i, generally referred to as the **van't Hoff factor.** This factor is sometimes defined in an alternative, but exactly equivalent, manner, as the ratio of the observed lowering of the vapor pressure, elevation of boiling point, depression of the freezing point or osmotic pressure to the corresponding value calculated from the theoretical molecular weight of the solute. Thus, if Δ represents the experimental value of one of these colligative properties, and Δ_0 is the expected value if the solution behaved ideally, then by definition

$$i = \frac{\Delta}{\Delta_0} = \frac{M_0}{M}. \tag{31.1}$$

For salts such as NaCl, KNO$_3$, MgSO$_4$, etc., consisting of two radicals, the van't Hoff factor i tends towards a limiting value of 2.0 in dilute solution; for salts made up of three radicals, of which two may be the same or all three different, e.g., K$_2$SO$_4$, CaCl$_2$, NaHSO$_4$, etc., the value of i approaches 3.0 as the concentration decreases. In general, the van't Hoff factor has an integral value at infinite dilution equal to the total number of radicals constituting the salt.

Problem: The freezing point depression of a 5.00×10^{-3} molal aqueous solution of potassium sulfate was found to be 0.0265°. Calculate the value of i for this solution.

The molal depression constant for water is 1.86°, and hence the theoretical depression Δ_0 for a 0.00500 molal solution is $1.86 \times 5.00 \times 10^{-3} = 0.00930°$. Since the observed depression Δ is 0.0265°, it follows that

$$i = \frac{\Delta}{\Delta_0} = \frac{0.0265}{0.0093} = 2.85.$$

The fundamental significance of the results just described was realized by S. Arrhenius (1887); he was able to correlate the abnormal colligative properties with the fact that the corresponding solutions were good conductors of electricity. The suggestion was made that *when an acid, base or salt is dissolved in water it splits up, or dissociates, spontaneously into positively and negatively charged ions*; this is the basis of the **theory of electrolytic dissociation.** A salt such as sodium chloride will dissociate into two ions, thus

$$\text{NaCl} = \text{Na}^+ + \text{Cl}^-,$$

whereas potassium sulfate will yield three ions upon dissociation,

$$K_2SO_4 = 2K^+ + SO_4^{--}.$$

The number of charges carried by an ion is equal to its normal valence (§ 10b).

The presence of free ions would account for the ability of the solutions to conduct an electric current, for electricity is always carried by charged particles, either ions or electrons. Further, the formation of the free ions explains the abnormal colligative properties of these solutions. As already seen, the properties considered in this chapter depend on the number of molecules present in the solution; if each ion behaves in this respect as a molecule, and there is no apparent reason why it should not, then a molecule of sodium chloride, for example, will produce twice the lowering of vapor pressure, elevation of boiling point, etc., to be expected for the single molecule. This will account for the limiting value of 2.0 for the van't Hoff factor for sodium chloride and analogous salts. Similarly, because potassium sulfate, calcium chloride, etc., dissociate into three ions, the van't Hoff factor should approach a value of 3.0. The experimental facts can thus be explained in a satisfactory manner by the theory of electrolytic dissociation.

It was stated earlier that the van't Hoff factor for sodium chloride, for example, tends towards a limiting value of 2.0 at infinite, i.e., very high, dilution; at appreciable concentrations it is less than 2.0, e.g., about 1.85 in a 0.05 molal solution. The ratio of the observed value of i to the limiting value, the latter being equal to ν, the number of ions produced by one molecule when it dissociates, is called the **osmotic coefficient;** it is often represented by the symbol g, so that

$$g = \frac{i}{\nu}. \tag{31.2}$$

At infinite dilution i must always equal ν, so that g will then be unity; at appreciable concentrations, however, g is less than unity, and the difference $1 - g$ can be regarded as a measure of the departure of the actual solution from ideal behavior after allowing for dissociation into ions. For an ideal solution the value of $1 - g$ would be zero. The variations of $1 - g$ with molality for a number of salts are shown in Fig. 59; it is seen that the deviations from ideal behavior increase with concentration, and are more marked the higher the valence of the ions formed in the solution.

There are two main reasons why the observed values of the osmotic coefficient g are less than unity. In the first place, the van't Hoff factor i can only be equal to ν if every molecule in the solution were dissociated into ions; in other words, it would be necessary for dissociation to be complete. Consequently, incomplete dissociation would be one way of accounting for the fact that $1 - g$ is greater than zero. At one time this was thought to be the main reason for the discrepancy, but it has been realized in recent years that for simple salts, e.g., sodium and potassium chlorides, nitrates, etc., and for the strong mineral acids, e.g., nitric and hydrochloric acids, such is not the case. These substances, called "strong electrolytes," are split up into free ions to a very large extent at all reasonable concentrations, and the fact that the osmotic coefficient is less than unity, i.e., that i is less than ν, is ascribed to electrostatic attractions between the oppositely charged ions. This aspect of the subject of solutions and the relationship of ions to the conductance of solutions will be considered more fully in later chapters.

31c. The Activity Concept.—In addition to the osmotic coefficient, the departure from ideal behavior may be represented in terms of a property known as the **activity.** The activity concept was introduced by G. N. Lewis (1907), and although it has been widely applied in the study of solutions of

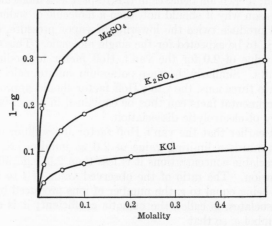

FIG. 59. Deviations of electrolytes from ideal behavior

electrolytes, e.g., salts, acids and bases, it is equally applicable to nonelectrolytes and even to gases. Various methods have been used for developing the idea of activity; the following is simple and is adequate for present purposes.

Consider a system of two large vessels, one containing a solution in equilibrium with its vapor at the pressure p', and the other containing another solution, of the same solvent and solute at a different concentration, whose vapor pressure is p''. The external pressure, e.g., 1 atm., and the temperature T are the same for both vessels. One mole of solvent is then vaporized isothermally and reversibly from the first solution at constant pressure p', by the method described in § 23e; the quantity of solution is supposed to be so large that the removal of 1 mole of solvent does not appreciably affect the concentration or vapor pressure. The vaporization has been carried out reversibly, and so every stage represents a state of equilibrium. Further, the temperature and pressure have remained constant, and hence by equation (26.26) there is no change of free energy.

The mole of vapor at pressure p' is now removed and compressed or expanded at constant temperature until its pressure is changed to p'', the vapor pressure of the second solution. If the pressures are sufficiently low for the vapor to be treated as an ideal gas without incurring serious error, as is generally the case, the increase of free energy is given by equation (26.21) as

$$\Delta F = RT \ln \frac{p''}{p'}. \tag{31.3}$$

Finally, the mole of vapor at the constant pressure p'' is condensed isothermally and reversibly into the second solution. The change of free energy for this stage, like that for the first stage, is again zero; the total free energy change for the transfer of 1 mole of solvent from the first solution to the second is thus given by equation (31.3).

Let F' represent the actual free energy of 1 mole of solvent in the one solution and F'' the value in the other solution, then since the latter solution gains 1 mole while the former loses 1 mole, the free energy increase ΔF is equal to $F'' - F'$; it is thus possible to write, from equation (31.3),

$$F'' - F' = RT \ln \frac{p''}{p'}. \tag{31.4}$$

If both solutions behave ideally, so that Raoult's law is applicable, the vapor pressure is proportional to the mole fraction of the solvent in the particular solution [equation (27.5)]; hence, for ideal solutions, equation (31.4) becomes

$$F'' - F' = RT \ln \frac{x''}{x'}, \tag{31.5}$$

where x' and x'' are the mole fractions of the solvent in the two solutions.

For *nonideal solutions* this result is not applicable, but the **activity** of the solvent, represented by a, is defined in such a way that the free energy of transfer of 1 mole of solvent from one solution to the other is given *exactly* by

$$F'' - F' = RT \ln \frac{a''}{a'}. \tag{31.6}$$

This means, in a sense, that the activity is the property for a real solution that takes the place of the mole fraction for an ideal solution, in the free energy equation.

Although the definition of activity as represented by equation (31.6) has been derived with particular reference to the solvent, an exactly similar result is applicable to the solute. If F' is the free energy of 1 mole of solute in one solution, and F'' is the value in another solution, the increase of free energy accompanying the transfer of 1 mole of *solute* from the first solution to the second is then given by equation (31.6), where a' and a'' are, by definition, the activities of the *solute* in the two solutions.

It should be noted that equation (31.6) does not define the actual or absolute activity, but rather the *ratio* of the activities of the particular substance in two solutions. In order to be able to express activities numerically, it is convenient to choose for each constituent of the solution a reference state, or **standard state,** *in which the activity is arbitrarily taken as unity.* The activity of a component, solvent or solute, in any solution is thus really the ratio of its value in the given solution to that in the chosen standard state. The actual standard state chosen for each component is the most convenient for the purpose, and varies from one to the other, as will be seen shortly. If the solution indicated by the single prime is taken as representing the standard state, then a' will be unity, and equation (31.6) may be written in the general form

$$F - F^0 = RT \ln a, \tag{31.7}$$

the double primes being omitted, and a superscript zero is used, in accordance with the widely accepted convention, to identify the standard state of unit activity. This equation defines the activity or, more correctly, the activity relative to the chosen standard state, of either solvent or solute in a given solution.

31d. The Activity Coefficient.—The deviation of a solution from ideal behavior can be represented by means of the quantity called the **activity coefficient,** which may be expressed in terms of various standard states. In this discussion the solute and solvent may be considered separately; the treatment of the activity coefficient of the *solute* in dilute solution will be given first. If the molar concentration, or molarity, of the solute is c moles (or g. ions) per liter, it is possible to express the activity a by the relationship

$$a = fc \qquad \text{or} \qquad f = \frac{a}{c}, \tag{31.8}$$

where f is the activity coefficient of the solute. Upon inserting this into equation (31.7) there is obtained the expression

$$F - F_c^0 = RT \ln fc, \tag{31.9}$$

applicable to ideal and nonideal solutions. An ideal (dilute) solution is defined as one for which f is unity, but for a nonideal solution it differs from unity. Since solutions tend to a limiting behavior as they become more dilute, it is postulated that at the same time f approaches unity, so that at, or near, infinite dilution, equation (31.8) becomes

$$a_0 = c_0, \tag{31.10}$$

that is, the activity of the solute is then equal to its molar concentration. The standard state of unit activity may thus be defined as *a hypothetical solution of unit molar concentration possessing the properties of a very dilute solution.**

---

* The word "hypothetical" is employed in this definition because a real solution at a concentration of 1 mole (or g. ion) per liter will generally not behave ideally in the sense of having the properties of a very dilute solution.

Another standard state for solutes that is employed especially in the study of galvanic cells (Chapter XIV) is that based on the relationships

$$a = \gamma m \quad \text{or} \quad \gamma = \frac{a}{m}, \tag{31.11}$$

where m is the molality of the solute, i.e., moles (or g. ions) per 1000 g. solvent, and γ is the appropriate activity coefficient. Once again it is postulated that γ approaches unity as the solution becomes more and more dilute, so that at, or near, infinite dilution it is possible to unite

$$a_0 = m_0, \tag{31.12}$$

the activity being now equal to the molality. The standard state of unit activity is consequently defined as *a hypothetical solution of unit molality possessing the properties of a very dilute solution.* The difference between the actual value of the activity coefficient γ and unity is a measure of the departure of the actual solution from an ideal solution, regarded as one having the same properties as at high dilution.

In view of equations (31.10) and (31.12), it is evident that in the defined *ideal dilute solutions* the activity is equal to the molarity or to the molality, respectively. It follows, therefore, that the activity may be thought of as an idealized molarity (or molality) which may be substituted for the actual molarity (or molality) to allow for departure from ideal dilute solution behavior. The activity coefficient is then the ratio of the ideal molarity (or molality) to the actual molarity (or molality). At infinite dilution both f and γ must, by definition, be equal to unity, but at appreciable concentrations, the activity coefficients differ from unity and from one another. However, it is possible to derive an equation relating f and γ, and this shows that the difference between them is quite small in dilute solutions.

When treating the *solvent*, the standard state of unit activity almost invariably chosen is that of the pure liquid; the mole fraction of the solvent is then also unity. The activity coefficient f_x of the solvent in any solution is then defined by

$$a = f_x x \quad \text{or} \quad f_x = \frac{a}{x}, \tag{31.13}$$

where x is the mole fraction of the solvent. In the pure liquid state of the solvent a and x are both equal to unity, and the activity coefficient is then also unity on the basis of the chosen standard state.

31e. Determination of Activities and Activity Coefficients.—Several methods have been devised for the determination of activities; two only will be mentioned here, but others will be referred to in Chapters XIV and XV. Without going into details, it can be seen in a general way that measurements of vapor pressure, freezing point depression, etc., might be used to determine departure from ideal behavior, and hence to evaluate activities. The vapor pressure method has been used particularly to obtain the activity of the solvent, in the following manner. The equation (31.4) is applicable to any solution, ideal or nonideal, provided only that the vapor behaves as an ideal gas; comparison of this with equation (31.6) shows that the activity of the solvent in a solution must be proportional to the vapor pressure of the solvent over the given solution. If a represents the activity of the solvent in the solution, and p is its vapor pressure, then $a = kp$, where k is a proportionality constant. The value of this constant can be determined by making use of the standard state postulated above, namely that $a = 1$ for the pure solvent, i.e., when the vapor pressure is p^0; it follows, therefore, that k, which is equal to a/p, is $1/p^0$, and hence,

$$a = \frac{p}{p^0}. \tag{31.14}$$

The activity of the solvent in a solution can thus be determined from measurements of the vapor pressure of the solution (p) and of the pure solvent (p^0) at a given temperature. It is obvious that for an ideal solution obeying Raoult's law p/p^0 will be equal to x, the mole fraction of solvent. The activity coefficient as given by equation (31.13) will then be unity. It is with the object of obtaining this result that the particular standard state of pure solvent was chosen. For a nonideal solution the activity coefficient of the solvent will, of course, differ from unity, and its value can be determined by dividing the activity as given by equation (31.14) by the mole fraction of the solvent.

The determination of activities and activity coefficients from vapor pressure measurements may be illustrated by the data in Table XXXV; the first

TABLE XXXV. ACTIVITY OF ACETONE IN ACETONE-CHLOROFORM MIXTURES AT 35.2° C

Mole Fraction	Vapor Pressure	Activity	Activity Coefficient
1.000	344.5 mm.	1.000	1.000
0.9405	322.9	0.937	0.997
0.8783	299.7	0.870	0.991
0.8165	275.8	0.801	0.981
0.7103	230.7	0.670	0.943

column gives the mole fraction of acetone in acetone-chloroform mixtures, while in the second column are quoted the corresponding vapor pressures of acetone over these solutions at 35.2° C. The activities and activity coefficients of the acetone, regarded as the solvent, are derived by means of equations (31.14) and (31.13), respectively.

The theory of the freezing point method for evaluating activity coefficients is somewhat more complicated than that based on vapor pressures; consequently the final result only will be given here, viz.,

$$\ln a = - \frac{L_f}{RT_0^2} \Delta T_f, \tag{31.15}$$

where a is the activity of the solvent in a solution giving a freezing point depression of ΔT_f. As usual, L_f is the molar heat of fusion of the solvent, and T_0 is its freezing point.

For many purposes it is of more interest to know the activity, or activity coefficient, of the solute rather than that of the solvent. Fortunately, there is a simple equation, which can be derived from thermodynamics, that relates the activity a_1 of solvent to that of the solute, a_2; thus,

$$n_2 d \ln a_2 = -n_1 d \ln a_1, \qquad (31.16)$$

where n_1 and n_2 are the numbers of moles of solvent and solute, respectively, in the solution. If the values of a_1 for the solvent are known, from vapor pressure or freezing point measurements, at a series of concentrations, the activity a_2 of the solute can be determined by graphical integration of equation (31.16).

The foregoing descriptions of methods for the evaluation of activities and activity coefficients refer particularly to solutes that are nonelectrolytes; the procedures have been adapted to electrolytes, but the calculations are somewhat involved. Special methods have also been devised for solutes of this type; these will be described in later sections.

READING REFERENCES

1. **Simple boiling point apparatus.** Hoshall, *Journal of Chemical Education*, **8**, 353 (1931).
2. **Improved boiling point apparatus.** Davis, *ibid.*, **10**, 47 (1933).
3. **Osmosis and osmotic pressure.** Davidson, *ibid.*, **11**, 499 (1934).
4. **Raoult.** Getman, *ibid.*, **13**, 153 (1936).
5. **Molecular weight by isopiestic method.** Mason and Gardner, *ibid.*, **13**, 188 (1936).
6. **Simple apparatus for boiling point and freezing point.** Chandler, *ibid.*, **15**, 166 (1938).
7. **Boiling point apparatus.** Jackson, *ibid.*, **17**, 472 (1940).
8. **Freezing point experiments.** Miller and Lucasse, *ibid.*, **17**, 522 (1940).
9. **Freezing points with camphor as solvent.** Gunn, *ibid.*, **18**, 188 (1941).
10. **Simplified Cottrell pump.** Steinbach and Conery, *ibid.*, **21**, 535 (1944).

REVIEW QUESTIONS

1. State Raoult's law in words and in terms of two alternative equations.
2. How can Raoult's law be used to determine molecular weights? Outline the experimental methods.
3. Develop an equation for the relation of the rise of boiling point to (*a*) the mole fraction of solute, (*b*) the molality of the solution. State the results in words.
4. What is the molal boiling point elevation constant? How is it related to the physical properties of the solvent?
5. How can the rise of boiling point be used for molecular weight determination? Outline the experimental methods.
6. Derive an equation relating the lowering of the freezing point to (*a*) the mole fraction of solute, (*b*) the molality of the solution. State the results in words.
7. What is the molal freezing point depression constant? How is it related to the physical properties of the solvent?

8. Show how the lowering of freezing point can be used for the determination of molecular weights. Outline the experimental procedures.

9. Define and explain semipermeable membrane, osmosis and osmotic pressure. How is osmotic pressure measured?

10. Explain the terms plasmolysis and isotonic.

11. How is osmotic pressure affected by concentration and temperature? Express the conclusions in the form of an equation.

12. Give an account of the mechanism of semipermeable membranes and osmotic pressure.

13. What is the general relationship between escaping tendency, vapor pressure and osmotic pressure?

14. Develop an equation for osmotic pressure in relation to other properties of a solution by means of thermodynamics. Under what conditions does this reduce to the van't Hoff equation?

15. How is the osmotic pressure related to the rise of boiling point and lowering of freezing point? Why are such properties called colligative?

16. What is meant by an ideal solution? What kind of solutions may be expected to behave ideally?

17. Explain the conditions under which abnormal molecular weights may be obtained from measurements on colligative properties of nonelectrolyte solutions.

18. What is the van't Hoff factor of electrolytic solutions? How did it lead to the development of the theory of electrolytic dissociation?

19. What is the osmotic coefficient? Illustrate graphically how it depends on the concentration and valence of the ions.

20. Explain the development of an expression for the activity of a nonideal solution. What is meant by the standard state?

21. Define the activity coefficient of a solute in terms of (a) molality, (b) concentration.

22. Outline some of the methods used for the determination of the activities of nonelectrolytes.

PROBLEMS

I

1. Calculate the vapor pressure of a solution containing 10.0 g. of a nonvolatile solute of molecular weight 125, dissolved in 75.0 g. of acetone (CH_3COCH_3) at 25° C. The vapor pressure of pure acetone is 229.2 mm. at 25° C.

2. When 0.362 g. of a nonvolatile substance was dissolved in 25.4 g. of acetone, the rise of boiling point was found to be 0.388°. The heat of vaporization of acetone at its boiling point, 56.1° C, is 124.5 cal. per g. Calculate the molecular weight of the solute.

3. A solution of 0.123 g. of a solute, of molecular weight 58.1, dissolved in 25.0 g. of acetic acid freezes at 0.340° below pure acetic acid (16.6° C). Calculate the molal depression constant for acetic acid, and compare it with the value derived from the heat of fusion (43.2 cal. per g.) and the freezing point.

4. The vapor pressure ratio p^0/p for a one molal aqueous solution of sucrose, i.e., 1 mole of sucrose to 1000 g. of water, was found to be 1.020 at 20° C. Taking the density of water as unity, calculate (a) the theoretical osmotic pressure, (b) the value from the Morse equation, in atm. at 20° C. The total volume of the solution is 1211 ml.; calculate the osmotic pressure according to the van't Hoff equation. (The experimental value was 26.64 atm.)

5. The osmotic pressure of normal blood is about 7.5 atm. at body temperature, 37° C; calculate its freezing point. (The density of water at 37° C is 0.993 g. per ml.; latent heat of fusion of ice at 0° C is 79.8 cal. per g.)

6. A solution of 2.53 g. of p-cresol ($CH_3C_6H_4OH$) in 100 g. benzene gave a freezing point depression of 1.11°, while 12.34 g. in 100 g. benzene depressed the freezing point by 3.77°. What conclusions can be drawn from these results?

7. A solution of 0.815 g. of anhydrous barium chloride dissolved in 23.0 g. of water gave a boiling point elevation of 0.210°. How many ions are formed when one molecule of barium chloride dissociates in aqueous solution?

8. Calculate the free energy change ΔF in calories, including the sign, accompanying the transfer of one mole of benzene vapor at 25° C from pure liquid benzene to an ideal solution containing 1 mole of benzene to 4 moles of another substance.

9. What is the activity of the water in the one molal sucrose solution referred to in problem 4? (The usual convention concerning the standard state should be employed.)

II

1. The vapor pressure of pure water at 25° C is 23.756 mm. When 6.00 g. of a nonvolatile substance were dissolved in 100 g. of water the vapor pressure at 25° C was found to be 23.332 mm. What is the molecular weight of the solute?

2. When 0.300 g. of a substance of molecular weight 60.8 was dissolved in 33.7 g. of carbon tetrachloride (CCl_4) the boiling point elevation was found to be 0.755°. Calculate the molal elevation constant of carbon tetrachloride, and compare it with the value derived from the boiling point (76.75° C) and the heat of vaporization (46.4 cal. per g.).

3. When 0.412 g. of naphthalene ($C_{10}H_8$) was dissolved in 10.0 g. of camphor the freezing point of the latter was lowered by 13°. Calculate the molecular weight of another substance which gave a depression of 9.5° when 1.00 g. was dissolved in 8.55 g. camphor. What is the molal depression constant of camphor?

4. The osmotic pressure of a sucrose ($C_{12}H_{22}O_{11}$) solution was found to be 58.37 atm. at 30° C. The vapor pressure of pure water at this temperature is 31.824 mm. and its density is 0.995 g. per ml. Calculate the relative lowering of vapor pressure of the sucrose solution, and hence derive its concentration in terms of molality, i.e., the number of moles of sucrose to 1000 g. of water, assuming Raoult's law applies. (The actual concentration is 2.0 molal.)

5. The freezing point of sea water is $-2.30°$ C; calculate its osmotic pressure in atm. at 20° C, taking the density of pure water as unity. The heat of fusion of ice is 79.8 cal. per g.

6. A solution of 0.771 g. acetic acid ($C_2H_4O_2$) in 25.0 g. of water gave a freezing point depression of 0.937°. A solution of 0.611 g. acetic acid in 20.0 g. of benzene gave a freezing point depression of 1.254°. Explain the significance of these results.

7. A 0.01 molal solution of potassium ferrocyanide exhibits a freezing point depression of 0.070°. Calculate the van't Hoff factor and the osmotic coefficient of this solution at the freezing point.

8. The free energy change ΔF for the transfer of one mole of a given substance from an ideal solution in which its mole fraction is 0.275 to another solution was found to be $+2.42 \times 10^{10}$ ergs at 0° C. Assuming ideal behavior, what is the composition of the second solution in terms of mole per cent?

9. Determine the activity of the water in the sucrose solution referred to in problem II, 4, on the basis of the usual convention.

CHAPTER X

CHEMICAL EQUILIBRIUM

EQUILIBRIUM CONSTANTS

32a. Reversible Reactions.—It is probable that all chemical reactions can take place in both directions, but in many cases the extent of the reverse reaction is so small as to be negligible. Such chemical reactions may thus be regarded as proceeding to completion in one direction. Consider, for example, the reaction between two parts of hydrogen and one part of oxygen; explosion of a mixture of these gases at ordinary temperatures, by means of an electric spark, results in complete conversion into water. There is no detectable residue of the reacting gases, provided they were present in the correct proportion. Nevertheless, at temperatures above about 1500° C, water vapor is decomposed to an appreciable extent into hydrogen and oxygen. The reverse reaction thus definitely occurs at high temperatures, and it undoubtedly takes place to some extent under ordinary conditions. Because this is so small as to be virtually undetectable, the combination of hydrogen and oxygen is regarded as a reaction which proceeds to completion at normal temperatures and pressures.

When the conditions are such that *forward and reverse reactions can both occur to a noticeable extent*, the process is described as a **reversible reaction.** If such a process takes place in a closed vessel, so that the products of the forward reaction do not escape, the reactants cannot combine completely. As the products accumulate they tend to react so as to reverse the process and regenerate the reacting substances; hence the reaction does not go to completion in either direction. If hydrogen and oxygen were heated together in a closed space at a temperature of 2000° C, for example, some of the reacting gases would remain unchanged, no matter how long the process was allowed to continue. Similarly, to take the case of a reaction which is appreciably reversible at much lower temperatures, a mixture of hydrogen gas and iodine vapor will not unite completely to form hydrogen iodide if heated in a closed vessel at 450° C. In the vicinity of this temperature hydrogen and iodine react to yield hydrogen iodide, but the latter decomposes to an appreciable extent into its constituent elements; the reversible nature of the reaction is indicated by writing

$$H_2 + I_2 \rightleftharpoons 2HI.$$

Finally, reference may be made to a reversible process occurring in a liquid phase at ordinary temperatures; this is the esterification reaction between ethanol and acetic acid leading to the formation of ethyl acetate and water.

If equal molecular amounts of the reactants are taken, the action apparently ceases when only two-thirds of the initial amounts of alcohol and acetic acid have been used up.

It has been found that after the lapse of a sufficient interval of time all reversible reactions reach a state of **chemical equilibrium,** that is, *a state in which no further change in the composition with time can be detected,* provided the temperature and pressure are not altered. If the conditions are properly chosen, *exactly the same state of equilibrium may be attained from either direction for a given reversible reaction.* The results in Fig. 60 show that this is true for the hydrogen-iodine reaction carried out in a closed vessel at 425° C.

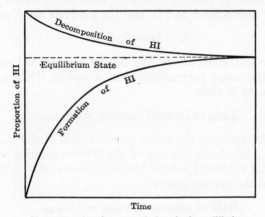

Fig. 60. Attainment of chemical equilibrium

The lower curve indicates the increase in the proportion of hydrogen iodide with time in a mixture consisting initially of equimolecular amounts of hydrogen and iodine only; the upper curve shows the rate of change in composition starting with pure hydrogen iodide. It is seen that in both cases the same state of equilibrium is reached, at the extreme right of the diagram, when there is no further appreciable change in the composition of the reacting gases. At a temperature of 425° C the equilibrium consists of 12 molecular per cent of hydrogen, 12 per cent of iodine vapor and 76 per cent of hydrogen iodide.

Since the composition of the system at equilibrium undergoes no further change if the temperature and pressure are not altered, there are evidently two possibilities. Either all chemical reaction has ceased entirely so that the system is stationary, or the forward and reverse directions are taking place simultaneously at exactly the same rate. It is now universally accepted that the latter condition is actually operative and that the system is in a state of **dynamic equilibrium.**

32b. The Law of Mass Action.—The concept of dynamic equilibrium, in conjunction with what is called the **law of mass action,** enunciated by C. M. Guldberg and P. Waage (1864), provides a means for determining the rela-

CHEMICAL EQUILIBRIUM**

tionship between the quantities of reacting substances and products that are present in a system at equilibrium. According to the aforementioned law, the *rate of a chemical reaction is proportional to the active masses of the reacting substances.* The quantity referred to as the "active mass" is generally taken as the molar concentration, that is, the number of moles in unit volume; hence, *the rate of a chemical reaction is proportional to the molar concentrations of the reacting substances.* It should be noted that the terms "mass action" and "active mass" may be somewhat misleading, for it is not the mass of reacting substance that is important, but rather the concentration, that is. the mass per unit volume.

Consider a perfectly general reversible reaction in which the reactants are the atoms or molecules A and B, and the products are C and D; thus,

$$A + B \rightleftharpoons C + D.$$

According to the law given above, the rate of the forward reaction will be proportional to the molar concentrations of A and B; if the proportionality constant is taken as k, then

$$\text{Rate of forward reaction} = k c_A c_B,$$

where c is used to represent the molar concentration of the species indicated by the subscript. Similarly, the rate of the reverse reaction will be proportional to the molar concentrations of C and D; hence, if k' is the proportionality constant for the reverse reaction,

$$\text{Rate of reverse reaction} = k' c_C c_D.$$

When the state of chemical equilibrium is attained, the rates of forward and reverse reactions must be equal, so that

$$k c_A c_B = k' c_C c_D, \tag{32.1}$$

where the various concentration terms now refer to the values *at equilibrium.* By rearrangement of equation (32.1), it is seen that

$$\frac{c_C \times c_D}{c_A \times c_B} = \frac{k}{k'} = K, \tag{32.2}$$

the constant K being called the **equilibrium constant** of the reaction.

The process considered above involved a single molecule of each of the reactants and products for simplicity; in practice, however, reactions are frequently encountered in which two or more molecules may be concerned. To derive the equilibrium constant for a general reaction, viz.,

$$aA + bB + \cdots \rightleftharpoons lL + mM + \cdots,$$

use is made of a more complete form of the law of mass action which states that *the rate of a reaction is proportional to the molar concentration of each reacting substance raised to the power of the number of its molecules taking part in the reaction,* as expressed by the chemical equation. Consequently, for the general case referred to above,

$$\text{Rate of forward reaction} = kc_A^a c_B^b \cdots$$

$$\text{Rate of reverse reaction} = k'c_L^l c_M^m \cdots$$

and when equilibrium is attained,

$$kc_A^a c_B^b \cdots = k'c_L^l c_M^m \cdots$$

Hence,

$$\frac{c_L^l \times c_M^m \times \cdots}{c_A^a \times c_B^b \times \cdots} = \frac{k}{k'} = K, \tag{32.3}$$

which is the general expression for the equilibrium constant. It should be noted that the reciprocal of K as defined by equation (32.3) would also be a constant; however, the convention adopted by physical chemists when expressing the equilibrium constant of a reaction is to place in the numerator the concentrations of the reaction products, i.e., of the substances on the right-hand side of the reaction as written. If the reaction were written in the opposite direction, viz.,

$$l\text{L} + m\text{M} + \cdots \rightleftharpoons a\text{A} + b\text{B} + \cdots ,$$

as it might very well be, the equilibrium constant would be inverted, in accordance with convention; thus,

$$K = \frac{c_A^a \times c_B^b \times \cdots}{c_L^l \times c_M^m \times \cdots}.$$

It will be seen in § 36a that the equilibrium constant frequently varies with the temperature of the reaction; at each temperature the constant K will have a definite value, depending on the nature of the reaction. If the reversible process is one whose equilibrium lies well to the side of the products, at the given temperature, e.g., the hydrogen-oxygen reaction below about 2000° C, the equilibrium constant will be large. On the other hand, if the equilibrium constant is small, it follows that in the equilibrium condition the extent of the reverse reaction predominates over that of the forward reaction.

The importance of the foregoing deductions lies in the fact that they have led to a definite connection between the concentrations of the reactants and products of a reversible process when the state of equilibrium is attained. No matter what are the initial amounts of the reacting species, A, B, etc., and whether any or all of the products L, M, etc., are present at the commencement or not, the concentrations at equilibrium must be related to one another in such a way that equation (32.3) holds. Once the value of the equilibrium constant is determined, from a single measurement at a given temperature, it is possible to calculate the composition of the system at equilibrium for any specified initial state at the same temperature. Some examples of this type of calculation will be given later.

32c. The Le Chatelier Principle.—It will be seen subsequently that the effect of temperature and pressure on the position of equilibrium of a reversible reaction can be calculated quantitatively. In the meantime it is of interest to consider a convenient rule, known as the **Le Chatelier principle,** whereby the same general conclusions may be reached in a qualitative manner. The principle, which is based fundamentally on the second law of thermodynamics, may be stated in the following form. *If a change occurs in one of the factors, such as temperature or pressure, under which a system is in equilibrium, the system will tend to adjust itself so as to annul, as far as possible, the effect of that change.*

Consider a reversible reaction involving gases, such as that between nitrogen and hydrogen, on the one hand, and ammonia, on the other hand, i.e.,

$$N_2 + 3H_2 \rightleftharpoons 2NH_3,$$

the system being at equilibrium at a constant temperature and under a given external pressure. Suppose this pressure is increased; then according to the Le Chatelier principle a change should take place in the system which will tend to counteract the pressure increase. Such a change would be brought about by a diminution of the number of molecules in the system at equilibrium. An examination of the equation for the reaction shows that a total of four molecules of nitrogen and hydrogen yield two molecules of ammonia. Hence, increase of pressure will favor the formation of ammonia from nitrogen and hydrogen, since this change will be accompanied by a decrease in the number of molecules. In other words, when the pressure is increased, the position of equilibrium in the reaction under consideration will be shifted to the right, favoring the increased formation of ammonia. On the other hand, a decrease of pressure would move the equilibrium to the left, thus decreasing the extent to which ammonia is formed from its elements. In general, it follows from the Le Chatelier principle that increase of pressure favors the process which is associated with the diminution in the number of molecules present at equilibrium, while decrease of pressure will have the effect of increasing this number.

The qualitative influence of temperature on the position of equilibrium of a reversible reaction can be readily derived in an analogous manner. If the temperature is raised the Le Chatelier principle requires the equilibrium system to change in such a manner as to absorb heat. That is to say, increase of temperature will favor the endothermic direction of the process; this is the one for which ΔH has a positive value (§ 24a). Decrease of temperature, on the other hand, will shift the equilibrium in the direction of the exothermic reaction, that is, the one in which heat is evolved and ΔH is negative. Considering the nitrogen-hydrogen-ammonia equilibrium once more, it is known that for the reaction as written above ΔH is negative, viz., -22.10 kcal., at 25° C. Hence, increase of temperature will cause the position of equilibrium to be shifted to the left, for ΔH is positive, i.e., heat is absorbed, in this direction; a lowering of temperature, however, will favor the increased formation of ammonia at equilibrium, since this change is accompanied by a negative ΔH value, i.e., heat is evolved.

It may be noted that the Le Chatelier principle is applicable to all types of equilibria, even those involving physical, rather than chemical, changes. In these cases, however, there can be no alteration in the number of molecules, and the effect of increase of pressure is to favor the formation of the state occupying the smaller volume. This conclusion may be illustrated by reference to the influence of pressure on the melting point of a solid. At this temperature solid and liquid are in equilibrium, and if the pressure is raised, the state occupying the larger volume will be converted into that having the smaller volume. With the water system, for instance, the volume of a given mass of liquid is less than that of the same mass of solid under normal conditions; hence, increase of pressure will cause the solid to be converted into liquid. In other words, if the pressure is raised, while the temperature is maintained constant, the ice will melt. In order to retain the solid-liquid equilibrium at the higher pressure it would consequently be necessary to lower the temperature, that is, the melting point is lowered. It is seen, therefore, that because the specific volume of liquid water is less than that of ice, increase of pressure should cause a decrease in the melting point (or freezing point), in agreement with experiment. The same result can, of course, be derived from the Clapeyron-Clausius equation (§ 22a), since this· equation and the Le Chatelier principle are in effect equivalent, both being direct consequences of the second law of thermodynamics.

32d. Forms of the Equilibrium Constant: Gas Reactions.—It will be shown in § 37a that a rigid thermodynamic deduction leads to an exact expression for the equilibrium constant of a reversible chemical reaction; for the general case this may be written as

$$K = \frac{a_L^l \times a_M^m \times \cdots}{a_A^a \times a_B^b \times \cdots}, \tag{32.4}$$

where the a terms represent the *activities* (§ 31c) of the respective species at equilibrium. This result is applicable to reversible reactions of all types, irrespective of whether gases, liquids or solids are concerned. For convenience, homogeneous reversible chemical reactions involving gases only will be considered at present; homogeneous processes occurring in solution and those (heterogeneous) in which solids take part will be treated later.

If the reactants A, B, etc., and the products L, M, etc., of the reaction are *ideal gases or approximate closely to ideal behavior*, the activity of each substance is proportional to its partial pressure and also to its molar concentration. For an ideal system it is thus possible to write equation (32.4) for the equilibrium constant in the alternative forms, viz.,

$$K_p = \frac{p_L^l \times p_M^m \times \cdots}{p_A^a \times p_B^b \times \cdots} \tag{32.5}$$

and

$$K_c = \frac{c_L^l \times c_M^m \times \cdots}{c_A^a \times c_B^b \times \cdots}, \tag{32.6}$$

where the p and c terms are the partial pressures and concentrations, respectively, at equilibrium. The two equilibrium constants are represented by K_p and K_c; in the former the various activity terms are replaced by the corresponding partial pressures, while in the latter concentrations, in moles per unit volume, are used. It should be mentioned that these expressions are applicable only to a system involving ideal gases. For real gases, the actual concentration (or partial pressure) must be replaced by the activity, which may be regarded as an ideal concentration (or ideal partial pressure).

If the reaction takes place at moderate pressures and relatively high temperatures, the deviations from ideal behavior are not great, and equations (32.5) and (32.6) may be employed with a fair degree of accuracy. Under these conditions the values of K_p and K_c are found to be almost independent of the pressure, as they should be. At high pressures, however, when the departure from ideal behavior is appreciable, the substitution of concentration or partial pressure for activity is no longer justifiable; in these circumstances K_p and K_c derived from equations (32.5) and (32.6) vary with the pressure. The true or thermodynamic equilibrium constant, as given by equation (32.4), is an exact constant, and does not depend in any way on the pressure.

Since equation (32.3), derived from the law of mass action of Guldberg and Waage, is identical with equation (32.6), which holds only for ideal gases, it might be considered, at first sight, that the law, as enunciated in § 32b was applicable to ideal substances only. This is, however, not strictly the case. It is generally accepted at the present time that the rate of a chemical reaction is actually proportional to the molar concentrations of the reacting substances, irrespective of whether they behave ideally or not. The reason why equation (32.3) does not apply to nonideal systems is because the proportionality constants k and k' are then not exactly constant. These "constants" may vary with pressure, and hence the "equilibrium constant" for the reaction, which is equal to k/k' according to equation (32.3), will also depend upon the pressure. If the reacting substances and the reaction products behave ideally, k and k' are exact constants at each temperature, and then K will have the same property.

In the subsequent treatment it will be assumed, as a first approximation, that the gases concerned do not deviate markedly from ideal behavior under the experimental conditions existing at equilibrium. It will then be possible to utilize equations (32.5) and (32.6) to express the equilibrium constants with respect to partial pressures and concentrations, respectively. A simple relationship between K_p and K_c can be readily obtained, as follows. By equation (11.19) the partial pressure p_i of any gas in a mixture of ideal gases occupying a total volume v at the temperature T is related to the number of moles n_i of the given gas by the expression

$$p_i v = n_i RT,$$

$$p_i = \frac{n_i}{v} RT. \tag{32.7}$$

The quantity n_i/v is equal to the number of moles in unit volume, and this is the same as the molar concentration c_i; it follows, therefore, that

$$p_i = c_i RT. \tag{32.8}$$

If the equilibrium partial pressures in equation (32.5) are replaced by the corresponding values of cRT, according to equation (32.8), it is seen that

$$K_p = \frac{c_L^l \times c_M^m \times \cdots}{c_A^a \times c_B^b \times \cdots} \times \frac{(RT)^{l+m+\cdots}}{(RT)^{a+b+\cdots}} = K_c(RT)^{[(l+m+\cdots)-(a+b+\cdots)]}$$

$$= K_c(RT)^{\Delta n}, \tag{32.9}$$

where $\Delta n = (l + m + \cdots) - (a + b + \cdots)$ is equal to the increase in the number of molecules in the chemical reaction as written. If the reaction is one in which the number of molecules of reactant is equal to the number of molecules of products, Δn is zero; for such a reaction K_p and K_c are identical.

Problem: For the reversible reaction $N_2 + 3H_2 \rightleftharpoons 2NH_3$ at 500° C, the value of K_p, with partial pressures in atm., is 1.44×10^{-5} at low pressures, where the gases behave almost ideally. Calculate the corresponding value of K_c with concentrations in moles per liter.

Since the pressures in K_p are in atm., while K_c is required in terms of moles per liter, it can be seen from equations (32.7) or (32.8) that R must be in liter-atm. deg.$^{-1}$ mole^{-1}, i.e., 0.0820. Further, Δn is here equal to $2 - 4$, i.e., -2; T is $273 + 500 = 773°$ K; hence, by equation (32.9),

$$K_p = K_c \times (0.082 \times 773)^{-2},$$

$$K_c = 1.44 \times 10^{-5}/(0.082 \times 773)^{-2} = 5.79 \times 10^{-2}.$$

32e. Experimental Determination of Equilibrium Constants.—The experimental method used for the determination of the equilibrium constant of a gas reaction depends on the nature of the reaction and the temperature. Two types of procedure have been most generally employed. In the first of these the reacting substances are sealed into glass or silica bulbs, and are heated at the required temperature for sufficient time for equilibrium to be established. The bulbs are then cooled very rapidly so as to fix or "freeze" the equilibrium, and the contents are analyzed in some convenient manner. The second procedure is the "flow method," in which the gases are passed through a tube, frequently containing a catalyst, heated to the appropriate temperature. The catalyst facilitates the attainment of equilibrium without affecting its position (§ 61a). The exit gases are cooled rapidly by passing through a capillary tube, and they are then collected and analyzed.

In the experiments just described it is, of course, essential that a state of equilibrium should be reached before the composition of the system is determined by analysis. The chief criterion of chemical equilibrium is that the same condition is approached from either side of the reaction (see Fig. 60), and that it does not change further with time, in the case of the observations made with sealed bulbs, or with decreasing rate of passage of the gases, in the flow method. From the analytically determined concentrations of the reactants and products in the system when equilibrium is attained, the equilibrium constant can be calculated by means of equation (32.6).

If the reaction being studied is accompanied by a change in the number of molecules, the equilibrium constant can sometimes be determined by measurements of the volume occupied by a known mass at a given pressure and temperature. In other words, vapor density measurements, such as those described in § 14d, may be employed. It was seen in § 14g that when a substance dissociates in the vapor state, the fraction of dissociation can be determined from the experimental pressure, volume and temperature data. It will be shown below that provided equilibrium is attained in the vapor, the dissociation fraction can be used to calculate the equilibrium constant.

HOMOGENEOUS GASEOUS EQUILIBRIA

33a. Reactions without Change in the Number of Molecules.—It is convenient to consider homogeneous reversible reactions, involving gas only, under two main headings; first, reactions in which the number of molecules of reactants is the same as the number of molecules of products and, second, those in which there is a change in the number of molecules. Instances of the former type of equilibria will be discussed in this section. One of the most completely studied reversible reactions between gases is that involving gaseous hydrogen and iodine, on the one hand, and hydrogen iodide, on the other hand, viz.,

$$H_2 + I_2 \rightleftharpoons 2HI.$$

In this case a total of two gaseous molecules of reactants produce two gaseous molecules of product, so that there is no net change in the number of molecules, i.e., Δn is zero. As seen in § 32d, for reversible reactions of this type the equilibrium constants K_p and K_c will be identical; it is thus immaterial which is considered, since the results will be the same in each case, and in any event the subscript p or c may be omitted.

The equilibrium constant for the reaction under consideration is determined by heating mixtures of hydrogen and iodine at a constant temperature, and analyzing the system when equilibrium is reached. The results are confirmed by approaching the equilibrium from the opposite direction, by starting with hydrogen iodide alone and determining the amounts of hydrogen and iodine formed. If n_{H_2}, n_{I_2} and n_{HI} are the numbers of moles of hydrogen, iodine and hydrogen iodide, respectively, present at equilibrium, and v is the volume of the system, the respective molar concentrations are then

$$c_{H_2} = \frac{n_{H_2}}{v}, \qquad c_{I_2} = \frac{n_{I_2}}{v} \qquad \text{and} \qquad c_{HI} = \frac{n_{HI}}{v}.$$

The equilibrium constant for the reaction, omitting the subscript, is thus

$$K = \frac{c_{HI}^2}{c_{H_2} \times c_{I_2}} = \frac{(n_{HI}/v)^2}{(n_{H_2}/v)(n_{I_2}/v)}$$

$$= \frac{n_{HI}^2}{n_{H_2} \times n_{I_2}}. \tag{33.1}$$

It will be noted that the volume v has disappeared from the final result, and hence need not be known. This is characteristic of all reactions in which the number of molecules remains unchanged; the volume factor appears an equal number of times in the numerator and denominator of the expression for the equilibrium constant, and hence the values cancel each other.

The accuracy of equation (33.1) was first confirmed by the classical work of M. Bodenstein (1897), but the results of the more recent experiments of A. H. Taylor and R. H. Crist (1941) at 457.6° C are quoted in Table XXXVI.

TABLE XXXVI.   THE HYDROGEN-IODINE-HYDROGEN IODIDE REACTION AT 457.6° C

$c_{H_2} \times 10^2$ mole liter^{-1}	$c_{I_2} \times 10^2$ mole liter^{-1}	$c_{HI} \times 10^2$ mole liter^{-1}	K
0.5617	0.05936	1.270	48.38 *
0.3841	0.1524	1.687	48.61 *
0.4580	0.09733	1.486	49.54 *
0.1696	0.1696	1.181	48.48 †
0.1433	0.1433	1.000	48.71 †
0.4213	0.4213	2.943	48.81 †

* Equilibrium approached from hydrogen and iodine.
† Equilibrium approached from hydrogen iodide.

The approximate constancy of the figures in the last column, in spite of the variations in the amounts of the substances present at equilibrium, is a satisfactory verification of equation (33.1). The equilibrium constant for the reaction as written above is thus 48.7 at 457.6° C.

Once the equilibrium constant for the reaction is known, it is possible to calculate the composition of the equilibrium system for any given initial conditions, at the same temperature. Suppose a mixture of a moles of hydrogen and b moles of iodine vapor are heated together until equilibrium is attained; at this point it is found that y moles of each have disappeared, thus producing $2y$ moles of hydrogen iodide. At equilibrium, therefore, the system contains $a - y$ moles of hydrogen, $b - y$ moles of iodine vapor and $2y$ moles of hydrogen iodide. Insertion of these values for n_{H_2}, n_{I_2} and n_{HI}, respectively, in equation (33.1) then gives

$$K = \frac{4y^2}{(a - y)(b - y)}. \tag{33.2}$$

If the initial amounts a and b of hydrogen and iodine are known, in addition to the equilibrium constant, it is obviously possible to evaluate y by means of equation (33.2); the number of moles of hydrogen iodide present at equilibrium is then $2y$.

Problem: A mixture of 1.24×10^{-2} mole of H_2 and 2.46×10^{-2} mole of I_2 was heated at $457.6°$ C until equilibrium was attained; how many moles of HI were then present?

Let $2y$ represent the number of moles of HI formed at equilibrium; the number of moles of H_2 remaining will then be $0.0124 - y$, while the number of moles of I_2 will be $0.0246 - y$. Since the equilibrium constant K, from Table XXXVI, is 48.7 at $457.6°$ C, it follows, by equation (33.2) that

$$K = 48.7 = \frac{4y^2}{(0.0124 - y)(0.0246 - y)}.$$

The two solutions of this quadratic equation are

$$2y = 5.75 \times 10^{-2} \quad \text{and} \quad 2y = 2.31 \times 10^{-2} \text{ mole.}$$

The former of these has obviously no physical significance as it is larger than twice the initial amount of either H_2 or I_2; it follows, therefore, that 2.31×10^{-2} mole of HI is present at equilibrium.

According to the principle of Le Chatelier, pressure should have no effect on the equilibrium composition at a given temperature. Since there is no variation in the number of molecules accompanying the reaction, it is evident that the system is not able to adjust itself so as to counteract an increase or decrease of external pressure. It is to be expected, therefore, that change of pressure should not alter the position of equilibrium; this has been confirmed experimentally. The same conclusion may be drawn from an examination of the equilibrium constant expressed in terms of partial pressures, viz.,

$$K = \frac{p_{HI}^2}{p_{H_2} \times p_{I_2}}. \tag{33.3}$$

The partial pressure of any gas in a mixture, as given by equation (11.22) or (11.23), is equal to the product of the total pressure P and the mole fraction of that gas, where the mole fraction is equal to the number of moles of the gas divided by the total number in the mixture. It follows, therefore, that the equilibrium partial pressures of hydrogen, iodine and hydrogen iodide, respectively, are

$$p_{H_2} = \frac{n_{H_2}}{N} P, \qquad p_{I_2} = \frac{n_{I_2}}{N} P \quad \text{and} \quad p_{HI} = \frac{n_{HI}}{N} P,$$

where N is equal to the total number of molecules, i.e., $n_{H_2} + n_{I_2} + n_{HI}$. If these partial pressures are inserted into equation (33.3) the result is

$$K = \frac{\left(\dfrac{n_{HI}}{N} P\right)^2}{\dfrac{n_{H_2}}{N} P \times \dfrac{n_{I_2}}{N} P} = \frac{n_{HI}^2}{n_{H_2} \times n_{I_2}}. \tag{33.4}$$

This quantity is, as it should be, indentical with equation (33.1), but the point to which attention must be called is that the P, i.e., the total (or external) pressure, factors have cancelled one another. In other words, the composition of the system at equilibrium, as represented by n_{H_2}, n_{I_2} and n_{HI}, is independent of the external pressure. Exactly the same result holds for any reaction in which there are equal numbers of molecules on both sides of the chemical equation. The expression for the partial pressure equilibrium constant will have an equal number of P factors in the numerator and denominator, and the equilibrium composition of the system will thus be unaffected by the total pressure.

The ΔH value for the combination of hydrogen and iodine vapor is negative, thus

$$H_2(g) + I_2(g) = 2HI(g) \qquad \Delta H = -3.0 \text{ kcal.}$$

at about 400° C. It follows, therefore, from the Le Chatelier principle, that increase of temperature will favor the reverse reaction, that is, the decomposition of hydrogen iodide, since this is accompanied by an absorption of heat, i.e., ΔH is positive in this direction. A decrease in the amount of hydrogen iodide at equilibrium will mean a decrease in the equilibrium constant; hence, in the present case, the equilibrium constant should decrease with increasing temperature. The same general result is true for all reactions for which ΔH is negative, irrespective of whether they involve a change or not in the total number of molecules. The quantitative relationship between the equilibrium constant and the change in heat content will be given in § 36a.

Another reversible reaction of the type in which the numbers of molecules are equal on both sides of the equation is the combination of nitrogen and oxygen to yield nitric oxide, viz.,

$$N_2 + O_2 \rightleftharpoons 2NO.$$

This reaction formed the basis of what was at one time the most important process for the fixation of atmospheric nitrogen. By using methods identical with those given above, the equilibrium constant for the reaction is found to be

$$K = \frac{n_{NO}^2}{n_{N_2} \times n_{O_2}}, \tag{33.5}$$

where the n's are the numbers of moles of the various gases at equilibrium. These values are, of course, independent of the external (total) pressure. For the nitrogen-oxygen reaction, ΔH is positive, viz., approximately 43 kcal. at 2000° C; hence, in accordance with the Le Chatelier principle the equilibrium constant here increases with increasing temperature. It is for this reason that the extremely high temperatures obtainable with a flaming electric arc were employed in the industrial process for converting atmospheric nitrogen and oxygen into nitric oxide.

The reversible reaction

$$CO_2 + H_2 \rightleftharpoons CO + H_2O,$$

in which the water is present in the gaseous state, is also of considerable importance; it is generally known as the "water gas" reaction. The equilibrium constant is given by

$$K = \frac{n_{CO} \times n_{H_2O}}{n_{CO_2} \times n_{H_2}}, \tag{33.6}$$

where, as before, the n's are the numbers of moles of the indicated species present at equilibrium. As in the preceding case, ΔH for the water gas reaction is positive; hence, the equilibrium constant increases as the temperature is raised.

Problem: Starting with equimolar amounts of carbon monoxide and steam, calculate the molar percentage composition of the water gas system at equilibrium at $1000°$ K; the equilibrium constant at this temperature is 0.719.

Since the numbers of moles of CO and H_2O are equal at the commencement, they must obviously remain equal throughout the reaction; let these values be n_1 at equilibrium. Similarly, the numbers of moles of CO_2 and H_2 must be equal; let these be n_2 at equilibrium. It follows then from the expression for the equilibrium constant, i.e., equation (33.6),

$$K = 0.719 = \frac{n_1^2}{n_2^2},$$

$$\frac{n_1}{n_2} = \sqrt{0.719} = 0.848.$$

The amounts of CO, H_2O, CO_2 and H_2 at equilibrium are therefore present in the molar ratio of 0.848 : 0.848 : 1.00 : 1.00; the molar percentages of CO and H_2O are consequently each

$$\frac{0.848}{(2 \times 0.848) + (2 \times 1.00)} \times 100 = 22.94\%.$$

The molar percentages of CO_2 and H_2 are then each 27.06%. The composition of the water gas at equilibrium at $1000°$ K is thus CO, 22.94; H_2O, 22.94; CO_2, 27.06; H_2, 27.06 moles per cent.

33b. Reactions with Change in the Number of Molecules.—For gaseous reactions in which the numbers of molecules of reactants and of products are different, the composition of the system at equilibrium depends on the total pressure. This is in harmony with the principle of Le Chatelier, which requires an increase of external pressure to be accompanied by such a shift of the equilibrium composition as will decrease the total number of molecules present. It is important to understand that *the pressure merely changes the position of equilibrium, i.e., the composition of the system at equilibrium; the equilibrium constant is, however, unaffected by the external (total) pressure.* The concentrations or partial pressures of the various constituents must adjust themselves when the total pressure is changed so as to leave the equilibrium constant unaffected.

The dissociation of nitrogen tetroxide to form nitrogen dioxide, viz.,

$$N_2O_4 \rightleftharpoons 2NO_2,$$

is a simple instance of a reversible reaction in which there is a change in the number of molecules. The equilibrium constant K_p in terms of partial pressures is given by

$$K_p = \frac{p_{NO_2}^2}{p_{N_2O_4}}. \tag{33.7}$$

In this case, of course, K_p and K_c must be distinguished; the increase Δn in the number of molecules in the reaction is equal to $2 - 1$, i.e., 1, and hence by equation (32.9), K_p is equal to $K_c \times RT$. Since it is the common practice to use K_p for equilibria involving gases, this form of the equilibrium constant will be employed in the subsequent discussion.

If $n_{N_2O_4}$ and n_{NO_2} are the numbers of moles of gaseous tetroxide and dioxide present in the system at equilibrium, and N, equal to $n_{N_2O_4} + n_{NO_2}$, is the total number of moles, the respective partial pressures are defined by

$$p_{N_2O_4} = \frac{n_{N_2O_4}}{N} P \quad \text{and} \quad p_{NO_2} = \frac{n_{NO_2}}{N} P$$

where P is the total pressure. Insertion of these values into equation (33.7) then gives

$$K_p = \frac{\left(\dfrac{n_{NO_2}}{N} P\right)^2}{\dfrac{n_{N_2O_4}}{N} P} = \frac{n_{NO_2}^2}{n_{N_2O_4} \times N} P. \tag{33.8}$$

It will be observed that the expression for K_p now contains the value of the total pressure P. Since K_p is a constant, it follows that the numbers of moles n_{NO_2} and $n_{N_2O_4}$ at equilibrium must adjust themselves as the pressure is altered. It is apparent from equation (33.8) that if P is increased, n_{NO_2} might be expected to decrease while $n_{N_2O_4}$ increases in order to maintain K_p constant. That is to say, increase of pressure should displace the equilibrium in the direction of the nitrogen tetroxide, i.e., to the left of the reaction as written above. This is in the direction of a decrease in the number of molecules, as required by the Le Chatelier principle. However, while this principle merely indicates the direction in which the equilibrium is shifted, equation (33.8) permits the actual equilibrium composition at any pressure to be calculated, provided the value of K_p is known, at the same temperature.

For this purpose, the equilibrium constant K_p may be expressed in a somewhat different form. Suppose the system contains initially 1 mole of N_2O_4, and let α be the fraction that has dissociated into NO_2 when equilibrium is attained; there are then $1 - \alpha$ moles of undissociated N_2O_4 and 2α moles of NO_2 in the given volume. The total number of moles is $1 - \alpha + 2\alpha$, i.e., $1 + \alpha$, at equilibrium; hence, the partial pressures of N_2O_4 and NO_2 are

$$p_{N_2O_4} = \frac{1 - \alpha}{1 + \alpha} P \quad \text{and} \quad p_{NO_2} = \frac{2\alpha}{1 + \alpha} P,$$

respectively, where P is the total pressure. Introducing these values into equation (33.7) the expression for the equilibrium constant becomes

$$K_p = \frac{\left(\dfrac{2\alpha}{1 + \alpha}\right)^2 P^2}{\left(\dfrac{1 - \alpha}{1 + \alpha}\right) P} = \frac{4\alpha^2 P}{1 - \alpha^2}. \tag{33.9}$$

It is evident from this result that if K_p is known the fraction of the N_2O_4 dissociated at equilibrium, and hence the composition of the system, can be readily calculated at any pressure. Such calculations are, of course, based on the fundamental assumption that the gases behave ideally over the whole range of pressure concerned.

It was seen in § 14g that the dissociation fraction α can be determined from pressure-volume measurements; if sufficient time has been allowed for equilibrium to be attained, the value of α found in this manner, for a given pressure, may be inserted in equation (33.9) and K_p determined. For example, the fraction of N_2O_4 dissociated into NO_2 at 35° C and a total pressure of 1 atm. is found to be 0.270; the equilibrium constant, with partial pressures expressed in atm., is then given by equation (33.9) as

$$K_p = \frac{4 \times (0.270)^2 \times 1}{1 - (0.270)^2} = 0.315.$$

Problem: Calculate the fraction of dissociation of N_2O_4 at 35° C and a total pressure of 10 atm., assuming ideal behavior. Show that the result is in agreement with the Le Chatelier principle.

From equation (33.9) it is seen that

$$\alpha = \sqrt{\frac{K_p}{4P + K_p}},$$

and since K_p at 35° C is 0.315, as seen above, it follows that at a pressure of 10 atm.,

$$\alpha = \sqrt{\frac{0.315}{(4 \times 10) + 0.315}} = 0.0884.$$

Comparison of this result with the value of α at a pressure of 1 atm., viz., 0.270 given above, shows that increase of pressure is accompanied by a decrease in the extent to which N_2O_4 is dissociated into NO_2; higher pressures thus favor the formation of N_2O_4, as required by the Le Chatelier principle.

Another familiar reversible gas reaction in which there is a change in the number of molecules is the dissociation of phosphorus pentachloride, viz.,

$$PCl_5 \rightleftharpoons PCl_3 + Cl_2.$$

In this case, as in the previous one, increase of pressure moves the position of equilibrium in the direction of the smaller number of molecules, i.e., to the left in the reaction as written, and hence causes a decrease in the extent of dissociation. An expression for the dissociation constant may be obtained in the usual manner. If there is initially present 1 mole of PCl_5, and α is the fraction dissociated, forming α moles of PCl_3 and α moles of Cl_2, when equilibrium is reached, there remain $1 - \alpha$ moles of undissociated PCl_5. The total number of moles is thus $1 - \alpha + \alpha + \alpha$, i.e., $1 + \alpha$. The equilibrium partial pressures of the various constituents are then given by

$$p_{PCl_5} = \frac{1 - \alpha}{1 + \alpha} P, \qquad p_{PCl_3} = \frac{\alpha}{1 + \alpha} P \quad \text{and} \quad p_{Cl_2} = \frac{\alpha}{1 + \alpha} P.$$

The equilibrium constant K_p for the reaction is thus,

$$K_p = \frac{p_{PCl_3} \times p_{Cl_2}}{p_{PCl_5}} = \frac{\left(\dfrac{\alpha}{1 + \alpha}\right) P \times \left(\dfrac{\alpha}{1 + \alpha}\right) P}{\left(\dfrac{1 - \alpha}{1 + \alpha}\right) P} = \frac{\alpha^2 P}{1 - \alpha^2}. \qquad (33.10)$$

It is thus possible to calculate the equilibrium constant from the experimentally determined fraction of dissociation at a known total pressure.

The variation of α with pressure may be derived by solving equation (33.10); thus,

$$\alpha = \sqrt{\frac{K_p}{K_p + P}}. \qquad (33.11)$$

If the pressure P is high it is often possible to neglect K_p in comparison with P in the denominator of this expression; it then reduces to the simple form $\alpha = \sqrt{K_p/P}$. It is obvious from these results that the extent to which phosphorus pentachloride dissociates must decrease with increasing pressure, as deduced above from the Le Chatelier principle.

The dissociation of nitrogen tetroxide and of phosphorus pentachloride are both reactions for which ΔH is positive; the dissociation is, in each case, accompanied by the absorption of heat. It follows, therefore, that increase of temperature increases the extent to which these substances dissociate when equilibrium is attained. For these reactions the equilibrium constant should increase as the temperature is raised, and this has been found to be true by direct experimental observations.

A reversible reaction of great industrial importance is the combination of nitrogen and hydrogen to yield ammonia, thus

$$N_2 + 3H_2 \rightleftharpoons 2NH_3.$$

For this reaction as written, ΔH is negative, that is to say, the reaction is exothermic; it is immediately evident from the principle of Le Chatelier, therefore, as shown in § 32c, that the formation of ammonia at equilibrium should be favored by high pressures and low temperatures. These are just the conditions which are aimed at in the large-scale synthesis of ammonia from its elements. In order to speed up the attainment of equilibrium, however, the temperature is raised to some extent and, in addition, a catalyst is employed.

It can be shown that the maximum conversion of nitrogen and hydrogen into ammonia is obtained when the reactants are present in the same ratio as that in which they react, namely, one mole of nitrogen to three of hydrogen. It will be supposed, therefore, that the system initially contains nitrogen and hydrogen in the molecular proportion of 1 to 3; this will, of course, be maintained throughout the reaction, since the gases are used up in the same ratio. In the study of the reversible reaction under consideration, the amount of ammonia present, after equilibrium is attained in the presence of a catalyst, is determined by analysis. The results may therefore be expressed in terms of the mole fraction x, or the mole per cent $100\ x$, of ammonia in the equilibrium system at a definite temperature and pressure. The sum of the mole fractions of nitrogen and hydrogen must then be $1 - x$, and since these gases are present in the ratio of 1 to 3, it follows that the respective mole fractions are

$$x_{N_2} = \tfrac{1}{4}(1 - x) \qquad \text{and} \qquad x_{H_2} = \tfrac{3}{4}(1 - x).$$

The partial pressures are obtained in each case by multiplying by the total pressure $P;$ hence, the equilibrium constant K_p will be

$$K_p = \frac{p_{NH_3}^2}{p_{N_2} \times p_{H_2}^3} = \frac{(xP)^2}{\tfrac{1}{4}(1 - x)P \times \{\tfrac{3}{4}(1 - x)P\}^3} = \frac{256x^2}{27(1 - x)^4 P^2}. \qquad (33.12)$$

From the experimentally determined value of x it is possible to calculate the equilibrium constant. Alternatively, once K_p at a given temperature is known, the mole fraction of ammonia formed at equilibrium may be derived for any given pressure, or the pressure may be estimated at which the mole fraction attains a particular value.

Problem: In a mixture of 1 part of N_2 to 3 parts of H_2, the mole per cent of NH_3 at equilibrium was found to be 1.20 at 500° C and a total pressure of 10 atm. Calculate the pressure at which the equilibrium mixture at this temperature contains 10.40 mole per cent of NH_3.

It is first necessary to derive K_p by utilizing the fact that when P is 10 atm. the experimental value of $100x$ is 1.20, i.e., $x = 0.0120$; hence, by equation (33.12),

$$K_p = \frac{256 \times (0.0120)^2}{27 \times (1 - 0.012)^4 \times 10^2} = 1.43 \times 10^{-5},$$

with the pressure in atm. It is now required to calculate P corresponding to $100x = 10.40$, i.e., $x = 0.104$; thus,

$$K_p = 1.43 \times 10^{-5} = \frac{256 \times (0.104)^2}{27 \times (1 - 0.104)^4 \times P^2},$$

$$P = 105 \text{ atm.}$$

It is not actually necessary to evaluate K_p in this case; the arithmetic is simplified by not doing so, since 256 and 27 in the two expressions cancel.

(It may be noted that experimentally $100x$ is found to be 10.40 at 100 atm. The difference between this pressure and the calculated value of 105 atm. is to be ascribed to departure of the gases, particularly the ammonia, from ideal behavior at these high pressures.)

33c. Influence of Products on Dissociation.—As a consequence of the fact that the composition of a system at equilbrium is always determined by the equilibrium constant, it can be readily shown that the presence of one or other of the products of a particular dissociation will repress that dissociation. For example, if phosphorus pentachloride is vaporized into a space containing chlorine gas, the extent to which the pentachloride dissociates will be less than if the chlorine were not initially present. The reason for this may be readily seen by considering the general dissociation reaction

$$A \rightleftharpoons B + C,$$

for which the expression for the equilibrium constant is

$$K_p = \frac{p_B \times p_C}{p_A}. \tag{33.13}$$

If an excess of one of the dissociation products, e.g., B, is present, the value of p_B is increased, and in order to maintain the constancy of the fraction in equation (33.13) it is necessary for p_C to decrease while p_A increases to some extent. Since C arises from the dissociation of A, it is evident that this reaction will occur to a lesser extent than it would if the excess of B were not present. Similarly, an excess of C, instead of B, would have the same effect of decreasing the extent of dissociation of A. If the equilibrium constant of the reaction is known, the new position of equilibrium can be readily calculated.

Problem: The value of K_p for the dissociation of PCl_5 at 250° C is 1.78, with pressures in atm. Calculate the fraction of dissociation at equilibrium when 0.040 mole PCl_5 is vaporized in a vessel containing 0.20 mole Cl_2 gas, (i) when a constant pressure of 2 atm. is maintained, (ii) when the volume is kept constant at 4.0 liters. Compare the results with those for the same final pressures in the absence of excess chlorine.

(i) Let y be the number of moles PCl_5 dissociated at equilibrium; the fraction of dissociation α is then $y/0.04$. At equilibrium the vessel will contain $0.04 - y$ mole PCl_5, y mole PCl_3 and $0.2 + y$ mole Cl_2; the total number of moles is thus $0.24 + y$. Since the total pressure is constant at 2 atm., it follows that

$$K_p = 1.78 = \frac{p_{PCl_3} \times p_{Cl_2}}{p_{PCl_5}} = \frac{\dfrac{y}{0.24 + y} 2 \times \dfrac{0.2 + y}{0.24 + y} 2}{\dfrac{0.04 - y}{0.24 + y} 2}$$

$$y = 0.0205, \qquad \alpha = 0.0205/0.04 = 0.512.$$

The value of α in the absence of excess chlorine may be obtained directly from equation (33.11), or by replacing 0.2 moles Cl_2 by zero in the foregoing calculations; in each case it is found that α is 0.686.

(ii) In this case the pressure is not given, and so a somewhat different method of calculation must be employed; use is made of the relationship $p_i = n_i RT/v$ [equation (32.7)] to obtain the partial pressures. As before, y is taken as the number of moles of PCl_5 dissociated at equilibrium; then

$$p_{PCl_5} = (0.04 - y)\frac{RT}{v}, \qquad p_{PCl_3} = y\frac{RT}{v} \qquad \text{and} \qquad p_{Cl_2} = (0.2 + y)\frac{RT}{v}$$

$$K_p = 1.78 = \frac{y\dfrac{RT}{v} \times (0.2 + y)\dfrac{RT}{v}}{(0.04 - y)\dfrac{RT}{v}} = \frac{y(0.2 + y)}{0.04 - y} \cdot \frac{RT}{v}.$$

The temperature T is $250°$ C, i.e., $523°$ K, and v is given as 4.0 liters; since the pressures in K_p are in atm., R must be in liter-atm. deg.$^{-1}$ mole^{-1}, i.e., 0.0820; hence,

$$1.78 = \frac{y(0.2 + y)}{0.04 - y} \times \frac{0.082 \times 523}{4.0},$$

$$y = 0.0173, \qquad \alpha = 0.432.$$

The total pressure is equal to the sum of the three partial pressures, i.e., to $(0.24 + y)RT/v$; now that y is known, this can be evaluated as 2.76 atm. At this pressure the fraction of PCl_5 dissociated in the absence of added chlorine is found from equation (33.11) to be 0.626. The results show that in both cases (i) and (ii), the presence of an excess of chlorine produces an appreciable decrease in the extent of dissociation of the PCl_5.

33d. Combination of Equilibria.—In some equilibria two or more different reversible reactions, which have some reactants or products in common, are taking place simultaneously. If this is the case, the equilibrium constants of these simultaneous reactions are related to one another. Consider, for example, the water gas reaction

$$CO_2 + H_2 = CO + H_2O,$$

for which the partial pressure equilibrium constant is

$$K_p = \frac{p_{CO} \times p_{H_2O}}{p_{CO_2} \times p_{H_2}}. \tag{33.14}$$

In addition to this reaction there will be at least two other reversible processes involving some of the same substances; these are

$$(1) \quad 2H_2O \rightleftharpoons 2H_2 + O_2 \qquad \text{and} \qquad (2) \quad 2CO_2 \rightleftharpoons 2CO + O_2,$$

for which the equilibrium constants in terms of partial pressures are

$$K_1 = \frac{p_{H_2}^2 \times p_{O_2}}{p_{H_2O}^2} \qquad \text{and} \qquad K_2 = \frac{p_{CO}^2 \times p_{O_2}}{p_{CO_2}^2}, \tag{33.15}$$

respectively. When the system as a whole is in equilibrium, the three reversible reactions are all simultaneously in a state of equilibrium. It follows then that the partial pressures in equations (33.14) and (33.15) refer to the same system, and hence it is seen that

$$K_p = \sqrt{\frac{K_2}{K_1}}. \tag{33.16}$$

This gives the relationship between the various equilibrium constants. Similar results can be obtained in other cases.

The importance of equations of the type of (33.16) is that they can often be used to determine the equilibrium constant for a reaction which cannot be obtained by direct measurement with any degree of accuracy. For example, in the reaction considered above, if K_p for the water gas reaction and K_1 for the dissociation of water vapor are determined by experiment, the equilibrium constant K_2 for the dissociation of carbon dioxide, at the same temperature, can be calculated.

HOMOGENEOUS EQUILIBRIA IN LIQUID SYSTEMS

34a. The Esterification Reaction.—For reactions occurring in the liquid phase, the exact expression for the equilibrium constant is still given by equation (32.4); if the various components behave ideally, the activities may be replaced by their respective mole fractions (§ 31c). For the general reversible reaction

$$a\text{A} + b\text{B} + \cdots \rightleftharpoons l\text{L} + m\text{M} + \cdots$$

occurring in an ideal liquid system, the equilibrium constant may be written as

$$K_x = \frac{x_{\text{L}}^l \times x_{\text{M}}^m \times \cdots}{x_{\text{A}}^a \times x_{\text{B}}^b \times \cdots}, \tag{34.1}$$

where the x's are the mole fractions of the indicated substances. *If the various components are all present in dilute solution, the mole fractions may be replaced by the respective molar concentrations*, to which they are then proportional. Under these conditions, the equilibrium constant, now represented by K_c, is given by

$$K_c = \frac{c_{\text{L}}^l \times c_{\text{M}}^m \times \cdots}{c_{\text{A}}^a \times c_{\text{B}}^b \times \cdots}. \tag{34.2}$$

One of the most familiar instances of a reversible reaction in a homogeneous liquid system is that between acetic acid and ethanol to form the ester, ethyl acetate, and water; thus,

$$\underset{\text{acid}}{\text{CH}_3\text{COOH}} + \underset{\text{alcohol}}{\text{C}_2\text{H}_5\text{OH}} \rightleftharpoons \underset{\text{ester}}{\text{CH}_3\text{COOC}_2\text{H}_5} + \underset{\text{water}}{\text{H}_2\text{O}}.$$

If the mixture is assumed to behave ideally, the equilibrium constant is

$$K_x = \frac{x_{\text{ester}} \times x_{\text{water}}}{x_{\text{acid}} \times x_{\text{alcohol}}}. \tag{34.3}$$

The mole fraction of a given substance is equal to the number of moles n of that substance divided by the total number of moles N; since there are the same number of factors in the numerator and denominator in equation (34.3) the N's cancel, so that

$$K_x = \frac{n_{ester} \times n_{water}}{n_{acid} \times n_{alcohol}}. \tag{34.4}$$

By taking known amounts of alcohol and acetic acid in a sealed tube, heating them at 100° C to permit equilibrium to be reached, and then analyzing the resulting mixture, the equilibrium constant was found to be 4.0.

Once the equilibrium constant is known, it is possible to calculate the composition of the equilibrium system for any given initial amounts of the two reactants, in the presence or absence of the products. If a and b are the numbers of moles of acetic acid and alcohol present at the commencement, and y is the number of moles of ester, and also of water, produced at equilibrium, there will then remain $a - y$ moles of acid and $b - y$ moles of alcohol; it is assumed here that neither of the products is present in the initial system. Substituting these values in equation (34.4), the result is

$$K_x = \frac{y \times y}{(a - y)(b - y)}. \tag{34.5}$$

Since K_x has been determined experimentally, it is a simple matter to solve the quadratic equation (34.5) so as to give the value of y for any particular initial amounts of acid and alcohol. The data in Table XXXVII are quoted

TABLE XXXVII. THE ACETIC ACID-ETHANOL-ESTER-WATER EQUILIBRIUM

Acid	Alcohol	Ester Formed	
a	b	y (calc.)	y (obs.)
1.00 mole	0.18 mole	0.171 mole	0.171 mole
1.00	0.33	0.301	0.293
1.00	0.50	0.423	0.414
1.00	1.00	0.667	0.667
1.00	2.00	0.850	0.858
1.00	8.00	0.970	0.966

from the classical work of M. Berthelot and P. St. Gilles (1862) at 100° C; the number of moles of ethyl acetate y, as calculated from equation (34.5), with K_x taken as 4.0, are compared with the observed values. The agreement is seen to be very satisfactory; such deviations as do occur are due partly to experimental errors and partly to deviations from ideal behavior.

It will be apparent from the results in Table XXXVII that as the proportion of alcohol to acetic acid increases so also does the amount of ester formed at equilibrium. When the initial mixture consists of 1 mole of alcohol to 1 mole of acid, only 0.667 mole of ester is formed; that is, 66.7 per cent of the acetic acid is esterified. However, when the proportion of alcohol is increased to 8 moles to 1 mole of acid, it is seen that 96.6 per cent of the acid is converted into ester. This is an illustration of the concentration or "mass action" effect in reversible reactions. Since the equilibrium constant must always be maintained, the presence of excess of any reactant will tend to increase the proportion of the products formed at equilibrium. Similarly, if the products are already present, the extent of the forward reaction is diminished. An example of this latter type of behavior was considered in § 33c, dealing with the repression of dissociation by a reaction product. In the present case, the proportion of ester formed at equilibrium can be greatly decreased if the system initially contains an appreciable amount of water, which is one of the reaction products.

Problem: Calculate the per cent of acid that is esterified when a mixture consisting initially of 1 mole of acetic acid, 1 mole of ethanol and 1 mole of water attains equilibrium at 100° C.

Let y be the number of moles of ester formed; the system at equilibrium then contains $1 - y$ mole of acid, $1 - y$ mole of alcohol, y mole of ester and $1 + y$ mole of water. Since the equilibrium constant at 100° C is 4.0,

$$K_x = 4.0 = \frac{y(1 + y)}{(1 - y)(1 - y)}$$

$$y = 0.543.$$

The other value of y is impossible. Consequently 54.3 per cent of the acid is esterified, compared with 66.7 per cent in the absence of the water.

The equilibrium constant for the acetic acid-ethanol reaction is almost independent of temperature. It is to be expected, therefore, from the Le Chatelier principle that the reaction is accompanied by a very small heat change; the actual value is only about 0.4 kcal.

34b. Reversible Reactions in Dilute Solution.—When a reaction occurs in dilute solution molar concentrations may be employed in place of mole fractions. The dissociation of nitrogen tetroxide into the dioxide has been studied in dilute solutions in chloroform, and the results may be used to evaluate the equilibrium constant. The extent of dissociation was determined from the darkening in color of the solution; the tetroxide is almost colorless while the dioxide has a dark brown color. The equilibrium constant K_c [equation (34.2)] is given by the expression

$$K_c = \frac{c_{NO_2}^2}{c_{N_2O_4}}$$

and the results in Table XXXVIII are for concentrations in moles per liter of chloroform solution at 8.2° C. The constancy of the values in the last

TABLE XXXVIII.   THE DISSOCIATION OF NITROGEN TETROXIDE IN SOLUTION AT 8.2° C

$c_{N_2O_4}$	c_{NO_2}	K_c
0.129 mole liter^{-1}	1.17×10^{-3} mole liter^{-1}	1.07×10^{-5}
0.227	1.61	1.14
0.324	1.85	1.05
0.405	2.13	1.13
0.778	2.84	1.04

column shows that in the solutions studied the molar concentrations may be used in place of the activities without incurring serious error. As in other cases, a knowledge of the equilibrium constant makes it possible to calculate the composition of the system at equilibrium for any given initial composition of the system.

Problem: A solution is made up of 0.5 mole N_2O_4 in 450 ml. of chloroform; calculate the concentration of NO_2 in the solution at equilibrium at 8.2° C.

Let y be the number of moles of N_2O_4 that have dissociated, leaving $0.5 - y$ mole N_2O_4 and forming $2y$ mole NO_2 in 450 ml., i.e., 0.45 liter. The mean value of K_c from Table XXXVIII is 1.08×10^{-5}, with concentrations in moles per liter; hence,

$$K_c = 1.08 \times 10^{-5} = \frac{c_{NO_2}^2}{c_{N_2O_4}} = \frac{\left(\dfrac{2y}{0.45}\right)^2}{\dfrac{0.5 - y}{0.45}} = \frac{4y^2}{0.45(0.5 - y)},$$

$$y = 7.79 \times 10^{-4} \text{ mole.}$$

The concentration of NO_2 is $2y/0.45$, i.e., $2 \times 7.79 \times 10^{-4}/0.45 = 3.46 \times 10^{-3}$ mole per liter.

Heterogeneous Chemical Equilibria

35a. Activity of Solid Phase.—When a reaction involves one or more solids, in addition to a gas or a liquid phase, i.e., the reaction is **heterogeneous,** the activity of each solid in the expression for the equilibrium constant has a constant value, irrespective of the amount of solid present. By convention, *the activity of a pure solid substance is always taken as unity.* Consider, for purposes of illustration, the dissociation of solid calcium carbonate to form solid calcium oxide and carbon dioxide; if this reaction occurs in a closed space, the equilibrium

$$CaCO_3(s) \rightleftharpoons CaO(s) + CO_2(g)$$

is established. Utilizing the general equation (32.4) for the equilibrium constant, it is seen that

$$K = \frac{a_{CaO} \times a_{CO_2}}{a_{CaCO_3}}, \tag{35.1}$$

where the a's represent the activities. According to the convention given above, the activities of the two solids, $CaCO_3$ and CaO, are unity, so that equation (35.1) becomes

$$K = a_{CO_2}. \tag{35.2}$$

If the pressures are not too high and the temperatures are not too low, the carbon dioxide gas may be regarded as behaving ideally; the activity is then proportional to its partial pressure in the equilibrium system, i.e., to p_{CO_2}. It is then possible to write equation (35.2) in the form

$$K_p = p_{CO_2},$$

the subscript p in K_p being used to indicate that the activity has been expressed in terms of partial pressures. It follows, therefore, according to these arguments that the partial pressure of carbon dioxide in equilibrium with solid calcium carbonate and calcium oxide, generally called the **dissociation pressure** of calcium carbonate, should have a constant value at each temperature. This is exactly what has been found to be true experimentally; the dissociation pressure is independent of the quantities of the two solids, provided they are both present.

Apart from the fact that it leads to correct results, there are several ways of showing that the activity of a pure solid is constant, irrespective of its amount. For example, it was seen in § 31e that the activity of a liquid is proportional to its vapor pressure, and the same is true of a solid. Every pure solid has a definite and constant vapor pressure at each temperature (§ 22b); like the vapor pressure of a liquid, this does not depend on the quantity of the solid phase. Consequently, the activity of the pure solid has a constant value, which depends only on the temperature. By defining the activity as the vapor pressure relative to that of the pure substance, as in equation (31.14), it is seen that the activity of a pure solid is unity at all temperatures. This is in fact the convention adopted above and always employed in physical chemistry.

It is evident from the foregoing discussion that when writing the equilibrium constant for a heterogeneous reaction between solids and gases, the terms for the solids are all taken as unity, and hence may be ignored; each gas, however, is represented by its partial pressure at equilibrium. If these rules are borne in mind the derivation of the expression for the equilibrium constant for a heterogeneous reaction is a very simple matter.

35b. Reactions between Solids and Gases.—For purposes of classification reactions between solids and gases may be divided into two types according to the numbers of solids and gases involved.

I. Two Solids and One Gas.—The dissociation of calcium carbonate, or of any metallic carbonate, is an example of this kind of reaction. Other illustrations are provided by the dissociation of oxides, e.g.,

$$2Ag_2O(s) \rightleftharpoons 4Ag(s) + O_2(g),$$

and of salt hydrates, e.g.,

$$CuSO_4 \cdot 5H_2O(s) \rightleftharpoons CuSO_4 \cdot 3H_2O(s) + 2H_2O(g).$$

In each case the equilibrium constant is determined by the pressure of a single gas; hence, if the reaction occurs in a closed space, there will be a definite dissociation pressure of the gas at each temperature. It is of interest to note that a system consisting of a higher and a lower salt hydrate, or of a salt hydrate and the anhydrous salt, e.g.,

$$Na_2SO_4 \cdot 10H_2O(s) \rightleftharpoons Na_2SO_4(s) + 10H_2O(g),$$

exerts a definite equilibrium (dissociation) pressure of water vapor which depends only on the temperature. One essential condition is, however, that *both* solid salts, as well as the water vapor, must be present, although the amounts of the various constituents of the system are immaterial. The subject of the dissociation of salt hydrates, etc., will be considered from the standpoint of the phase rule in Chapter XII.

II. One Solid and Two Gases.—A familiar instance of this type of system is the dissociation of many ammonium salts; one of these which has been studied in some detail is ammonium hydrosulfide, NH_4HS. This salt dissociates into ammonia and hydrogen sulfide at quite low temperatures, viz.,

$$NH_4HS(s) \rightleftharpoons NH_3(g) + H_2S(g),$$

and remembering that the activity of the solid is to be taken as unity, the equilibrium constant is

$$K_p = p_{NH_3} \times p_{H_2S}.$$

When solid ammonium hydrosulfide was heated at 20° C, the total pressure of the vapor was found to be 0.468 atm. The actual vapor pressure of the solid salt is small and may be neglected; hence, the 0.468 atm. is due to the ammonia and hydrogen sulfide gases. Since these are produced in equimolecular amounts when the ammonium hydrosulfide dissociates, the partial pressure of each must be one half of 0.468, i.e., 0.234 atm.; that is,

$$p_{NH_3} = p_{H_2S} = 0.234 \text{ atm.,}$$

and consequently,

$$K_p = p_{NH_3} \times p_{H_2S} = 5.48 \times 10^{-2}.$$

The same value for the equilibrium constant should be obtained if the hydrosulfide is vaporized into a space already containing some ammonia or hydrogen sulfide gas. Let p be the initial pressure of one of these gases, e.g., the ammonia, and let y be the pressure of each gas resulting from the dissociation of the solid ammonium hydrosulfide; it follows then that

$$p_{NH_3} = p + y \quad \text{and} \quad p_{H_2S} = y$$

$$K_p = p_{NH_3} \times p_{H_2S} = (p + y)y. \tag{35.3}$$

Neglecting, as before, the actual vapor pressure of the solid, the total pressure is equal to the sum of the partial pressures of the two gases, i.e., to $p + 2y$. If the value of p, the initial excess pressure of ammonia, or of hydrogen sulfide, is known, and the total pressure at equilibrium, i.e., $p + 2y$, is measured, y can be calculated; it is thus possible to evaluate K_p from equation (35.3). The results obtained in this manner by J. P. Magnusson (1907) are recorded in Table XXXIX; the values of K_p in the last column are seen to be almost constant, and approximately equal to the result, i.e., 5.48×10^{-2}, obtained above from the dissociation of the pure hydrosulfide.

The figures in Table XXXIX illustrate, once again, the repression of dissociation by excess of either of the reaction products. The normal dissociation pressure of each gas is 0.234 atm. at 20° C. In the first three lines the systems contain an excess of hydrogen sulfide, and the partial pressure of

TABLE XXXIX. DISSOCIATION OF AMMONIUM HYDROSULFIDE AT $20°$ C

p_{NH_3}	p_{H_2S}	$p_{NH_3} \times p_{H_2S}$
0.0509 atm.	1.084 atm.	5.52×10^{-2}
0.115	0.481	5.54
0.140	0.397	5.43
0.531	0.104	5.50
0.711	0.0748	5.60
0.924	0.0587	5.42

ammonia, i.e., p_{NH_3}, is seen to be less than the normal dissociation pressure. Similarly, in the last three lines, where the ammonia is in excess, p_{H_2S} is smaller than 0.234 atm. in each case.

The dissociation of ammonium carbamate is of interest, since three molecules of gas are produced; thus

$$NH_4COONH_2(s) \rightleftharpoons 2NH_3(g) + CO_2(g),$$

and hence,

$$K_p = p_{NH_3}^2 \times p_{CO_2}. \tag{35.4}$$

Since the vapor pressure of the solid salt is itself very small, the total observed pressure P at equilibrium is due to the ammonia and carbon dioxide gases. Since there are two molecules of the former for each one of the latter, the partial pressure of the ammonia must be twice that of the carbon dioxide. In other words, p_{NH_3} is equal to two-thirds of the total pressure, i.e., $\frac{2}{3}P$, while p_{CO_2} is one half of this value, i.e., $\frac{1}{3}P$; consequently, by equation (35.4),

$$K_p = \tfrac{4}{27}P^3.$$

The equilibrium constant can thus be determined from measurements of the total pressure, in the absence of excess of either of the products. As in the case of ammonium hydrosulfide, the products repress the dissociation of the carbamate.

A different kind of process involving one solid and two gases is the industrially important equilibrium,

$$C(s) + CO_2(g) \rightleftharpoons 2CO(g),$$

for which

$$K_p = \frac{p_{CO}^2}{p_{CO_2}}. \tag{35.5}$$

Other reactions in the same category are

$$2C(s) + H_2(g) \rightleftharpoons C_2H_2(g) \quad \text{and} \quad C(s) + 2H_2(g) \rightleftharpoons CH_4(g).$$

III. One Solid and Three Gases.—In the reaction between solid carbon and steam represented by

$$C(s) + H_2O(g) \rightleftharpoons CO(g) + H_2(g),$$

three gases and one solid are present at equilibrium; in this case,

$$K_p = \frac{p_{CO} \times p_{H_2}}{p_{H_2O}}. \tag{35.6}$$

Attention may be called to the fact that the combination of the equilibrium constants in equations (35.5) and (35.6) gives that for the water gas reaction. Thus, if the former is divided by the latter, the result is identical with equation (33.14). This is an interesting illustration of the combination of two heterogeneous equilibria to yield the constant for a homogeneous equilibrium. Many other examples of a similar nature are to be found in the chemical literature.

TEMPERATURE AND EQUILIBRIUM

36a. The van't Hoff Equation.—The qualitative effect of temperature on chemical equilibrium is given by the principle of Le Chatelier, but an exact relationship can be derived by means of thermodynamics, as will be shown in § 37d. For homogeneous or heterogeneous gas reactions the variation of K_p with temperature is given by the expression

$$\frac{d \ln K_p}{dT} = \frac{\Delta H}{RT^2}, \tag{36.1}$$

sometimes known as the **van't Hoff equation**; in this expression ΔH is the heat of the reaction at constant pressure, R is the gas constant and T is the absolute temperature. Stated in words, this equation means that if $\ln K_p$ is plotted against the absolute temperature, the slope of the curve at any temperature is equal to $\Delta H/RT^2$.

Since K_p is equal to $K_c (RT)^{\Delta n}$, by equation (32.9), while ΔH is related to ΔE, the heat of reaction at constant volume, by equation (24.2), i.e., $\Delta H = \Delta E + RT(\Delta n)$, it can be readily shown that a modified form of equation (36.1) giving the variation of K_c with temperature is

$$\frac{d \ln K_c}{dT} = \frac{\Delta E}{RT^2}. \tag{36.2}$$

It will be observed that equation (36.1) is of the same form as the Clapeyron-Clausius equation (16.8); the latter may, in fact, be regarded as a special case of the former. When a liquid or a solid is in equilibrium with its own vapor, the pressure of the latter is equivalent to the equilibrium constant of the vaporization process. Hence, K_p in equation (36.1) may be replaced by the vapor pressure p; further, the change in heat content accompanying vaporization at constant pressure is the heat of vaporization L_v(or L_s). If these substitutions are made, the van't Hoff equation becomes identical with the special form of the Clapeyron-Clausius equation that is applicable to liquid-vapor and solid-vapor equilibria. It may be noted that in this form the equation cannot be applied to solid-liquid equilibria, i.e., to melting, since the external pressure may not be regarded as the equilibrium constant of the melting process.

The general agreement between the van't Hoff equation (36.1) and the Le Chatelier principle is at once evident; according to the former, K_p must increase with temperature if ΔH is positive, whereas it will decrease with increasing temperature if ΔH is negative. These are equivalent to the conclusions reached in § 32c.

36b. Integration of the van't Hoff Equation.—In order to utilize equation (36.1) for purposes of calculation, it must be integrated, just as was the Clapeyron-Clausius equation in § 16e. If the heat of reaction ΔH is taken as constant over a small range of temperature, general integration of the van't Hoff equation gives

$$\ln K_p = -\frac{\Delta H}{RT} + \text{constant}, \qquad (36.3)$$

or

$$\log K_p = -\frac{\Delta H}{2.303RT} + \text{constant}, \qquad (36.4)$$

which are exactly analogous to equations (16.10) and (16.11), respectively. These expressions show that the plot of $\log K_p$ against $1/T$, i.e., the reciprocal of the absolute temperature, should yield a straight line; the slope of this line will be $-\Delta H/2.303R$. The experimental data for a number of reversible reactions have been found to satisfy this requirement, provided the temperature range is not too large, so that ΔH remains almost constant.

For practical purposes it is more convenient to integrate equation (36.1) between the definite temperature limits of T_1 and T_2 or, what is the same thing, to subtract the two forms of equation (36.4) for these two temperatures; the result is

$$\log \frac{(K_p)_2}{(K_p)_1} = -\frac{\Delta H}{2.303R}\left(\frac{1}{T_2} - \frac{1}{T_1}\right) = \frac{\Delta H}{2.303R}\left(\frac{T_2 - T_1}{T_1 T_2}\right), \qquad (36.5)$$

where $(K_p)_1$ and $(K_p)_2$ are the equilibrium constants at the temperatures T_1 and T_2, respectively. If ΔH is expressed in calories, R is 1.987 cal. deg.$^{-1}$ mole^{-1}, and hence equation (36.5) becomes

$$\log \frac{(K_p)_2}{(K_p)_1} = \log (K_p)_2 - \log (K_p)_1 = \frac{\Delta H}{4.576}\left(\frac{T_2 - T_1}{T_1 T_2}\right), \qquad (36.6)$$

which is exactly analogous to equation (16.13). It may be noted that provided the equilibrium constants $(K_p)_1$ and $(K_p)_2$ are expressed in the same pressure units, the actual units are immaterial, since equations (36.5) and (36.6) involve the ratio of these constants. By means of equation (36.6) it is possible to calculate the equilibrium constant $(K_p)_2$ at the absolute temperature T_2, from the value $(K_p)_1$ at the temperature T_1, provided the heat of reaction ΔH at constant pressure is known. Alternatively, if the equilibrium constants have been determined at two temperatures, the heat of reaction can be evaluated.

It should be emphasized that equations (36.5) and (36.6) are based on the approximation of a constant value of ΔH over the temperature range from T_1 to T_2. For exact calculations allowance should be made for the possible variation of the heat of reaction with temperature, although for approximate purposes a mean value of ΔH may be employed. It was seen in § 24h that the variation of the heat of reaction with temperature can be expressed by means of equation (24.7), viz.,

$$\Delta H = \Delta H_0 + aT + \tfrac{1}{2}bT^2 + \tfrac{1}{3}cT^3 + \cdots,$$

where a, b, c, etc., are determined by the heat capacities of the substances taking part in the reaction. This value for ΔH may be substituted in the van't Hoff equation (36.1) with the result,

$$\frac{d \ln K_p}{dT} = \frac{\Delta H_0}{RT^2} + \frac{a}{RT} + \frac{b}{2R} + \frac{c}{3R}T + \cdots \tag{36.7}$$

Integration of this equation then gives a complete expression for the variation of the equilibrium constant with temperature [see equation (37.24)].

Problem: The equilibrium constant K_p for the reaction $N_2 + 3H_2 \rightleftharpoons 2NH_3$ is 1.64×10^{-4} at 400° C and 0.144×10^{-4} at 500° C. Calculate the mean heat of formation of 1 mole of ammonia from its elements in this temperature range.

Let T_1 be 400° C, i.e., $400 + 273 = 673°$ K, and T_2 be 500° C, i.e., 773° K; then $(K_p)_1$ is 1.64×10^{-4} and $(K_p)_2$ is 0.144×10^{-4}. These values may be inserted into equation (36.6) to evaluate ΔH in calories for the reaction; thus,

$$\log 0.144 \times 10^{-4} - \log 1.64 \times 10^{-4} = \frac{\Delta H}{4.576}\left(\frac{773 - 673}{673 \times 773}\right)$$

$$\Delta H = -25,140 \text{ cal.}$$

This is the heat of the reaction as written, in which two moles of NH_3 are formed; the mean heat of formation of one mole of NH_3 is thus $-12,570$ cal. or -12.57 kcal.

36c. Heterogeneous Reactions.—The equations derived above apply to heterogeneous reactions in which solids and gases are concerned. As seen in § 35a, the equilibrium constant for the dissociation of a carbonate is equivalent to the dissociation pressure of carbon dioxide. It follows, therefore, from equation (36.4) that the plot of $\log p_{CO_2}$ for various temperatures against $1/T$ should be a straight line, at least as long as ΔH remains constant. The results for the dissociation of calcium carbonate in the temperature range from 600° C to 1000° C are plotted in Fig. 61; the points fall approximately on a straight line, and from its slope, which is equal to $-\Delta H/2.303R$, the heat content change accompanying the reaction is found to be 40.4 kcal. in the given range of temperature.

Problem: The total pressure developed when solid HgO is heated so as to form mercury vapor and oxygen gas, according to the reaction $2HgO(s) \rightleftharpoons 2Hg(g) + O_2(g)$, is 141 mm. at 380° C, and 387 mm. at 420° C. Assuming ΔH to remain constant, calculate the temperature at which HgO dissociates freely in air. (This occurs when the equilibrium partial pressure of the oxygen is equal to its partial pressure in the air, i.e., 0.21 atm.)

The first step is the evaluation of ΔH for the reaction. Since both the mercury and the oxygen are in the gaseous state, K_p is given by

$$K_p = p_{Hg}^2 \times p_{O_2}.$$

The partial pressure of mercury is twice that of the oxygen, and since these two together make up the total observed pressure, it follows that at 380° C, i.e., 653° K,

$$p_{Hg} = \tfrac{2}{3} \times 141 = 94 \text{ mm.}, \quad \text{and} \quad p_{O_2} = 47 \text{ mm.},$$

while at 420° C, i.e., 693° K,

$$p_{Hg} = \tfrac{2}{3} \times 387 = 258 \text{ mm.}, \quad \text{and} \quad p_{O_2} = 129 \text{ mm.}$$

Hence,

$$(K_p)_1 \text{ at } 653° \text{ K} = (94)^2 \times 47 = 4.15 \times 10^5$$

$$(K_p)_2 \text{ at } 693° \text{ K} = (258)^2 \times 129 = 8.59 \times 10^6$$

and by equation (36.6)

$$\log 8.59 \times 10^6 - \log 4.15 \times 10^5 = \frac{\Delta H}{4.576} \left(\frac{693 - 653}{653 \times 693} \right)$$

$$\Delta H = 68,110 \text{ cal.}$$

If the partial pressure of oxygen is to be 0.21 atm., i.e., 159.6 mm., the partial pressure of the mercury vapor must be $2 \times 159.6 = 319.2$ mm.; K_p is then $(319.2)^2 \times 159.6 = 1.63 \times 10^7$. Taking ΔH as 68,110 cal., the temperature T must now be found

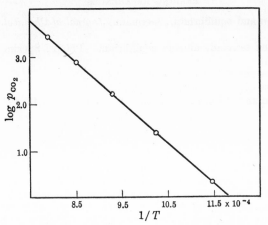

FIG. 61.   Dissociation of calcium carbonate

at which K_p has this value; combining this with either of the experimental K_p's, e.g., $(K_p)_1$, equation (36.6) gives

$$\log 4.15 \times 10^5 - \log 1.63 \times 10^7 = \frac{68,110}{4.576} \left(\frac{653 - T}{653 \times T} \right)$$

$$T = 702° \text{ K.}$$

Mercuric oxide should thus dissociate freely in air when the temperature reaches 702° K, i.e., $702 - 273 = 429°$ C.

36d. Reactions in Solution.—The appropriate form of the van't Hoff equation for reactions in solution at constant pressure is

$$\frac{d \ln K_x}{dT} = \frac{\Delta H}{RT^2}. \tag{36.8}$$

If the substances taking part are all in dilute solution, this expression becomes

$$\frac{d \ln K_c}{dT} = \frac{\Delta H}{RT^2}. \tag{36.9}$$

Attention should be called to the difference between equations (36.2) and (36.9); although both are concerned with K_c, the former, for gases, has ΔE on the right hand side, while the latter, for dilute solutions, has ΔH. Actually, for reactions in solution ΔH and ΔE are not appreciably different, and so a general equation of the form of (36.2) might be regarded as applicable to both gases and solutions. The equations (36.8) and (36.9) may be integrated in the usual manner, and the results are exactly similar to those already obtained for gas reactions. Since the subject presents no new features it need not be discussed further here, but an important application of equation (36.9) will be given in § 53h.

READING REFERENCES

1. **Mass action and equilibrium.** Germann, *Journal of Chemical Education*, **11**, 328 (1934).
2. **The nitrogen tetroxide-dioxide equilibrium.** Phipps, Spealman and Cooke, *ibid.*, **12**, 318 (1935).
3. **Law of mass action.** Adams, *ibid.*, **17**, 22 (1940).
4. **Law of mass action.** Frost, *ibid.*, **18**, 272 (1941).
5. **Dissociation and law of mass action.** Wakeham, *ibid.*, **18**, 493 (1941).

REVIEW QUESTIONS

1. Explain, with examples, the meaning of a reversible chemical reaction. Show how a state of chemical equilibrium is attained.

2. State the law of mass action and use it to derive an expression for the equilibrium constant of a homogeneous reversible reaction in the most general case.

3. State the Le Chatelier principle. Illustrate its application to determine the influence of temperature and pressure on the condition of equilibrium in the following cases: $N_2 + 3H_2 \rightleftharpoons 2NH_3$ (ΔH negative); $N_2 + O_2 \rightleftharpoons 2NO$ (ΔH positive); $2SO_2 + O_2 \rightleftharpoons 2SO_3$ (ΔH negative); $CO_2 + C(s) \rightleftharpoons 2CO$ (ΔH negative).

4. Give the expressions for the equilibrium constants K_p and K_c for a homogeneous gas reaction. How are these quantities related?

5. Outline the experimental methods used in determining equilibrium constants.

6. Derive an expression for the equilibrium constant for the hydrogen, iodine, hydrogen iodide reaction. What is the effect of changing (a) pressure, (b) volume, at constant temperature? How are K_p and K_c for this reaction related?

7. Give examples of other reactions which are similar in behavior to the hydrogen-iodine reaction.

8. Derive an expression for the equilibrium constant for the dissociation of nitrogen tetroxide in terms of the fraction dissociated.

9. Derive an expression for the equilibrium constant for the dissociation of phosphorus pentachloride in terms of the fraction dissociated.

10. Derive an expression for the equilibrium constant for the $N_2 + 3H_2 \rightleftharpoons 2NH_3$ reaction in terms of the mole fraction of ammonia at equilibrium. What conclusion can be drawn as to the effect of pressure?

11. Describe, with examples, the effect on dissociation of introducing one of the products.

12. How may two simultaneous equilibria be combined to give the equilibrium constant for a given reaction?

13. Derive an equation for the equilibrium constant of the esterification reaction. Show how it may be used to calculate the amount of ester formed under specified conditions.

14. Derive an equation for the equilibrium constant of the $N_2O_4 \rightleftharpoons 2NO_2$ reaction in dilute solution.

15. How is the expression for the equilibrium constant modified if one or more of the reactants or products is in the solid state? Illustrate by reference to the dissociation of a carbonate and an oxide.

16. Show how the equilibrium constant for the dissociation of (a) ammonium hydrosulfide, (b) ammonium carbamate, can be expressed.

17. Write down the forms of the van't Hoff equation for the influence of temperature on K_p and K_c. Integrate the expression for K_p and show how the results may be used to calculate heats of reaction.

18. Explain the application of the van't Hoff equation to (a) heterogeneous gas reactions, (b) reactions in solution.

PROBLEMS

I

1. The value of K_p for the reaction $2H_2O(g) + 2Cl_2(g) = 4HCl(g) + O_2(g)$ is 0.039 at 450° C, with pressures in atm. Assuming ideal behavior of the gases, calculate K_c for concentrations in moles per liter.

2. When a mixture of 1 mole of nitrogen and 0.25 mole of oxygen is allowed to come to equilibrium at over 3000° C, 0.125 mole of nitric oxide is formed. Calculate the molar composition of the gas obtained at equilibrium when equal molecular amounts of nitrogen and oxygen are heated at the same temperature.

3. At a temperature of 2000° K and a total pressure of 1 atm. steam is dissociated to the extent of 0.504 per cent according to the reaction $2H_2O(g) \rightleftharpoons 2H_2(g) + O_2(g)$. Calculate the equilibrium constant, and determine the percentage of dissociation of steam at the same temperature and a total pressure of 10 cm. (Since the dissociation is small, the partial pressure of the steam may be taken as equal to the total pressure, in order to avoid having to solve a cubic equation.)

4. At 1000° K, carbon dioxide is dissociated to the extent of 2×10^{-5} per cent according to the reaction $2CO_2 \rightleftharpoons 2CO + O_2$ at a total pressure of 1 atm. Combine this result with the value of K_p of 3.45 for the reaction $2SO_2 + O_2 \rightleftharpoons 2SO_3$ to calculate the equilibrium constant at 1000° K for the gas reaction $SO_2 + CO_2 = SO_3 + CO$.

5. Trichloracetic acid (CCl_3COOH) when heated with amylene (C_5H_{10}) reacts to form the ester (amyl trichloracetate) according to the reversible reaction $CCl_3COOH + C_5H_{10} \rightleftharpoons CCl_3COOC_5H_{11}$. When a mixture consisting of 1 mole of the acid and 4.12 moles of amylene is heated 0.814 mole of ester is formed at equilibrium at 100° C

What will be the molar composition at equilibrium when the system consists initially of 1 mole of acid and 1 mole of amylene?

6. The constant for the equilibrium between double molecules of benzoic acid and single molecules in benzene solution, i.e., $(C_6H_5COOH)_2 \rightleftharpoons 2C_6H_5COOH$ is 0.00219 at 10° C, with concentrations in moles per liter. Determine the weights of single and double molecules present in a 0.1 molar solution, i.e., one containing 12.2 g. benzoic acid in 1 liter of benzene.

7. When steam is heated with iron in a closed vessel at moderate temperatures the equilibrium $3Fe(s) + 4H_2O(g) \rightleftharpoons Fe_3O_4(s) + 4H_2(g)$ is established. At a given temperature the equilibrium system was found to contain steam at a partial pressure of 5.2 mm. and hydrogen at 75.6 mm. Calculate the partial pressures of the gases when iron is allowed to come to equilibrium, at the same temperature, with steam initially at 1 atm. pressure.

8. Solid ammonium hydrosulfide is in equilibrium with gaseous ammonia and hydrogen sulfide, according to the reaction $NH_4HS(s) \rightleftharpoons NH_3(g) + H_2S(g)$. At 25.1° C, the total gas pressure in equilibrium with the solid is 0.658 atm. Calculate the partial pressure of each gas when the solid hydrosulfide is allowed to dissociate into a closed space containing an initial pressure of 0.45 atm. of hydrogen sulfide.

9. The value of K_p for the dissociation of iodine vapor into atoms, i.e., $I_2(g) \rightleftharpoons 2I$ is 1.14×10^{-2} at 800° C and 4.74×10^{-2} at 900° C. Determine the value of the mean heat of dissociation in this temperature range.

10. The value of K_p for the equilibrium $C(s) + CO_2(g) \rightleftharpoons 2CO(g)$ is 43.07 at 900° C; what is the value at 1000° C, taking ΔH as constant and equal to $+40.3$ kcal. in this temperature range?

II

1. Calculate the value of the ratio K_p/K_c for the reaction $NO_2(g) \rightleftharpoons NO(g) + \frac{1}{2}O_2(g)$ at 250° C, where K_p is expressed in terms of atm. and K_c in moles per liter.

2. A mixture of 1.82 moles of hydrogen and 2.63 moles of iodine vapor were heated at a definite temperature until equilibrium was attained; it was then found that the amount of iodine had been decreased to 0.88 moles. What will be the composition of the system when 5.00 moles of hydrogen iodide are heated until equilibrium is attained at the same temperature?

3. Carbon dioxide gas is dissociated according to the reaction $2CO_2 \rightleftharpoons 2CO + O_2$ to an extent of 0.546 per cent at 1800° K and a total pressure of 1 atm. What would be the molecular composition of the equilibrium system at a total pressure of 0.200 atm. at the same temperature? (To avoid solving cubic equation, see note to problem I, 3.)

4. When carbon dioxide and carbon are heated at 1000° C, equilibrium is attained in the reaction $C(s) + CO_2(g) \rightleftharpoons 2CO(g)$ at a total pressure of 30 atm. when the gas contains 83 mole per cent of carbon monoxide. Combine this result with the value of K_p of 1.66 for the reaction $CO_2 + H_2 \rightleftharpoons CO + H_2O$ to calculate the equilibrium constant at 1000° C for the reaction $C(s) + H_2O(g) \rightleftharpoons CO(g) + H_2(g)$.

5. A mixture consisting of 1.00 gram of ethanol and 4.00 grams of acetic acid is heated until equilibrium is attained at 100° C. What is the composition by weight of the resulting mixture? (The value of the equilibrium constant is given in § 34a.)

6. When 0.130 mole of nitrogen tetroxide is dissolved in 1 liter of chloroform, it is dissociated at equilibrium to the extent of 0.45 per cent into nitrogen dioxide, according to the reaction $N_2O_4 \rightleftharpoons 2NO_2$, at 8° C. Determine the equilibrium composition of the solution obtained by dissolving 0.050 mole of the tetroxide in 850 ml. of chloroform.

7. In the reaction $Fe(s) + CO_2(g) \rightleftharpoons FeO(s) + CO(g)$, the partial pressure of carbon dioxide was found to be 0.740 atm. and that of the monoxide was 1.34 atm. when equilibrium was attained at 800° C. Calculate the partial pressures of the gases when iron is allowed to come to equilibrium with carbon dioxide initially at a pressure of 0.500 atm. at 800° C.

8. Solid ammonium cyanide is in equilibrium with gaseous ammonia and hydrogen cyanide, according to the reaction $NH_4CN(s) \rightleftharpoons NH_3(g) + HCN(g)$. The total pressure of the gases in equilibrium with the solid at 11° C is 0.298 atm. Calculate the partial pressures of the two gases when ammonium cyanide is allowed to dissociate into a closed space containing an initial pressure of 0.250 atm. of ammonia gas.

9. The value of K_p for the equilibrium $Fe(s) + H_2O(g) \rightleftharpoons FeO(s) + H_2(g)$ is 2.38 at 900° C and 1.67 at 1100° C. Calculate the mean value of ΔH in this temperature range.

10. For the equilibrium $2SO_2 + O_2 \rightleftharpoons 2SO_3$, the value of K_p is 3.45 at 727° C; calculate the value at 827° C, taking ΔH as constant and equal to -45.2 kcal. over this temperature range.

CHAPTER XI

FREE ENERGY AND CHEMICAL EQUILIBRIUM

EQUILIBRIUM CONSTANT AND FREE ENERGY

37a. Derivation of the Equilibrium Constant.—In the preceding chapter the subject of chemical equilibrium has been considered essentially from the practical and experimental points of view; in the present chapter the theoretical and thermodynamic aspects will be given some attention. It will be seen that among the results are exact derivations of the expression for the equilibrium constant and of the van't Hoff equation. In addition a criterion for indicating whether a particular chemical reaction is theoretically possible or not will be developed.

Consider, again, the general equation

$$aA + bB + \cdots \rightleftharpoons lL + mM + \cdots,$$

and suppose that the reactants A, B, etc., and the products L, M, etc., are not necessarily present in their equilibrium amounts, but *in any arbitrarily chosen state.** If the molar free energies of the various substances taking part in the reaction are F_A, F_B, $\cdots$, F_L, F_M, $\cdots$, in these arbitrary states, then

$$\text{Free energy of products} = lF_L + mF_M + \cdots$$

$$\text{Free energy of reactants} = aF_A + bF_B + \cdots$$

The increase of free energy ΔF accompanying the reaction with the reactants and products in the specified states is the difference between these two quantities; hence,

$$\Delta F = (lF_L + mF_M + \cdots) - (aF_A + bF_B + \cdots). \quad (37.1)$$

The molar free energy F of a substance in any state can be expressed in terms of its activity a in that state by means of equation (31.7), which may be written as

$$F = F^0 + RT \ln a, \quad (37.2)$$

where F^0 is the molar free energy in the standard state of unit activity. If the values of F_A, F_B, $\cdots$, F_L, F_M, $\cdots$, in equation (37.1) are replaced by the corresponding expressions as derived from equation (37.2), it is seen that

$$\Delta F = [l(F_L^0 + RT \ln a_L) + m(F_M^0 + RT \ln a_M) + \cdots]$$
$$- [a(F_A^0 + RT \ln a_A) + b(F_B^0 + RT \ln a_B) + \cdots], \quad (37.3)$$

---

* The word "state" here refers essentially to the partial pressure or concentration of any substance present in the system; the temperature may be regarded as constant.

where a_A, a_B, $\cdots$, a_L, a_M, $\cdots$, are the activities of the various substances involved in the reaction *in their arbitrary states.* Upon rearranging equation (37.3) the result is

$$\Delta F = \Delta F^0 + RT \ln \frac{a_L^l \times a_M^m \times \cdots}{a_A^a \times a_B^b \times \cdots},$$ (37.4)

where ΔF^0, the increase in free energy accompanying the reaction when all the reactants and products are *in their respective standard states*, is given by an equation analogous to (37.1), viz.,

$$\Delta F^0 = (lF_L^0 + mF_M^0 + \cdots) - (aF_A^0 + bF_B^0 + \cdots).$$ (37.5)

It will be noted that the quantity whose logarithm is involved in equation (37.4), which may be called the arbitrary **reaction quotient,** is exactly similar in form to the expression for the equilibrium constant. It should be clearly understood, however, that in the latter the activities of reactants and products are the values when the system as a whole is in equilibrium, whereas in the reaction quotient in equation (37.4) the activities correspond to the arbitrary specified states for the various substances, and *these may or may not correspond to a condition of equilibrium.*

It was seen in § 26b that for a system in equilibrium the free energy change ΔF is zero, provided the temperature and pressure at equilibrium are not allowed to alter. Consequently, when the arbitrarily chosen conditions represent those for equilibrium, ΔF in equation (37.4) may be put equal to zero, so that

$$\Delta F^0 = -RT \ln \left(\frac{a_L^l \times a_M^m \times \cdots}{a_A^a \times a_B^b \times \cdots} \right)_e$$ (37.6)

where the subscript e indicates that *the activities are those for the system at equilibrium.* Since the standard free energy change ΔF^0 refers to the reactants and products in the definite states of unit activity, it is apparent that ΔF^0 must be constant; consequently, the right-hand side of equation (37.6) must also be constant. The gas constant R has, of course, a definite value, and so it follows that if the temperature T is constant,

$$\left(\frac{a_L^l \times a_M^m \times \cdots}{a_A^a \times a_B^b \times \cdots} \right)_e = \text{constant} = K.$$ (37.7)

This is the exact expression for the equilibrium constant K, as given in equation (32.4); it has been derived here from thermodynamic considerations alone, without the assumption of the law of mass action. As seen in Chapter X, it may be simplified for systems which do not depart appreciably from ideal behavior. For gaseous reactions, the activity terms may be replaced by the respective partial pressures, while for reactions in solution mole fractions or, in dilute solutions, concentrations may be employed.

37b. The Reaction Isotherm.—If the symbol K for the equilibrium constant, as given by equation (37.7), is substituted in equation (37.6) the result is

$$\Delta F^0 = -RT \ln K. \tag{37.8}$$

This is a very important equation, for it relates the standard free energy change of a reaction to the experimentally determinable equilibrium constant. If this value for ΔF^0 is now inserted in equation (37.4) it follows that the free energy change for the reaction with reactants and products in any arbitrary states is given by

$$\Delta F = -RT \ln K + RT \ln \frac{a_L^l \times a_M^m \times \cdots}{a_A^a \times a_B^b \times \cdots}, \tag{37.9}$$

where the a's refer to the activities in these arbitrary states. The arbitrary reaction quotient in terms of activities may be represented by the symbol Q_a, that is,

$$Q_a = \frac{a_L^l \times a_M^m \times \cdots}{a_A^a \times a_B^b \times \cdots}, \tag{37.10}$$

so that equation (37.9) becomes

$$\Delta F = -RT \ln K + RT \ln Q_a, \tag{37.11}$$

which is a form of what is known as the **reaction isotherm** (J. H. van't Hoff, 1886). It is evident that if the arbitrary states happen to correspond to those for the system at equilibrium, Q_a will become identical with the equilibrium constant K, since the expressions for both these quantities are of exactly the same form [see equations (37.7) and (37.10)]. By equation (37.11), the value of ΔF would then be zero, as indeed it should be for an equilibrium system.

It was seen in § 31c that the standard state of unit activity may be defined in any convenient manner, and so it is obvious that the standard free energy change ΔF^0 must depend upon the particular choice of standard states. For gases, it is the usual practice to choose the state of unit activity as the ideal gas at 1 atm. pressure; consequently, for gas reactions equation (37.8) becomes

$$\Delta F_p^0 = -RT \ln K_p \tag{37.12}$$

where K_p is the equilibrium constant with partial pressures expressed in atm., ideal behavior being assumed. For these conditions, therefore, equation (37.11) may be written as

$$\Delta F = -RT \ln K_p + RT \ln Q_p, \tag{37.13}$$

where Q_p is now the reaction quotient with the arbitrary states of reactants and products given in terms of pressures in atm. From this form of the reaction isotherm the free energy change for a reaction taking place between gaseous reactants, at specified pressures, to form gaseous products, also at specified pressures, can be calculated. The same equation is applicable to heterogeneous reactions involving gases and solids.

Attention may be drawn to the fact that although ΔF^0 depends on the particular standard states that are chosen, the value of ΔF is, as it should be, independent of their nature. This may be readily seen by writing equation (37.13) in the simple form

$$\Delta F = RT \ln \frac{Q_p}{K_p}, \tag{37.14}$$

from which it is evident that ΔF is determined by the *ratio* of Q_p to K_p. Consequently, as long as both of these quantities are expressed in terms of the same standard states, that is, in terms of the same units, the result will be independent of the particular standard states employed.

Problem: The equilibrium constant K_p for the reaction $2H_2(g) + O_2(g) \rightleftharpoons 2H_2O(g)$ at $2000°$ K is about 1.55×10^7 with partial pressures in atm. Calculate (i) the free energy change accompanying the reaction of two moles of hydrogen at 0.100 atm. and one mole of oxygen at 0.100 atm. to form water vapor at 1.00 atm.; (ii) the standard free energy change for the same reaction at $2000°$ K, assuming ideal behavior of the gases.

(i) The arbitrary reaction quotient Q_p in terms of pressures in atm. is given by

$$Q_p = \frac{p_{H_2O}^2}{p_{H_2}^2 \times p_{O_2}} = \frac{1}{(0.1)^2 \times 0.1} = 10^3.$$

Converting equation (37.14) to common logarithms, this becomes

$$\Delta F = 2.303RT \log \frac{Q_p}{K_p} = 2.303R \times 2000 \times \log \frac{10^3}{1.55 \times 10^7},$$

since T is $2000°$ K. If ΔF is required in calories, R may be taken as 1.987, so that

$$\Delta F = 2.303 \times 1.987 \times 2000 \log \frac{10^3}{1.55 \times 10^7}$$

$$= -38,340 \text{ cal.} = -38.34 \text{ kcal.}$$

(ii) The standard free energy change ΔF_p^0, for standard states of 1 atm., is merely $-RT \ln K_p$; hence,

$$\Delta F_p^0 = -RT \ln K_p = -2.303 \times 1.987 \times 2000 \log 1.55 \times 10^7$$

$$= -65,800 \text{ cal.} = -65.80 \text{ kcal.}$$

For reactions in dilute solution, the standard state is chosen as the (hypothetical) ideal solution of unit concentration, i.e., 1 mole (or 1 gram ion) per liter, or of unit molality, i.e., 1 mole per 1000 grams of solvent. Under these conditions the standard free energy change is given by

$$\Delta F_c^0 = -RT \ln K_c, \tag{37.15}$$

and the reaction isotherm becomes

$$\Delta F = -RT \ln K_c + RT \ln Q_c = RT \ln \frac{Q_c}{K_c}, \tag{37.16}$$

where Q_c is the arbitrary reaction quotient with the states of the reactants and products expressed in terms of concentrations in their ideal solutions. If the solutions are sufficiently dilute, the actual concentrations may be employed in place of the ideal values.

37c. Criteria of Spontaneous Reaction.—The essential importance of the reaction isotherm lies in the fact that it provides a means of determining whether a particular reaction is possible or not, under a given set of conditions. It was seen in § 26b that for a thermodynamically irreversible process taking place at constant temperature and pressure, ΔF must be negative, that is, the free energy of the system diminishes. If a particular physical or chemical change is to be theoretically possible it must be able to occur spontaneously; spontaneous processes are, however, irreversible in the thermodynamic sense (§ 25b), and hence it follows that *a reaction can take place spontaneously only if it is accompanied by a decrease of free energy*, i.e., ΔF must be negative, at constant temperature and pressure. This result applies to any process, physical or chemical; it is immaterial whether the latter is reversible, in the chemical sense, or if it goes to virtual completion.

If the value of ΔF under a given set of conditions is positive, the reaction cannot possibly occur spontaneously under those conditions, although it may be able to do so if the conditions are altered. In the problem of the preceding section, it was seen that for the combination of hydrogen and oxygen at 0.1 atm. pressure to form water vapor at 1 atm. pressure at 2000° K, the free energy change was negative. The reaction can therefore take place spontaneously under these conditions. Suppose, however, the hydrogen and oxygen pressures were greatly reduced, or that of the water vapor was increased, so that Q_p became greater than K_p, the value of ΔF would be positive and the reaction would not be possible. Under these conditions the reverse reaction, i.e., the dissociation of water vapor, will tend to occur. By writing the reaction isotherm in the general form.

$$\Delta F = RT \ln \frac{Q}{K},$$

it is seen that a particular process will be possible theoretically if the reaction quotient Q is less than the corresponding equilibrium constant K; ΔF will then involve the logarithm of a fraction and hence will be negative. If, however, the arbitrary pressures or concentrations are such as to make Q greater than K, the value of ΔF will be positive, and the reaction will not be possible under these conditions.

It should be borne in mind, of course, that a change in temperature may affect the value of the equilibrium constant K to such an extent that a reaction which previously could not occur spontaneously, for a given value of the quotient Q, can now do so. At some temperatures K is less than Q, but as the temperature is altered K may become greater than Q; the sign of ΔF will thus reverse from positive to negative, and the reaction becomes possible, when the temperature is changed.

It is of interest to consider the physical significance of the conclusion that a reaction will be able to take place spontaneously if Q is less than K, but not if Q is greater than K. A comparison of equations (37.7) and (37.10), which define Q and K respectively, shows that when $Q < K$, the arbitrary activities (or concentrations) of the products are relatively less than those in the equilibrium state. The occurrence of the reaction will mean that the amounts of the products are increased, while those of the reactants decrease correspondingly; in other words, the state of the system will tend to move spontaneously towards the state of equilibrium. On the other hand, if $Q > K$, the products will be present in excess of the equilibrium activities, and for the reaction to continue would mean a still greater departure from equilibrium; such a change would never occur spontaneously. In these circumstances, of course, the reaction would tend to take place in the reverse direction.

Although any reaction accompanied by a decrease of free energy is theoretically possible, this is no indication that the process will actually occur with a measurable speed. In a series of analogous reactions, the rates at which the processes occur are roughly in the order of the free energy decrease, but in general, for different reactions, there is no connection between the magnitude of the decrease of free energy and the rate at which the reaction occurs. For example, at ordinary temperatures and pressures the free energy change for the combination of hydrogen and oxygen to form water has a very large negative value, yet the reaction, in the absence of a catalyst, is so slow that no detectable amount of water would be formed in years. The passage of an electric spark or the presence of a suitable catalyst, however, facilitates the occurrence of a reaction which the free energy change shows to be theoretically possible. The factors which determine the rate of a reaction, as distinct from its theoretical possibility, will be considered in Chapter XVIII.

37d. Derivation of the van't Hoff Equation.—From the results already obtained it is a simple matter to deduce the van't Hoff equation (36.1) for the variation of the equilibrium constant with temperature. Omitting the p subscript from the symbol ΔF^0 in equation (37.12) for simplicity, this equation for a gas reaction is

$$\Delta F^0 = -RT \ln K_p. \tag{37.17}$$

The left-hand side refers to a process in which each of the reactants and products is in its standard state of 1 atm. pressure, assuming ideal behavior; the right-hand side is, of course, independent of pressure. It is thus possible to differentiate equation (37.17) with respect to temperature at constant pressure; the result is

$$\left(\frac{d(\Delta F^0)}{dT}\right)_P = -R \ln K_p - RT \frac{d \ln K_p}{dT},$$

the subscript P implying constant pressure. Multiplying through by T, and substituting ΔF^0 for $-RT \ln K_p$, according to equation (37.17), this becomes

$$T\left(\frac{d(\Delta F^0)}{dT}\right)_P = \Delta F^0 - RT^2 \frac{d \ln K_p}{dT}. \qquad (37.18)$$

The Gibbs-Helmholtz equation (26.34), deduced in Chapter VIII, modified by the introduction of the superscript zero for the special case when all the substances taking part in the process are in their standard states, is

$$\Delta F^0 = \Delta H^0 + T\left(\frac{d(\Delta F^0)}{dT}\right)_P. \qquad (37.19)$$

Comparison of equations (37.18) and (37.19) immediately leads to the result

$$RT^2 \frac{d \ln K_p}{dT} = \Delta H^0 ,$$

$$\frac{d \ln K_p}{dT} = \frac{\Delta H^0}{RT^2}. \qquad (37.20)$$

This is the correct form of the van't Hoff equation, with ΔH^0, the change in heat content for the reaction, i.e., the heat of reaction at constant pressure, with the reactants and products in their standard states. However, it is a matter of experience that the heat content change does not vary appreciably with the pressures of the substances concerned, and so ΔH^0 may be replaced by ΔH without specifying the conditions, thus making the result more general, as in equation (36.1).

37e. Standard Free Energy of Reaction.—The significance of the standard free energy change ΔF^0 is that it is the increase of free energy associated with a reaction taking place under such conditions that each of the reactants and products is in its standard state, e.g., for a reaction involving ideal gases every gas taking part is at a partial pressure of 1 atm. Consequently, the sign of the standard free energy gives an indication of whether the process is possible or not under these conditions; if the value is negative it means that the reaction with reactants and products in their standard states can take place at the particular temperature.

In addition to the application just described, the quantity ΔF^0 has other uses which make it an important property in the study of reactions. In the first place, it has a definite value at every temperature for any given reaction, and it is related to the equilibrium constant at the same temperature by the familiar equation (37.8). The tabulation of standard free energies is thus equivalent to the tabulation of equilibrium constants. In the second place, since the free energy, like the heat content, is a property which depends only on the state of a system, *it is possible to add and subtract free energy changes for different reactions*, just as was done for heat changes in § 24e. Further, reversal of a particular reaction does not alter the standard free energy change but merely reverses the sign.

By utilizing these facts the ΔF^0 values of reactions which cannot be studied directly can be obtained by combining the known values for other reactions. For example, it is known that at 25° C,

$$2H_2O(g) = 2H_2(g) + O_2(g) \qquad \Delta F^0 = 109.3 \text{ kcal.}$$

$$CO_2(g) + H_2(g) = H_2O(g) + CO(g) \qquad \Delta F^0 = \quad 6.8$$

Multiplication of the second equation by two and addition of the first equation then gives for the reaction

$$2CO_2(g) = 2CO(g) + O_2(g)$$

$$\Delta F^0 = (2 \times 6.8) + 109.3 = 122.9 \text{ kcal.}$$

Without going into details, it should be evident that in view of the definition of ΔF^0 in terms of the negative logarithm of the equilibrium constant, the addition and subtraction of standard free energies is equivalent to the division and multiplication of equilibrium constants, respectively, as in § 33d. In other words, the use of free energies is analogous to the treatment of equilibrium constants by means of a slide rule.

If the standard free energy for a reaction involving a substance in a particular state, e.g., gaseous, is known, and that for another state, e.g., liquid, is required, the difference can usually be calculated and appropriate allowance made. The procedure can be simply illustrated by reference to the reaction

$$H_2(g) + \tfrac{1}{2}O_2(g) = H_2O(g).$$

The standard free energy change is half that given above for the dissociation of two moles of water vapor, with the sign changed, i.e., ΔF^0 at 25° C is -54.65 kcal. Suppose it is required to find ΔF^0 for the reaction

$$H_2(g) + \tfrac{1}{2}O_2(g) = H_2O(l);$$

it is necessary to know the standard free energy change accompanying the process

$$H_2O(g) = H_2O(l),$$

so that this may be added to the -54.65 kcal. The standard state of the water as vapor is at a pressure of 1 atm., assuming ideal behavior, while the standard state of liquid water is pure water (§ 31d). Hence, the required ΔF^0 is the free energy change for the transfer of 1 mole of water vapor from a pressure of 1 atm. to the pressure of vapor in equilibrium with pure liquid water at 25° C. This is obviously equal in magnitude but opposite in sign to the quantity calculated in the problem in § 26a; the value is consequently -2050 cal., i.e., -2.05 kcal. The standard free energy change for the formation of 1 mole of liquid water from its elements at 25° C is thus $-54.65 - 2.05$, i.e., -56.70 kcal.

Various procedures have been employed for the evaluation of the standard free energies of reactions. When the equilibrium constant can be determined

332 FREE ENERGY AND CHEMICAL EQUILIBRIUM 37f

experimentally, ΔF^0 can of course be calculated from equation (37.8). On the other hand, if the reaction is one that goes virtually to completion, so that it is not possible to measure the equilibrium constant, the value of ΔF^0 may often be obtained by the combination of results for two or more reactions for which the data are available, as described above. For a reaction that can be made to take place in a suitable galvanic cell, the standard free energy can be derived from the electromotive force of the cell (§ 49e). Another approach, which has received much attention in recent years, is based on the determination of entropy; this subject will be treated in the latter part of the present chapter.

37f. Standard Free Energy and Temperature.—Just as the equilibrium constant changes with temperature so also must the standard free energy, and the expression for this variation can be readily obtained. If both sides of equation (36.3), obtained by the integration of the van't Hoff equation on the assumption that ΔH is constant, i.e.,

$$\ln K_p = -\frac{\Delta H}{RT} + \text{constant}, \qquad (37.21)$$

are multiplied by RT and the sign changed, the result is

$$-RT \ln K_p = \Delta H - IT, \qquad (37.22)$$

where the gas constant R has been multiplied by the integration constant in equation (37.21) to give the new constant I. The value of this constant can evidently be calculated if the equilibrium constant K_p at any temperature T, and the change of heat content ΔH are known. The left-hand side of equation (37.22) is equal to ΔF^0, and hence

$$\Delta F^0 = \Delta H - IT. \qquad (37.23)$$

If ΔH were independent of temperature, this equation would provide a very simple method for determining ΔF^0 (or K_p) at any temperature, provided K_p was known at one particular temperature; all that would be necessary is a knowledge of the heat of reaction ΔH, and the constant I, obtained in the manner just described.

For a relatively small range of temperature, equation (37.23) may be employed in conjunction with a mean value of ΔH to give a fair indication of the variation of ΔF^0 with temperature. When the temperature range is considerable, however, it is necessary to make allowance for the fact that ΔH is not constant. General integration of equation (36.7), in which ΔH has been expressed as a function of the temperature, gives

$$\ln K_p = -\frac{\Delta H_0}{RT} + \frac{a}{R} \ln T + \frac{b}{2R} T + \frac{c}{6R} T^2 + \cdots + \text{constant}. \qquad (37.24)$$

If this is treated in the same manner as equation (37.21), it is found that the variation of ΔF^0 with temperature is represented by

$$\Delta F^0 = \Delta H_0 - aT \ln T - \tfrac{1}{2}bT^2 - \tfrac{1}{6}cT^3 + \cdots - IT. \qquad (37.25)$$

The values of ΔH_0, a, b, c, etc., are derived from measurements of the heat of reaction and from the heat capacities of the substances taking part in the reaction; the constant I can then be calculated from a knowledge of ΔF^0, or K_p, at any one temperature. In this way it is possible to obtain an expression which gives the standard free energy change of a particular reaction over a considerable range of temperature.

Problem: Utilizing the data given in the problem in § 24h, for the reaction $N_2(g)$ $+ 3H_2(g) \rightleftharpoons 2NH_3(g)$, together with the fact that K_p is 1.43×10^{-5}, with partial pressures in atm., at 500° C, derive a general expression for the variation with temperature of ΔF^0 for the formation of 1 mole of NH_3 from its elements.

From the results in § 24h, it is seen that ΔH_0 is $-19,130$ cal, $a = -9.92$, $b = -2.3$ $\times 10^{-3}$ and $c = 10.2 \times 10^{-6}$ cal.; these values may be inserted in equation (37.25). The constant I may then be calculated by utilizing the fact that K_p is 1.43×10^{-5} at 500° C, i.e., 773° K. It is more instructive, however, to follow through the detailed treatment, instead of merely substituting in a formula. The expression for ΔH is

$$\Delta H = -19,130 - 9.92T - 1.15 \times 10^{-3}T^2 + 3.4 \times 10^{-6}T^3 \text{ cal.},$$

and hence

$$\frac{d \ln K_p}{dT} = \frac{\Delta H}{RT^2} = -\frac{19,130}{RT^2} - \frac{9.92}{RT} - \frac{1.15 \times 10^{-3}}{R} + \frac{3.4 \times 10^{-6}}{R} T.$$

Upon integration this gives

$$\ln K_p = \frac{19,130}{RT} - \frac{9.92}{R} \ln T - \frac{1.15 \times 10^{-3}}{R} T + \frac{1.7 \times 10^{-6}}{R} T^2 + \text{const.}$$

Multiplication through by RT and changing the sign gives $-RT \ln K_p$, which is equal to ΔF^0, so that

$$\Delta F^0 = -19,130 + 9.92T \ln T + 1.15 \times 10^{-3}T^2 - 1.7 \times 10^{-6}T^3 - IT$$

in calories.

At 773° K, the value of K_p is 1.43×10^{-5}, so that

$$\Delta F^0 = -RT \ln K_p = -2.303 \times 1.987 \times 773 \log 1.43 \times 10^{-5}$$

$$= 17,140 \text{ cal.}$$

If this is substituted in the expression for ΔF^0 with T equal to 773°, it is found that I is 18.94.

The problem requires an expression for ΔF^0 for 1 mole of NH_3; that given above is for 2 moles, as in the chemical equation. It is necessary, therefore, to divide by two; the final result is

$$\Delta F^0 = -9,565 + 4.96T \ln T + 5.75 \times 10^{-4}T^2 - 8.5 \times 10^{-7}T^3 - 9.47T \text{ calories.}$$

From this expression ΔF^0 can be calculated for any temperature, within the range for which the equation for ΔH is applicable.

37g. Standard Free Energies of Compounds.—For purposes of calculation it is convenient to tabulate the molar free energies of substances in their standard states, i.e., 1 atm. pressure for (ideal) gases, and the pure state for liquids and solids. Since these are employed to calculate standard free energy *changes* in reactions, it is not necessary to know the *absolute* free energies of the various substances concerned. The situation is exactly similar to that considered in connection with the study of heat contents in § 24c. Just as in the latter case, a convention is adopted according to which *the free energy of all elements in their standard states is arbitrarily taken as zero at all temperatures.* The standard free energy change ΔF^0 for the reaction between hydrogen and oxygen at 25° C to form 1 mole of water in the gaseous state is -54.65 kcal., as seen in § 37e. By convention, the free energies of the hydrogen and oxygen gases are both taken as zero, and hence the molar standard free energy of water vapor, i.e., at 1 atm. pressure, would be -54.65 kcal. at 25° C. Similarly, the value for liquid water would be -56.7 kcal. per mole.

By the use of the methods referred to in § 37e and § 38d, the standard free energy changes accompanying the formation of various compounds from their elements have been determined, and these, in accordance with the convention given above, represent the standard (molar) free energies of the substances. Some of the results obtained in this manner are recorded in Table

TABLE XL.   STANDARD MOLAR FREE ENERGIES OF FORMATION OF COMPOUNDS AT 25° C

Solids and Liquids		Gases	
	ΔF^0		ΔF^0
$H_2O(l)$	-56.7 kcal.	H_2O	-54.6 kcal.
$CH_3OH(l)$	-40.0	HCl	-22.7
$C_2H_5OH(l)$	-40.2	CH_4	-12.8
$C_6H_6(l)$	$+29.4$	C_2H_4	$+16.3$
$CH_3COOH(l)$	-95.0	H_2S	-7.8
$AgCl(s)$	-26.2	C_2H_6	-7.8
$HgO(s)$	-13.8	CO_2	-94.2
$PbO(s)$	-45.0	NH_3	-3.9
$PbS(s)$	$+18.0$	CO	-32.7
$PbSO_4(s)$	-176.5	SO_2	-69.6

XL for a temperature of 25° C. The physical meaning of these data may be understood more clearly by writing out the equations in full, e.g.,

$$\tfrac{1}{2}H_2(g,\ 1\ \text{atm.}) + \tfrac{1}{2}Cl_2(g,\ 1\ \text{atm.}) = HCl(g,\ 1\ \text{atm.}) \qquad \Delta F^0 = -22.7\ \text{kcal.}$$

$$C(s) + O_2(g,\ 1\ \text{atm.}) = CO_2(g,\ 1\ \text{atm.}) \qquad \Delta F^0 = -94.2$$

$$C(s) + 2H_2(g,\ 1\ \text{atm.}) + \tfrac{1}{2}O_2\ (g,1\ \text{atm.}) = CH_3OH(l) \qquad \Delta F^0 = -40.0$$

By indicating the pressures of the gases it is perhaps unnecessary to insert the zero superscript in the symbol ΔF^0, since they represent alternative methods of stating the same facts. However, both are given here for the sake of completeness, and to facilitate an understanding of the significance of the results; in any event the standard state of a gas refers to the *ideal* gas at 1 atm.

The standard free energies in Table XL can be used to calculate the standard free energy changes for reactions at 25° C, in the same way as the heat contents were employed in § 24c to calculate heats of reaction. For example, in the following reaction

$$CH_4(g) + 2O_2(g) = CO_2(g) + 2H_2O(l),$$
$$\quad -12.8 \qquad 0 \qquad\quad -94.2 \quad -2 \times 56.7$$

the standard free energy values, allowing for the number of moles in each case, are inserted below the formula for each reactant and product. The standard free energy change for the complete reaction at 25° C is then given by

$$\Delta F^0 = [(-94.2) + (-2 \times 56.7)] - [(-12.8) + 0] = -194.8 \text{ kcal.}$$

If the value of ΔF^0 for a reaction is known at one temperature, it is theoretically possible to derive the values for other temperatures by the procedure described in § 37f.

Problem: Calculate the equilibrium constant K_p at 25° C for the reaction

$$2H_2S(g) + SO_2(g) = 2H_2O(g) + 3S(s).$$

From Table XL it is seen that for this reaction

$$\Delta F^0 = [(-2 \times 54.6) + 0] - [(-2 \times 7.8) + (-69.6)]$$
$$= -24.0 \text{ kcal. or } -24,000 \text{ cal.}$$

Since $-\Delta F^0 = RT \ln K_p$, it follows that $\ln K_p = -\Delta F^0/RT$, or

$$\log K_p = -\frac{\Delta F^0}{2.303RT} = \frac{24,000}{2.303 \times 1.987 \times 298.2} = 17.59$$

$$K_p = 3.9 \times 10^{17} \text{ at } 25° \text{ C.}$$

The high value of K_p indicates that the reaction as written above goes virtually to completion at ordinary temperatures.

ENTROPY AND FREE ENERGY

38a. The Third Law of Thermodynamics.—It was seen in § 26a that the free energy change associated with a given process is related to the corresponding heat content and entropy changes by the equation

$$\Delta F = \Delta H - T\Delta S. \tag{38.1}$$

If all the substances concerned are in their standard states, this becomes

$$\Delta F^0 = \Delta H^0 - T\Delta S^0, \tag{38.2}$$

or, in view of the fact that ΔH does not vary appreciably with the pressure or concentration of the reactants and products, as stated earlier,

$$\Delta F^0 = \Delta H - T\Delta S^0. \tag{38.3}$$

The heat content changes ΔH of many reactions are known or can be determined without difficulty from calorimetric measurements; hence, if the entropy changes were known there would be available a method for determining free energy changes. This would be particularly useful for reactions which go to virtual completion; for such reactions it is not possible to determine the equilibrium constant, and hence ΔF^0, by direct experiment.

If the *absolute entropies* of elements and their compounds in their standard states could be measured or their values calculated, the standard entropy change for a reaction involving these substances could be determined. The problem of evaluating standard free energy changes thus reduces itself to one of obtaining the absolute entropies of the materials taking part in the reaction.* The fundamental difficulty lies in the establishment of an entropy zero for each substance, but this has been overcome by the enunciation of what has become known as the **third law of thermodynamics**. Like the other laws of thermodynamics, this is largely a law of experience; in other words, it leads to results which are in agreement with those obtained by direct experiment. In addition, however, it has a certain amount of theoretical support. In its simplest terms the law may be stated in the following manner: *the entropy of a perfect crystalline solid of a pure substance is zero at the absolute zero of temperature.* With this postulate the problem of obtaining absolute entropies may be regarded as solved, for in principle the change of entropy with temperature can be determined by experimental methods; hence, the actual entropy of an element or compound at any desired temperature may be obtained.

38b. Determination of Entropy from Thermal Measurements.—If equation (25.13) for a small entropy change at constant pressure is integrated between the absolute temperatures of zero and T, the result is

$$S_T - S_0 = \int_0^T C_P \frac{dT}{T} = \int_0^T C_P \, d \ln T, \qquad (38.4)$$

where S_T and S_0 are the entropies at the temperature T and at the absolute zero, respectively; C_P is the heat capacity of the substance at constant pressure. According to the third law of thermodynamics, S_0 is zero for a perfect crystalline solid, and hence *the entropy of a solid substance* at any temperature is given by

$$S = \int_0^T C_P \frac{dT}{T} = \int_0^T C_P d \ln T. \qquad (38.5)$$

The molar entropy can thus be determined by plotting the experimental values of the heat capacity C_P against $\ln T$ (or C_P/T against T) for a number of temperatures, and measuring the area beneath the curve from zero to the temperature at which the entropy is required (see § 25e). Reliable

---

* It should be pointed out that the situation with regard to ΔS^0 is quite different from that with ΔF^0 and ΔH; the evaluation of the latter may be based on a convention, i.e., zero for elements, but this is not possible for ΔS^0. The reason is that free energy and heat content changes can be determined by direct experiment, but this is not possible for entropy changes. The only way these can be evaluated is from the actual (absolute) entropies of the substances concerned in the process.

heat capacity determinations cannot be made below about 10° or 15° K; it is fortunate, therefore, that at very low temperatures the necessary data can be obtained from the Debye equation (21.2), the value of the characteristic temperature θ being readily derived from measurements at higher temperatures. Actually the Debye equation gives C_V, but the difference between C_P and C_V at low temperatures is so small as to be negligible. The evaluation of the entropy of a crystalline solid may be illustrated by reference to Fig. 62; the heat capacities plotted on the curve BC are the experimental values, the point B corresponding to the lowest temperature, i.e., 10° or 15° K, at which satisfactory measurements are possible. The portion AB, down

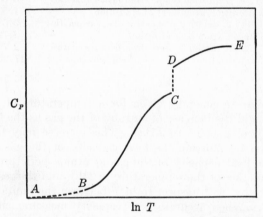

Fig. 62. Evaluation of entropy of crystalline solid

to the absolute zero, is then derived from the low temperature form of the Debye specific heat equation, i.e., equation (21.2). It is evident from this equation that the heat capacity of a solid must approach zero rapidly at temperatures below about 10° K, and so this part of the curve has little influence on the accuracy of the results. The area enclosed by the curve ABC, the ln T axis and the ordinate corresponding to any given temperature is equivalent to the entropy of the solid at that temperature.

If the solid undergoes an enantiotropic change of crystalline form on heating (§ 20b), the heat capacity curve will not be continuous, but will show a break, e.g., CD in Fig. 62, at the transition point. To the entropy obtained from the area under the two curves ABC and DE must now be added the entropy of transition, that is, the heat absorbed in the transition divided by the transition temperature on the absolute scale (§ 25f).

If the substance being studied is a liquid or a gas at the temperature at which the entropy is required, the heat capacity measurements on the crystalline solid are made up to its melting point, and the entropy at that temperature is determined in the manner just described. Heat capacity data of the liquid up to its boiling point are now plotted, in the same way, against ln T, and the area under the curve gives the increase in entropy in passing from the melting point to the boiling point; this is then added to the entropy of the solid at its melting point. The addition of the entropies of fusion and vaporization (§ 25f) to this total gives the entropy of the *gas* (vapor) at the boiling point. An illustration of the results obtained in this manner for nitrogen is given in Table XLI (W. F. Giauque and J. O. Clayton, 1933); the values are in E.U., i.e., cal. per deg., per mole. The entropy of nitrogen gas at 77.32° K and 1 atm. pressure is thus 36.31 E.U. per mole.

TABLE XLI.   THE MOLAR ENTROPY OF NITROGEN GAS AT THE BOILING POINT

0° to 10° K from Debye equation	0.458 E.U.
10° to 35.61° K (transition point) from heat capacities	6.034
Entropy of transition, from heat of transition	1.536
35.61° to 63.14° K (melting point) from heat capacities	5.589
Entropy of fusion, from heat of fusion	2.729
63.14° to 77.32° K (boiling point) from heat capacities	2.728
Entropy of vaporization, from heat of vaporization	17.239
Total	36.31 E.U.

Molar entropies are generally given for a temperature of 25° C, and so it is necessary to add the increase of entropy of the gas as the temperature is raised from the boiling point to 25° C. This increase may be obtained in the usual manner, by plotting the heat capacity of the gas against ln T. Alternatively, the heat capacity of the gas at atmospheric pressure may be expressed as a function of the temperature (§ 24h), and the resulting expression can be integrated with respect to ln T between the limits of the boiling point and 25° C. When accurate heat capacity measurements of the gas are not available, the values may be obtained by calculations involving statistical methods (§ 38c). The entropy of the gas at 25° C and a pressure of 1 atm. having been obtained, the addition of a small correction for deviation from ideal behavior gives the standard molar entropy at this temperature.

38c. Entropy of Gases by the Statistical Method.—During recent years remarkable progress has been made in the calculation of entropy and other thermodynamic properties of gases by methods based on the quantum theory of energy and the science of statistical mechanics. The total energy of a molecule is made up of various kinds, e.g., translational, rotational, vibrational and electronic; there is also nuclear energy, but this need not be considered for the present purpose. Instead of being continuously variable in amount, each of these energies is quantized; in other words, a molecule can have only certain definite values of the various forms of energy, or it can occupy only certain specific energy levels (§ 9c). If ϵ_0, ϵ_1, ϵ_2, etc., represent the energies of a single molecule in the various possible levels, a quantity called the **partition function,** and to which the symbol Z will be given here,* is defined by

$$Z = g_0 e^{-\epsilon_0/kT} + g_1 e^{-\epsilon_1/kT} + g_2 e^{-\epsilon_2/kT} + \cdots , \qquad (38.6)$$

* Although some writers use Z for the partition function, the symbol Q is perhaps more frequently employed; it is avoided here, however, because this letter has been used to indicate the "reaction quotient" in the earlier part of this chapter.

where g_0, g_1, g_2, etc., are the **statistical weights** of the various levels, that is, the number of states of the molecule possessing the energies ϵ_0, ϵ_1, ϵ_2, etc., respectively; k is the Boltzmann constant, i.e., the gas constant per single molecule, and T is the absolute temperature. The summation in equation (38.6), which defines the partition function, includes an exponential term for every permitted energy level of the molecule. By utilizing the relationship between entropy and probability given in § 25h, in conjunction with statistical methods for calculating the probability, the following relationships between the partition function and various thermodynamic properties for 1 mole of an *ideal gas* are obtained:

$$S = R\left[\ln\frac{Z}{N} + T\left(\frac{d\ln Z}{dT}\right)_P\right]$$

$$E = RT^2\left(\frac{d\ln Z}{dT}\right)_V$$

$$C_V = \left(\frac{dE}{dT}\right)_V = \frac{d}{dT}\left[RT^2\left(\frac{d\ln Z}{dT}\right)\right]_V$$

where N is the Avogadro number and R is the usual molar gas constant.

The evaluation of the partition function, in accordance with equation (38.6), requires a knowledge of all the energy levels of the molecule. For the forms of energy other than translational the necessary information can be obtained from the spectra of the gas molecules concerned, particularly if these are not too complicated. The translational contribution to the partition function can be derived from a relatively simple formula, but for the other kinds of energy an accurate partition function can be obtained only by summing the exponential terms in equation (38.6). The amount of labor involved is very large, but it has been greatly reduced by means of certain devices. Where reliable spectroscopic data are available, the use of the partition function method leads to values for thermodynamic constants which are probably more accurate than the best data obtained from thermal, e.g., heat capacity, and similar measurements. If precise values are not required, or there are not sufficient data for their calculation, it is possible to make use of relatively simple, but somewhat approximate, expressions to determine the contribution to the partition function made by the vibrational and rotational energies of the molecule.

In general, where entropy values of gases have been obtained by both the statistical and heat capacity (thermal) methods the results are in excellent agreement, thus providing experimental support for the third law of thermodynamics upon which the latter method is based. There are, however, a few cases, notably hydrogen, water, nitric oxide, carbon monoxide and nitrous oxide, where the thermal entropies are lower than the statistical values. The discrepancies in these instances are due to the fact that the solids do not constitute perfect crystals in the sense required by the third law of thermodynamics. With hydrogen there are reasons for believing that rotation persists in the solid state, even at very low temperatures. On the other hand, with NO, CO and N_2O, i.e., NNO, the similarity of the atoms makes it possible for the molecules to be oriented in the crystal in two alternative ways, viz., CO and OC, NO and ON, NNO and ONN. As a consequence of these various factors the crystals are not perfect, and the entropy is then finite, instead of being zero, at the absolute zero. For these substances the entropy values obtained by the statistical method are the correct ones to be used in thermodynamic calculations.

38d. Application of Entropy Data.—By the use of thermal and statistical methods, the standard molar entropies of a number of elements and compounds have been determined; some of the values at 25° C are recorded in Table XLII in the usual entropy units, i.e., cal. per deg., per mole. From

TABLE XLII.   STANDARD MOLAR ENTROPIES AT 25° C

Solids and Liquids				Gases			
	S^0		S^0		S^0		S^0
Graphite	1.39 E.U.	Hg(l)	17.8 E.U.	H_2	31.23 E.U.	O_2	49.03 E.U.
Zn(s)	9.9	Br_2(l)	18.4	CH_4	44.4	CO_2	51.07
Ag(s)	10.3	AgCl(s)	23.4	HCl	44.64	C_2H_4	52.3
Na(s)	12.25	AgI(s)	26.6	H_2O	45.17	Cl_2	53.31
I_2(s)	14.0	CH_3OH(l)	30.3	N_2	45.79	C_2H_6	55.0
H_2O(l)	15.9	C_2H_5OH(l)	38.4	NH_3	46.4	CH_3OH	56.63
HgO(s)	16.6	C_6H_6(l)	41.9	CO	47.32	Br_2	58.67
NaCl(s)	17.2	$C_6H_5CH_3$(l)	52.4	C_2H_2	48.0	I_2	62.29

these data it is possible to derive the standard entropy change ΔS^0 for any reaction involving the substances concerned. For such a reaction as the formation of liquid benzene from its elements, viz.,

$$6C \text{ (graphite)} + 3H_2(g) = C_6H_6(l),$$

the value of ΔS^0 is seen to be given by

$$41.9 \text{ (for } C_6H_6) - [6 \times 1.39 \text{ (for 6C)} + 3 \times 31.23 \text{ (for } 3H_2)] = -60.1 \text{ E.U.}$$

As seen in § 38a, a knowledge of the standard entropy change, in conjunction with the change of heat content in the reaction, permits the evaluation of the standard free energy change of the process. In this way it is possible to determine the equilibrium constant of a reaction from purely thermal measurements or from thermal measurements, which give ΔH, in conjunction with statistical calculations based on spectroscopic information. It is of interest to mention that in certain cases accurate ΔH values have been obtained from spectroscopic data (§ 62d), and since the entropy can also be obtained from similar measurements, it has been found possible to calculate free energy changes and equilibrium constants of some reactions with great precision merely from a study of the spectra of the molecules concerned.

Problem: The heat of formation of liquid benzene at 25° C is 12.3 kcal. per mole (Table XXVI); calculate the standard free energy of formation of this substance at 25° C.

The value of ΔH for the reaction $6C(s) + 3H_2(g) = C_6H_6(l)$ is 12,300 cal., and since ΔS^0 has been found above to be -60.1 cal. deg.$^{-1}$ mole^{-1}, it follows from equation (38.3) that at $25°$ C, i.e., $298.2°$ K,

$$\Delta F^0 = 12,300 + 298.2 \times 60.1 = 30,200 \text{ cal. mole}^{-1}.$$

The use of entropy data makes possible the determination of standard free energies of formation and the standard free energy changes of reactions which could not be obtained by the direct experimental methods described in § 37e. In fact many of the values quoted in Table XL, especially for organic compounds, were actually derived in this manner. It may be noted that although the results, in the first place, apply at $25°$ C, they can be adjusted to any desired temperature by the procedures described in § 37f.

REVIEW QUESTIONS

1. Derive the expression for the equilibrium constant by means of thermodynamics.
2. Derive the equation for the reaction isotherm in terms of (a) activities, (b) partial pressures.
3. Show how ΔF may be used as a criterion of spontaneous reaction under any given conditions. How may the value of ΔF be changed?
4. Derive the van't Hoff equation for the influence of temperature on the equilibrium constant.
5. What is meant by the standard free energy change of a reaction? Explain its importance. How may standard free energy changes be determined?
6. Derive an expression for the free energy change as a function of the temperature (a) assuming ΔH to be constant, (b) allowing for the variation of ΔH with temperature.
7. What is meant by the standard free energy of a compound? Illustrate the use of such standard free energies.
8. State the third law of thermodynamics and explain its importance in connection with free energy and heat content changes.
9. Describe the determination of entropies from heat capacity and related (thermal) measurements.
10. Outline the statistical method for the calculation of entropies and other thermodynamic quantities. Explain why the results are sometimes different from those obtained by the thermal method.
11. Illustrate the application of standard entropies to the calculation of free energy changes.

PROBLEMS

I

1. For the reaction $2HI(g) \rightleftharpoons H_2(g) + I_2(g)$, the equilibrium constant at $458°$ C is 48.7. Calculate the standard free energy of formation of one mole of hydrogen iodide gas at this temperature.
2. The value of K_p for the reaction $2CO + O_2 = 2CO_2$ is 3.27×10^7 at $2000°$ K, with pressures in atm. What is the value of ΔF accompanying the transfer of two moles of CO at 0.01 atm. and one mole of O_2 at 0.05 atm. to form CO_2 at 1.0 atm. at this temperature?

3. In which direction will the reaction referred to in the preceding problem proceed spontaneously under the specified conditions? If the arbitrary pressures of CO and O_2 are maintained at 0.01 and 0.05 atm., respectively, how must that of the CO_2 be adjusted so as to make the reverse reaction possible?

4. The standard free energy change of the reaction $SO_2(g) + Cl_2(g) = SO_2Cl_2(g)$ is -1.90 kcal. at $25°$ C. What is the standard molar free energy of formation of sulfuryl chloride (SO_2Cl_2)? (Use the data in Table XL.)

5. Using the data in Table XL, evaluate the standard free energy changes of the following reactions at $25°$ C: $H_2(g) + CO_2(g) = H_2O(g) + CO(g)$; $3H_2(g) + SO_2(g) = H_2S(g) + 2H_2O(g)$; $CH_4(g) + \frac{1}{2}O_2(g) = CH_3OH(l)$. Determine the equilibrium constant in each case.

6. For the reaction $CH_4(g) + 2O_2(g) = CO_2(g) + 2H_2O(l)$ the standard free energy change is -194.8 kcal. at $25°$ C. The value of ΔH^0 for the reaction at the same temperature is -212.8 kcal. Calculate the standard entropy change for the reaction in cal. deg.$^{-1}$, and compare with the result derived from Table XLII.

7. The heat of formation of one mole of hydrogen chloride is -22.0 kcal. at $25°$ C. By combining this result with the entropy values in Table XLII, determine the equilibrium constant of the gas reaction $2HCl \rightleftharpoons H_2 + Cl_2$ at $25°$ C.

II

1. For the reaction $N_2O_4(g) \rightleftharpoons 2NO_2(g)$, the value of K_p is 0.318 at $35°$ C. Calculate the standard free energy change accompanying the dissociation of one mole of nitrogen tetroxide at this temperature.

2. The value of K_p for the reaction $2SO_2 + O_2 = 2SO_3$ is 3.45 at $1000°$ K, with pressures in atm. Determine the value of ΔF for the transfer of two moles of SO_2 at 0.1 atm. and one mole of oxygen at 0.2 atm. to form SO_3 at 1.0 atm. at this temperature.

3. In which direction will the reaction referred to in the preceding problem proceed spontaneously under the specified conditions? If the arbitrary pressures of SO_2 and O_2 are maintained at 0.1 and 0.2 atm. respectively, how must that of the SO_3 be adjusted so as to make the reverse reaction possible?

4. The standard free energy change of the reaction $CO(g) + Cl_2(g) = COCl_2(g)$ is -16.3 kcal. at $25°$ C. What is the standard molar free energy of formation of carbonyl chloride ($COCl_2$)? (Use data in Table XL.)

5. By means of the data in Table XL, calculate the standard free energy changes of the following reactions at $25°$ C: $4HCl + O_2 = 2H_2O(g) + 2Cl_2$; $CO + 2H_2 = CH_3OH(l)$; $CO + PbO(s) = CO_2 + Pb(s)$. Determine the equilibrium constant in each case.

6. For the reaction $2H_2S(g) + SO_2(g) = 2H_2O(g) + 3S(s)$, the standard free energy change is -24.0 kcal. at $25°$ C. The value of ΔH^0 for the reaction at the same temperature is -34.4 kcal. Calculate the standard entropy change for the reaction in cal. deg.$^{-1}$. The standard molar entropy of SO_2 is 59.2 E.U. and that of solid sulfur is 7.6 E.U. per g. atom; determine the molar entropy of H_2S at $25°$ C. (Use Table XLII.)

7. The heat content change of the reaction $C_2H_4 + H_2 = C_2H_6$ is -31.5 kcal. at $25°$ C. By utilizing the entropy data in Table XLII, calculate the equilibrium constant of this reaction at $25°$ C.

CHAPTER XII

PHASE EQUILIBRIA

SOLUTIONS OF GASES IN LIQUIDS

39a. Solubility of Gases.—It was pointed out in § 36a that there is no essential difference between a chemical equilibrium and the physical equilibrium involving the vapor and the liquid (or solid) phase of a substance as measured by the vapor pressure. It is nevertheless desirable to treat physical equilibria between phases separately from chemical equilibria. The present chapter will therefore be devoted to a consideration of the phenomena associated with phase equilibria, particularly in systems of two components. In place of the law of mass action and the equilibrium constant, use will be made of the phase rule, enunciated in § 22e, to study the conditions of equilibrium. In certain cases, however, the van't Hoff equation will be applied to determine the influence of temperature.

The first type of system to be considered is that of a gas and a liquid; the former dissolves in the latter, and a state of equilibrium is reached when the liquid is saturated with the gas. The amount of gas that has then dissolved depends on the temperature and pressure, as well as on the nature of the gas and the liquid solvent. At a given temperature and pressure the solubilities of a series of gases in a given liquid generally increase in the order of their ease of liquefaction; thus, in any solvent, hydrogen and helium are generally the least soluble gases, whereas carbon dioxide and ammonia are much more soluble. Chemical reaction between the gas and the solvent, as undoubtedly occurs when ammonia, hydrogen chloride or carbon dioxide is dissolved in water, results in an increased solubility.

There are no universally accepted units for expressing the solubilities of gases; as will be seen later, there are theoretical reasons for employing mole fractions, but as the latter are often small they are not convenient for general use. Since the solubility of a gas is usually determined by measuring the volume, rather than the weight, that has dissolved, the **absorption coefficient** of R. Bunsen (1857) is frequently used. This is defined as *the volume of gas, reduced to 0° C and 1 atm. pressure, dissolved by unit volume of solvent at the temperature of the experiment under a partial pressure of 1 atm. of the gas.* The absorption coefficients of a few common gases at 20° C in three solvents of different types are quoted in Table XLIII. Although the actual values vary from one solvent to another, the order of increasing solubilities of gases is approximately the same in each case.

It will be noted that in the evaluation of the absorption coefficient the volume of dissolved gas is supposed to be measured at 0° C and 1 atm. pres-

343

TABLE XLIII.   ABSORPTION COEFFICIENTS OF GASES AT 20° C

Solvent	H₂	He	N₂	O₂	CO	CO₂
Water	0.017	0.009	0.015	0.028	0.025	0.88
Ethanol	0.080	0.028	0.130	0.143	0.177	3.0
Benzene	0.066	0.018	0.104	0.163	0.153	—

sure. Since 1 mole of any gas under these conditions occupies approximately 22.4 liters, it follows that *if the absorption coefficient is divided by 22.4, the result gives the solubility of the gas expressed in moles per liter*, at the experimental temperature and 1 atm. pressure.

When gases dissolve in water there is generally a liberation of heat (§ 24g); hence, the Le Chatelier principle indicates that increase of temperature should result in a decrease of solubility. It is for this reason that gases may be readily expelled from solution by boiling. Certain solutions of the hydrogen halides in water are apparent exceptions to this rule, but chemical reaction between the gas and the solvent is undoubtedly a complicating factor in these cases. The solubility of a gas expressed in moles per unit volume of liquid, at a constant pressure, may be regarded as the constant of the equilibrium existing between the gas molecules in solution and those in the gas phase. As seen above, the absorption coefficient divided by 22.4 gives the solubility in moles per liter; hence, this coefficient, represented by α, may be regarded as a measure of the equilibrium constant, and if this replaces K in the van't Hoff equation (36.9), the influence of temperature on the solubility of a gas can be expressed by

$$\frac{d \ln \alpha}{dT} = \frac{\Delta H}{RT^2},\tag{39.1}$$

or after integration between the limits of T_1 and T_2, assuming ΔH to be constant,

$$\log \frac{\alpha_2}{\alpha_1} = \frac{\Delta H}{2.303R}\left(\frac{T_2 - T_1}{T_1 T_2}\right).\tag{39.2}$$

In these equations ΔH is the change of heat content accompanying the solution of 1 mole of gas, and its value may be calculated, in the manner described in § 36b, if the solubilities α_1 and α_2 are known at two temperatures T_1 and T_2. It may be mentioned that ΔH is actually the *differential* heat of solution of the gas (§ 24g) in the saturated solution.

The absorption coefficients of helium, nitrogen, oxygen and carbon dioxide at 0° and 30° C, in water as solvent, are recorded in Table XLIV. The

TABLE XLIV.   INFLUENCE OF TEMPERATURE ON SOLUBILITIES OF GASES IN WATER

		Absorption Coefficients		
Temperature	He	N₂	O₂	CO₂
0°	0.0094	0.0235	0.0489	1.713
30°	0.0081	0.0134	0.0261	0.665

relative influence of temperature is seen to be greater for carbon dioxide than for the other gases; this means that the heat of solution is largest in this instance, a fact which is no doubt related to the chemical reaction which occurs between carbon dioxide and water.

39b. Influence of Pressure: Henry's Law.—The influence of pressure on the solubility of a gas was expressed by W. Henry (1803); his conclusions, generally known as Henry's law, may be stated in the following form: *the mass of gas dissolved by a given volume of solvent, at constant temperature, is proportional to the pressure of the gas in equilibrium with the solution.* If w is

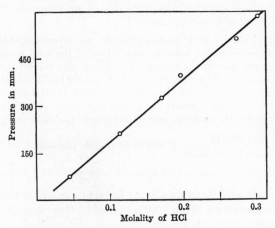

FIG. 63.   Solubility of hydrogen chloride in benzene

the mass of gas dissolved by unit volume of solvent at the equilibrium pressure p, then according to Henry's law,

$$w = kp \qquad (39.3)$$

where k is a proportionality constant. If a gas obeys equation (39.3) the plot of the solubility against the pressure should give a straight line passing through the origin. The results for the solubility of hydrogen chloride in dry benzene at 30° C are represented in Fig. 63; the points are seen to fall close to a straight line, as required by Henry's law. Provided the pressures are not too high or the temperatures too low, most gases obey Henry's law, especially if they are not very soluble. When chemical reaction takes place between the gas and the solvent, e.g., hydrogen chloride, ammonia or carbon dioxide in water, Henry's law fails to hold if the total solubility is considered. However, if an estimate is made of the quantity of gas that is in the free, or uncombined, state in the solution, this is found to increase in proportion to the pressure as required by equation (39.3).

When gases dissolve from a mixture, instead of from the pure gas, the solubility of each constituent is proportional to its own partial pressure; in other words, Henry's law applies to each gas independently of the pressure of the others present in the mixture. The Bunsen absorption coefficient, as seen above, is proportional to the molar concentration of the gas dissolved at constant pressure, viz., 1 atm. It follows, then, that the solubility of a gas in a mixture, expressed either in terms of the volume at 0° C and 1 atm., or of moles, dissolved by unit volume, is proportional to αp, where α is the absorption coefficient and p is the partial pressure of the gas.

Problem: Air consists of 78.06 per cent by volume of nitrogen and 21.00 per cent of oxygen, the remainder being inert gases. Utilizing the absorption coefficients in Table XLIII calculate the molar composition of the gas dissolved in water saturated with air at 20° C, assuming ideal behavior of the oxygen and nitrogen. (The solubility of the inert gases is small and may be ignored.)

If the gases behave ideally, their partial pressures are proportional to the number of moles of each, and hence to the volume composition; if the total pressure of the air is 1 atm., the partial pressure of the nitrogen is consequently 0.7806 atm., while that of the oxygen is 0.2100 atm. The absorption coefficients are 0.0150 and 0.0280, respectively; the solubilities are therefore in the ratio of 0.7806 × 0.0150 volumes (or moles) of nitrogen to 0.2100 × 0.0280 volumes (or moles) of oxygen, i.e., 0.0117 to 0.00588. Neglecting the inert gases, the mole per cent of nitrogen in the dissolved gas is given by

$$\frac{0.0117}{0.0117 + 0.00588} \times 100 = 66.6 \text{ mole per cent.}$$

The dissolved gas therefore contains 66.6 moles of nitrogen to 33.4 moles of oxygen.

39c. Henry's Law and Raoult's Law.—In equation (39.3) the quantity w is the mass of gas dissolved in unit volume, and hence it may be taken as equal to the concentration of gas molecules in the saturated solution. If this solution is moderately dilute, the concentration is proportional to the mole fraction of the dissolved substance, and so it is possible to write the Henry's law equation (39.3) as

$$x_2 = k'p_2 \qquad \text{or} \qquad p_2 = \frac{x_2}{k'}, \tag{39.4}$$

where x_2 is the mole fraction of solute (gas) in the solution when the pressure of the gas above the solution is p_2; k' is a proportionality constant which is related to k in equation (39.3).

According to Raoult's law, as stated in the form of equation (27.5), the pressure p_1 of the solvent vapor in equilibrium with a solution in which the mole fraction of the solvent is x_1 is given by

$$p_1 = x_1 p_1^0, \tag{39.5}$$

where p_1^0 is the vapor pressure of the pure solvent. It can be shown by means of thermodynamics that if a solution behaves ideally, an expression analogous to equation (39.5) must apply to the solute if it is volatile; thus,

$$p_2 = x_2 p_2^0, \tag{39.6}$$

where the subscript 2 refers to the solute. Comparison of equations (39.4) and (39.6) shows a distinct similarity; in fact the two equations would become identical if k' were equal to $1/p_2^0$, where p_2^0 is the vapor pressure of the liquefied gas at the temperature at which the solubility is measured. This condition is approached in a few cases, representing *ideal* solutions of gases in liquids; for such solutions Henry's law and Raoult's law, as applied to the solute, may be regarded as identical. For the majority of solutions of gases in liquids, however, the behavior is not ideal, and although k' in equation (39.4) is approximately constant, in accordance with Henry's law, it is not equal to $1/p_2^0$, as would be required by Raoult's law.

The relationship between Henry's law and Raoult's law shows that the solubility of a gas may be considered from two points of view; in equation (39.4), for example, x_2 may be regarded as the solubility of the gas, in mole fractions, under the pressure p_2, or alternatively, p_2 may be taken as the vapor pressure of a volatile solute when it is present to the extent of mole fraction x_2 in the solution. From the latter aspect it is possible to calculate the ideal solubility of any gas, for then the solubility x_2 is related to the pressure p_2 by means of the Raoult equation (39.6); writing this in the form of equation (39.4), it follows that

$$x_2 = \frac{p_2}{p_2^0},\qquad(39.7)$$

where p_2^0, as seen above, is the vapor pressure of the pure liquefied gas at the temperature of the solution. These conclusions may be illustrated by reference to a particular case; thus, at 25° C, pure liquid ethane has a vapor pressure of 42 atm., i.e., $p_2^0 = 42$ atm. Consequently, by equation (39.7), the ideal solubility of ethane *in any solvent* at 25° C and a pressure p_2 of 1 atm. is given by

$$x_2 = \tfrac{1}{42} = 0.024 \text{ mole fraction.}$$

The actual solubility of ethane in n-hexane at 25° C is 0.017 mole fraction at 1 atm. pressure; the difference between the observed and calculated values shows that the solution of ethane in n-hexane does not behave ideally.

MIXTURES OF TWO LIQUIDS

40a. Ideal Systems and Raoult's Law.—A system consisting of a mixture of two volatile liquids is essentially similar to a solution of a gas in a volatile liquid, the temperature being low enough for the gas to liquefy under the applied pressure. For practical purposes, however, it is best to consider mixtures of liquids from the aspect of vapor pressure, whereas in the previous section the solution of a gas was treated mainly from the point of view of solubility. Nevertheless, it should be realized, as indicated above, that there is no real difference between these two approaches to the study of systems of two components involving gaseous and liquid phases. The particular method employed is the one which happens to lead to the most useful results.

When a system consists of two liquids, such as water and alcohol, or benzene and toluene, which are soluble (miscible) in one another in all proportions, no distinction can, or need, be drawn between solvent and solute.

With such systems, therefore, the practice is to replace the subscripts 1 and 2 by the letters A and B. The symbol p_A then represents the partial pressure of the component A in the vapor, while p_B is that of the component B, when the vapor and liquid phases are in equilibrium. The total vapor pressure P is equal to the sum of the two partial pressures, i.e., $p_A + p_B$, in accordance with Dalton's law of partial pressures (§ 11g). The tacit assumption is made here that the vapors behave as ideal gases; the pressures are generally so low that this approximation does not cause appreciable errors.

In order to evaluate the partial pressures of the vapors in equilibrium with a mixture of two volatile liquids, the principle generally employed is to determine both the total pressure P and the composition of the vapor. If the latter is stated in terms of the respective mole fractions x'_A and x'_B, it follows from equation (11.23) that *

$$p_A = x'_A P \quad \text{and} \quad p_B = x'_B P. \tag{40.1}$$

The partial vapor pressures of the two components in equilibrium with a liquid mixture of given composition can thus be determined. The values depend not only on the nature of the substances and their proportions present in the mixture, but also, of course, on the temperature.

In accordance with the definitions of §§ 27a and 31a, an **ideal system of two liquids** is described as *one in which both constituents obey Raoult's law over the whole range of concentrations and at all temperatures*, i.e.,

$$p_A = x_A p_A^0 \quad \text{and} \quad p_B = x_B p_B^0 \tag{40.2}$$

for all values of the mole fractions x_A and x_B in the liquid, and at all temperatures; p_A^0 and p_B^0 are the vapor pressures of the pure liquids A and B, respectively, at each temperature. Theoretical considerations show that for an ideal liquid system defined in this manner, there are neither heat nor volume changes when the two liquids are mixed.

Without entering into detailed arguments, it can be shown in a general way that Raoult's law might be expected to hold for a mixture in which the presence of the molecules of B has no effect on the forces existing between the molecules of A, and vice versa (§ 31a). A mixture of two liquids behaving in this manner with respect to each other might well show no volume or heat change, and it is reasonable to describe its behavior as ideal. The vapor pressure of the pure liquid A is determined essentially by two factors; first, the "escaping tendency" of the molecules, which depends on the (van der Waals) forces acting between the A molecules in the liquid and, second, the number of A molecules available. If the molecular forces remain unchanged in a mixture, the escaping tendency of the A molecules will be the same in the solution as in the pure liquid; however, the proportion of A molecules in the liquid is less in the former case, and hence the vapor pressure of A will be reduced in proportion. If n_A is the number of molecules (or moles) of A,

---

* It should be noted that x'_A and x'_B refer to the mole fractions of A and B in the vapor; it is for this reason that the primes are used.

and n_B is the number of molecules (or moles) of B in the mixture, the proportion of A molecules in the mixture is $n_A/(n_A + n_B)$, which is the mole fraction x_A of A. The vapor pressure p_A of the component A in the mixture should thus be proportional to x_A, viz.,

$$p_A = k \frac{n_A}{n_A + n_B} = kx_A, \tag{40.3}$$

where k depends on the escaping tendency of the A molecules in the solution. If, as postulated above, this escaping tendency is the same as in the pure liquid, when x_A is unity and the vapor pressure is p_A^0, it follows from equation (40.3) that k is equal to p_A^0, and so this equation becomes

$$p_A = x_A p_A^0,$$

which is the statement of Raoult's law as applied to the component A [equation (40.2)]. Exactly the same result can be obtained in an analogous manner for the component B, so that if the intermolecular forces remain unchanged when A and B are mixed, Raoult's law should apply to both substances in the mixture.

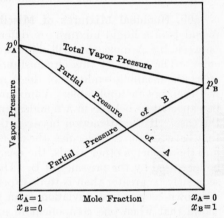

FIG. 64. Vapor pressures of ideal liquid system

The variation with the composition of the liquid of the partial and total vapor pressures at a given temperature for an ideal system, to which the Raoult equations (40.2) are applicable, is shown in Fig. 64. The plot of the partial pressure of each constituent against its respective mole fraction in the liquid should be a straight line passing through the origin, as shown by the thin lines; the total vapor pressure, equal to the sum of the partial vapor pressures, is then also a straight line, as shown in the figure. If the mixture is really ideal, a similar diagram, but with different actual pressures, would be obtained at any temperature at which the liquids can exist.

As is to be anticipated, from the discussion of intermolecular forces and Raoult's law, ideal, or approximately ideal, behavior is exhibited almost exclusively by mixtures of two similar liquids. The following are examples of mixtures which have been found experimentally to obey Raoult's law over the whole range of compositions, at least at one temperature: ethylene bromide and ethylene chloride, n-hexane and n-heptane, n-butyl chloride and n-butyl bromide, and carbon tetrachloride and silicon tetrachloride.

Problem: The vapor pressures of pure CCl_4 and $SiCl_4$ at 25° C are 114.9 mm. and 238.3 mm., respectively. Assuming ideal behavior, calculate the total vapor pressure of a mixture of equal weights of the two liquids.

The molecular weights of CCl_4 (A) and $SiCl_4$ (B) are 153.8 and 169.9, respectively, so that the mixture consists of $w/153.8$ moles of A and $w/169.9$ moles of B; the mole fraction of CCl_4 is then

$$x_A = \frac{w/153.8}{(w/153.8) + (w/169.9)} = 0.525.$$

The mole fraction x_B of $SiCl_4$ is then $1 - x_A$, i.e., 0.475. The partial vapor pressures are consequently,

$$p_A = x_A p_A^0 = 0.525 \times 114.9 = 60.3 \text{ mm.}$$
$$p_B = x_B p_B^0 = 0.475 \times 238.3 = 113.2 \text{ mm.,}$$

and the total vapor pressure is therefore $60.3 + 113.2 = 173.5$ mm.

40b. Nonideal Mixtures of Miscible Liquids.—If the two components A and B of a liquid mixture are different in character, the molecular forces between the A molecules will differ from those acting between the B molecules. The result of this circumstance will be that the presence of B will affect the escaping tendency of the A molecules, and vice versa; Raoult's law will then not be applicable. A mixture of two dissimilar liquids would thus be expected to behave in a nonideal manner, and this has been found to be the case. If the attraction between the B molecules is much stronger than that between the A molecules, the effect is to force the latter out of the liquid into the vapor; in other words, the escaping tendency of the A molecules will be increased by the presence of B. The partial vapor pressure of A will consequently be greater than is to be expected from Raoult's law; such behavior is known as **positive deviation** from the ideal law. Theoretical treatment shows that when one component of a mixture exhibits positive deviations, the other component must do the same; the nonideal system as a whole is then said to show positive deviations from Raoult's law. The type of vapor pressure curves obtained at a given temperature for mixtures of this kind is shown in Fig. 65, where the dotted lines indicate ideal behavior. If the positive deviations are large, and especially if the vapor pressures of the pure liquids are not very different, the curve for the total vapor pressure of the mixture will exhibit a maximum. Such behavior is not uncommon and is of importance in connection with distillation, as will be seen later (§ 40d).

If the two liquids constituting the mixture are both nonpolar, e.g., carbon tetrachloride and heptane, or if both are moderately polar, e.g., ether and acetone, the positive deviations from ideal behavior are not large. On the other hand, if one component is slightly polar while the other is highly polar or, more particularly, if the mixture consists of a polar and a nonpolar compound, e.g., an alcohol and a hydrocarbon, considerable positive deviations may occur. Such large deviations may lead to the liquids becoming immiscible to some extent (§ 40e).

If the two constituents of a mixture are such that the molecules of A and B *attract one another strongly*, and particularly if a compound between A and B is formed to some extent in the liquid, the vapor pressure of each constituent will be less than that required by the Raoult equation. This type of nonideal behavior is described as **negative deviation** from Raoult's law. The vapor pressure curves at constant temperature are then of the form shown in Fig. 66, where, as before, the dotted lines indicate ideal behavior. It will be observed that the vapor pressure curve may well have, and in fact frequently does have, a minimum for a particular composition. Systems exhibiting negative deviations from Raoult's law are pyridine and acetic acid, chloroform and ethyl ether, and the halogen acids and water; in every case there are good reasons for believing that the molecules of the two components attract one another strongly, even to the extent of interaction or partial compound formation in the liquid state.

An examination of Figs. 65 and 66 shows that as the system approaches pure A, i.e., very dilute B or pure B, i.e., very dilute A, in composition, the

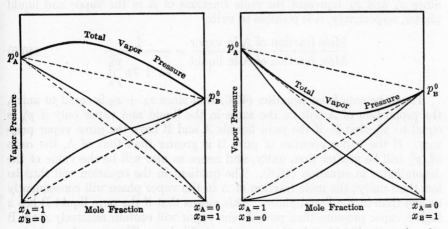

FIG. 65. System exhibiting positive deviations from Raoult's law

FIG. 66. System exhibiting negative deviations from Raoult's law

partial vapor pressure of A or B, respectively, approximates the ideal (Raoult law) value, irrespective of whether positive or negative deviations occur at other compositions. This is the justification for the statement in § 31a that for dilute solutions Raoult's law is almost invariably applicable to the solvent. It may be mentioned that it can be shown theoretically that Henry's law applies to the constituent present in small amount, i.e., the solute, over the same range that Raoult's law holds for the one present in excess, i.e., the solvent. A system of this kind is sometimes called an "ideal dilute solution" (cf. 31d).

40c. Composition of Liquid and Vapor.—If the vapors behave ideally, the partial pressure of each component of a mixture will be proportional to its mole fraction in the vapor [equation (40.1)]; if these are x'_A and $1 - x'_A$, respectively, then

$$\frac{x'_A}{1 - x'_A} = \frac{p_A}{p_B},$$

and hence,

$$x'_A = \frac{p_A}{p_A + p_B}. \tag{40.4}$$

If a liquid mixture behaves ideally, p_A and p_B may be replaced by $x_A p_A^0$ and $x_B p_B^0$, respectively, where x_A and x_B refer to the mole fractions in the liquid; equation (40.4) consequently becomes

$$x_A' = \frac{x_A p_A^0}{x_A p_A^0 + x_B p_B^0},$$ (40.5)

$$\frac{x_A'}{x_A} = \frac{1}{x_A + x_B \dfrac{p_B^0}{p_A^0}}.$$

Since x_A' and x_A represent the mole fractions of A in the vapor and liquid phases, respectively, it is possible to write

$$\frac{\text{Mole fraction of A in vapor}}{\text{Mole fraction of A in liquid}} = \frac{1}{x_A + x_B \dfrac{p_B^0}{p_A^0}}.$$ (40.6)

It can be seen from equation (40.6) that since $x_A + x_B$ is equal to unity, the proportion of A will be the same in the liquid and vapor only if p_A^0 is equal to p_B^0, that is, if the pure liquids A and B have the same vapor pressure. If the vapor pressure of pure B is greater than that of A, the ratio p_B^0/p_A^0 will be greater than unity, and hence so also will be the value of the denominator in equation (40.6). The quotient in the equation will thus be less than unity; the mole fraction of A in the vapor phase will consequently be less than in the liquid phase. This means that if the pure liquid B has a higher vapor pressure than pure A, the vapor will contain relatively more B than does the liquid with which it is in equilibrium. The general conclusion, derived here for a system obeying Raoult's law, is that *the vapor always contains relatively more of the more volatile, i.e., higher vapor pressure, component than does the liquid phase.* The same result is applicable to all liquid mixtures whether they behave ideally or not; for ideal liquid systems the composition of the vapor can be calculated by means of equations (40.5) or (40.6), but for nonideal solutions further information is necessary.

Problem: Calculate the composition of the vapor in equilibrium at 25° C with the mixture of CCl_4 and $SiCl_4$ referred to in the problem in § 40a.

From the data and results of the previous problem, $p_A^0 = 114.9$ mm., $p_B^0 = 238.3$ mm., $x_A = 0.525$ and $x_B = 0.475$; hence, by equation (40.5),

$$x_A' = \frac{0.525 \times 114.9}{(0.525 \times 114.9) + (0.475 \times 238.3)} = 0.348$$

$$x_B' = 1 - x_A' = 0.652.$$

The vapor thus contains 0.348 mole fraction of CCl_4 and 0.652 mole fraction of $SiCl_4$. The same result may be obtained directly from the problem in § 40a, since the number of moles of each constituent in the vapor is proportional to its partial pressure. (It should be noted that the vapor is relatively richer in B, i.e., $SiCl_4$, than is the liquid; pure $SiCl_4$ has a higher vapor pressure than CCl_4 at 25° C.)

The composition of the vapor in equilibrium with a liquid containing known amounts of two components can either be calculated, as shown above for an ideal system, or determined experimentally. In either event, the results for a definite temperature can be plotted in the manner shown in Fig. 67, I and II; in I the pure component A has a higher vapor pressure than B, while in II the reverse is the case. At any value of the total pressure P, the point l on the curve marked "liquid" gives the composition of the liquid in equilibrium with vapor whose composition is indicated by the point v on the curve marked "vapor." It is seen from the figures that in both cases the vapor in equilibrium with any liquid (except pure A or pure B) is relatively richer in the component having the higher vapor pressure, viz., A in I and

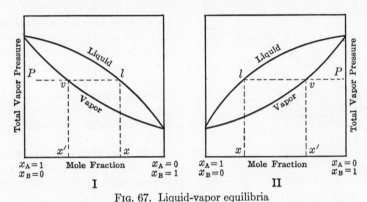

FIG. 67. Liquid-vapor equilibria

B in II. The curves in Fig. 67 are typical of systems which behave ideally or which show small deviations from ideal behavior. Corresponding curves can be obtained for systems in which the total vapor pressure has a maximum or minimum, at a given temperature; the "liquid" and "vapor" curves are always related to one another in such a way as to satisfy the condition that the vapor of the mixture shall contain a relatively larger proportion of the more volatile component. At the maximum or minimum point, however, the liquid and vapor curves touch; at such points, therefore, the liquid and vapor in equilibrium with each other have the same composition.

40d. Distillation of Liquid Mixtures.—If a liquid mixture were distilled at a constant temperature, i.e., isothermally, the composition of the condensate or distillate, which is theoretically the same as that of the vapor in equilibrium with the liquid, could be determined from curves of the type shown in Fig. 67. It is more interesting, however, and in closer agreement with general practice, to consider distillation at constant pressure, e.g., 1 atm. The boiling point of a mixture is the temperature at which the total vapor pressure is 1 atm., and hence the distillation is being carried out at the boiling point. However, just as the vapor pressure varies with the composition of the mixture, so also will the boiling point   Three main types of such variation may be distinguished.

First, if the system is one which is ideal or which does not deviate greatly from ideal behavior, the vapor pressure will vary regularly with the composition and there will be no maximum or minimum (see Fig. 67). In this case the boiling point also will vary in a regular manner from that of one pure component to that of the other. Second, if the system exhibits positive deviations from Raoult's law to such an extent that the vapor pressure-composition curve has a maximum, the corresponding boiling point curve will exhibit a minimum. Since there is at each temperature a particular mixture having a total vapor pressure higher than that of any other mixture, there

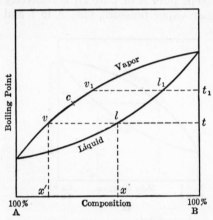

must be a corresponding mixture having a lower boiling point than any other. Third, if the system is of the type showing negative deviations from ideal behavior, the vapor pressure curve may have a minimum; in this case there will be a particular mixture possessing a maximum on the boiling point-composition curve. These three types of variation of boiling point with composition will be considered in turn.

FIG. 68. Boiling points of mixtures increase regularly

I. The Boiling Point Increases Regularly.—The properties of a system of this type may be depicted by the experimental curves in Fig. 68, for a constant pressure of 1 atm. These curves should not be confused with those in Fig. 67, which are for a constant temperature, although the two sets of curves are related to one another in an inverse manner. If the vapor pressure of a component in Fig. 67 is high, the boiling point in Fig. 68 will be low; hence, Fig. 68 may be regarded as equivalent, at least in form, to Fig. 67, I. In the latter the component A has the higher vapor pressure, and this falls regularly as the proportion of B is increased; consequently, in Fig. 68 the boiling point increases regularly from A to B.

The curve marked "liquid" in Fig. 68 gives the temperature at which liquids of different compositions attain a vapor pressure of 1 atm.; in other words, this represents the variation of boiling point with composition. The "vapor" curve gives the composition of the vapor that is in equilibrium with any liquid at its boiling point. For example, at the temperature t, the liquid of composition l (mole fraction x) boils, and the composition of the vapor is given by the point v (mole fraction x'). If a liquid of the particular composition represented by the point l is heated, it will boil at the temperature t, and the vapor which comes off at the commencement has the composition v; if the vapor is condensed, the resulting liquid condensate will also have this composition.

It is evident from the curves that the vapor is relatively richer in A, the component of higher vapor pressure, than is the liquid; hence, the residual liquid will become richer in B, and its boiling point must consequently rise. This accounts for the gradual increase of temperature observed when a liquid mixture is distilled. Suppose the distillation, that is, the removal by condensation of the vapor of the boiling liquid, is continued until the temperature rises from t to t_1. The liquid in the distilling flask now has the composition represented by l_1; it is therefore much richer in B than the original liquid l. The vapor which initially had the composition v now corresponds to v_1, so that the collected distillate, i.e., the condensed vapor, will have a composition approximately midway between v and v_1, e.g., at c. Clearly, the distillate is relatively richer in A than is the original mixture. By partially distilling the mixture l, therefore, it is possible to separate it into a condensate which contains relatively more A, the more volatile component, and a residue in the flask containing relatively more of B, the less volatile component. The condensate may be partially distilled in the same manner, and this will give a distillate even richer in the substance A.

The results described in the preceding paragraph illustrate the fundamental principles of **fractional distillation,** whereby a mixture of two or more liquids having appreciably different boiling points can be separated from one another. The liquid is boiled and separated into **fractions** boiling within certain ranges of temperature, by condensing the vapor. The first fractions are richer in the lower boiling point component, while the final fractions contain more of the higher boiling point component than the original mixture. The various fractions are then redistilled, the residue from one fraction being added to the distillate from the next; eventually pure A is obtained from the earlier fractions, and pure B from those at the other end of the series. In practice, both in the laboratory and in industry, additional advantage is gained by the use of a **fractionating column** in which the vapor rising from the boiling liquid meets a downflow of cooler liquid produced by partial condensation of the vapor. It can be seen from Fig. 68 that if the temperature of the vapor is lowered, it will condense to some extent, giving a vapor still richer in the more volatile component A; at the same time the proportion of B in the liquid is increased. The vapor passing up the column, therefore, contains even more A than did the vapor which left the boiling liquid. Similarly, the liquid returning to the distilling flask will be relatively richer in B, the less volatile component.

Any mixture of two liquids giving a boiling point-composition curve of the type shown in Fig. 68 can, theoretically, be separated into its components by fractional distillation. The greater the difference in the boiling points, that is to say, the steeper the boiling point curve, the more readily can the separation be achieved. The fractional distillation of liquid air, petroleum, benzene-toluene mixtures, and alcohol-water mixtures are all processes of industrial importance in which partial or complete separation of the components can be achieved.

II. Systems with a Boiling Point Minimum.—When there is a particular mixture having a boiling point lower than any other, the boiling point-com-

position curves are of the form shown in Fig. 69. The liquid and vapor curves
touch at the minimum M, so that here liquid and vapor in equilibrium have the same composition, as already mentioned. The liquid mixture represented by M will, therefore, boil at a constant temperature and will distil over completely without change of composition. Liquids of this kind *which are not pure substances but which nevertheless distil unchanged at a definite temperature* are called **constant boiling mixtures** or **azeotropic mixtures** (Greek: *to boil without change*). The compositions as well as the boiling points of such mixtures change with pressure, thus proving that they are not definite compounds.

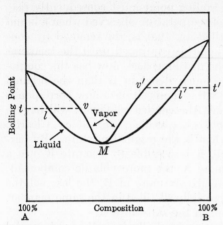

Fig. 69. System with minimum boiling point

Some instances of minimum constant boiling point mixtures at 1 atm. pressure are given in Table XLV.

TABLE XLV.   MINIMUM CONSTANT BOILING MIXTURES AT 1 ATM.

| | | | | Constant Boiling Mixture | |
A	B. Pt.	B	B. Pt.	A (mole %)	B. Pt.
Ethyl acetate	77.1° C	Ethanol	78.26° C	53.6	71.8° C
Ethyl acetate	77.1°	Water	100.00°	69.5	70.4°
Ethanol	78.26°	Water	100.00°	89.4	78.15°
Carbon tetrachloride	76.5°	Ethanol	78.26°	60.3	64.95°

The results to be expected when a system of the type having a boiling point curve with a minimum is distilled may be seen from Fig. 69. When the liquid l boils at the temperature t, the vapor first evolved has the composition v, and is consequently relatively richer in B than is the liquid. As distillation proceeds, the residual liquid in the flask tends toward pure A in composition. If the condensate is redistilled, however, it is apparent that the vapor approaches in composition that of the mixture at the minimum boiling point. Fractional distillation will thus ultimately result in a distillate of composition M, although the final residue will approach pure A. Complete separation of the two constituents is thus impossible. An analogous conclusion is reached by consideration of the liquid l'; the composition of the distillate will again tend toward M, while the residue now approaches pure B. For systems having a minimum boiling point it is consequently possible to obtain in a pure state by fractional distillation only the component present in excess of the amount required to give the constant boiling mixture; this component remains in the final residue in the flask. The composition of the distillate always tends toward that of the mixture having the minimum boiling point, i.e., maximum vapor pressure.

III. Systems with a Boiling Point Maximum.—Mixtures which exhibit marked negative deviations from Raoult's law, often yield systems for which the vapor pressure curve has a minimum, and hence the boiling point-composition curve has a maximum, as in Fig. 70. The liquid and vapor curves meet at the maximum boiling point M, where again the two phases have the same composition. The liquid M is thus an azeotropic mixture of maximum boiling point; it distils without change of composition at a definite temperature. Here, again, the composition varies regularly with the external (total) pressure, indicating that the constant boiling mixture is not a definite compound, as was at one time considered possible.* Maximum boiling point systems are not common, the most familiar being those formed by water and a halogen acid. It is of interest to mention that the composition of the constant boiling mixture is so definite, *at a given external pressure,* that the distillate is used for the purpose of making standard solutions of hydrochloric acid for quantitative analysis.

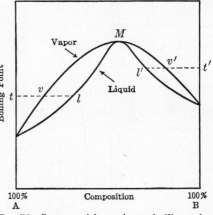

It will be evident from the curves in Fig. 70 that separation of the components of a maximum boiling point system by fractional distillation is not possible. The composition of the vapor, and hence of the condensate, will tend toward A if the original mixture lies to the left of M, while it will approach pure B if the mixture was originally to the right of M. In every case, however, the composition of the residue in the distilling flask will tend toward that of the mixture M of maximum boiling point. It is thus possible to obtain in a pure state only that constituent which is present in excess of the amount required by the azeotropic mixture.

FIG. 70. System with maximum boiling point

40e. Partially Miscible Liquids.—When two liquids are so markedly different in nature that the system exhibits large positive deviations from ideal behavior, there occurs the phenomenon of **partial miscibility,** that is, limited solubility of each liquid in the other. If alcohol is added to acetic acid or to water, or vice versa, there is no limit to the proportion of one liquid that can be added to the other without the formation of two separate layers. Such

---

* It may seem, at first sight, that the statement at the end of § 40b, referring to negative deviations from Raoult's law as being sometimes due to partial compound formation in the liquid, is a contradiction of the conclusion that the mixture of maximum boiling point is not a compound. Actually there is no such contradiction. Interaction between the components of the mixture may lead to a vapor pressure minimum, and hence a boiling point maximum, but the composition of the system at which this occurs bears no simple relationship to the nature of the compound, if any, or to the extent of its presence in the mixture.

liquids are said to be completely miscible. On the other hand, if a small quantity of phenol, ether or aniline is added to water, the substance will at first dissolve completely, but if the addition is continued, a condition is reached when no further solution occurs, and two liquid layers are formed. The two liquids are then only partially miscible with one another. Among other pairs of liquids that are partially miscible at ordinary temperatures are aniline and hexane, carbon disulfide and methyl alcohol, and water and amyl or butyl alcohol. When the relative quantities of the two components A and B are such that two liquid layers coexist, one of the layers is a satu-

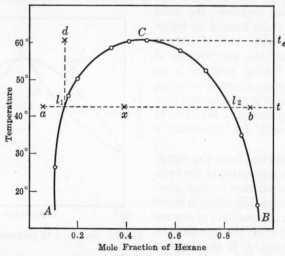

Fig. 71. Partially miscible liquids: the aniline-hexane system

rated solution of A in B while the other is a saturated solution of B in A, e.g., aniline in water and water in aniline. The two liquid layers or phases in equilibrium are called **conjugate solutions**.

The compositions of the conjugate solutions at a given temperature and pressure are quite definite, and may be determined experimentally. As long as two liquid layers are present in equilibrium, at the particular temperature, their compositions are independent of the actual or relative amounts of the layers. If the values of these compositions for a number of different temperatures and a constant pressure, e.g., 1 atm., are plotted, a curve of the kind shown in Fig. 71 is obtained; the one given is actually for the aniline-hexane system. At any temperature t the points l_1 and l_2 give the compositions of the two conjugate solutions, that is, of the two layers in equilibrium with each other at this temperature. It is seen from the shape of the curve ACB that as the temperature is raised the compositions of the two layers become closer; this is because the solubility of each liquid in the other increases with increasing temperature. At the temperature t_c the two layers have become identical in composition; they are, in fact, one layer the composition of which is represented by the point C, the maximum of the curve. The temperature t_c is known as the **critical solution temperature** or as the (upper) **consolute temperature** of the system. *Above this temperature the two liquids, which had previously been partially miscible, become completely miscible in all proportions*, and only one liquid layer is then possible. The consolute temperatures, and the corresponding compositions, expressed in weight per cent, for a number of systems are recorded in Table XLVI.

TABLE XLVI. CONSOLUTE TEMPERATURES AND COMPOSITIONS

System		Consolute	Composition	
A	B	Temperature	A	B
Aniline	Hexane	59.6° C	52%	48%
Methanol	Cyclohexane	49.1°	29	71
Methanol	Carbon disulfide	40.5°	20	80
Water	Phenol	65.9°	34	66
Benzene	Sulfur	163°	35	65
Water	Aniline	167°	15	85

Actually all systems whose compositions lie outside the curve ACB consist of only one liquid layer, while those represented by points within the curve are made up of two layers, the compositions of which are given by the points on the curve for the same temperature. Thus, the point x, for example, indicates a system of two layers whose respective compositions are represented by l_1 and l_2. These facts may be used to draw a number of interesting conclusions. A mixture whose composition and temperature are given by the point a consists of a single layer; it is an unsaturated solution of hexane in aniline. If the proportion of hexane is increased, the temperature remaining constant, the point representing the system will move to the right along the horizontal line. When the composition just falls on the curve ACB, i.e., at l_1, the second layer of composition l_2 will just commence to form. As the mole fraction of hexane is increased still further, the relative amount of the layer l_1 will decrease while the l_2 layer will increase; but, *the composition of each layer will remain unchanged as long as the two phases are present*, at the given temperature. Eventually, when sufficient hexane has been added for the system to have the composition l_2, the layer l_1 will have just ceased to exist. From l_2 to b, and beyond, the mixture of hexane and aniline then consists of a single layer which is now an unsaturated solution of aniline in hexane. Conclusions similar to the foregoing can, of course, be derived at any temperature lying below the consolute temperature t_c, or for the addition of either component of the system.

Another way in which a single layer may be converted into two layers, or vice versa, is by changing the temperature. Consider, for instance, the point d lying outside the curve ACB; it is immaterial whether this point is above or below the critical solution temperature t_c.* The system consists of a single

* In order to simplify the figure, d has been chosen vertically above the point l_1; this is, however, not necessary. The general conclusions are applicable to any point outside the curve ACB.

layer; in the particular case chosen it happens to be an unsaturated solution of hexane in aniline. Suppose that the composition of the mixture is maintained constant, but the temperature is lowered. The state of the system will move vertically downward in Fig. 71, and it will remain one layer until the curve ACB is reached, at the point l_1; here the second layer, composition l_2, just commences to form. *If the temperature is lowered still further, the compositions of the conjugate layers will no longer remain unchanged;* the representative points will move down the curve from l_1 toward A for the first (aniline rich) layer, and from l_2 toward B for the second (hexane rich) layer. Incidentally, it can be shown that the proportion of the aniline layer to the hexane layer will decrease as the temperature is lowered.

Although systems with an upper consolute temperature, such as in Fig. 71, are probably of more common occurrence, there are instances in which the curve is reversed, so that there is a **lower consolute temperature.** That is to say, the two liquids become completely miscible *below* a certain temperature. In systems of this type the mutual solubilities of the two components decrease with increasing temperature. However, there is experimental evidence to show that this decrease of solubility does not continue as the temperature is raised, for after a certain point a normal solubility behavior, similar to Fig. 71, commences. Where the liquids are such that measurements over a considerable temperature range are possible, it is found that systems possessing a lower consolute temperature also exhibit an upper consolute temperature. There are thus two temperature limits outside which the liquids are completely miscible, and between which they are partially miscible. Most of the systems of this type that have been studied hitherto consist of water and an amine, e.g., nicotine or methyl piperidine, or water and an ether or ketone, e.g., methyl ethyl ketone. The increased solubility as the temperature is lowered is undoubtedly due to increasing compound formation between the two components in the liquid state. The system, which shows positive deviations from ideal behavior at one temperature, thus tends to exhibit negative deviations as the temperature is lowered.

For the sake of clarity, it should be noted that mixtures with a lower consolute temperature probably always have an upper temperature of this kind, although it may not be accessible experimentally if it is above the temperature at which either of the liquids ceases to exist. A system with an upper consolute temperature, however, does not necessarily have a lower consolute point; it is very doubtful, for example, whether aniline and hexane, or methyl alcohol and carbon disulfide, would unite to a sufficient extent to give an increased mutual solubility with decreasing temperature. An alcohol or phenol with water might conceivably do so, but the temperatures would then be below those at which the liquids solidify.

40f. Distillation of Partially Miscible Liquids.—As long as only one liquid layer is present, distillation of a system of partially miscible liquids is the same in principle as for a completely miscible pair. The vapor always contains relatively more than the residual liquid of the component, or mixture of components, having the highest vapor pressure. When the liquid being distilled consists of two layers, or if two layers are formed in the flask during the course of the distillation as a result of the change in composition, the situation is changed. *As long as the two layers are present, irrespective of their relative amounts, the total vapor pressure remains constant,* and the system boils, i.e., distils, at a definite temperature. The composition of the vapor is also constant, as long as the two layers are present, and so the distillate has a constant composition. This composition will, in general, not be the same as that of the mixture being distilled, and so the proportions of the two components in the residual liquid will alter. This means that the relative amounts of the two layers will alter, but their respective compositions, as well as the temperature and vapor pressure, will remain unchanged. The distillate of constant composition will thus continue to be collected, and the boiling point will be constant, as long as there are two conjugate layers in the flask. Eventually, one or other of the two layers will be used up completely, leaving one only; then the boiling point will rise, and the composition of the vapor, and distillate, will change continuously, just as for completely miscible liquids.

It is opportune at this juncture to refer once more to the phase rule which was introduced at the end of Chapter VI, and applied there to systems of one component. In the systems of pairs of liquids at present being considered, there are clearly two components, so that C, as defined in § 22e, is equal to 2. When there are two conjugate solutions in equilibrium with vapor, as is assumed to exist in the process of distillation, the system consists of three phases, namely, two liquids and one vapor; hence, P, the number of phases, is 3. According to the phase rule equation (22.6), the number of degrees of freedom F is given by

$$F = C - P + 2$$
$$= 2 - 3 + 2 = 1,$$

so that the system is univariant, having one degree of freedom. This result implies that only one of the variables, either temperature, pressure or concentration, needs to be fixed in order to define the system completely. In the present case, the distillation is presumably carried out at the fixed pressure of 1 atm., and this is the one degree of freedom. Consequently, the mere act of distilling the system of two liquid layers at a definite pressure means that the temperature and compositions of the three phases, viz., two liquid and one vapor, are fixed. The phase rule says nothing about the relative amounts of the layers, but it clearly indicates that as long as the two liquid layers are present, each will have a definite composition, and the composition of the vapor in equilibrium with them will, likewise, be constant. Further, the temperature, that is, the boiling point, will not change. These conclusions, drawn from the phase rule, are in exact agreement with the actual results described above.

When one of the liquids has disappeared, so that there is now only one liquid and one vapor phase, P is equal to 2; the phase rule then gives

$$F = 2 - 2 + 2 = 2,$$

and the system is bivariant, with two degrees of freedom. Even if the pressure is fixed at 1 atm., there is still one variable; the equilibrium temperature, i.e., the boiling point of the mixture, can then vary, and as this changes corresponding changes occur in the compositions of both liquid and vapor. The phase rule thus provides a concise summary of the experimental facts.

40g. Completely Immiscible Liquids: Steam Distillation.—It is probably true that no two liquids are absolutely insoluble in each other, but with certain pairs, e.g., mercury and water, and carbon disulfide and water, the mutual solubility is so small that the liquids may be regarded as virtually immiscible. For systems of this type, each liquid exerts its own vapor pressure, independent of the other, and the total vapor pressure is the sum of the separate vapor pressures of the two components in the pure state at the given temperature. The composition of the vapor can be readily calculated by assuming that the gas laws are obeyed; the number of molecules (or moles) of each constituent in the vapor will then be proportional to its partial pressure, that is to say, to the vapor pressure of the substance in the pure state. If p_A^0 and p_B^0 are the vapor pressures of the pure liquids A and B, respectively, at the given temperature, and n_A' and n_B' are the numbers of moles of each present in the vapor, then if the liquids are completely immiscible, the total pressure P at the same temperature is given by

$$P = p_A^0 + p_B^0, \tag{40.7}$$

and the composition of the vapor by

$$\frac{n_A'}{n_B'} = \frac{p_A^0}{p_B^0}. \tag{40.8}$$

To express the ratio of A to B in the vapor in terms of the actual weights w_A and w_B, the numbers of moles must be multiplied by the respective molecular weights, M_A and M_B; hence, from equation (40.8),

$$\frac{w_A}{w_B} = \frac{n_A' M_A}{n_B' M_B} = \frac{p_A^0 M_A}{p_B^0 M_B}. \tag{40.9}$$

A system of two immiscible liquids will boil, that is, distil freely, when the total vapor pressure P is equal to the atmospheric pressure. The boiling point of the mixture is thus lower than that of either constituent, since the total pressure of the vapor is the sum of the two separate vapor pressures. Further, since the total vapor pressure is independent of the relative amounts of the two liquids, the boiling point, and hence the composition of the vapor and distillate, will remain constant as long as the two layers are present. The same conclusion can be readily derived from the phase rule, as in the case of a system of two partially miscible liquids.

The properties just described are utilized in the process of **steam distillation,** whereby a substance that is immiscible, or almost immiscible, with water, and that has a relatively high boiling point, can be distilled at a much lower temperature by passing steam through it. The same result should, theoretically, be obtained by boiling a mixture of water and the particular immiscible substance, but by bubbling steam through the latter the system is kept agitated, and equilibrium is attained between the vapor and the two liquids. The mixture distils freely when the total pressure of the two components is equal to that of the atmosphere. For example, when a mixture of water and chlorobenzene is distilled at an external pressure of 740.2 mm., the liquid is found to boil at a temperature of 90.3° C; at this temperature the vapor pressure of pure water is 530.1 mm., and that of chlorobenzene is 210.1 mm., making a total of 740.2 mm. The composition of the distillate, which is equal to that of the vapor, as given by equation (40.9), is then

$$\frac{\text{Wt. of chlorobenzene } (w_A)}{\text{Wt. of water } (w_B)} = \frac{p_A^0 M_A}{p_B^0 M_B} = \frac{210.1 \times 112.5}{530.1 \times 18.02} = 2.47.$$

The distillate should thus contain 2.47 parts by weight of chlorobenzene to one part of water, that is, 71.2 per cent by weight of the former; the actual value found by experiment was 71.4 per cent.

It is seen that chlorobenzene, which has a normal boiling point of 132° C, can be distilled with steam at a temperature about 40° lower, the distillate containing over 70 per cent of the organic compound. An examination of the calculation shows that the high proportion by weight of chlorobenzene in the steam distillate is due largely to the high molecular weight of this substance, viz., 112.5, as compared with that of water. In addition, this case is a particularly favorable one because chlorobenzene has a relatively high vapor pressure in the region of 90° to 100° C. In order that a liquid may be distilled efficiently in steam, it should therefore be immiscible with water, it should have a high molecular weight, and its vapor pressure should be appreciable in the vicinity of 100° C. A liquid which is partially miscible with water, such as aniline, may be effectively distilled in steam, provided the solubility is not very great. In calculating the composition of the distillate, however, the pressures p_A^0 and p_B^0 in equation (40.9) would have to be replaced by the actual partial pressures.

Attention may be called to the fact that equation (40.9) can be employed to determine the (approximate) molecular weight of a substance that is almost immiscible with water. This can be done provided the composition of the steam distillate and the vapor pressures of the two components are known.

Problem: The hydrocarbon terpinene was found to distil freely in steam at a temperature of 95° C, when the atmospheric pressure was 744 mm.; the vapor pressure of pure water at this temperature is 634 mm. The distillate contained 55 per cent by weight of terpinene; calculate its molecular weight.

If the terpinene is designated by A, and the water by B, it follows that at 95° C, the boiling point of the mixture, p_B^0 is 634 mm., and hence p_A^0 is equal to $P - p_B^0$, i.e., 744 − 634 = 110 mm. The ratio w_A/w_B in equation (40.9) is 55/45, since the distillate contains 55 per cent of terpinene (A) and 45 per cent of water (B); it follows, therefore, from equation (40.9) that

$$\frac{55}{45} = \frac{110 \times M_A}{634 \times 18}$$

$$M_A = 127.$$

(The actual value is 136.)

40h. The Distribution Law.—If to a system of two liquid layers, consisting of two immiscible or slightly miscible components, there is added a third substance which is soluble in both layers, this substance is found to distribute, or divide, itself between the two layers in a definite manner. It has been shown experimentally that at equilibrium, at constant temperature, the ratio of the concentrations in the two layers has a definite value, independent of the actual amount of the dissolved substance; thus, if c_1 and c_2 are the concentrations of this substance in the two layers, then

$$\frac{c_1}{c_2} = \text{constant.} \tag{40.10}$$

In words, therefore, *the dissolved substance, irrespective of its total amount, distributes itself between the two layers in a constant concentration ratio, at constant temperature.* This may be regarded as the statement of the **distribution law;** the ratio, equal to the constant in equation (40.10), is referred to as the **distribution ratio.**

An interesting conclusion may be drawn by considering the two liquid layers to be in contact with excess of the pure solute, either solid or liquid, so that when equilibrium is attained both solutions are saturated with the dissolved substance. If the saturation solubilities in the two liquid layers are s_1 and s_2, respectively, the distribution law then gives

$$\frac{c_1}{c_2} = \frac{s_1}{s_2} = \text{distribution ratio.} \tag{40.11}$$

The distribution ratio should thus be equal to the ratio of the solubilities of the substance in the two layers. It will be shown below that the distribution law in the form of equation (40.10) can usually be applied only to dilute solutions; hence, equation (40.11) will hold only if the solute is sparingly soluble in both solvents, so that the saturated solutions are dilute. In any event, even if the equation is not exact, it is generally true that the solute distributes itself in such a manner as to have a higher concentration in the layer in which it normally has the larger saturation solubility. This fact is made use of in the familiar process employed in the organic laboratory of extracting an aqueous solution with ether or other solvent that is immiscible, or partially miscible, with water.

The distribution law is actually one of wide applicability, for it should hold for the distribution of a dissolved substance between any two phases, e.g., liquid-liquid, gas-liquid, liquid-solid, etc. Henry's law for the influence of pressure on the solubility of a gas is, in fact, a form of the distribution law; this follows directly from equation (39.3), as may be readily shown. According to this equation w/p is a constant; w is the mass of gas in unit volume of the solution, and hence it is proportional to the concentration of gas in the solution, while the pressure p is related to the concentration in the gas phase. The ratio of the concentrations of the gas in the two phases, viz., liquid and gas, is thus constant by Henry's law.

It was seen in § 26c that when two phases are in equilibrium the molar free energy of a given substance will be the same in both phases. By means of equation (31.7) the molar free energy of the dissolved substance in any two phases may be represented by

$$F_1 = F_1^0 + RT \ln a_1 \quad \text{and} \quad F_2 = F_2^0 + RT \ln a_2,$$

where a_1 and a_2 are the activities of the solute in the two phases. When the system is at equilibrium F_1 and F_2 must be equal, so that

$$RT \ln \frac{a_1}{a_2} = F_2^0 - F_1^0.$$

At constant temperature the standard free energies F_1^0 and F_2^0 are constant, and so also are R and T; it follows, therefore, that

$$\frac{a_1}{a_2} = \text{constant}, \tag{40.12}$$

which is the exact form of the distribution law. For systems which are ideal or do not depart appreciably from ideal behavior, the ratio of the activities may be replaced by the ratio of the mole fractions, i.e., x_1/x_2 should be constant. Further, for dilute solutions or for gases, the ratio of the concentrations may be used in place of the ratio of the mole fractions, and so in these circumstances c_1/c_2 should be constant, in agreement with the simple form of the distribution law equation (40.10).

In spite of the theoretical limitations of the simple form of the law to dilute, almost ideal solutions, it has been found to hold in many cases, *provided the dissolved substance has the same molecular weight in both solvents*. The results obtained in some experiments on the distribution of succinic acid between water (c_1) and ether (c_2) are given in Table XLVII; the ratio c_1/c_2 is

TABLE XLVII.   DISTRIBUTION OF SUCCINIC ACID BETWEEN WATER AND ETHER AT $25°$ C

c_1	0.191	0.370	0.547	0.749 mole liter^{-1}
c_2	0.0248	0.0488	0.0736	0.101
c_1/c_2	7.69	7.58	7.43	7.41

seen to be approximately constant over an appreciable range of concentrations. When the dissolved substance does not have the same molecular weight in the two liquid phases, the simple form of the distribution law breaks down. The reason for this is that the law is applicable only to the molecular species that are common to the two layers. Consider, for example, the distribution of benzoic acid between water and benzene. In the former liquid the acid consists mainly of C_6H_5COOH molecules; there is some ionization, but this is small and may be ignored here. In the benzene solution, on the other hand, the benzoic acid is largely associated (§ 31a) to form double molecules, $(C_6H_5COOH)_2$, with a relatively small proportion of single molecules, C_6H_5-COOH. The distribution law, as expressed by equation (40.10), holds for the species present in both layers, namely the single C_6H_5COOH molecules. If allowance is made for this modification, the law is found to be obeyed in a satisfactory manner.

Suppose a given solute A has a normal molecular weight in one solvent, in which the concentration is c_1, while in the second solvent it exists mainly as the associated molecule A_n, the total concentration being c_2. In the latter solvent there will be an equilibrium between associated and simple molecules, thus,

$$A_n \rightleftharpoons nA,$$

and assuming the solution to be dilute, the equilibrium constant is

$$K_c = \frac{c_A^n}{c_{A_n}}, \qquad (40.13)$$

where c_A is the concentration of simple molecules and c_{A_n} of associated molecules in the second solvent. It then follows from equation (40.13) that

$$c_A = \text{constant} \times \sqrt[n]{c_{A_n}}. \qquad (40.14)$$

If the solute is mainly in the associated form, as is benzoic acid in benzene except at high dilutions, c_{A_n} may be identified with c_2, the total concentration in the second layer; hence, from equation (40.14),

$$c_A \approx \text{constant} \times \sqrt[n]{c_2}. \qquad (40.15)$$

As stated above, the distribution law applies to the species that the two liquid phases have in common, namely the simple A molecules; in this case, therefore, it should take the form

$$\frac{c_1}{c_A} = \text{constant},$$

and upon introducing the value of c_A given by equation (40.15), the result is

$$\frac{c_1}{\sqrt[n]{c_2}} = \text{constant}. \qquad (40.16)$$

The modified distribution law derived in this manner may be tested by means of the data for the distribution of benzoic acid between water and benzene, quoted in Table XLVIII. It can be seen that c_1/c_2 is far from con-

TABLE XLVIII. DISTRIBUTION OF BENZOIC ACID BETWEEN WATER AND BENZENE

c_1	c_2	c_1/c_2	$c_1/\sqrt{c_2}$
4.88×10^{-3} mole liter^{-1}	3.64×10^{-2} mole liter^{-1}	0.134	0.0256
8.00	8.59	0.093	0.0273
16.0	33.8	0.047	0.0275
23.7	75.3	0.030	0.0273

stant, but $c_1/\sqrt{c_2}$ remains almost unchanged over a range of concentrations. It is apparent that n in equation (40.16) is equal to 2, so that benzoic acid exists mainly as $(C_6H_5COOH)_2$ molecules in the particular benzene solutions used in these experiments.

The fact that the simple distribution law applies only to the molecular species common to the two layers has found a number of useful applications in physical chemistry. For example, when iodine is dissolved in an aqueous solution of potassium iodide it combines to some extent with the iodide ions to form the I_3^- ion thus

$$I_2 + I^- = I_3^-,$$

and it is of interest to know how much of the free iodine I_2 is left in the solution. This can be found by studying, first, the distribution of iodine between water and an organic solvent, e.g., carbon disulfide, carbon tetrachloride or chloroform, and finding the distribution ratio. The experiments are then repeated with the same organic liquid and a solution of iodine in potassium iodide. By determining the concentration of iodine in the organic solvent, in which I_2 molecules only are present, and assuming the distribution ratio just found, the concentration of free iodine in the iodide solution can be calculated.

Problem: The distribution ratio of iodine between carbon disulfide and water is found to be 625. When iodine is distributed between carbon disulfide and a 0.125 molar solution of KI, the concentration of iodine in the former layer is found to be 0.1896 mole per liter; the total concentration in the aqueous KI layer is 0.02832 mole per liter. What is the concentration of I_3^- ions in the latter layer?

The concentration of free I_2 in the KI layer must be equal to the concentration in the carbon disulfide divided by the distribution ratio for free iodine, i.e., 0.1896/625 mole per liter; hence,

$$\text{Conc. of } I_2 \text{ in KI layer} = \frac{0.1896}{625} = 0.000303 \text{ mole per liter.}$$

The total concentration of iodine in this layer is 0.02832 molar, and so the concentration of I_3^- ions is $0.02832 - 0.00030 = 0.02802$ mole per liter.

GAS-SOLID SYSTEMS

41a. Salt Hydrates: Application of Phase Rule.—The nature of the equilibrium between a gas and a solid depends on whether the two combine to form compounds or not; the discussion here will be restricted to cases in which compounds are formed, since these are of wider interest. Simple examples of gas-solid equilibria of this type are the dissociation of solid calcium carbonate to form calcium oxide and carbon dioxide, and the dissociation of salt hydrates. These systems have already been studied in Chapter X from the aspect of the equilibrium constant; in the present chapter the point of view will be somewhat different, use being made of the phase rule and of equilibrium diagrams.

Consider the dissociation of solid $CuSO_4 \cdot 5H_2O$ to form solid $CuSO_4 \cdot 3H_2O$ and water vapor, thus

$$CuSO_4 \cdot 5H_2O(s) \rightleftharpoons CuSO_4 \cdot 3H_2O(s) + 2H_2O(g).$$

This is a system of two components (C = 2), since the proportions of two independent substances, e.g., $CuSO_4$ and H_2O, must be specified in order that the composition of each phase may be defined. There are three phases (P = 3), namely two solids and one gas; hence, by the phase rule

$$F = C - P + 2 = 2 - 3 + 2 = 1.$$

The system at equilibrium is consequently univariant; this means that only one variable, e.g., the temperature, need be fixed to define the equilibrium

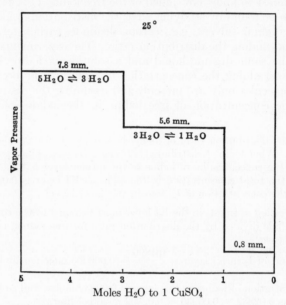

FIG. 72.   Dehydration of copper sulfate at 25°

completely. At a given temperature, therefore, there should be a definite pressure of water vapor in equilibrium with the two hydrates. This conclusion is, of course, identical with that derived from a consideration of the equilibrium constant in § 35a. Once again, it is apparent that the two solid phases must be present in addition to the vapor, for otherwise the system would not be univariant. It is necessary therefore to speak of the aqueous vapor pressure or dissociation pressure of a *salt hydrate system, the two solid phases being named;* the bare expression "dissociation pressure of a salt hydrate" generally has no exact significance.

An examination of the variation of the equilibrium pressure with the total composition of a salt hydrate is of interest. Starting with pure $CuSO_4 \cdot 5H_2O$, for example, the solid may be gradually dehydrated, and the vapor pressure determined at constant temperature, from time to time during the dehydration. The results obtained at 25° C are shown in Fig. 72. The process of removal of water may be followed by passing from left to right of the diagram. At first, the equilibrium vapor pressure is 7.8 mm. of mercury, and this remains constant as long as the system contains more water than $CuSO_4 \cdot 3H_2O$; when this point is reached the pressure falls sharply to 5.6 mm. It then stays constant at this value until the composition of the system is $CuSO_4 \cdot H_2O$, when it falls again, to 0.8 mm., where it remains until the salt is completely anhydrous; the pressure of the water vapor then sinks to zero. It is evident from these results that there are three consecutive equilibria involving the hydrates of copper sulfate, viz.,

$$CuSO_4 \cdot 5H_2O(s) \rightleftharpoons CuSO_4 \cdot 3H_2O(s) + 2H_2O(g) \quad p = 7.8 \text{ mm. at } 25° \text{ C.}$$

$$CuSO_4 \cdot 3H_2O(s) \rightleftharpoons CuSO_4 \cdot H_2O(s) + 2H_2O(g) \quad 5.6 \text{ mm.}$$

$$CuSO_4 \cdot H_2O(s) \rightleftharpoons CuSO_4(s) + H_2O(g) \quad 0.8 \text{ mm.}$$

It is seen from Fig. 72 that as long as the two particular solid phases are present, the equilibrium pressure remains constant, irrespective of the relative amounts of these two phases; this result is in agreement with the phase rule and the equilibrium constant.

It may be mentioned that if the starting material is anhydrous copper sulfate and water vapor is gradually added, the results are the same as those depicted in Fig. 72; in this case, the state of the system is initially at the right and it moves to the left as water is added.

41b. Salt Hydrate Equilibria and Temperature.—The dehydration of the copper sulfate hydrates has been studied at other temperatures, and the results found to be similar to those just described; the vapor pressures are, however, higher the higher the temperature. At 50° C, for example, the three systems mentioned above give equilibrium vapor pressures of 45.4, 30.9 and 4.5 mm., respectively. It appears that above 102° C the pentahydrate is not stable, and $CuSO_4 \cdot 3H_2O$ is then the first stable hydrate; at such temperatures only two horizontal portions would appear in the vapor pressure-dehydration curve.

The variation of vapor pressure of the salt hydrate system with temperature may be represented in the manner depicted in Fig. 73; this diagram is not quantitative, as is Fig. 72, but it is of the proper form. The lowest three curves show the variation with temperature of the equilibrium vapor pressure of the indicated system; the uppermost curve gives the vapor pressure of an aqueous saturated solution of $CuSO_4 \cdot 5H_2O$. The data in Fig. 73 may be correlated with those in Fig. 72; in fact each of the two diagrams is a section, at a definite composition and at a definite temperature, respectively, of a three-dimensional model in which the variations of vapor pressure, temperature and concentration are shown simultaneously.

Suppose water is gradually added to the anhydrous salt while the system is kept at a constant temperature; starting from a (Fig. 73), where the vapor pressure is zero (anhydrous salt), the pressure increases along the vertical line af (constant temperature). Between a and b the anhydrous salt and vapor exist without interaction; at b, which is the vapor pressure of the $CuSO_4$-$CuSO_4 \cdot H_2O$ system at the given temperature, the monohydrate commences to form, and the pressure remains constant as long as some anhydrous salt remains. The point b in Fig. 73 thus corresponds to the lowest horizontal step in Fig. 72. When the formation of $CuSO_4 \cdot H_2O$ is complete, a further small addition of water causes some $CuSO_4 \cdot 3H_2O$ to form, so that the vapor pressure rises suddenly to c in Fig. 73. Here again the pressure remains constant until the whole salt is in the form of trihydrate. The point c is equivalent to the second step in Fig. 72. If more water is now added to the system, $CuSO_4 \cdot 5H_2O$ is produced and the vapor pressure rises to d; it will remain unchanged until the whole solid is converted into pentahydrate. The point d is consequently equivalent to the uppermost line in Fig. 72.

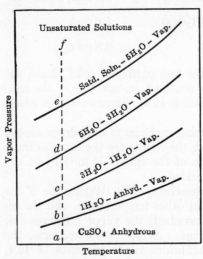

If the addition of water is continued further, the pentahydrate commences to dissolve, a saturated solution being formed; the vapor pressure, at the stipulated constant temperature, is then given by the point e. Although there is now only one solid phase, there is still a total of three phases present, viz., solid $CuSO_4 \cdot 5H_2O$, solution and vapor; the system is still univariant, according to the phase rule, and the vapor pressure will have a definite value at each temperature as long as the three phases coexist in equilibrium. Ultimately, the addition of sufficient water results in the whole of the solid salt being dissolved and the solution is unsaturated. There are now two phases only, and hence the vapor pressure varies with the concentration of the solution, the values falling on the line ef.

Fig. 73. Variation of vapor pressure with temperature

41c. Deliquescence and Efflorescence.—The results described above may be utilized to explain the phenomena of deliquescence and efflorescence. Consider, first, **deliquescence** (Latin: *to become liquid*), which may be described as *the act whereby a solid takes up water vapor from the atmosphere and eventually forms an unsaturated solution.* It should be clear from Fig. 73 that, in general, if a salt is exposed to water vapor at a pressure which is greater than that of the saturated solution of the highest hydrate, e.g., a vapor pressure corresponding to a point such as f in the figure, it will gradually take up water and finally form an unsaturated solution. *A substance will be deliquescent, therefore, when the vapor pressure of its saturated solution is less than the pressure of water vapor in the atmosphere.* Water will continue to deposit on the solid until eventually an unsaturated solution is formed having the same vapor pressure, at the room temperature, as the pressure of water vapor in the air. In order that a substance may be deliquescent, the vapor pressure of the saturated solution must be low, in fact lower than the normal partial pressure of water in the atmosphere. This condition will arise only if the substance is very soluble, and hence it is highly soluble salts, such as calcium chloride, that deliquesce. A saturated solution of calcium chloride has a vapor pressure of 4 to 5 mm. at ordinary temperatures, and this is generally below the pressure of water vapor in the air.

It will be obvious from the foregoing arguments that deliquescence is a relative property, since it depends on the actual pressure of water vapor in the atmosphere, and this varies with time and place. In exceptionally dry atmospheres even calcium chloride will not deliquesce, that is, actually turn into a liquid, although it will probably take up some water vapor. Copper sulfate is not normally deliquescent, for at room temperatures the vapor pressure of its saturated aqueous solution is higher than the usual vapor pressure of water in the atmosphere. If the lower hydrates of copper sulfate are exposed to normal air, in which the water vapor pressure is above 7 or 8 mm., water will be taken up and the pentahydrate will be formed. If the atmospheric water vapor pressure is below 7.8 mm. at 25° C, as might well be the case, the hydration process would stop at the trihydrate (Fig. 72).

The phenomenon of **efflorescence** (Latin: *to blossom*), that is, *the loss of water by a hydrated salt,* is observed *when the vapor pressure of a salt hydrate system is greater than that of water vapor in the air.* Dehydration of the salt will then occur in the effort for equilibrium to be attained between the hydrate system and the surrounding atmosphere. Normally, the vapor pressures of the systems involving $Na_2CO_3 \cdot 10H_2O$, $Na_2SO_4 \cdot 10H_2O$ or $Na_2HPO_4 \cdot 12H_2O$, as the higher hydrate, are greater than that of water in the atmosphere, and so these substances effloresce. Like deliquescence, however, the property of efflorescence is a relative one which depends on the atmospheric conditions. In a very dry atmosphere, even $CuSO_4 \cdot 5H_2O$ would effloresce, whereas under very moist conditions sodium carbonate and sodium sulfate might not display this property.

SOLID-LIQUID SYSTEMS

42a. Freezing Point and Solubility Curves.—The conditions of equilibrium between solid and liquid phases in a system of two components may be considered from two points of view. If the liquid mixture (solution) is in equilibrium with the solid phase of the component present in excess, that is, the solid solvent, the solution is said to be at its freezing point. The curve representing the variation of the equilibrium temperature with the composition of the liquid phase is referred to as the **freezing point curve.** On the other hand, if the solid phase in equilibrium with the solution is that of the substance present in smaller amount, that is, the solid solute, the liquid phase is said to be a **saturated solution,** and the curve showing the variation of its composition with temperature is called a **solubility curve.**

It was pointed out earlier that there is no fundamental difference between solute and solvent, and the distinction between solubility and freezing point curves is merely a matter of convenience. When the two components of the system are similar chemically, e.g., both are metals or oxides, or when they are organic compounds of not very different melting point, it is not possible to distinguish clearly between solvent and solute. The curves representing the conditions of equilibrium of solid and liquid phases at different temperatures are called freezing point curves, irrespective of which component constitutes the solid phase. On the other hand, if one of the substances differs from the other, e.g., a salt and water, or if the system consists of two organic compounds with very different melting points, e.g., benzene and naphthalene, it is generally possible to make the conventional distinction between solvent and solute. In this case the term "solubility" is used when the solid phase is the solute, and "freezing point" when it is the solvent.

Although the influence of temperature on the solid-liquid equilibrium will be considered more fully later, some general remarks on the subject may be made here. The variation of freezing point or solubility in a given system is determined by the heat of fusion of the solid solvent or heat of solution of the solid solute, respectively. If the solution is ideal, the heat of fusion of the solid solvent in the solution is the same as that of the solid solvent into the pure liquid solvent; that is to say, it is equal to the normal heat of fusion of the solid. Since there is no essential difference between the solvent and solute, it can be seen that if the solution is ideal, the heat of solution of the solute should also be equal to its own heat of fusion. This has been found to be approximately true for solutions involving chemically related substances, e.g., naphthalene in benzene, which do not deviate greatly from ideal behavior. For nonideal solutions, such as those of salts in water, the heat of solution may be quite different from the heat of fusion.

42b. Condensed Systems.—Since three degrees of freedom, viz., temperature, pressure and concentration, are possible for a two-component system, a complete graphical representation of the conditions of equilibrium would require the use of three dimensions. Solid models are frequently employed for this purpose, but from the point of view of liquid-solid equilibria it is the practice to disregard the vapor phase and to fix an arbitrary constant pressure, generally 1 atm. Experimental studies are then made with vessels open to the atmosphere. It should be understood that since the pressure is generally not the equilibrium value, the system as a whole is not strictly in true equilibrium. For a solid-liquid system, however, the effect of pressure is relatively small (§ 22a), and so the results at atmospheric pressure will be very little different from those which would be obtained if the system were in equilibrium with vapor. A system in which only solid and liquid phases are considered is called a **condensed system.** The graphical representation of the conditions of equilibrium in a condensed system of two components is simplified by the fact that there are now only two variables, namely, temperature and concentration (composition); it is thus possible to use ordinary rectangular coordinates. Solid-liquid equilibria of a number of types and of varying degrees of complexity are known; some of the more important simpler cases will now be described.

42c. Solid Phases Consist of Pure Components.—If a liquid mixture of two similar components A and B is cooled, solid will commence to separate at a definite temperature, namely the freezing point. The actual value of the freezing point will depend on the composition of the liquid mixture, and if the results for a series of such mixtures of components varying from pure A to pure B are plotted against the corresponding compositions, two curves, like

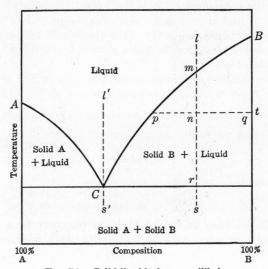

FIG. 74. Solid-liquid phase equilibria

AC and BC in Fig. 74, are obtained. The points A and B are the freezing points of the pure components; the addition of B to A lowers the freezing point (§ 29a) along AC, and similarly A added to B lowers the freezing point of the latter along BC. If the freezing point and composition of a given mixture are such as to fall on the curve AC, the solid which separates is pure A; on the other hand, if the freezing system is represented by a point on BC, pure solid B will separate from the liquid. The curves AC and BC may be regarded as representing the conditions of temperature under which liquid phases of various compositions are in equilibrium with the solid phase A or the solid phase B, respectively. Since it gives the conditions of equilibrium of different phases, Fig. 74 is sometimes called a **phase diagram.**

At the point C, where the curves AC and BC meet, obviously *both solids* A and B must be in equilibrium with the liquid phase. There are consequently three phases present, and since the system involves two components, there can be only one degree of freedom, according to the phase rule; thus, P = 3, C = 2, and hence,

$$F = C - P + 2 = 2 - 3 + 2 = 1.$$

For a condensed system, such as that being considered, the pressure is arbitrarily fixed at 1 atm., and this represents the one degree of freedom; the condensed system has thus effectively no degrees of freedom, that is to say, it is then an invariant condensed system. This means that the mere fact of the existence of the two solid phases A and B in equilibrium with the liquid, at 1 atm. pressure, completely defines the point C; there is thus only one temperature where this equilibrium is possible, as the phase diagram actually indicates. The point C, where the freezing point curves AC and BC meet, is the lowest temperature at which any liquid mixture can be in equilibrium with solid A or B; consequently, it is the lowest temperature at which any mixture of solid A and B will melt. For this reason C has been called the **eutectic point** (Greek: *easily melting*). It is the lowest temperature at which the existence of liquid phase for the given system is possible at the arbitrarily fixed pressure, viz., 1 atm.

A number of examples of two-component systems which give equilibrium diagrams of the type in Fig. 74 are mentioned in Table XLIX. It is seen

TABLE XLIX. TWO-COMPONENT SYSTEMS WITH SIMPLE EUTECTIC

A	M. Pt.	B	M. Pt.	Eutectic
Antimony	630° C	Lead	326° C	246° C
Bismuth	268°	Cadmium	317°	146°
Silicon	1412°	Aluminum	657°	578°
Potassium chloride	790°	Silver chloride	451°	306°
o-Nitrophenol	44.1°	p-Toluidine	43.3°	15.6°
Benzene	5.4°	Methyl chloride	−63.5°	−79°

that the components may both be metals, or one may be a metal and the other a nonmetal. In some cases both are salts, while in others they are organic compounds. Systems involving a salt and water are sometimes of this type, as will be seen in § 42e.

By means of the phase diagram it is possible to foretell the behavior of any system upon heating or cooling. Consider, for purposes of illustration, a system of composition represented by the line ls in Fig. 74; l represents the system above its freezing point, when it consists of liquid phase only, and s is the same system completely solidified, since it is below the eutectic temperature. If the liquid l is cooled, no solid will separate until the temperature corresponding to the point m on the freezing point curve BC is reached; at this temperature solid B will commence to deposit. As the temperature continues to fall, the state of *the system as a whole* will be represented by points lying between m and r, of which n may be chosen as an example. Such points indicate mixtures of solid B and of liquid whose composition changes, becoming relatively richer in A, as the temperature falls. At the typical point n, at the temperature t, the composition of the liquid phase is given by the point p, while the solid consists of pure B, as indicated by the other end q of the constant temperature **tie line** passing through n. It is apparent, therefore, that as the temperature falls from m to r, the composition of the liquid phase must correspondingly change from m to C, pure solid B separating all the time. When the eutectic temperature is reached at r, the second solid, that is A, commences to deposit in addition to B; the temperature must now remain constant until all the liquid has solidified, since the phase rule shows that there is only one temperature at which the liquid can be in equilibrium with two solid phases. When the whole system has solidified completely, the temperature of the mixed solids A and B can fall from r to s. If the solid s is heated until it liquefies completely, the changes described above take place exactly in the reverse order.

If the original liquid l were on the left side of the eutectic point, that is to say, if it were richer in the component A, there would be a similar series of changes on cooling. In this case, however, solid A would separate first; the temperature would then continue to fall, while the composition of the liquid changed, until the eutectic was reached. The second solid B would now deposit, and the temperature would again remain constant until the system was completely solid.

In the special case in which the composition of the liquid l' coincides exactly with that of the eutectic point, solid will separate on cooling only when the eutectic temperature is reached at C. The two solid phases A and B will deposit simultaneously, and the temperature will remain constant until the liquid has disappeared.

42d. Cooling Curves: Thermal Analysis.—It is apparent from the results described in the preceding section that upon cooling a liquid mixture, solid A or B commences to separate when the temperature reaches a point on the curve AC or BC, respectively. The solid continues to deposit as the temperature falls, but when the eutectic is reached, and both solids separate, the temperature remains constant. The separation of solid A or B is always accompanied by the evolution of heat, the reverse of the heat of fusion; consequently, at the point equivalent to m in Fig. 74, the rate of cooling will be diminished. The cooling will thus continue from m to r at a slower rate than before, until the eutectic point is attained when the temperature remains constant. If the temperature of the system while cooling, starting with the molten liquid l, were plotted against the time, a **cooling curve,** such as is shown in Fig. 75, would be expected; the letters in this figure correspond to those in Fig. 74. From l to m the liquid cools rapidly, then at m solid commences to separate and the rate of cooling is slowed down; the cooling curve thus shows a break at the temperature m, i.e., the freezing point, where solid first commences to form. As the composition of the liquid phase changes, the temperature falls from m to r; at r, the eutectic point, the temperature remains constant, along rr', until solidification is complete. When no more liquid is left, cooling of the solid can proceed from r' to s.

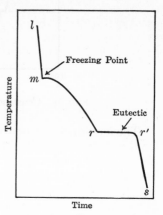

FIG. 75. Cooling curve

From the cooling curve for a mixture of any definite composition, it is thus possible to obtain the freezing point of that mixture and the eutectic temperature for the system. The former will, of course, vary with the composition, but the latter remains the same throughout. The closer the composition of the original system is to that of the eutectic, the shorter will be the portion *mr* and the longer the halt *rr'* at the eutectic temperature. If the liquid mixture coincides exactly with the composition at the eutectic point, the region *mr* will not exist; the cooling curve will then not show a break until the eutectic temperature is reached.

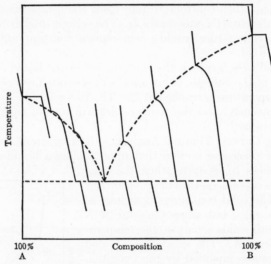

FIG. 76.   Construction of phase diagram by thermal analysis

The facts described above form the basis of the method of **thermal analysis** for the study of solid-liquid phase equilibria, especially those involving metals. A series of mixtures of known amounts of the two constituents A and B are made up, and each mixture is heated until it melts to a homogeneous liquid. It is then allowed to cool steadily, and the temperature is recorded at regular intervals so as to obtain the cooling curve, as in Fig. 75. The first break in the curve occurs at the freezing point of the particular mixture; this temperature is plotted against the composition of the mixture, thus giving the appropriate point on the curve *AC* or *BC* of the equilibrium (phase) diagram, Fig.74. The second break, where the temperature remains constant, gives the eutectic point, and for a system of the type under consideration this should be the same for all the mixtures. In order to complete the diagram it is necessary to know the freezing points (or melting points) of pure A and B; these can be determined by means of cooling curves, for the pure liquid will solidify at a constant temperature. The general nature of the results is represented schematically in Fig. 76; the various cooling curves, for pure A and

B and for a number of mixtures, are superimposed, at the appropriate compositions, on a temperature-composition diagram. The dashed lines, drawn through the first break (freezing point) of each cooling curve, correspond to AC and BC in Fig. 76; the horizontal line is drawn through the eutectic temperature. It can thus be seen how the thermal analysis procedure is used to derive the phase diagram for a system of two components.

42e. Systems Involving a Salt and Water: Freezing Mixtures.—Although there is no fundamental difference between the properties of a system involving a salt and water, and that of a binary system of two metals, or two salts,

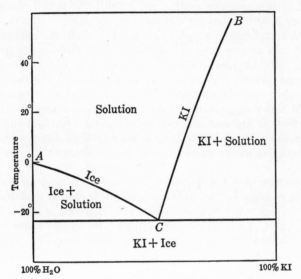

Fig. 77.   System of a salt (KI) and water

etc., it is of interest to give special attention to the former. There is one limitation to the complete study of many salt-water systems: the melting point of the salt is often so high that it is above the critical temperature of the water in the solution. It is consequently then impossible to follow the two-component system up to the melting points of both components. The complete phase diagrams have been obtained in a few cases, however, by working at high pressures to prevent evaporation of the water.

The equilibrium diagram for potassium iodide and water is depicted in Fig. 77; it is seen to be of the general type being considered, although the melting point of potassium iodide, at the extreme right, is not attained. The two curves, AC and BC, represent the conditions of equilibrium of liquid phases, i.e., potassium iodide solutions, of various compositions with a solid phase; the latter is solid water, i.e., ice, along AC, and solid potassium iodide along BC. Since ice separates from the potassium iodide solutions along AC, it is convenient to regard this curve as giving the freezing points of the solutions; on the other hand, BC may be considered as the *solubility curve* of potassium iodide, since the solid is in equilibrium with solutions that are obviously saturated with this salt. The relatively steep rise of the curve CB shows that the solubility of potassium iodide increases slowly with temperature. The dependence of solubility on temperature varies with the nature of the salt and the solvent, for reasons which will be examined in § 42h.

The freezing point and solubility curves meet at C, the eutectic point, where both ice and potassium iodide deposit from solution at $-23°$ C; this is the lowest temperature at which an aqueous solution of potassium iodide can exist, at atmospheric pressure. All solutions when cooled will ultimately show a halt in temperature at this point until the liquid phase has disappeared. Since a system having the same composition as the eutectic freezes at a constant temperature, as seen above, the salt-water mixture depositing at this point was at one time considered to be a definite compound, i.e., a salt hydrate. The physical properties, such as heat of solution and density, of the solid are, however, equal to the mean values of the two components, suggesting that it is really a mixture. If a compound were formed the actual values would differ appreciably from the respective means. Further, the separate crystals of ice and salt can be observed when the eutectic solid is placed under the microscope. There is no doubt, at the present time, that the solid separating at the eutectic point is a mixture and not a definite salt hydrate.

The production of a freezing mixture from a salt and ice, as well as the thawing of ice or snow by the addition of a salt, is readily explained by means of a phase diagram, such as that in Fig. 77. If a salt is added to ice and a little water at 0° C, some of the salt will dissolve in the water so that there will now be present salt, ice and solution. Such a system can only be in stable equilibrium at the eutectic temperature, which is usually well below 0° C, and so the ice will melt and the salt will continue to dissolve in the water produced. Melting of the ice is always, and solution of the salt is generally, accompanied by an absorption of heat, and so the temperature of the system will fall; this fall will continue until one of the solid phases, ice or salt, is used up. If there are present relatively large quantities of both ice and salt, however, the temperature will continue to decrease until the eutectic point is reached. This is the principle of the ice-salt freezing mixture; the actual temperature attained depends on the eutectic point for the given system, and this varies with the nature of the salt. The freezing mixture will stay at the eutectic temperature until sufficient heat is absorbed from the surroundings to cause all the ice to melt or all the salt to dissolve. There is now only one solid phase present, and so the temperature will change with the composition of the solution, along AC or BC.

42f. The Two Components Form a Solid Compound.—If the components A and B form a stable solid compound AB, the phase diagram obtained by plotting the results of a thermal analysis, or of any equivalent procedure, is of the type shown in Fig. 78. In addition to the branches AC and BE, which represent the compositions of liquids in equilibrium with solid A and B, respectively, at different temperatures, there is a central portion CDE rising to a maximum. This portion of the phase diagram gives the conditions of equilibrium of liquid systems with the solid compound AB; in accordance with both theory and experiment, the maximum D of the curve occurs when the composition of the liquid is identical with that of the compound. The particular diagram in Fig. 78 shows the formation of a compound containing equimolecular amounts of A and B; hence, the point D' vertically below D, is midway between pure A and pure B on the molecular composition axis.* From the position of the maximum, i.e., D or D', it is consequently possible

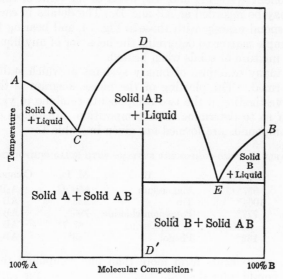

Fig. 78. Compound with congruent melting point

to derive, without the necessity for chemical analysis, the formula of the solid compound which separates from the liquid phase along the curve CDE.

Since the liquid at the maximum point D has the same composition as the solid with which it is in equilibrium, the temperature at D is actually the melting point of the compound. In this case, the compound is fairly stable at its melting point, and *solid and liquid of the same composition can coexist;* the compound AB is then said to have a **congruent melting point.** It will be noted that at the temperature D the two-component system has become virtually a one-component system, the one component being the compound AB; the temperature at D is consequently just as definite as are the melting points of the pure components A and B. The melting point of the

* In order to simplify the interpretation of the phase diagram the composition of the liquid in Fig. 78 is assumed to be in mole per cent; this makes the point D', representing the compound AB, fall midway along the composition axis. It should be noted, however, that it is a common practice to represent the compositions in weight per cent, as in Fig. 74; in this event, the molecular composition at D' would have to be calculated instead of being read off by inspection.

compound may lie above, below or between the melting points of the two single components; instances of all three types are well known.

It will be evident that in Fig. 78 there are now two eutectic points, viz., C and E; at the former the solids A and AB deposit, while at the latter the solid phases are B and AB. The details of the phase diagram can best be understood by regarding it as made up of two diagrams of the simple type shown in Fig. 74 placed side by side. To the left of the dividing line DD' in Fig. 78 the figure gives the conditions of solid-liquid phase equilibrium of the two-component system A and AB, while to the right of the line the two components may be regarded as AB and B. The details in each part of the diagram correspond exactly with those in Fig. 74, and bearing these facts in mind it is a simple matter to determine the behavior of any liquid upon cooling, or of any mixture of solids when heated.

There are many examples of binary systems in which stable solid compounds are formed. The plotting of the phase diagram is the recognized method for investigating if the two components combine to yield such compounds, and if so to determine their composition. Instances of systems in which solid compounds are formed are given in Table L.

TABLE L.   TWO-COMPONENT SYSTEMS WITH SOLID COMPOUNDS

A	M. Pt.	B	M. Pt.	Compound	M. Pt.
Aluminum	657° C	Magnesium	650° C	A_3B_4	463° C
Gold	1064°	Tin	232°	AB	425°
Calcium chloride	777°	Potassium chloride	790°	AB	754°
Diphenylamine	52.8°	Benzophenone	47.7°	AB	40.2°
Urea	132°	Phenol	43°	AB_2	61°

When two components form more than one compound there will be a curve on the equilibrium diagram analogous to CDE for each compound. In each case the composition of the maximum of any curve is identical with that of the solid compound depositing from liquid phases represented by that curve, and the temperature of the maximum gives the melting point of the particular compound. A phase diagram of this type, involving ferric chloride and water, will be referred to presently (Fig. 81); four stable compounds are formed in this system.

The sharpness of the maximum in a phase diagram gives an indication of the stability of the compound at its melting point; if the maximum is flat, it means that the compound tends to decompose to a great extent. Sometimes the compound is so unstable that it decomposes completely at a temperature below its melting point; *the solid cannot then be in equilibrium with a liquid having the same composition as itself.* The compound is then said to have an **incongruent melting point.**

The equilibrium (phase) diagram for this type of behavior is represented in Fig. 79, in which it is supposed that a 1 : 2 compound AB_2 is formed. At the temperature of the incongruent melting point E, which is below the hypothetical melting point D, the compound AB_2 dissociates completely into its constituents. Along the curve CE, therefore, solid AB_2 separates, but along EB the solid phase consists of pure B.   If a liquid such as l, lying to the right of E, is cooled, the first solid to separate will be B; then when the temperature reaches E the compound AB_2 commences to form.   Since there are now one liquid and two solid phases, the condensed system is invariant; the temperature at E will thus remain constant until the solid B has been completely replaced by solid compound, or the liquid phase disappears.

Compounds with incongruent melting points are found in the following systems: gold-antimony ($AuSb_2$); magnesium-nickel (Mg_2Ni, congruent; Mg-

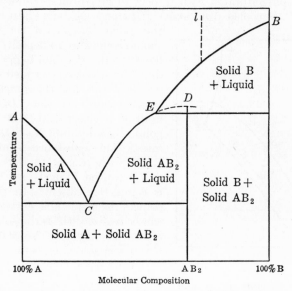

FIG. 79.   Compound with incongruent melting point

Ni_2, incongruent); sodium-bismuth ($NaBi$, congruent; Na_3Bi, incongruent); potassium chloride-cupric chloride ($2KCl \cdot CuCl_2$); picric acid-benzene (AB); and acetamide-salicylic acid (AB).

42g. The Formation of Salt Hydrates.—For systems consisting of a salt and water, the compounds are salt hydrates; these generally have incongruent melting points, since they decompose into anhydrous salt and water, or into a lower hydrate and water, below their melting points, i.e., the appropriate maxima in the phase diagram.   A case which has been well studied is the system consisting of sodium sulfate and water; part of the phase diagram is reproduced in Fig. 80.   Along the curve AB the liquid solution is in equilibrium with ice, while along BC the solid phase is $Na_2SO_4 \cdot 10H_2O$; the latter curve may thus be regarded as the solubility curve of this salt.   Before a maximum is attained, an incongruent melting point, or **transition point,** is reached at C; here the decahydrate $Na_2SO_4 \cdot 10H_2O$ decomposes into the anhydrous salt Na_2SO_4 and water.   At the point C the decahydrate and anhydrous salts are in equilibrium with saturated solution; there are thus two solid phases and one liquid, and so the condensed system is invariant. The equilibrium will thus occur at one particular temperature, the transition point, at each pressure. The transition temperature for the $Na_2SO_4 \cdot 10H_2O$-Na_2SO_4 system at 1 atm. pressure is 32.383° C; it is so definite that it has been suggested as a fixed point in thermometry. The curve CD gives the compositions of solutions in equilibrium with anhydrous sodium sulfate, and so it is the solubility curve of this salt. It will be noted that this curve slopes to the left, indicating that the solubility *decreases* with increasing temperature.

If a solution, saturated with respect to anhydrous sodium sulfate along the curve DC, is cooled from above the transition temperature, then when

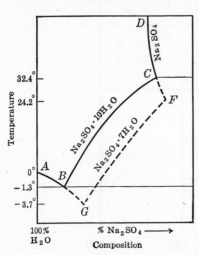

FIG. 80.   The sodium sulfate-water system

this point is reached the decahydrate should commence to deposit. Sometimes, however, this does not happen; the anhydrous form remains, in metastable equilibrium (§ 22d), and the composition of the solution continues along DC, beyond C, until F is reached at 24.2° C. At this point a new hydrate $Na_2SO_4 \cdot 7H_2O$ separates. This substance is always metastable with respect to the decahydrate, and it can be formed only if the latter is completely absent. In these circumstances the metastable curves BG and GF can be realized; GF is the solubility curve of the heptahydrate $Na_2SO_4 \cdot 7H_2O$, and G is a metastable eutectic. The point F is the transition point at which heptahydrate and anhydrous salt are in metastable equilibrium with saturated solution. The fact that the metastable solubility curve GF lies to the right of the stable curve BC, shows that at a given temperature the metastable form is more soluble than the stable form. The addition of a small crystal of the decahydrate will cause the excess salt to precipitate as $Na_2SO_4 \cdot 10H_2O$, and the concentration will fall from GF to BC. The statement that a *metastable form is more soluble than the stable form at the same temperature* represents a rule of universal applicability.

One of the best known systems involving salt hydrates with congruent melting points is that formed by ferric chloride and water, the phase diagram for which is given in Fig. 81. Four stable hydrates are known, namely $Fe_2Cl_6 \cdot 12H_2O$, $Fe_2Cl_6 \cdot 7H_2O$, $Fe_2Cl_6 \cdot 5H_2O$ and $Fe_2Cl_6 \cdot 4H_2O$; the double formula Fe_2Cl_6 is used for ferric chloride in order to avoid the use of fractional numbers of molecules of water in two of the four cases. It will be evident from Fig. 81 that each hydrate has a definite (congruent) melting point; this point may be alternatively regarded, in each case, as the temperature at which the saturated solution of the hydrate has the same composition as the solid phase.

42h. Influence of Temperature on Solubility of Salts.—It was stated in § 42a that when a solid forms an ideal solution in a liquid, heat should be absorbed when it dissolves, the amount being numerically equal to the heat of fusion of the pure solid solute. Although solutions of salts do not behave ideally, it is true that in the majority of cases heat is absorbed when a salt dissolves in water; the solubility of that particular salt then increases with increasing temperature in accordance with the requirement of the Le Chatelier principle. There are a few salts, such as anhydrous sodium sulfate, referred to above, calcium sulfate and chromate, and cerium sulfate, for which

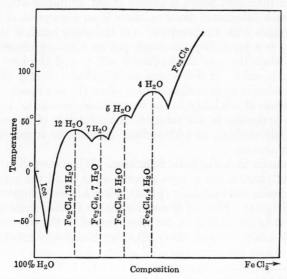

FIG. 81. Salt hydrates with congruent melting points (FeCl$_3$-H$_2$O)

the solubility decreases as the temperature is raised. This means that when these substances dissolve, in the region of the saturated solutions, there is an evolution of heat, just as is the case with gases. An examination of the nature of the compounds showing the reversed temperature effect on solubility reveals the fact that they are usually anhydrous salts. When a solid dissolves in a liquid, two distinct processes occur; in the first place, work must be done against the electrostatic and other forces that hold the ions together in the crystal, and in the second place, the ions unite with the molecules of water to form **hydrated ions.** There are many reasons for expressing the belief that ions in solution do not consist merely of bare units, such as Na$^+$, Cl$^-$, SO$_4$$^{--}$, etc., but are combined with, or in some way associated with, a number of water molecules. There may be definite compound formation, such as in Cu(H$_2$O)$_4$$^{++}$, but in any event there are also probably a number of water dipoles (§ 171) which are held to the ion by forces of electrostatic attraction. A positive ion, for example, will attract the negative parts of a number of dipolar molecules, and similarly a negative ion will attract the positive regions of such molecules. The process of hydration is accompanied by the liberation of energy, and it is this factor which makes it possible for salts to dissolve in water while they are insoluble in nonpolar organic liquids, such as hydrocarbons, etc. In the latter, no process analogous to hydration, that is, solvation, is possible, and no means is available to supply some, or all, of the energy required to break up the salt crystal into individual ions in solution; the salt thus remains in the solid state and does not dissolve.

If the ions are largely hydrated in the crystal, as is the case with $Na_2SO_4 \cdot 10H_2O$, the energy which must be supplied to overcome the forces in the solid is greater than that which is gained in the hydration stage in the solution. When such substances dissolve, there is an absorption of heat and the solubility increases with temperature. On the other hand, if the salt is anhydrous, there is a possibility, although not an absolute necessity, that the heat evolved when the ions are hydrated will exceed the heat absorbed in disintegrating the solid. If this occurs, as it evidently does in the cases mentioned above, there is an evolution of heat when the salt dissolves, and hence there is a decrease of solubility as the temperature is raised. Provided there is appreciable hydration in the solution, the solubility of an anhydrous salt will increase only slightly, as with sodium chloride, or it will decrease with increasing temperature.

42i. Continuous Series of Solid Solutions.—When the solid that separates from the liquid phase is not a pure substance, as in all the preceding cases, but a homogeneous solid solution (§ 20a), there are some important changes in the phase diagram. First, *it is possible for the freezing point of one component to be raised by the addition of the other;* second, if the two solids A and B are completely soluble in each other, like two completely miscible liquids, *it is not possible to have more than one solid phase.* A homogeneous solid solution constitutes a single phase, irrespective of its composition, and since there is only one liquid phase, the condensed system can never consist of more than two phases. By the phase rule, therefore, the minimum number of degrees of freedom, corresponding to the maximum number of phases, is thus given by

$$F = C - P + 2 = 2 - 2 + 2 = 2.$$

Even after fixing the pressure, for the condensed system, there still remains one degree of freedom; an invariant system is thus impossible in the present case and there will be no singular point or discontinuity, such as a eutectic, on the phase diagram. Three types of freezing point curves have been obtained, depending on whether the freezing points of all mixtures lie between those of the pure components, or whether there is a mixture with a maximum or a minimum freezing point.

I. The Freezing Point Increases Regularly.—A typical equilibrium diagram of the kind in which the freezing points of all mixtures lie between those of the pure components A and B is shown in Fig. 82. The upper, or **liquidus,** curve L gives the composition of the liquid phase in equilibrium with solid solution whose composition is indicated by the corresponding point on the ower, or **solidus,** curve S. At any temperature t, for example, the liquid represented by the point y will be in equilibrium with solid solution z; it is evident that *the composition of the solid phase changes continuously with that of the liquid from which it separates.* At any temperature, however, the liquid phase always contains relatively more of the component by the addition of which the freezing point is depressed, namely A in the present case.

If the liquid represented by the point l is cooled, freezing will commence at y (temperature t) and the composition of the solid phase separating will be given by z. As cooling proceeds, the composition of the system as a whole will be represented by points on the vertical line ls between y and z'; these will represent mixtures of liquid and solid solutions whose compositions are given by the appropriate points on the curves L and S. The composition of the liquid changes steadily from y to y', while at the same time that of the solid goes from z to z'. It should be noted that if the system is to remain in equilibrium upon cooling, the compositions of both liquid and solid phases must change continuously. When the composition of the liquid reaches the point y', at the tempera-ture t', the solid phase with which it

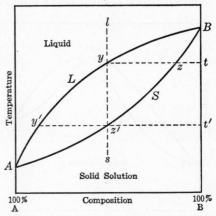

FIG. 82. Continuous series of solid solutions

is in equilibrium, namely z', has the same composition as the original liquid. In other words, at this temperature solidification is complete, and $z's$ represents the cooling of the solid. Separa-tion of solid thus commences at y, and is complete at z'; for this reason the liquidus curve L is sometimes called the *freezing point curve*, while the solidus curve S is called the *melting point curve*. When the liquid l is cooled, solid first separates at the freezing point t; on the other hand, when the solid s, of the same composition, is heated liquid first appears at the melting point t'.

The cooling curve of a liquid from which a solid solution separates differs from that considered previously (§ 42d). Upon cooling the liquid l, solid first separates at y, and hence there will be a change in the rate of cooling which will be indicated by a break in the cooling curve at the temperature t. As cooling proceeds, and solid continues to separate, the temperature will fall steadily. Finally, at the temperature t', when solidification is complete, the solid will commence to cool more rapidly. There are thus two breaks in the curve, in opposite directions, at t and t'; in this way the points y and z', on the liquidus and solidus curves, respectively, are obtained for any mixture of known composition. By carrying out these cooling observations with a number of mixtures, as well as with pure A and B, that is by thermal analy-sis, the complete phase diagram can be plotted. It will be noted that since the system has no invariant point, there is no complete arrest in the cooling curves, such as is obtained at a eutectic.

Substances of similar constitution or closely related elements are usually isomorphous and form completely miscible solid solutions, provided their lattice dimensions are not very different (§ 20a); examples are cobalt-nickel, gold-silver, gold-platinum, silver chloride-sodium chloride, lead bromide-lead chloride, and naphthalene-β-naphthol.

II. The Freezing Point Curve Has a Maximum.—The type of equilibrium diagram depicted in Fig. 83 is not common; it is seen that each component *raises* the freezing point of the other, and that the liquidus and solidus curves

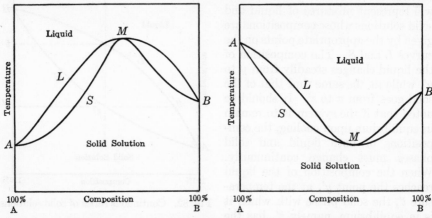

Fig. 83. Solid solutions with maximum melting point

Fig. 84. Solid solutions with minimum melting point

touch at the maximum M. At this point the liquid and solid in equilibrium evidently have the same composition; the liquid solution will then freeze, and the solid solution will melt sharply at a definite temperature, given by the maximum M, just like a pure substance. Nevertheless, the maximum point does not represent a compound; it is merely a consequence of the fact that the liquidus and solidus curves must touch at the maximum.

One of the rare cases of a freezing point curve with a maximum is the system d- and l-carvoxime; the components have the same melting point (72° C), and the curve is symmetrical with a maximum at 91.4° C. The composition at the maximum in this case corresponds to equimolecular amounts of the two components; the solid phase is, however, not a compound but a solid solution.

III. The Freezing Point Curve Has a Minimum.—A number of systems yielding completely miscible solid solutions have freezing point curves with a minimum, as in Fig. 84. Here, as in other cases, the liquidus curve lies above the solidus curve, and the two touch at the minimum M. At this point the solid and liquid in equilibrium again have the same composition, and the solid will melt and the liquid will freeze sharply, like a pure substance. The solid phase is actually a solid solution of definite composition, but the molecular proportions of the constituents A and B do not necessarily correspond to simple whole numbers as would be the case for a definite compound.

Among systems forming a continuous series of solid solutions and giving phase diagrams with minima the following may be mentioned: copper-manganese, copper-gold, cobalt-manganese, arsenic-antimony, mercuric bromide-mercuric chloride, potassium chloride-potassium bromide, and p-chloroiodo-benzene-p-dichlorobenzene.

42j. Partially Miscible Solid Solutions.—It frequently happens that two substances can form solid solutions with one another to a limited extent only,

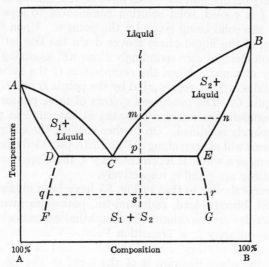

Fig. 85.   Partially miscible solid solutions with eutectic point

so that between definite concentration limits, depending upon the temperature, two conjugate solid solutions can exist. The phenomenon of partial miscibility of solids is analogous to that occurring with partially miscible liquids. Solid A can dissolve a certain quantity of solid B to form a single solid solution, and similarly solid B can dissolve a limited amount of A, but if these concentrations are exceeded two solid phases, each of which is a homogeneous solution of A and B, are produced. Since it is now possible to have three phases, viz., two solid solutions and one liquid, the condensed system can be invariant, and so the solid-liquid equilibrium curves will exhibit a discontinuity. Two types of behavior are found in practice, the nature of the discontinuity being somewhat different in the two cases.

I. The Discontinuity Is a Eutectic Point.—In Fig. 85, AC and BC are the liquidus curves, and AD and BE are the corresponding solidus curves; along AD the solid phases may be regarded as solutions of B in excess of A (S_1 type), and along BE the solid solutions are of A in excess of B (S_2 type).

The liquidus curves meet at C which is the eutectic point for the system. It differs in one respect from the ordinary eutectic of Fig. 74; the solid phases in equilibrium are not the pure components A and B, as in the latter case, but the conjugate solid solutions whose compositions are represented by the points D and E. The eutectic C is, however, a true invariant point for the condensed system of two components; it is the lowest temperature at which liquid can exist. Just as the compositions of two conjugate liquid solutions vary with the temperature (see Fig. 71), so also do those of the conjugate solid solutions. This variation is indicated by the curves DF and EG. Theoretically, a consolute temperature might be expected above DE, but in this region liquid only occurs, and the solids have no real existence.

If a liquid l is cooled, solid solution commences to separate at m, the composition of the solid being given by the point n. Upon further cooling, the composition of the liquid phase moves down the line mC, while that of the solid solution changes correspondingly along nE, assuming equilibrium to be continuously attained. When the composition of the system reaches the point p, two solid solutions, represented by the points D and E, separate from the eutectic liquid C. The condensed system of three phases is now invariant, and the temperature remains constant at the eutectic point until the liquid has completely solidified. On further cooling, the compositions of the two solid solutions will change along DF and EG, provided equilibrium exists. When the system as a whole is represented by s, there are two solid solutions whose compositions are q and r, respectively.

Phase diagrams similar to that in Fig. 85 have been obtained for the systems gold-nickel, bismuth-lead, cadmium-tin, potassium nitrate-thallous nitrate, silver chloride-cuprous chloride, and naphthalene-monochloroacetic acid.

II. The Discontinuity Is a Transition Point.—When the addition of one component raises the melting point of the other, and the solids are only partially miscible, the phase diagram is of the form of Fig. 86. The liquidus curve AC gives the compositions of the liquids in equilibrium with solid solutions (S_1 type) along the solidus curve AD; similarly, BC is the liquidus curve corresponding to the solidus curve BE (S_2 type of solid solutions). The point C represents an invariant condensed system, for there are here three phases, viz., two solid solutions and one liquid, in equilibrium. It is not a eutectic point, since it is not the lowest temperature at which liquid exists, but it is frequently called a *transition point*, for reasons which will be evident shortly. The compositions of the conjugate solid solutions in equilibrium with liquid at the transition point are indicated by D and E. Upon cooling, these change along the lines DF and EG, respectively, in a manner analogous to that observed for partially miscible liquids.

The behavior upon cooling mixtures lying to the right of D or to the left of C can be readily derived from previous considerations, but in the region between C and D the phenomena are unusual. When the liquid l is cooled, solid solution of composition n commences to separate at m; the composition of the liquid phase moves down mC, while that of the solid in equilibrium with it changes correspondingly along nE. When the transition point is reached at p, two solid solutions, D and E, are in equilibrium with liquid of composition C. Since the condensed system is now invariant, the temperature remains constant until one of the phases disappears. In this case, however, it is not the liquid that is removed by complete solidification. The liquid remains, but the solid solution E (S_2 type) gradually diminishes in amount while D (S_1 type) increases; it is for this reason that the temperature is described as a transition point. When the former solid solution has completely disappeared the system is again univariant; the temperature can then continue to fall once more from p to s, the composition of the liquid changing

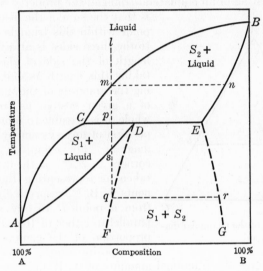

FIG. 86. Partially miscible solid solutions with transition point

along CA, and that of the solid solution (S_1 type) along DA. At the point s, the system has completely solidified in the form of a single solid solution. The temperature of the solid may now fall to q when two solid solutions, of composition q and r, respectively, will form if the system attains equilibrium.

Systems forming two series of solid solutions with a transition point are cadmium-mercury, silver chloride-lithium chloride, silver nitrate-sodium nitrate, and p-iodochlorobenzene-p-diiodobenzene.

SYSTEMS OF THREE COMPONENTS

43a. Graphical Representation of Three-Component Systems.—For systems of three components it is possible to have four degrees of freedom, since temperature, pressure and the concentrations of two components may be independently variable.* In order to simplify the graphical representation of

* Although there are three components, the concentrations of two components define the composition of the system completely; thus, x per cent of A, and y per cent of B, means $100 - x - y$ per cent of C.

the conditions of equilibrium for three components, the procedure usually adopted is to consider a condensed system, that is, the vapor is ignored. This reduces the number of degrees of freedom to three, and hence a three-dimensional model can be used to represent the compositions of equilibrium systems at different temperatures.

In order to understand the type of figure that is used, it is convenient to consider, in the first place, the condition of constant temperature; it is then required to indicate in a simple manner the composition of a system of three independent components. For this purpose it is the common practice to use a diagram consisting of an equilateral triangle; the property which is utilized is that the sum of the distances from any point within this triangle drawn parallel to the three sides is always equal to the length of the side of the triangle. By taking this length as unity, and expressing the amounts of the three components of a given system as fractions of the whole, it is possible to represent the composition of any system by a point in the diagram. For example, in Fig. 87 the corners A, B, C of the triangle may be taken as representing the pure components A, B, C, respectively; the distance from a point P to any side, measured parallel to either of the others, gives the proportion of the component occupying the opposite corner. Thus, the distances Pa, Pb and Pc give the fractional amounts of A, B and C, respectively, in the system represented by the point P.

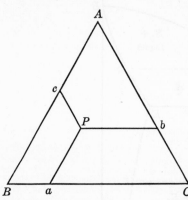

FIG. 87.   Principle of the triangular diagram

Any point within the triangle indicates a system of three components, but a point situated on one of the sides represents two components only; a point on the edge BC would mean the amount of A is zero, and similarly along AC there is no B, whereas on the line AB the component C would be absent. A point on the edge AB of the triangle, for example, would imply a two-component system containing definite amounts of A and B only. To facilitate the plotting of the points corresponding to various compositions on the triangular diagram, the sides are divided into ten, or more, equal parts, and a series of lines are drawn parallel to the three sides, thus producing a network of small equilateral triangles within the large one. Special graph paper, based on these principles, can be purchased for use in plotting the experimental results for three-component systems. The triangular diagram, as described above, has a number of properties which make it of great value for the study of phase equilibria.

If it is required to represent variations of temperature as well as composition, a prism having an equilateral triangular cross-section is used, the temperature being measured vertically; an illustration of such a model is given below (see Fig. 88). A section through the prism at any definite temperature is thus a triangular diagram of the type just described.

43b. Systems with Solid Phases.—In the study of three-component systems considerable complexity is possible; in addition to the vapor, which is neglected, there may be one, two or three liquid phases, and three different solid phases, apart from the possibility of solid compounds formed by combination of two or more of the components. The maximum number of phases which can coexist, for a system of three components, excluding the vapor, is four; this represents an invariant condensed system, i.e., one with no degrees of freedom. Since C is three, the phase rule leads to the result

$$F = C - P + 2 = 3 - 4 + 2 = 1,$$

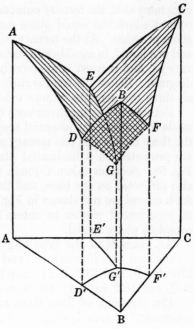

for a system of four phases; the one remaining degree of freedom is the pressure, and as this is fixed for the condensed system, the system is effectively invariant. It is thus impossible for P to exceed four, so that there cannot be more than four phases in equilibrium at any arbitrary pressure.

In view of the many possibilities that can arise for a system of three components, it is necessary to make a choice of one or two special types for consideration here; those chosen are of interest because they have a bearing on problems of industrial importance. The first type of system to be examined is that in which the three components A, B and C are completely miscible when liquid, so that only one liquid phase can exist; further, it is supposed that the solids A, B and C

FIG. 88. Three component system with solid phases

separate out in the pure state, and there is no formation of compounds or of solid solutions. The conditions of equilibrium of solid and liquid phases for each pair of components, that is, for A and B, B and C, and C and A, respectively, is then given by a simple eutectic curve of the type considered in Fig. 74. The phase equilibria in the three-component system are then represented by means of a triangular prism, as shown in Fig. 88. Each vertical face of the prism depicts a two-component system; thus for A and B, the solid-liquid equilibrium (freezing point) curve is *ADB*, and for the binary systems B and C, and A and C, the equilibrium curves are *BFC* and *CEA*, respectively. The points *D*, *E* and *F* are the binary (two-component) eutectics, at which two solid phases can exist in contact with binary liquid (§ 42c).

If now the ternary (three-component) system is considered, the conditions of equilibrium are given by points within the prism. Points lying on the surfaces $AEGD$, $BFGD$ and $CFGE$ represent the conditions under which one of the solids, A, B and C, respectively, is in equilibrium with ternary liquid; the position of the point on the surface gives the composition of the latter. The lines along which two surfaces join are the **ternary eutectic curves,** and they indicate the conditions of temperature and liquid composition for the separation of two solid phases from the liquid; thus, along DG, FG and EG the pairs of solids are A and B, B and C, and A and C, respectively. These three lines meet at G, the **ternary eutectic point** for the system; it is the only temperature at which the liquid phase can be in equilibrium with three solids, at the given pressure. At the ternary eutectic there are four phases, viz., three solid and one liquid, in equilibrium; hence, as seen above, the condensed system is invariant, and it must consequently be represented by a definite point on the diagram. Below the temperature G the ternary liquid, i.e., liquid containing all three components, cannot exist.

Because of the inconvenience of a three-dimensional model, an attempt is made to indicate the essential results on a planar diagram. For this purpose the three binary and one ternary eutectic points, and the curves joining them, are projected on a horizontal plane, as shown at the base of the prism in Fig. 88. Sections taken through the prism at a number of temperatures are also projected on the base, and the values of the temperatures are indicated. Such curves are not shown in Fig. 88, but by means of them it is possible for an experienced worker to obtain a satisfactory picture of the nature of the complete phase model.

An example of the type of system just considered is that involving the metals lead (A), bismuth (B) and tin (C); the melting points are 326° for A, 270° for B, and 232° for C; the binary eutectics are 128° for A-B, 134° for B-C, and 182° for A-C; the ternary eutectic temperature is 96° C.

43c. Systems of Two Salts and Water.—An interesting type of three-component system is that consisting of water and two salts having an ion in common; if the salts do not possess a common ion the system is one of four components.* Fundamentally the system of two salts and water does not differ from the type considered in the preceding section; the essential distinction, however, lies in the fact that the melting points of the two salts are so much higher than that of the water that the complete phase-equilibrium diagram cannot be realized. It is found more convenient to study the salt-water system at constant temperature, as well as at a definite pressure, and to plot the curves representing the conditions of equilibrium of the solid salts and

* The reason for this is as follows. For a system of two salts with an ion in common, e.g., KCl and NaCl, and water, the composition of any phase can be expressed in terms of three components, e.g., KCl, NaCl and H_2O; this is true whether double salts are formed or not. If there is no common ion, e.g., KCl and $NaNO_3$, there is a possibility of the separation of KNO_3 and NaCl as solid phases; consequently it is necessary to specify four components, e.g., KCl, $NaNO_3$, KNO_3 and H_2O, in order to be able to express the composition of every possible solid phase or solution. Pure NaCl, or a mixture with any other salt, could be expressed in terms of x $NaNO_3$ + y KCl − z KNO_3.

the ternary liquids at that temperature. This means that the solubility of each salt is determined in an aqueous solution containing varying amounts of both, at constant temperature and pressure. The experimental method used is to make up various mixtures of the two salts with an ion in common, and dissolve them in water at a temperature slightly higher than that at which the system is to be studied. The solution is then allowed to come to equilibrium at the experimental temperature; the clear liquid and the residual solid are removed, and both are analyzed. In this way the composition of the liquid

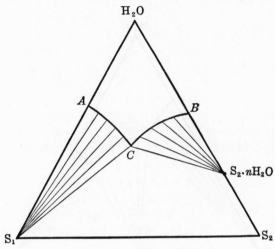

Fig. 89. Two salts and water

containing the two salts in solution, and the nature of the solid salt in equilibrium with it are determined; the results for a number of solutions are then plotted on a triangular diagram in the usual manner.

When two salts S_1 and S_2 do not form a compound or solid solution, the solubility curves, giving the compositions of the solutions in equilibrium with either solid S_1 or S_2 are of the type shown in AC and CB in Fig. 89. The points along the curve AC give the compositions of the solutions from which the solid S_1 separates at the given temperature; the tie lines radiating from the corner of the triangle to the curve AC indicate that S_1 is the solid phase which separates from these solutions. In the case of the curve BC it has been supposed, for purposes of illustration, that the solid phase which separates is a hydrated salt, represented by the formula $S_2 \cdot n H_2 O$. If the salt S_2 had separated in the anhydrous form, the tie lines from BC would have converged in the S_2 corner of the triangle. The point C, where the two solubility curves meet, gives the composition of the solution in equilibrium with the two solids S_1 and S_2 (or $S_2 \cdot n H_2 O$) at the given temperature; this point is referred to as an **isothermal invariant point.** At C there are, apart from vapor, three phases, viz., two solid and one liquid, and the phase rule shows that the three-component system then has two degrees of freedom. These are the pressure and temperature which have been fixed, and so the condensed system is effectively invariant.

It may be mentioned that the system $NaCl-Na_2SO_4-H_2O$ gives a phase-equilibrium diagram of the type shown in Fig. 89 at temperatures below 17.9° C; S_1 is NaCl, which separates in the anhydrous form, and $S_2 \cdot nH_2O$ is $Na_2SO_4 \cdot 10H_2O$. The shape and position of the curves and the nature of the solid phases change with temperature; thus, between 17.9° and 32.4° the anhydrous solid Na_2SO_4 can separate from the solution, as well as $Na_2SO_4 \cdot$

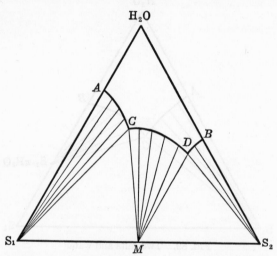

FIG. 90. Two salts and water: formation of a double salt

$10H_2O$, and the solubility curve has three parts. Above 32.4° C the hydrated salt cannot exist in contact with solution, and then the solid phases are NaCl and Na_2SO_4.

If, in addition to the pure components S_1 and S_2, or their hydrates, one or more compounds, i.e., double salts, can separate from the solution at the experimental temperature, the solubility curve will have an additional portion, e.g., CD in Fig. 90, along which the solid phase is the compound of composition indicated by the point M. In this case it is seen that the compound, or double salt, like the single salts S_1 and S_2, is anhydrous; if it were hydrated the tie lines from CD would meet at a point within the triangle, as required for a phase containing all three components. A diagram of the type shown in Fig. 90 is given by the system $NH_4NO_3-AgNO_3-H_2O$ at ordinary temperatures; the compound M has the composition $NH_4NO_3 \cdot AgNO_3$. If more than one double salt is formed, there will be an additional portion of the solubility curve for each one that can separate from solution at the given temperature. Thus, for the system $(NH_4)_2SO_4-NH_4NO_3-H_2O$, there are two compounds, viz., $(NH_4)_2SO_4 \cdot 2NH_4NO_3$ and $(NH_4)_2SO_4 \cdot 3NH_4NO_3$, for each of

43c   REVIEW QUESTIONS   **395**

which, in addition to the pure components $(NH_4)_2SO_4$ and NH_4NO_3, there is a curve in the equilibrium diagram. By changing the temperature the nature of the curves is changed, and there is generally a definite transition point above or below which each double salt can no longer exist in contact with solution.

READING REFERENCES

1. **Experiments on boiling point curves.** Soday and Bennett, *Journal of Chemical Education,* **7,** 1336 (1930).
2. **Teaching the phase rule.** Wood, *ibid.,* **7,** 2100 (1930).
3. **Sublimation.** Robertson, *ibid.,* **9,** 1713 (1932).
4. **Boiling point of miscible liquids.** Collins, Morrison and Stone, *ibid.,* **10,** 749 (1933).
5. **Chemistry of Portland cement clinker.** Fisk, *ibid.,* **11,** 195 (1934).
6. **Constant boiling hydrochloric acid.** Cadbury, *ibid.,* **12,** 292 (1935).
7. **Constant boiling hydrochloric acid.** Sheldon, *ibid.,* **12,** 318 (1935).
8. **Ternary liquid systems.** Vernon and Brown, *ibid.,* **14,** 143 (1937).
9. **Constant boiling hydrobromic acid.** Heisig and Amdur, *ibid.,* **14,** 187 (1937).
10. **Negative solubility coefficients.** Bateman and Fernelius, *ibid.,* **14,** 315 (1937).
11. **Molecular weights by steam distillation.** Carson, *ibid.,* **14,** 537 (1937).
12. **Experiments on two-component systems.** Vernon, *ibid.,* **15,** 88 (1938).
13. **Negative solubility coefficients.** Bacon, *ibid.,* **15,** 494 (1938).
14. **Maximum boiling points.** Vernon, *ibid.,* **16,** 20 (1939).
15. **Negative solubility coefficients.** Kobe, *ibid.,* **16,** 183 (1939).
16. **Introduction to the phase rule.** Deming, *ibid.,* **16,** 215, 260 (1939).
17. **Boiling points for partially miscible liquids.** Randall and Avila, *ibid.,* **17,** 536 (1940).
18. **Structure of water.** Forbes, *ibid.,* **18,** 18 (1941).
19. **Phase rule experiments.** Mason, Rosen and Swift, *ibid.,* **18,** 473 (1941).
20. **Distillation of partially miscible liquids.** Jasper, Campbell and Marshall, *ibid.,* **18,** 540 (1941); Jasper, Farrell and Madoff, *ibid.,* **21,** 536 (1944).
21. **Phase models for ternary system.** Sutton, *ibid.,* **19,** 238 (1942).
22. **Deliquescence and efflorescence.** Steinbach, *ibid.,* **20,** 146 (1943).
23. **Relative weights of phases in equilibrium.** Spicer and Metcalf, *ibid.,* **20,** 199 (1943).
24. **Extraction with solvents.** Sharefkin and Wolfe, *ibid.,* **21,** 449 (1944).
25. **Two-component systems.** Lucasse, Koob and Miller, *ibid.,* **21,** 454 (1944).

REVIEW QUESTIONS

1. Define the absorption coefficient of a gas. How does it vary with the nature of the gas, the solvent and the temperature?
2. State Henry's law in words and in the form of an equation. When does the law fail? How does it apply to a mixture of gases?
3. Show that Henry's law and Raoult's law are related. How may the relationship be used to calculate the ideal solubility of a gas?
4. What is the criterion of an ideal system of two liquids? Under what circumstances would the mixture be expected to behave ideally? Draw the vapor pressure-composition curves for an ideal system at constant temperature.

5. Under what conditions are (a) positive, (b) negative, deviations from ideal behavior to be expected? Draw the corresponding vapor pressure-composition curves for constant temperature.

6. Derive an equation for the ratio of the amounts of a given component in vapor and liquid phases at equilibrium for an ideal mixture of two liquids. State the general result in words.

7. Indicate the types of curves showing the composition of liquid and vapor in equilibrium at constant temperature for an ideal or approximately ideal system. What conclusions can be drawn from these curves?

8. Draw the type of boiling point curve for a system of two liquids whose boiling point increases regularly with composition. What information can be obtained from such curves?

9. Explain fractional distillation and the action of a fractionating column.

10. What is a constant boiling (azeotropic) mixture? Under what conditions are such mixtures obtained? Draw and explain the appropriate boiling point-composition curves.

11. Draw the general form of the solubility curve for two partially miscible liquids. Utilize the diagram to explain the behavior of such a system upon varying (a) the composition at constant temperature, (b) the temperature at constant composition.

12. What is meant by the critical solution (consolute) temperature? Account for the existence of upper and lower consolute temperatures.

13. Explain what happens when a system of two partially miscible liquids is distilled. Utilize the phase rule to account for the results.

14. Describe the vapor pressure properties of a mixture of two immiscible liquids. How are the facts utilized in steam distillation? What are the conditions under which steam distillation will be successful?

15. Explain how distillation in steam may be used to estimate the molecular weight of a liquid.

16. State the distribution law in words, and define the distribution ratio for a solute between two liquids. How is this related to the solubilities in the liquids?

17. Derive the exact form of the distribution law. Show under what conditions it reduces to the simple form generally used.

18. How must the distribution law be modified when the solute is associated in one of the solvents? Show how the distribution measurements can give information concerning the association.

19. Why is it necessary to refer to the vapor pressure of a salt hydrate *system?* Draw the vapor pressure-composition diagram for the hydrates of copper sulfate at constant temperature, and explain its meaning.

20. By means of a figure, explain the effect of pressure on a salt hydrate system at constant temperature.

21. Define efflorescence and deliquescence. Explain the occurrence of these phenomena. Show how they depend on the amount of moisture in the atmosphere.

22. Show that the solubility and freezing point curves for a two-component system are related, and are sometimes indistinguishable.

23. What is a condensed system? What advantage is presented by considering such a system? How is the use of the phase rule affected?

24. Draw and explain the phase diagram for a system of two substances which do not form a compound or solid solution. What is the significance of the eutectic temperature?

25. By means of a phase diagram, explain the basis of thermal analysis. Indicate the nature of the cooling curves obtained for mixtures of different compositions.

26. Draw the equilibrium diagram for a salt-water system. Account for the behavior of salt-ice freezing mixtures.

27. Draw and explain the phase diagram for a two-component system in which a solid compound is formed.

28. Distinguish between compounds with congruent and incongruent melting points. Draw the phase diagram for the latter case.

29. Draw and explain the phase diagram for the system Na_2SO_4-H_2O. What information does it provide concerning the solubility of a metastable form?

30. Draw and explain the phase diagram for the system $FeCl_3$-H_2O.

31. What information can be obtained from the influence of temperature on the solubilities of salts and salt hydrates?

32. Draw the phase diagrams for systems in which there is one series of solid solutions. Explain why there cannot be a eutectic mixture, even though the freezing point curve may have a maximum or minimum.

33. Draw and explain the types of phase diagram for a system forming two partially miscible solid solutions, when there is a (a) eutectic, (b) a transition point.

34. How is a three-component system represented graphically, (a) at constant temperature, (b) to include temperature?

35. Draw and explain the phase diagram for a system of three components A, B, C, when each pair forms a simple eutectic system. How may the essential results be represented in a plane?

36. Draw and explain the phase diagram at constant temperature for a system of two salts (with a common ion) and water. What modifications are introduced when (a) a salt hydrate, (b) a double salt, separates out?

PROBLEMS

I

1. It was found by experiment that 1 liter of water dissolved 0.0523 g. of oxygen at 10° C and an atmospheric pressure of 748 mm. The vapor pressure of water at 10° C is 9.2 mm. Assuming Henry's law and ideal behavior, calculate the absorption coefficient of oxygen gas.

2. Using the data in Table XLIV calculate the (differential) heat of solution of nitrogen, and thence the weight of the gas dissolved by 1 liter of water at 1 atm. pressure and 15° C.

3. From data in Table XLIII calculate the molar composition of the dissolved gas when excess of electrolytic gas (2 vols. H_2 to 1 vol. O_2) is shaken with water at 20° C.

4. A mixture of benzene, C_6H_6 (vapor pressure 268 mm.) and ethylene chloride, $C_2H_4Cl_2$ (vapor pressure 236 mm.) behaves ideally at 50° C. What is the total vapor pressure of a liquid mixture consisting of equal weights of the two components? What is the molar composition of the vapor?

5. A mixture of nitrobenzene ($C_6H_5NO_2$) and water, which are virtually immiscible, boils at 99.0° C when the external pressure is 753.0 mm. The vapor pressure of pure water at 99.0° is 733.2 mm. Calculate the weight composition of the distillate.

6. In the distribution of benzoic acid between water (c_1) and benzene (c_2) the results were as follows:

| c_1 | 2.304 | 4.608 | 7.299 | 9.964 × 10⁻³ mole per liter |
| c_2 | 9.76 | 36.24 | 89.24 | 166.2 × 10⁻³ |

Show that the benzoic acid exists as double molecules in benzene solution, if simple molecules are present in water.

7. An aqueous solution contains 5.00 g. solute per liter; when 1 liter of the solution is extracted with 50 ml. of ether, 0.84 g. of solute are dissolved out. Assuming the solute to have the same molecular weight in both water and ether, how much will be left after the liter of solution is extracted by a second 50 ml. of ether. What would be the amount left if there were one extraction only with 100 ml. of ether?

8. Sketch the form of the phase equilibrium diagram for a system of two components A and B having the following properties: m. pt. of A, 245°; m. pt. of B, 187°; m. pt. of compound AB_2, 162°; eutectic of A and AB_2, 124°; eutectic of AB_2 and B, 154°.

II

1. From the data in Table XLIII, calculate the weight of oxygen dissolved by 1 liter of ethanol at 20° C and 5 atm. pressure of oxygen, assuming Henry's law and ideal behavior.

2. Calculate the mean (differential) heat of solution of oxygen in water over the temperature range from 0° to 30° C, utilizing the data in Table XLIV. Determine the absorption coefficient at 20° C and compare it with that in Table XLIII.

3. An equilibrium mixture, obtained at 500° C, consisting of 1.20 mole per cent of NH_3, 24.7 mole per cent of N_2 and 74.1 mole per cent of H_2, is cooled rapidly to fix the equilibrium. A large volume is shaken with water at 20° C; what is the composition, in mole per cent, of the dissolved gas? (The absorption coefficient of ammonia at 20° C is 710.)

4. The vapor in equilibrium with a liquid mixture of benzene and toluene, which behaves ideally at 60° C, contains 44 per cent by weight of the former. What is the weight composition of the liquid? The vapor pressures of pure benzene and toluene are 389 mm. and 140 mm. respectively.

5. Iodobenzene distils freely in steam at a temperature of 98.2° C when the external pressure is 758 mm.; at this temperature the vapor pressure of pure water is 712 mm. The distillate contains 42.2 per cent by weight of iodobenzene; what is its molecular weight?

6. The distribution of acetic acid between water (c_1) and benzene (c_2) gave the following results:

c_1	0.245	0.314	0.375	0.500 mole per liter
c_2	0.043	0.071	0.094	0.149

How can these results be explained?

7. When iodine was distributed between water and carbon tetrachloride, the concentration in the water layer was 0.1934, and in the other layer it was 16.54 g. iodine per liter. One liter of a solution containing 0.25 g. of iodine was extracted successively twice with 10 ml. of carbon tetrachloride; how much iodine was removed in this manner?

8. Sketch the form of the phase equilibrium diagram for a system of two components A and B having the following properties: m. pt. of A, 122°; m. pt. of B, 195°; compound AB having an incongruent melting point at 110°; eutectic of A and AB, 98°.

CHAPTER XIII

THE CONDUCTANCE OF ELECTROLYTES

The Laws of Electrolysis

44a. Electrolytic Conduction.—Solid and liquid substances which are able to conduct the electric current can be divided roughly into two categories. There are, first, the **metallic conductors** or **electronic conductors** in which the electricity is carried by the electrons. It was seen in § 19e, II that a metal probably consists of a rigid lattice of positive ions, i.e., atoms which have lost some electrons, and a system of relatively mobile electrons removed from the atoms. When an electrical pressure or potential is applied, the electrons are forced to stream in one direction, while the positive ions remain stationary; the flow of electricity is thus not accompanied by any movement of matter. Since the electrons carry negative charges, the direction in which they stream is opposite to that conventionally regarded as the direction of the positive current.

Conducting materials of the second type are known as **electrolytic conductors or electrolytes,** and the properties of these conductors will be given detailed consideration in this and succeeding chapters. *Electrolytes are distinguished from metallic conductors by the fact that the current is carried by ions and not by electrons.* As already seen (§ 10b), ions consist of atoms or groups of atoms which have lost or gained electrons, thus acquiring positive or negative charges, respectively. The application of an electrical potential causes these charged particles of matter to move, the positive ions in the direction of the current and the negative ions in the opposite direction.* It follows, therefore, that passage of an electric current through an electrolyte is always accompanied by a transfer of matter. This transfer is manifested by changes of concentration, and also by visible separation of material at the points where the electric current enters and leaves the electrolyte. Although many molten salts and hydroxides are electrolytic conductors, the treatment here will be restricted to electrolytes consisting of a salt, acid or base dissolved in a suitable solvent, such as water. It has been shown in § 31b that, in accordance with the theory of electrolytic dissociation, such solutions contain ions produced by the spontaneous dissociation of the dissolved acid, base or salt.

In order to pass a current of electricity through an electrolyte, two suitable pieces of metal (or carbon), called **electrodes,** are inserted in the solution; these are connected to the poles of a battery (Fig. 91) or other source of electrical

---

* The term **ion** originates from a Greek word meaning "to go"; it was applied to charged particles because of their movement under the influence of an electrical force.

pressure or, as it is generally called, **electromotive force** (abbreviated to E.M.F.). The electrode at which the positive current enters the solution is called the positive electrode or **anode** (Greek: ana, *up*), while that at which the current leaves is known as the negative electrode or **cathode** (Greek: cata, *down*). The ions which carry a positive charge move through the solution in the direction of the positive current, that is, toward the cathode; these ions are consequently called **cations.**

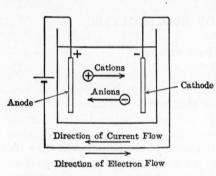

FIG. 91.   Flow of current and electrons

Similarly, the negative ions travel in the opposite direction, toward the anode; they are thus referred to as **anions.** The function of the applied E.M.F. is to direct the ions to the appropriate electrodes, and also to cause a movement of electrons, from the anode to the cathode, *outside the cell*, as indicated in Fig. 91. The flow of electrons is thus accompanied by a removal of electrons from the anode and their transfer, through the external connecting wire, to the cathode. As will be seen below, the supply of electrons at the anode is provided by the negatively charged anions, while the same number of electrons at the cathode are removed by the positively charged cations.

When a cation, carrying a positive charge, reaches the cathode it acquires (negative) electrons which are available at this electrode, thus having its charge neutralized. Since cations generally consist of a positively charged atom of a metal or of hydrogen, the neutralization of the charge leaves the neutral metal or hydrogen deposited upon the cathode. This result is in accord with the statement made above that the passage of an electric current through an electrolyte is usually associated with the visible separation of matter. Similarly, when an anion, which is negatively charged, reaches the anode, the electrons are removed, leaving the discharged neutral atom or group of atoms. If the anion is a halogen or hydroxyl ion, the discharged material may appear as the free halogen or as oxygen, respectively. Some anions, such as sulfate and nitrate, are not usually discharged from aqueous solutions, and so other processes, accompanied by the removal of electrons, frequently take place at the anode. One of these, which is always liable to occur, is the abstraction of electrons from the atoms of the actual metal constituting the anode; the atoms are thus converted into the corresponding positively charged cations which pass into solution. Such attackable metals as copper, zinc and cadmium usually dissolve when they are made anodes. On the other hand, platinum and gold fall into the category of "unattackable metals" that pass into solution to a small extent, or not at all, when they are used as anodes.

In the foregoing discussion it has been supposed, for the sake of simplicity, that the ions which carry the current are the ones discharged at the anode or cathode; this is, however, not necessarily the case. The ions carrying most of the current are generally those present in largest quantity, but these may not be actually discharged. The factors determining the order in which ions have their charges neutralized at the electrodes will be considered in §§ 51b, 51c.

44b. Faraday's Laws of Electrolysis.—The decomposition of electrolytic solutions by means of the electric current, in the manner just described, is known as **electrolysis**. While investigating the phenomena of electrolysis, M. Faraday (1833) discovered certain relationships between the quantity of electricity passing through an electrolyte and the amount of any material liberated at the electrode. The **quantity of electricity** *is equal to the product of the current strength and the time for which it is passed;* the nature of the units employed will be described more fully below. In the meantime, the results obtained by Faraday may be considered in the form of the two **laws of electrolysis,** as follows.

I. *The amount of chemical change produced by an electric current, that is, the amount of any substance deposited or dissolved, is proportional to the quantity of electricity passed.*

II. *The amounts of different substances deposited or dissolved by the same quantity of electricity are proportional to their chemical equivalent weights.*

The first law may be confirmed by passing currents of different strengths and for various periods of time through a given solution, e.g., copper sulfate or silver nitrate, and determining the amounts of material deposited on the cathode, e.g., copper or silver, or dissolved from the anode, if the latter is attackable. According to the law enunciated above, these amounts should be proportional to the product of the current strength and the time; thus, if w is the weight of a given metal deposited on the cathode, I is the strength of the current, e.g., in amperes, and t is the time in seconds for which it passes, w will be found to be proportional to $I \times t$ as I and t are varied. The nature of the electrolyte should, of course, be the same for all the experiments of one series.

In order to test the second law, the same current is passed simultaneously through a number of different solutions, e.g., dilute sulfuric acid, silver nitrate and copper sulfate. The amounts of material liberated at the cathodes, viz., hydrogen, silver and copper, will be proportional to the respective equivalent weights, i.e., 1 to 107.88 to 31.78. The amounts of silver or copper dissolved from anodes of these metals will be found to be exactly the same as those deposited on the cathode. Further, if in the sulfuric acid solution oxygen is evolved at an unattackable (platinum) anode, the weight will be proportional to its equivalent weight, i.e., 8.00.

Combination of the two laws of electrolysis leads to the conclusion that the weight w of material deposited or dissolved at an electrode is proportional to $I \times t \times e$, where e is the equivalent weight of the material. It is thus possible to write

$$w = \frac{I \times t \times e}{F},$$ (44.1)

where $1/F$ is the proportionality constant. The significance of this constant may be seen by taking the quantity $I \times t$ equal to F; then the weight w of substance deposited (or dissolved) is equal to e, the equivalent weight. In other words, F, called the **faraday**, *is the quantity of electricity which must be passed in order to deposit or dissolve 1 gram equiv. of any substance.* It is important to note that this quantity of electricity is always the same, irrespective of the nature of the substance deposited or dissolved.

In order to assess the value of the faraday, it is necessary to consider the question of units of current and quantity of electricity. The practical unit of current, the international **ampere,** abbreviated to **amp.,** is defined as *the current which flowing for 1 sec. will cause the deposition of 1.11800 milligram of silver* from a solution of a silver salt. The unit quantity of electricity, called the **coulomb,** is then *the quantity of electricity passing when 1 amp. flows for 1 sec.* Combining the definitions of the ampere and the coulomb, it follows that the passage of one coulomb results in the deposition of 0.001118 gram of silver. The quantity of electricity required to deposit 1 g. equiv., i.e., 107.88 grams, of silver, and hence 1 g. equiv. of any substance, is consequently given by

$$F = \frac{107.88}{0.001118} = 96,494 \text{ coulombs.}$$

This is obviously the value of the faraday in international coulombs. In view of the uncertainties connected with atomic weights, impurities in the silver, etc., it is best to round off the last two figures, and to write

$$F = 96,500 \text{ coulombs.}$$

Insertion of this value in equation (44.1) then gives a complete summary of Faraday's laws in the form

$$w = \frac{I \times t \times e}{96,500}, \tag{44.2}$$

where w is the weight in grams, I is the current strength in amperes, and t is the time in seconds for which the current is passed.

An important use of equation (44.2) lies in its application to the measurement of quantity of electricity or of current strength. The apparatus used for the purpose is known as a **coulometer,** and by its means the amount of a given material, e.g., silver, copper, iodine or a mixture of hydrogen and oxygen, set free in electrolysis can be measured. Thus, if w is determined in this way, and the equivalent weight e of the substance is known, the quantity of electricity passed, i.e., $I \times t$, can be derived from equation (44.2). If the time t is measured, the current strength I, assumed to be constant, can be calculated.

Problem: The passage of a constant current through a dilute solution of sulfuric acid, with platinum electrodes, for 1 hr. resulted in the liberation of 336 ml. of mixed hydrogen and oxygen, reduced to S.T.P. Calculate the strength of the current.

The passage of 1 faraday, i.e., 96,500 coulombs, results in the simultaneous liberation of 1 equiv., i.e., 8 grams, of oxygen, and 1 equiv., i.e., 1 gram, of hydrogen; this represents $\frac{1}{4}$ mole of O_2 and $\frac{1}{2}$ mole of H_2, making a total of $\frac{3}{4}$ mole of gas per faraday. The volume of $\frac{3}{4}$ mole of gas at S.T.P. is $\frac{3}{4} \times 22.4 = 16.8$ liters; hence

16.8 liters of $H_2 + O_2$ gases are liberated by 96,500 coulombs.

The actual volume of gas obtained in the experiment was 0.336 liter; hence,

0.336 liters of $H_2 + O_2$ gases are liberated by $\dfrac{96,500}{16.8} \times 0.336$ coulombs.

Since the current is passed for 1 hr., i.e., 3600 sec., the current in amp. is obtained by dividing the number of coulombs by 3600; thus

$$\text{Current strength} = \frac{96,500 \times 0.336}{16.8 \times 3600} = 0.536 \text{ amp.}$$

There is little doubt that Faraday's laws are exact; they have been found to hold at high and low temperatures, as well as under normal conditions, for nonaqueous solutions and fused salts, as well as for aqueous solutions. Provided the correct equivalent weight is employed, there are no exceptions to equation (44.2). The laws also apply to chemical changes at the anode and cathode which do not involve deposition on, or solution of, the electrode; for example, ions are frequently oxidized at the anode or reduced at the cathode.* For such reactions equation (44.2) may still be employed if the appropriate equivalent weight is used; thus, in the reduction of ferric (Fe^{+++}) to ferrous (Fe^{++}) ions, or the reverse oxidation process, the equivalent weight is equal to the atomic weight of iron, i.e., 55.85.

Apparent exceptions to Faraday's laws sometimes arise when two or more processes occur simultaneously at an electrode; for example, the deposition of a metal, such as zinc or nickel, may be accompanied by the evolution of hydrogen. The quantity of metal liberated at the cathode is then not in accord with equation (44.2); however, if allowance is made for the fact that part of the current is utilized in an alternative process, the laws are found to be obeyed.

44c. Significance of Faraday's Laws.—Apart from their practical value, Faraday's laws have an important theoretical significance. The discharge at a cathode, or formation at an anode, of 1 g. equiv. of any ion requires the passage of one faraday of electricity; hence, it is reasonable to suppose that this represents the charge carried by 1 g. equiv. of any ion. If the ion has a valence of z, then 1 mole or 1 gram ion of these ions will contain z gram equiv., and will consequently carry z faradays, i.e., zF coulombs, where F is 96,500. The number of individual ions in 1 gram ion is equal to the Avogadro number, and so the electrical charge carried by a single ion is equal to zF/N. Since z is an integer, one for a univalent ion, two for a bivalent ion, and so

* Strictly speaking all processes occurring at anode and cathode are oxidation and reduction in the most general sense, since they all involve the removal or addition of electrons, respectively (see § 47c).

on, it follows that the charge of electricity carried by a single ion is a multiple of a fundamental unit charge whose value is F/N. This result, derived from Faraday's laws, implies that *electricity, like matter, is atomic in nature*, and that F/N is the "atom" or unit of electric charge. There are many reasons for identifying this unit charge with the charge of an electron, i.e., ϵ, so that

$$\epsilon = \frac{F}{N}.$$

This conclusion is supported by the value of the electronic charge calculated from this relationship in § 4b; the result derived in this manner is virtually identical with that obtained from the most accurate oil drop experiments.

The identification of F/N with the electronic charge suggests that a univalent (singly charged) cation, e.g., Na^+, for which z is 1, is formed when an atom loses a single electron, so that its positive charge is equal to the electronic charge. A bivalent cation, e.g., Ca^{++}, for which z is 2, results from the loss of two electrons, and so on. Similarly, a univalent anion, e.g., Cl^-, is formed when an atom gains an electron and becomes an ion. In general, therefore, an ion carries the number of charges equal to its valence, and it differs from the corresponding uncharged particle by this number of electrons. These results are in complete harmony with the conclusions reached from the electronic theory of valence (§ 10b).

One final consequence of Faraday's laws may be mentioned; since equivalent amounts of different ions are discharged at the anode and cathode, for a given current, it follows that when a solution is electrolyzed the number of electrons taken up by the cations at the cathode must be equal to the number released simultaneously at the anode. This will, presumably, be also equal to the number of electrons which pass through the external connection from the anode to the cathode.

THE MIGRATION OF IONS

45a. Transference Numbers.—Although positive and negative ions are discharged in equivalent amounts at the two electrodes, these ions do not necessarily move at the same speed toward the cathode and anode, respectively, under the influence of an applied E.M.F. This can be seen in a simple pictorial manner by considering Fig. 92, which represents the electrolytic vessel containing an equivalent number of positive and negative ions, indicated by plus and minus signs. Since the solution must always be electrically neutral, the cations and anions must always remain equivalent in number; if they are both univalent, then the numbers must be equal. The condition of the solution at the commencement of electrolysis is shown in Fig. 92, I. Suppose that the *cations only* are able to move under the influence of an applied potential, and that two of these ions move from left to right in a given time; the condition attained will then be as in Fig. 92, II. At each electrode there are two ions unpaired, and this means that two electrons are given up at the anode, accompanied by the discharge of two anions; the same number of electrons have passed round the external connection, and are taken up by the two ions at the cathode, leading to their discharge. It is seen, therefore, that although only positive ions are assumed to be able to move, equivalent amounts of positive and negative ions are discharged at the cathode and anode, respectively. A condition of this kind actually exists in certain solid and fused electrolytes, where all the current is carried by the cations.

If while the cations are moving in one direction, three anions are carrying electricity in the opposite direction, so that the ionic velocities are in the ratio of 2 to 3, the result will be as shown in Fig. 92, III. Five ions, equal

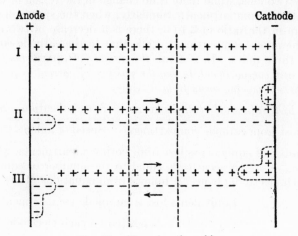

FIG. 92. The migration of ions

to the sum of two and three, are seen to be discharged at each electrode, in spite of the difference in the speeds of the ions. Exactly analogous results would be obtained for any speeds of the two ions, and so there is no difficulty in correlating Faraday's laws with the fact that the oppositely charged ions in a solution may have different velocities.

It can be seen from the two cases just considered and, in fact, from any particular choice of the ionic speeds, that the total number of ions discharged, and hence the total quantity of electricity carried through the solution, is proportional to the sum of the speeds of the two ions. If u_+ is the velocity of the cations and u_- that of the anions in the same solution, and under the same conditions, the quantity of electricity passing will be proportional to the sum, $u_+ + u_-$. The amount carried by each ion is proportional to its own speed, i.e., to u_+ or to u_-, as the case may be, and so *the fraction of the total current carried by each ionic species*, which is called its **transference number,** is given by

$$t_+ = \frac{u_+}{u_+ + u_-} \quad \text{and} \quad i_- = \frac{u_-}{u_+ + u_-}, \tag{45.1}$$

where t_+ and t_- are the transference numbers of the cations and anions, respectively, in the given electrolyte. It is evident from equation (45.1) that the faster the speed of one ion relative to that of the other, the greater will be the fraction of the total current carried by the former. It should be noted that the actual ionic velocities are not important in determining the transference numbers; the relative velocities are the significant quantities.

45b. Determination of Transference Numbers: The Hittorf Method.— An examination of Fig. 92 shows that in II, where two cations have moved while the anions were stationary, the number of positive and negative ions in the vicinity of the anode, i.e., in the anode compartment, has decreased from 8 to 6, i.e., by two ions, while there is no change in the region of the cathode, i.e., in the cathode compartment. Similarly, when the speeds of the cations and anions are in the ratio of 2 to 3, there is a decrease of two units in the material in the anode compartment, while that in the cathode compartment decreases by three units. In general, *the number of equivalents of electrolyte removed from any compartment during the passage of current is proportional to the speed of the ion moving away from it;* thus,

$$\frac{\text{Equivalents lost from anode compartment}}{\text{Equivalents lost from cathode compartment}} = \frac{\text{Speed of cation}}{\text{Speed of anion}} = \frac{u_+}{u_-}. \quad (45.2)$$

The total number of equivalents lost from both compartments, which is proportional to $u_+ + u_-$, is seen to be equal to the number of equivalents deposited on each electrode; hence, it follows from equations (45.1) and (45.2),

$$\frac{u_+}{u_+ + u_-} = t_+ = \frac{\text{Equivalents lost from anode compartment}}{\text{Equivalents deposited on each electrode}}, \quad (45.3)$$

and

$$\frac{u_-}{u_+ + u_-} = t_- = \frac{\text{Equivalents lost from cathode compartment}}{\text{Equivalents deposited on each electrode}}. \quad (45.4)$$

These two expressions provide a basis for the experimental determination of transference numbers by the method proposed by W. Hittorf (1853).

By Faraday's laws, the number of equivalents discharged at each electrode must be equal to the equivalents of any substance deposited in another cell by the same quantity of electricity. The practice, therefore, is to include a coulometer (§ 44b) in the same circuit as the experimental solution, so that the same quantity of electricity passes through them both. The number of equivalents of metal, e.g., silver or copper, deposited in the coulometer gives the denominator of equations (45.3) and (45.4). The numerators can then be obtained by measuring the fall in concentration of the solution in the vicinity of the anode and cathode, respectively, in the experimental vessel. Since the sum of the two transference numbers t_+ and t_- must be unity, it is not necessary to measure the concentration changes in both anode and cathode compartments, except for confirmatory purposes; the determination of the transference number of one ion thus automatically gives the value for the other ion.

When carrying out transference number measurements by means of the Hittorf (analytical) method, precautions must be taken to avoid the possibility of mixing between the anode and cathode solutions; for this reason it is desirable to have a "middle compartment," analogous to that depicted between the dashed lines in Fig. 92, in which the concentration remains unchanged when current is passed. Further, diffusion and convection must be made negligible, so that the measured concentration changes can really be ascribed to ionic transference and not to extraneous factors. One form of apparatus, which has been used for the study of solutions of alkali and alkaline earth chlorides, is shown diagrammatically in Fig. 93; two right-angle bends are introduced below the anode A and also above the cathode C, in order to minimize the possibility of mixing of the solutions in different parts of the apparatus. The latter is filled with the experimental solution whose *weight concentration* must be known; suitable electrodes A and C are inserted, and these are connected in series with a coulometer and a source of current. A current of 0.01 to 0.02 amp. is passed for two or three hours, so as to produce appreciable, but not too large, changes of concentration; the stopcocks S_1 and S_2 are then closed. The liquid isolated above S_1 represents the anode solution, while that below S_2 is the cathode solution; these are removed and analyzed. The concentration of the "middle compartment," between the two stopcocks, should be unchanged after the electrolysis. The quantity of material, e.g., silver,

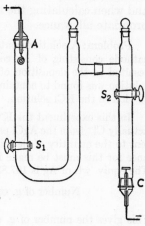

FIG. 93. Apparatus for application of Hittorf method

deposited by the current in the coulometer is determined, and from this the number of equivalents can be calculated.

Since the change in concentration of the solution is accompanied by a change of density, and hence of volume, the loss of material from anode or cathode compartment must be determined with reference to a definite *weight* of solvent present after current has passed. Thus, if the analysis of x grams of anode solution showed it to contain y grams of the dissolved substance (electrolyte) *at the end* of the experiment, then the latter was associated with $x - y$ grams of water. The amount of electrolyte, say m grams, associated with this same weight of water *at the beginning*, is calculated from the known weight concentration of the original solution. The decrease of electrolyte in the anode compartment is thus $m - y$ grams, or $(m - y)/e$ gram equiv., where e is the equivalent weight of the experimental substance. If g is the number of gram equiv. deposited in the coulometer during the electrolysis, it follows from equation (45.3) that the transference number of the cation t_+ is given by

$$t_+ = \frac{m - y}{e \times g}. \tag{45.5}$$

The transference number of the anion t_- is of course equal to $1 - t_+$.

In this treatment, as in Fig. 92, it is assumed that the discharge of an ion leads to its complete removal from the solution. Although this is generally true for cations, which are deposited as metals, it is not the case for anions. It frequently happens that these ions are not removed upon discharge, but an equivalent amount of anode material passes into solution. This occurs, for example, if a solution of silver nitrate is electrolyzed with a silver anode; the latter dissolves to an extent equivalent to the NO_3^- ions that would have been discharged according to Fig. 92. The concentration of the anode compartment is thus increased by this amount of silver nitrate, and when calculating the transference number it is necessary to make the appropriate allowance.

Problem: A solution containing 3.654 g. KCl per 100 g. was electrolyzed, using a cathode consisting of Ag coated with AgCl. After the passage of current which resulted in the deposition of 1.9768 g. Ag in a coulometer, 122.93 g. of the cathode solution was found to contain 5.136 g. KCl. Calculate the transference number of the K^+ ion in the KCl solution.

In this experiment the K^+ ions are not discharged (and removed) at the cathode; actually Cl^- from the AgCl passes into solution to form KCl in amount exactly equivalent to the quantity of electricity, i.e., to the Ag deposited in the coulometer. Allowance for this must be made in determining the loss from the cathode compartment. The equiv. wt. of Ag is 107.88; hence,

$$\text{Number of g. equiv. of Ag deposited} = \frac{1.9768}{107.88} = 0.01832.$$

This gives the number of g. equiv. of Cl^- from the cathode which have entered the cathode solution as KCl.

After electrolysis the cathode solution contains $122.93 - 5.14 = 117.79$ g. of H_2O to 5.136 g. KCl; the equiv. wt. of KCl is 74.56, and consequently,

$$\text{Number of g. equiv. of KCl in cathode solution} = \frac{5.136}{74.56} = 0.06888.$$

If the Cl^- had not been removed from the cathode, the number of g. equiv. of KCl, associated with 117.79 g. H_2O, would have been $0.06888 - 0.01832 = 0.05056$.

Before electrolysis 100 g. solution contained 3.654 g. KCl, so that the weight of H_2O was $100 - 3.65 = 96.35$ g.; this was associated with $3.654/74.56 = 0.04900$ g. equiv. KCl. Hence 117.79 g. H_2O (present in the cathode solution after electrolysis) was associated before electrolysis with

$$\frac{0.04900 \times 117.79}{96.35} = 0.05991 \text{ g. equiv. KCl.}$$

The loss of electrolyte from the cathode compartment is thus $0.05991 - 0.05056 = 0.00935$ g. equiv. Since 0.01832 g. equiv. was deposited in the coulometer, it follows that the transference number of the ion leaving the cathode compartment, i.e., the anion, is given by

$$t_- = \frac{0.00935}{0.01832} = 0.510.$$

The transference number t_+ of the cation is thus $1 - 0.510 = 0.490$.

45c. The Moving Boundary Method.—A more direct method for the determination of transference numbers is based on a study of the rate of movement of the boundary between two ionic solutions. This method is capable of considerable accuracy, and as a result of improvements in the apparatus it has been largely used in recent years in place of the Hittorf method. If it is required to determine the transference numbers of the ions in the electrolyte MA, e.g., potassium chloride, it is necessary to have another, i.e., "indicator," electrolyte, M'A, e.g., lithium chloride, having an ion in common with the experimental substance. Further, the ion M', which is different from M, must have a smaller velocity than the latter; this condition is satisfied, in the case under consideration, by the lithium ion, which migrates more slowly than the potassium ion under the influence of the same applied E.M.F.

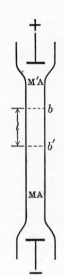

Imagine the two solutions, i.e., of MA and M'A, in an electrolysis apparatus, part of which consists of a uniform vertical tube, as depicted in Fig. 94. A suitable anode is placed in the indicator solution M'A, and a cathode is inserted in the experimental solution. The actual nature of the anode and cathode is immaterial, provided they do not cause gas evolution or other interference. By means of a special device, which constitutes an important part of the method, a sharp boundary is produced between the two solutions at b. When a current is passed, the M (potassium) ions move downward toward the cathode, and these are followed by the M' (lithium) ions, thus maintaining the sharp boundary. The latter ions are chosen with this end in view, for if the M' ions were the faster moving ions the boundary would become blurred. After the passage of a measured quantity Q of electricity, the boundary has moved from b to b', and this distance l is measured. In observing the boundary, especially

Fig. 94. Moving boundary method for transference numbers

between two colorless electrolytes, use is made of the difference in the refractive indices of the indicator and experimental solutions. The method of calculating the transference numbers is then as follows.

If one faraday of electricity is passed through the apparatus, the quantity carried by the cation is equal to its transference number, i.e., t_+ faraday; hence, t_+ gram equiv. of the cation (potassium ion) must pass any given point, moving in the downward direction. If the concentration of the MA (potassium chloride) solution in the vicinity of the boundary is c gram equiv. per unit volume,* this boundary must move through a volume t_+/c while one faraday is passing through the apparatus. The boundary is observed to move from b to b', through the distance l, for the passage of Q coulombs; hence, the distance moved for one faraday is $l \times F/Q$, where F is the fara-

---

* The symbol c is used to represent concentrations in gram equiv., as distinct from concentrations in gram ions or moles, for which c is employed.

day, i.e., 96,500 coulombs. If the area of cross section of the tube in which the boundary moves is a, the volume through which it moves is $l \times a \times F/Q$; this must be equal to t_+/c, as given above, so that

$$\frac{l \times a \times F}{Q} = \frac{t_+}{c},$$

$$t_+ = \frac{l \times a \times F \times c}{Q}. \qquad (45.6)$$

It is thus possible to calculate the transference number of the cation (potassium ion) from the data available. In accurate work a correction must be applied for volume changes occurring as a result of chemical reactions at the electrodes, for these will affect the movement of the boundary. The correction is negligible except for relatively concentrated solutions.

Problem: In a moving boundary experiment with 0.100 N KCl, using 0.065 N LiCl as indicator solution, a constant current of 0.005893 amp. was passed for 2130 sec., and the boundary was observed to move through 5.60 cm. in a tube of 0.1142 sq. cm. cross section. Calculate the transference numbers of the K^+ and Cl^- ions.

The values of l and a are given, while that of the faraday is known; hence, Q and c must be derived from the data to calculate t_+ by equation (45.6). The quantity of electricity Q in coulombs is the product of the current in amp. and the time in sec., i.e., 0.005893×2130 coulombs. The concentration c must be expressed in g. equiv. per cc., since l is in cm. and a in cm.^{2}. The solution of KCl contains 0.100 g. equiv. per liter, and this is 10^{-4} g. equiv. per ml., or per cc., with sufficient accuracy; hence, c is 10^{-4}, and by equation (45.6),

$$t_+ = \frac{5.60 \times 0.1142 \times 96,500 \times 10^{-4}}{0.005893 \times 2130} = 0.492.$$

The transference number of the K^+ ion is thus 0.492, and hence that of the Cl^- ion must be $1 - 0.492 = 0.508$.

45d. Results of Transference Number Measurements.—Some of the most recent values of the transference numbers of the cations in various electrolytes at a number of concentrations at 25° C are quoted in Table LI. The

TABLE LI.   TRANSFERENCE NUMBERS OF CATIONS AT 25° C

Concn.	HCl	LiCl	NaCl	KCl	KNO$_3$	BaCl$_2$	K$_2$SO$_4$
0.01 N	0.825	0.329	0.392	0.490	0.508	0.440	0.483
0.02	0.827	0.326	0.390	0.490	0.509	0.437	0.485
0.05	0.829	0.321	0.388	0.490	0.509	0.432	0.487
0.10	0.831	0.317	0.385	0.490	0.510	0.425	0.489
0.20	0.834	0.311	0.382	0.489	0.512	0.416	0.491
0.50	—	0.300	—	0.489	—	0.399	0.491

corresponding anion transference numbers may be obtained in each case by subtracting the cation transference number from unity. It will be noted that the transference numbers vary to some extent with the concentration of the electrolyte; this fact is of great significance, for it implies that the speeds of the ions, upon which the transference numbers depend [equation (45.1)], are not constant but may change as the concentration of the solution is altered.

An examination of the cation transference numbers of the three alkali chlorides, viz., lithium, sodium and potassium chlorides, as given in Table LI, reveals the fact that the values increase in this order. Since these three electrolytes have the same anion, it is apparent that the speeds of the cations must increase in the order lithium, sodium, potassium. Of these ions, lithium is the smallest and potassium the largest, as may be expected from general considerations of atomic weight and atomic structure, and as has been verified by X-ray diffraction measurements on crystals. It would be anticipated, therefore, that lithium, the smaller ion, should have a higher velocity than the potassium ion, which is larger. The fact that the reverse is actually the case, as shown by transference and other measurements, is a strong argument in favor of the hydration of ions in solution (§ 42h). Because of the small size of the *bare* lithium ion, there is a strong electrostatic field in its vicinity, and so it is able to attract a relatively large number of water dipoles. The larger bare potassium ion cannot hold as many, because of the weaker field at its circumference. The result is that the highly hydrated lithium ion in solution is actually larger than the hydrated potassium ion; this explains why the former ion moves with a smaller speed than the latter.

More direct experimental evidence for the hydration of ions in solution has been obtained in connection with transference studies. If the ions carry molecules of water with them in their migration, the cations will take some water out of the anode compartment, for example, while the anions will bring some water in with them. If the anions and cations are hydrated to different extents, the net result should be a change in the amount of water in the compartment. This change will be a measure of the difference in the extents of hydration of the positive and negative ions. That such changes in the water content do occur as a result of ionic migration has been proved in two ways: first, by observations on the volumes of the anode and cathode solutions separated by a parchment membrane, and second, by showing that the concentration of a nonelectrolyte, such as urea or a sugar, which is not affected by the current, actually changes in the course of electrolysis. The volume and concentration changes are to be attributed to the net addition or removal of water by the hydrated ions.

EQUIVALENT CONDUCTANCE

46a. Electrolytic Conductance.—Solutions, like metallic conductors, obey **Ohm's law** which relates the electrical pressure or E.M.F. applied to a conductor and the strength of the current passing. The law states that *the current strength* (I) *is directly proportional to the applied* E.M.F. (E), *and inversely proportional to the resistance* (R); thus, with the appropriate units,

$$I = \frac{E}{R}.$$ (46.1)

The practical unit of current strength, the ampere, has been already defined in § 44b; the international unit of resistance, the **ohm,** is defined as *the resistance at 0° C of a column of mercury 106.30 cm. long, of uniform cross section, weighing 14.4521 gram.* The corresponding unit of E.M.F., the **volt,** is then given by expressing the Ohm's law equation (46.1) in the form

$$\text{Amperes} = \frac{\text{Volts}}{\text{Ohms}}, \tag{46.2}$$

so that *the volt is the magnitude of the* E.M.F. *which must be applied to a resistance of one ohm in order to pass a current of one ampere.*

The resistance of any uniform conductor varies directly as its length (l cm.) and inversely as its area of cross section (a sq. cm.), so that

$$R = \text{R} \frac{l}{a} \text{ ohms,} \tag{46.3}$$

where R, a constant for the given conductor, is known as the **specific resistance;** it is effectively *the resistance in ohms of a specimen one cm. in length ($l = 1$) and one sq. cm. in cross section ($a = 1$),* that is, R is the resistance between opposite faces of a 1 cm. cube of the material.

The **specific conductance** of any conductor is defined as *the reciprocal of the specific resistance,* and may be represented by the symbol κ. Since by definition κ is equal to $1/\text{R}$, equation (46.3) becomes

$$R = \frac{1}{\kappa} \cdot \frac{l}{a} \text{ ohms,} \tag{46.4}$$

and hence,

$$\kappa = \frac{l}{aR} \text{ ohms}^{-1} \text{ cm.}^{-1} \tag{46.5}$$

Since R is in ohms, l in cm. and a in sq. cm., the units of κ are seen to be ohms^{-1} cm.$^{-1}$. The conductance C is defined as the reciprocal of the resistance, so that by equation (46.4),

$$C = \kappa \frac{a}{l} \text{ ohms}^{-1}. \tag{46.6}$$

The specific conductance κ is thus seen from equation (46.6) to be *the conductance between opposite faces of a 1 cm. cube.* The unit of conductance, indicated above as ohm^{-1}, is frequently referred to as a "reciprocal ohm" or "mho."

For electrolytic solutions, it is convenient to define a quantity called the **equivalent conductance** and represented by the symbol Λ (Greek: capital *lambda*); it is a measure of the conducting power of all the ions produced by 1 gram equiv. of electrolyte in a given solution. Imagine two large electrodes set 1 cm. apart, and suppose the whole of the solution containing 1 gram equiv. is placed between these electrodes; the area of the electrodes covered will then be v sq. cm., where v cc. is the volume of the solution containing the 1 gram equiv. of solute. The conductance of this system, which is equal to the equivalent conductance Λ, can be derived from equation (46.6), with l equal to 1 cm., and the area of cross section a equal to v sq. cm.; thus,

$$\Lambda = \kappa v \text{ ohms}^{-1} \text{ cm.}^{2}, \tag{46.7}$$

where v is the volume in cc. of the solution containing 1 gram equiv. of solute. If c is the concentration of the solution in *gram equiv. per liter*, then v is equal to $1000/c$, neglecting the difference between ml. and cc. Consequently, equation (46.7) becomes

$$\Lambda = 1000 \frac{\kappa}{c} \text{ ohms}^{-1} \text{ cm.}^{2} \tag{46.8}$$

The equivalent conductance of a solution can thus be readily derived if its concentration and specific conductance are known. The latter can be obtained by means of equation (46.5) from the resistance R of the electrolytic conductor of known dimensions l and a; the next problem to consider, therefore, is the determination of the resistance of an electrolyte.

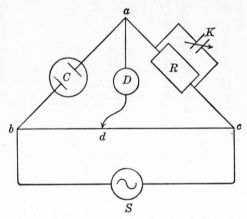

Fig. 95.   Measurement of resistance of electrolyte

46b. Measurement of Resistance of Electrolyte.—The resistance of an electrolytic solution is most frequently determined by means of some form of Wheatstone bridge circuit. In the earliest measurements, direct current was employed, but this caused the results to be erratic because of the so-called "polarization" due to gases liberated at the electrodes. Following the suggestion of F. W. Kohlrausch (1868), a rapidly alternating current is now generally used. The direction of the current is reversed about a thousand times per second, so that the "polarizations" produced by successive pulses counteract one another. The Wheatstone bridge arrangement is shown in Fig. 95; C is the cell containing the solution whose resistance is to be measured, and R is a variable standard resistance. The source of the alternating current is indicated by S, and D is a suitable current detector; K is a variable electrical condenser for compensating the electrical capacity of the cell. The point of contact d is moved along the uniform wire or other resistance bc, until no current can be detected in D. When this condition is attained, the ratio of the resistances in the bridge arms, i.e., ab and ac, is equal to the ratio of bd to dc. The resistance in ab is that of the cell C, i.e., R_c, and that in the arm ac is the known resistance R, so that

$$\frac{R_c}{R} = \frac{bd}{dc}.$$

By observing the ratio bd/dc at the point of balance of the bridge, when no current passes through D, the value of R_c can be derived directly, since R is known.

For approximate measurements, an induction coil may be used as the source S of alternating current; in modern work, however, some form of vacuum-tube oscillator, producing vibrations of 1000 to 2000 cycles per sec., is

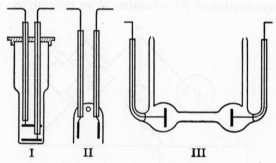

I   II   III
FIG. 96.   Types of conductance cells

almost invariably employed. The best form of detector D is a tuned telephone earpiece, but its sensitivity may be increased by means of an audio-frequency vacuum-tube amplifier. Various types of cells C have been used for conductance work; Fig. 96, I, shows a simple cell often employed in the laboratory, while Fig. 96, II depicts a "dipping cell" that is useful for industrial measurements. Where accurate results are required, cells designed specially to avoid errors due to electrostatic capacity effects are used; one of these (G. Jones and G. M. Bollinger, 1931) is represented in Fig. 96, III. The electrodes in the cell are of stout platinum, and they are generally coated with a layer of finely divided platinum black; this tends to decrease the effect of polarization. Exceptionally pure water, known as **conductance water**, made by redistilling good distilled water in a special apparatus, should be employed in preparing solutions for conductance studies.

Instead of attempting to measure the dimensions l and a of the conductance cell, which are required for calculating the specific conductance by equation (46.5), the cell is standardized by means of a solution of known conductance. For a given cell both l and a, and hence the quantity l/a, are constant; if the constant l/a, known as the **cell constant,** is represented by k, it follows from equation (46.5) that

$$\kappa = \frac{k}{R}. \tag{46.9}$$

A solution, generally one of potassium chloride, whose specific conductance is known accurately from measurements made in cells of known dimensions, is placed in the experimental cell and the resistance R is measured; the cell constant k for the given cell can then be calculated from equation (46.9). Once the cell constant is known, the specific conductance of any solution can be determined by measuring its resistance when filled with the given solution.

Problem: The measured resistance of a cell containing 0.1 g. equiv. of KCl in 1000 ml. at 25° C was found to be 3468.9 ohms; the specific conductance of this solution is known, with considerable accuracy, to be 0.012856 ohm^{-1} cm.$^{-1}$ at 25° C. An exactly 0.1 N solution of another substance in the same cell had a resistance of 4573.4 ohms; calculate the equivalent conductance of this electrolyte at the given concentration. (The conductance of the water is so small that it may be neglected.)

For the KCl solution, R is 3468.9 ohms and κ is 0.012856 ohm^{-1} cm.$^{-1}$, and hence the cell constant is given by equation (46.9) as

$$k = \kappa R = 0.012856 \times 3468.9 = 44.597 \text{ cm.}^{-1}$$

Hence, for the other electrolyte,

$$\kappa = \frac{k}{R} = \frac{44.597}{4573.4} = 0.009751 \text{ ohm}^{-1} \text{ cm.}^{-1}$$

The equivalent conductance is given by equation (46.8); since the solution is exactly 0.1 N, it follows that c is 10^{-1} g. equiv. *per liter*, and hence

$$\Lambda = 1000\,\frac{\kappa}{c} = \frac{1000 \times 0.009751}{10^{-1}} = 97.51 \text{ ohms}^{-1} \text{ cm.}^2$$

46c. Results of Conductance Measurements.—The results of conductance measurements are usually expressed as the equivalent conductances for a series of concentrations. Some reliable values for a number of electrolytes in aqueous solution at 25° C are recorded in Table LII; the concentrations are in gram equiv. per liter. These data show that the equivalent conductance,

TABLE LII. EQUIVALENT CONDUCTANCES AT 25° C IN OHMS^{-1} CM.^{2}

Concn.	HCl	NaCl	KCl	AgNO$_3$	$\frac{1}{2}$BaCl$_2$	$\frac{1}{2}$NiSO$_4$
0.0005 N	422.7	124.5	147.8	131.4	136.0	118.7
0.001	421.4	123.7	146.9	130.5	134.3	113.1
0.005	415.8	120.6	143.5	127.2	128.0	93.2
0.01	412.0	118.5	141.3	124.8	123.9	82.7
0.02	407.2	115.8	138.3	121.4	119.1	72.3
0.05	399.1	111.1	133.4	115.2	111.5	59.2
0.10	391.3	106.7	129.0	109.1	105.2	50.8

and hence the conducting power of the ions in 1 gram equiv. of any electrolyte, invariably increases with decreasing concentration. The figures, however, appear to approach a limiting value in very dilute solutions; this limiting value, which is of considerable significance, can often be obtained by extrapolating the measured equivalent conductances against a suitable function, generally the square root, of the concentration. The limiting equivalent conductance is represented by the symbol Λ_0, and it is called the **equivalent conductance at infinite dilution.** In a sense this expression is somewhat mis-

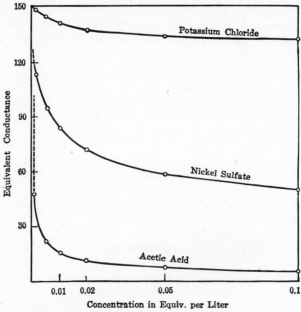

Fig. 97.   Conductances of electrolytes of different types

leading because an infinitely dilute solution would be pure water; what is implied, however, is a solution so dilute that further dilution does not change the equivalent conductance, which then has its limiting value.

It will be seen from Table LII that the equivalent conductances of substances like hydrochloric acid, alkali halides and sodium hydroxide do not change very greatly with concentration; this is also evident from Fig. 97 in which the equivalent conductance of potassium chloride is plotted against the concentration. Electrolytes of this type, which generally consist of solutions of strong acids and bases, and of many simple salts, are known as **strong electrolytes.** The weak acids and bases, particularly the organic carboxylic acids and amines, behave in a different manner; these are called **weak electrolytes.** An aqueous solution of acetic acid is a typical weak electrolyte, and the variation of its equivalent conductance with concentration is also shown in Fig. 97. The values are seen to be low at concentrations less than about 0.01 N, and then to increase very rapidly in extremely dilute solutions. It is, of course, impossible to draw a sharp distinction between strong and weak electrolytes, and many substances exhibit intermediate behavior; this may be seen from the curve for nickel sulfate in Fig. 97. The salts of the transition metals, such as manganese, nickel, iron, cobalt, copper, zinc, etc., particularly those of dibasic acids, such as the sulfates, behave in this intermediate manner.

It should be pointed out that the behavior of a particular electrolyte is dependent upon the nature of both the solvent and solute. A particular substance which is a strong electrolyte in water may become an intermediate, or even a weak, electrolyte in a solvent of low dielectric constant. It was seen in § 17k that the force of electrostatic attraction between two oppositely charged particles is inversely proportional to the dielectric constant of the medium separating the charges. In a solvent of high dielectric constant, such as water, the attraction between ions of opposite charge is small; hence, the ions are relatively free to carry the electric current. In a medium of low dielectric constant, however, the ions attract one another so strongly, that they are much less free to move under the influence of an applied E.M.F. It is thus possible to account qualitatively for the change in behavior of a given electrolyte in solvents of different dielectric constants; a more quantitative treatment of this subject is described below.

46d. The Interionic Attraction Theory.—When the theory of electrolytic dissociation was first enunciated (§ 31b) the decrease of equivalent conductance with increasing concentration was attributed to the diminution in the extent to which the salt was dissociated into ions in solution. In other words, the falling off in the equivalent conductance was ascribed to a decrease in the degree (or fraction) of ionization as the concentration of the solution was increased. The conductance of a solution of a given solute depends on two factors, namely, the number of ions and their speeds. In supposing that the changes in equivalent conductance were due to the variation in the degree of ionization, the responsibility for the change was placed entirely upon the number of ions produced from 1 gram equiv. of electrolyte. The tacit assumption is involved, therefore, that the speeds of the ions do not vary appreciably with the concentration. Although this may be approximately true for weak electrolytes, it is certainly not the case for strong electrolytes. It will be recalled that in § 45d attention was drawn to the variation of transference numbers with concentration, and it was there pointed out that this result implies a variation of the ionic speeds. It follows, therefore, that the dependence of the speeds of the ions on the concentration of the solution must be, at least partly, responsible for the change in the equivalent conductance.

The view widely adopted at the present time is that *strong electrolytes*, such as the halides and nitrates of the alkali and alkaline earth metals, *are completely ionized at all reasonable concentrations.* This postulate is in harmony with the electronic theory of valence (§ 10b) and with the results obtained from the study of crystals of salts by X-rays (§ 19b). It is now generally accepted that even in the solid state a salt consists of positive and negative ions held together by forces of electrostatic attraction, and that the molecule, as such, does not exist in the crystal. It is reasonable to suppose, therefore, that when a salt is dissolved in water, the ions, which already exist in the solid, become free to move and conduct electricity. It follows then that substances having ionic lattices, i.e., the strong electrolytes, may be regarded as being completely ionized at all reasonable concentrations, as suggested above.

If this is the case, the variation of equivalent conductance with concentration cannot be ascribed to a change in the number of ions obtained from 1 gram equiv. of electrolyte, for this is constant; the degree of ionization, in other words, is equal to unity at all concentrations. The falling off in the equivalent conductance must then be due to a decrease in ionic velocity with increasing concentration. This is the basis of the **interionic attraction theory** of electrolytic conductance; the theory is applicable to all types of electrolytes, but its importance lies particularly in connection with strong electrolytes. The basis of the theory in its simplest terms is that in a dilute solution the ions are relatively far apart, and so they exert little influence upon one another. As the concentration is increased, however, and the ions come closer together, the attraction between ions of opposite charge results in a decrease of their speeds, and consequently in the equivalent conductance of the solution.

The quantitative treatment of the theory of interionic attraction is due mainly to the work of P. Debye and E. Hückel (1923), and of L. Onsager (1926). The fundamental idea underlying the deductions is that as a consequence of the electrical attraction between positive and negative ions, there are, on the average, more ions of unlike sign than of like sign in the neighborhood of any ion. Every ion may, therefore, be regarded as being surrounded by a centrally symmetric **ionic atmosphere** having a resultant charge whose sign is opposite to that of the ion itself. When an E.M.F. is applied, so that the ions are caused to move, the oppositely charged ionic atmospheres take some time to readjust themselves; the result is that the ion tends to move ahead, leaving its atmosphere behind. Since the ion and its atmosphere have opposite charges, there is an electrostatic attraction between them which slows down the motion of the ion. This effect on the speed of an ion is known as the **asymmetry (or relaxation) effect,** because it arises from a lack of symmetry in the atmosphere of a moving ion, resulting from the slowness of readjustment (or relaxation) of the ionic atmosphere.

Another factor which results in a retardation of the ionic motion is the tendency of the applied E.M.F. to move the oppositely charged ionic atmosphere, with its associated molecules of water of hydration, in a direction opposite to that in which the central ion is moving. An additional retarding influence is thus exerted on the moving ion, since the atmosphere tends to drag the ion with it; this is known as the **electrophoretic effect,** because it is somewhat analogous to that opposing the movement of a colloidal particle in an electric field (§ 57e).

By expressing the magnitudes of these effects in terms of properties of the ions and the solvent, and assuming ionization to be complete, the following equation was derived for a uni-univalent strong electrolyte, that is, an electrolyte like potassium chloride which yields two univalent ions in solution, viz.,

$$\Lambda = \Lambda_0 - \left[\frac{82.4}{(DT)^{\frac{1}{2}}\eta} + \frac{8.20 \times 10^5}{(DT)^{\frac{3}{2}}} \Lambda_0 \right] \sqrt{c}, \qquad (46.10)$$

where D is the dielectric constant of the solvent, η is its viscosity, and T is the absolute temperature; c is the concentration of the solution in moles per liter or gram equiv. per liter, since they are identical in this case. It is seen that equation (46.10), generally known as the **Onsager equation**, accounts for the falling off in the equivalent conductance Λ from the limiting value Λ_0 with increasing concentration of the electrolyte. The first term in the brackets is due to the electrophoretic effect, while the second represents the asymmetry effect; the sum of these two terms multiplied by the square root of the concentration gives the difference between Λ_0 and Λ at any concentration.

It should be noted that the dielectric constant D appears in the denominator of both terms; this means that in solvents of lower dielectric constant, such as methanol, ethanol, nitromethane, acetonitrile, etc., the equivalent conductance usually falls off with concentration more rapidly than in water. This conclusion is in general agreement with the experimental fact, referred to earlier, that a strong electrolyte approaches the behavior of a weak electrolyte in a solvent of low dielectric constant.

By writing A and B in place of the two quotients in equation (46.10), this becomes

$$\Lambda = \Lambda_0 - (A + B\Lambda_0)\sqrt{c}, \qquad (46.11)$$

where A and B are constants for a given solvent that depend only on the temperature. For water at $25°$ C, A is 60.20 and B is 0.229, so that for solutions of strong uni-univalent electrolytes in water the theoretical treatment leads to the result

$$\Lambda = \Lambda_0 - (60.2 + 0.229 \, \Lambda_0)\sqrt{c} \qquad (46.12)$$

at $25°$. This means that the plot of the equivalent conductance Λ against the square root of the concentration, i.e., $\sqrt{c}$, should give a straight line of slope $60.2 + 0.229 \, \Lambda_0$; such has been found to be true for a number of uni-univalent electrolytes, as the results in Fig. 98 indicate. The experimental data are represented by the small circles, while the dashed lines give the theoretical slopes as derived from equation (46.12); the agreement is seen to be excellent up to concentrations of about 2×10^{-3} gram equiv. per liter.

In more concentrated solutions deviations begin to occur, as may be seen from the figure; these are due to approximations and simplifications made in the derivation of the Onsager equation (46.10). The problem of the quantitative treatment of solutions of even moderate concentrations is too difficult to be possible at present. Nevertheless, the fact that the theoretical equa-

tion has been found satisfactory in dilute solutions, suggests that the fundamental postulates of complete ionization of strong electrolytes and of the
mutual interaction of the ions in solution, as stated above, provide a sound
basis for the interpretation of the variation of equivalent conductance with
concentration.

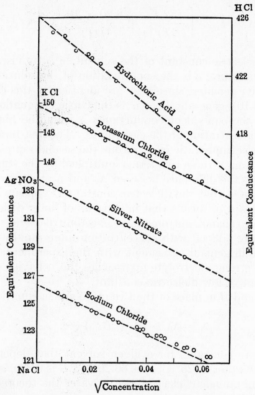

FIG. 98.   Test of the Onsager equation

46e. Incomplete Dissociation.—For certain electrolytes, the plot of
Λ against $\sqrt{c}$ is approximately linear, but the slope is appreciably greater
than would be expected from the Onsager equation. In these cases the conductance is less than required by theory, and it appears that not all the ions
are available for carrying the current. A fraction α, called the **degree of
dissociation** of the electrolyte, may be defined as *the fraction of the solute which
is dissociated into ions that are free to carry current* at a given concentration.
It can then be shown that the appropriate form of equation (46.11) is

$$\Lambda = \alpha[\Lambda_0 - (A + B\Lambda_0)\sqrt{\alpha c}]. \qquad (46.13)$$

This equation is particularly applicable to intermediate electrolytes, such as
those consisting of ions of high valence, and to solutions in solvents of low

dielectric constant. Since A, B and Λ_0 may be regarded as known, it should be possible to solve equation (46.13) in order to evaluate the degree of dissociation α of the electrolyte at any concentration c. In practice it is found convenient to do this by means of a series of approximations, because equation (46.13) involves $\alpha^{3/2}$, and so it is effectively of the third order.

For weak electrolytes, such as the weak organic acids and bases, the degree of dissociation is small, and the factor $\sqrt{\alpha c}$ in equation (46.13) is less than 0.01. Further, since the quantity $A + B\Lambda_0$ lies between 80 and 150 for most electrolytes, it follows that the correction term $(A + B\Lambda_0)\sqrt{\alpha c}$ is generally not more than 1.5 for a weak electrolyte. The equivalent conductance at infinite dilution Λ_0 is about 250 and 400 ohm^{-1} cm.^{2} for bases and acids, respectively, and so the value of the correction term is negligible in comparison; thus, equation (46.13) can be reduced to the simple, but somewhat approximate, form

$$\Lambda = \alpha\Lambda_0$$

for a weak electrolyte. The degree of dissociation is then given by

$$\alpha = \frac{\Lambda}{\Lambda_0} \cdot \tag{46.14}$$

It may be pointed out that this result is equivalent to the assumption, made in the early development of the ionic theory, that the falling off in equivalent conductance with concentration is due solely to incomplete dissociation of the solute into ions, and not to changes in the velocities of the latter. It can be seen from the foregoing arguments, however, that this is true only when the electrolyte is so weak, and hence the concentration αc of free ions is so small, that the correction term $(A + B\Lambda_0)\sqrt{\alpha c}$ in equation (46.13) is negligible. This term allows for the decrease of ionic velocity due to ionic interaction, and in weak electrolytes this is evidently so small that the speeds of the ions may be regarded as remaining almost constant.

It should be emphasized that equation (46.14) is applicable to weak electrolytes only; it cannot be used to calculate the degree of dissociation of strong, moderately strong, or intermediate electrolytes, for which the interionic attraction term is appreciable. For such solutions, the fraction Λ/Λ_0 is given the noncommittal name of the **conductance ratio.** It is only for weak electrolytes that the conductance ratio is *approximately* equal to the degree of dissociation; for accurate values of α, it is always necessary to employ the more complete equation (46.13).

Problem: The equivalent conductance Λ of an aqueous solution of 1.0283×10^{-3} g. equiv. acetic acid per liter is 48.15 ohms^{-1} cm.^{2} at 25°; Λ_0 is 390.7 ohms^{-1} cm.^{2} Calculate the degree of dissociation, from equation (46.13), and compare the result with the conductance ratio.

For weak and moderately weak electrolytes, the value of α in equation (46.13) may be derived as follows. As a first approximation, α in the correction term $\sqrt{\alpha c}$ is taken as the conductance ratio, i.e., Λ/Λ_0; in the present case this is $48.15/390.7 =$

0.1232. Since the constant A and B for water at 25° C are 60.2 and 0.229, equation (46.13) may be written as

$$\Lambda = \alpha[\Lambda_0 - (A + B\Lambda_0)\sqrt{\alpha c}]$$

$$48.15 = \alpha[390.7 - (60.2 + 0.229 \times 390.7)\sqrt{0.1232 \times 1.0283 \times 10^{-3}}],$$

since Λ is 48.15 for the concentration 1.0283×10^{-3} g. equiv. per liter. The value of α is thus found to be 0.1238. This is not greatly different from the conductance ratio, i.e., 0.1232, as is to be expected for a weak electrolyte.

46f. Significance of the Degree of Dissociation.—The quantity α, referred to above as the degree of dissociation, represents the fraction of the solute which yields completely free ions. The fact that α is less than unity for many electrolytes may be due to two causes; these are, however, indistinguishable as far as conductance is concerned. Although many salts undoubtedly exist in the ionic form even in the solid state, so that they may be regarded as completely, or almost completely, ionized at all reasonable concentrations, *the ions are not necessarily free to move independently.* As a result of electrostatic attraction, ions of opposite sign may form a certain proportion of what are termed **ion-pairs**; these are not definite molecules, but they behave as if they were nonionized molecules. Any particular ion-pair has a temporary existence only, for there is a continual interchange between the various ions in the solution; nevertheless, at any instant a number of oppositely charged ions will be paired off in this manner, and so are made unavailable for carrying the electric current. In cases of this kind α will be less than unity, and *the electrolyte will be incompletely dissociated, in spite of the fact that it is completely ionized.*

It is thus seen to be essential to distinguish between "dissociation" and "ionization," a distinction which was not evident in the original ionic theory. The term "ionization" applies to the total number of ions, irrespective of whether they are free or are held in ion-pairs; "dissociation," on the other hand, refers only to the ions that are free to carry current. The free ions are, of course, still subject to the effects of the ionic atmosphere which results in a retardation of their velocities with increasing concentration. These effects, it must be understood, are quite distinct from, and additional to, the formation of ion-pairs.

For strong electrolytes, such as alkali and alkaline earth halides and nitrates, in particular, the ionization is complete, and there are no covalent, nonionized molecules, even though dissociation may be incomplete in fairly concentrated solutions. A solution of sodium chloride, for example, probably contains no actual nonionized NaCl molecules, although there may be transient ion-pairs (Na^+Cl^-) held together by electrostatic forces. Weak electrolytes, and also many intermediate electrolytes, however, exist to some extent in the form of nonionized molecules. A solution of acetic acid, for instance, undoubtedly contains neutral covalent molecules of CH_3COOH, as well as acetate (CH_3COO^-) and hydrogen (H^+) ions; some of these may be held together as ion-pairs ($CH_3COO^-H^+$). The degree of dissociation α

represents the fraction of the acetic acid present as free ions capable of carrying the current; the remaining fraction $1 - \alpha$ includes both nonionized molecules and ion-pairs. Neither of these is able to transport electricity, and so the ordinary conductance measurements cannot differentiate between them.

Both theoretical and experimental observations suggest that *the extent of formation of ion-pairs for a given ionic concentration is greater the smaller the size of the ions, the higher their valence, and the lower the dielectric constant of the solvent*. The size of the ion referred to is its effective size in solution, which includes molecules of solvent; this may differ considerably from the size of the bare ion, as seen in § 45d. It follows, therefore, that hydration in aqueous solution, or solvation in general, is an important factor in ion-pair formation.

In solvents of low dielectric constant, where the force of attraction between ions of opposite sign is large, there is an increased tendency for the occurrence of ion-pairs. There are reasons for believing that even **ion-triplets** or **triple ions,** involving the association of three ions, are formed in sufficiently concentrated solutions. These triple ions, e.g. $(M^+A^-M^+)$, or $(A^-M^+A^-)$, formed from the simple ions M^+ and A^- differ from the ion-pairs (M^+A^-) in having a net charge; they are consequently able to conduct the electric current. The existence of such triple ions accounts for the observation that the equivalent conductances of some electrolytes in solvents of low dielectric constant pass through a minimum, and then increase with increasing concentration. The initial decrease is due partly to the increased formation of nonconducting ion-pairs. As the concentration is increased, the latter are converted into conducting triple ions; consequently the equivalent conductance passes through a minimum and then increases.

46g. The Independent Conductance of Ions.—In the so-called state of infinite dilution, all forces of interaction between the ions will have ceased to exist; both ionization and dissociation are then complete, and all the ions that can possibly be derived from the given electrolyte are free to carry current. It is evident that if any relationships exist between the equivalent conductances of different electrolytes, these are the conditions under which they can best be studied. If the Λ_0 values for the sodium and potassium salts of the same anion are examined, it will be found that there is a constant difference, irrespective of the nature of the anion; the following results, for example, were obtained at $18°$ C:

KCl	$\Lambda_0 = 130.0$ ohms^{-1} cm.^{2}		KNO$_3$	$\Lambda_0 = 126.3$ ohms^{-1} cm.^{2}
NaCl	108.9		NaNO$_3$	105.2
Difference	21.1		Difference	21.1

The same difference of 21.1 ohms^{-1} cm.^{2} is found for the equivalent conductances at infinite dilution of any pair of sodium and potassium salts of the same anion. Analogous results have been obtained with other pairs of salts, having either a cation or an anion in common. The conclusion to be drawn from these observations, as pointed out by F. W. Kohlrausch (1875), is that *at infinite dilution, each ion makes a definite contribution toward the equivalent conductance of an electrolyte*, irrespective of the nature of the other ion with which it is associated in the solution. The value of *the equivalent conductance of any electrolyte at infinite dilution is thus made up of the sum of two independent factors, one characteristic of each ionic species;* hence,

$$\Lambda_0 = \lambda_+ + \lambda_- \qquad (46.15)$$

where λ_+ and λ_- (Greek: *lambda*) are known as the **ion conductances** of cation and anion, respectively, at infinite dilution. The ion conductance is a definite constant for each ion in a given solvent, the value depending only on the temperature.

The ion conductances can be determined by a method of trial and error, from the known equivalent conductances at infinite dilution, obtained from experimental data as described in § 46c. A more satisfactory procedure, however, is to make use of the measured transference numbers. The ability of an electrolyte to transport current, and hence its conductance, is determined by the product of the total charge carried by the ions and their speeds. For equivalent solutions at infinite dilution, where ionization is complete, the total charge of the ions is constant, and hence the limiting equivalent conductance of an electrolyte must depend only on the ionic velocities. If the total conductance is the sum of the individual ion conductances, as expressed by equation (46.15), it follows that the ion conductance must be directly proportional to the ionic speed; thus,

$$\lambda_+ = ku_+ \quad \text{and} \quad \lambda_- = ku_- \qquad (46.16)$$

$$\Lambda_0 = \lambda_+ + \lambda_- = k(u_+ + u_-), \qquad (46.17)$$

where k is a universal constant for all electrolytes. It must be understood, of course, that the λ and u values in these equations refer to infinite dilution. From equations (46.16) and (46.17) it follows immediately that

$$\frac{\lambda_+}{\Lambda_0} = \frac{u_+}{u_+ + u_-} \quad \text{and} \quad \frac{\lambda_-}{\Lambda_0} = \frac{u_-}{u_+ + u_-}. \qquad (46.18)$$

The fractions involving the ionic velocities are seen to be equal to the respective transference numbers, by the equations (45.1); the equations (46.18) may consequently be written in the general form

$$\frac{\lambda_0}{\Lambda_0} = t_0 \quad \text{or} \quad \lambda_0 = t_0 \Lambda_0, \qquad (46.19)$$

where the zero subscripts have been inserted to emphasize the fact that infinite dilution is to be understood. It can thus be seen that the ion conductance of any ion can be obtained from a knowledge of Λ_0 for an electrolyte containing that ion, and its transference number in the same electrolyte extrapolated to infinite dilution.

Problem: The value of Λ_0 for NaCl is found by extrapolation of the data in Table LII to be 126.45 ohms^{-1} cm.^{2}; similarly, by extrapolation of the results in Table LI, the transference number of the cation (Na$^+$) in NaCl is 0.3965 at infinite dilution. Calculate the ion conductance of the Cl$^-$ ion at 25° C.

The transference number of the Cl^- ion in NaCl at infinite dilution is evidently $1 - 0.3965 = 0.6035$; hence, by equation (46.19) it follows that

$$\lambda_{Cl^-} = 0.6035 \times 126.45 = 76.31 \text{ ohms}^{-1} \text{ cm.}^2$$

By utilizing the best conductance and transference number data at 25° the ion conductances quoted in Table LIII have been obtained. It should

TABLE LIII.   ION CONDUCTANCES AT INFINITE DILUTION AT 25° C

Cation	λ_+	Anion	λ_-
H^+	349.82 ohms^{-1} cm.^{2}	OH^-	198.5 ohms^{-1} cm.^{2}
K^+	73.52	Br^-	78.4
NH_4^+	73.4	I^-	76.8
Ag^+	61.92	Cl^-	76.34
Na^+	50.11	NO_3^-	71.44
Li^+	38.69	ClO_4^-	68.0
$\frac{1}{2}Ba^{++}$	63.64	HCO_3^-	44.5
$\frac{1}{2}Mg^{++}$	53.06	$\frac{1}{2}SO_4^{--}$	79.8

be noted that since these are actually *equivalent* ion conductances, symbols such as $\frac{1}{2}Ba^{++}$ and $\frac{1}{2}SO_4^{--}$ are employed.

Attention may be called to the fact that although the ion conductance is a definite property of the ion, and is independent of the nature of the solute of which it is a part, the transference number of a given ion varies with the electrolyte. The reason for this apparent anomaly is that the transference number is the fraction of the current carried by the given ion, and this obviously depends on the nature of the other ion present in the solution. Thus, the value of t_0 for a given ion, e.g., the chloride ion, in equation (46.19) varies from one chloride to another; however, the limiting conductances Λ_0 of these chlorides vary correspondingly in an inverse manner, so that the product $t_0\Lambda_0$, which gives λ_0 for the chloride ion, remains constant.

46h. Application of Ion Conductances.—An important use of ion conductances is to determine the limiting conductances at infinite dilution of certain electrolytes which cannot be, or have not been, evaluated from direct experimental data. For example, with a weak electrolyte the extrapolation to infinite dilution is very uncertain (see Fig. 97), and with sparingly soluble salts the range of measurements is too small for extrapolation to be possible. The value of Λ_0 in these cases can, however, be obtained by adding the ion conductances. The equivalent conductance of acetic acid at infinite dilution, for instance, is the sum of the conductances of the hydrogen and acetate ions; the former is derived from a study of strong acids and the latter from measurements on acetates. It is therefore possible to write

$$\Lambda_{0(CH_3COOH)} = \lambda_{H^+} + \lambda_{CH_3COO^-}$$

$$= 349.8 + 40.9 = 390.7 \text{ ohms}^{-1} \text{ cm.}^2 \text{ at } 25° \text{ C.}$$

The same result can be derived in another manner which is often convenient, since it avoids the necessity of separating the conductance of an electrolyte into the contributions of its constituent ions. The limiting equivalent conductance of any electrolyte, that is, $\Lambda_{0(MA)}$, is equal to $\lambda_{M^+} + \lambda_{A^-}$; consequently,

$$\Lambda_{0(MCl)} + \Lambda_{0(NaA)} - \Lambda_{0(NaCl)} = (\lambda_{M^+} + \lambda_{Cl^-}) + (\lambda_{Na^+} + \lambda_{A^-}) - (\lambda_{Na^+} + \lambda_{Cl^-})$$

$$= \lambda_{M^+} + \lambda_{A^-} = \Lambda_{0(MA)},$$

so that

$$\Lambda_{0(MA)} = \Lambda_{0(MCl)} + \Lambda_{0(NaA)} - \Lambda_{0(NaCl)}, \qquad (46.20)$$

where $\Lambda_{0(MCl)}$, $\Lambda_{0(NaA)}$ and $\Lambda_{0 (NaCl)}$ are the equivalent conductances at infinite dilution of the chloride of the metal M, i.e., MCl, of the sodium salt of the anion A^-, i.e., NaA, and of sodium chloride, respectively. Any convenient anion may be used instead of the chloride ion, and similarly the sodium ion may be replaced by another metallic cation or by the hydrogen ion.

Problem: The equivalent conductances at infinite dilution of HCl, CH_3COONa and NaCl are 426.16, 91.0 and 126.45 ohms^{-1} cm.^{2}, respectively, at 25° C. Calculate the value of Λ_0 for acetic acid.

$$\Lambda_{0(HCl)} = \lambda_{H^+} + \lambda_{Cl^-} = 426.16$$

$$\Lambda_{0(CH_3COONa)} = \lambda_{Na^+} + \lambda_{CH_3COO^-} = 91.0$$

$$\Lambda_{0(NaCl)} = \lambda_{Na^+} + \lambda_{Cl^-} = 126.45$$

Adding the first two lines and subtracting the last line, it follows that

$$\lambda_{H^+} + \lambda_{CH_3COO^-} = \Lambda_{0(CH_3COOH)} = 426.16 + 91.0 - 126.45$$

$$= 390.7 \text{ ohms}^{-1} \text{ cm.}^2 \text{ at } 25° \text{ C.}$$

In order to determine the limiting equivalent conductance of a sparingly soluble salt, the procedure is to add the conductances of the constituent ions; thus, at 25° C for silver chloride,

$$\Lambda_{0(AgCl)} = \lambda_{Ag^+} + \lambda_{Cl^-} = 61.92 + 76.34 = 138.3 \text{ ohms}^{-1} \text{ cm.}^2,$$

while for barium sulfate,

$$\Lambda_{0(\frac{1}{2}BaSO_4)} = \lambda_{\frac{1}{2}Ba^{++}} + \lambda_{\frac{1}{2}SO_4^{--}} = 63.64 + 79.8 = 143.4 \text{ ohms}^{-1} \text{ cm.}^2$$

46i. Ionic Mobilities.—It was shown above that the ion conductance is proportional to the speed of the ion, as indicated by equation (46.16); the actual velocity of an ion is proportional to the **potential gradient,** that is, to the applied E.M.F. divided by the distance between the electrodes. It can be deduced theoretically that for a potential gradient of 1 volt per cm. the constant k in equation (46.16) is equal to the faraday, F; thus,

$$u_0 = \frac{\lambda_0}{F}, \qquad (46.21)$$

where F is 96,500 coulombs, u_0 is the limiting speed of the ion in cm. per sec., for a potential gradient of 1 volt per cm., and λ_0 is the ion conductance in ohms^{-1} cm.^{2}. The velocity of an ion under this potential gradient is called the **ionic mobility**, and some of the values calculated from equation (46.21), using the ion conductances in Table LIII, are given in Table LIV. It will

TABLE LIV. CALCULATED IONIC MOBILITIES AT 25° C

Cations	Mobility cm. per sec.	Anions	Mobility cm. per sec.
Hydrogen	36.2 $\times 10^{-4}$	Hydroxyl	20.5 $\times 10^{-4}$
Potassium	7.61	Sulfate	8.27
Barium	6.60	Chloride	7.91
Sodium	5.19	Nitrate	7.40

be observed that apart from hydrogen and hydroxyl ions, most ions have mobilities of about 6×10^{-4} cm. per sec. at 25° C, under unit potential gradient. Increasing the temperature increases the speeds of nearly all ions by about 2 per cent per degree. The exceptionally high mobilities, and ionic conductances, of the hydrogen and hydroxyl ions have been ascribed to an unusual type of conductance mechanism which is operative for these ions in water.

Problem: A potential of 5.60 volts is applied to two electrodes placed 9.80 cm. apart; how far would an NH_4^+ ion be expected to move in 1 hr. in a dilute solution of an ammonium salt at 25° C?

The ion conductance for NH_4^+ is 73.4 ohms^{-1} cm.^{2} at 25° from Table LIII; hence, the mobility is $73.4/96,500 = 7.61 \times 10^{-4}$ cm. per sec. The potential gradient in the problem is $5.60/9.80 = 0.571$ volt per cm., and so the actual velocity of the NH_4^+ ion is $7.61 \times 10^{-4} \times 0.571 = 4.34 \times 10^{-4}$ cm. per sec. In 1 hr., i.e., 3600 sec., the distance moved by the ion in dilute solution, i.e., approximately infinite dilution, would be $4.34 \times 10^{-4} \times 3600 = 1.56$ cm.

Ionic mobilities have been determined by direct experiment, utilizing a principle similar to that employed in the moving boundary method for transference numbers (§ 45c). The concentrations of the solutions must be adjusted so that the potential gradient is uniform; the rate of movement of the boundary then gives the speed of the ion under the influence of this potential gradient. From the result the ionic mobility, i.e., the speed for a gradient of 1 volt per cm., can be calculated. The values obtained in this manner are in satisfactory agreement with those recorded in Table LIV, derived from the ion conductances. The latter, of course, refer to infinite dilution, and hence the experimental results, which are obtained in solutions of finite concentration, will be somewhat lower.

46j. Determination of Solubilities by Conductance Measurements.—If a sparingly soluble electrolyte ionizes in a simple manner, it is possible to calculate its solubility from conductance measurements. If s is the solubility, in gram equiv. per liter, of a given salt, and κ is the specific conductance of the saturated solution, then the equivalent conductance, according to equation (46.8), is given by

$$\Lambda = 1000 \, \frac{\kappa}{s} \cdot$$

If the salt is sparingly soluble the saturated solution will be so dilute that Λ will not differ appreciably from the limiting value at infinite dilution; it is thus possible to write

$$\Lambda_0 = 1000 \, \frac{\kappa}{s},$$

$$s = 1000 \, \frac{\kappa}{\Lambda_0} \cdot \qquad (46.22)$$

Since the specific conductance κ can be determined by experiment, and Λ_0 can be derived from the ion conductances, as shown in § 46h, it is possible to calculate the solubility of the salt. This method for determining solubilities can be used only if the solute undergoes simple dissociation into ions of known conductance. Further, the saturated solution must be dilute and dissociation must be virtually complete, so that the actual equivalent conductance is not appreciably different from the limiting value.

Problem: For a saturated solution of AgCl at 25° C, κ was found to be 3.41×10^{-6} ohm^{-1} cm.$^{-1}$; the value of κ for the water used to make up the solution was 1.60×10^{-6} ohm^{-1} cm.$^{-1}$. Determine the solubility of AgCl in water, in moles per liter, at 25° C.

The actual specific conductance of the AgCl is the difference between the values for the saturated solution and for the water; hence, κ for the AgCl is $(3.41 - 1.60) \times 10^{-6}$, i.e., 1.81×10^{-6} ohm^{-1} cm.$^{-1}$. The Λ_0 for AgCl at 25° is 138.3 ohms^{-1} cm.^{2}, as found above from the ion conductances of Ag$^+$ and Cl$^-$; hence, by equation (46.22),

$$s = \frac{1000 \times 1.81 \times 10^{-6}}{138.3} = 1.31 \times 10^{-5} \text{ g. equiv. per liter.}$$

In this case g. equiv. and moles are identical; the solubility of AgCl is therefore 1.31×10^{-5} mole per liter at 25°.

46k. Conductance Titrations.—If a solution of a strong acid is gradually neutralized by a strong base, e.g., sodium hydroxide, the hydrogen ions of the former are replaced by the metal ions, e.g., Na$^+$ ions, having a much lower conductance (Table LIII). The conductance of the solution will therefore decrease steadily as the base is added. When neutralization is complete the further addition of alkali cannot remove any more hydrogen ions, and so the conductance will no longer decrease. In fact there will be an increase due to the excess of the strong base now present in the solution. It follows, therefore, that the variation of the conductance with the addition of alkali will be of the form shown in Fig. 99, I, the minimum corresponding to the equivalence point, i.e., the theoretical end point, of the neutralization. It is evident from these curves that conductance measurements can be used to determine the equivalence point in a strong acid-base titration. The conductance is measured at six or eight points, after the addition of known amounts of alkali; two lines are then drawn through these points in a plot of the conductance against the quantity of alkali added, as in Fig. 99. The intersection of the lines gives the required end point. If the alkali solution is much more concentrated than, e.g., about ten times, that of the acid there is little volume change, and these lines are virtually straight. It is thus possible to determine the end point by making four observations, two each side of the equivalence point, and drawing two straight lines through the points.

When a moderately weak acid, e.g., acetic acid, is neutralized by a strong base the initial conductance is low, and after a small decrease which is sometimes observed, the conductance increases; this is because the salt formed, e.g., sodium acetate, is a strong electrolyte and hence is more highly ionized than the weak acid. At the equivalence point there is a further increase of conductance, since the strong base is an even better conductor than the salt because of the high conductance of the hydroxyl ion. The variation of conductance with the addition of alkali is similar to that in Fig. 99, II. If the acid is very weak, e.g., boric acid or phenol, the initial decrease of conductance upon neutralization is not observed, the titra-

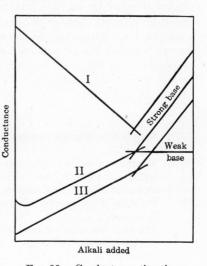

Fig. 99. Conductance titrations

tion curves being of the type shown in Fig. 99, III. In each case the end point is given by the intersection of two (almost) straight lines, provided the volume change is kept small, as stated above. When titrating a weak or very weak acid the sharpness of the intersection at the end point may be improved by using a weak base for neutralization. Such a base has a very small conductance, and so the curve is almost horizontal after the equivalence point has been attained (Fig. 99).

The conductance method can be used to determine the end point in the titration of a salt of a weak acid, e.g., sodium acetate, by a strong acid, e.g., hydrochloric acid. As the reaction proceeds the strong electrolyte sodium acetate is replaced by sodium chloride which has approximately the same conductance; the conductance of the solution thus remains almost constant, since the contribution of the acetic acid is negligibly small. When the equivalence point is reached the conductance commences to increase rapidly because of the free strong (hydrochloric) acid that is now present. Precipitation titrations, e.g., the addition of sodium chloride to silver nitrate, or the reverse, may also be followed by conductance measurements. Since the solubility of silver chloride is low, its contribution to the conductance is extremely small; the conductance of the solution thus remains almost constant until the equivalence point is reached, and then it commences to increase. In each instance the end point can be ascertained from the intersection of two straight lines.

The conductometric titration procedure has many advantages. It can be used for the analysis of dilute solutions, provided no extraneous electrolytes are present, and also for very weak acids, when other methods of titration fail. Mixtures of strong and weak acids, and colored solutions can be readily titrated by the conductance method. Since the end point is determined graphically there is no need to take special precautions as the equivalence point is approached, as in ordinary titrations. Finally, it is not necessary to measure the actual conductance of the solution; any quantity that is proportional to the conductance, e.g., the reading on a conductance bridge or resistance box, is adequate. This may be plotted against the volume of titrant, as in Fig. 99.

READING REFERENCES

1. **Simple transference number apparatus.** Collins, *Journal of Chemical Education*, **11**, 52 (1934).
2. **Mechanism of the conduction process.** Longsworth, *ibid.*, **11**, 420 (1934).
3. **Solutions of electrolytes.** Davidson, *ibid.*, **12**, 24 (1935).
4. **Demonstration of migration of ions.** Fedorow, *ibid.*, **12**, 93 (1935).
5. **Problem of electrolytic solutions.** Kraus, *ibid.*, **12**, 567 (1935).
6. **Nonaqueous solutions.** Davidson, *ibid.*, **14**, 218 (1937).
7. **Transference number determinations.** Hoyt, *ibid.*, **14**, 472 (1937).
8. **Simple conductance bridge.** Evans, *ibid.*, **15**, 389 (1938).
9. **Discovery of galvanoplasty and electrotyping.** Heinrich, *ibid.*, **15**, 565 (1938).
10. **Conductance bridge.** Hovorka and Mendenhall, *ibid.*, **16**, 239 (1939).
11. **Conductance bridge assembly.** Luder and Vernon, *ibid.*, **17**, 229 (1940).
12. **Vacuum tube oscillator for conductance.** Hull, *ibid.*, **17**, 329 (1940).
13. **Vacuum tube oscillator.** Hudson and Hobbs, *ibid.*, **19**, 147 (1942).
14. **Significance of conductance at infinite dilution.** Van Rysselberghe, *ibid.*, **20**, 131 (1943).

REVIEW QUESTIONS

1. What is meant by an electrolyte? Give examples.

2. Explain, with the aid of a figure, the terms anode, cathode, anion and cation. How is the direction of electron flow related to that of current flow?

3. State Faraday's laws of electrolysis in words. How can the laws be verified experimentally?

4. Derive an equation which summarizes Faraday's laws. What is the significance of the faraday?

5. Define ampere and coulomb. What is the value of the faraday in coulombs?

6. Explain the principle and use of a coulometer.

7. Explain, with the aid of a figure, why the fact that oppositely charged ions may have different speeds is not contrary to Faraday's laws.

8. What is meant by the transference number? What is the basis of its determination by the Hittorf method? Describe the experimental application of this method.

9. Describe the moving boundary method for determining transference numbers.

10. How is it possible to account for the fact that the speeds of the ions Li^+, Na^+, K^+ increase in this order?

11. Explain the meaning of specific resistance, specific conductance and equivalent conductance. Derive equations for them in terms of measurable quantities.

12. Describe and explain the principles used in the measurement of the resistance of electrolytes.

13. Outline the general nature of the variation of equivalent conductance with concentration for strong, weak and intermediate electrolytes. What is the meaning of equivalent conductance at infinite dilution?

14. Describe the basis of the interionic attraction theory of electrolytes. Explain the various effects which influence the velocity of an ion in solution under the influence of an applied electric field.

15. State the Onsager equation in its general form for a uni-univalent electrolyte, and explain the significance of the various terms. What modification must be made for an incompletely dissociated electrolyte?

16. Explain how the degree of dissociation of a moderately strong electrolyte may be determined. When does the degree of dissociation approximate to the conductance ratio?

17. Explain the distinction which must be made between ionization and dissociation. What are ion-pairs and ion-triplets? How does their presence affect the properties of electrolytes?

18. State and explain the significance of the law of independent migration of ions. How are the ion conductances related to the transference numbers?

19. Describe the use of ion conductances to determine the equivalent conductance of (a) a weak electrolyte, (b) a sparingly soluble salt.

20. What is meant by the ionic mobility? How may the mobility of an ion be determined (a) from the ion conductance, (b) by direct measurement?

21. Describe the use of conductance measurement for the determination of the solubility of a sparingly soluble salt.

22. How may conductance methods be used to determine the end point in (a) neutralization, (b) precipitation, titrations? What advantages does the conductometric procedure have over conventional titration methods?

PROBLEMS

I

1. A constant current, which gave a reading of 0.500 amp. on a meter, was passed through a solution of copper sulfate for exactly 1 hour; the deposit on the cathode weighed 0.5960 g. What is the error of the meter?

2. A solution containing 0.7422 g. of potassium chloride per 100 g. was electrolyzed using a silver anode, so that the discharged chloride ions were removed as solid silver chloride. After the passage of current, which resulted in the deposition of 0.6136 g. of silver in a coulometer, the anode solution, weighing 117.51 g., contained 0.6659 g. of potassium chloride. Calculate the transference numbers of the K^+ and Cl^- ions.

3. A solution containing 10.06 g. of $CuSO_4$ in 100 g. was electrolyzed between copper electrodes. After electrolysis, which resulted in the deposition of 0.5008 g. of silver in a coulometer, 54.565 g. of the anode solution was found to contain 5.726 g. of $CuSO_4$. Calculate the transference numbers of the Cu^{++} and SO_4^{--} ions.

4. In a moving boundary experiment with 0.02 N sodium chloride, using cadmium chloride as indicator, a current of 0.001600 amp. was passed through a tube of uniform

cross section of 0.1115 sq. cm. The time taken for the boundary to traverse a distance of 7.0 cm. was 2414 sec. Calculate the transference number of the Na^+ ion.

5. A conductance cell has two parallel electrodes of 1.25 sq. cm. area and 10.50 cm. apart. When filled with a solution of an electrolyte the resistance was found to be 1996 ohms. Calculate the constant of the cell and the specific conductance of the solution.

6. A conductance cell was standardized by means of 0.02 N potassium chloride, having a specific conductance of 2.767×10^{-3} ohm^{-1} cm.$^{-1}$. When filled with this solution the cell resistance was found to be 4364 ohms. Calculate the cell constant. What is the specific resistance of a solution which has a resistance of 3050 ohms in this cell?

7. From the specific conductance of exactly 0.02 N potassium chloride given in the preceding problem, calculate the equivalent conductance of this solution.

8. The equivalent conductance of the sodium salt of crotonic acid at infinite dilution is 83.30 ohms^{-1} cm.^{2} at 25° C. What is the value of Λ_0 for crotonic acid?

9. The equivalent conductance of crotonic acid at a concentration of 1.705×10^{-3} g. equiv. per liter is 39.47 ohms^{-1} cm.^{2} at 25° C. Calculate the degree of dissociation, using the Onsager equation, and compare it with the conductance ratio. (The value of Λ_0 for crotonic acid is given by the preceding problem.)

10. The value of Λ_0 for ammonium chloride is 149.7 ohms^{-1} cm.^{2} at 25° C; the transference number of the cation, extrapolated to infinite dilution, is 0.4907. Calculate the ionic conductance and the mobility of the NH_4^+ and Cl^- ions.

11. The value of Λ_0 for sodium chloride is 126.25 ohms^{-1} cm.^{2} at 25° C. Calculate the equivalent conductance at exactly 0.01 N, using the Onsager equation. (Compare the result with that given by experiment in Table LII.)

12. The solubility of barium sulfate is 2.42 mg. per liter at 25° C. Calculate the specific conductance of the saturated solution, exclusive of that of the water, assuming complete dissociation.

II

1. Calculate the weight of iodine that would be liberated from potassium iodide solution by the same quantity of electricity which resulted in the liberation of 34.0 ml. of oxygen from a solution of sulfuric acid. How many coulombs of current were passed?

2. A solution containing 0.4312 g. of lithium chloride per 100 g. water was electrolyzed, using a silver anode so that the discharged chloride ions were removed as solid silver chloride. After the passage of current, which resulted in the deposition of 0.7394 g. of silver in a coulometer, 128.61 g. of anode solution contained 0.4606 g. of lithium chloride. Calculate the transference numbers of the Li^+ and Cl^- ions.

3. A solution of cadmium sulfate contained 11.560 g. of $CdSO_4$ in 100 g. After electrolysis, using a cadmium anode, the anode solution weighing 171.66 g. contained 20.722 g. of $CdSO_4$; at the same time 1.869 g. of silver were deposited in a coulometer. Determine the transference numbers of the Cd^{++} and SO_4^{--} ions.

4. In the moving boundary experiment described in problem I, 4, the boundary moved 10.0 cm. in 3453 sec. Calculate the transference number of the Na^+ ion.

5. When a solution of specific conductance 1.342×10^{-2} ohm^{-1} cm.$^{-1}$ was placed in a cell with parallel electrodes the resistance was found to be 170.5 ohms. The area of the electrodes was 1.86 sq. cm.; determine the distance apart of the electrodes and the cell constant.

6. What would be the specific conductance of a solution which had a resistance of 7546 ohms when placed in the cell referred to in the preceding problem?

7. If the concentration of the solution referred to in problem 6 is precisely 0.005 N, what is its equivalent conductance?

8. The equivalent conductance of the potassium salt of benzoic acid at infinite dilution is 105.88 ohms^{-1} cm.^{2} at 25° C. What is the value of Λ_0 for benzoic acid?

9. The equivalent conductance of benzoic acid at a concentration of 1.495 $\times$ 10^{-3} g. equiv. per liter is 75.68 ohms^{-1} cm.^{2} at 25° C. Calculate the degree of dissociation, using the Onsager equation, and compare it with the conductance ratio. (The value of Λ_0 for benzoic acid is given by the preceding problem.)

10. The value of Λ_0 for sodium chloride is 126.45 ohms^{-1} cm.^{2} at 25°, and the limiting conductance of the Cl$^-$ ion is 76.34 ohms^{-1} cm.^{2}. Calculate the limiting transference numbers and mobilities of the Na$^+$ and Cl$^-$ ions.

11. The value of Λ_0 for ammonium chloride is 149.7 ohms^{-1} cm.^{2} at 25° C. Calculate the equivalent conductance at exactly 0.01 N, using the Onsager equation. (The experimental value is 141.3 ohms^{-1} cm.^{2}.)

12. If the specific conductance of a saturated aqueous solution of silver bromide, after subtracting that of the water, were 1.174 $\times$ 10^{-7} ohm^{-1} cm.$^{-1}$ at 25° C, what would be the solubility of silver bromide in g. per liter?

CHAPTER XIV

ELECTROMOTIVE FORCE

GALVANIC CELLS

· **47a. E.M.F. and Its Measurement.**—A **galvanic** or **voltaic cell** consists essentially of two electrodes combined in such a manner that when they are connected by a conducting material, such as a metallic wire, an electric current will flow. Each electrode, in general, involves an electronic (metallic) and an electrolytic conductor in contact; at the surface of separation between the metal and the solution there exists a difference of electrical potential,

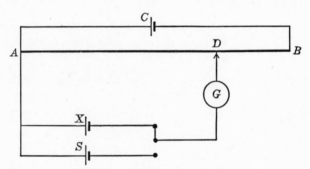

FIG. 100.   Measurement of E.M.F.

called the **electrode potential.** The E.M.F. of the cell is then equal to the algebraic sum of the two electrode potentials, appropriate allowance being made, as described later, for the sign of each potential difference.

For reliable measurement of the E.M.F. of a galvanic cell it is necessary to use some form of potentiometer, the essential principle of which can be understood from Fig. 100. A "working cell" C of constant E.M.F., generally a storage cell, is connected across the conductor AB of fairly high resistance. The cell X, which is being studied, is connected to A, and through a galvanometer G to a contact D which can be moved along AB. The direction of the cell X and the position of D are adjusted until no current flows through the galvanometer; the fall of potential between A and D due to the working cell C is then exactly compensated by the E.M.F. of the experimental cell X, that is, E_X. By means of a suitable switch the cell X is now replaced by a standard cell S, of accurately known E.M.F., equal to E_S, and the contact is adjusted until a point of balance is reached at D' (not shown in the figure).

434

The fall of potential between A and D' is consequently equal to E_S. The fall of potential between A and any point on AB is proportional to the resistance of that part of the conductor; it follows, therefore, that

$$\frac{E_X}{E_S} = \frac{\text{Fall of potential between } A \text{ and } D}{\text{Fall of potential between } A \text{ and } D'}$$

$$= \frac{\text{Resistance of } AD}{\text{Resistance of } AD'}.$$

In its simplest form, AB may be a uniform wire; then the resistances AD and AD' are proportional to the lengths AD and AD'. Alternatively a set of resistance coils may be used, from which the values may be derived directly. In any event, the ratio of the resistances AD to AD' can be determined, and since E_S, the E.M.F. of the standard cell is known, the E.M.F. of the experimental cell, i.e., E_X, can be calculated.

The majority of E.M.F. measurements at the present time are made by means of special potentiometers, operating on the foregoing principle, which can be purchased from instrument makers. In these, the conductor AB consists of a number of resistance

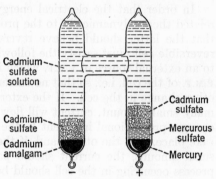

FIG. 101. The Weston standard cell

coils with a movable contact, together with a slide wire for fine adjustment. A standard cell is used for calibration purposes, and the E.M.F. of the cell being studied can then be read off with an accuracy of 0.1 millivolt, i.e., 10^{-4} volt, or better.

The standard cell that is widely employed for E.M.F. measurements is some form of the **Weston cell**; it is highly reproducible, its E.M.F. remains constant over long periods of time, and it has a small temperature coefficient. In order to retain constancy of E.M.F. while in use, only very minute currents should be drawn from the cell, as is actually done if the potentiometer is operated properly. The "negative" electrode of the Weston cell consists of a 12.5 per cent cadmium amalgam in a saturated solution of cadmium sulfate, $3CdSO_4 \cdot 8H_2O$, and the "positive" electrode is mercury, covered with solid mercurous sulfate, in the same solution; thus,

12.5% Cd in Hg | 3 $CdSO_4 \cdot 8H_2O(s)$ saturated solution $Hg_2SO_4(s)$ | Hg.

The cell is usually set up in an H-shaped vessel, as shown in Fig. 101, connection to the cadmium amalgam and mercury electrodes being made by platinum wires sealed through the glass. The E.M.F. of the Weston cell is 1.018300 international volt at 20.0° C, and it decreases by the small amount of 4×10^{-5} volt for every degree rise of temperature.*

For ordinary laboratory work, an "unsaturated" Weston cell is often employed; it contains a solution of cadmium sulfate saturated at 4.0° C, and consequently unsaturated at room temperatures. The E.M.F. of this cell is 1.0186 volt, and the variation with temperature is so small as to be negligible.

47b. Reversible Cells.—During the operation of a galvanic cell a chemical reaction takes place at each electrode, and it is the energy of these reactions that provides the electrical energy of the cell. If there is an over-all chemical reaction, the cell is referred to as a **chemical cell.** In some cells, however, there is no resultant chemical reaction, but there is a change of energy due to the transfer of solute from one concentration to another; such cells are called **concentration cells.**

In order that the electrical energy produced by a galvanic cell may be related thermodynamically to the process occurring in the cell, it is essential that the latter should behave reversibly in the thermodynamic sense. A **reversible cell** must satisfy the following conditions. If the cell is connected to an external source of E.M.F. which is adjusted so as exactly to balance the E.M.F. of the cell, i.e., so that no current flows, there should be no chemical or other change in the cell. If the external E.M.F. is decreased by an infinitesimally small amount, current will flow from the cell, and a chemical or other change, proportional in extent to the quantity of electricity passing, should take place. On the other hand, if the external E.M.F. is increased by a very small amount, the current should pass in the opposite direction, and the process occurring in the cell should be exactly reversed.

It may be noted that galvanic cells can only be expected to behave reversibly when the currents passing are infinitesimally small, so that the system is always virtually in equilibrium (§ 23e). If large currents flow, concentration gradients arise within the cell because diffusion is relatively slow; in these circumstances the cell cannot be regarded as existing in a state of equilibrium. It is important to recall, in this connection, that in the potentiometric method of measuring E.M.F.'s, described above, an infinitesimal or zero current is drawn from the cell at the point of balance. The E.M.F. obtained in this way is as close to the reversible value as is experimentally possible. If an attempt had been made to determine the E.M.F. with an ordinary voltmeter, which takes an appreciable current, the result would have been in error.

A familiar instance of a reversible cell is the **Daniell cell,** consisting of a zinc electrode immersed in an aqueous solution of zinc sulfate, and a copper electrode in copper sulfate solution, viz.,

$$\text{Zn} \mid \text{ZnSO}_4 \text{ soln.} \mid \text{CuSO}_4 \text{ soln.} \mid \text{Cu},$$

the two solutions being usually separated by a porous partition. Provided there is no spontaneous diffusion through this partition, and the electrodes

---

* In order to comply with the convention in common use by physical chemists (see § 47d) the Weston cell as written above has a positive E.M.F., i.e., +1.0183 volt; if the positions of the two electrodes were reversed the E.M.F. would be −1.0183 volt.

are not attacked by the solutions when the external circuit is open, this cell behaves in a reversible manner. If the external circuit is closed by an E.M.F. just less than that of the Daniell cell, the chemical reaction taking place in the cell is

$$Zn + Cu^{++} = Zn^{++} + Cu,$$

i.e., zinc dissolves from the zinc electrode to form zinc ions in solution, while copper ions are discharged and deposit copper on the other electrode. On the other hand, if the external E.M.F. is slightly greater than that of the cell, the reverse process occurs; the copper electrode dissolves while metallic zinc is deposited on the zinc electrode.

47c. Reversible Electrodes.—The electrodes constituting a reversible cell are **reversible electrodes,** and three chief types of such electrodes are known; *the combination of any two reversible electrodes gives a reversible cell.* The first type of reversible electrode involves a *metal or a nonmetal in contact with a solution of its own ions,* e.g., zinc in zinc sulfate solution, or copper in copper sulfate solution, as in the Daniell cell. The nonmetals which, at least in principle, yield reversible electrodes are hydrogen, oxygen and the halogens, the corresponding ions being hydrogen, hydroxyl and halide ions, respectively. Since the electrode materials in these cases are nonconductors, and often gaseous, finely divided platinum or other unattackable metal, which comes rapidly into equilibrium with the hydrogen, oxygen, etc., is employed for the purpose of making electrical contact (see § 55b). Electrodes of the first kind are reversible with respect to the ions of the electrode material, e.g., metal, hydrogen, oxygen or halogen; if the electrode material is a univalent metal or hydrogen, represented by M, the reaction which takes place at such an electrode, when the cell of which it is part operates, is then

$$M \rightleftharpoons M^+ + \epsilon,$$

where ϵ indicates an electron, and M^+ implies a *hydrated (or solvated) ion in solution.* The direction of the reaction depends on the direction of the flow of current through the cell. If the electrode material is a univalent non-metal A, the ions are negative, and the corresponding reaction is

$$A^- \rightleftharpoons A + \epsilon.$$

As will be seen later, the potentials of these electrodes depend on the concentration (or activity) of the reversible ions in the solution; in the case of a gas electrode, the pressure of the gas is also important.

Electrodes of the second type involve *a metal and a sparingly soluble salt of this metal in contact with a solution of a soluble salt of the same anion;* an example is the important electrode consisting of silver, solid silver chloride and a solution of a soluble chloride, such as hydrochloric acid, viz.,

$$Ag \mid AgCl(s) \quad HCl \text{ soln.}$$

The electrode reaction in this case may be written as

$$Ag(s) + Cl^- \rightleftharpoons AgCl(s) + \epsilon,$$

the chloride ion being that in the solution of the soluble chloride, e.g., hydrochloric acid. These electrodes behave as if they were reversible with respect to the common anion, namely, the chloride ion in this case. The silver-silver chloride electrode is thermodynamically equivalent to a chlorine gas electrode, with the gas at a pressure equal to that in equilibrium with silver chloride dissociating at the experimental temperature, according to the reaction

$$AgCl(s) \rightleftharpoons Ag(s) + \tfrac{1}{2}Cl_2(g).$$

Electrodes of the second type have been made with other insoluble halides, e.g., silver bromide and iodide, and mercurous chloride, and also with insoluble sulfates, oxalates, etc.

The third important type of reversible electrode consists of *an unattackable metal, e.g., gold or platinum, immersed in a solution containing both oxidized and reduced states of an oxidation-reduction system*, e.g., Sn^{++++} and Sn^{++}, Fe^{+++} and Fe^{++}, or $Fe(CN)_6^{---}$ and $Fe(CN)_6^{----}$. The purpose of the unattackable metal is to act as a conductor for making electrical contact, just as in the case of a gas electrode. The oxidized and reduced states are not necessarily ionic; for example, an important type of reversible electrode to be considered later (§ 55c, II) involves the organic compound quinone, together with hydrogen ions, as the oxidized state, while the neutral molecule hydroquinone is the reduced state. Electrodes of the kind under consideration, consisting of conventional oxidized and reduced forms, are sometimes called **oxidation-reduction electrodes**; the chemical reactions taking place at these electrodes are either oxidation of the reduced state or reduction of the oxidized state, e.g.,

$$Sn^{++} \rightleftharpoons Sn^{++++} + 2\epsilon$$
$$Fe(CN)_6^{----} \rightleftharpoons Fe(CN)_6^{---} + \epsilon,$$

depending upon the direction of the current. In order that the electrode may behave reversibly it is essential that the system contain both oxidized and reduced states.

The three types of reversible electrodes described above differ formally as far as their construction is concerned; nevertheless, they are all based on the same fundamental principle which it is important to understand clearly. *A reversible electrode always involves an oxidized and a reduced state*, using the terms "oxidized" and "reduced" in their broadest sense; thus, oxidation refers to the liberation of electrons while reduction implies the taking up of electrons. If the electrode consists of a metal M and its ions M^+, the former is the reduced state and the latter is the oxidized state; similarly, for an anion electrode, the A^- ions are the reduced state while A represents the oxidized state. In the silver-silver chloride electrode, the metallic silver and the chloride ions together form the reduced state of the system while silver chloride is the oxidized state. It can be seen, therefore, that all three types of reversible electrode are made up from the reduced and oxidized states of a given system, and in every case the electrode reaction may be written in the general form

$$\text{Reduced State} \rightleftharpoons \text{Oxidized State} + n\epsilon,$$

where n is the number of electrons by which the oxidized and reduced states differ.

47d. Reactions in Reversible Cells.—A reversible electrode consists of an oxidized and a reduced state, and the reaction which occurs at such an electrode, when it forms part of an operating cell, is either oxidation, i.e., reduced state → oxidized state + electrons, or reduction, i.e., oxidized state + electrons → reduced state. It can be readily seen, therefore, that in a reversible cell, consisting of two reversible electrodes, a flow of electrons, and hence a flow of current, can be maintained if oxidation occurs at one electrode and reduction at the other electrode. According to the convention widely adopted, *the* E.M.F. *of the cell is positive when in its normal operation oxidation takes place at the left-hand electrode of the cell as written*, reduction occurring at the right-hand electrode. If the reverse is the case, so that reduction is taking place at the left-hand electrode, the E.M.F. of the cell, by convention, will have a negative sign.

The Daniell cell, represented by

$$\text{Zn} \mid \text{M ZnSO}_4 \text{ soln.} \mid \text{M CuSO}_4 \text{ soln.} \mid \text{Cu,}$$

has an E.M.F. of 1.10 volt, and by the convention its sign is positive. This means that when the cell operates oxidation occurs at the left-hand electrode; that is to say, metallic zinc atoms are being oxidized to form zinc ions in solution, i.e.,

$$\text{Zn} = \text{Zn}^{++} + 2\epsilon.$$

At the right-hand electrode there must, therefore, be reduction of the cupric ions, from the copper sulfate solution, to copper atoms, i.e.,

$$\text{Cu}^{++} + 2\epsilon = \text{Cu.}$$

The electrons liberated at the zinc electrode travel along the external connecting circuit and are available for the discharge (reduction) of the cupric ions at the copper electrode. The complete cell reaction, obtained by adding the separate electrode reactions, is consequently

$$\text{Zn} + \text{Cu}^{++} = \text{Zn}^{++} + \text{Cu,}$$

as stated in § 47b. Since two electrons are involved for each zinc (or copper) atom taking part in the reaction, the whole process as written, with quantities in gram atoms or gram ions, takes place for the passage of two faradays of electricity.*

* The "practical" convention, employed in connection with cells for yielding current, e.g., Daniell cell, Leclanché cell, secondary (lead-acid or iron-nickel-alkali) cells, etc., is to call the "negative" pole the electrode at which the process is oxidation when the cell is producing current; the "positive" electrode is the one at which reduction is the spontaneous process. The reason for this is that oxidation is accompanied by the liberation of electrons, and so the electrode metal acquires a "negative" charge; similarly, the reduction electrode will acquire a "positive" charge, because electrons are taken up from it. According to the widely used convention, as employed in this book, the E.M.F. of a cell is positive when it is set up in such a way that the "negative," i.e., oxidation, electrode is to the left, and the "positive," i.e., reduction, electrode is to the right.

When writing the reaction taking place in a cell for which the sign of the E.M.F. is not stated, the convention is to assume that the sign is positive; thus, the oxidation is supposed to be taking place at the left-hand electrode. For example, in the cell

$$H_2(g) \mid HCl \; soln. \quad AgCl(s) \mid Ag(s),$$

consisting of a hydrogen electrode at the left, and a silver-silver chloride electrode at the right, both in contact with the same solution of hydrochloric acid, the hydrogen gas is oxidized to hydrogen ions, thus

$$\tfrac{1}{2}H_2(g) = H^+ + \epsilon.$$

At the right-hand electrode reduction of silver chloride takes place, i.e.,

$$AgCl(s) + \epsilon = Ag(s) + Cl^-,$$

so that the complete reaction, with quantities in moles, gram ions or gram atoms, is

$$\tfrac{1}{2}H_2(g) + AgCl(s) = H^+ + Cl^- + Ag(s)$$

for the passage of one faraday. The H^+ and Cl^- ions, of course, represent hydrochloric acid in the aqueous solution.

If the cell just considered were written in the reverse direction, viz.,

$$Ag(s) \mid AgCl(s) \quad HCl \; soln. \mid H_2(g),$$

then, according to the usual convention, the cell reaction would be exactly opposite to that derived above, namely

$$H^+ + Cl^- + Ag(s) = \tfrac{1}{2}H_2(g) + AgCl(s).$$

In this case, it is presumed that the solid silver and the chloride ions are oxidized to solid silver chloride at the left-hand electrode, while hydrogen ions are reduced to hydrogen gas at the right-hand electrode.

Free Energy Changes in Cells

48a. Free Energy and E.M.F.—It was seen in § 26a that the free energy change accompanying a process is equal to the reversible work, other than that due to a volume change, at constant temperature and pressure. When a reversible cell operates, producing an infinitesimal current, the electrical work is thermodynamically reversible in character, and does not include any work due to a volume change. Further, since the temperature and pressure remain constant, *it is possible to identify the electrical work done in a reversible cell with the free energy change accompanying the chemical or other process taking place in the cell.* The work done in a cell is equal to the product of the E.M.F. and the quantity of electricity passing. The practical **unit of electrical energy** is defined as the energy developed when one coulomb is passed under the influence of an E.M.F. of one volt; this unit is called the **volt-coulomb,** and is equivalent to one international joule. The calorie defined by the

U. S. Bureau of Standards is equivalent to 4.1833 int. joules, and hence 1 volt-coulomb is equivalent to 1/4.1833, i.e., 0.2390 (defined), calorie.

If the E.M.F. of a reversible cell is E volts, and the process taking place is associated with the passage of n faradays, i.e., nF coulombs, the electrical work done *by* the system is consequently nFE volt-coulombs or int. joules. The corresponding increase of free energy is equal to the electrical work done *on* the system; it is consequently possible to write

$$\Delta F = -nFE. \tag{48.1}$$

This is an extremely important relationship, for it lies at the basis of the whole treatment of reversible cells, and, in addition, it has many practical applications.

The identification of the free energy change of a chemical reaction with the electrical work done when the reaction takes place in a reversible cell can be justified experimentally in the following manner. By the Gibbs-Helmholtz equation (26.34),

$$\Delta F = \Delta H + T \left(\frac{d(\Delta F)}{dT} \right)_P,$$

where ΔH is the heat change accompanying the cell reaction; if ΔF is replaced by $-nFE$, the result is

$$-nFE = \Delta H - nFT \left(\frac{dE}{dT} \right)_P$$

$$\Delta H = -nF \left[E - T \left(\frac{dE}{dT} \right)_P \right]. \tag{48.2}$$

It is seen from equation (48.2) that if the E.M.F. of the reversible cell, i.e., E, and its temperature coefficient dE/dT, at constant pressure, are known, it is possible to evaluate the heat change of the reaction occurring in the cell. The result may be compared with that obtained by direct thermal measurement; good agreement would then confirm the view that $-nFE$ is equal to the free energy increase, since equation (48.2) is based on this postulate.

Problem: The E.M.F. of the cell

$$\text{Ag} \mid \text{AgCl}(s) \quad \text{KCl soln.} \quad \text{Hg}_2\text{Cl}_2(s) \mid \text{Hg},$$

is $+0.0455$ volt at 25° C, and the temperature coefficient is $+3.38 \times 10^{-4}$ volt per degree. What is the reaction taking place in the cell, and what is the heat content change at 25° C, expressed in calories?

Since the E.M.F. is positive, oxidation occurs at the left-hand electrode, viz.,

$$\text{Ag} + \text{Cl}^- = \text{AgCl}(s) + \epsilon,$$

while at the right-hand electrode the mercurous chloride is reduced to mercury, thus,

$$\tfrac{1}{2}\text{Hg}_2\text{Cl}_2(s) + \epsilon = \text{Hg} + \text{Cl}^-,$$

so that the complete cell reaction for 1 faraday is

$$\text{Ag} + \tfrac{1}{2}\text{Hg}_2\text{Cl}_2(s) = \text{AgCl}(s) + \text{Hg}.$$

For this particular cell, E is $+0.0455$ volt, and dE/dT is $+3.38 \times 10^{-4}$ volt degree^{-1}; since the reaction as written requires 1 faraday, n is equal to 1. These values may be inserted into equation (48.2), and if F is taken as 96,500 coulombs, ΔH will be in volt-coulombs, i.e., int. joules; to convert to calories it is then necessary to multiply by 0.2390. Consequently at 25° C, when T is $273 + 25 = 298°$ K,

$$\Delta H = -1 \times 96{,}500 \times 0.2390 \, (0.0455 - 298 \times 3.38 \times 10^{-4})$$

$$= 1273 \text{ calories, i.e., } 1.27 \text{ kcal.}$$

Some of the results obtained in the calculation of heat content changes from E.M.F. measurements at 25° C are recorded in Table LV; the values de-

TABLE LV. HEAT CHANGES FROM E.M.F. MEASUREMENTS

Cell Reaction	E volt	dE/dT $\times 10^4$	ΔH kcal. E.M.F.	Thermal
Cd + PbCl$_2$ = CdCl$_2$ + Pb	0.1880	-4.80	-15.25	-14.65
Cd + 2AgCl = CdCl$_2$ + 2Ag	0.6753	-6.50	-40.08	-39.53
Pb + 2AgCl = PbCl$_2$ + 2Ag	0.4900	-1.86	-25.16	-24.17

rived from direct thermochemical determinations are given in the last column for purposes of comparison. The agreement between the results for ΔH derived from E.M.F. measurements and from thermal data is seen to be satisfactory. It is probable, in fact, that the former are more accurate than the latter.

48b. E.M.F.'s of Reversible Cells.—The free energy change accompanying a given reaction depends on the concentrations or, more accurately, the activities, of the reactants and the products, as was seen in Chapter XI. It is evident, therefore, that the E.M.F. of a reversible cell, in which a particular reaction takes place when producing current, will vary with the activities of the substances present in the cell. The exact connection can be readily derived in the following manner. Suppose the general reaction

$$a\mathrm{A} + b\mathrm{B} + \cdots \rightleftharpoons l\mathrm{L} + m\mathrm{M} + \cdots$$

occurs in a reversible cell; the corresponding free energy change is then given by equation (37.4), viz.,

$$\Delta F = \Delta F^0 + RT \ln \frac{a_\mathrm{L}^l \times a_\mathrm{M}^m \times \cdots}{a_\mathrm{A}^a \times a_\mathrm{B}^b \times \cdots}, \qquad (48.3)$$

where a_A, a_B, $\cdots$, a_L, a_M, $\cdots$, now represent the activities of A, B, $\cdots$, L, M, $\cdots$, *as they occur in the reversible cell*. If, as in § 37b, the arbitrary reaction quotient, in terms of activities, is represented by the symbol Q_a, then equation (48.3) may be written as

$$\Delta F = \Delta F^0 + RT \ln Q_a. \qquad (48.4)$$

As before, ΔF^0 is the free energy change when all the substances taking part in the cell reaction are in their standard states.

If E is the E.M.F. of the cell under consideration when the various substances have the arbitrary activities a_A, a_B, $\cdots$, a_L, a_M, $\cdots$, as given above, and the reaction as written occurs for the passage of n faradays, it follows from equation (48.1) that ΔF, as given by equations (48.3) or (48.4), is also equal to $-nFE$. Further, if the E.M.F. of the reversible cell is E^0 when all the substances involved are in their standard states, then ΔF^0 is equal to $-nFE^0$. Substituting these values for ΔF and ΔF^0 into equation (48.4), and dividing through by $-nF$, the result is

$$E = E^0 - \frac{RT}{nF} \ln Q_a. \qquad (48.5)$$

This expression is seen to relate the E.M.F. of a cell to the activities of the substances taking part; E^0, the standard E.M.F., is a constant for the given cell reaction, varying only with the temperature, at 1 atm. pressure.

The foregoing results may be illustrated by reference to the cell

$$H_2(g) \mid HCl \; soln. \quad AgCl(s) \mid Ag,$$

for which, as seen above, the cell reaction is

$$\tfrac{1}{2}H_2(g) + AgCl(s) = H^+ + Cl^- + Ag(s)$$

for the passage of one faraday. The reaction quotient in terms of activities is

$$Q_a = \frac{a_{H^+} \times a_{Cl^-} \times a_{Ag}}{a_{H_2}^{1/2} \times a_{AgCl}},$$

but since the silver and the silver chloride are present in the solid state, their activities are unity, in accordance with the convention referred to in § 35a; hence,

$$Q_a = \frac{a_{H^+} \times a_{Cl^-}}{a_{H_2}^{1/2}}.$$

Inserting this expression into equation (48.5), with n equal to unity, the E.M.F. of the cell is given by

$$E = E^0 - \frac{RT}{F} \ln \frac{a_{H^+} \times a_{Cl^-}}{a_{H_2}^{1/2}}. \qquad (48.6)$$

The E.M.F. is thus seen to be dependent upon the activities of the hydrogen and chloride ions in the solution of hydrochloric acid, and of the hydrogen gas in the cell. If the substances taking part in the cell behaved ideally, the activities in equation (48.6) could be replaced by the corresponding concentrations of the hydrogen and chloride ions, and by the pressure of the hydrogen gas. The resulting form of equation (48.6), viz.,

$$E = E^0 - \frac{RT}{F} \ln \frac{c_{H^+} \times c_{Cl^-}}{p_{H_2}^{1/2}}, \qquad (48.7)$$

could be used if the solution of hydrochloric acid were dilute, and the pressure of the hydrogen gas were low.

REVERSIBLE ELECTRODE POTENTIALS

49a. Single Electrode Potentials.—There is at present no known method whereby the potential of a single electrode can be measured; it is only the E.M.F. of a cell, made by combining two electrodes, that can be determined experimentally. However, by choosing an arbitrary zero of potential, much as the freezing point of water is chosen as the zero of the centigrade temperature scale, it is possible to express the potentials of individual electrodes. *The arbitrary zero of potential is taken as the potential of a reversible hydrogen electrode, with gas at 1 atm. pressure, in a solution of hydrogen ions of unit activity.* This particular electrode, viz., H_2(1 atm.), H^+ ($a = 1$), is known as the **standard hydrogen electrode,** for reasons which will be evident shortly. The convention, therefore, is to take the potential of the standard hydrogen electrode as zero; electrode potentials based on this zero are said to refer to the **hydrogen scale.** If any electrode, e.g., M, M^+ is combined with the standard hydrogen electrode, so as to make a complete cell, viz.,

$$M \mid M^+ \text{ soln.} \mid H^+ (a = 1) \mid H_2 \text{ (1 atm.)},$$
$$E \qquad\qquad\qquad\qquad 0$$

the E.M.F. of this cell, i.e., E, is equal to the potential of the M, M^+ electrode on the hydrogen scale.

When any reversible electrode is combined with a standard hydrogen electrode, as just indicated, an oxidation reaction takes place at the former, while the hydrogen ions are reduced to hydrogen gas at the latter. The electrode (oxidation) process may be written in the general form given at the end of § 47c, viz.,

$$\text{Reduced state} = \text{Oxidized state} + n\epsilon,$$

and the corresponding hydrogen electrode reaction is

$$nH^+ + n\epsilon = \tfrac{1}{2}nH_2(g).$$

The complete cell reaction for the passage of n faradays is consequently

$$\text{Reduced state} + nH^+ = \text{Oxidized state} + \tfrac{1}{2}nH_2(g). \qquad (49.1)$$

The E.M.F. of the cell, which is equal to the potential of the reversible electrode under consideration, is then given by equation (48.5) as

$$E = E_{\text{el.}}^0 - \frac{RT}{nF} \ln \frac{(\text{Oxidized state}) \times a_{H_2}^{n/2}}{(\text{Reduced state}) \times a_{H^+}^n}, \qquad (49.2)$$

where parentheses have been used to represent the activities of the oxidized and reduced states as they actually occur in the cell. In the standard hydrogen electrode, the pressure of the gas is 1 atm., and hence the activity a_{H_2} is unity (§ 37b); further, by definition, the activity of the hydrogen ions a_{H^+} in the electrode is also unity. It can thus be seen that equation (49.2) for the electrode potential can be reduced to the simple form

$$E = E_{\text{el.}}^0 - \frac{RT}{nF} \ln \frac{(\text{Oxidized state})}{(\text{Reduced state})}. \qquad (49.3)$$

This is the general equation for the **oxidation potential** *of any reversible electrode; $E^0_{el.}$* is the corresponding **standard electrode potential,** that is, *the potential of the electrode when all the substances concerned are in their standard states of unit activity.** The qualification "oxidation" is used because it describes the process taking place at the electrode; the corresponding "reduction potentials" will be considered presently.

49b. Expressions for Electrode Potentials.—The application of equation (49.3) may be illustrated by reference to a few simple cases of different types. Consider, first, an electrode consisting of a metal in contact with a solution of its own cations, e.g., copper in copper (cupric) sulfate solution. The electrode (oxidation) reaction is

$$Cu = Cu^{++} + 2\epsilon,$$

the Cu being the reduced state and Cu^{++} the oxidized state; in this case n is 2, and hence by equation (49.3)

$$E = E^0_{el.} - \frac{RT}{2F} \ln \frac{a_{Cu^{++}}}{a_{Cu}}.$$

The activity a_{Cu} of the solid metal is unity, by convention, and hence

$$E = E^0_{el.} - \frac{RT}{2F} \ln a_{Cu^{++}}, \tag{49.4}$$

so that the electrode potential is dependent upon the standard (oxidation) potential $E^0_{el.}$ of the Cu, Cu^{++} system, and on the activity $a_{Cu^{++}}$ of the cupric ions in the copper sulfate solution. · The result may be generalized, so that for any metal M (or hydrogen) in equilibrium with a solution of its ions M^+ of valence n, the oxidation potential of the M, M^+ electrode is given by

$$E = E^0_{el.} - \frac{RT}{nF} \ln a_{M^+}, \tag{49.5}$$

where a_{M^+} is the activity of the M^+ ions in the solution. For a univalent ion, e.g., hydrogen, silver, cuprous, etc., n is 1; for a bivalent ion, e.g., zinc, nickel, ferrous, cupric, mercuric, etc., n is 2, and so on.

The second application of equation (49.3) will be made to an electrode in which a nonmetal, e.g., oxygen at 1 atm. pressure, is in contact with its own anions, i.e., hydroxyl ions. The electrode (oxidation) reaction is

$$2OH^- = \tfrac{1}{2}O_2 \text{ (1 atm.)} + H_2O(l) + 2\epsilon,$$

and hence the electrode potential is given by equation (49.3) as

$$E = E^0_{el.} - \frac{RT}{2F} \ln \frac{a_{O_2}^{1/2} \times a_{H_2O}}{a_{OH^-}^2}. \tag{49.6}$$

* As far as possible standard electrode potentials will be distinguished by the use of a subscript, e.g., $E^0_{el.}$, E^0_{Ag}, etc.; the standard E.M.F. of a complete cell will then be indicated by E^0_{cell}.

Since the oxygen gas is at 1 atm. pressure, the activity a_{O_2} is unity, and so also is that of the water, i.e., a_{H_2O} is 1, by convention; * hence equation (49.6) becomes

$$E = E^0_{el.} + \frac{RT}{F} \ln a_{OH^-}. \quad (49.7)$$

The general equation for the oxidation potential of any electrode reversible with reference to the anion A^- of valence n is

$$E = E^0_{el.} + \frac{RT}{nF} \ln a_{A^-}, \quad (49.8)$$

where a_{A^-} is the activity of the A^- ions in the given electrode solution. This equation holds also for the Ag, AgCl, Cl^- electrode which, as already seen, is reversible with respect to chloride ions. It should be noted, in comparing equations (49.5) and (49.8), that in the former, for cations, the second term on the right-hand side is preceded by a negative sign, while in the latter, for anions, the sign is positive.

The third type of electrode to which equation (49.3) will be applied is to the so-called "oxidation-reduction" electrodes, consisting of a piece of platinum or gold in contact with a solution containing both oxidized and reduced states, these terms being used in their restricted sense. A simple illustration is the ferric-ferrous system, for which the oxidation reaction is

$$Fe^{++} = Fe^{+++} + \epsilon,$$

for the passage of one faraday. According to equation (49.3), therefore,

$$E = E^0_{el.} - \frac{RT}{F} \ln \frac{a_{Fe^{+++}}}{a_{Fe^{++}}}, \quad (49.9)$$

where $a_{Fe^{+++}}$ and $a_{Fe^{++}}$ are the activities of the ferric and ferrous ions, respectively, in the given electrode solution.

Quite frequently hydrogen ions are involved in the oxidation-reduction system, as is the case, for example, with quinone-hydroquinone; the oxidation reaction here is

$$C_6H_4(OH)_2 = C_6H_4O_2 + 2H^+ + 2\epsilon,$$
$$\text{hydroquinone} \qquad \text{quinone}$$

for two faradays. Writing a_{H_2Q} for the activity of the hydroquinone and

---

* Strictly speaking a_{H_2O} is equal to unity for pure water. All cells, however, and other systems of electrochemical interest, must contain electrolytes, which lower the activity of the water. According to § 31e, a_{H_2O} is equal to p/p^0, where p is the aqueous vapor pressure of the given solution and p^0 is that of water at the same temperature. It is thus readily shown, e.g., by Raoult's law, that for a 0.1 N solution of (total) strong electrolyte a_{H_2O} is about 0.996, and for a N solution it is approximately 0.97. Consequently, as long as the total concentration of electrolyte is not too great, e.g., 0.1 N or less, as is usually the case, a_{H_2O} is not greatly different from unity.

a_Q for that of the quinone in the electrode solution, it follows from equation (49.3) that

$$E = E_{el.}^0 - \frac{RT}{2F} \ln \frac{a_Q \times a_{H^+}^2}{a_{H_2Q}}$$

$$= E_{el.}^0 - \frac{RT}{2F} \ln \frac{a_Q}{a_{H_2Q}} - \frac{RT}{F} \ln a_{H^+}. \qquad (49.10)$$

It should be evident from the foregoing examples that it is not a difficult matter to derive the equation for the oxidation potential of any electrode; all that is necessary is to write down the electrode reaction, and then to insert the appropriate activities of the oxidized and reduced states into equation (49.3). The result is then simplified by using the convention concerning the standard states of unit activity; thus for any metal present in the pure state, for any pure solid compound, e.g., silver chloride, mercurous sulfate, etc., for a gas at 1 atm. pressure, and for water forming part of a dilute solution, the activity is taken as unity. The corresponding activity factors may then be omitted from the electrode potential equation.

It has been seen that in every galvanic cell, oxidation occurs at one electrode, but a reduction process takes place at the other electrode; the equations just derived give the potential of the former, and now reference must be made to the potential of the electrode at which reduction is occurring. The situation is, fortunately, quite simple; the **reduction potential** of any electrode is equal to the oxidation potential for the same electrode but *with the sign reversed*. It is quite unnecessary, and in fact undesirable, to write out separate formulae for reduction potentials. The procedure that is recommended is to derive the oxidation potential for the given electrode and then merely to reverse the sign. For example, the reduction potential of the copper-cupric ion electrode, for which the reaction is

$$Cu^{++} + 2\epsilon = Cu,$$

would be given by an equation identical with (49.4) but with the sign reversed. Similarly, the reduction potential of the ferrous-ferric electrode, where the reaction is

$$Fe^{+++} + \epsilon = Fe^{++},$$

is expressed by equation (49.9) with the reversed sign.

49c. Sign of Electrode Potential.—In order to facilitate the representation of electrodes, a simple convention is adopted; when the electrode is a metal M, and the process is oxidation to M^+ ions, the reduced state of the system is written to the left and the oxidized state to the right, viz., M, M^+, as in the electrochemical equation $M \rightarrow M^+ +$ electrons. Examples of oxidation electrodes are thus

$$Cu, Cu^{++} \text{ (or Cu, CuSO}_4 \text{ soln.);} \qquad Zn, Zn^{++} \text{ (or Zn, ZnSO}_4 \text{ soln.);}$$

$$Ag, Ag^+ \text{ (or Ag, AgNO}_3 \text{ soln.)}$$

The potentials of such electrodes are given by equations (49.3) or (49.5). On the other hand, if the electrodes are represented in the reverse manner, i.e., M^+, M, with the oxidized state to the left and the reduced state to the right, e.g.,

$$Cu^{++}, Cu \text{ (or } CuSO_4 \text{ soln., Cu)}; \quad Zn^{++}, Zn \text{ (or } ZnSO_4 \text{ soln., Zn)};$$

$$Ag^+, Ag \text{ (or } AgNO_3 \text{ soln., Ag)},$$

the electrode process is reduction, and the potentials are opposite in sign to those of the corresponding oxidation electrodes.

If the electrode material is a nonmetal, as in hydrogen, oxygen and halogen electrodes, and in the so-called "oxidation-reduction" electrodes, an inert metal, usually platinum, is employed to act as the conducting material and functions as part of the electrode system. If the symbol Pt, representing any inert conductor, is written to the left, e.g.,

$$Pt, H_2(g), H^+; \quad Pt, Cl_2(g), Cl^-; \quad Pt, I_2(s), I^-; \quad Pt, Fe^{+++}, Fe^{++},$$

the convention is that an oxidation process is implied. *The order of writing the components*, e.g., $Cl_2(g)$, Cl^- or Cl^-, $Cl_2(g)$, Fe^{+++}, Fe^{++} or Fe^{++}, Fe^{+++}, *is immaterial*. On the other hand, if the symbol Pt is written to the right, as in

$$H^+, H_2(g), Pt; \quad Cl^-, Cl_2(g), Pt; \quad I^-, I_2(s), Pt \quad \text{or} \quad Fe^{+++}, Fe^{++}, Pt,$$

the electrode process is reduction, and the sign of the potential is reversed.

If two reversible electrodes are combined to form such cells as

$$Zn \mid ZnSO_4 \text{ soln.} \mid CuSO_4 \text{ soln.} \mid Cu,$$

$$Ag \mid AgCl(s) \quad HCl \text{ soln.} \mid Cl_2(g), Pt,$$

$$Pt, I_2(s) \mid KI \text{ soln.} \mid K_4Fe(CN)_6, K_3Fe(CN)_6 \text{ soln.} \mid Pt,$$

then, in accordance with the convention given above, the reaction at the left-hand electrode is oxidation, while at the right-hand electrode a reduction process is taking place when the cell operates spontaneously to produce current upon closing the external circuit. It should be noted that this is exactly in agreement with the convention adopted in § 47d. *The* E.M.F. *of the complete cell is then equal to the algebraic sum of the potentials of the two electrodes*, one being an oxidation potential and the other a reduction potential. An important point to which attention may be called is that since the E.M.F. of a cell is equal to the sum of an oxidation and a reduction electrode potential, it i equivalent to *the difference of two oxidation potentials*. As a consequence, the E.M.F. of a cell is independent of the arbitrary potential chosen as the zero of the potential scale; the actual value, whatever it may be, cancels out when taking the difference of the two oxidation potentials based on the same, e.g., hydrogen, scale. Illustrations of the calculation of the E.M.F.'s of cells from electrode potential data will be given in later sections.

49d. Reference Electrodes.—In order to measure the potential of any electrode on the hydrogen scale, all that is necessary, in principle, is to combine the electrode with a standard hydrogen electrode, i.e., one with gas at 1 atm. pressure and a solution of hydrogen ions of unit activity, and to determine the E.M.F. of the resulting cell. As seen in § 49a, this value is identical with the required electrode potential. For a number of reasons the direct use of the hydrogen electrode is not convenient, and hence several subsidiary reference electrodes have been devised. The most common of these is the **calomel electrode**; it consists of mercury in contact with a solution of potassium chloride saturated with mercurous chloride (calomel). Three different concentrations of potassium chloride have been employed, namely 0.1 N, 1.0 N and a saturated solution. The potentials of these electrodes have been measured against the standard hydrogen electrode, so that the values are known; they are as follows on the hydrogen scale at 25° C:

$$0.1 \text{ N KCl, Hg}_2\text{Cl}_2(s), \text{ Hg} \qquad +0.334 \text{ volt}$$

$$1.0 \text{ N KCl} \qquad +0.280$$

$$\text{Satd. KCl} \qquad +0.242.$$

Because the calomel electrodes are employed as reference electrodes, for the determination of the oxidation potentials of other electrodes, they have been deliberately represented here as reduction electrodes. In order to obtain the potential of any given electrode, it is combined with a reference electrode, and the E.M.F. of the resulting cell is measured; the potential of the reference electrode, as stated above, is then subtracted to give the required electrode potential.

A difficulty that arises in the determination of electrode potentials is that it is frequently necessary to have two different solutions in contact. For example, the potential of a Zn, ZnSO$_4$ soln. electrode may be measured by combining it with a calomel electrode, e.g., 0.1 N KCl, Hg$_2$Cl$_2(s)$, Hg; in the resulting cell there will be a junction between two different solutions. Such a liquid-liquid contact introduces an additional potential, known as a **liquid junction potential**. In certain simple cases it is possible to calculate the value of this potential with fair accuracy, but in most instances the calculation is too difficult and uncertain to be significant. It is therefore the general practice to try to reduce the value of the liquid junction potential as much as possible, and this may be achieved by the use of a **salt bridge**. This generally consists of a tube or a convenient vessel containing a saturated solution of potassium chloride which is employed to connect the solutions in the two electrodes. It is because potassium and chloride ions have almost identical mobilities (see Table LIV) that potassium chloride possesses the property of being able to minimize liquid junction potentials (see § 50b). When potassium chloride cannot be used, e.g., if one of the electrodes contains a silver salt, a saturated solution of ammonium nitrate is employed as a salt bridge. It is doubtful whether the potentials are ever eliminated entirely, but at least they can be reduced in magnitude so that the actual value is negligible for measurements not requiring the highest degree of accuracy. When a salt bridge is used, and it is supposed that the liquid junction potential is eliminated, a double line is inserted between the symbols for the two solutions, e.g.,

$$Zn \mid M \ ZnSO_4 \ soln. \parallel 0.1 \ N \ KCl \ Hg_2Cl_2(s) \mid Hg.$$

Problem: The E.M.F. of the cell just given, containing molar $ZnSO_4$, was found to be 1.094 volt; determine the (oxidation) potential of the Zn, $ZnSO_4$ soln. electrode on the hydrogen scale.

Let E_{Zn} be the value of the required potential, i.e., of the left-hand electrode of the cell; the (reduction) potential of the 0.1 N KCl calomel electrode, as given above, is $+0.334$ volt. The total E.M.F. of the cell is thus $E_{Zn} + 0.334$, and this is found by direct measurement to be 1.094 volt; hence,

$$E_{Zn} + 0.334 = 1.094, \quad \text{and} \quad E_{Zn} = +0.760 \text{ volt.}$$

(The result can be obtained directly by the rule given previously; the potential of the reference electrode is subtracted from that of the cell.)

The great advantage of the calomel electrode is its convenient construction; vessels of various types have been employed, some of which are shown

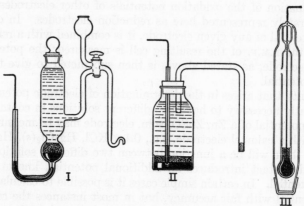

FIG. 102.   Forms of calomel electrode

in Fig. 102. In each case a small quantity of pure mercury is covered with a paste of pure mercurous chloride, mercury and potassium chloride solution. The vessel is then filled with the appropriate solution of potassium chloride which has been saturated with calomel. Electrical connection with the mercury is made by means of a platinum wire sealed into a glass tube, or through the walls of the vessel. The solution of potassium chloride is brought into contact with the other solution, e.g., in the salt bridge, by means of a siphon tube, as in Fig. 102, I and II. The compact form of calomel electrode (Fig. 102, III), as used with many commercial potentiometers, is dipped directly into the solution of the other electrode; connection between the two solutions occurs at the relatively loose ground glass joint.

For work of special accuracy where liquid junctions can be avoided by the use of a single electrolyte, e.g., a chloride solution, the silver-silver chloride electrode has been employed as a reference electrode. It usually consists of a silver wire coated with a layer of silver chloride; this is inserted directly into the solution of the chloride in the experimental electrode. The potential of the silver chloride electrode has been determined from measurements on cells consisting of this electrode combined with a hydrogen electrode in solutions of hydrochloric acid. In this way the E.M.F. of the cell

$$\text{Ag} \mid \text{AgCl}(s) \; \text{Cl}^- \; (a = 1) \; \text{H}^+ \; (a = 1) \mid \text{H}_2 \; (1 \text{ atm.})$$

has been found to be -0.2224 volt at $25°$ C. Since the potential of the right-hand electrode is zero, by convention, the oxidation potential of the silver chloride electrode is also -0.2224 volt, and hence the corresponding reduction potential, with chloride ions at unit activity, is

$$\text{Cl}^- \; (a = 1) \; \text{AgCl}(s) \mid \text{Ag}, \qquad +0.2224 \text{ volt at } 25° \text{ C.}$$

49e. Standard Oxidation Potentials.—According to the equations derived in § 48b, the potential of any electrode is determined by the standard potential $E_{el.}^0$, and by the activity or activities of the ions taking part in the electrode process. These activities are variable, but the standard potential is a definite property of the electrode system, having a constant value at a given temperature. If these standard potentials were known, it would be a simple matter to calculate the actual potential of any electrode, in a solution of given concentration or activity, by using the appropriate form of equation (49.3). The standard potentials of many electrodes have been determined, with varying degrees of accuracy, and the results have been tabulated. The principle of the method used to evaluate $E_{el.}^0$ for a given electrode system is to measure the potential E of the electrode, on the hydrogen scale, in a solution of known activity; from these two quantities the standard potential $E_{el.}^0$ can be calculated at the experimental temperature, using equation (49.3). Actually the procedure is more complicated than is indicated, because the activities are uncertain, but the details need not be considered here. The results obtained for the **standard oxidation potentials** of a number of electrodes at $25°$ C are recorded in Table LVI; the appropriate electrode process is given in each case.

It should be remembered that the standard potential refers to the condition in which all the substances in the cell are in their standard states of unit activity; gases such as hydrogen, oxygen and chlorine are thus at 1 atm. pressure. With bromine and iodine, however, the standard states are chosen as the pure liquid and solid, respectively; the solutions are therefore saturated with these elements in the standard electrodes. For all ions the standard state of unit activity is taken as *the hypothetical ideal solution* of unit molality (see § 31c), or, in other words, a solution for which the product $m\gamma$ is unity, where m is the molality of the ion and γ its activity coefficient.

Electrode	Reaction	$E^0_{el.}$
K, K$^+$	K $\rightarrow$ K$^+$ + ϵ	+2.924
Na, Na$^+$	Na $\rightarrow$ Na$^+$ + ϵ	+2.714
Zn, Zn^{++}	Zn $\rightarrow$ Zn^{++} + 2ϵ	+0.761
Fe, Fe^{++}	Fe $\rightarrow$ Fe^{++} + 2ϵ	+0.441
Cd, Cd^{++}	Cd $\rightarrow$ Cd^{++} + 2ϵ	+0.402
Co, Co^{++}	Co $\rightarrow$ Co^{++} + 2ϵ	+0.283
Ni, Ni^{++}	Ni $\rightarrow$ Ni^{++} + 2ϵ	+0.236
Sn, Sn^{++}	Sn $\rightarrow$ Sn^{++} + 2ϵ	+0.140
Pb, Pb^{++}	Pb $\rightarrow$ Pb^{++} + 2ϵ	+0.126
Pt, $\frac{1}{2}$H$_2$, H$^+$	$\frac{1}{2}$H$_2$ $\rightarrow$ H$^+$ + ϵ	$\pm$0.000
Pt, Sn^{++}, Sn^{++++}	Sn^{++} $\rightarrow$ Sn^{++++} + 2ϵ	$-$0.15
Pt, Cu$^+$, Cu^{++}	Cu$^+$ $\rightarrow$ Cu^{++} + ϵ	$-$0.16
Ag, AgCl(s), Cl$^-$	Ag + Cl$^-$ $\rightarrow$ AgCl + ϵ	$-$0.2224
Cu, Cu^{++}	Cu $\rightarrow$ Cu^{++} + 2ϵ	$-$0.340
Pt, Fe(CN)$_6^{\equiv}$, Fe(CN)$_6^{=}$	Fe(CN)$_6^{\equiv}$ $\rightarrow$ Fe(CN)$_6^{=}$ + ϵ	$-$0.356
Pt, O$_2$, OH$^-$	2OH$^-$ $\rightarrow$ $\frac{1}{2}$O$_2$ + H$_2$O + 2ϵ	$-$0.401
Pt, I$_2$(s), I$^-$	I$^-$ $\rightarrow$ $\frac{1}{2}$I$_2$ + ϵ	$-$0.536
Pt, Fe^{++}, Fe^{+++}	Fe^{++} $\rightarrow$ Fe^{+++} + ϵ	$-$0.771
Ag, Ag$^+$	Ag $\rightarrow$ Ag$^+$ + ϵ	$-$0.799
Hg, Hg$_2^{++}$	Hg $\rightarrow$ $\frac{1}{2}$Hg$_2^{++}$ + ϵ	$-$0.799
Pt, Hg$_2^{++}$, Hg^{++}	Hg$_2^{++}$ $\rightarrow$ 2Hg^{++} + 2ϵ	$-$0.906
Pt, Br$_2$(l), Br$^-$	Br$^-$ $\rightarrow$ $\frac{1}{2}$Br$_2$ + ϵ	$-$1.066
Pt, Cl$_2$(g), Cl$^-$	Cl$^-$ $\rightarrow$ $\frac{1}{2}$Cl$_2$ + ϵ	$-$1.358
Pt, Ce^{+++}, Ce^{++++}	Ce^{+++} $\rightarrow$ Ce^{++++} + ϵ	$-$1.61

The standard reduction potentials, corresponding to the oxidation potentials in Table LVI, but involving the reverse electrode processes, would be obtained by reversing the sign in each case; thus, for example, for the zinc electrode

$$\text{Zn, Zn}^{++} \qquad E^0_{el.} = +0.761 \text{ volt} \qquad \text{Zn} = \text{Zn}^{++} + 2\epsilon$$

$$\text{Zn}^{++}, \text{Zn} \qquad E^0_{el.} = -0.761 \text{ volt} \qquad \text{Zn}^{++} + 2\epsilon = \text{Zn},$$

whereas for the chlorine electrode

$$\text{Pt, Cl}_2(g), \text{Cl}^- \qquad E^0_{el.} = -1.358 \text{ volt} \qquad \text{Cl}^- = \tfrac{1}{2}\text{Cl}_2(g) + \epsilon$$

$$\text{Cl}^-, \text{Cl}_2(g), \text{Pt} \qquad E^0_{el.} = +1.358 \text{ volt} \qquad \tfrac{1}{2}\text{Cl}_2(g) + \epsilon = \text{Cl}^-.$$

49f. Applications of Electrode Potentials.—There are numerous applications of electrode potentials in various branches of chemistry; some of these will be considered here, while others will be found in later sections. In order to make practical use of the electrode potential equations developed in § 49b, it is necessary to insert values for R and F in the factor RT/nF which appears in all such equations. The potential is always expressed in volts, and since F is known to be 96,500 coulombs, the value of R must be in volt-coulombs, i.e., in int. joules; thus R is 8.314 abs. joules or 8.312 int. joules deg.$^{-1}$

$mole^{-1}$. Taking equation (49.5) for the oxidation potential of an electrode reversible with respect to cations, that is

$$E = E_{el.}^0 - \frac{RT}{nF} \ln a_{M^+},$$

inserting the values of R and F given above, and introducing the factor 2.303 to convert natural logarithms to common logarithms, i.e., to the base 10, the result is

$$E = E_{el.}^0 - \frac{2.303 \times 8.312}{96,500} \cdot \frac{T}{n} \log a_{M^+}$$

$$= E_{el.}^0 - 1.984 \times 10^{-4} \frac{T}{n} \log a_{M^+}. \tag{49.11}$$

At 25° C, i.e., T is 298.16° K, which is the temperature most frequently employed for accurate electrochemical measurements, this equation becomes

$$E = E_{el.}^0 - \frac{0.05915}{n} \log a_{M^+}. \tag{49.12}$$

Similarly, for the oxidation potential of an anion electrode at 25° C,

$$E = E_{el.}^0 + \frac{0.05915}{n} \log a_{A^-}. \tag{49.13}$$

The general form of the equation at 25° C, which is applicable to all reversible electrodes [see equation (49.3)], is

$$E = E_{el.}^0 - \frac{0.05915}{n} \log \frac{\text{(Oxidized state)}}{\text{(Reduced state)}}, \tag{49.14}$$

where the parentheses are used to indicate activities.

I. Approximate Determination of Ionic Activities.—By means of the standard potentials in Table LVI and the appropriate form of the general equation (49.14), it is possible to evaluate the oxidation electrode potential for any specified activity of the reversible ions in the electrode solution. On the other hand, if the potential of a particular electrode is measured in a solution of its ions at an unknown activity, the value of the latter can be calculated. This is particularly useful for the determination of very small ionic activities, such as are encountered in the study of sparingly soluble salts and of complex ions. It is important to mention that the results obtained in this manner are not strictly ionic activities; a careful study of thermodynamics shows that it is theoretically impossible to determine the activity of a single ionic species. The quantity actually measured is a kind of mean value of the activities of two or more ions; for many purposes, such as those connected with the study of hydrogen ions in Chapter XVI, the value derived from electrode potential measurements may be taken as approximately equal to the corresponding molalities in gram ions per 1000 grams of solvent. In dilute aqueous solution this is roughly equivalent to the concentration in gram ions per liter.

Problem: The E.M.F. of the cell

$$Ag \mid AgCl(s) \qquad 0.1 \text{ N KCl} \qquad Hg_2Cl_2(s) \mid Hg$$

is $+0.0455$ volt at $25°$ C; calculate the approximate activity (or concentration) of the Ag^+ ions in the saturated solution of AgCl in 0.1 N KCl.

The (reduction) potential of the right-hand electrode, i.e., 0.1 N KCl, $Hg_2Cl_2(s)$, Hg is $+0.334$ (§ 49d); hence, if E_{Ag} is the (oxidation) potential of the silver electrode,

$$E_{Ag} = +0.0455 - 0.334 = -0.2885 \text{ volt.}$$

For an electrode reversible with respect to Ag^+ ions, n is 1, and so equation (49.12) becomes

$$E_{Ag} = E_{Ag}^0 - 0.05915 \log a_{Ag^+}.$$

From Table LVI, E_{Ag}^0 for the Ag, Ag^+ electrode is -0.799 volt; hence

$$-0.2885 = -0.799 - 0.05915 \log a_{Ag^+}$$

$$\log a_{Ag^+} = -8.630 = 0.370 - 9$$

$$a_{Ag^+} = 2.34 \times 10^{-9} \text{ gram ion per 1000 grams of water.}$$

Since the aqueous solution is dilute, the approximate activity or concentration of the silver ions is 2.34×10^{-9} gram ion per liter.

(It may be noted that although the left-hand electrode is generally regarded as being reversible to Cl^- ions, it is treated here as being reversible to Ag^+ ions. This does not affect the results, for both points of view may be used.)

II. Influence of Ionic Concentration on Electrode Potential.—The oxidation potential of a cation electrode in a solution of ionic activity x is given by the general equation

$$E_1 = E_M^0 - \frac{RT}{nF} \ln x.$$

If the solution is diluted so as to decrease the activity of the cations to one-tenth of its initial value, that is to say to $0.1x$, the electrode potential becomes

$$E_2 = E_M^0 - \frac{RT}{nF} \ln 0.1x.$$

The resulting change of potential is obtained by subtracting E_1 from E_2; thus,

$$E_2 - E_1 = -\frac{RT}{nF} (\ln 0.1x - \ln x) = \frac{RT}{nF} \ln 10.$$

Inserting the values of R, F and T (for $25°$ C), and converting the logarithms, as explained above, this becomes

$$E_2 - E_1 = \frac{0.05915}{n} \text{ volt.} \qquad (49.15)$$

It can be seen, therefore, that at 25° C every tenfold *decrease* in ionic activity or, approximately, in the concentration, of the *cations* results in the oxidation potential becoming *more positive* by $0.05915/n$ volt, where n is the valence of the ions. For bivalent ions, such as Zn^{++}, Cd^{++}, Fe^{++}, Cu^{++}, etc., the value of n is 2, and hence the electrode potential changes by $0.05915/2$, i.e., 0.0296 volt, for every tenfold change of ionic activity; a hundredfold change, which is equivalent to two successive tenfold changes, would mean an alteration of 0.05915 volt in the potential at 25° C. For univalent ions, n is 1, and hence tenfold and hundredfold changes in the activities of the reversible ions produce potential changes of 0.05915 and 0.1183 volt, respectively. The *alteration of potential* is not determined by the actual ionic concentrations or activities, but by the *ratio* of the two concentrations, that is, by the relative change of concentration. Thus, a change from 1.0 gram ion to 0.1 gram ion per liter produces the same change in potential as a decrease from 10^{-6} to 10^{-7} gram ion per liter; in each case the ratio of the two concentrations is the same, viz., 10 to 1.

It will have been noted that the formula of mercurous chloride is written as Hg_2Cl_2, and not $HgCl$, and that of the mercurous ion is represented by Hg_2^{++} in Table LVI. One argument for the use of the double formula is the fact that a tenfold change in the concentration of mercurous nitrate solution was found to alter the potential by 0.029 volt at ordinary temperatures. This result indicates that for the mercurous ions n is 2, so that they carry two unit charges per ion; the formula must consequently be Hg_2^{++} and not Hg^+.

An equation similar to (49.15), but with a negative sign, can be derived for electrodes reversible with respect to anions; for such ions, therefore, a tenfold *decrease* of concentration or activity, at 25° C, causes the oxidation potential to become $0.05915/n$ volt *more negative*. For reduction potentials, the changes are of the same magnitude as for oxidation potentials, but the signs are reversed in each case.

Problem: Calculate the oxidation potential of an oxygen gas electrode, at 1 atm. pressure, in (i) a N solution of strong acid, (ii) a neutral solution, at ordinary temperature.

The electrode under consideration is Pt, O_2, OH^-; hence equation (49.13) is applicable with $E_{el.}^0$ equal to -0.401 and n equal to 1. It will be seen in § 53g that the OH^- ion concentration in (i) N acid solution is about 10^{-14}, and (ii) 10^{-7} g. ion per liter in a neutral solution. These may be taken as approximately equal to the corresponding activities, expressed in molalities. The oxygen potentials at about 25° C are thus:

(i) $\qquad E = -0.401 + 0.059 \log 10^{-14} = -1.23$ volt

(ii) $\qquad E = -0.401 + 0.059 \log 10^{-7} = -0.81$ volt.

III. Potentiometric Titration.—One of the most interesting applications of electrode potentials is in connection with **potentiometric titration,** or **electrometric titration,** that is, the detection of the end point of a titration in quantitative analysis by measurement of electrode potential. Suppose a standard solution of silver nitrate is being titrated by means of a solution of sodium chloride; as the titration proceeds, silver chloride is precipitated, and the concentration of the silver ions remaining in solution decreases steadily. The potential of a silver electrode, which in this case acts as the **indicator electrode,** changes correspondingly. The change of potential is quite small, at first, since a hundredfold decrease of concentration alters the potential by only 0.118 volt. However, when the end point of the titration is approached, the *relative* change of concentration of silver ions for a given amount of sodium chloride added increases rapidly; there is a corresponding rapid change in the silver electrode potential, for the reason stated above. The end point can thus be found by determining the quantity of titrant added when the rate of change of the electrode potential is a maximum. A silver electrode can thus be used as an indicator for the quantitative analysis of chloride solutions, or of solutions of any anion forming an insoluble silver salt, e.g., bromide, iodide, cyanide, thiocyanate and phosphate. Other metal electrodes may be adapted to the analysis of other anion solutions.

The general form of the potentiometric titration curve, showing the variation of the potential of the indicator electrode with the amount of titrant added, is depicted in Fig. 103; the sharp change of potential at the end point is evident. In order to determine the position of the end point with some degree of precision, it is necessary to find the point at which the slope of the titration curve is a maximum. The method adopted to find this point is to plot the ratio of the change ΔE of electrode potential, for the addition of a definite small volume ΔV of titrant solution, to the volume ΔV, that is, $\Delta E/\Delta V$, against the total volume of added titrant. Provided ΔV is not large, $\Delta E/\Delta V$ is a close approximation to the slope of the titration curve in Fig. 103, and it has a maximum value at the end point, as shown in Fig. 104. The height of this maximum, and the accuracy with which the end point can be estimated, are smaller the more dilute the solutions being titrated and the more soluble the precipitated salt.

The principles described above can be used for other forms of titration; for example, in the titration of an acid solution by a base, there is a rapid relative change in the hydrogen ion concentration as the end point is approached (§ 55g). The position of this point can consequently be obtained from measurements of the potential of a suitable hydrogen indicator electrode, in the same way as a silver electrode was employed in the precipitation titration. The accuracy of the neutralization titration depends on the concentration of the solutions, and also on the strength of the acid and base; if the acid or base, or both, are too weak, the point at which $\Delta E/\Delta V$ is a maximum cannot be detected satisfactorily and accurate titration is not possible. Problems associated with the neutralization of acids and bases will be considered more fully in Chapter XVI.

Titrations involving conventional oxidizing and reducing agents, e.g., permanganate or dichromate and ferrous ions, can also be followed potentiometrically; here again the potential of the system undergoes a rapid change at the end point, provided the oxidation and reduction reactions go to virtual completion (see § 49h). The indicator electrode employed for this type of titration consists of an unattackable electrode, such as one of platinum, as explained in § 47c. It is in connection with oxidation-reduction titrations that the potentiometric method has found its greatest usefulness, since there are few indicators available such as are used in neutralization titrations.

The potentiometric procedure can be employed with colored solutions, and often in dilutions at which ordinary titrations with colored indicators

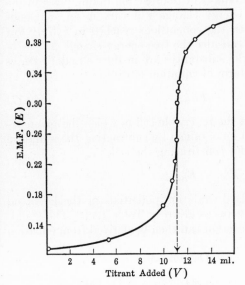

FIG. 103.   Potentiometric titration

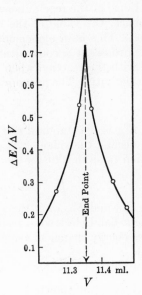

FIG. 104.   Potentiometric end point

would be very inaccurate. The general method is to place the indicator electrode in the solution to be titrated and to combine it with a reference electrode of constant potential, e.g., a calomel electrode, thus forming a complete cell. The E.M.F. of this cell is measured, by a suitable potentiometer, as various known amounts of titrant solution are added. The actual potential of the indicator electrode need not be known; since the potential of the reference electrode remains constant, the E.M.F. of the complete cell will undergo the same changes as does the potential of the indicator electrode. The end point of the titration is then the point at which $\Delta E/\Delta V$ is a maximum, where ΔE is given by the changes in the E.M.F. of the cell. Numerous devices have been developed in order to simplify the titration procedure, and to increase the ease and accuracy of determining the end point.

49g. Standard Free Energy Changes and Spontaneous Reactions.—According to the arguments in § 37c, a reaction can take place spontaneously if it is accompanied by a decrease of free energy, i.e., when ΔF is negative. If the reaction can be made to take place, for the passage of n faradays, in a reversible cell of E.M.F. equal to E, then by equation (48.1)

$$\Delta F = -nFE, \tag{49.16}$$

so that ΔF is negative if E is positive. Consequently, *when the* E.M.F. *of a reversible cell is positive, the corresponding cell reaction will take place spontaneously.*

The E.M.F. of a cell and even its sign depend on the activities, or concentrations, of the reactants and products of the reaction taking place in the cell; hence, the value of the free energy change will vary in an analogous manner. This is in agreement with the conclusions reached in § 37c. For many purposes it is convenient to consider the free energy change ΔF^0 associated with the reaction when all the substances are in their standard states of unit activity. The appropriate form of equation (49.16) is

$$\Delta F^0 = -nFE^0_{cell}, \tag{49.17}$$

where E^0_{cell} is the standard E.M.F. of the reversible cell in which the given reaction occurs; the value of E^0_{cell} can be obtained by subtracting the standard oxidation potentials of the electrodes constituting the cell, i.e.,

$$E^0_{cell} = E^0_{left} - E^0_{right},$$

where E^0_{left} and E^0_{right} are the standard oxidation potentials of the left-hand and right-hand electrodes, respectively, as given in Table LVI. The standard free energy change of the cell reaction can then be derived from equation (49.17).

Consider, for example, the particular Daniell cell

$$Zn \mid ZnSO_4 \ (a_{Zn^{++}} = 1) \parallel CuSO_4 \ (a_{Cu^{++}} = 1) \mid Cu$$
$$+0.761 \qquad\qquad\qquad\qquad\qquad\qquad -(-0.340)$$

for which the reaction, as seen earlier, is

$$Zn + Cu^{++} = Zn^{++} + Cu$$

for the passage of two faradays. The standard oxidation potential of the left-hand, i.e., Zn, Zn^{++}, electrode is $+0.761$ volt (Table LVI), while the standard oxidation potential of the right-hand, i.e., Cu, Cu^{++}, electrode is -0.340 volt; the standard E.M.F. of the complete cell E^0_{cell} is thus $+0.761 - (-0.340) = 1.101$ volt at 25° C, and by equation (49.17)

$$\Delta F^0 = -2 \times 96,500 \times 1.101 = -212,500 \text{ joules}$$

$$= -212,500 \times 0.2390 = -50,790 \text{ cal., i.e., } -50.79 \text{ kcal., at 25° C.}$$

Since E^0_{cell}, the standard E.M.F. of the cell, is positive, the standard free energy change ΔF^0 is negative, and the reaction as written is spontaneous; hence, metallic zinc can react spontaneously with cupric ions at unit activity to produce metallic copper and zinc ions also at unit activity.

Suppose it is required to determine whether the reaction

$$Cd + 2H^+ \ (a = 1) = Cd^{++} \ (a = 1) + H_2 \ (1 \text{ atm.}),$$

that is, the displacement of hydrogen ions from solution by metallic cadmium, is possible theoretically, when all the substances are in their standard states. This reaction would occur in the cell

$$Cd \mid Cd^{++} \ (a = 1) \parallel H^+ \ (a = 1) \mid H_2 \ (1 \text{ atm.}),$$
$$+0.402 \qquad\qquad\qquad\qquad 0$$

the standard E.M.F. of which is the same as the oxidation potential of the cadmium electrode, i.e., $+0.402$ volt at $25°$ C. Since E_{cell}^0 is positive, ΔF^0 is negative, and the reaction should be capable of taking place spontaneously. The actual value of the standard free energy change could be determined, if required, from equation (49.17), using $n = 2$ for the cell reaction as written above.*

An illustration of another kind is provided by the cell

$$Ag \mid AgClO_4 \ (a = 1) \parallel Fe(ClO_4)_2, \ Fe(ClO_4)_3 \ (a = 1) \mid Pt$$
$$-0.799 \qquad\qquad\qquad\qquad\qquad -(-0.771)$$

for which the reaction is

$$Ag(s) + Fe^{+++} = Ag^+ + Fe^{++}$$

for the passage of one faraday. The standard oxidation potential of the left-hand (Ag, Ag^+) electrode is -0.799 volt, while the reduction potential of the right-hand (Fe^{++}, Fe^{+++}, Pt) electrode is $- \ (-0.771)$, i.e., $+0.771$ volt (Table LVI). The standard E.M.F. of the cell depicted is thus $-0.799 + 0.771 = -0.028$ volt; since E_{cell}^0 is negative, ΔF^0 is positive, and the reaction as written will not occur spontaneously, for the reactants and products in their standard states. For the reverse reaction, however, ΔF^0 will be negative, so that the process

$$Fe^{++} + Ag^+ = Fe^{+++} + Ag(s)$$

can be spontaneous if all the substances taking part are at unit activity.

An examination of the foregoing results, or a general consideration of the situation, will reveal the fact that the standard E.M.F. of a cell is positive when the standard oxidation potential of the left-hand electrode is greater algebraically than the standard oxidation potential of the right-hand electrode, that is, when the former lies above the latter in Table LVI. When this is the case, the cell reaction will be capable of occurring spontaneously, oxidation taking place at the left-hand side and reduction at the right-hand side. It follows, therefore, that any system in Table LVI should be able, theoreti-

---

* If the cell reaction had been written as $\frac{1}{2}Cd + H^+ = \frac{1}{2}Cd^{++} + \frac{1}{2}H_2$, which is quite justifiable, n would be 1 and ΔF^0 would be half the value for the process as represented above; this is correct since the quantities involved are now half those in the equation given above.

cally, to reduce any system lying below it in the table, while it is itself oxidized, provided all the substances concerned are in their standard states of unit activity. Thus, as seen above, zinc (higher in the table) reduces cupric ions to copper (lower in the table), while it is itself oxidized to zinc ions; similarly, cadmium reduces hydrogen ions to hydrogen gas, and is itself oxidized to cadmium ions. In general, any metal higher in Table LVI will displace from solution, i.e., reduce, the ions of a metal (or of hydrogen) lower in the table of standard oxidation potentials.

It is important to remember that these conclusions are strictly applicable only when the ions are all at unit activity. By changing the activity it is possible for a process to be reversed, particularly if the standard potentials of the systems involved are not far apart. For example, copper should be unable to displace hydrogen ions from solution, since the Cu, Cu^{++} system has a lower oxidation potential than the H_2, H^+ system; this is true in so far as copper does not normally liberate hydrogen from acid solution. However, if the concentration of the cupric ions is decreased very greatly by the formation of complex ions, e.g., with cyanide or bromide, the oxidation potential is increased (§ 49f, II) until it is greater than that of hydrogen against hydrogen ions in the same solution. In these circumstances, the displacement of hydrogen ions by metallic copper, with the evolution of hydrogen gas, becomes possible.

Similar observations have been made in connection with the Ag, Ag^+ and Fe^{++}, Fe^{+++} systems; as seen above, if all the substances are in their standard states of unit activity, the spontaneous reaction should be the reduction of silver ions to metallic silver by ferrous ions, as is actually the case. The standard oxidation potentials of the two systems are not very different, although that of the Fe^{++}, Fe^{+++} system is the higher. In the presence of thiocyanate ions, which maintain a low concentration of Ag^+ ions by the precipitation of silver thiocyanate, in addition to removing many of the Fe^{+++} ions in the form of a complex, the potentials are reversed, and metallic silver then reduces the ferric compound to the ferrous state.

Although the standard potentials provide some indication, therefore, of the direction in which a particular reaction may be expected to proceed spontaneously, especially if the potentials are appreciably different for the two systems involved, the results may sometimes be misleading. The real criterion, which is always satisfactory, is the one given at the beginning of this section; namely, that the E.M.F. of the actual cell, i.e., E, with the substances at the given activities, and not necessarily E^0_{cell}, when the activities are all unity, should be positive for the reaction to be spontaneous. In other words, the actual oxidation potential of the left-hand electrode must be greater algebraically than that of the right-hand electrode if the reaction occurring in the cell is to proceed spontaneously.

Problem: According to the results in Table LVI, metallic Pb cannot displace Sn^{++} ions from solution to form metallic Sn when the ions are all at unit activity; can this displacement occur if Pb is placed in a solution in which the activity of the Sn^{++} ions is 1.0 g. ion per liter and that of the Pb^{++} ions is 0.1 g. ion per liter?

The problem reduces itself to the question of finding whether ΔF for the reaction

$$Pb(s) + Sn^{++}(a = 1.0) = Pb^{++}(a = 0.1) + Sn(s)$$

is negative or not. The reaction as written will take place spontaneously in the cell

$$Pb \mid Pb^{++}(a = 0.1) \parallel Sn^{++}(a = 1.0) \mid Sn$$

provided its E.M.F. is positive, for then ΔF will be negative. Two procedures, which are ultimately identical, may be employed to determine E and ΔF.

First, the potentials of the two electrodes may be calculated from equation (49.12); for the left-hand electrode, E_{Pb}^0 is $+0.126$ volt, n is 2 and $a_{Pb^{++}}$ is 0.1, so that at 25° C,

$$E_{Pb} = +0.126 - \frac{0.05915}{2} \log 0.1 = +0.156 \text{ volt.}$$

For the right-hand electrode, E_{Sn}^0 is $+0.140$ volt, n is 2 and $a_{Sn^{++}}$ is 1.0, so that

$$E_{Sn} = +0.140 - \frac{0.05915}{2} \log 1.0 = +0.140 \text{ volt.}$$

The E.M.F. of the cell as written is the algebraic sum of the oxidation potential of the lead electrode and the reduction potential of the tin electrode, i.e., $+0.156 - 0.140 = +0.016$ volt. Since E is positive, ΔF, equal to $-2 \times 96,500 \times 0.016 = -3087$ joules, is negative. The reaction under consideration will thus take place spontaneously with the specified activities; the change of activities consequently permits the reaction to take place in the direction which is not possible when the activities of both ions are unity.

The second method of calculating E is to make use of the general equation (48.5); in the present case this is,

$$E = E_{cell}^0 - \frac{RT}{2F} \ln \frac{a_{Pb^{++}} \times a_{Sn}}{a_{Pb} \times a_{Sn^{++}}},$$

with n equal to 2. The activities of the solid lead and tin are both unity, by the usual convention, and hence at 25° C this equation for the E.M.F. of the cell is

$$E = E_{cell}^0 - \frac{0.05915}{2} \log \frac{a_{Pb^{++}}}{a_{Sn^{++}}}.$$

The value of E_{cell}^0 is equal to $E_{Pb}^0 - E_{Sn}^0$, i.e., $+0.126 - 0.140 = -0.014$ volt; hence,

$$E = E_{cell}^0 - \frac{0.05915}{2} \log \frac{0.1}{1.0} = +0.016 \text{ volt,}$$

as found above.

49h. Equilibrium Constants.—For many purposes it is more convenient to calculate the equilibrium constant of a reaction, instead of the free energy change; this constant provides the same information from a slightly different viewpoint. The equilibrium constant is related to the standard free energy change by equation (37.8), viz.,

$$\Delta F^0 = -RT \ln K,$$

and since ΔF^0 is equal to $-nF E^0_{\text{cell}}$, by equation (49.17), it follows that

$$E^0_{\text{cell}} = \frac{RT}{nF} \ln K, \qquad (49.18)$$

or at 25°, with E^0_{cell} in volts,

$$E^0_{\text{cell}} = \frac{0.05915}{n} \log K. \qquad (49.19)$$

By means of these equations the equilibrium constant of any reaction can be readily calculated from the standard E.M.F. of the reversible cell in which the reaction occurs.

The reaction in the Daniell cell, for example, is

$$\text{Zn}(s) + \text{Cu}^{++} = \text{Zn}^{++} + \text{Cu}(s)$$

for the passage of two faradays, i.e., $n = 2$, and the equilibrium constant is given by

$$K = \left(\frac{a_{\text{Zn}^{++}}}{a_{\text{Cu}^{++}}}\right)_e, \qquad (49.20)$$

where the subscript e is used to show that the activities are the values when the reacting system attains equilibrium. The activities of the solid zinc and copper are, as usual, taken as unity. The standard E.M.F. of the cell, as seen above, is equal to $E^0_{\text{Zn}} - E^0_{\text{Cu}}$, i.e., 1.101 volt at 25° C; hence, by equations (49.19) and (49.20),

$$1.101 = \frac{0.05915}{2} \log \left(\frac{a_{\text{Zn}^{++}}}{a_{\text{Cu}^{++}}}\right)_e$$

$$\left(\frac{a_{\text{Zn}^{++}}}{a_{\text{Cu}^{++}}}\right)_e = 1.7 \times 10^{37}.$$

The ratio of the activities of the zinc and copper ions in the solution at equilibrium will be approximately equal to the ratio of the concentrations under the same conditions; hence, when a system consisting of metallic zinc and copper and their bivalent ions in aqueous solution attains equilibrium, the ratio of the zinc ion to the cupric ion concentration is extremely large. If zinc is placed in a solution of cupric ions, the latter will be displaced to form metallic copper until the $c_{\text{Zn}^{++}}/c_{\text{Cu}^{++}}$ ratio in the solution is about 10^{37}. In other words, the zinc will displace the copper from the solution until the quantity of cupric ions remaining is extremely small.

Stannous chloride is frequently employed for the reduction of ferric to ferrous ions, according to the reaction

$$\text{Sn}^{++} + 2\text{Fe}^{+++} = \text{Sn}^{++++} + 2\text{Fe}^{++}.$$

This process is made up of the oxidation process

$$\text{Sn}^{++} = \text{Sn}^{++++} + 2\epsilon,$$

and the reduction

$$2Fe^{+++} + 2\epsilon = 2Fe^{++},$$

so that it can take place for the passage of two faradays in the reversible cell

$$Pt \mid Sn^{++}, Sn^{++++} \quad \| \quad Fe^{++}, Fe^{+++} \mid Pt.$$

The E^0_{cell} value for this cell is equal to $E^0_{Pt, Sn^{++}, Sn^{++++}} - E^0_{Pt, Fe^{++}, Fe^{+++}}$, i.e., $-0.15 - (-0.771) = +0.621$ volt (Table LVI); hence, at 25° C, by equation (49.19),

$$0.621 = \frac{0.05915}{2} \log K,$$

$$K = \left(\frac{a_{Sn^{++++}} \times a^2_{Fe^{++}}}{a^2_{Fe^{+++}} \times a_{Sn^{++}}}\right)_e = 1.0 \times 10^{21}.$$

The high value of the equilibrium constant means that when equilibrium is attained in the ferrous-ferric and stannous-stannic mixture, the concentrations (activities) of stannous and ferric ions must be negligibly small in comparison with those of the stannic and ferrous ions. In other words, when a stannous salt is added to a solution of ferric ions, the latter are reduced virtually completely to ferrous ions, within the limits of analytical accuracy.

It is apparent from these calculations that the large equilibrium constants, indicating almost complete reaction from left to right, are due to the high value of the standard E.M.F. of the cell, i.e., E^0_{cell} [see equation (49.19)], in which the reaction may be supposed to occur. The further the standard potentials of the two systems concerned are apart in Table LVI, the greater will be E^0_{cell}, and hence the more complete will be the reaction as written. This is in general accord with the conclusions reached in § 49g.

If the two standard potentials are not very different, all the substances involved will be present in somewhat similar concentrations at equilibrium, and the reaction will not be complete in either direction. This may be illustrated by reference to the reaction

$$Ag^+ + Fe^{++} = Ag(s) + Fe^{+++},$$

for which it can be readily shown, from the known Ag, Ag^+ and Pt, Fe^{++}, Fe^{+++} standard potentials, that

$$K = \left(\frac{a_{Fe^{+++}}}{a_{Ag^+} \times a_{Fe^{++}}}\right)_e = 2.97.$$

This value of the equilibrium constant shows that appreciable concentrations of silver and ferrous ions must be present at equilibrium; the reaction, therefore, does not normally approach completion, and so it could not be used for analytical purposes. It may be recalled that in the presence of thiocyanate ions the reverse reaction, i.e., the reduction of ferric ions by metallic silver, takes place to a considerable extent. This is not due to any change in the equilibrium constant, which must always have the same value at a given temperature, but to the fact that the precipitation of the silver ions as silver thiocyanate makes a_{Ag^+} very small, so that $a_{Fe^{+++}}$ must be diminished correspondingly in order to maintain the value of the equilibrium constant. The reaction under consideration consequently takes place from right to left.

The equilibrium constant of a process can be obtained in another manner, which is fundamentally identical with that just described, although the approach is somewhat different. When the activities of various substances present in a reversible cell happen to correspond to the equilibrium values, the E.M.F. of the cell will be zero. This statement can be proved in various ways; for example, it is known that for a system at equilibrium, at constant temperature and pressure, ΔF is zero (§ 26b); consequently, since ΔF is equal to $-nFE$, the E.M.F. of the cell, i.e., E, containing the equilibrium system must be zero. If the E.M.F. of the cell is zero, it follows that the potentials of the two electrodes must be identical; the activities (or concentrations) for which the two electrodes of a cell have the same (oxidation) potential must consequently be the equilibrium values.

Problem: Utilize the fact that two electrodes must have the same potential when equilibrium is attained to calculate K for the familiar reaction $Zn + Cu^{++} = Zn^{++} + Cu$.

If $(a_{Zn^{++}})_e$ and $(a_{Cu^{++}})_e$ represent the activities of the respective ions when equilibrium is attained, the potentials of the Zn, Zn^{++} and Cu, Cu^{++} electrodes, which must then be equal, are given by

$$E_{Zn} = E_{Zn}^0 - \frac{RT}{2F} \ln (a_{Zn^{++}})_e = +0.761 - 0.02958 \log (a_{Zn^{++}})_e$$

$$E_{Cu} = E_{Cu}^0 - \frac{RT}{2F} \ln (a_{Cu^{++}})_e = -0.340 - 0.02958 \log (a_{Cu^{++}})_e.$$

Equating these potentials, it is seen that

$$+0.761 - 0.02958 \log (a_{Zn^{++}})_e = -0.340 - 0.02958 \log (a_{Cu^{++}})_e$$

$$\left(\frac{a_{Zn^{++}}}{a_{Cu^{++}}}\right)_e = K = 1.7 \times 10^{37},$$

which is identical with the result obtained previously. The two methods of calculation are, of course, the same, although the point of view is somewhat different.

In the foregoing treatment standard electrode potentials have been employed to calculate equilibrium constants; the reverse calculation is equally possible and has, in fact, been used in certain cases. For example, the standard potential of Sn, Sn^{++} given in Table LVI was obtained in this manner. Finely divided metallic lead and tin were shaken with solutions containing stannous and plumbous perchlorates until the equilibrium in the reaction

$$Sn(s) + Pb^{++} = Sn^{++} + Pb(s)$$

was reached; the ratio of the concentrations of stannous and plumbous ions at equilibrium, i.e., $(c_{Sn^{++}}/c_{Pb^{++}})_e$, was found to be 2.98 at 25° C. Assuming the ratio of the concentrations to be equal to the ratio of the activities in terms of molalities, as is probably the case if the solutions are dilute, it follows that

$$K = \left(\frac{a_{\mathrm{Sn}^{++}}}{a_{\mathrm{Pb}^{++}}}\right)_e = 2.98.$$

The reaction under consideration may be separated into the oxidation and reduction processes, viz.,

$$\mathrm{Sn}(s) = \mathrm{Sn}^{++} + 2\epsilon \quad \text{and} \quad \mathrm{Pb}^{++} + 2\epsilon = \mathrm{Pb}(s),$$

so that the complete reaction, as written above, takes place in the reversible cell

$$\mathrm{Sn} \mid \mathrm{Sn}^{++} \parallel \mathrm{Pb}^{++} \mid \mathrm{Pb}$$

for the passage of two faradays, i.e., n is 2. The E^0 for the complete cell is equal to $E^0_{\mathrm{Sn}} - E^0_{\mathrm{Pb}}$, where E^0_{Pb} is known to be $+0.126$ volt at $25°$ C; hence, by equation (49.19),

$$E^0 = E^0_{\mathrm{Sn}} - 0.126 = \frac{0.05915}{2} \log 2.98$$

$$= 0.014,$$

$$E^0_{\mathrm{Sn}} = +0.140 \text{ volt.}$$

The standard potential of the Sn, Sn^{++} electrode is thus $+0.140$ volt at $25°$ C.

Concentration Cells

50a. Concentration Cells with Transference.—Imagine two electrodes of the same metal (or hydrogen), represented by M, in contact with two solutions in which the corresponding M^+ ion activities are a_1 and a_2. Suppose the electrodes are combined to form a cell in which the liquid junction potential is assumed to be eliminated; thus,

$$\mathrm{M} \mid \mathrm{M}^+ (a_1) \parallel \mathrm{M}^+ (a_2) \mid \mathrm{M}.$$

This is a form of **concentration cell,** since its E.M.F. depends on the difference in the concentrations (activities) of two solutions of the same electrolyte. The oxidation potential of the left-hand electrode is given by equation (49.5) as

$$E_1 = E^0_{\mathrm{M}} - \frac{RT}{nF} \ln a_1,$$

and the reduction potential of the right-hand electrode is

$$-E_2 = -E^0_{\mathrm{M}} + \frac{RT}{nF} \ln a_2.$$

The E.M.F. of the cell is equal to $E_1 - E_2$, in the usual manner, so that

$$E = E_1 - E_2 = \frac{RT}{nF} \ln \frac{a_2}{a_1}. \tag{50.1}$$

It is seen, therefore, that the E.M.F. of the concentration cell depends on the ratio of the ionic activities in the two solutions; as mentioned earlier, single ion activities do not have precise thermodynamic significance, and so the ratio a_2/a_1 may be taken as (approximately) equal to the ratio of the *mean activities* (see below) of the ions in the respective solutions.

If the liquid junction potential between the two solutions is not eliminated, the E.M.F. of the concentration cell has a different value from that obtained above. Consider, for example, the cell

$$\text{Pt, H}_2 \text{ (1 atm.)} \mid \text{HCl}(a_1) \mid \text{HCl}(a_2) \mid \text{H}_2 \text{ (1 atm.), Pt}$$

in which the two solutions of hydrochloric acid are in contact, as indicated by the dotted line. In this cell there is a direct transfer of electrolyte from the more concentrated to the more dilute solution; it is, therefore, referred to as a **concentration cell with transference.** When one faraday passes through the cell, 1 gram atom of hydrogen gas is oxidized at the left-hand electrode to yield 1 gram ion of hydrogen ions; the same amount of hydrogen ions is reduced to form 1 gram atom of hydrogen gas which is liberated at the right-hand electrode. If t_+ and t_- are the transference numbers of the hydrogen cations and the chloride anions, representing the fractions of the current carried by the respective ions, then during the passage of the one faraday through the cell, t_+ faradays will be carried by t_+ gram ion of hydrogen ions in one direction (from left to right), while t_- faradays will be carried by t_- gram ion of chloride ions in the opposite direction, as shown below.

Pt, H$_2$(1 atm.) $\mid$ H Cl (a_1) ⋮ H Cl (a_2) $\mid$ H$_2$(1 atm.), Pt

½ H$_2$(g) → H$^+$(soln.) $\xrightarrow{\;t_+\;}$ H$^+$ H$^+$(soln.) → ½ H$_2$(g)

Cl$^-$ $\xleftarrow{\;t_-\;}$

The net result is the transfer of $1 - t_+$, that is, t_-, gram ion of hydrogen ions and t_- gram ion of chloride ions from right to left, i.e., from the solution represented by the subscript 2 to that indicated by the subscript 1. Utilizing equation (31.6), it follows that the free energy change accompanying the transfer is given by

$$\Delta F = t_- RT \ln \frac{(a_+)_1}{(a_+)_2} + t_- RT \ln \frac{(a_-)_1}{(a_-)_2}, \tag{50.2}$$

where a_+ and a_- refer to the activities of the hydrogen and chloride ions, respectively, in the indicated solutions. The **mean activity** of an electrolyte is defined as *the geometric mean of the activities of the component ions;* if a_1

and a_2 are the mean activities of the hydrochloric acid in the two solutions, it follows by the definition that

$$a_1^2 = (a_+)_1(a_-)_1 \quad \text{and} \quad a_2^2 = (a_+)_2(a_-)_2.$$

Utilizing these results, equation (50.2) becomes

$$\Delta F = 2t_- RT \ln \frac{a_1}{a_2}. \tag{50.3}$$

The free energy change, by equation (48.1), is also equal to $-EF$, since n is 1, for the passage of one faraday; hence, from equation (50.3),

$$E = 2t_- \frac{RT}{F} \ln \frac{a_2}{a_1}. \tag{50.4}$$

50b. Liquid Junction Potential.—The equation (50.4) just derived, for the E.M.F. of the concentration cell with transference, includes the potential at the junction between the two solutions of hydrochloric acid. If this potential could be eliminated entirely, the E.M.F. of the corresponding concentration cell would be given (approximately) by equation (50.1) as

$$E = \frac{RT}{F} \ln \frac{a_2}{a_1}, \tag{50.5}$$

since n is 1; the difference between equations (50.4) and (50.5) thus gives the value of the liquid junction potential E_l, so that

$$E_l = (2t_- - 1) \frac{RT}{F} \ln \frac{a_2}{a_1}. \tag{50.6}$$

Although this expression for the liquid junction potential was developed by considering a cell containing hydrochloric acid solutions, it holds equally for any two solutions of uni-univalent electrolytes with mean activities a_1 and a_2. Remembering that t_- is also equal to $1 - t_+$, it can be readily seen that the factor $2t_- - 1$ in equation (50.6) is equivalent to $t_- - t_+$, so that the equation can be written as

$$E_l = (t_- - t_+) \frac{RT}{F} \ln \frac{a_2}{a_1}. \tag{50.7}$$

It is apparent from this result that the sign and magnitude of the liquid junction potential depends on the transference numbers of the anions and cations. If the transference numbers of the two ions of the electrolyte are not very different, the liquid junction potential will be small. This conclusion is of general applicability, and it accounts for the use of concentrated solutions of potassium chloride to minimize liquid junction potentials (§ 49d); the transference numbers of the potassium and chloride ions in this electrolyte are approximately equal, as is evident from the data in Table LI.

Problem: Calculate the liquid junction potential at 25° C between two solutions of HCl of mean activities 0.1 and 0.01, respectively; the mean value of the cation transference number (t_+) in this range may be taken as 0.828 (Table LI).

Since t_+ is 0.828, t_- is 0.172, so that equation (50.7) becomes, at 25° C,

$$E_l = (0.172 - 0.828) \times 0.05915 \log \frac{0.01}{0.1}$$

$$= 0.039 \text{ volt.}$$

(This result gives an indication of the magnitude of liquid junction potentials; the value is increased by increasing the ratio of the concentrations, or activities, of the two solutions. For hydrochloric acid, and other acids, the potentials are exceptionally high, because of the large transference number of the hydrogen ion.)

50c. Concentration Cells without Transference.—It is apparent from § 47d that for the cell

$$\text{Pt, } H_2 \text{ (1 atm.) } | \text{ HCl}(a_1) \qquad \text{AgCl}(s) | \text{ Ag,}$$

the reaction is

$$\tfrac{1}{2}H_2 \text{ (1 atm.) } + \text{AgCl}(s) = H^+(a_+)_1 + Cl^-(a_-)_1 + \text{Ag}(s),$$

where $(a_+)_1$ and $(a_-)_1$ are the activities of the hydrogen and chloride ions in the hydrochloric acid solution of mean activity a_1. If the cell is reversed, and the mean activity of the solution is changed to a_2, viz.,

$$\text{Ag } | \text{ AgCl}(s) \qquad \text{HCl}(a_2) | \text{ H}_2 \text{ (1 atm.), Pt}$$

the reaction is

$$H^+(a_+)_2 + Cl^-(a_-)_2 + \text{Ag}(s) = \tfrac{1}{2}H_2 \text{ (1 atm.) } + \text{AgCl}(s).$$

If the two cells as written are joined together to give the combined cell

$$\text{Pt, } H_2 \text{ (1 atm.) } | \text{ HCl}(a_1) \quad \text{AgCl}(s) | \text{ Ag } | \text{ AgCl}(s) \quad \text{HCl}(a_2) | \text{ H}_2 \text{ (1 atm.), Pt,}$$

the over-all reaction, for the passage of one faraday, is obtained by summing the separate reactions in the two component cells; thus,

$$H^+(a_+)_2 + Cl^-(a_-)_2 = H^+(a_+)_1 + Cl^-(a_-)_1.$$

The cell reaction for the passage of one faraday, i.e., n is 1, is thus the transfer of 1 gram ion of hydrogen ions and 1 gram ion of chloride ions from the solution represented by the subscript 2, to that indicated by the subscript 1. Again, by means of equation (31.6), the free energy accompanying the transfer is

$$\Delta F = RT \ln \frac{(a_+)_1}{(a_+)_2} + RT \ln \frac{(a_-)_1}{(a_-)_2},$$

and since ΔF is also equal to $-EF$, since n is unity, it follows, by exactly the same arguments as in § 50a, that

$$E = \frac{2RT}{F} \ln \frac{a_2}{a_1}, \qquad (50.8)$$

where a_1 and a_2 are, as before, the mean activities of the ions in the two solutions.

A cell of the type described is called a **concentration cell without transference,** for the E.M.F. depends on the relative concentrations (activities) of the two solutions concerned; the operation of the cell is not accompanied by the *direct* transfer of electrolyte from one solution to the other. The transfer occurs indirectly, as shown above, as the result of chemical reactions. A comparison of the concentration cell with transference in § 50a with that for the same solutions without transference shows that the change of type is achieved by introducing an intermediate electrode, $AgCl(s) \mid Ag \mid AgCl(s)$, between the two solutions. In general, any concentration cell with transference, in which the electrodes are reversible with respect to the cation, can be converted into one without transference by separating the two solutions, in the manner indicated above, by means of an electrode that is reversible with respect to the anion of the electrolyte. In the case under consideration, the end electrodes are hydrogen electrodes, and so the intermediate electrode is reversible with respect to the chloride ion. If the end electrodes had been anion electrodes, then a concentration cell without transference would be obtained by using a suitable cation electrode to separate the two solutions.

The E.M.F. of a cell *with transference*, represented by the symbol E_t, is given by equation (50.4) as

$$E_t = 2t_- \frac{RT}{F} \ln \frac{a_2}{a_1}.$$

The E.M.F. of the same cell, that is, with the same end electrodes and with the same solutions, *without transference*, represented by E, is given by equation (50.8); it is immediately evident that

$$\frac{E_t}{E} = t_-. \tag{50.9}$$

The ratio of the E.M.F.'s of the two concentration cells, one with transference and the other without transference, is thus equal to the transference number of the anion, in this case. If the end electrodes had been reversible with respect to the anion, the ratio E_t/E would give the transference number of the cation. This method for the determination of transference numbers, by measuring the E.M.F.'s of cells with and without transference, has been employed in a number of cases. A difficulty arises in practice because the transference number varies with the concentration, although in the foregoing treatment the tacit assumption has been made that it is constant. Mathematical methods have been devised to allow for this variation.

50d. Determination of Activities and Activity Coefficients.—The measurement of the E.M.F.'s of concentration cells without transference provides one of the most convenient methods for evaluating the activities and activity coefficients of electrolytes. As seen in § 50c, the concentration cell without transference may be regarded as made up of two similar cells connected in opposite directions; these cells differ only in the activities a_1 and a_2 of the electrolytes contained in them. If E_1 and E_2 are the E.M.F.'s of these partial cells, or half-cells, in which the mean activities are a_1 and a_2, respectively, the E.M.F. of the whole cell is equal to $E_1 - E_2$; hence, by equation (50.8), for the particular cells described in § 50c,

$$E_1 - E_2 = \frac{2RT}{F} \ln \frac{a_2}{a_1}. \tag{50.10}$$

If in one of the two solutions the activity, e.g., a_2, is unity, the corresponding E.M.F. of the half-cell containing that solution is the standard E.M.F., i.e., E^0; equation (50.10) then reduces to the form

$$E - E^0 = -\frac{2RT}{F} \ln a, \tag{50.11}$$

where E represents the E.M.F. of the half-cell

$$H_2 \text{ (1 atm.)} \mid HCl(m) \qquad AgCl(s) \mid Ag,$$

in which m is the molality of the hydrochloric acid solution, and a is its mean activity; the standard E.M.F. of this cell with a equal to unity is then E^0. If the quantity $(2RT/F) \ln m$ is added to both sides of equation (50.11) the result is

$$E + \frac{2RT}{F} \ln m - E^0 = -\frac{2RT}{F} \ln \frac{a}{m}. \tag{50.12}$$

As seen in § 31d, the ratio of the activity to the molality, i.e., a/m, is equal to the activity coefficient γ; in the present case the ratio a/m in equation (50.12) is the mean activity coefficient of the electrolyte (hydrochloric acid) in the solution of molality m. Making this substitution, and inserting the values of R, T and F, in the usual manner, equation (50.12) becomes, at 25° C,

$$E + 0.1183 \log m - E^0 = -0.1183 \log \gamma. \tag{50.13}$$

Since the E.M.F. of the half-cell, i.e., E, can be measured for any molality m of the electrolyte, it should be possible to evaluate the corresponding activity coefficient γ, from equation (50.13), provided E^0 were known. Several methods, of varying degrees of accuracy, are available for the determination of E^0; one of the simplest will be described here. At infinite dilution the solution behaves ideally, and then a and m are identical, so that γ, equal to a/m, is unity; $\log \gamma$ is then zero, and hence, by equation (50.13), $E + 0.1183 \log m$ gives the value of E^0. The procedure is to plot the experimental values of $E + 0.1183 \log m$, for various molalities m of the electrolyte, against a convenient function of m, and to extrapolate the curve to m equal to zero, i.e., to infinite dilution. The extrapolated result gives E^0, which is found to be $+0.2224$ volt at 25° C for the cell depicted above (see § 49d). It is thus possible to determine the activity coefficient γ of hydrochloric acid at any molality; the product of the molality and the activity coefficient gives the corresponding mean activity of the electrolyte.

Concentration cells with transference have also been employed for the evaluation of activity coefficients; the calculations require, in addition, a knowledge of transference numbers over a range of concentrations. The procedure is too involved to be described here. The actual values for the activity coefficients of a number of electrolytes at various molalities will be given in Chapter XV, where the reasons for the difference between the activity and the concentration (or molality), that is, the departure from ideal behavior, will be considered.

50e. Gas Concentration Cells.—An interesting, and theoretically important, type of concentration cell is obtained when the two electrodes consist of a gas at different pressures, p_1 and p_2, in contact with the same solution of the corresponding ions (see § 55b), e.g.,

$$\text{Pt, H}_2(p_1) \mid \text{Solution of hydrogen ions} \mid \text{H}_2(p_2), \text{Pt}.$$

The oxidation reaction at the left-hand electrode is

$$\text{H}_2(p_1) = 2\text{H}^+ + 2\epsilon,$$

while the reduction at the right-hand electrode is

$$2\text{H}^+ + 2\epsilon = \text{H}_2(p_2),$$

the hydrogen ions referring to the same solution. The complete cell reaction for the passage of two faradays is thus

$$\text{H}_2(p_1) = \text{H}_2(p_2),$$

that is, the transfer of 1 mole of hydrogen gas from the electrode of pressure p_1 to that of pressure p_2. If these pressures are not too high, and the gas may be supposed to behave ideally, the free energy change accompanying this transfer from p_1 to p_2 is given by equation (26.22) as

$$\Delta F = RT \ln \frac{p_2}{p_1}. \tag{50.14}$$

If E is the E.M.F. of the cell, the free energy change ΔF is also given by $-2EF$, since n is 2; hence, from equation (50.14),

$$E = \frac{RT}{2F} \ln \frac{p_1}{p_2}. \tag{50.15}$$

This equation has been verified for hydrogen gas pressures from 0.005 to 100 atm. At higher pressures deviations are observed, mainly because of departure of the gas from ideal behavior.

Expressions similar to equation (50.15) can be derived for cells with chlorine or oxygen electrodes; in the latter case, it should be remembered that four faradays must pass through the cell for the transfer of 1 mole of gas from one electrode to the other, i.e., n is equal to 4 for the cell reaction. It will be noted that the E.M.F. of a gas cell of the type considered is independent of the concentration of the electrolyte.

Problem: Calculate the E.M.F. at 25° C of a hydrogen gas cell in which the left-hand electrode is at a pressure (p_1) of 0.1 atm. and the right-hand electrode (p_2) at 1 atm.

The E.M.F. required is given by equation (50.15); at 25° C, this becomes

$$E = \frac{0.05915}{2} \log \frac{p_1}{p_2} = 0.02958 \log \frac{0.1}{1.0}$$

$$= -0.02958 \text{ volt.}$$

(Since the E.M.F. is negative, the oxidation potential of the left-hand electrode is smaller than that of the right-hand electrode. This is to be expected, since the spontaneous reaction must involve the transfer of gas from the higher pressure, i.e., right-hand, to the lower pressure, i.e., left-hand. The oxidation must therefore occur at the former and reduction at the latter. The reverse would be the case for an oxygen or chlorine cell, since these yield negative ions; the oxidation process would then occur at the electrode of lower pressure.)

THE DISCHARGE OF IONS

51a. Decomposition Voltage and Discharge Potential.—One of the essential characteristics of a reversible cell is that the reaction occurring in the cell can be reversed by the application of an external E.M.F. just greater than that of the cell itself. For example, the cell

$$\text{Zn} \mid \text{M ZnBr}_2 \text{ solution} \mid \text{Br}_2 \ (l), \text{Pt}$$

will have an E.M.F. of about 1.83 volt, made up of approximately $+0.76$ volt, for the oxidation potential of the zinc electrode, minus approximately -1.07, i.e., plus $+1.07$ volt, for the reduction potential of the bromine electrode (Table LVI). The reactions at the two electrodes are

$$\text{Zn} = \text{Zn}^{++} + 2\epsilon \quad \text{and} \quad \text{Br}_2 + 2\epsilon = 2\text{Br}^-,$$

so that zinc dissolves at one electrode while bromine passes into solution at the other. If an external E.M.F. just greater than 1.83 volt is applied to a molar solution of zinc bromide, therefore, these processes should be reversed; zinc ions should be discharged to form metallic zinc at one electrode (cathode), while bromine ions should be utilized to liberate free bromine at the other electrode (anode). The application of an E.M.F. of about 1.8 volt should thus be capable of causing continuous electrolysis of a solution of zinc bromide, accompanied by the liberation of zinc at the cathode and bromine at the anode. The **decomposition voltage** of an electrolyte is defined as *the minimum external E.M.F. which must be applied between two electrodes in the electrolyte in order to bring about continuous electrolytic decomposition.* The decomposition voltage of zinc bromide solution should thus be about 1.8 volt, and this has been verified by direct experiment. In general, therefore, the decomposition voltage of any solution should be approximately equal to the E.M.F. of the galvanic cell consisting of the substances liberated at the two electrodes in contact with the same solution. This agreement is to be expected, of course, only if the electrodes behave reversibly, and it has been confirmed for a number of such cases. It will be seen shortly, however, that certain ions are not discharged reversibly, and then the rule fails to hold. For the present, however, reversible behavior will be assumed.

The decomposition voltage may be separated into two parts, representing the potentials which must be applied to each of the electrodes. Thus, in the continuous electrolysis of zinc bromide solution, the potential at the cathode must be just greater than the reversible Zn, $ZnBr_2$ soln. potential, and that at the anode must just exceed the reversible $ZnBr_2$ soln., Br_2, Pt, potential. The **discharge potential** or **deposition potential** at any electrode is defined as *the potential at which the continuous deposition of material (or discharge of ions) commences at that electrode.* This should be equal to the reversible potential of the deposited material in the same solution, as has been verified in many instances, such as the deposition of zinc, cadmium, copper, silver, mercury, chlorine, bromine and iodine from solutions of their ions. The metals nickel, cobalt and iron behave somewhat abnormally in this connection, for reasons not clearly understood; however, the abnormality disappears as the temperature is raised, and the deposition potentials of these metals approach the ordinary reversible potentials.

In certain electrolyses the discharge of anions does not occur readily, but an equivalent electrical process, namely the passage of the anode metal into solution, takes place. An instance of this behavior is found with a silver anode in a solution of silver nitrate; the process occurring at the anode is not the discharge of an anion, but the metallic silver enters the solution as silver ions. In cases of this kind the potential of the anode, again, just exceeds the reversible potential of the metal in the given solution, e.g., silver in silver nitrate.

51b. Consecutive Electrode Processes.—If an electrolyte contains a number of different positive and negative ions then, provided there are no disturbing factors, *each ionic discharge will take place as the appropriate potential is reached.* When the external E.M.F. applied to an electrolytic cell is gradually increased, the potentials of the electrodes change until the discharge potentials of the most easily discharged ions are attained. The cations that are discharged most readily are those having the largest (algebraic) *reduction potential,* since the free energy of the process

$$M^+ + \epsilon = M$$

will then have its greatest negative value, indicating a considerable tendency for the discharge process to occur. The largest reduction potential corresponds to the smallest oxidation potential; hence, the lower the oxidation potential, the more easily will the metallic ion be discharged. This means that for solutions of approximately equivalent ionic concentrations, *metals lower in Table LVI will be deposited before those higher in the table.* Consider, for example, the electrolysis of a solution containing molar zinc and copper sulfates; the oxidation potentials of the respective metals in these solutions are $+0.76$ and -0.34 volt. It follows, therefore, from the foregoing arguments that the cupric ions will be discharged first and metallic copper will be deposited on the cathode. If the electrolysis is prolonged to such an extent that the copper ions in the solution are almost exhausted, the cathode potential will increase until that for zinc deposition is attained. In general, if a solution contains a number of different cations, each will be deposited in turn, starting from the one with the lowest oxidation potential *in the given solution*. This is the principle used in the separation of metals by electrolysis for analytical and other purposes.

Sometimes two metals have potentials that are not very different in the particular electrolyte; then simultaneous deposition of both metals occurs in the form of an alloy. Such is the case, for example, for copper and zinc in a solution containing their complex cyanides. Although the potentials of these metals differ considerably in sulfate solutions, the ionic concentrations are so changed in the complex cyanide solutions as to bring their respective potentials close together. When these solutions are electrolyzed, an alloy of zinc and copper, i.e., brass, is deposited on the cathode. Other alloys can be obtained in an analogous manner.

It should be pointed out that all aqueous solutions contain hydrogen ions, as will be explained more fully in the next chapter, and consequently the discharge of these ions, with the liberation of hydrogen, is a possibility to be taken into consideration. The discharge of certain cations, such as those of tin, nickel, iron, etc., is almost invariably accompanied by the evolution of hydrogen, particularly if the electrolytic solution is appreciably acid.

51c. Processes at the Anode.—The behavior at an anode is, in general, analogous to that at a cathode; the process associated with the largest negative free energy change, whether it be solution of the metallic anode to form cations or the discharge of anions, will take place first. Subsequent anodic processes will follow in order of decreasing negative free energy change. The reaction taking place at the anode is always an oxidation, and so *anodic processes take place in order of decreasing oxidation potential*, since ΔF is equal to $-nFE$ [equation (48.1)]. For solutions of approximately the same ionic concentration, the order of anodic processes, viz., formation of cations or discharge of anions, is that of the potentials in Table LVI; the higher the process in this table, the more easily does it occur at an anode.

If a copper electrode is placed in an acid solution of M copper sulfate, three anodic processes are possible; these are first, solution of the copper to form cupric ions at a potential of -0.34 volt (Table LVI); second, discharge of hydroxyl ions, which are always present in aqueous solution, at about -1.2 volt (see § 49f, II, problem); and third, discharge of SO_4^{--} ions, probably at a very high negative potential, e.g., about -2 volts. It is evident, therefore, that when an external E.M.F. is applied to the copper anode, the first process to occur will be that of the anode passing into solution as cupric ions, since the reaction $Cu = Cu^{++} + 2\epsilon$ has the highest oxidation potential. The next possible process is the discharge of hydroxyl ions, but this will not occur unless for some reason the solution of the anode is prevented. At an unattackable anode, such as platinum, where anion discharge is the only possible process, hydroxyl ions would be discharged and oxygen evolved. The discharge of SO_4^{--} ions, with a large negative potential, is in any event highly improbable. The same, incidentally, is true of other similar ions, such as NO_3^-, PO_4^{---}, etc., which do not correspond to stable uncharged molecules; they have high negative oxidation potentials, and their discharge from aqueous solutions does not commonly take place.

The consecutive discharge of anions may be illustrated by reference to the electrolysis of a N solution of neutral potassium iodide; such an electrolyte contains iodide and hydroxyl ions, whose oxidation potentials in the given electrolyte are about -0.54 (Table LVI) and -0.80 volt (see § 49f, II, problem), respectively. When this solution is electrolyzed by means of an external E.M.F., using a platinum anode, it is evident that iodide ions will be discharged preferentially. If the supply of these ions is exhausted, the anode potential will change, and hydroxyl ion discharge and oxygen evolution will occur.

51d. Carriage of Current and Discharge of Ions.—Attention may be called here to an important matter in connection with electrolysis and ionic discharge that was referred to briefly in § 44a. It is essential to distinguish clearly between the ions *carrying the current to the electrode* and those actually *discharged at the electrode*. The carriage of current depends on the concentrations and speeds of the various ionic species present in the solution, whereas the discharge potential is determined essentially by the reversible potential in the given solution of the particular ion discharged. The two aspects of the problem are quite independent and should not be confused. As long as the appropriate quantity of electricity is transferred across the solution and at the electrodes, it is immaterial which ions perform the respective functions. In an acid solution of copper sulfate, for instance, the current is carried toward the anode almost exclusively by sulfate ions, and toward the cathode largely by hydrogen ions and to some extent by cupric ions; nevertheless, cupric ions only are discharged at the cathode, while at an inert, unattackable anode, such as one of platinum, hydroxyl ions are discharged, although they play a negligible part in the carriage of current.

51e. The Decomposition of Water.—When aqueous solutions of acids or bases are electrolyzed, with platinum or other unattackable electrodes, the products are usually hydrogen gas at the cathode and oxygen gas at the anode. It can be shown that a reversible cell consisting of a hydrogen gas electrode and an oxygen gas electrode, each at 1 atm. pressure, has an E.M.F. of about 1.2 volt in any dilute aqueous solution.* If the discharge of hydrogen and hydroxyl ions occurred reversibly, the decomposition voltage of a solution of acid or base should be 1.2 volt. The experimental results obtained in a number of instances, using platinum for both cathode and anode, are quoted in Table LVII (M. Le Blanc, 1893); in each case hydrogen and oxygen gas were liberated at the respective electrodes.

* This result may be derived very simply from the fact that ΔF^0 for the reaction $H_2(g) + \frac{1}{2}O_2(g) = H_2O(l)$, occurring in the hydrogen-oxygen cell for the passage of two faradays, is $-56,700$ cal. at 25° C.

TABLE LVII. DECOMPOSITION VOLTAGES OF AQUEOUS SOLUTIONS OF ACIDS AND BASES

Acid	Volts	Base	Volts
Phosphoric	1.70	Tetramethylammonium OH	1.74
Nitric	1.69	Ammonia	1.74
Sulfuric	1.67	Sodium hydroxide	1.69
Perchloric	1.65	Potassium hydroxide	1.67

It is evident that the decomposition voltages of the aqueous solutions of acids and bases differ considerably from 1.2 volt, although they are all approximately constant at 1.7 volt. The fact that the decomposition voltage is the same for a variety of acids and bases suggests that the electrolytic processes occurring at the anode and the cathode, respectively, are identical in all the solutions. The only process which could be common to all these solutions is the decomposition of water; hydrogen ions are discharged at the cathode, to yield hydrogen gas, while hydroxyl ions are discharged at the anode, leading to the evolution of oxygen, in every case. In a dilute solution of sulfuric acid, for example, the only cations are hydrogen ions, and so these must be discharged at the cathode. The most abundant anions in the solution are the sulfate ions, and these undoubtedly carry the current to the anode, but the hydroxyl ions have the higher oxidation potential, and so they are actually discharged in spite of their extremely low concentration in acid solution (see § 53g). Similarly, in a solution of sodium hydroxide, it is easy to understand that hydroxyl ions are discharged at the anode. At the cathode, however, hydrogen ions are most easily discharged, although their concentration is small in comparison with that of the sodium ions; the discharge of the latter requires a much larger cathode potential.

51f. Overvoltage.—Although the decomposition voltage of an aqueous solution of an acid or base is constant, in many cases, at about 1.7 volt, with smooth platinum electrodes, the value is different if other metals are employed as electrode materials. With a lead anode and a platinum cathode in dilute sulfuric acid, the decomposition voltage is lowered to about 1.6 volt, but if the cathode is lead and the anode is platinum the value is increased to 2.25 volts. It is apparent that the decomposition voltage of a solution, from which hydrogen and oxygen gases are liberated, depends on the individual nature of the cathode and of the anode. At each electrode the potential is in excess of the calculated reversible value by an amount that is dependent upon the nature of the metal and upon whether it forms the cathode or the anode. *The difference between the potential of an electrode at which gas evolution occurs and the theoretical reversible potential for the same solution* is called the **overvoltage**. By measuring the separate potentials at cathode and anode, when hydrogen and oxygen, respectively, are being evolved, and subtracting the calculated reversible potentials for the same solution, the cathodic and anodic overvoltages can be determined.

The results for a few common electrodes at ordinary temperatures are given in Table LVIII; it should be mentioned that these values refer to the condition when visible gas evolution commences and are to be regarded as

TABLE LVIII. CATHODIC AND ANODIC OVERVOLTAGES

Electrode	Hydrogen	Oxygen
Platinized platinum	~0.00 volt	0.25 volt
Iron	0.08	0.25
Smooth platinum	0.09	0.45
Nickel	0.21	0.06
Cadmium	0.48	0.43
Lead	0.64	0.31
Zinc	0.70	—
Mercury	0.78	—

approximate only. The actual overvoltage varies with the state of the electrode surface, as the difference between the results for smooth and platinized (blackened) platinum shows; it also depends to some extent on the nature of the electrolyte, and on the current strength per unit area of electrode. Overvoltages invariably decrease with increasing temperature.

According to the data in Table LVIII, the hydrogen overvoltage at a smooth platinum cathode is 0.09 volt, while the oxygen overvoltage at an anode of this metal is 0.45 volt; the total excess potential is thus 0.54 volt. If this is added to the reversible E.M.F. of the hydrogen-oxygen cell, i.e., 1.2 volt, which is the theoretical decomposition voltage for the simultaneous liberation of hydrogen and oxygen, the result approximates the actual decomposition voltage of 1.7 volt.

Problem: An aqueous solution is electrolyzed with a lead anode and a mercury cathode so that oxygen and hydrogen, respectively, are evolved. Calculate the approximate decomposition voltage at ordinary temperatures.

The oxygen overvoltage at a lead anode is 0.31, and the hydrogen overvoltage at a mercury cathode is 0.78 volt; the total overvoltage is thus 0.31 + 0.78 = 1.09 volt. This must be added to the theoretical decomposition voltage, i.e., 1.2, giving 2.29 or about 2.3 volts for the actual value.

The existence of an overvoltage, or potential in excess of the reversible value, which must be applied to an electrode in order to make a particular ionic discharge process occur, means that one of the stages in the process is slow. In the discharge of hydrogen ions, for instance, the initial state consists of hydrated hydrogen ions in the solution, and the final state is the bubble of evolved hydrogen gas; in between these states there is undoubtedly a number of stages, at least one of which takes place slowly and hence gives rise to an overvoltage. The exact nature of the slow stage is not clearly understood, and since the subject is highly controversial, with much difference of opinion, it will not be discussed here. However, no matter what the actual cause of overvoltage, the fact remains that it is a phenomenon of great practical consequence.

In a solution containing approximately molar zinc sulfate and sulfuric acid, the reversible (oxidation) potentials of zinc and hydrogen are about +0.76 volt and 0.0 volt, respectively. It is to be expected, therefore, that when such a solution is electrolyzed hydrogen alone, and no zinc, should be liberated at the cathode. In actual practice, however, considerable amounts of zinc are deposited, in addition to hydrogen, in spite of the large difference in the reversible potentials. The explanation for this behavior is to be found in the high overvoltage for hydrogen evolution at a zinc cathode. From the data in Table LVIII, this is seen to be about 0.7 volt, and so the evolution of hydrogen will not take place until a potential of 0.7 volt is attained, instead of about 0.0 volt. The former potential is so close to that for zinc ion discharge (0.76 volt) in the same solution that simultaneous deposition of hydrogen and zinc occurs. The fact that zinc can be deposited on the cathode by the electrolysis of an acid solution of zinc sulfate is thus to be attributed to the high hydrogen overvoltage of zinc. The deposition of other metals lying above hydrogen in the table of electrode potentials (Table LVI) is also largely due to overvoltage effects.

Overvoltage also plays an important part in the industrial production of sodium hydroxide and chlorine by the electrolysis of sodium chloride solutions. If the discharge of hydroxyl ions were reversible it should occur in preference to that of chloride ions, so that oxygen would be evolved, and not chlorine. Because of the high overvoltage accompanying the evolution of oxygen, and the small, or zero, overvoltage for chlorine, the order of the two anode processes is reversed and chlorine is actually obtained.

Problem: In an alkali-chlorine cell a saturated (about 6 N) solution of sodium chloride is electrolyzed, at ordinary temperatures, between a steel cathode (hydrogen overvoltage 0.2) and a graphite anode (oxygen overvoltage 0.6 volt; chlorine overvoltage negligible). Explain the nature of the electrode processes.

Cathode. The cations present in the solution are H^+ and Na^+; the concentrations (approx. activities) are 10^{-7} (for a neutral solution, see § 53g) and 6 g. ion per liter, respectively. The standard oxidation potentials (Table LVI) are $+2.71$ and ± 0.0 volt, respectively; hence, the reversible potentials in the given electrolyte are, by equation (49.12),

$$E_H = 0 - 0.059 \log 10^{-7} = +0.41 \text{ volt}$$

$$E_{Na} = +2.71 - 0.059 \log 6 = +2.66 \text{ volt.}$$

Since the hydrogen overvoltage is 0.2, the potential for the discharge of hydrogen ions and the evolution of hydrogen gas is about $+0.41 + 0.2 = 0.61$ volt (note signs!); this is so much below that required for Na^+ ion discharge, that the former process obviously takes place in preference (§ 51b). [Only by raising the potential to 2.66 volt, e.g., by a large increase of current, would discharge of Na^+ ions (as is often erroneously suggested for normal electrolysis) become possible.] Incidentally, this is another illustration of the fact that the ions carrying the current are not necessarily those discharged (§ 51d). The removal of H^+ ions by discharge leaves an excess of OH^- ions in the solution (§ 53g), and this accounts for the formation of sodium hydroxide.

Anode. The anions present are OH^- and Cl^-, the concentrations being 10^{-7} and 6 g. ion per liter, as for H^+ and Na^+, respectively. The standard oxidation potentials of O_2 and Cl_2 are -0.40 and -1.36, respectively, and hence the reversible potentials in the given electrolyte are, by equation (49.13),

$$E_O = -0.40 + 0.059 \log 10^{-7} = -0.81 \text{ volt}$$

$$E_{Cl} = -1.36 + 0.059 \log 6 = -1.31 \text{ volt.}$$

Allowing for the overvoltage (0.6 volt), the oxygen evolution potential resulting from the discharge of OH^- ions, is $-0.81 - 0.6 = -1.41$ volt (note signs!), and hence discharge of chlorine ions, and the formation of chlorine gas, will take place in preference. By increasing the anode potential, however, oxygen evolution would tend to occur.

READING REFERENCES

1. **Displacement series of metals.** Taft and Stareck, *Journal of Chemical Education*, **7**, 1520 (1930).

2. **Corrosion.** Rohrman, *ibid.*, **10**, 141, 215, 297 (1933).

3. **E.M.F. and oxidation-reduction reactions.** Lochte, *ibid.*, **10**, 373 (1933).

4. **Aspects of electrode potentials.** Bennett, *ibid.*, **13**, 56 (1936).

5. **Potentiometric experiments.** Miller and Lucasse, *ibid.*, **13**, 581 (1936).

6. **Concentration cell measurements.** Hoyt, *ibid.*, **14**, 185 (1937).

7. **E.M.F. and equilibrium constant.** Livingston and Lingane, *ibid.*, **15**, 320 (1938).

8. **Transference numbers by E.M.F.** Masson and Mellon, *ibid.*, **16**, 512 (1939); **17**, 96 (1940).

9. **Sign of electrode potential.** Hoyt, *ibid.*, **17**, 530 (1940).

10. **Silver-silver chloride electrode.** Redlich and Maranville, *ibid.*, **20**, 10 (1943).

11. **Primary cells in silicic acid gels.** Steinbach, *ibid.*, **21**, 32 (1944).

12. **Electromotive series.** Hall, *ibid.*, **24**, 403 (1944).

REVIEW QUESTIONS

1. Explain the principle used in the measurement of E.M.F. by the potentiometer method. Describe the form of standard cell in general use.

2. What is a reversible cell in the thermodynamic sense? Give an example of such a cell and explain its behavior.

3. Describe, with examples, the three chief types of reversible electrodes. State the reactions occurring in each case and generalize the results.

4. How is the nature of the cell reaction determined? Give examples. What is the reaction taking place at each electrode and in the complete cell?

5. What is the connection between the E.M.F. of a reversible cell and the free energy change of the reaction occurring in the cell? How may the result be confirmed by means of the Gibbs-Helmholtz equation?

6. Derive a general expression for the E.M.F. of any cell in terms of the activities of the substances taking part in the cell reaction. Illustrate by reference to a particular cell.

7. Explain the meaning of the hydrogen scale for stating electrode potentials. Derive a general equation for the potential of any electrode on the hydrogen scale. What is meant by the standard electrode potential?

8. Derive the general equation for the potential of a reversible electrode consisting of (a) a metal in a solution of its ions, (b) a nonmetal in a solution of its ions, (c) an "oxidation-reduction" system.

9. Distinguish between the oxidation and reduction potentials of the same electrode. How do these potentials differ? Explain the convention generally employed.

10. How is the E.M.F. of a cell related to the potentials of the separate electrodes on the basis of the usual convention?

11. Describe the use of the calomel reference electrode for the determination of single electrode potentials. What is the purpose of a salt bridge in this connection?

12. Explain the principle used in the determination of standard oxidation potentials. Give some examples of electrodes, the electrode reactions and the standard oxidation potentials.

13. Describe the application of electrode potentials to the determination of ionic activities. Mention some specific uses of such determinations.

14. Describe the variation of the potential of an electrode with the concentrations of the ions in the solution. How may this variation be used to determine the number of charges (valence) carried by an ion?

15. Explain, with the aid of a figure, the principle involved in potentiometric titrations.

16. How may the E.M.F. of a cell be used to indicate whether a particular reaction can occur spontaneously? Illustrate with examples, and state the general conclusions reached.

17. Explain the use of standard electrode potentials for the determination of (a) standard free energy changes, (b) equilibrium constants, of cell reactions. What can be stated about the electrode potentials in a reversible cell at equilibrium?

18. Derive the equation for the E.M.F. of a concentration cell with transference. How is the result affected if the liquid junction potential is assumed to be eliminated?

19. Derive the value of the liquid junction potential between two solutions of the same electrolyte. How does the result account for the use of potassium chloride as a salt bridge?

20. Derive an equation for the E.M.F. of a concentration cell without transference. How is this used to determine transference numbers?

21. Describe a method for determining activity coefficients by E.M.F. measurements.

22. Derive the equation for the E.M.F. of a gas concentration cell in which the gas is (a) hydrogen, (b) oxygen, at different pressures.

23. What is meant by the decomposition voltage? How is it related to the electrode potentials?

24. What are the factors which determine the order in which the various possible (a) cathode, (b) anode, processes occur in electrolysis? Illustrate with examples.

25. What is meant by overvoltage? Account for the fact that the decomposition voltage, when hydrogen and oxygen are liberated, is 1.7 volts using platinum electrodes. How would the decomposition voltage be changed if lead electrodes were employed?

26. Account for the fact that (a) zinc is deposited from an acid solution of zinc sulfate, and (b) chlorine is liberated from a neutral chloride solution, upon electrolysis, although hydrogen and oxygen, respectively, might have been expected.

PROBLEMS *

I

1. The E.M.F. of the cell Pb, $PbCl_2(s)$ KCl soln. AgCl(s), Ag is $+0.4900$ volt at $25°$, and it decreases by 1.86×10^{-3} volt for every $10°$ rise of temperature. State the cell reaction and calculate the free energy change and heat content change for this reaction at $25°$ C.

2. Write the equations for the chemical reactions taking place in the following cells, and thence derive expressions for the E.M.F.'s in terms of the activities of the

* In connection with the matter of significant figures, it should be understood that statements such as $a = 0.1$, 0.05 M, etc., are intended to imply that these figures may be taken as exact. Unless otherwise stated, temperatures are to be taken as $25°$ C.

various substances involved: Pt, $H_2(g)$, HCl soln. $Hg_2Cl_2(s)$, Hg; and Zn, Zn^{++} || Sn^{++}, Sn^{++++}, Pt.

3. State the process occurring at each electrode, and the complete reaction, in the following cell: Pt, $Fe(CN)_6^{----}$, $Fe(CN)_6^{---}$ || I^-, $I_2(s)$, Pt. By means of the data in Table LVI, determine (a) the standard E.M.F. of the cell, including the sign, (b) the standard free energy of the cell reaction in kcal.

4. Referring to the cell in the preceding problem, in what direction does the reaction proceed spontaneously with all substances in their standard states? What would be the ratio of the activities of $Fe(CN)_6^{---}$ to $Fe(CN)_6^{----}$ necessary to reverse the direction?

5. By means of the data in Table LVI, calculate the equilibrium constant at $25°$ C of the reaction $2Hg + 2Fe^{+++} = Hg_2^{++} + 2Fe^{++}$, representing the reduction of ferric ions by means of mercury, which takes place in the cell Hg, Hg_2^{++} || Fe^{++}, Fe^{+++}, Pt. In which direction does the spontaneous reaction proceed when all the substances are in their standard states?

6. Calculate the change in potential of (a) a zinc electrode, (b) a silver electrode, when the concentration (activity) of the reversible ions in the solution is changed from 0.1 to 0.005 molal.

7. Calculate the potential of each electrode, and the E.M.F. of the complete cell in the following cases: Cd, Cd^{++} ($a = 0.01$) || Cl^- ($a = 0.5$), Cl_2 (1 atm.), Pt; and Pt, Cu^+ ($a = 10^{-5}$), Cu^{++} ($a = 0.1$) || Cu^{++} ($a = 0.05$), Cu. State whether the cell as written will function spontaneously, i.e., with positive current passing through the cell from left to right.

8. Calculate the activities (or ratio of activities) of the reversible ions in the following electrodes at the given (oxidation) potentials: Zn, Zn^{++} ($E = +0.795$ volt); and Pt, Fe^{++}, Fe^{+++} ($E = -0.783$ volt).

9. Determine the liquid junction potential at $25°$ C between 0.1 and 0.005 M solutions of lithium chloride in which the mean ionic activity coefficients are 0.792 and 0.924, respectively. The transference number required may be estimated from the data in Table LI.

10. The E.M.F. of the cell with transference Ag, AgCl(s) KCl 0.01 M ⋮ KCl 0.025 M AgCl(s), Ag is -0.02434 volt. The cell with the same extreme electrodes, but without transference, is -0.04963 volt at $25°$ C. Calculate the mean transference numbers of the K^+ and Cl^- ions in the given concentration range of potassium chloride.

11. Calculate the reversible E.M.F. of the cell, including the sign, consisting of two oxygen electrodes, at pressures of 1.00 atm. (at the left) and 0.025 atm. (at the right) at $25°$ C.

II

1. The E.M.F. of the cell Zn, $ZnSO_4 \cdot 7H_2O(s)$ $ZnSO_4$ soln. $Hg_2SO_4(s)$, Hg is 1.4328 volt at $15°$ and 1.4268 volt at $20°$ C. State the cell reaction, and calculate the free energy change and heat content change for this reaction at $20°$ C.

2. Write the equations for the chemical reactions taking place in the following cells, and thence derive expressions for the E.M.F.'s in terms of the activities of the various substances involved: Pt, $H_2(g)$, H_2SO_4 soln. $PbSO_4(s)$, Pb; and Cd, Cd^{++} || Ce^{+++}, Ce^{++++}, Pt.

3. State the process occurring at each electrode, and the complete reaction, in the following cell: Cu, Cu^{++} || Fe^{++}, Fe^{+++}, Pt. By means of the data in Table LVI, determine (a) the standard E.M.F. of the cell, including the sign, (b) the standard free energy change of the cell reaction in kcal.

4. Referring to the cell in the preceding problem, in what direction does the reac-

tion proceed spontaneously with all substances in their standard states? What would be the ratio of the activities of Fe^{+++} to Fe^{++} necessary to reverse the direction?

5. By means of the data in Table LVI, calculate the equilibrium constant at 25° C of the reaction $2Ag + 2Hg^{++} = 2Ag^+ + Hg_2^{++}$, representing the reduction of mercuric ions by means of silver, which takes place in the cell Ag, $Ag^+ \parallel Hg_2^{++}$, Hg^{++}, Pt. In which direction does the reaction proceed when all the substances are in their standard states?

6. Calculate the change in potential of (a) a hydrogen electrode, (b) a copper electrode, when the concentration of the reversible ions in the solution is changed from 0.001 to 0.25 molal.

7. Calculate the potential of each electrode, and the E.M.F. of the complete cell in the following cases: Pt, Fe^{++} $(a = 0.1)$ Fe^{+++} $(a = 0.01) \parallel Fe^{++}$ $(a = 0.002)$, Fe; and Ag, Ag^+ $(a = 0.025) \parallel H^+$ $(a = 10^{-4}) \mid H_2$ (1 atm.), Pt.

8. Calculate the activities (or ratio of activities) of the reversible ions in the following electrodes at the given (oxidation) potentials: Pt, $Br_2(l)$, Br^- $(E = -1.128$ volt); and Pt, Hg_2^{++}, Hg^{++} $(E = -0.943$ volt).

9. The liquid junction potential between 0.05 and 0.1 M solutions of hydrochloric acid has been determined experimentally to be -0.01119 volt at 25° C. Calculate the ratio of the activity coefficients in the two solutions, using transference number data from Table LI. (The experimental value is 1.044.)

10. The E.M.F. of the cell with transference Ag, AgCl(s) 0.1 M HCl ⋮ 0.01 M HCl AgCl(s), Ag is 0.09253 volt at 25° C. If the liquid junction is completely eliminated, e.g., by the use of a salt bridge, the E.M.F. is 0.05590 volt. Calculate the mean transference numbers of the H^+ and Cl^- ions in the given range of concentrations of hydrochloric acid.

11. The E.M.F. of a cell consisting of two hydrogen electrodes is $+0.0464$ volt at 25° C. The pressure of the gas in the left-hand electrode is 10 atm.; what is the gas pressure in the other?

CHAPTER XV

EQUILIBRIA IN ELECTROLYTES

ACTIVITY COEFFICIENTS

52a. The Dissociation Constant.—In a solution of any electrolyte there should be an equilibrium between the free ions, on the one hand, and undissociated molecules, on the other hand; the latter may consist of both true nonionized, covalent molecules, if any are present, and also of ion-pairs held together by electrostatic forces (§ 46f). Writing the equilibrium in the form

$$MA \rightleftharpoons M^+ + A^-,$$

the equilibrium constant, called the **dissociation constant,** is given by equation (37.7) as

$$K = \frac{a_{M^+} \times a_{A^-}}{a_{MA}}, \tag{52.1}$$

where, as usual, the a factors are the activities of the indicated species. The activity may be represented as the product of the concentration c, in gram ions or moles per liter, and the activity coefficient f (§ 31d); hence, equation (52.1) may be written as

$$K = \frac{c_{M^+} \times c_{A^-}}{c_{MA}} \cdot \frac{f_{M^+} \times f_{A^-}}{f_{MA}}. \tag{52.2}$$

Suppose α is the degree of dissociation of the electrolyte, that is, the fraction of the electrolyte present in the form of free ions (§ 46e), and c is its *total concentration* in moles per liter; c_{M^+} and c_{A^-} are then each equal to αc, while c_{MA} is equal to $(1 - \alpha)c$. It follows, therefore, that

$$K = \frac{\alpha c \times \alpha c}{(1 - \alpha)c} \cdot \frac{f_{M^+} \times f_{A^-}}{f_{MA}}$$

$$= \frac{\alpha^2 c}{1 - \alpha} \cdot \frac{f_{M^+} \times f_{A^-}}{f_{MA}}. \tag{52.3}$$

The degree of dissociation α can be derived from conductance measurements, for both strong and weak electrolytes, as indicated in § 46e, but a complete evaluation of the dissociation constant K requires a knowledge of activity coefficients. For weak electrolytes the ionic concentrations are low, and the solutions do not deviate appreciably from ideal behavior; the activity coefficients thus are not greatly different from unity. Fairly good values of the

483

dissociation constant can consequently be obtained even if the activity coefficient factor in equation (52.3) is ignored, that is, taken as unity. For strong electrolytes, however, except at extreme dilutions, there is marked departure from ideality; the activity coefficient factor then differs considerably from unity, and also varies with the concentration. It is necessary, therefore, to inquire further into the subject of activity coefficients, particularly of strong electrolytes.

52b. Mean Activity Coefficients of Strong Electrolytes.—Three methods have been chiefly employed for the determination of the mean activity coefficients of strong electrolytes; the freezing point and E.M.F. methods (§§ 31e, 50d) have been used for solutions of all kinds, whereas the procedure based on vapor measurements has also been employed for less dilute solutions. The results obtained by these methods, as well as in other ways, are in good agreement with one another and may be accepted as accurate. Mean activity coefficients are usually expressed in terms of molalities, and some of the most reliable data for a number of electrolytes at 25° C are quoted in Table LIX. For dilute aqueous solutions there is little difference between activity coefficients based on molalities and those based on concentrations in moles per liter; hence, the figures in Table LIX may be employed in equations such as (52.3).

TABLE LIX. MEAN ACTIVITY COEFFICIENTS AT 25° C

Molality	HCl	NaCl	KCl	CaCl$_2$	ZnCl$_2$	H$_2$SO$_4$	LaCl$_3$	ZnSO$_4$
0.001	0.966	0.966	0.966	0.888	0.881	—	0.853	0.734
0.005	0.930	0.928	0.927	0.789	0.767	0.643	0.716	0.477
0.01	0.906	0.903	0.902	0.732	0.708	0.545	0.637	0.387
0.02	0.878	0.872	0.869	0.669	0.642	0.455	0.552	0.298
0.05	0.833	0.821	0.816	0.584	0.556	0.341	0.417	0.202
0.10	0.798	0.778	0.770	0.524	0.502	0.266	0.356	0.148
0.50	0.769	0.679	0.652	0.510	0.376	0.155	0.303	0.063
1.00	0.811	0.656	0.607	0.725	0.325	0.131	0.387	0.044
2.00	1.011	0.670	0.577	1.554	—	0.125	0.954	0.035
3.00	1.31	0.719	0.572	3.38	—	0.142	—	0.041

An examination of the mean activity coefficients recorded in the table brings to light a number of interesting facts. It will be observed, in the first place, that the values always decrease at first as the concentration is increased, but they generally pass through a minimum and then increase again. This is seen more clearly in Fig. 105, where the activity coefficients of a few electrolytes have been plotted against the square root of the corresponding molality. At high concentrations the activity coefficients often exceed unity, so that the mean activity of the electrolyte is actually greater than the concentration. In dilute solutions of strong electrolytes, therefore, the deviations from ideal behavior make the activity, which may be regarded as the effective or ideal concentration, less than the actual concentration; in concentrated solutions, however, the effective concentration is greater than the actual value, since the activity coefficient exceeds unity. It will be seen, further, from Table LIX, that electrolytes of the same valence type, e.g., sodium and potassium chlorides, etc., or calcium and zinc chlorides, etc., have almost identical activity coefficients at the same concentration, in dilute solution. Finally, it will be noted, from Fig. 105 and from the values in the table, that the deviation from ideal behavior, that is, the departure of the activity coefficients from unity, at a given concentration is greater the higher the product of the valences of the two ions constituting the electrolyte.

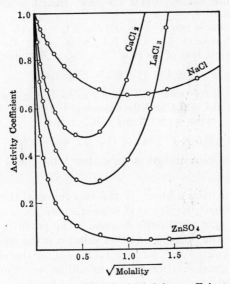

FIG. 105. Mean ionic activity coefficients

52c. The Ionic Strength.—In order to represent the variation of activity coefficient with concentration, especially in the presence of added electrolytes, a quantity called the **ionic strength** has been introduced (G. N. Lewis and M. Randall, 1921); it is a measure of the intensity of the electrical field due to the ions in a solution. The ionic strength is usually represented by the symbol μ, and is defined as *half the sum of the terms obtained by multiplying the molality (or concentration) of each ion in the solution by the square of its valence.* Thus, if a solution contains a number of different ionic species, indicated by the subscripts 1, 2, 3, etc., so that their respective molalities are m_1, m_2, m_3, etc., in gram ions per 1000 grams of solvent, and z_1, z_2, z_3, etc., are the corresponding valences, i.e., the charges carried by the ions, then the ionic strength is given by

$$\mu = \tfrac{1}{2}(m_1 z_1^2 + m_2 z_2^2 + m_3 z_3^2 + \cdots), \tag{52.4}$$

the sum being taken for all the ions present. For a single electrolyte, such as sodium chloride or potassium sulfate, the equation reduces to two terms, one for the positive and one for the negative ion, viz.,

$$\mu = \tfrac{1}{2}(m_+ z_+^2 + m_- z_-^2). \tag{52.5}$$

Problem: Calculate the ionic strength of (i) 0.1 molal KCl, (ii) 0.2 molal K_2SO_4, (iii) a solution containing 0.1 molal KCl and 0.2 molal K_2SO_4.

(i) The molality of each ion in 0.1 molal KCl is 0.1, i.e., $m_+ = 0.1$ and $m_- = 0.1$; also $z_+ = 1$ and $z_- = 1$, since both ions are univalent; hence,

$$\mu = \tfrac{1}{2}(0.1 \times 1^2 + 0.1 \times 1^2) = 0.1.$$

(For any single uni-univalent electrolyte the ionic strength is always equal to the molality of the solution.)

(ii) Since K_2SO_4 produces two K^+ ions and one SO_4^{--} ion, the molality of the ions in 0.2 molal K_2SO_4 is thus $m_+ = 2 \times 0.2 = 0.4$, and $m_- = 0.2$; the valence of the K^+ ion is 1, i.e., z_+ is 1, while that of the SO_4^{--} ion, i.e., z_-, is 2; hence,

$$\mu = \tfrac{1}{2}(0.4 \times 1^2 + 0.2 \times 2^2) = 0.6.$$

(iii) In the mixture of 0.1 molal KCl and 0.2 molal K_2SO_4, the total molality m_1 of the K^+ ions is $0.1 + 0.4 = 0.5$, and the valence z_1 is 1; for the Cl^- ions, m_2 is 0.1 and z_2 is 1; for the SO_4^{--} ions, m_3 is 0.2 and z_3 is 2; hence,

$$\mu = \tfrac{1}{2}(0.5 \times 1^2 + 0.1 \times 1^2 + 0.2 \times 2^2) = 0.7.$$

(It will be noted that the ionic strength of the mixture is the sum of the ionic strengths of the constituents.)

It has been found from a study of the experimental data that in dilute solutions, *the mean activity coefficient of a given electrolyte is approximately the same in all solutions of a given ionic strength.* The particular ionic strength may be partly due to the presence of other salts; it is the *total* ionic strength, however, which determines the activity coefficient of the electrolyte under consideration. This generalization which, as will be seen shortly, has a theoretical basis, holds only for solutions of relatively low ionic strength; as the concentration is increased, the specific influence of the added salts becomes apparent.

52d. The Debye-Hückel Theory.—The fact that solutions of electrolytes do not behave ideally, and give activity coefficients that differ from unity, has been accounted for quantitatively, at least for dilute solutions; this has been achieved by means of the interionic attraction theory described in connection with conductance in § 46d. When an ideal solution is diluted there is a definite change of free energy which depends only on the initial and final concentrations of the solute. In the case of an ionic solution, however, there is an additional free energy change equivalent to the work done against the electrostatic attraction in removing an ion from its oppositely charged ionic atmosphere. This difference between the actual and ideal free energy of dilution is related to the activity coefficient of the ion in the given solution.

On the basis of these arguments, P. Debye and E. Hückel (1923) were able to derive the expression

$$\log f_i = -1.823 \times 10^6 \frac{z_i^2}{(DT)^{3/2}} \sqrt{\mu} \tag{52.6}$$

for the variation of the activity coefficient f_i of an ion i of valence z_i with the *total* ionic strength μ of the solution; the symbols D and T represent the dielectric constant of the solvent and the absolute temperature, respectively. For a given solvent and temperature, D and T have definite values which may be inserted; equation (52.6) then takes the general form

$$\log f_i = -Az_i^2 \sqrt{\mu}, \tag{52.7}$$

where A is a constant for the solvent at the specified temperature. The mean activity coefficient f of an electrolyte, which is the quantity determined by experiment (§ 52b), is equal to the geometric mean of the activity coefficients of the individual ions; hence,

$$\log f = -Az_+z_- \sqrt{\mu}, \tag{52.8}$$

where z_+ and z_- are the (numerical) valences of the two ions. For water as solvent at 25° C, the dielectric constant D is 78.54 and T is 298.16° K; the constant A is then found to be 0.509, so that equation (52.8) becomes

$$\log f = -0.509z_+z_- \sqrt{\mu}. \tag{52.9}$$

The foregoing equations represent what has been called the **Debye-Hückel limiting law**; the term "limiting" is used because the derivation is such that

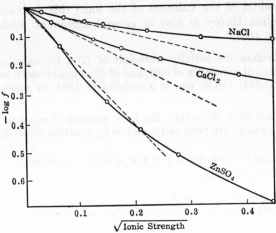

FIG. 106. Test of the Debye-Hückel limiting law

the results are applicable only to very dilute solutions approaching the limit of infinite dilution.

For an ideal solution the activity coefficient f is unity, and hence $\log f$ would be zero; the fact that $\log f$ is negative, according to the Debye-Hückel equations, means that the activity coefficient should be less than unity, as it actually is in dilute solutions of electrolytes. According to equation (52.8) the plot of $\log f$ against $\sqrt{\mu}$, the square root of the ionic strength, should be a straight line, passing through the origin, with a slope equal to $-Az_+z_-$ (see Fig. 106). Measurements of activity coefficients of various electrolytes, some of which will be referred to more explicitly in § 52f, in aqueous and non-aqueous solutions, at various temperatures, have established the quantitative accuracy of the Debye-Hückel equations for dilute solutions. The experimental values of log f, for three salts of different valence types in aqueous solution, are plotted against $\sqrt{\mu}$ in Fig. 106; the dashed lines show the behavior to be expected from equation (52.8) or (52.9). It is evident that the experimental results approach the values required by the Debye-Hückel limiting law as infinite dilution is attained.

It can be readily shown in other ways that the Debye-Hückel theory is in general agreement with conclusions already noted from experimental data. By equation (52.8) or (52.9) the activity coefficient of a given electrolyte, for which z_+ and z_- are constant, should depend only on the ionic strength of the solution; this is identical with the rule of Lewis and Randall mentioned in the preceding section. Further, the Debye-Hückel limiting equations contain no reference to the specific nature of the electrolyte, apart from the valence of the ions; hence, as noted in § 52b, electrolytes of the same valence type should have equal activity coefficients at the same concentration or ionic strength. Finally, the value of log f, which is a measure of the deviation of the activity coefficient from unity, should be numerically proportional to z_+z_-, the product of the valences of the ions; this derivation from the interionic attraction theory is also in general agreement with the experimental facts (Fig. 105).

Problem: Calculate the activity coefficient of (i) a uni-univalent electrolyte, e.g., HCl, NaCl, etc., at a molality of 0.01, and of (ii) a uni-bivalent, or bi-univalent, electrolyte, e.g., Na_2SO_4, $CaCl_2$, etc. at a molality of 0.001, in aqueous solution at 25° C.

(i) For a uni-univalent electrolyte, the ionic strength is equal to the molality; hence μ is 0.01; z_+ and z_- are both unity, and so by equation (52.9), for an aqueous solution at 25°,

$$\log f = -0.509 \times 1 \times 1 \times \sqrt{0.01} = -0.0509$$
$$f = 0.889.$$

(The experimental value is about 0.90.)

(ii) For the 0.001 molal uni-bivalent electrolyte μ is $\frac{1}{2}(0.002 \times 1^2 + 0.001 \times 2^2)$ = 0.003; hence

$$\log f = -0.509 \times 1 \times 2 \times \sqrt{0.003} = -0.0558$$
$$f = 0.879.$$

(The experimental value is about 0.88.)

If the Debye-Hückel equations held at appreciable concentrations, it would mean that the activity coefficient would decrease steadily with increasing ionic strength, i.e., with increasing concentration. It is evident from the results in Table LIX and Fig. 105 that this is not the case; beyond a certain concentration, which varies with the nature of the electrolyte, the activity decreases more slowly, passes through a minimum, and then increases as the concentration is increased. Although the valence type is still an important factor, the behavior becomes a property of the individual electrolyte.

To account for the variation of activity coefficient with the ionic strength in solutions that are not very dilute, two empirical corrections have been applied to the Debye-Hückel treatment; one makes allowance for the sizes of the ions, and the other for the aggregation of water molecules in the vicinity of every ion. The effect of these factors is to add a correction term, proportional to the ionic strength, to the limiting equation; thus, the more complete expression, which holds at higher concentration, is of the form

$$\log f = -Az_+z_-\sqrt{\mu} + C\mu, \qquad (52.10)$$

where C is an empirical constant which can only be evaluated from experimental data; the value of C depends on the nature of the electrolyte, but no method has yet been devised for its calculation theoretically.

Since equation (52.10) involves two terms, each being a function of the ionic strength, but of opposite sign, it can obviously satisfy the condition that the activity coefficient should have a minimum value at a particular ionic strength. At low concentrations the $-Az_+z_-\sqrt{\mu}$ term predominates, but as the concentration increases the $C\mu$ term becomes more important; hence, the activity coefficient will decrease with increasing ionic strength in dilute solutions, but it will increase in more concentrated solutions. It was seen above that the activity coefficient can be greater than unity, so that the activity exceeds the concentration; the physical interpretation of this fact is that the attraction between the ions and the solvent (dipole) molecules results in such a segregation of the latter that the *effective* concentration of the solution, relative to the *free* solvent molecules, becomes greater than the actual concentration.

As explained in § 31b deviation of a solution from ideal behavior can also be expressed in terms of the osmotic coefficient g; for an ideal solution $1 - g$ should be zero, and the value should increase with increasing departure from ideality. According to the Debye-Hückel theory, for dilute solutions,

$$1 - g = Bz_+z_-\sqrt{\mu} \qquad (52.11)$$

where B is a constant, for a given solvent and temperature, equal to $0.768A$. It can be seen from equation (52.11) that $1 - g$ should increase with increasing ionic strength or concentration, the effect being more marked the higher the valence of the ions constituting the electrolyte. This deduction from theory is in agreement with the experimental results, as shown in Fig. 59.

52e. Solubility Equilibria: The Solubility Product.—When a solution is saturated with a salt there is an equilibrium between the solid state and the ions in solution; the rate at which ions pass from the solid crystal lattice into the solution is then equal to the rate at which the ions return to the lattice. To consider a simple case, such as that of the sparingly soluble salt silver chloride in contact with its saturated solution, the equilibrium may be represented by

$$AgCl(s) \rightleftharpoons Ag^+ + Cl^-,$$

where Ag^+ and Cl^- refer, as usual, to the hydrated ions in solution. The corresponding equilibrium constant is given in the familiar manner as

$$K = \frac{a_{Ag^+} \times a_{Cl^-}}{a_{AgCl}}, \tag{52.12}$$

where the a's are the activities. Since the silver chloride is present in the solid state, its activity may be taken as unity, in accordance with convention (§ 35a); equation (52.12) then reduces to

$$K_s = a_{Ag^+} \times a_{Cl^-}, \tag{52.13}$$

where the constant K_s is known as the **solubility product** of the silver chloride. In general, for any electrolyte having the general formula M_xA_y, in contact with its saturated solution, the equilibrium between the solid and the ions in solution is

$$M_xA_y(s) \rightleftharpoons xM^+ + yA^-,$$

and the solubility product is given by

$$K_s = a_{M^+}^x \times a_{A^-}^y. \tag{52.14}$$

If the activity of an ion is written as the product of its concentration in gram ions per liter and the corresponding activity coefficient, as in § 52a, the expression for the solubility product of silver chloride [equation (52.13)] becomes

$$K_s = (c_{Ag^+} \times c_{Cl^-})(f_{Ag^+} \times f_{Cl^-}). \tag{52.15}$$

If the solid is sparingly soluble, as is the case with silver chloride, and the solution does not contain added electrolyte, the ionic strength of the medium will be low and the activity coefficients will not differ greatly from unity. In these circumstances, equation (52.15) may be reduced to the approximate expression

$$K_s = c_{Ag^+} \times c_{Cl^-}, \tag{52.16}$$

or, in general, from equation (52.14)

$$K_s = c_{M^+}^x \times c_{A^-}^y. \tag{52.17}$$

This is the form in which the solubility product principle is frequently employed, although it is applicable only if the ionic strength of the solution is small. The significance of the principle is that *when a solution is saturated with a given salt, the product of the activities (or concentrations) of its constituent ions, raised to the appropriate powers, must be constant*, irrespective of the nature of the other electrolytes present in the solution.

The solubility product of a sparingly soluble substance may be derived from a knowledge of the solubility in pure water. For example, if S_0 mole per liter is the solubility of silver chloride in water, then since this salt is probably completely dissociated, even in the saturated solution, the concentration of both silver and chloride ions is S_0 gram ion per liter; hence, by equation (52.16),

$$K_s = c_{Ag^+} \times c_{Cl^-} = S_0^2.$$

It was shown in § 46j that the solubility of silver chloride in pure water, as derived from conductance measurements, is 1.31×10^{-5} mole per liter at 25° C; the solubility product is consequently $(1.31 \times 10^{-5})^2$, i.e., 1.72×10^{-10}. It may be noted that at this low concentration it is reasonably justifiable to assume both complete dissociation and an activity coefficient of unity for the electrolyte, as has been done in the foregoing calculations.

Another method for determining solubility products is based on the evaluation of ionic activities by measurements of electrode potential; this procedure may also be illustrated by reference to silver chloride. A solution of 0.1 N potassium chloride is saturated with silver chloride, and the silver ion activity a_{Ag^+} is determined by means of a silver electrode; the value, as shown by the problem in § 49f, I, is found to be 2.34×10^{-9} gram ion per 1000 grams of water or, with sufficient accuracy, 2.34×10^{-9} gram ion per liter at 25° C. The chloride ion activity a_{Cl^-} in the solution may be taken as equal to the mean activity of the 0.1 N potassium chloride, in which the silver chloride is dissolved; this is equal to the product of the concentration, i.e., 0.1, and the mean activity coefficient 0.77 (Table LIX), so that a_{Cl^-} is 0.077. The solubility product is then given by

$$K_s = a_{Ag^+} \times a_{Cl^-} = 2.34 \times 10^{-9} \times 0.077$$
$$= 1.80 \times 10^{-10},$$

a result in satisfactory agreement with that obtained above by a fundamentally different procedure.

Problem: The silver ion activity in a saturated solution of Ag_2CrO_4 in 0.1 M K_2CrO_4 was found to be 6.4×10^{-6} g. ion per liter at 25° C; assuming the mean activity coefficient of the K_2CrO_4 to be equal to that of another uni-bivalent electrolyte at the same concentration, calculate the solubility of Ag_2CrO_4 in pure water at 25° C.

From Table LIX, the mean activity coefficient of a uni-bivalent electrolyte at 0.1 M is about 0.5; hence, the activity of the CrO_4^{--} ions in 0.1 M K_2CrO_4 may be taken as $0.1 \times 0.5 = 0.05$. The solubility product of Ag_2CrO_4 is then

$$K_s = a_{Ag^+}^2 \times a_{CrO_4^{--}} = (6.4 \times 10^{-6})^2 \times 0.05$$
$$= 2.05 \times 10^{-12}.$$

If s mole per liter is the solubility of Ag_2CrO_4 in water, and the salt is assumed to be completely dissociated, c_{Ag^+} is equal to $2s$ and $c_{CrO_4^{--}}$ is s g. ion per liter; the solubility product is then $(2s)^2 \times s = 4s^3$, so that

$$4s^3 = 2.05 \times 10^{-12}$$
$$s = 8.00 \times 10^{-5} \text{ mole per liter.}$$

52f. Solubility and Activity Coefficient.—The exact form of the solubility product law for silver chloride is given by equation (52.15), and if the solution is saturated in pure water, both c_{Ag^+} and c_{Cl^-} are equal to the solubility S_0. Further, the product of the ionic activity coefficients may be replaced by f_0^2, where f_0 is the mean activity coefficient of silver chloride in its saturated solution in pure water; it follows, therefore, from equation (52.15) that

$$K_s = S_0^2 f_0^2. \tag{52.18}$$

If S is the solubility of the silver chloride in any aqueous solution containing added electrolytes, *other than silver salts or chlorides*, and f is the mean activity coefficient of the silver and chloride ions in this solution, then

$$K_s = S^2 f^2. \tag{52.19}$$

Combination of this result with equation (52.18) gives

$$S_0 f_0 = S f,$$

and upon taking logarithms and rearranging, the result is

$$\log \frac{S}{S_0} = \log f_0 - \log f. \tag{52.20}$$

Although this equation has been derived for a uni-univalent electrolyte, viz., silver chloride, it can be shown to hold for a substance of any valence type. By its use the mean activity coefficient f of the sparingly soluble salt

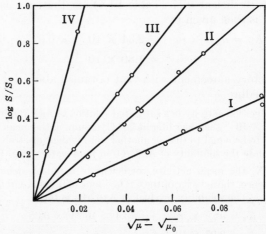

Fig. 107. Solubility and the Debye-Hückel theory

can be determined at various ionic strengths from solubility measurements in the presence of added electrolytes, provided the activity coefficient f_0 is known in water.

An interesting application of equation (52.20) is to test the Debye-Hückel limiting law equation (52.8); thus, writing $-A z_+ z_- \sqrt{\mu}$ for $\log f$, it is seen that

$$\log \frac{S}{S_0} = A z_+ z_- (\sqrt{\mu} - \sqrt{\mu_0}), \tag{52.21}$$

where μ_0 and μ are the ionic strengths of the solutions containing the sparingly soluble salt only, and that in which other electrolytes are also present, respectively. It follows from equation (52.21) that the plot of $\log S/S_0$

against $\sqrt{\mu} - \sqrt{\mu_0}$ should be a straight line of slope Az_+z_-, where z_+ and z_- are the numerical valences of the ions of the sparingly soluble substance. Solubility measurements have been made on a number of salts of different valence types, viz., 1-1 (I), 1-2 (II), 3-1 (III) and 3-3 (IV), in the presence of various added electrolytes at a number of ionic strengths; the experimental data are indicated by the small circles in Fig. 107. The full lines show the theoretical slopes to be expected from the Debye-Hückel theory; the agreement is seen to be excellent in dilute solutions.

It is evident from Fig. 107 that in the presence of neutral salts, not containing a common ion, the solubility of a sparingly soluble salt increases with increasing ionic strength, that is, with increasing concentration of the neutral salts. The reason for this will be apparent from equation (52.19); as the ionic strength of the medium is increased, the activity coefficient f decreases, and hence the solubility S must increase in order that the solubility product K_s may remain constant. However, if the ionic strength is made sufficiently large, the activity coefficient will pass through a minimum and then increase; the solubility of the sparingly soluble salt should thus attain a maximum value and then decrease, as the ionic strength of the solution is increased by the addition of neutral salts. This behavior was observed many years ago, but it could not be explained until the concept of activity and activity coefficients was developed.

52g. Influence of Common Ion on Solubility.—If the solution contains an excess of one or other of the ions produced by the sparingly soluble salt, this must be taken into consideration in the application of the solubility product principle. For instance, if a solution which is being saturated with silver chloride already contains one of the ions of this salt, e.g., the chloride ion, then the term c_{Cl^-} in equation (52.16) will represent the *total* concentration of chloride ion in the solution. Since this is greater than that in a solution containing no excess of chloride ion, the value of c_{Ag^+} required according to equation (52.16) will be less in the former case, in order that the product of c_{Ag^+} and c_{Cl^-} may remain constant. The silver ion concentration in a saturated solution of silver chloride containing an excess of chloride ions, e.g., due to the presence of potassium chloride in the solution, will be less than in a solution in pure water. The silver chloride may be regarded as completely dissociated in solution; hence, the silver ion concentration is a measure of the solubility of the salt. It follows, consequently, that silver chloride is less soluble in the presence of an excess of chloride ions than it is in pure water. The same conclusion may be reached with reference to a solution containing excess of silver ions, instead of chloride ions. In general, *if there is no formation of complex ions to disturb the equilibrium, the solubility of any salt is less in a solution containing a common ion than in water alone;* this fact finds frequent application in analytical chemistry.

The solubility of a salt in the presence of a common ion may be calculated in the following manner; for simplicity, the saturating salt will be assumed to be silver chloride and the common ion to be the chloride ion. Suppose the addition of x mole per liter of potassium chloride reduces the solubility of silver chloride from S_0 to S mole per liter. The concentration c_{Ag^+} of silver ions in the solution, assuming the silver chloride to be completely dissociated, will then be S gram ion per liter, and that of the chloride ions, i.e., c_{Cl^-}, will be $S + x$, the potassium chloride being also taken to be completely dissociated. It follows, therefore, that

$$K_s = c_{Ag^+} \times c_{Cl^-} = S(S + x), \qquad (52.22)$$

assuming the solutions to be dilute enough for the activity coefficients to be unity. Under these conditions K_s is also equal to S_0^2, as seen above; hence, by equation (52.22),

$$S(S + x) = S_0^2, \qquad (52.23)$$

$$S = -\tfrac{1}{2}x + \sqrt{\tfrac{1}{4}x^2 + S_0^2}. \qquad (52.24)$$

The solubility S of the salt in the presence of x mole per liter of added common ion can thus be calculated, if the solubility S_0 in water is known. In the event that the solubility S is small, so that it may be neglected in comparison with x in equation (52.23), S is approximately equal to S_0^2/x; on the other hand, if x is small in comparison with S_0, equation (52.24) gives

$$S = -\tfrac{1}{2}x + S_0. \qquad (52.25)$$

Problem: The solubility of silver nitrite in pure water is 0.0269 mole per liter; what is the solubility in the presence of 0.0118 mole per liter of silver nitrate, assuming the salts to be completely dissociated and the activity coefficients to be unity?

Since S_0 is 0.0269 and x is 0.0118 mole per liter, equation (52.24) gives

$$S = -0.0059 + \sqrt{\tfrac{1}{4}(0.0118)^2 + (0.0269)^2} = 0.0216 \text{ mole per liter.}$$

If x is treated as small in comparison with S_0, equation (52.25) would give S as 0.0210 mole per liter. (The experimental value is 0.0224 mole per liter.)

52h. Complex Ions.—In certain cases excess of a common ion brings about a marked increase, instead of a decrease, in the solubility of a sparingly soluble salt. Instances of this type of behavior are to be found in the solubility of silver cyanide and several other insoluble cyanides in alkali cyanide solutions, and of mercuric iodide in iodide solutions. The results, however, do not violate the solubility product principle. The increase of solubility is due to the removal of the simple ions by the formation of complex ions; for example, the silver ions produced by silver cyanide when it dissolves are removed by the formation of the complex $Ag(CN)_2^-$ ions in the presence of excess cyanide ions. As a result, the silver cyanide must continue to dissolve in order to increase the concentration of free silver ions to the point that the solubility product $a_{Ag^+} \times a_{CN^-}$ is attained. When this condition is reached considerable amounts of silver will be in the solution, although almost the whole will be in the form of $Ag(CN)_2^-$ ions. It is of interest to mention that the solubility product of silver sulfide is so very low, viz., about 10^{-50}, that it can be precipitated from a cyanide solution of silver; even the small concentration of free silver ions in the presence of excess of cyanide ions is sufficient to enable the solubility product of the sulfide to be readily exceeded.

The solubility of silver chloride, and also of silver and cupric oxides, in the presence of ammonia can also be accounted for by the formation of complex ions which markedly decrease the concentration of the free metal ions. This and other aspects of complex ion formation are more profitably studied in connection with qualitative and quantitative analysis.

ACIDS AND BASES

53a. The Proton Transfer Theory.—Acids and bases have been defined in a number of different ways, but a point of view that has proved useful in several aspects of physical chemistry is that associated with the names of J. N. Brønsted (1923) and T. M. Lowry (1923).* As a result of various studies, particularly on the catalytic influence of nonionized molecules of acids and bases and of certain ions (§ 61b), a concept of acids and bases has been developed which has proved useful in the study of equilibria in solutions. *An acid is defined as a substance with a tendency to lose a proton, and a base is a substance with a tendency to gain a proton.* A proton, as seen in § 6c, is a hydrogen nucleus or a "bare" hydrogen ion, H^+, that is, without the water of hydration that the hydrogen ion undoubtedly has in solution (see § 10e). The "strength" of an acid is a measure of its tendency to lose a proton, and the "strength" of a base is similarly a measure of its tendency to take up a proton.

According to the foregoing definitions there must be a relationship between an acid and a base; when an acid loses a proton the residue will have some tendency to regain the proton, and hence it will be a base. It is thus possible to write the general expression

$$A \rightleftharpoons H^+ + B.$$
acid   proton   base

The acid and base which differ by a proton, in accordance with this relationship, are said to form a **conjugate pair**; every acid must have its conjugate base, and every base its conjugate acid. It will be seen presently that acids and bases do not necessarily have to be nonionized molecules; in fact, at least one of the members of a conjugate pair must be ionic in character. This is one of the important results of the proton concept of acids and bases; ions, as well as molecules, can possess acidic or basic character.

In order that an acid may exhibit its acidic properties it is necessary that a substance capable of accepting a proton, i.e., a base of some kind, should be present. In a solution of hydrogen chloride in benzene there are no molecules that are able to take up the proton from the hydrogen chloride; however, if a base, such as ammonia or an amine, is added to the solution, the proton can be transferred to the base. Many solvents, such as water and alcohols, are bases because the molecules are able to take up pro-

---

* In its widest sense, a base has been defined as a substance capable of furnishing a pair of electrons to a bond, while an acid is able to accept a pair of electrons (G. N. Lewis, 1938). The Brønsted-Lowry acids and bases are thus a more or less limited group in a larger field.

tons; in fact, the ionization of acids in water and similar solvents is probably to be ascribed to the transfer of a proton from the acid to the solvent molecule. The ionization equilibrium of hydrochloric acid in water, for example, may be written as

$$HCl + H_2O \rightleftharpoons H_3O^+ + Cl^-,$$

acid   base   acid   base
          (solvent)

and other acids ionize in an analogous manner.

An examination of this equation will reveal a number of interesting points. First, it implies that the hydrogen ion in aqueous solution is not H^+, i.e., a proton, but it consists of at least one water molecule in addition; its *minimum formula* is thus that of the hydronium ion H_3O^+ (see § 10e), although there are probably several other, less firmly bound, molecules of water associated with this unit, as is the case with other ions in aqueous solution. Second, the H_3O^+ ion has itself a tendency to lose a proton, thus re-forming its conjugate base, the water molecule; thus,

$$H_3O^+ \rightleftharpoons H^+ + H_2O,$$

acid   proton   base

and in the hydrochloric acid equilibrium represented above, this proton passes to the chloride ion; the latter must, consequently, be the conjugate base of hydrochloric acid, i.e.,

$$Cl^- + H^+ \rightleftharpoons HCl.$$

base   proton   acid

The conclusion to be drawn is that the chloride ion is a base according to the definition adopted here; in fact, *the anion of any acid is the base conjugate to that acid.*

Another important general result is that interaction between an acid (HCl) and a base (H_2O) leads to the formation of another acid (H_3O^+) conjugate to the base, and of another base (Cl^-) conjugate to the acid. Actually, all types of acid-base reactions can be represented as an equilibrium between two acid-base systems, viz.,

$$\text{Acid 1} + \text{Base 2} \rightleftharpoons \text{Acid 2} + \text{Base 1,} \tag{53.1}$$

where Acid 1 and Base 1 are the conjugate acid and base of one system, and Acid 2 and Base 2 are those of the other system, e.g., the solvent. The forward reaction involves the transfer of a proton from Acid 1 to Base 2, while the reverse reaction is the transfer of a proton from Acid 2 to Base 1.

The general expression for the ionization equilibrium of an acid HA in water is represented by

$$HA + H_2O \rightleftharpoons H_3O^+ + A^-,$$

and the position of equilibrium, i.e., to the right or left of the equation, depends on the "strengths" of the acids and bases concerned. If the acid HA is a strong acid, e.g., HCl, it will tend to give up its proton readily, and even f the base H_2O is fairly weak, it will take up the proton to a sufficient extent to permit the equilibrium to lie considerably to the right; the extent of ionization will then be large. In this case, the reverse reaction, that is, the transfer of a proton from the acid H_3O^+ to the base A^- will occur to a small extent only. In other words, if the acid HA is a strong acid, its conjugate base A^- will be a very weak base. Since hydrochloric acid is a strong acid, its conjugate base, the chloride ion, is very weak. On the other hand, if HA is a very weak acid, such as a phenol, the equilibrium lies well to the left, so that the reverse process takes place to an appreciable extent; the anion A^- of a very weak acid, e.g., the phenoxide ion, will be a moderately strong base. The fact that for a weak acid the acid-solvent equilibrium lies to the left means that ionization occurs to a small extent only; an aqueous solution of a weak acid is consequently a weak electrolyte (§ 46c).

The general rule that there is a reciprocal relationship between the strength of an acid and that of its conjugate base is applicable to acids of all types, irrespective of whether they consist of neutral molecules or of ions. The reverse is, of course, also true; the weaker the base the stronger will be its conjugate acid. Water, for example, is a very weak base, and its conjugate acid H_3O^+ is a strong acid.

Just as the ionization of an acid requires a solvent that can act as a base, so the ionization of a base requires a solvent having acid character. It happens that water and related solvents actually possess both acidic and basic properties; hence, bases, as well as acids, can ionize in water. With the base ammonia, for example, the ionization equilibrium is

$$NH_3 + H_2O \rightleftharpoons NH_4^+ + OH^-,$$

   base   acid   acid   base

       (solvent)

the NH_4^+ ion being the acid conjugate to the base NH_3, and OH^- is the base conjugate to the acid H_2O. Since NH_3 is a weak base, NH_4^+ is a moderately strong acid; on the other hand, H_2O is a very weak acid and so OH^- is a strong base. Further, because neither NH_3 nor H_2O is strong, the ionization equilibrium in this case lies to the left; an aqueous solution of ammonia is thus a weak electrolyte. The ionizations of other weak bases, which are generally amines, i.e., substituted ammonias, are similar to that given above for ammonia; the corresponding ammonium ions are the conjugate acids, and the solutions are slightly ionized.

Although strong acids, such as HCl, HNO_3, $HClO_4$, etc., consist of covalent molecules that are not appreciably ionized in the pure state, the so-called strong bases, such as the alkali or alkaline-earth hydroxides, are invariably ionic in character even in the solid state. The basic character of these strong bases is due to the OH^- ions which are always present and interaction with the solvent is not an essential preliminary. Strictly speaking, therefore, such substances as NaOH, $Ca(OH)_2$, etc., like sodium acetate, etc., are to be regarded as "salts," rather than as bases, for it is the OH^- that is the real base.

53b. Influence of Solvent.—In view of the general equilibrium represented by equation (53.1), viz.,

$$\text{Acid } 1 + \text{Base } 2 \rightleftharpoons \text{Acid } 2 + \text{Base } 1,$$

the ionization of any Acid 1 will depend to some extent on the basic strength of the solvent acting as Base 2. The situation is, in fact, very similar to that encountered in the study of oxidation-reduction equilibria; the higher the standard oxidation potential of one system compared with that of the other, the further will the reaction proceed to completion (§ 49h). Similarly, in the case of acid-base equilibria, the greater the tendency of Acid 1 to lose a proton, i.e., the greater its strength, compared with that of Acid 2, the further will the ionization process occur. If Acid 2 is very weak, i.e., the solvent is a moderately strong base, the equilibrium will lie well to the right; on the other hand, if Acid 2 is fairly strong, i.e., the solvent is a very weak base, the equilibrium will lie to the left. The behavior of a particular acid must therefore depend on the proton accepting tendency, that is, the basic strength, of the solvent.

These conclusions may be illustrated by reference to three solvents of increasing basic character, viz., glacial acetic acid, water and liquid ammonia. In spite of the fact that acetic acid normally behaves as an acid, it is nevertheless able to take up a proton to a small extent, thus acting as a very weak base. The ionization of an acid HA in glacial acetic acid as solvent is thus represented by

$$\text{HA} + \text{CH}_3\text{COOH} \rightleftharpoons \text{CH}_3\text{COOH}_2^+ + \text{A}^-,$$

acid	base	acid	base
	(solvent)		

but the equilibrium cannot lie far to the right, so that even strong acids, such as hydrochloric acid, can only be slightly ionized in this solvent. By means of conductance and other measurements, the extent of ionization of a number of acids, which are strong acids in aqueous solution, have been determined, using glacial acetic acid as solvent. The order of their ionization, and hence of their tendency to lose a proton, is found to be as follows:

$$\text{HClO}_4 > \text{HBr} > \text{H}_2\text{SO}_4 > \text{HCl} > \text{HNO}_3.$$

This gives the correct order of the strengths of these acids although they appear to be equally strong in aqueous solution.

Water is a stronger base than acetic acid, and so the ionization equilibria for these strong acids in aqueous solution lie well to the right; it is consequently not possible to distinguish between their relative strengths, except perhaps in concentrated solutions. For weak acids, like formic, lactic, acetic, propionic, phosphoric acids, etc., the equilibria do not proceed so far, and it is possible to determine the order of their strengths in aqueous solution, as will be seen in § 53c.

With liquid ammonia as solvent, the proton-accepting tendency of the base is so great that even with an acid as weak as acetic acid, the ionization equilibrium, viz.,

$$CH_3COOH + NH_3 \rightleftharpoons NH_4^+ + CH_3COO^-,$$

$$\text{acid} \qquad \underset{\text{(solvent)}}{\text{base}} \qquad \text{acid} \qquad \text{base}$$

lies so far to the right that the acid behaves like a strong acid. In fact, all acids stronger than acetic acid appear to be about equally strong in liquid ammonia as solvent; acetic and hydrochloric acids, for example, behave as if they had almost the same strength.

The influence of the solvent on the ionization and apparent strength of bases, other than hydroxides, is similar in nature. In water it is possible to distinguish between the strengths of various weak bases, because water is a relatively weak acid. If the solvent has stronger acid character, this distinction is no longer possible. In pure acetic acid as solvent all bases stronger than aniline, which is a very weak base in water, behave as strong bases. This fact is made use of in the analytical titration, by means of acid, of bases which are too weak to be titrated satisfactorily in aqueous solution.

An extreme type of solvent effect occurs when the solvent has only acidic and no basic properties, as is the case with liquid hydrogen fluoride. Not even the strongest acid can ionize *as an acid* when dissolved in this solvent, but it may ionize *as a base*. As mentioned previously, acetic acid has some slight tendency to accept a proton, and when it is dissolved in liquid hydrogen fluoride it ionizes as a base; thus,

$$CH_3COOH + HF \rightleftharpoons CH_3COOH_2^+ + F^-.$$

$$\text{base} \qquad \underset{\text{(solvent)}}{\text{acid}} \qquad \text{acid} \qquad \text{base}$$

The behavior may again be compared with that in oxidation-reduction processes; a particular system may behave as an oxidizing agent to one having a higher oxidation potential, but it will be a reducing agent to a system with a lower potential. So the acidic or basic character of a substance, such as acetic acid, will depend on the tendency of the solvent to gain or lose protons, respectively. A substance such as hydrogen chloride has virtually no basic character, and so it will not ionize when dissolved in hydrogen fluoride, although acetic, nitric, sulfuric and other acids, which contain an oxygen atom, and can take up protons to some extent, will give conducting systems.

53c. Dissociation Constants.—The comparison of the strengths of acids or bases, other than the strongest, in a given solvent, such as water, is conveniently made by utilizing the dissociation constant of the acid or base (§ 52a).

I. Acids.—For any acid HA dissolved in water, for example, the ionization equilibrium is

$$HA + H_2O \rightleftharpoons H_3O^+ + A^-,$$

and the equilibrium constant in terms of activities is

$$K = \frac{a_{H_3O^+} \times a_{A^-}}{a_{HA} \times a_{H_2O}}.$$ (53.2)

If the concentration of dissolved substances in the water is not too large, the activity a_{H_2O} of the water molecules is approximately equal to that in pure water, and this, by convention, is taken as unity. The equilibrium constant in equation (53.2) may now be represented as K_a, given by

$$K_a = \frac{a_{H_3O^+} \times a_{A^-}}{a_{HA}},$$ (53.3)

which is exactly analogous to equation (52.1); this is the general expression for the true dissociation constant of the acid HA. The formula H_3O^+ is used for the hydrogen ion in aqueous solution to show that the proton is associated with one strongly bound molecule of water; however, for simplicity of representation it is adequate to use the symbol H^+, *provided it is clearly understood that this does not refer to a proton, but to the hydrogen ion as it exists in solution.* With this simplification, equation (53.3) for the dissociation constant K_a of the acid may be written as

$$K_a = \frac{a_{H^+} \times a_{A^-}}{a_{HA}}.$$ (53.4)

As in § 52a, each activity term may be replaced by the product of the corresponding concentration and activity coefficient, so that

$$K_a = \frac{c_{H^+} \times c_{A^-}}{c_{HA}} \cdot \frac{f_{H^+} \times f_{A^-}}{f_{HA}}.$$ (53.5)

As before, α may be taken as the degree of dissociation of the acid HA in the aqueous solution of total concentration c mole per liter; c_{H^+} and c_{A^-} are then both equal to αc, while c_{HA}, the concentration of the undissociated portion, is given by $(1 - \alpha)c$, and equation (53.5) becomes

$$K_a = \frac{\alpha^2 c}{1 - \alpha} \cdot \frac{f_{H^+} \times f_{A^-}}{f_{HA}}.$$ (53.6)

If the solution of the acid HA behaves ideally, the activity coefficient factor in equation (53.6) would be equal to unity, and the first factor on the right-hand side would be equal to the dissociation constant. Although this is not the case for actual solutions, nevertheless for a weak electrolyte, it is possible to write

$$k_a = \frac{\alpha^2 c}{1 - \alpha},$$ (53.7)

where k_a is approximately constant, becoming equal to the dissociation constant K_a at infinite dilution when the activity coefficients are all unity.

The degree of dissociation α can be derived from conductance measurements (§ 46e), but if the approximation is made of neglecting the variation of ionic speeds with concentration, the degree of dissociation may be identified with the conductance ratio [equation (46.14)]. Thus, replacing α by the ratio Λ/Λ_0, where Λ is the equivalent conductance of the acid solution at the concentration c, and Λ_0 is the limiting value at infinite dilution, equation (53.7) for the dissociation constant takes the somewhat more approximate form

$$k_a' = \frac{\Lambda^2 c}{\Lambda_0(\Lambda_0 - \Lambda)}. \tag{53.8}$$

The equivalent conductances Λ at 25° C of acetic acid solutions at various concentrations are recorded in Table LX; from these, together with the limiting conductance Λ_0 of 390.7 ohms^{-1} cm.^{2}, obtained in § 46h, the values of k_a' have been calculated. These are seen to be approximately constant, as is to be expected; in order that they should be exactly constant it would be necessary to apply corrections for the activity coefficients, as in equation (53.6), and also to allow for the variation of the ionic speeds, by means of equation (46.11), in calculating the degree of dissociation. The corrected values of α are given in the fourth column of Table LX; these are seen to be

TABLE LX.   DISSOCIATION CONSTANT OF ACETIC ACID

$c \times 10^3$	Λ	Λ/Λ_0	α	k_a'	k_a
0.02801	210.38	0.5384	0.5393	1.763×10^{-5}	1.768×10^{-5}
0.11135	127.75	0.3270	0.3277	1.768	1.779
0.21844	96.49	0.2470	0.2477	1.769	1.781
1.02831	48.15	0.1232	0.1238	1.779	1.797
2.41400	32.22	0.08247	0.08290	1.789	1.809
5.91153	20.96	0.05364	0.05401	1.797	1.823
9.8421	16.37	0.04189	0.04222	1.803	1.832
20.000	11.57	0.02961	0.02987	1.806	1.840
52.303	7.202	0.01843	0.01865	1.809	1.854

only slightly larger than the conductance ratios in the third column. The last column gives k_a obtained from equation (53.7), using the corrected degrees of dissociation; the variation from constancy is somewhat greater than with k_a', because in deriving the latter there is a partial cancellation of errors.

In order to obtain the true dissociation constant K_a, it is necessary to extrapolate k_a', or better k_a, to infinite dilution; this can be very conveniently done with the aid of the Debye-Hückel limiting law. By combining equations (53.6) and (53.7) it is seen that

$$K_a = k_a \frac{f_{H^+} \times f_{A^-}}{f_{HA}}. \tag{53.9}$$

Provided the ionic strength of the medium is not too high, the activity coefficient of the undissociated molecules HA does not differ greatly from unity; hence, equation (53.9) may be written as

$$K_a = k_a(f_{H^+} \times f_{A^-}) = k_a f^2, \tag{53.10}$$

where f is the mean activity coefficient of the ions. According to the Debye-Hückel limiting equation (52.8)

$$\log f = -A\sqrt{\mu}, \tag{53.11}$$

since both ions are univalent, and z_+ and z_- are equal to unity. In the present case, the ionic strength μ of the solution is equal to the ionic concentration αc, as is true for all uni-univalent electrolytes; hence, taking logarithms of equation (53.10) and substituting equation (53.11), with μ equal to αc, the result after rearrangement is

$$\log k_a = \log K_a + 2A\sqrt{\alpha c}. \tag{53.12}$$

The plot of $\log k_a$ against $\sqrt{\alpha c}$, the values of which can be obtained from the data in Table LX, should thus be a straight line of slope $2A$; for water

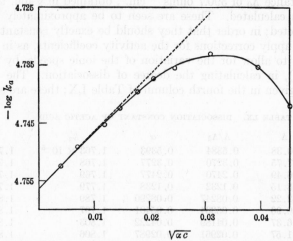

FIG. 108.   Dissociation constant of acetic acid (MacInnes and Shedlovsky)

at 25° C, A is 0.509, and so the slope should be 1.018. Further, according to equation (53.12), the intercept on the $\log k_a$ axis, for $\sqrt{\alpha c}$ equal to zero, should give $\log K_a$; this is actually the extrapolated value of $\log k_a$ at infinite dilution. The results for acetic acid are shown in Fig. 108; the theoretical limiting slope, according to equation (53.12), is indicated by the dashed line. The experimental and theoretical slopes are seen to approach one another in dilute solution, thus providing support for the Debye-Hückel limiting equation. The extrapolated value of $\log k_a$, which is equal to $\log K_a$, is -4.7564, so that K_a for acetic acid at 25° C is 1.752×10^{-5}.

The treatment just described, utilizing conductance data appropriately corrected, provides one of the most accurate devices for the evaluation of the dissociation constants of acids that are not too weak. Another highly accurate method, which can be used for very weak acids in addition, is based on E.M.F. measurements of special galvanic cells free from liquid junctions. A somewhat more approximate procedure involves the determination of hydrogen ion concentrations (activities) in solutions containing a mixture of known amounts of the acid and its salt; the equation required for this purpose is derived in § 53e.

II. Bases.—The ionization of a base B in aqueous solution may be represented as

$$B + H_2O \rightleftharpoons BH^+ + OH^-,$$

so that the dissociation constant K_b of the base is given by

$$K_b = \frac{a_{BH^+} \times a_{OH^-}}{a_B},$$ (53.13)

the activity a_{H_2O} of the water being taken as unity. The undissociated, including nonionized, portion of the base is represented by B, whereas BH^+ is the ionized portion; hence, if α is the degree of dissociation, the concentrations of BH^+, OH^- and B are given by αc, αc and $(1 - \alpha)c$, respectively. It can thus be readily seen that quation (53.13) can be reduced to a form exactly analogous to equation (53.6), viz.,

$$K_b = \frac{\alpha^2 c}{1 - \alpha} \cdot \frac{f_{BH^+} \times f_{OH^-}}{f_B}.$$ (53.14)

It is thus possible to obtain K_b for a moderately weak base by utilizing conductance data in a manner exactly analogous to that described above for acetic acid. Methods based on E.M.F. measurements and on hydrogen ion determinations have also been used. One of the difficulties experienced in making accurate measurements on certain bases, such as ammonia and the lower amines, is their volatility; in addition, many amines are unstable when exposed to air, especially in the presence of light. For these reasons there are not many accurate data for the dissociation constants of bases.

III. Polybasic (or Polyprotonic) Acids.—A dibasic acid, such as carbonic or oxalic acid, has two protons which can be lost from the molecule; similarly, a tribasic acid, such as phosphoric or citric acid, can lose three protons. These protons are detached from the acid molecule in turn, so that there are a number of stages of ionization corresponding to the basicity of the acid. The three ionization stages of phosphoric acid, for example, are as follows:

1st stage: $H_3PO_4 + H_2O \rightleftharpoons H_3O^+ + H_2PO_4^-$

2nd stage: $H_2PO_4^- + H_2O \rightleftharpoons H_3O^+ + HPO_4^{--}$

3rd stage: $HPO_4^{--} + H_2O \rightleftharpoons H_3O^+ + PO_4^{---}.$

The corresponding dissociation constants for the three stages are given by

$$K_1 = \frac{a_{H^+} \times a_{H_2PO_4^-}}{a_{H_3PO_4}}$$ (53.15)

$$K_2 = \frac{a_{H^+} \times a_{HPO_4^{--}}}{a_{H_2PO_4^-}}$$ (53.16)

$$K_3 = \frac{a_{H^+} \times a_{PO_4^{---}}}{a_{HPO_4^{--}}}.$$ (53.17)

Conductance methods have been used for evaluating the dissociation constants of dibasic acids, but the results are not accurate because of certain approximations that must be made in the calculations. For polybasic acids it is therefore the general practice to employ E.M.F. methods. The values of the dissociation constants of successive stages of a polybasic (or polyprotonic) acid always decrease steadily; thus, for phosphoric acid K_1 is 7.52×10^{-3}, K_2 is 6.22×10^{-8} and K_3 is 4.8×10^{-13} at $25°$ C. The reason for this decreasing tendency for the proton to be lost in successive ionizations is that in the first stage the positively charged proton is detached from an uncharged molecule, e.g., H_3PO_4, but in the later stages it must be removed from an ion of increasingly negative charge, e.g., $H_2PO_4^-$ and HPO_4^{--}. On account of the electrostatic attraction, the removal of the proton becomes increasingly difficult in successive stages, and so the dissociation constants decrease correspondingly. This conclusion is applicable to dibasic, tribasic, and polybasic acids of all types.

Attention may be called to a matter of general interest; in the first stage of ionization of phosphoric acid, $H_2PO_4^-$ is the base conjugate to the acid H_3PO_4, but in the second stage $H_2PO_4^-$ functions as an acid. Similarly, HPO_4^{--} is the conjugate base in the second stage of ionization, but is the acid in the third stage. In general, the intermediate ion (or ions) of a polyprotonic acid will possess both acidic and basic character; such ions are therefore said to be "amphiprotic" or "amphoteric" (Greek: amphi, *both*).

IV. Results.—The dissociation constants at $25°$ C of a number of acids and bases are recorded in Table LXI; as a general rule, change of temperature has a relatively small effect on the dissociation constant. An acid hav-

TABLE LXI. DISSOCIATION CONSTANTS OF ACIDS AND BASES AT $25°$ C

Monobasic Acids

Acid	K_a	Acid	K_a
Formic	1.774×10^{-4}	Lactic	1.37×10^{-4}
Acetic	1.752×10^{-5}	Glycolic	1.48×10^{-4}
Benzoic	6.31×10^{-5}	Phenol	1.20×10^{-10}
Chloroacetic	1.33×10^{-3}	Hydrogen cyanide	7.24×10^{-10}
Phenylacetic	4.90×10^{-5}	Boric	5.75×10^{-10}

Polybasic Acids

Acid	K_1	K_2	K_3
Oxalic	5.02×10^{-2}	5.18×10^{-5}	—
Phthalic	1.29×10^{-3}	3.80×10^{-6}	—
Carbonic	4.47×10^{-7}	5.62×10^{-11}	—
Hydrogen sulfide	6.3×10^{-8}	1.3×10^{-12}	—
Citric	8.7×10^{-4}	1.8×10^{-5}	4.0×10^{-6}
Phosphoric	7.52×10^{-3}	6.22×10^{-8}	4.8×10^{-13}

Bases

Base	K_b	Base	K_b
Ammonia	1.74×10^{-5}	Aniline	4.1×10^{-10}
Methylamine	5.0×10^{-4}	Diphenylamine	6.9×10^{-14}
Dimethylamine	7.4×10^{-4}	Pyridine	1.6×10^{-9}
Trimethylamine	7.4×10^{-5}	Quinoline	3.5×10^{-10}

ing a dissociation constant of about 10^{-2} to 10^{-3} is regarded as "moderately strong"; if the value is 10^{-4} to 10^{-7}, the acid is referred to as "weak"; if it is in the region of 10^{-8} to 10^{-11} the acid may be described as "very weak," while an "extremely weak" acid would have a dissociation constant of 10^{-12} or less. This classification is, of course, very rough, although it is useful for some purposes. The strong acids have large dissociation constants; the values have to be obtained by special methods and are not known with any degree of certainty.

53d. Hydrogen Ion Concentration in Acid Solutions.—Provided the solutions are not too concentrated, a strong acid, such as hydrochloric acid, may be regarded as being completely ionized in aqueous solution; the hydrogen ion concentration is then equal to the total acid concentration. Thus, if the concentration of a solution of hydrochloric acid is 0.1 mole per liter, the hydrogen ion concentration c_{H^+} will be 0.1 gram ion per liter. Further, the addition of the salt of the strong acid will have little effect on the hydrogen ion concentration, although it may affect the activity to some extent. The value of c_{H^+} in a solution of 0.1 mole of hydrochloric acid and 0.1 mole of sodium chloride per liter may thus be taken as remaining at 0.1 gram ion per liter.

With weak acids the situation is quite different, because ionization is far from complete, even in the most dilute solutions that are generally encountered. From a knowledge of the dissociation constant, however, it is possible to calculate the degree of dissociation, and hence the hydrogen ion concentration. In this connection, it is sufficient, for most purposes, to use the approximate equation (53.7). If the degree of dissociation α is small, $1 - \alpha$ in the denominator will be almost equal to unity, so that the equation becomes

$$k_a = \alpha^2 c,$$

$$\alpha = \sqrt{\frac{k_a}{c}}. \tag{53.18}$$

For acids of k_a about 10^{-4} to 10^{-5}, this approximation is satisfactory, if the concentration c of the acid solution is about 0.1 mole per liter or more; for weaker acids it is applicable at even lower concentrations. Since the hydrogen ion concentration c_{H^+} is equal to αc, as already seen, it follows from equation (53.18) that

$$c_{H^+} = \alpha c = \sqrt{c k_a}. \tag{53.19}$$

The hydrogen ion concentration in a solution of a weak acid is thus (approximately) proportional to the square root of its dissociation constant, at a given acid concentration.

If α is too large to be neglected in comparison with unity, then it is necessary to treat equation (53.7) as a quadratic in α, and to solve it accordingly; it is then found that

$$c_{H^+} = -\tfrac{1}{2}k_a + \sqrt{\tfrac{1}{4}k_a^2 + c k_a}. \tag{53.20}$$

In the great majority of cases $\frac{1}{4}k_a^2$ is quite negligible in comparison with ck_a, and a very satisfactory compromise between equations (53.19) and (53.20) is

$$c_{H^+} = -\tfrac{1}{2}k_a + \sqrt{ck_a}. \tag{53.21}$$

If c_{H^+} is calculated from one of these equations, the corresponding degree of dissociation α may then be obtained upon dividing by c, the concentration of acid, i.e., α is equal to c_{H^+}/c.

Problem: Calculate the hydrogen ion concentration in a precisely 0.1 molar solution of acetic acid, using the approximate and more exact equations.

Since k_a is 1.752×10^{-5}, and c is precisely 0.1, it follows from equation (53.19) that

$$c_{H^+} = \sqrt{0.1 \times 1.752 \times 10^{-5}} = 1.324 \times 10^{-3} \text{ g. ion per liter.}$$

From equation (53.21), on the other hand,

$$c_{H^+} = -(\tfrac{1}{2} \times 1.752 \times 10^{-5}) + \sqrt{0.1 \times 1.752 \times 10^{-5}} = 1.315 \times 10^{-3} \text{ g. ion per liter.}$$

Equation (53.20) gives an identical result, to four significant figures. The degree of dissociation at this concentration is $c_{H^+}/c = 1.32 \times 10^{-3}/0.1 = 1.32 \times 10^{-2}$.

53e. Solutions of Weak Acid and Salt.—In accordance with the general principles of equilibrium, the addition of one of the products of dissociation should suppress the extent of dissociation (see § 33c); hence, the degree of dissociation of a weak acid, such as acetic acid, will be diminished by the presence either of excess of hydrogen ions, e.g., from a strong acid, or of acetate ions, e.g., from an acetate. In a mixture of acetic acid and its salt sodium acetate, the acid will thus be dissociated to a smaller extent than for the same concentration in water; the hydrogen ion concentration will thus be decreased by the addition of the salt.

The problem of calculating the hydrogen ion concentration of a mixture of a weak acid and one of its highly ionized salts, e.g., a sodium or potassium salt, is of practical importance; the method employed is based on the expression for the dissociation constant. Starting with equation (53.4), a slight rearrangement gives

$$a_{H^+} = K_a \frac{a_{HA}}{a_{A^-}} = K_a \frac{c_{HA}}{c_{A^-}} \cdot \frac{f_{HA}}{f_{A^-}}, \tag{53.22}$$

where, in the last expression, the activities have been replaced by the products of the concentrations and activity coefficients. As already seen, the activity coefficient f_{HA} of the undissociated molecules may be taken as unity, provided the ionic strength of the solution is not too high, and so equation (53.22) becomes

$$a_{H^+} = K_a \frac{c_{HA}}{c_{A^-}} \cdot \frac{1}{f_{A^-}}. \tag{53.23}$$

This result is reasonably exact, but in order to simplify the calculations an approximate form is frequently employed. Taking the activity coefficient of the A^- ions as unity, and replacing the activity term a_{H^+} by the corresponding concentration of hydrogen ions, equation (53.23) becomes

$$c_{H^+} = k_a \frac{c_{HA}}{c_{A^-}}. \tag{53.24}$$

In order to indicate that the equation is not exact, the symbol K_a has been replaced by k_a, in accordance with the usual practice (§ 53c, I).

The equation (53.24) has been derived from a consideration of the dissociation of the acid HA alone; nevertheless, it must hold under any conditions. Even if the solution contains added common ions, e.g., A^- ions, the equilibrium between hydrogen and A^- ions, on the one hand, and undissociated molecules HA, on the other hand, must always be maintained, and equations (53.22), (53.24), etc., will apply. However, if A^- ions are added to the solution, e.g., in the form of the completely ionized salt NaA, the quantity c_{A^-} in equation (53.24) represents the *total concentration* of A^- ions produced by the ionization of the acid HA and of the salt NaA. Since the presence of the latter must suppress the ionization of the former, the concentration of A^- ions derived from HA may be neglected; hence, as a fair approximation, c_{A^-} may be identified with the concentration of A^- ions produced from the salt NaA. As already indicated, this salt is supposed to be completely ionized, and so it is possible to write

$$c_{A^-} = \text{Concentration of completely ionized salt} = [\text{salt}],$$

the symbol [salt] being used as an abbreviation.

Because of the very small extent of ionization of the weak acid, especially in the presence of the salt, the quantity c_{HA}, representing the concentration of undissociated molecules, may be taken, as a first approximation, as being equal to the total concentration of the acid; hence,

$$c_{HA} = \text{Total concentration of weak acid} = [\text{acid}].$$

Inserting these expressions for c_{A^-} and c_{HA} in equation (53.24), the result is

$$c_{H^+} = k_a \frac{[\text{acid}]}{[\text{salt}]}, \tag{53.25}$$

from which the hydrogen ion concentration of the solution consisting of a given concentration of a weak acid and its completely ionized salt can be calculated, provided the dissociation constant of the acid is known. It is evident from this equation that the greater the proportion of salt to acid, the smaller will be the hydrogen ion concentration. This is to be expected, since the A^- ions formed by dissociation of the salt must repress the ionization of the acid HA. When salt and acid are present in equivalent amounts, that is when [salt] = [acid], the value of c_{H^+} is equal to k_a, the dissociation constant of the acid.

Incidentally, it may be mentioned that equation (53.25) is the basis of the approximate method for determining dissociation constants, referred **to** in § 53c, I; the hydrogen ion concentration of a mixture of the acid and its salt, in known amounts, is determined by means of a hydrogen electrode (§§ 55b, 55c). The value of k_a is then obtained by means of equation (53.25). Corrections for the activity coefficients, which have so far been neglected, should be applied to improve the accuracy of the results.

Problem: Calculate the hydrogen ion concentration of a solution containing 0.1 molar acetic acid and 0.05 molar sodium acetate.

In this case, [acid] = 0.1 and [salt] = 0.05; k_a is 1.75×10^{-5}, and consequently,

$$c_{H^+} = 1.75 \times 10^{-5} \times \frac{0.1}{0.05} = 3.50 \times 10^{-5} \text{ g. ion per liter.}$$

(This may be compared with 1.32×10^{-3} g. ion per liter for 0.1 molar acetic acid in the absence of sodium acetate, as found in the preceding problem.)

The degree of dissociation of a weak acid in the presence of its salt can be readily derived from the hydrogen ion concentration; since these ions arise almost entirely from the dissociation of the weak acid,* it follows that c_{H^+} is equal to αc, where c is the concentration of the acid. The degree of dissociation is consequently equal to c_{H^+}/c, just as in a solution of the acid alone. In the presence of the salt, however, c_{H^+} is greatly reduced, and so also is the degree of dissociation.

The foregoing treatment of weak acids can be applied to weak bases; replacing k_a by k_b in equations (53.19), (53.20), etc., these equations give the hydroxyl ion concentration c_{OH^-} in solutions of weak bases. Similarly, an equation analogous to (53.25) can be derived with k_b in place of k_a, with c_{OH^-} for c_{H^+}, and [base] for [acid], where [base] refers to the total concentration of weak base. The salt, of course, must be a strongly ionized salt of the base, e.g., ammonium chloride if ammonia is the base. Just as the salt of a weak acid decreases the hydrogen ion concentration, so the salt of a weak base will diminish the hydroxyl ion concentration of the solution of the base. These facts find many applications in analytical chemistry.

53f. The Ionic Product of Water.—Since water behaves as both an acid and a base, that is to say, a molecule of water is capable of losing as well as gaining a proton, there must exist *in all aqueous solutions*, as well as in pure water, the proton transfer equilibrium represented by

$$H_2O + H_2O \rightleftharpoons H_3O^+ + OH^-.$$

The equilibrium constant is then

$$K = \frac{a_{H_3O^+} \times a_{OH^-}}{a_{H_2O}^2},$$

and if, as in other cases, the solution is so dilute that the activity of the water may be taken as unity (see §49 b, footnote), the result is

$$K_w = a_{H_3O^+} \times a_{OH^-} \text{ (or } a_{H^+} \times a_{OH^-}), \tag{53.26}$$

* Some hydrogen ions are produced by the ionization of the water (§ 53f), but these are neglected.

where the constant K_w is known as the **ionic product** of water. This means that *in pure water or in any dilute aqueous solution, the product of the activities of the hydrogen and hydroxyl ions is constant*, at a given temperature. For moderately dilute solutions the activities may be replaced by the corresponding concentrations, so that the relationship

$$k_w = c_{H^+} \times c_{OH^-} \qquad (53.27)$$

is approximately correct; k_w is used here in place of K_w because of the approximate nature of the result. Before considering some of the consequences of the constancy of the ionic product, some description will be given of the methods used for its determination.

I. Conductance Method.—Because of the equilibrium under consideration, even the purest water will contain a certain proportion of hydrogen and hydroxyl ions, and hence it will possess a definite electrical conductance. It has been estimated from accurate measurements that the specific conductance, that is, the conductance of a 1 cm. cube, of perfectly pure water is 5.54×10^{-8} ohm^{-1} cm.$^{-1}$ at 25° C. The equivalent conductances of hydrogen and hydroxyl ions at the very small concentrations existing in pure water may be taken as equal to the values at infinite dilution, i.e., 349.8 and 198.5 ohms^{-1} cm.^{2}, respectively (Table LIII). The total conductance of 1 gram equiv. of hydrogen and hydroxyl ions in very dilute solution would thus be $349.8 + 198.5 = 548.3$ ohms^{-1} cm.^{2}; it follows, therefore, that a 1 cm. cube, that is, 1 cc., of pure water contains

$$\frac{5.54 \times 10^{-8}}{548.3} = 1.01 \times 10^{-10} \text{ gram equiv. per cc.}$$

of hydrogen and hydroxyl ions. Since the ions are univalent, gram equiv. and gram ions are identical, and so the concentration of hydrogen ions and of hydroxyl ions is 1.01×10^{-7} gram ion per 1000 cc., i.e., per liter; thus, in pure water, where the hydrogen and hydroxyl ions are present at the same concentration,

$$c_{H^+} = c_{OH^-} = 1.01 \times 10^{-7} \text{ gram ion per liter.}$$

By equation (53.27), therefore,

$$k_w = c_{H^+} \times c_{OH^-} = 1.02 \times 10^{-14} \text{ at } 25° \text{ C.}$$

Since the ionic concentrations in pure water are very small, the activity coefficients are virtually unity, and so 1.02×10^{-14} may be taken as the value of K_w.

II. E.M.F. Methods.—The simplest, although approximate, E.M.F. method for determining the ionic product of water employs a galvanic cell with liquid junction, viz.,

$$\text{Pt, H}_2 \text{ (1 atm.)} \mid \text{KOH (0.01 N)} \parallel \text{HCl (0.01 N)} \mid \text{H}_2 \text{ (1 atm.), Pt,}$$

from which it is supposed that the liquid junction potential has been completely eliminated in a suitable manner. The E.M.F. of this cell, according to equation (50.1), is given by

$$E = \frac{RT}{F} \ln \frac{a'_{H^+}}{a_{H^+}}, \qquad (53.28)$$

where a'_{H^+} and a_{H^+} represent the hydrogen ion activities in the right-hand and left-hand solutions, i.e., in 0.01 N hydrochloric acid and 0.01 N potassium hydroxide, respectively. If a_{OH^-} is the hydroxyl ion activity in the latter solution, then by the ionic product principle,

$$a_{H^+} \times a_{OH^-} = K_w,$$

$$a_{H^+} = K_w/a_{OH^-},$$

and substitution of this value for a_{H^+} in equation (53.28) gives

$$E = \frac{RT}{F} \ln \frac{a'_{H^+} \times a_{OH^-}}{K_w}$$

$$= 0.05915 \log \frac{a'_{H^+} \times a_{OH^-}}{K_w} \qquad (53.29)$$

at 25°. The value of a'_{H^+} is equal to the product of the concentration of the hydrogen ions in 0.01 N HCl, i.e., 0.01 gram ion per liter, and the activity coefficient in the solution; from the data in Table LIX, as well as by means of the Debye-Hückel equation, this activity coefficient is found to be about 0.90, so that a'_{H^+} is 0.01 × 0.90, i.e., 0.009 gram ion per liter. Similarly, a_{OH^-} is the hydroxyl ion activity in 0.01 N KOH; this is, likewise, approximately 0.009 gram ion per liter. The E.M.F. of the cell was found to be 0.5874 volt at 25° C, so that by equation (53.29),

$$0.5874 = 0.05915 \log \frac{0.009 \times 0.009}{K_w}$$

$$K_w = 0.95 \times 10^{-14} \text{ at } 25° \text{ C}.$$

This result obtained by an entirely different procedure, is very close to that given by the conductance method.

The most accurate values of the ionic product of water have been derived from measurements with galvanic cells free from liquid junctions; the results for a series of temperatures are summarized in Table LXII. It will be seen

TABLE LXII.   IONIC PRODUCT OF WATER

Temperature	0°	10°	20°	25°	30°	40°	50°
K_w	0.113	0.292	0.681	1.008	1.468	2.917	5.474 × 10⁻¹⁴

that K_w increases rapidly with increasing temperature. The concentration of hydrogen and hydroxyl ions in pure water at any temperature are equal; expressed in gram ion per liter, these are given by the square root of the ionic product [see equation (53.27)]; i.e.,

$$c_{H^+} = c_{OH^-} = \sqrt{K_w}. \qquad (53.30)$$

At ordinary temperatures K_w is very close to 10^{-14}, and so the concentration of hydrogen and hydroxyl ions in pure water may be taken, for most purposes, as 10^{-7} gram ion per liter.

53g. The pH Scale.—In a 1.0 N solution of a strong acid the hydrogen ion concentration c_{H^+} is about 1 gram ion per liter; the ionic product $c_{H^+} \times c_{OH^-}$ must always be approximately 10^{-14} in any dilute aqueous solution, at ordinary temperatures, and hence the concentration of hydroxyl ions c_{OH^-} in this acid solution is of the order of 10^{-14} gram ion per liter. Similarly, in a 1.0 N solution of an alkali hydroxide, c_{OH^-} is about 1 gram ion per liter; consequently c_{H^+} must be in the vicinity of 10^{-14} gram ion per liter in order to maintain the constancy of the ionic product of water. It is seen, therefore, that hydrogen and hydroxyl ion concentrations in ordinary aqueous solutions can vary from about 1 to 10^{-14} gram ion per liter. In order to cover this very large range of concentration, S. P. L. Sørensen (1909) suggested a convenient scale which has come into general use. *The negative logarithm of the hydrogen ion activity is called the pH of the solution;* thus,

$$pH = - \log a_{H^+} = \log \frac{1}{a_{H^+}}. \tag{53.31}$$

Since individual ion activities cannot be determined with any certainty, the definition of equation (53.31) is modified by using hydrogen ion concentrations in place of activities; thus, $pH \approx - \log c_{H^+}$.

Problem: Calculate (i) the pH of a solution in which c_{H^+} is 5.46×10^{-5} g. ion per liter, (ii) the hydrogen ion concentration of a solution of pH 8.752.

(i) $pH = - \log c_{H^+} = - \log (5.46 \times 10^{-5}) = \log 10^5 - \log 5.46$
         $= 5 - 0.737 = 4.263.$

(ii) $- \log c_{H^+} = pH = 8.752$
     $\log c_{H^+} = -8.752 = -9 + 0.248$
       $c_{H^+} = \text{antilog} (-9) \times \text{antilog } 0.248 = 1.770 \times 10^{-9}$ g. ion per liter.

The logarithmic method of representation has been extended to other quantities which vary over a range of magnitudes; for example, pOH is used for hydroxyl ion activities (or concentrations), so that by analogy with equation (53.31),

$$pOH = - \log a_{OH^-} = \log \frac{1}{a_{OH^-}}. \tag{53.32}$$

For most purposes, however, pOH may be defined as $\approx - \log c_{OH^-}$. Dissociation constants of acids and bases, and the ionic product of water are frequently expressed in a similar manner; thus,

$$pK_a = - \log K_a \quad \text{and} \quad pK_w = - \log K_w, \tag{53.33}$$

where pK_a and pK_w are called the **dissociation exponents** of the acid and of water, respectively.

Upon taking logarithms of equation (53.27) and changing the signs throughout, it is seen that

$$- \log c_{H^+} - \log c_{OH^-} = - \log k_w$$

$$pH + pOH = pk_w, \tag{53.34}$$

giving a relationship which holds for water or any dilute aqueous solution. Since k_w is about 10^{-14} at ordinary temperatures (about 25° C), pk_w or $- \log k_w$ is 14.0; hence,

$$pH + pOH = 14. \tag{53.35}$$

The sum of pH and pOH is thus equal to 14 in water or in any dilute aqueous solution at ordinary temperatures.

The hydrogen and hydroxyl ion concentrations in pure water are each 10^{-7} gram ion per liter, and hence pH and pOH are both 7.0; this is taken as the criterion of a **neutral solution,** i.e., a solution of pH 7.0 at ordinary temperatures. If the hydrogen ion concentration exceeds 10^{-7} gram ion per liter, the pH is less than 7.0,* and the solution is said to be **acidic;** the pOH is correspondingly greater than 7.0, since the sum of pH and pOH must remain equal to 14.0. In an **alkaline solution,** on the other hand, the hydrogen ion concentration is less than 10^{-7} gram ion per liter; the pH is then greater than 7.0 while the pOH is smaller than this value. The relationship between pH, pOH, c_{H^+} and c_{OH^-}, at about 25° C, may be summarized in the manner represented below.

c_{H^+}	1	10^{-1}	10^{-2}	10^{-3}	10^{-4}	10^{-5}	10^{-6}	10^{-7}	10^{-8}	10^{-9}	10^{-10}	10^{-11}	10^{-12}	10^{-13}	10^{-14}
c_{OH^-}	10^{-14}	10^{-13}	10^{-12}	10^{-11}	10^{-10}	10^{-9}	10^{-8}	10^{-7}	10^{-6}	10^{-5}	10^{-4}	10^{-3}	10^{-2}	10^{-1}	1
pH	0	1	2	3	4	5	6	7	8	9	10	11	12	13	14
pOH	14	13	12	11	10	9	8	7	6	5	4	3	2	1	0

$\longleftarrow$ ———— Acidic ———— $\longrightarrow$ Neutral $\longleftarrow$ ———— Alkaline ———— $\longrightarrow$

The range of pH from zero to 14 covers the range of hydrogen and hydroxyl ion concentrations from a molar solution of strong acid, at one extreme, to a molar solution of a strong base, at the other extreme. Solutions with hydrogen ion activity exceeding 1 gram ion per liter are known; these have small negative pH's, but values less than zero in water are not common.

Problem: Calculate the hydroxyl ion concentration in a solution of pH 4.75 at 25° C.

Since pH + pOH = 14, it follows that pOH = 14 − 4.75 = 9.25.

$$\log c_{OH^-} = -pOH = -9.25 = -10.0 + 0.75$$

$$c_{OH^-} = 5.62 \times 10^{-10} \text{ g. ion per liter.}$$

---

* It should be noted that since pH is equal to $- \log c_{H^+}$, or to $\log 1/c_{H^+}$, the pH *decreases* as the hydrogen ion concentration *increases,* and vice versa.

53h. Neutralization of Strong Acid and Strong Base.—In a dilute solution of a strong acid in water the ionization reaction

$$HA + H_2O \rightleftharpoons H_3O^+ + A^-$$

may be regarded as being virtually complete; a dilute solution of hydrochloric or nitric acid thus behaves as if the acid were entirely in the form of H_3O^+ ions. Similarly, as already mentioned, a strong base, such as sodium hydroxide, in dilute solution is probably completely dissociated; the basic character of the solution is due to OH^- ions. According to these arguments, the neutralization of any *strong acid by a strong base in dilute solution* may be represented by the proton transfer process

$$H_3O^+ + OH^- = H_2O + H_2O,$$

which is independent of the nature of the strong acid or base. This result explains the observation that the heat change ΔH accompanying the neutralization of a strong acid by a strong base in dilute solution has the constant value of -13.69 kcal. at $20°$ C. The observed heat change is, in every case, that for a reaction between hydrogen and hydroxyl ions, and hence it is a constant, independent of the nature of the acid and base, provided they are both strong and the solution is dilute.

It will be observed that the reaction depicted above is exactly the reverse of that given in § 53f for the self-ionization of water. It should be possible to calculate the heat of reaction in the latter case from the variation with temperature of the equilibrium constant, i.e., the ionic product, by means of the integrated form of the van't Hoff equation (§ 36a). The form analogous to equation (36.6) is

$$\log \frac{(K_w)_2}{(K_w)_1} = \frac{\Delta H}{4.576}\left(\frac{T_2 - T_1}{T_1 T_2}\right).$$

According to Table LXII, the value of K_w is 0.681×10^{-14} at $20°$ C, i.e., $293.16°$ K, and 1.468×10^{-14} at $30°$ C, i.e., $303.16°$ K; hence,

$$\log \frac{1.468}{0.681} = \frac{\Delta H}{4.576} \times \frac{10}{293.16 \times 303.16}$$

$$\Delta H = 13.56 \text{ kcal.}$$

The mean value of ΔH between $20°$ and $30°$ C for the ionic dissociation of water is thus 13.56 kcal., which is very close, but of opposite sign, to that for the neutralization of a strong acid by a strong base in dilute solution. The agreement supports the view that this neutralization is effectively the combination of a hydrogen and a hydroxyl ion. The acidity of a strong acid in dilute solution may thus be attributed to the H_3O^+ ion, and the alkalinity of a strong base is due to the OH^- ion.

With an aqueous solution of a weak acid, such as acetic acid, the acidity is due partly to H_3O^+ ions, but mainly to the nonionized CH_3COOH molecules; the neutralization with a strong base is thus represented almost entirely by the reaction

$$CH_3COOH + OH^- = CH_3COO^- + H_2O.$$

The change of heat content of the reaction would not necessarily be the same as for the neutralization of a strong acid; the values observed are actually different and depend on the nature of the weak acid. However, if the results obtained at a number of concentrations are extrapolated to infinite dilution, when ionization of the weak acid to form H_3O^+ ions, or of the weak base to yield OH^- ions, would be complete, the value of ΔH is found to be the same as for a strong acid and a strong base.

53i. Amino-Acids.—The amino-acids are **amphoteric electrolytes** or **ampholytes,** *possessing both acidic and basic groups*; they are consequently capable of being neutralized by a base or an acid, respectively. If an acid is added the amino-acid exercises its basic function, while the addition of a base causes the acidic property of the ampholyte to be apparent. The aliphatic amino-acids are usually represented by the general formula NH_2RCOOH; the simplest of these substances, i.e., glycine or aminoacetic acid, is NH_2-CH_2COOH. There are, however, many excellent reasons for stating that in aqueous solution these substances exist in the form of **dual ions,*** having the structure $^+NH_3RCOO^-$; each of these ions carries both a positive and a negative charge, and so it is electrically neutral. Nevertheless, these dual ions have properties quite different from those of the uncharged, neutral molecules NH_2RCOOH. The acidic function of the amino-acid is exercised by the $^+NH_3$— group, which is a substituted ammonium ion, while the basic property is exhibited by the —COO^- radical. The acidic ionization is therefore represented by

$$^+NH_3RCOO^- + H_2O = H_3O^+ + NH_2RCOO^-,$$

and the basic ionization is

$$^+NH_3RCOO^- + H_2O = {}^+NH_3RCOOH + OH^-.$$

The relative extents of the two ionizations in pure water will depend on the dissociation constants of the acidic and basic groups in the ampholyte, and these will determine the pH of the solution. If the pH is changed by the addition of an alkali, or other base, the acidic ionization will be favored, but the addition of an acid will favor the basic ionization process. At a certain pH, known as the **isoelectric point** of the ampholyte, the two ionizations take place to the same extent, so that the solution contains equivalent amounts of the negative and positive ions, NH_2RCOO^- and $^+NH_3RCOOH$. The physical properties, e.g., viscosity, solubility, etc., of an amino-acid are frequently a maximum or a minimum at the isoelectric point; for example, the solubility of an ampholyte is generally a minimum at the isoelectric pH.

---

* Such ions are also referred to as "zwitterions" (hybrid ions), ampholyte ions or dipolar ions.

Attention may be called to the fact that aromatic amino-sulfonic acids, e.g., sulfanilic acid, probably exist in the dual-ion form in solution, but the aromatic amino-carboxylic acids, e.g., the aminobenzoic acids, are present mainly as uncharged molecules, viz., $NH_2C_6H_4COOH$, and not as dual ions.

READING REFERENCES

1. **Modern conception of acids and bases.** Hall, *Journal of Chemical Education*, **7**, 782 (1930).
2. **Acids, bases and salts.** Steffens, *ibid.*, **12**, 115 (1935).
3. **Nomenclature of acids and bases.** Alyea, *ibid.*, **16**, 535 (1939).
4. **Acids and bases in nonprotonic solvents.** McReynolds, *ibid.*, **17**, 116 (1940).
5. **Acids and bases: general discussion.** Hall, Briscoe, Hammett and Johnson, *ibid.*, **17**, 124, 128, 131, 132 (1940).
6. **Interpretation of pH.** Gorman, *ibid.*, **17**, 343 (1940).
7. **Solubility product.** Zuffanti, *ibid.*, **17**, 433 (1940).
8. **Dissociation constants, pH, etc.** Porges and Clark, *ibid.*, **17**, 571 (1940).
9. **Theory of the solubility product.** Denbigh, *ibid.*, **18**, 126 (1941).
10. **Acids and bases in organic chemistry.** Davidson, *ibid.*, **18**, 154 (1941).
11. **Proton transfer theory of acids and bases.** Alyea, *ibid.*, **18**, 206 (1941).
12. **pH.** Sammis, *ibid.*, **19**, 490 (1942).
13. **Acids and bases: critical reevaluation.** Ginnel, *ibid.*, **20**, 250 (1943).
14. **Electronic theory of acids and bases.** Luder, McGuire and Zuffanti, *ibid.*, **20**, 344 (1943).

REVIEW QUESTIONS

1. Derive an exact expression for the dissociation constant in terms of the degree of dissociation.

2. Describe, with the aid of a figure, the general conclusions concerning the effect of concentration on the activity coefficients of electrolytes of different valence types.

3. Define ionic strength in words and in the form of an equation. What is the experimental rule concerning the activity coefficient of a given electrolyte and the ionic strength of the (dilute) solution?

4. Outline the basis of the Debye-Hückel theory of electrolytes. Give the form of the Debye-Hückel limiting law equation. State some facts that support this equation.

5. How is the Debye-Hückel equation modified for moderately concentrated solutions? Show that the modification is in general agreement with experiment.

6. Derive the exact expression for the solubility product. How may it be simplified for dilute solutions? State the conclusion in words.

7. Describe two methods for determining solubility products. Give some applications of the solubility product principle.

8. Derive an equation relating the solubility product of a sparingly soluble salt to the ionic strength of the medium. Show how it may be used to test the Debye-Hückel theory.

9. How may the presence of neutral salts without a common ion cause (*a*) a decrease, (*b*) an increase, of solubility of a sparingly soluble salt? How can a salt with a common ion bring about an increase?

10. Explain the proton transfer theory of acids and bases. What is meant by a conjugate pair? Why are certain ions regarded as acids or bases?

11. Why does the apparent (relative) strength of an acid depend on the nature of the solvent? Refer to the behavior of acids in different solvents.

12. How does the nature of the solvent affect the apparent (relative) strength of a base? Why are alkali hydroxides strong bases in all solvents in which dissociation is appreciable?

13. Derive an equation for the dissociation constant of an acid. Explain how the dissociation constant may be obtained from conductance measurements.

14. How can the true dissociation constant of an acid be obtained by extrapolation of experimental data, using the Debye-Hückel equation?

15. Derive an equation for the dissociation constant of a base in terms of its degree of dissociation.

16. Explain the dissociation in stages of a polybasic, e.g., tribasic, acid. Why do the dissociation constants of successive stages decrease?

17. Derive an equation for the hydrogen ion concentration in a solution of a weak acid.

18. Derive an equation for the hydrogen ion concentration in a solution of a mixture of a weak acid and its salt. When is the hydrogen ion concentration equal to the dissociation constant of the acid?

19. What is meant by the ionic product of water? What is its accepted value at $25°$ C? Describe two methods for its evaluation.

20. Explain the meaning of pH, pOH and pK_w. How are these quantities related?

21. How may (a) neutral, (b) acidic, (c) alkaline, aqueous solutions be defined in terms of pH?

22. What is the evidence that the neutralization of a strong acid by a strong base always involves the same fundamental process? What is this process?

23. Describe the acidic and basic ionizations of an aliphatic amino-acid. What is the effect of adding alkali or acid, respectively? What is meant by the isoelectric point?

PROBLEMS

I

1. Calculate the ionic strengths of the following solutions: 0.025 molal NaCl; 0.025 molal $CuSO_4$; 0.025 molal $LaCl_3$.

2. By means of the Debye-Hückel limiting law, calculate the mean ionic activity coefficients in (a) 0.005 molal NaBr, (b) 0.001 molal $ZnSO_4$. (Compare the results with the experimental values given in, or inferred from, Table LIX.)

3. The silver ion activity in a 0.01 M solution of potassium bromide saturated with silver bromide is 8.2×10^{-11} g. ion per liter at $25°$ C. Calculate the expected solubility product of silver bromide and its solubility in pure water in g. per liter.

4. The solubility product of calcium fluoride (CaF_2) is 3.9×10^{-11} at $25°$ C. Calculate the expected solubility of this salt, in g. per liter, (a) in pure water, (b) in 0.10 M sodium fluoride solution.

5. The solubility of barium iodate [$Ba(IO_3)_2$] in pure water is 5.46×10^{-4} mole per liter at $25°$ C. Estimate the solubility of this salt in 0.01 M sodium chloride, assuming the Debye-Hückel limiting law to be applicable.

6. Use the results of problem I, 9 (Chapter XIII) to calculate the approximate dissociation constant k_a of crotonic acid [equation (53.7)]. Evaluate the true dissociation constant K_a, assuming the activity coefficients of the univalent ions to be given by the Debye-Hückel limiting equation [see equation (53.12)].

7. Calculate the values of c_{H^+}, c_{OH^-} and pOH corresponding to each of the following pH values: (a) 0.88, (b) 4.52, (c) 9.84, at $25°$ C.

8. Determine the pH and pOH values corresponding to each of the following hydrogen ion concentrations (activities): (a) 1.20, (b) 2.45 $\times$ 10^{-3}, (c) 7.86 $\times$ 10^{-11}, g. ion per liter at 25° C. What are the pH and pOH values in (d) 0.01 M hydrochloric acid, (e) 0.01 M sodium hydroxide at 25° C?

9. Evaluate the hydrogen ion concentration and pH of 0.05 molal phenylacetic acid, by accurate and approximate methods, at 25° C.

10. Calculate the hydrogen ion concentration and pH of a solution consisting of 0.05 molal lactic acid and 0.122 molal sodium lactate at 25° C.

II

1. Calculate the ionic strengths of the following solutions: 0.05 molal KBr; 0.05 molal K$_3$Fe(CN)$_6$; 0.05 molal La$_2$(SO$_4$)$_3$.

2. By means of the Debye-Hückel limiting law, calculate the mean ionic activity coefficients in (a) 0.02 molal KI, (b) 0.001 molal LaCl$_3$. (Compare the results with the experimental values given in, or inferred from, Table LIX.)

3. The lead ion (Pb^{++}) activity in a 0.005 M solution of potassium iodate (KIO$_3$) saturated with lead iodate [Pb(IO$_3$)$_2$] is 1.3 $\times$ 10^{-8} g. ion per liter at 25° C. Calculate the solubility product of lead iodate, and the expected solubility in pure water, in g. per liter.

4. The solubility product of silver bromate (AgBrO$_3$) is 4.1 $\times$ 10^{-13} at 25° C. Calculate the expected solubility of this salt, in g. per liter, (a) in pure water, (b) in 0.05 M potassium bromate (KBrO$_3$) solution.

5. The solubility of a salt MA$_3$, where M is a trivalent and A a univalent ion, is 5.04 $\times$ 10^{-5} mole per liter in water at 25° C. Calculate the solubility in 0.005 M barium chloride, assuming the Debye-Hückel limiting law to be applicable.

6. Use the results of problem II, 9 (Chapter XIII) to calculate the approximate dissociation constant k_a of benzoic acid [equation (53.7)]. Evaluate the true dissociation constant K_a, assuming the activity coefficients of the univalent ions to be given by the Debye-Hückel limiting equation [see equation (53.12)].

7. Calculate the values of c_{H^+}, c_{OH^-} and pOH corresponding to each of the following pH values: (a) 0.45, (b) 2.28, (c) 10.79, at 25° C.

8. Determine the pH and pOH values corresponding to each of the following hydrogen ion concentrations (activities): (a) 1.35, (b) 5.28 $\times$ 10^{-6}, (c) 3.32 $\times$ 10^{-9}, g. ion per liter. What are the pH and pOH values in (d) 0.05 M hydrochloric acid, (e) 0.05 M potassium hydroxide at 25° C?

9. Evaluate the hydrogen ion concentration and pH of 0.1 molal phosphoric acid, treated as a monobasic acid, by accurate and approximate methods, at 25° C. (The second and third stages of dissociation may be neglected.)

10. Calculate the hydrogen ion concentration and pH of a solution consisting of 0.10 molal ammonia and 0.024 molal ammonium chloride at 25° C.

CHAPTER XVI

HYDROLYSIS AND NEUTRALIZATION

The Hydrolysis of Salts

54a. Incomplete Neutralization.—The term **neutralization** is generally applied to the reaction of one equivalent of an acid with one equivalent of a base; if the terms "acid" and "base" are employed in the sense defined in § 53a, the products are not necessarily a salt and water. They are, however, always the conjugate base and acid, respectively, of the reacting acid and base, in accordance with equation (53.1). The following reactions, for example, are all to be described as neutralizations:

$$
\begin{array}{llll}
H_3O^+ & + \quad\quad OH^- & = H_2O & + \quad\quad H_2O \\
CH_3COOH & + \quad (Na^+)OH^- & = H_2O & + (Na^+)CH_3COO^- \\
HCl & + \quad\quad NH_3 & = NH_4^+ & + \quad\quad Cl^- \\
HCl & + (Na^+)CH_3COO^- & = CH_3COOH & + (Na)^+Cl^- \\
NH_4^+(Cl^-) & + \quad (Na^+)OH^- & = H_2O & + \quad\quad NH_3 \quad\quad +(Na^+Cl^-)
\end{array}
$$

$$\text{Acid 1}\quad\quad\quad\quad \text{Base 2}\quad\quad\quad\quad \text{Acid 2}\quad\quad\quad\quad \text{Base 1}$$

The last two reactions are of special interest, since they belong to the category usually known as "displacement reactions." In the first of these, a strong acid displaces a weak acid, acetic acid, from its salt; in the second, a weak base, ammonia, is displaced from its hydrochloride by a strong base. A much better understanding of these processes can be obtained by treating them as neutralizations that are not fundamentally different from other acid-base reactions.

When equivalent amounts of strong acid and strong base are mixed, the reaction goes to virtual completion, leaving a very small concentration of free acid and base, viz., 10^{-7} gram ion per liter of H_3O^+ and of OH^- ions. If the acid or base, or both, are weak, the neutralization process is incomplete in aqueous, and similar, solutions. Suppose an acid HA reacts with a base B; the neutralization reaction is represented by

$$HA + B \rightleftharpoons BH^+ + A^-. \tag{54.1}$$

$$\text{acid}\quad\ \text{base}\quad\ \ \text{acid}\quad\ \ \text{base}$$

Since BH^+ is an acid and A^- is a base, a proton transfer equilibrium can be established with the solvent, e.g., water, acting as a base or acid, respectively; thus,

$$BH^+ + H_2O \rightleftharpoons H_3O^+ + B \tag{54.2}$$

$$\text{acid}\quad\ \text{base}\quad\ \ \text{acid}\quad\ \text{base}$$

$$A^- + H_2O \rightleftharpoons OH^- + HA. \tag{54.3}$$

$$\text{base}\quad\ \text{acid}\quad\ \ \text{base}\quad\ \text{acid}$$

518

In the first of these reactions the free base B is regenerated, while in the second the free acid HA is re-formed, so that they tend to oppose the neutralization. *This partial reversal of neutralization, or the prevention of complete neutralization, due to the action of the solvent water* is referred to as **hydrolysis**. In general, for any solvent capable of acting as an acid or base, or both, the phenomenon is known as **lyolysis** or **solvolysis**.

The conditions for hydrolysis to be appreciable can be readily derived from information already gained concerning the relative strengths of conjugate acids and bases. If the hydrolysis reaction indicated by equation (54.2) is to take place to any considerable extent, that is, if the equilibrium is to lie to the right-hand side, the acid BH^+ must be strong or moderately strong. Since there is a reciprocal relationship between the strengths of a conjugate pair (§ 53a), it is evident that the conjugate base B must be relatively weak. It follows, therefore, that the neutralization reaction in equation (54.1) will be incomplete, and hydrolysis of the type of equation (54.2) will take place if B is a weak base. It can be seen in an exactly analogous manner that if the hydrolytic reaction in equation (54.3) is to be appreciable, the base A^- must be strong, and hence the conjugate acid HA should be weak. The conclusion to be drawn, then, is that *neutralization is incomplete and hydrolysis occurs when the acid or base, or both, are weak*. Consideration will show that the phenomenon of lyolysis, in general, also depends on the acidic or basic character of the solvent, since this plays a part in the reactions which reverse the neutralization. The discussion in § 53b may be applied to the present problem with interesting consequences.

54b. The Hydrolysis of Salts.—The subject of hydrolysis can be regarded from two angles; in the treatment given above it has been considered from the point of view of incomplete neutralization of an acid by a base. Another approach to the phenomena of hydrolysis is to study the equilibria resulting when a salt is dissolved in water; the resulting situation is, of course, exactly the same as that which arises when the appropriate acid is neutralized by an equivalent of the base constituting the given salt. In treating this aspect of hydrolysis, it is convenient to consider salts of (I) weak acid and strong base, (II) weak base and strong acid, and (III) weak acid and weak base. Salts of strong acids and strong bases, e.g., sodium chloride, do not undergo hydrolysis; the conjugate base and acid, respectively, are so extremely weak that the reactions in equations (54.2) and (54.3) occur to a negligible extent.

I. Salt of Weak Acid and Strong Base.—When a salt such as sodium acetate, represented by NaOAc, is dissolved in water, it probably undergoes complete ionization (and dissociation) into Na^+ and OAc^- ions, provided the solution is not too concentrated. Since acetic acid (HOAc) is a weak acid, its conjugate base, the acetate ion (OAc^-) will be moderately strong; hence, the latter will react with water to an appreciable extent, in accordance with equation (54.3), i.e.,

$$(Na^+)OAc^- + H_2O \rightleftharpoons (Na^+)OH^- + HOAc.$$

The hydrolysis of the salt thus results in the partial regeneration of the free weak acid HOAc, and of the strong base $(Na^+)OH^-$ from which the sodium acetate was constituted. It will be observed that the hydrolytic process results in the formation of OH^- ions, and this must obviously be associated with a decrease of hydrogen ion concentration, since the product $c_{H^+} \times c_{OH^-}$ is constant. *A solution of the salt of a weak acid and a strong base thus reacts alkaline because of hydrolysis.* This accounts for the familiar fact that the "normal" alkali metal salts * of weak acids, such as cyanides, acetates, sulfides, borates, phosphates, carbonates, etc., are alkaline in solution, that is, the pH is greater than 7 in every case.

Since the cation of a strong base, i.e., Na^+, appears on both sides of the equilibrium represented above, it may be omitted; the general hydrolytic equilibrium for the salt NaA of a weak acid HA and a strong base then reduces to the form

$$A^- \quad + H_2O \rightleftharpoons OH^- + HA,$$

| unhydrolyzed | free | free |
| salt | base | acid |

which is identical with equation (54.3). Taking the activity of the water as unity, as is justifiable for a dilute solution, the exact equilibrium constant is given by

$$K_h = \frac{a_{OH^-} \times a_{HA}}{a_{A^-}}, \tag{54.4}$$

where K_h is known as the **hydrolysis constant** of the salt. In addition to the hydrolytic equilibrium, all other possible equilibria will be established in the solution, e.g., between the hydrogen and hydroxyl ions and water molecules, for which

$$K_w = a_{H^+} \times a_{OH^-}, \tag{54.5}$$

and also between hydrogen and A^- ions and molecules of undissociated acid HA, for which

$$K_a = \frac{a_{H^+} \times a_{A^-}}{a_{HA}}. \tag{54.6}$$

Combination of equations (54.4), (54.5) and (54.6) leads immediately to the result

$$K_h = \frac{K_w}{K_a}. \tag{54.7}$$

The hydrolysis constant K_h of the salt is thus inversely proportional to the dissociation constant K_a of the weak acid; the weaker the acid the greater is the hydrolysis constant of the salt.

Attention may be called to the fact that the quantity, i.e., K_h, defined by equation (54.4) is also the dissociation constant of the base A^- [see equation

---

* The so-called "acid salts," e.g., $NaHCO_3$, Na_2HPO_4, are sometimes alkaline; NaH_2PO_4 is acidic.

(53.13)], which is conjugate to the acid HA. It is seen, therefore, from equation (54.7) that the dissociation constant of the base is inversely proportional to the dissociation constant of its conjugate acid; the proportionality constant is equal to K_w, the ionic product of the solvent. This is the quantitative expression of the inverse relationship between the strengths of a conjugate acid and base, referred to in § 53a.

If the ionic strength of the solution is low, the activity terms in equation (54.4) may be replaced by the corresponding concentrations, in gram ions or gram moles per liter; hence, using k_h in place of K_h, it follows that equation (54.4) defining the hydrolysis may be written in the approximate form

$$k_h = \frac{c_{OH^-} \times c_{HA}}{c_{A^-}}, \qquad (54.8)$$

and by analogy with equation (54.7),

$$k_h = \frac{k_w}{k_a}. \qquad (54.9)$$

The **degree of hydrolysis** x is defined as *the fraction of the total salt present in solution that has undergone hydrolysis when equilibrium is attained.* If c mole per liter is the total concentration of the salt NaA in the solution, the concentration of unhydrolyzed salt will be $c(1 - x)$; this may be regarded as completely dissociated into Na^+ and A^- ions, and so it is possible to write

$$c_{A^-} = c(1 - x). \qquad (54.10)$$

In the hydrolytic reaction equivalent amounts of HA and OH^- are formed; although the former will ionize to a very small extent, this can be neglected, and c_{HA} and c_{OH^-} may be taken as equal. Since the HA and OH^- arise from the hydrolyzed part of the salt, it follows that

$$c_{HA} = c_{OH^-} = cx, \qquad (54.11)$$

and substitution of these values for c_{A^-}, c_{HA} and c_{OH^-} into equation (54.8) gives

$$k_h = \frac{cx^2}{1 - x}. \qquad (54.12)$$

Unless the acid is extremely weak or the solution is very dilute, x is small, and $1 - x$ in equation (54.12) may be replaced by unity without serious error, so that this equation reduces to $k_h = cx^2$; hence,

$$x \approx \sqrt{\frac{k_h}{c}} = \sqrt{\frac{k_w}{k_a c}}, \qquad (54.13)$$

the last expression being obtained by utilizing equation (54.9). By making use of equation (54.13) it is possible to calculate the degree of hydrolysis of a salt of a weak acid and a strong base at any desired concentration. It can be seen from this equation that the degree of hydrolysis is greater the weaker the acid, i.e., the smaller k_a, and the more dilute the solution, i.e., the smaller the total concentration c of the salt.

Problem: Calculate the degree of hydrolysis of a 0.01 molar solution of sodium acetate at 25° C.

For acetic acid, k_a is 1.75×10^{-5}, and taking k_w as 1.01×10^{-14} at 25° C, with c equal to 0.01, equation (54.13) gives

$$x = \sqrt{\frac{1.01 \times 10^{-14}}{1.75 \times 10^{-5} \times 0.01}} = 2.40 \times 10^{-4}.$$

The per cent hydrolysis is equal to $100x$, that is, 0.024 per cent.

According to equation (54.11), c_{OH^-} is equal to cx, and since c_{H^+} is equal to k_w/c_{OH^-}, it follows that, using equation (54.13),

$$c_{H^+} = \frac{k_w}{cx} = \sqrt{\frac{k_w k_a}{c}}. \tag{54.14}$$

Upon taking logarithms and changing the signs throughout, the result is

$$- \log c_{H^+} = -\tfrac{1}{2} \log k_w - \tfrac{1}{2} \log k_a + \tfrac{1}{2} \log c$$

$$pH = \tfrac{1}{2}pk_w + \tfrac{1}{2}pk_a + \tfrac{1}{2} \log c. \tag{54.15}$$

It is seen, therefore, that the pH, or alkalinity, of a solution of the salt of a weak acid and a strong base increases with decreasing acid strength, i.e., with increasing pk_a, and increasing concentration of the salt. It may be remarked that although the degree of hydrolysis x decreases with increasing concentration [equation (54.13)], the pH, or alkalinity, increases at the same time.

Problem: Calculate the pH of a 0.01 molar solution of sodium acetate at 25° C (see preceding problem).

For acetic acid k_a is 1.75×10^{-5}, and so $pk_a = -\log (1.75 \times 10^{-5}) = 4.76$; pk_w is 14, and c is 0.01; hence, by equation (54.15),

$$pH = \tfrac{1}{2} \times 14 + \tfrac{1}{2} \times 4.76 + \tfrac{1}{2} \log 0.01 = 8.38.$$

Since the pH of a neutral solution is 7.0, this solution is definitely alkaline.

It was mentioned in § 53c that the dissociation constant of an acid undergoes relatively little change with temperature; on the other hand, the ionic product of water increases rapidly (Table LXII). It is evident, therefore, from equations (54.7) and (54.9), that the hydrolysis constant will increase markedly with increasing temperature; the degree of hydrolysis will likewise increase, as required by equation (54.13).

II. Salt of Weak Base and Strong Acid.—Ammonium chloride may be taken as a typical salt of a weak base (ammonia) and a strong acid; since the NH_4^+ ion is a moderately strong acid, being conjugate to the weak base

NH_3, it will react with water to an appreciable extent, as in equation (54.2), i.e.,

$$NH_4^+(Cl^-) + H_2O \rightleftharpoons H_3O^+(Cl^-) + NH_3.$$

The salt is thus hydrolyzed with the formation, to some extent, of its constituent weak base and the strong (hydrochloric) acid $H_3O^+(Cl^-)$. In this case hydrolysis is accompanied by the liberation of hydrogen ions, and so *the solution of a salt of a weak base and a strong acid will have an acidic reaction.*

If B represents the weak base, the cation present in the salt will be BH^+, and the hydrolytic equilibrium may be represented by the general equation *

$$BH^+ + H_2O \rightleftharpoons H_3O^+ + B$$
$$\text{unhydrolyzed} \qquad\qquad \text{free} \qquad \text{free}$$
$$\text{salt} \qquad\qquad\qquad \text{acid} \qquad \text{base}$$

as in equation (54.2); the anion of the strong acid, e.g., Cl^-, is omitted since it appears on both sides of the equilibrium. By the use of arguments analogous to those employed in connection with the salt of a weak acid, the hydrolysis constant K_h is given by

$$K_h = \frac{a_{H_3O^+} \times a_B}{a_{BH^+}} = \frac{K_w}{K_b}, \tag{54.16}$$

where K_b is the dissociation constant of the weak base. In dilute solution, when concentrations may be employed in place of activities, it is found that

$$k_h = \frac{k_w}{k_b} = \frac{cx^2}{1-x}, \tag{54.17}$$

$$x \approx \sqrt{\frac{k_h}{c}} = \sqrt{\frac{k_w}{k_bc}}, \tag{54.18}$$

where x is the degree of hydrolysis in a salt solution of concentration c mole per liter. As in the previous case, the degree of hydrolysis is greater the weaker the base, i.e., the smaller k_b, and the more dilute the solution, i.e., the smaller the value of c. Since k_b does not vary greatly with temperature, the degree of hydrolysis, at a given concentration, increases with temperature.

It can be readily seen from equation (54.16) that K_h is equivalent to the dissociation constant of the acid BH^+ which is conjugate to the base B; it is evident, therefore, as before, that the dissociation constants of conjugate acid and base are inversely proportional to one another, the product being equal to K_w, the ionic product of the solvent.

* Although it may not be immediately obvious, this expression also represents the hydrolysis of salts of such weak bases as metallic hydroxides, e.g., ferric hydroxide. It is probable that the conjugate acid, represented by BH^+, is a hydrated ion of the metal, e.g., $Fe(H_2O)_n^{+++}$, and the weak base B is $Fe(H_2O)_{n-1}(OH)^{++}$. The general conclusions are, in any event, independent of the particular formula that may be proposed for the conjugate acid and base.

The concentration of hydrogen (H_3O^+) ions is here equal to the concentration of the hydrolyzed salt, i.e., to cx; hence, utilizing equation (54.18),

$$c_{H^+} = cx = \sqrt{\frac{k_w c}{k_b}},\qquad (54.19)$$

and,

$$pH = \tfrac{1}{2}pk_w - \tfrac{1}{2}pk_b - \tfrac{1}{2}\log c.\qquad (54.20)$$

It can be seen from this equation that, in general, the pH will be less than $\tfrac{1}{2}pk_w$, i.e., less than 7.0; the solution of the salt of a weak base and strong acid will thus have an acidic reaction, as mentioned above. Since salts of this type do not present any essentially new problems, it is not necessary to treat the subject in further detail.

III. Salt of Weak Acid and Weak Base.—If the acid and base from which the given salt is made are both weak, the respective conjugate acid and base will be fairly strong, and both will be able to react with water. When a salt such as ammonium acetate is dissolved in water, it dissociates virtually completely into NH_4^+ and OAc^- ions, and these acting as acid and base, respectively, take part in the hydrolytic equilibria

$$NH_4^+ + H_2O \rightleftharpoons H_3O^+ + NH_3 \qquad \text{and} \qquad OAc^- + H_2O \rightleftharpoons HOAc + OH^-.$$

Combining the two equations, by addition, the complete equilibrium may be written as

$$NH_4^+ + OAc^- + 2H_2O \rightleftharpoons H_3O^+ + OH^- + NH_3 + HOAc.$$

Since the normal equilibrium between water molecules and hydrogen and hydroxyl ions, viz.,

$$2H_2O \rightleftharpoons H_3O^+ + OH^-$$

exists in the aqueous solution in any case, it may be subtracted from the hydrolytic equilibrium, giving the result

$$NH_4^+ + OAc^- \rightleftharpoons NH_3 + HOAc.$$

The effect of the action of water upon the ammonium acetate is thus to bring about partial decomposition into the constituent acid and base, i.e., ammonia and acetic acid.

For any salt (BH^+A^-) of the weak base B and weak acid HA the hydrolytic equilibrium is consequently

$$BH^+ + A^- \rightleftharpoons B + HA$$
$$\text{unhydrolyzed} \qquad \text{free} \qquad \text{free}$$
$$\text{salt} \qquad \text{base} \qquad \text{acid}$$

and the hydrolysis constant is given by

$$K_h = \frac{a_B \times a_{HA}}{a_{BH^+} \times a_{A^-}} = \frac{K_w}{K_a K_b},\qquad (54.21)$$

where K_a and K_b are the dissociation constants of the weak acid HA and base B, respectively. Making the usual approximation of replacing activities by concentrations, it is seen that equation (54.21) gives

$$k_h = \frac{c_B \times c_{HA}}{c_{BH^+} \times c_{A^-}} = \frac{k_w}{k_a k_b}. \tag{54.22}$$

If c mole per liter is the total concentration of the salt, and x is the degree of hydrolysis, c_B and c_{HA} may both be set equal to cx, while c_{BH^+} and c_{A^-} are both equal to the concentration of the unhydrolyzed salt, i.e., to $c(1-x)$. Insertion of these values in equation (54.22) leads to the result

$$k_h = \frac{x^2}{1-x^2}, \tag{54.23}$$

and if x^2 is neglected in comparison with unity in the denominator,

$$x = \sqrt{k_h} = \sqrt{\frac{k_w}{k_a k_b}}. \tag{54.24}$$

In order to determine the hydrogen ion concentration of the solution, use is made of equation (53.24) which must hold in any solution containing the acid HA; thus,

$$c_{H^+} = k_a \frac{c_{HA}}{c_{A^-}} = k_a \frac{cx}{c(1-x)}$$

$$= k_a \frac{x}{1-x}.$$

Again x may be neglected in comparison with unity, so that c_{H^+} becomes equal to $k_a x$, and by equation (54.24),

$$c_{H^+} = \sqrt{\frac{k_w k_a}{k_b}} \tag{54.25}$$

$$\text{pH} = \tfrac{1}{2}pk_w + \tfrac{1}{2}pk_a - \tfrac{1}{2}pk_b. \tag{54.26}$$

If the dissociation constants of the weak acid and base are approximately equal, i.e., pk_a and pk_b are not very different, it is seen from equation (54.26) that the pH will be approximately $\tfrac{1}{2}pk_w$, i.e., about 7.0. *The solution will thus be approximately neutral in spite of hydrolysis.* If, however, the weak acid is somewhat stronger than the base, i.e., pk_a is less than pk_b, the solution will have an acidic reaction, for pH will be less than $\tfrac{1}{2}pk_w$. On the other hand, if the weak base is stronger than the acid, the pH will be greater than $\tfrac{1}{2}pk_w$ and the solution will react alkaline. A solution of a salt of a weak acid and a weak base may thus be considerably hydrolyzed, but the solution may be only slightly acidic or alkaline in reaction.

It appears from equations (54.24) and (54.25) that the degree of hydrolysis and the hydrogen ion concentration of a solution of a salt of a weak acid and weak base is independent of the concentration of the salt. This result is not exactly true, for in its derivation the tacit assumption is made that the acid BH^+ and the base A^- react with water to the same extent. This will be the case only if k_a and k_b are equal; hence, equations (54.24) and (54.25) are strictly applicable only under these conditions. However, detailed calculations have shown that provided the salt solution is not too dilute, the use of these equations does not lead to appreciable errors.

54c. Determination of Hydrolysis Constants.—A number of procedures of varying accuracy have been used for the study of hydrolysis. The most obvious, but indirect, method is to use equations (54.7), (54.16) or (54.21) which relate the hydrolysis constant to the dissociation constants of the weak acid or base and the ionic product of water. For example, K_a for acetic acid is known to be 1.75×10^{-5} and K_w is 1.01×10^{-14} at 25° C; hence, K_h for sodium acetate is given by equation (54.7) as 5.77×10^{-10}; from this result the degree of hydrolysis at any desired concentration can be obtained from equation (54.12) or (54.13).

Among the more direct methods, some are based on the determination of the hydrogen ion concentration of the salt solution, by one of the procedures described in §§ 55b, 55c. If the salt is one of a weak acid and a strong base, c_{H^+} is equal to k_w/cx by equation (54.14); hence, if c_{H^+} is determined by experiment, in a solution of salt of concentration c, the degree of hydrolysis x can be readily calculated, since k_w is known. With this information the hydrolysis constant can be obtained from equation (54.12). On the other hand, if the salt is one of a weak base and a strong acid, c_{H^+} is equal to cx, by equation (54.19), so that x and k_h can be evaluated.

Problem: The pH of a 0.1 molar solution of sodium acetate was found to be 8.88; calculate the hydrolysis constant of this salt.

A pH of 8.88 corresponds to a c_{H^+} value of 1.32×10^{-9} g. ion liter^{-1}; the degree of hydrolysis x is then given by equation (54.14) as

$$x = \frac{k_w}{cc_{H^+}} = \frac{10^{-14}}{0.1 \times 1.32 \times 10^{-9}} = 7.58 \times 10^{-5}.$$

Since $1 - x \approx 1$, it follows from equation (54.12) that

$$k_h = cx^2 = 5.75 \times 10^{-10}.$$

A different principle has been used in the conductance method of studying hydrolysis. In a solution containing c mole per liter of the salt of a weak monoacid base and a strong acid, for example, there will be present $c(1 - x)$ mole of unhydrolyzed salt and cx mole per liter of both free acid and free base. If the base is very weak, it may be regarded as completely nonionized, and so it will contribute nothing to the total conductance of the solution of the salt. The conductance of 1 gram equiv. of the salt is thus made up of the conductance of $1 - x$ gram equiv. of unhydrolyzed salt and x gram equiv. of free acid, i.e.,

$$\Lambda = (1 - x)\Lambda_c + x\Lambda_{HA}. \tag{54.27}$$

In this equation Λ is the apparent equivalent conductance of the solution, equal to 1000 κ/c, where κ is the observed specific conductance [equation (46.8)]; Λ_c is the hypothetical equivalent conductance of the unhydrolyzed salt, and Λ_{HA} is the equivalent conductance of the free acid in the salt solution. It follows from equation (54.27) that

$$x = \frac{\Lambda - \Lambda_c}{\Lambda_{HA} - \Lambda_c}, \tag{54.28}$$

and so the evaluation of the degree of hydrolysis requires a knowledge of Λ, Λ_{HA} and Λ_c. As mentioned above, Λ is obtained directly from the measured specific conductance of the hydrolyzed salt solution; the value of Λ_{HA} may be taken, approximately, as equal to that for the strong acid HA at infinite dilution. In order to determine Λ_c, an excess of the almost nonconducting weak base is added to the salt solution; this represses the hydrolysis to such an extent that the conductance of the resulting solution may be regarded as giving Λ_c for the unhydrolyzed salt.

Problem: The apparent equivalent conductance Λ of 0.0156 molar aniline hydrochloride solution is 111.5 ohms^{-1} cm.^{2} at 25° C; in the presence of excess aniline, which is practically a nonconductor, the equivalent conductance Λ_c is 99.9 ohms^{-1} cm.^{2}. The equivalent conductance Λ_{HA} of hydrochloric acid at 25° is 426 ohms^{-1} cm.^{2} Calculate the hydrolysis constant of aniline hydrochloride and the dissociation constant of aniline at 25° C.

By equation (54.28),

$$x = \frac{111.5 - 99.9}{426 - 99.9} = 0.0356,$$

and introduction of this value into equation (54.17) gives

$$k_h = \frac{cx^2}{1 - x} = \frac{0.0156 \times (0.0356)^2}{1 - 0.0356} = 2.05 \times 10^{-5}.$$

Since $k_h = k_w/k_b$, by equation (54.17), and $k_w = 1.0 \times 10^{-14}$,

$$k_b = \frac{k_w}{k_h} = \frac{1.0 \times 10^{-14}}{2.05 \times 10^{-5}} = 4.9 \times 10^{-10}.$$

(The accurate value of K_b for aniline obtained from E.M.F. measurements is 4.07 × 10^{-10} at 25° C.)

THE DETERMINATION OF HYDROGEN ION CONCENTRATIONS

55a. Buffer Solutions.—Aqueous solutions of a salt of a strong acid and strong base, e.g., sodium chloride, and of ammonium acetate have a pH of about 7, but the addition of 1 ml. of 0.1 molar hydrochloric acid to 1 liter alters the pH to 4 in the former solution, although it hardly affects the pH of the latter. The addition of an equivalent quantity of sodium hydroxide would likewise change the pH of sodium chloride solution from 7 to 10, but it would not appreciably alter that of the ammonium acetate solution. The solution of ammonium acetate thus has the property of resisting change of pH when acid or alkali is added, and this property is known as **buffer action**. In general, a **buffer solution** is *one which is resistant to change of* pH *upon the addition of acid or alkali*. Such solutions usually consist of a mixture of a weak acid and its salt (conjugate base) or of a weak base and its salt (conjugate acid); a salt of a weak acid and a weak base, such as ammonium acetate, also has some buffer action, as indicated above.

The buffer action of a solution of a weak acid HA and its highly ionized salt, e.g., NaA, which contributes A^- ions, is explained by the "neutralization" of added hydrogen ions by the anions A^- acting as a base; thus, since HA is a weak acid, the reaction

$$H_3O^+ + A^- = H_2O + HA$$

takes place to a considerable extent. If hydroxyl ions are added, they are removed by reaction with the HA in the solution,

$$OH^- + HA = H_2O + A^-.$$

If the buffer mixture consists of a weak base B and its salt, which provides BH^+ ions, the corresponding equations for the removal of hydrogen and hydroxyl ions by the constituents of the solution are

$$H_3O^+ + B = H_2O + BH^+ \quad \text{and} \quad OH^- + BH^+ = H_2O + B.$$

In view of these reactions it can be understood why a buffer solution of the type described resists change of pH when acid (H_3O^+ ions) or alkali (OH^- ions) are added. Similar reactions will occur upon the addition of any other acid or base.

Buffer solutions of definitely known pH are of great value in various aspects of chemistry, and the problem of preparing such solutions is of interest. The hydrogen ion concentration of a buffer solution, consisting of a weak acid and its salt, is given with fair approximation, in the pH range of 4 to 10, by equation (53.25), i.e.,

$$c_{H^+} = k_a \frac{[\text{acid}]}{[\text{salt}]}.$$

Upon taking logarithms, and changing the signs throughout, this becomes

$$- \log c_{H^+} = - \log k_a + \log \frac{[\text{salt}]}{[\text{acid}]}$$

$$pH = pk_a + \log \frac{[\text{salt}]}{[\text{acid}]}. \tag{55.1}$$

By means of equation (55.1) it is possible to calculate the pH of a buffer solution of known concentration; alternatively, it may be employed to prepare a buffer solution of definite pH. Before considering the matter, it is necessary to examine the conditions under which a maximum buffer action **or buffer capacity** is to be expected.

According to equation (55.1), the pH of a solution of a given acid and its salt is determined by the logarithm of the ratio of the salt concentration to that of the acid, i.e., by [salt]/[acid], since pk_a for the acid is constant. If a strong acid, i.e., H_3O^+ ion, is added to the solution, some of the buffer salt is converted into the buffer acid, and so the ratio [salt]/[acid] changes. For the solution to have maximum buffer capacity, the change should be as small as possible. It can be shown that this condition is realized when the concentrations of salt and acid are the same, that is, when the ratio [salt]/[acid] is equal to unity. Consider, for instance, a buffer solution containing 0.5 mole of salt and 0.5 mole of the weak acid, so that the ratio is unity. Suppose 0.1 mole of a strong acid (H_3O^+) is added to this solution; 0.1 mole of the salt will then be converted into the acid, and hence the ratio [salt]/[acid] becomes equal to 0.4/0.6, i.e., 0.67. The change in the ratio [salt]/[acid] is thus from 1.0 to 0.67; the corresponding change of pH is 0.17. Consider, on the other hand, a buffer solution consisting initially of 0.2 mole of salt and 0.8 mole of weak acid, making the same total concentration as in the previous case; the addition of 0.1 mole of strong acid changes the ratio [salt]/[acid] from 0.2/0.8, i.e., 0.25, to 0.1/0.9, i.e., 0.11, and the resulting pH change is 0.36. It is evident that the relative alteration in the [salt]/[acid] ratio from 1 to 0.67 is less than from 0.25 to 0.11, and produces a smaller change of pH.

In general, the resistance to change in the [salt]/[acid] ratio, and hence in the pH of the solution, upon the addition of acid or alkali, is greatest when the ratio is unity, as stated above. The buffer capacity is therefore a maximum in a solution containing equivalent amounts of a weak acid and its salt; it falls off as the ratio of salt to acid changes in either direction. Although it is difficult to give an exact limit, it is generally accepted that a solution has useful buffer capacity provided the value of [salt]/[acid] lies within the range of 10 to 0.1, i.e., ten parts of salt to one of acid, at one extreme, to one part of salt to ten of acid, at the other extreme.

For maximum buffer capacity, [salt]/[acid] is equal to unity, and hence, by equation (55.1), the pH will be equal to the pk_a of the acid. If the ratio [salt]/[acid] is equal to 10, then pH has the value $pk_a + 1$; on the other hand, for [salt]/[acid] equal to 0.1, the pH becomes $pk_a - 1$. It follows, therefore, that a particular acid can be employed for making useful buffer solutions of pH lying within the range of $pk_a - 1$ to $pk_a + 1$; the maximum buffer capacity is attained in the solution for which the pH is equal to pk_a for the given acid. Acetic acid, for example, has a pk_a of 4.76 at 25° C; hence, mixtures of sodium acetate and acetic acid can be used for preparing buffer solutions whose pH's are roughly in the range of 3.75 to 5.75. Outside this range the buffer capacity of the sodium acetate-acetic acid system is too small to be of practical value.

To make a buffer solution of given pH, it is first necessary to choose an acid * with a pk_a value as near as possible to the desired pH, so as to obtain

---

* Weak bases are rarely used for the preparation of buffer solutions on account of their volatility or instability; the arguments given apply to any mixture of conjugate acid and base, and so can be adapted to a buffer mixture of a weak base and its salt.

maximum buffer capacity. The actual ratio of acid to salt necessary can then be found from equation (55.1). For purposes of illustration, suppose it is required to prepare a buffer solution of pH 7.00; an examination of the dissociation constants of acids shows that the second stage dissociation exponent of phosphoric acid is 7.21 at 25° C (cf. § 53c). The weak "acid" is thus $H_2PO_4^-$, which can be derived from the highly ionized salt NaH_2PO_4; the corresponding "salt" contains the ion HPO_4^{--}, and this is obtained from the ionized salt Na_2HPO_4. The proportions of NaH_2PO_4 and Na_2HPO_4 required to give a pH of 7.00 are now calculated from equation (55.1); thus

$$7.00 = 7.21 + \log \frac{[salt]}{[acid]},$$

$$\frac{[salt]}{[acid]} = \frac{[Na_2HPO_4]}{[NaH_2PO_4]} = 0.62.$$

A mixture containing 0.62 mole of Na_2HPO_4 to 1 mole of NaH_2PO_4 will thus have a pH of 7.00; since the proportion of salt to acid does not differ greatly from unity, the solution will have appreciable buffer capacity.

Any given weak acid can be used for the preparation of buffer solutions over a limited range of pH only; hence, a number of different acids, and their salts, are required to cover the useful range of pH from about 2 to 12. Some of the recommended mixtures and their effective ranges are given in Table LXIII; the pH values for various compositions have been carefully checked

TABLE LXIII. BUFFER MIXTURES

Constituents	pH Range
Glycine and Glycine hydrochloride	1.0–3.7
Phthalic acid and Potassium acid phthalate	2.2–3.8
Acetic acid and Sodium acetate	3.7–5.6
Disodium citrate and Trisodium citrate	5.0–6.3
Monosodium phosphate and Disodium phosphate	5.8–8.0
Boric acid and Borax	6.8–9.2
Borax and Sodium hydroxide	9.2–11.0
Disodium phosphate and Trisodium phosphate	11.0–12.0

by experimental determinations with the hydrogen electrode (§ 55b). By following the directions given in the literature a solution of any desired pH value can be prepared with rapidity and precision.

Provided there is no chemical action, other than the establishment of acid-base equilibria, a mixture of two different buffer solutions will be effective over the pH ranges of both solutions separately. A simple and ingenious combination of this kind consists of citric acid and disodium hydrogen phosphate in various proportions; this is equivalent to a system of five acids, viz., three stages of citric acid and the first two stages of phosphoric acid. This system, with the constituents in various proportions, can be used for preparing buffer solutions having definite pH values between 2.2 and 8.0. The inclusion of diethylbarbituric acid (veronal) and boric acid extends the range to pH 12.

According to equation (55.1) the pH of a buffer solution is determined by the *ratio* of the concentrations of salt and acid, and not by their amounts; nevertheless, the buffer capacity at a given pH does depend on the actual concentrations. The more concentrated the solution the greater will be the resistance to change of pH upon the addition of an acid or a base. This can be readily proved by means of equation (55.1), using two hypothetical cases in which the salt and acid concentrations are different but the ratio is the same (see problem below). In practice the solutions employed are usually about 0.1 to 0.2 molar, because the use of more concentrated solutions introduces so-called "salt effects"; the ionic strength is then so high that it produces marked deviations from unity in the activity coefficients.

Problem: Two buffer solutions of pH 7.00 are prepared from Na_2HPO_4 and NaH_2PO_4 in the proper proportions; one contains 0.62 mole of "salt" and 1.00 mole of "acid" per liter, while the concentration of the other is one fourth of this, i.e., 0.155 mole of "salt" and 0.25 mole of "acid" per liter. To each solution is added NaOH to the extent of 0.05 mole per liter; calculate the change of pH in each case.

The addition of NaOH converts an equivalent amount of NaH_2PO_4, i.e., "acid," into Na_2HPO_4, i.e., "salt"; hence, in the first solution, [salt] becomes 0.62 + 0.05 = 0.67, while [acid] becomes 1.00 − 0.05 = 0.95. Since pk_a is 7.21, as given above, the pH of the solution after addition of NaOH is given by

$$pH = 7.21 + \log \frac{0.67}{0.95} = 7.06.$$

In the more dilute solution, [salt] becomes 0.155 + 0.05 = 0.205, while [acid] becomes 0.25 − 0.05 = 0.20, upon addition of the NaOH; hence, the pH is

$$pH = 7.21 + \log \frac{0.205}{0.20} = 7.22.$$

The pH is thus increased from 7.00 to 7.06 in the more concentrated buffer solution, and from 7.00 to 7.22 in the more dilute solution by the addition of the same amount of alkali; the former has therefore the greater buffer capacity.

55b. The Hydrogen Gas Electrode.—The standard potential of the hydrogen electrode with gas at 1 atm. pressure is zero, since this is the basis of the hydrogen scale of potentials (§ 49a). It follows then from equation (49.5) that the oxidation potential of a hydrogen electrode, with gas at 1 atm. pressure, in a solution containing hydrogen ions at an activity a_{H^+} is given by

$$E_H = -\frac{RT}{F} \ln a_{H^+}, \qquad (55.2)$$

since E^0 is zero, in this case, and n is unity; the electrode process is

$$\tfrac{1}{2}H_2(1 \text{ atm.}) + H_2O = H_3O^+ + \epsilon,$$

where, as before, H_3O^+ represents the hydrogen ion in solution. Converting the logarithms in equation (55.2), and taking the temperature to be 25° C, this becomes

$$E_H = -0.05915 \log a_{H^+}. \qquad (55.3)$$

Utilizing the definition of pH as $-\log a_{H^+}$, in this case, it is seen that

$$E_H = 0.05915 \text{ pH}. \tag{55.4}$$

If the hydrogen electrode is combined with a convenient reference electrode, the potential of which is represented by $E_{ref.}$, the measured E.M.F. of the cell, E, is equal to $E_H + E_{ref.}$; hence,

$$E = E_H + E_{ref.} = 0.05915 \text{ pH} + E_{ref.}$$

$$pH = \frac{E - E_{ref.}}{0.05915}. \tag{55.5}$$

This equation provides, in principle, a direct method for measuring the pH of any solution; a hydrogen gas electrode is combined with a reference electrode of known potential, and the E.M.F. of the resulting cell E is measured. The pH, at 25° C, can then be calculated from equation (55.5). It has been found, however, that if the reference electrode potentials given in § 49d are employed, the results are not quite consistent with those obtained in other ways; this is due to uncertainties in connection with liquid junction potentials and single ion activities. Better agreement is obtained by taking the potential of the calomel electrode with 0.1 N potassium chloride, in conjunction with a saturated potassium chloride salt bridge, i.e.,

$$\text{KCl satd.} \mid 0.1 \text{ N KCl} \quad Hg_2Cl_2(s) \mid Hg,$$

as +0.3358 volt at 25° C. Consequently, if E is the E.M.F. of a cell, consisting of a hydrogen electrode in a given solution and this calomel electrode, the pH of the solution at 25° C is determined by equation (55.5) in the form

$$pH = \frac{E - 0.3358}{0.05915}. \tag{55.6}$$

Since hydrogen gas is a nonconductor, it is necessary to have a device for making electrical contact between the gas and the solution of hydrogen ions; for this purpose the common practice is to employ a small sheet or wire of platinum coated with the finely divided metal, i.e., "platinized," by electrolysis of a solution of chloroplatinic acid. The platinum foil or wire, attached to a suitable connecting wire, is inserted in the experimental solution, and a stream of hydrogen gas is passed through the solution. The finely divided platinum permits rapid establishment of the equilibrium between gaseous hydrogen, on the one hand, and hydrogen ions in solution and electrons, on the other hand; the result is that the platinum acquires a potential that is characteristic of the hydrogen gas and hydrogen ion system. Various types of hydrogen electrode vessels have been devised for different purposes; a simple and convenient type of hydrogen electrode (J. H. Hildebrand, 1913) is shown in Fig. 109. A rectangular sheet of platinum, about 1 to 3 sq. cm. in area, is sealed into a glass tube, and platinized in the usual manner; this constitutes the actual electrode. The apparatus is inserted in the experimental solution, and hydrogen gas is passed in through the side tube; the outlet holes near the bottom are so arranged that as the gas bubbles out, the upper half of the platinum sheet is surrounded by hydrogen gas, while the lower half is immersed in the solution. The gas should be purified, so as to remove oxygen and other substances, and its partial pressure should be known, after making allowance for the aqueous vapor pressure of the solution. The potential of the electrode, measured by combination with a reference electrode, must be corrected to a pressure of 1 atm. by equation (50.15).

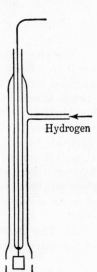

The hydrogen gas electrode cannot be employed in solutions containing oxidizing agents, such as nitrates, permanganates, ferric salts, etc., or other substances capable of reduction by hydrogen in the presence of finely divided platinum. The electrode does not behave satisfactorily in solutions containing ions of metals lying below hydrogen in the table of standard potentials, e.g., gold, silver, mercury and copper. In addition, traces of compounds of mercury, sulfur and arsenic "poison" the electrode, so that it will not function even in other solutions. In spite of these limitations, the hydrogen gas electrode has been extensively employed for precise measurements in cells with or without liquid junctions, and for the standardization of buffer solutions.

Hydrogen

Fig. 109. Hydrogen electrode: Hildebrand type

55c. Other Hydrogen Ion Electrodes.—The hydrogen gas electrode is the ultimate standard of reference for all pH measurements, but owing to the limitations and experimental difficulties associated with its use, other electrodes have been devised which are reversible with respect to hydrogen ions. The most important of these will be described below.

I. Oxygen Gas and Oxide Electrodes.—An oxygen gas electrode is theoretically reversible with respect to hydroxyl ions, and since the concentration of these ions is related to that of the hydrogen ions in the same solution (§ 53f), it should be possible to determine values of the latter by means of this electrode. Attempts have been made to set up oxygen gas electrodes in a manner similar to that adopted for hydrogen, but the results were always unsatisfactory. It is generally accepted, therefore, that this form of oxygen gas electrode does not behave in a reversible manner; nevertheless, it has been employed where accurate results are not required, for example, to detect sudden changes of pH, as in potentiometric titration (§ 49f, III).

An electrode consisting of a metal and its oxide is thermodynamically equivalent to an oxygen electrode operating at the dissociation pressure of the oxide. A useful electrode of this type, known as the **antimony electrode,** consists of antimony and its trioxide. The electrode reaction is

$$2Sb(s) + 3H_2O \rightleftharpoons Sb_2O_3(s) + 6H^+ + 6\epsilon,$$

and since the solid antimony and the trioxide, as well as the water, are in their standard states of unit activity, it follows that the potential is given by

$$E_{Sb} = E^0_{Sb} - \frac{RT}{F} \ln a_{H^+}. \tag{55.7}$$

The potential of the antimony electrode should thus depend on the hydrogen ion activity, or pH, of the solution in which it is placed.

The electrode is generally prepared by melting the antimony, and allowing it to solidify in the air to form a stick; in this way it becomes sufficiently oxidized for the further addition of oxide to be unnecessary. The antimony stick is inserted in the experimental solution, and its potential is measured by combination with a reference electrode. Since the standard potential E^0_{Sb} in equation (55.7) is somewhat variable, it is determined for the particular electrode by utilizing a buffer solution of known pH. Once E^0_{Sb} has been obtained, it can be used in conjunction with equation (55.7) to evaluated the hydrogen ion activity, or pH, of an experimental solution. The antimony electrode behaves satisfactorily in the pH range from 2 to 7, but in more acid or more alkaline solutions the solubility of the oxide interferes with the results.

II. The Quinhydrone Electrode.—It was seen in § 49b that the potential of the quinone-hydroquinone system is given by equation (49.10) as

$$E = E^0_{el.} - \frac{RT}{2F} \ln \frac{a_Q}{a_{H_2Q}} - \frac{RT}{F} \ln a_{H^+} \tag{55.8}$$

where a_Q and a_{H_2Q} refer to the activities of the quinone and hydroquinone, respectively; the potential is evidently dependent on the hydrogen ion activity of the solution, and hence it offers possibilities for the determination of the latter. For this purpose a small quantity of the compound quinhydrone, which consists of equimolar amounts of quinone and hydroquinone, is dissolved in the solution. The ratio of the concentrations of these two substances is thus equal to unity, and if the ratio of the activities is taken as equal to the ratio of the concentrations, a_Q/a_{H_2Q} is also equal to unity. The second term on the right-hand side of equation (55.8) is then zero, and so the potential of the **quinhydrone electrode** is given by

$$E_Q = E^0_Q - \frac{RT}{F} \ln a_{H^+} = E^0_Q + 0.05915 \text{ pH at } 25° \text{ C.} \tag{55.9}$$

By standardization of the quinhydrone electrode in buffer solutions of definite pH's, the value of E^0_Q is found to be -0.6994 volt at 25° C. For practical purposes the electrode is best combined with a calomel electrode with 0.1 N potassium chloride and a salt bridge, as in § 55b; the potential of the calomel electrode is taken as $+0.3358$ volt, so that E, the E.M.F. of the resulting cell is equal to $E_Q + 0.3358$. Consequently, by equation (55.9), using -0.6994 for E_Q^0,

$$E = E_Q + 0.3358 = -0.6994 + 0.05915 \text{ pH} + 0.3358$$

$$\text{pH} = \frac{E + 0.3636}{0.05915}. \quad (55.10)$$

Problem: A quinhydrone electrode in a solution of unknown pH (at the left) was combined, through a saturated KCl salt bridge, with a 0.1 N KCl, $Hg_2Cl_2(s)$, Hg electrode (at the right); the E.M.F. of the resulting cell was -0.1252 volt at 25° C. Calculate the pH of the solution.

By equation (55.10)

$$\text{pH} = \frac{-0.1252 + 0.3636}{0.05915} = \frac{0.2384}{0.05915}$$

$$= 4.03.$$

The quinhydrone electrode is easily set up by dissolving a small quantity of solid quinhydrone in the experimental solution, and then inserting an indicator electrode of clean gold or platinum. The electrode gives accurate results in solutions of pH less than 8; in more alkaline solutions errors arise, first, because of oxidation of the hydroquinone by oxygen of the air, and second, on account of the ionization of the hydroquinone as an acid. The quinhydrone electrode can be used in the presence of the ions of many metals which have a harmful effect on the hydrogen gas electrode. The potential of the electrode is affected, however, by neutral electrolytes which increase the ionic strength of the solution; under these conditions the ratio of the activities a_Q/a_{H_2Q} is not equal to unity, as was assumed in deriving equation (55.9). Because of its simplicity and the accuracy of which it is capable, the quinhydrone electrode has been widely used for pH measurements.

III. The Glass Electrode.—At the interface between glass and a solution with which it is in contact there is a difference of potential which has been found by experiment to be dependent

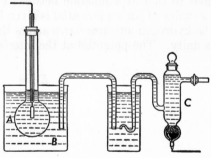

FIG. 110.   Glass electrode cell

upon the pH of the solution; this dependence corresponds to the usual type of equation for a reversible hydrogen electrode, viz.,

$$E_G = E_G^0 - 0.05915 \log a_{H^+} = E_G^0 + 0.05915 \text{ pH at } 25°C, \quad (55.11)$$

where E_G^0 is a constant for the given electrode. In its simplest form the glass electrode consists of a glass tube terminating in a thin-walled bulb, as shown at A in Fig. 110; a special glass of relatively low melting point and high electrical conductance is used for the purpose. The bulb contains a solution of constant hydrogen ion concentration and an electrode of definite potential; an Ag, AgCl(s) electrode in 0.1 molar hydrochloric acid, or a platinum wire inserted in a pH 4.00 buffer solution containing a small quantity of quinhydrone, is usually employed. The bulb is inserted in the experimental solution B, and the resulting glass electrode is combined with a reference electrode, e.g., a calomel electrode C, to form the cell

Ag | AgCl(s)   0.1 N HCl | glass | experimental solution ‖ calomel electrode,

whose E.M.F. can be determined. Because of the high resistance of the glass, viz., 10 to 100 million ohms, special vacuum-tube potentiometers are used for this purpose. Several commercial forms of apparatus are now available, by means of which the glass electrode potential can be measured with an accuracy of about 0.0005 volt or 0.01 pH unit. The constant E_G^0 in equation (55.11) is evaluated by standardizing the particular electrode in a number of buffer solutions of definitely known pH values.

The glass electrode can be employed in aqueous solutions of almost any kind, provided the pH lies within the range of 1 to 9; for higher pH's up to 12, special glass should be used. Because of its very wide applicability, its indifference to oxidizing agents, metallic ions, poisons, etc., and the simplicity of its operation, the glass electrode has been extensively adopted for pH determinations in chemical and biological laboratories and for industrial control purposes.

The theory of the glass electrode has not yet been completely worked out, but its action appears to be related to the transfer of hydrogen ions through the glass. A potential is set up at the glass-solution interface which is analogous to that at a junction between two solutions containing hydrogen ions; the value of such a potential is given by equation (50.7), but in this case only the hydrogen ions can move across the boundary, so that t_- is zero while t_+ is unity. The potential at the interface is then given by the expression

$$E_G = -\frac{RT}{F} \ln \frac{a_2}{a_1}, \qquad (55.12)$$

where a_1 and a_2 are the hydrogen ion activities on the two sides of the glass wall. One of these solutions, e.g., a_1, inside the glass bulb, is constant in nature, and so equation (55.12) reduces to

$$E_G = \text{constant} - \frac{RT}{F} \ln a_2,$$

which is identical in form with the experimental equation (55.11).

55d. Hydrogen Ion (Acid-Base) Indicators.—An acid-base or hydrogen ion **indicator** is a substance which, within certain limits, *varies its color according to the hydrogen ion concentration (or activity) of its environment.* It is thus possible to determine the pH of a solution by observing the color of a suitable indicator when placed in that solution. An acid-base indicator is almost invariably a substance which can exist in two tautomeric forms in equilibrium with one another,* the two forms having different structures and different colors. One or both of the tautomeric forms is a weak acid; if both forms are acids, then one should be very much weaker than the other. Suppose the two tautomeric weak acids with different structures are represented by HIn_A and HIn_B; their colors are different, and these will be referred to as color A and color B, respectively. The tautomeric and ionization equilibria in water can be represented by the scheme:

$$HIn_A + H_2O \rightleftharpoons H_3O^+ + In_A^- \quad \text{Color A}$$
$$\Updownarrow \qquad\qquad\qquad \Updownarrow$$
$$HIn_B + H_2O \rightleftharpoons H_3O^+ + In_B^- \quad \text{Color B.}$$

The anions In_A^- have the same structure and color as the nonionized HIn_A molecules; similarly, the anions In_B^- have the same structure and color as the molecules HIn_B. If the tautomeric equilibrium favors HIn_A over HIn_B, and if the former acid is much weaker than the latter, the system will contain very few HIn_B molecules and In_A^- ions; it is thus possible to approximate the actual condition of equilibrium in the form

$$HIn_A + H_2O \rightleftharpoons H_3O^+ + In_B^-. \tag{55.13}$$

The approximate equilibrium constant, taking the activity of the water as unity, is

$$k_{In} = \frac{c_{H^+} \times c_{In_B^-}}{c_{HIn_A}}, \tag{55.14}$$

where k_{In} is known as the **indicator constant**; the negative logarithm of this constant, i.e., $- \log k_{In}$, is represented by pk_{In}, and is called the **indicator exponent**. It should be noted that in equation (55.14) the quantity c_{H^+} refers to the hydrogen ion concentration of the solution containing the indicator, irrespective of whether it is due to the indicator alone or to other substances that may be present.

Upon rearrangement of equation (55.14), it is seen that

$$c_{H^+} = k_{In} \frac{c_{HIn_A}}{c_{In_B^-}}, \tag{55.15}$$

and hence the ratio of the concentrations of HIn_A and In_B^- present at equilibrium depends on the hydrogen ion concentration of the solution in which the indicator is present. Since the species HIn_A and In_B^- have different colors, viz., A and B, respectively, the actual color exhibited by the indicator will depend on the hydrogen ion concentration of the medium. In an acidic solution, that is, one containing excess of H_3O^+ ions, the equilibrium in equation (55.13) will be displaced to the left; the indicator will thus consist predominantly of the form HIn_A, and it will exhibit the color A. On the other

---

* The difference in the two tautomeric forms lies essentially in the point of attachment of a mobile hydrogen atom (proton).

hand, if the solution is alkaline, containing OH^- ions which combine with the H_3O^+ ions and reduce their concentration, the equilibrium will lie to the right, and the indicator will be largely in the In_B^- form; in alkaline, i.e., basic, solution the indicator will consequently have the color B. It is thus possible to account for the change in the indicator from color A in acid solution to color B in basic (alkaline) solution.

55e. Indicator Exponent and Useful Range.—If the depth or intensity of color is proportional to the concentration of the particular species producing that color, equation (55.15) may be written in the form

$$c_{H^+} = k_{In} \frac{\text{Color A}}{\text{Color B}}. \tag{55.16}$$

By taking logarithms and changing the signs throughout, this becomes

$$pH = pk_{In} + \log \frac{\text{Color B}}{\text{Color A}}. \tag{55.17}$$

By means of these equations it is possible to determine the constant (or exponent) of any given indicator. If a small quantity of the indicator is placed in a buffer solution of known pH, and the ratio of the intensities of color B to color A is estimated in a suitable manner, the exponent pk_{In} of the indicator can be derived by means of equation (55.17). For accurate work the ratio of the color intensities may be obtained from bsorption spectra measurements; for most purposes, however, some form of colorimeter may be used (§ 55f, II). In the simplest, the color of the indicator in the solution of known pH is matched by superposing two tubes containing varying amounts of the indicator in its acidic (color A) and basic (color B) forms, respectively.

Another method of determining pk_{In} is to utilize the fact, derived from equation (55.17), that when the intensities of color A and color B are equal, so that the ratio is unity, pk_{In} will be equal to the pH of the solution. In other words, an indicator shows its exact intermediate color in a solution whose pH is equal in value to the indicator exponent. Two tubes containing equal amounts of the indicator, one having the extreme acid color and the other the extreme alkaline color, are superposed; a buffer solution is then found in which the indicator appears the same as the two superposed colors. The pH of this buffer solution is then identical with the pk_{In} of the indicator.

By reversing the procedure described above it should be possible to utilize an indicator to determine the pH of a solution; thus, if the indicator exponent is known, and the ratio of color B to color A of the indicator in the given solution is measured, the pH of the latter can be evaluated by equation (55.17). In theory, the ratio of the intensities of color B to color A may have any value, but in practice it is possible to detect the proportions of the two colors in a mixture within certain limits only. For example, if 1 per cent of a blue color is mixed with 99 per cent of red, the eye cannot notice any difference from pure red. In general, it is necessary that there should be a minimum of about 10 per cent of a particular color before it can be easily detected in the presence of another color. The actual figure depends on the nature of the two colors, but for the present purpose it may be supposed that a minimum of about one part in ten is necessary before the color can be observed. It follows, therefore, according to equation (55.17), that before the basic color B of an indicator can be detected in the presence of an acid color A, the minimum pH is given by

$$\text{pH} = pk_{In} + \log \tfrac{1}{10} = pk_{In} - 1.$$

Similarly, the acidic color A will no longer be detectable in the presence of an excess of basic color B when the ratio of basic to acidic colors is 10 to 1, so that the pH is then determined by

$$\text{pH} = pk_{In} + \log \tfrac{10}{1} = pk_{In} + 1.$$

It is seen from these results that the **useful range** of an indicator is approximately one unit of pH on each side of the pk_{In} of the particular indicator. Since the useful range of an indicator is restricted to about two units of pH, it is evident that a number of indicators are required to cover the range of pH from zero to 14, i.e., from completely acid to completely alkaline solutions. A selection of useful indicators is given in Table LXIV to-

TABLE LXIV. SOME USEFUL INDICATORS

Indicator	Color		pk_{In}	pH range
	Acid	Alkaline		
Thymol blue	Red	Yellow	1.51	1.2–2.8
Methyl orange	Red	Yellow	3.7	3.1–4.4
Bromphenol blue	Yellow	Blue	3.98	3.0–4.6
Methyl red	Red	Yellow	5.1	4.2–6.3
Chlorphenol red	Yellow	Red	5.98	4.8–6.4
Bromcresol purple	Yellow	Purple	6.3	5.2–6.8
Bromthymol blue	Yellow	Blue	7.0	6.0–7.6
Phenol red	Yellow	Red	7.9	6.8–8.4
Cresol red	Yellow	Red	8.3	7.2–8.8
Thymol blue (2nd range)	Yellow	Purple	8.9	8.0–9.6
Phenolphthalein	Colorless	Red	9.4	8.3–10.0
Thymolphthalein	Colorless	Blue	9.4	9.2–10.6

gether with the values of their exponents and their acidic and alkaline colors; the effective range, as determined by experiment, is given in each case. In addition to these individual indicators, mixtures of indicators, known as **universal indicators,** have been found useful for approximate pH determinations. A convenient and simple form of universal indicator, covering the range of pH from 4 to 11, is made from methyl red, α-naphtholphthalein, thymolphthalein, phenolphthalein and bromthymol blue; the colors at different pH values are given below.

pH	4	5	6	7	8	9	10	11
Color	Red	Orange-red	Yellow	Green-yellow	Green	Blue-green	Blue-violet	Red-violet

55f. Determination of pH by Indicators: I. With Buffer Solutions.—If a number of buffer solutions of known pH are available, the estimation of the unknown pH of an experimental solution is a relatively simple matter. The pH is first determined approximately by means of a universal indicator; this permits the best indicator to be chosen from Table LXIV. A definite quantity of this indicator is then added to a certain volume of the test solution; the color produced is compared with those obtained, with the same concentration of indicator, in a series of buffer solutions of known pH. By matching the colors, the pH of the unknown solution may be estimated within 0.05 pH unit.

II. Without Buffer Solutions.—Provided the exponent of an appropriate indicator is known, the pH of an unknown solution can be obtained without the use of buffer solutions, by means of equation (55.17). The practical prob-

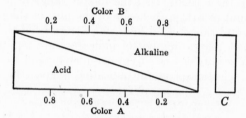

Fig. 111.   Bjerrum wedge for pH determination

lem is the determination of the ratio of the intensities of the two colors of the indicator when the latter is placed in the experimental solution. As mentioned above, absorption spectra and colorimeter methods have been employed for accurate work; for approximate purposes, a number of simple devices have been used.

In the "wedge method" of N. Bjerrum (1914), a rectangular box is divided by a diagonal glass sheet into two wedge-shaped compartments, as shown in plan in Fig. 111. A solution of the indicator which has been made definitely acid (color A) is placed in one wedge, and an alkaline solution (color B) is placed in the other. By viewing the combination from the front, a gradation of color, from pure A to pure B, can be seen as a result of the superposition of steadily varying proportions of the two individual colors. The test solution is placed in a narrow glass cell C of the same thickness as the combined wedges, and the indicator is added so that its concentration is the same as in the wedges. A position is then found at which the color of the test solution matches that of the superimposed acidic and basic colors in the wedges. The ratio of the depths of the wedge solutions at this point gives the ratio of the color intensities required for equation (55.17).

Problem: With bromphenol blue as indicator, a given solution shows the best color match in a Bjerrum wedge at a point where the thickness of the alkaline wedge is 0.85 of the total. What is the pH of the solution?

The thickness of the alkaline wedge (color B) is 0.85, and so that of the acid wedge (color A) must be 0.15; hence the ratio of color B to color A is 0.85/0.15.   The pk_{In} of bromphenol blue is 3.98 (Table LXIV); the required pH is thus given by equation (55.17) as

$$pH = 3.98 + \log \frac{0.85}{0.15} = 4.73.$$

Another simple procedure for determining the color ratio is the "drop ratio" method of L. J. Gillespie (1920).   A set of pairs, generally nine pairs, of test tubes is prepared, one tube of each pair contains acid and the other alkali.   Various numbers of drops of indicator, increasing from one to nine, are placed in the tubes containing acid, and a corresponding decreasing number of drops of indicator, from nine to one, are placed in the tubes containing alkali.   Each pair of tubes thus contains a total of ten drops of indicator, but the color as seen through the combination of both tubes varies regularly from one extreme to the other.   A quantity of the experimental solution, equal in volume to that in the tubes, is placed in a similar tube, and ten drops of the same indicator are added.   The color of this solution is then matched against the pairs of tubes.   The ratio of the numbers of drops of alkaline form (color B) to the number of drops of acidic form (color A) of the indicator, in the pair giving the best match, is then equal to the ratio of the amounts of color B to color A in the test solution.

Problem: With bromthymol blue as indicator, a given solution exhibits the best color match with a pair of tubes containing 3 drops of alkaline color and 7 drops of the acidic color; what is the pH of the solution?

The ratio of color B to color A is $\frac{3}{7}$; pk_{In} for bromthymol blue is 7.0, and so by equation (55.17),

$$pH = 7.0 + \log \tfrac{3}{7} = 6.63.$$

It should be remembered that the equations derived above are approximate, since they are based on the use of concentrations instead of activities in equation (55.14).   However, the errors introduced in this manner are not serious, provided the experimental solutions do not contain relatively large amounts of electrolytes, i.e., the ionic strength is low.   The presence of neutral salts in appreciable quantities may produce color changes of an indicator which are not due to changes of pH but to alterations in the activities; this is known as the **salt effect** of the indicator.   Erroneous results are also frequently obtained in the presence of proteins, and indicator methods are not satisfactory in solutions containing these substances.

55g. Neutralization Curves.—The changes in hydrogen ion concentration accompanying the addition of a base to an acid, or the reverse, are of importance for analytical purposes.   These changes can, of course, be followed by experimental determination of the pH values during the neutralization process, but the necessary information can be obtained by calculations based on some of the equations developed in earlier sections.   The treatment depends on the strength of the acid and base, and a few typical cases will be considered.

If the acid and base are both strong, the hydrogen ion concentration at any point in the course of neutralization may be taken as equal to the concentration of unneutralized acid (§ 53d). At the **equivalence point,** when equivalent amounts of strong acid and strong base have been mixed, the solution is neutral and the pH will be 7.0. The variation of hydroxyl ion concentration during the neutralization of a strong base can be determined in an analogous manner, as c_{OH^-} will be equal to the concentration of unneutralized base. Since $c_{H^+} \times c_{OH^-}$ is equal to 10^{-14}, the corresponding values for the hydrogen ions can be calculated. The complete results for the variation of pH when 0.1 N solutions of strong acid and strong base are added

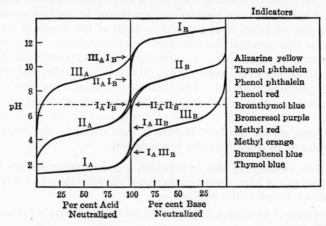

Fig. 112.   Neutralization curves for various acids and bases

to one another, in both directions, are represented by the curves I_A and I_B in Fig. 112. Starting from the extreme left, and proceeding to the right, curve I_A shows the change of pH as the strong base is added to the 0.1 N solution of strong acid; similarly, starting from the extreme right, and proceeding to the left, curve I_B indicates the change of pH when strong acid is added to the 0.1 N solution of strong base. The equivalence point of the titration occurs at the middle of the diagram, and it is evident that the attainment of this point is characterized by a very rapid change of pH, from about 4 to 10, or vice versa.

The change of pH in the course of the neutralization of a weak acid by a strong base can be calculated by means of a single equation, but this is too complicated to justify consideration here. Nevertheless, the information can be obtained, in most cases, without serious difficulty in the following manner. The pH of the acid solution before neutralization is given by equation (53.20); that at the equivalence point, when the solution corresponds to that of the salt of a weak acid and strong base, is obtained from equation (54.15). Between these extremes, when neutralization is partial, the system consists of the weak acid and its salt in varying proportions; the pH of such solutions, provided the values are between 4 and 10, can be calculated from equation (55.1). In this manner the whole of the neutralization curve, such as IIA in Fig. 112, can be obtained; this curve is actually for a 0.1 N solution of an acid of dissociation constant k_a equal to 10^{-5}, i.e., pk_a is 5. It should be noted that at the midpoint of the neutralization curve IIA the solution contains equivalent amounts of unneutralized acid and its salt; the pH is then equal to the pk_a of the acid (§ 53e).

The neutralization curve for a weak base by a strong acid can be derived in an analogous manner; the results for a 0.1 N solution of a weak base of k_b equal to 10^{-5}, i.e., pk_b is 5, are shown by curve IIB in Fig. 112. Similar methods are used for the neutralization of a very weak acid by a strong base, or of a very weak base by a strong acid; when the pH is less than 4 or greater than 10, a modified form of equation (55.1) must be used for the calculations. The curves IIIA and IIIB, respectively, are for 0.1 N solutions of an acid and base, respectively, whose dissociation constants are 10^{-9}.

The information contained in Fig. 112 is summarized in Table LXV; the

TABLE LXV.   CHARACTERISTICS OF TITRATION CURVES

Acid	Base	Curve	End Point
Strong	Strong	IA-IB	Very sharp
Weak	Strong	IIA-IB	Moderately sharp
Very weak	Strong	IIIA-IB	Not sharp
Strong	Weak	IA-IIB	Moderately sharp
Strong	Very weak	IA-IIIB	Not sharp
Weak	Weak	IIA-IIB	Not sharp

kind of pH change in the vicinity of the equivalence point for each type of acid-base neutralization is given in the last column. The actual position of the equivalence point in each case is indicated by an arrow in Fig. 112; it should be remembered that these refer to 0.1 N solutions of acids and bases having the specified dissociation constants. The general effect of decreasing the dissociation constants or the concentration of the solutions is to diminish the extent of the pH change at the equivalence point.

The curves in Fig. 112 provide the fundamental basis of the potentiometric determination of the end point of a neutralization titration (§ 49f, III). The change in potential of any form of hydrogen electrode, e.g., hydrogen gas, quinhydrone, etc., is directly proportional to the change in pH of the solution in which it is placed, as may be seen, for instance, from equations (55.4) and (55.11). It follows, therefore, that a plot of the hydrogen electrode potential during the course of a particular neutralization will have exactly the same form as the corresponding pH-neutralization curve in Fig. 112. Except when both acid and base are weak, or one of the reactants is very weak, or the solutions are too dilute, there will be a relatively sharp change in potential in the immediate vicinity of the equivalence point, from which the position of the latter may be determined, as explained earlier.

55h. Indicators in Neutralization Titrations.—Since an acid-base indicator changes color according to the pH of the solution in which it is placed, it is readily seen that such indicators may be used to detect the attainment of the equivalence point in a neutralization reaction. It is necessary, of course, to use an indicator which changes color at a pH in the vicinity of that at the equivalence point for the particular acid and base being neutralized. As already seen, this varies with the nature of the acid and base, and also, to some extent, with the concentration. The approximate positions on the pH scale at which some common indicators undergo a marked color change are shown at the right of Fig. 112.

In the neutralization of a 0.1 N solution of a strong acid by a strong base, the pH undergoes a very sharp change, from about pH 4 to 10, within 0.1 per cent of the equivalence point; any indicator changing color in this range can, therefore, be used to give a reliable estimate of the completion of neutralization. If the solution is diluted to 0.01 N, the change in pH at the equivalence point is less sharp, viz., from 5 to 9; hence, methyl orange, which could be used for the more concentrated solution, will now give results that are in error.

When a 0.1 N solution of a weak acid, of pk_a about 5, is neutralized by a strong base, the pH change at the equivalence point is moderately sharp (curve IIa-Ib, Fig. 112) and occurs between pH's of approximately 8 and 10. Of the common indicators, phenolphthalein is the only one that is satisfactory, although the less familiar thymolphthalein, changing at pH 9.5, could be used. Any indicator changing color below about pH 8 will be unsatisfactory for two reasons; first, the color will change before the theoretical end point, i.e., the equivalence point, and second, the color change will not be sharp, because of the relatively gradual change of pH in that region. For the titration of a weak base, of pk_b about 5, the attainment of the equivalence point is accompanied by a pH change from about 6 to 4 (curve IIb-Ia); methyl red is seen to be the ideal indicator, although methyl orange may be, and frequently is, used if the solutions are not too dilute. The best indicator for any particular acid or base is, of course, the one which changes its color as close as possible to the pH at the equivalence point.

It will be evident that for an indicator to change color sharply at the end point the pH-neutralization curve must rise rapidly as the equivalence point is attained; if this is not the case, there will be a gradual transition from acid to alkaline color (or the reverse) as the base (or acid) is added. No satisfactory indicator can consequently be obtained for the titration of a very weak acid (curve IIIa-Ib) or of a very weak base (curve IIIb-Ia); the same is true for the neutralization of a weak acid by a weak base (curve IIa-IIb).

The nature of the titration curves for displacement reactions can also be seen from Fig. 112. For example, if the sodium salt of a weak acid, of pk_a 5, is titrated with a strong acid, the pH change is shown by curve IIa, starting from the center of the diagram and proceeding to the left. The change of pH at the equivalence point, i.e., the extreme left, is obviously not sharp, and so it cannot be estimated with any degree of accuracy. If the displaced acid is very weak, e.g., pk_a about 9 or more, the variation of pH is shown by curve IIIa, from the center to the left of Fig. 112; the end point is accompanied by a moderately sharp change of pH from about 5 downward, so that a satisfactory end point can be detected by using methyl orange as indicator. It can thus be understood why no adequate end point can be obtained in the titration of sodium acetate by a strong acid, but with sodium carbonate or borate the results are satisfactory.

The foregoing conclusions are exactly what are to be expected by considering the displacement reaction

$$(Na^+)A^- + H_3O^+(Cl^-) = HA + H_2O + (Na^+Cl^-)$$

as a neutralization of the anion A^-, regarded as a base, by a strong acid (§ 54a). It is only when the acid HA is extremely weak that the conjugate base A^- is sufficiently strong to satisfy the condition for a satisfactory end point.

Problem: Calculate the pH at the equivalence point of the titration of 0.1 N solution of borax, by means of hydrochloric acid; the boric acid may be treated as a monobasic acid of k_a equal to 5.75×10^{-10}. What indicator would be suitable for this titration?

At the equivalence point of the given titration the solution would consist of 0.1 N boric acid, together with 0.1 N NaCl; the c_{H^+} is given by equation (53.19), with sufficient accuracy, i.e.,

$$c_{H^+} = \sqrt{ck_a} = \sqrt{0.1 \times 5.75 \times 10^{-10}} = 7.58 \times 10^{-6},$$

and hence the required pH at the equivalence point is

$$pH = - \log c_{H^+} = 5.12.$$

The best indicator for the titration would be methyl red, although methyl orange would be fairly satisfactory.

READING REFERENCES

1. **Buffer effect in blood and tissue.** Clausen, *Journal of Chemical Education,* **7,** 2850 (1930).
2. **Universal indicator experiments.** Foster and Gruntfest, *ibid.,* **14,** 274, 592 (1937).
3. **Hydrolysis of salts.** O'Brien and Kenney, *ibid.,* **16,** 140 (1939).
4. **Hydrolysis and other properties of ions.** Foster, *ibid.,* **17,** 509 (1940).
5. **Simple wedge colorimeter for pH.** Hirsch, *ibid.,* **18,** 7 (1941).
6. **Maximum buffer capacity region.** Park, *ibid.,* **18,** 171 (1941).
7. **Mixed indicators.** McGuire, *ibid.,* **18,** 271 (1941).

REVIEW QUESTIONS

1. Give examples of neutralizations of different types. Explain the nature of the acid and base in each case.
2. Explain the conditions under which the solvent prevents complete neutralization. Show how this leads to solvolysis (or lyolysis).
3. Explain the hydrolysis of a salt of a weak acid and a strong base. Derive expressions for the hydrolysis constant, the degree of hydrolysis and the pH of the solution.

4. Explain the hydrolysis of a salt of a strong acid and a weak base. Derive expressions analogous to those in the preceding question.

5. Explain the hydrolysis of a salt of a weak acid and a weak base. Derive the expressions analogous to those in the preceding questions.

6. Describe three methods for determining hydrolysis constants.

7. Explain the meaning of buffer action. Describe how a buffer solution of any desired pH may be prepared. Under what conditions is the buffer capacity a maximum?

8. Describe the determination of pH by means of a hydrogen gas electrode.

9. Describe the determination of pH by means of (a) an antimony, (b) a quinhydrone, (c) a glass, electrode.

10. Explain the theory of acid-base indicator action. Define the indicator constant and the indicator exponent.

11. What is the useful pH range of an indicator? How is it related to the indicator exponent?

12. Describe the use of indicators for the determination of pH (a) with the aid of buffer solutions, (b) without buffer solutions.

13. Draw the pH-neutralization curves of a number of typical acids and bases of different strengths. What is the general effect of changing the concentrations? What conclusions can be drawn from the results?

14. Describe the principle involved in the use of indicators for acid-base titrations.

15. Displacement titrations can be treated as neutralization in the widest sense: consider and justify this statement.

PROBLEMS *

I

1. Calculate the hydrolysis constant, the degree of hydrolysis, and pH of (a) 0.01 M sodium formate, (b) 0.1 M sodium phenoxide (phenolate).

2. Calculate the hydrolysis constant, the degree of hydrolysis and pH of (a) 0.02 M ammonium chloride, (b) 0.2 M pyridine hydrochloride.

3. A 0.05 M solution of the potassium salt of a weak monobasic acid was found to have a pH of 9.25 at 25° C. Calculate the degree of hydrolysis and the hydrolysis constant. Assuming the value of K_w for water, determine the dissociation constant of the weak acid.

4. Determine the hydrolysis constant, degree of hydrolysis and pH of 0.1 M ammonium acetate.

5. A buffer solution is made from 0.06 mole of acetic acid and 0.04 mole of sodium acetate per liter. What is the pH of the solution? Calculate the change of pH resulting from the addition of (a) 0.015 mole strong acid, (b) 0.03 mole strong base, per liter of the buffer solution.

6. A hydrogen gas electrode in a given solution, when combined with a 0.1 N KCl calomel electrode, gave a cell with an E.M.F. of 0.5562 volt at 25° C. What is the pH of the solution?

7. An antimony electrode when inserted in a solution of pH 5.00 gave a potential of 0.146 volt at 25° C. What is the pH of the solution in which the potential of the same electrode was 0.255 volt?

8. A given indicator when placed in a buffer solution of pH 4.63 was found to exhibit a color which corresponded to 24 per cent of the acid form to 76 per cent of the alkaline form. What is the exponent of the indicator?

* When not given, dissociation constants may be obtained from Table LXI.

9. Calculate the equivalence points (pH) for the titration of 0.1 M aniline by hydrochloric acid, and the reverse titration of 0.1 M aniline hydrochloride by sodium hydroxide. Which titration would give the sharper end point, and which indicator might be used to detect it? (The volume change in the titration may be neglected.)

II

1. Calculate the hydrolysis constant, the degree of hydrolysis, and pH of (a) 0.05 M sodium benzoate, (b) 0.2 M potassium cyanide.

2. Calculate the hydrolysis constant, the degree of hydrolysis, and pH of (a) 0.01 M methylamine hydrochloride, (b) 0.2 M aniline hydrochloride.

3. The pH of a 0.01 M solution of the sodium salt of phenylacetic acid was found to be 8.15 at 25° C. Calculate the degree of hydrolysis and the hydrolysis constant. Assuming the value of K_a for the acid given in Table LXI, calculate the ionic product of water at 25° C.

4. Equivalent amounts of aqueous solutions of a weak acid and weak base, each having a dissociation constant of 5.4×10^{-7} were mixed; how much of each will remain unneutralized? What is the hydrolysis constant of the salt formed?

5. It is required to make a buffer solution of total concentration 0.2 mole per liter having a pH of exactly 4.00, using lactic acid ($K_a = 1.37 \times 10^{-4}$). How would such a solution be prepared? Calculate the change of pH resulting from the addition of (a) 0.04 mole strong acid, (b) 0.04 mole strong base, per liter of the buffer solution.

6. The potential of a quinhydrone electrode was found to be -0.4162 volt at 25° C. What is the pH of the solution?

7. A cell consisting of a glass electrode inserted in a solution of pH 6.65 combined with a 0.1 N KCl calomel electrode, through a salt bridge, had an E.M.F. of 0.4924 volt at 25° C. What is the pH of a solution in which the same combination of glass and calomel electrodes has an E.M.F. of 0.1285 volt?

8. An indicator of pk_{In} equal to 6.16 was placed in a solution of unknown pH; the color was found to correspond to 6.3 parts of the acidic form to 3.7 parts of the alkaline color. What is the pH of the solution?

9. Treating phthalic acid as a monobasic acid with a dissociation constant equal to K_2, that is, 3.80×10^{-6}, calculate the pH at the equivalence point of the neutralization of a 0.1 molal solution by a strong base. What indicator might be used to indicate this end point? (The volume change in the titration may be neglected.)

CHAPTER XVII

SURFACE CHEMISTRY AND COLLOIDS

ADSORPTION

56a. Adsorption and Adsorbents.—An important property of surfaces is that known as **adsorption**; this term is used to describe *the existence of a higher concentration of any particular substance at the surface of a liquid or solid than is present in the bulk.* It is necessary to distinguish between "adsorption" and "absorption" as applied to solids; while the former refers to an excess concentration at the surface, the latter implies a more or less uniform penetration of the solid by a given substance. It is probable that adsorption occurs at all surfaces, but for the purpose of studying the phenomena of adsorption it is convenient to employ porous substances which have a large effective area for a given mass. Among the best known of these is charcoal, made by burning some form of wood, e.g., coconut shells, in a limited supply of air. It has long been known that charcoal can take up relatively large volumes of gases, and also that it can remove dyestuffs and other substances from solution, e.g., in the purification of sugar and other organic compounds. These are examples of adsorption of gases and from solution, respectively.

Silica gel, made by drying a gelatinous precipitate of silicic acid, and alumina, obtained by heating aluminum hydroxide, are important adsorbing materials, i.e., **adsorbents.** Other oxides, particularly chromium sesquioxide (Cr_2O_3) and zinc oxide, are used for adsorbing gases. Certain metals, such as platinum, palladium, copper and nickel, when prepared in a suitable manner are also able to adsorb gases, particularly hydrogen, in appreciable amounts. It should be clearly understood that although the large surface is of importance in determining the adsorbing properties of a given material, the extent and firmness of adsorption are dependent to a great extent on the nature of the adsorbent and the substance adsorbed. A given metal may adsorb one gas but not another; thus, nickel adsorbs hydrogen strongly, but the adsorption of nitrogen is quite small. For the further consideration of the phenomena of adsorption it is convenient to treat adsorption of gases and adsorption from solution separately.

56b. Adsorption of Gases.—*Increase of pressure and decrease of temperature increase the extent of the adsorption of a gas by a solid;* the curves in Fig. 113 show the quantities of nitrogen gas adsorbed by 1 gram of charcoal at various temperatures and pressures. It will be observed that, particularly at low temperatures, the adsorption of gas increases very rapidly as the pressure is raised; at higher temperatures this increase is less marked. Diminution of temperature, at a given pressure, is associated with a marked increase of the adsorption of gases. This fact is utilized in the production of high vacua; the partly evacuated apparatus is connected to a vessel containing charcoal cooled in liquid air. Under these conditions the adsorptive capacity of the charcoal is so high that it is able to take up a large proportion of the gas remaining in the apparatus, and so it brings about a considerable reduction of pressure. The fact that adsorption decreases with increasing temperature means, according to the Le Chatelier principle (§ 32c), that the adsorption

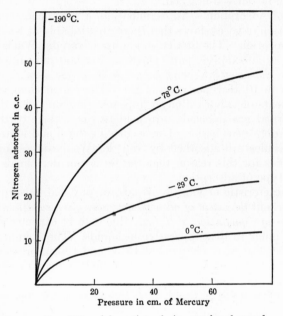

FIG. 113. Adsorption of nitrogen by charcoal

of a gas is accompanied by a decrease of heat content, i.e., an evolution of heat; this is known as the **heat of adsorption.** For every gas and solid there is a more or less definite heat of adsorption, although the actual value depends to some extent on the amount of gas already adsorbed by the solid.

The variation of gas adsorption with pressure at constant temperature can often be represented, over a limited range of pressure, by the empirical equation

$$a = kp^n, \tag{56.1}$$

where a is the amount of gas adsorbed by unit mass, e.g., 1 gram, of adsorbing material at the pressure p; k and n are constants for the given gas and adsorbent at the particular temperature. An equation of this type is known as an **adsorption isotherm,** since it is applicable at constant temperature. The value of n in equation (56.1) is less than unity, and so the quantity of gas adsorbed increases less rapidly than the pressure, as is evident from the curves in Fig. 113. Upon taking logarithms, equation (56.1) becomes

$$\log a = \log k + n \log p, \qquad (56.2)$$

so that the plot of log a against log p should be a straight line. The actual plots show a slight curvature, especially at low temperatures, so that the adsorption isotherm equation (56.1) can be regarded as approximate only, although it is convenient to use over a short range of pressure. A more exact isotherm will be derived in § 56d.

56c. Types of Adsorption.—An examination of the phenomena associated with the adsorption of gases shows that there are probably at least two different types of adsorption. The first type, known as **van der Waals adsorption,** is exhibited by all substances, particularly at low and moderately low temperatures; *it is characterized, chiefly, by relatively low heats of adsorption,* namely about 5 to 10 kcal. per mole of gas. These heat changes are of the same order as heats of vaporization; it appears, therefore, that the forces by which the adsorbed gas molecules are held to the surface of the solid are similar to the forces of cohesion of molecules in the liquid state. In other words, the molecules are adsorbed by van der Waals forces, or dispersion forces (§ 13f); it is for this reason that the term van der Waals adsorption is used for this type of adsorption.

Another characteristic of van der Waals, or physical, adsorption is that for a given adsorbent *the extent of adsorption, under given conditions, is roughly related to the ease of liquefaction of the gas;* this is to be expected if the forces concerned are similar to those operative in liquids. The volumes of various gases adsorbed by 1 gram of charcoal at 15° C and 1 atm. pressure are given in Table LXVI, together with the respective boiling points of the liquefied

TABLE LXVI.   VAN DER WAALS ADSORPTION OF GASES BY CHARCOAL

Gas	Volume Adsorbed	Boiling Point	Gas	Volume Adsorbed	Boiling Point
Sulfur dioxide	380 ml.	263.1° K	Carbon dioxide	48 ml.	— ° K
Chlorine	235	238.5°	Methane	16.2	111.7°
Ammonia	181	239.7°	Carbon monoxide	9.3	81.6°
Hydrogen sulfide	99	213.5°	Oxygen	8.2	90.2°
Hydrogen chloride	72	188.1°	Nitrogen	8.0	77.3°
Nitrous oxide	54	183.7°	Hydrogen	4.7	20.3°

gases. It is seen that there is a distinct parallelism between the extent of adsorption of a gas and the boiling point; the most easily liquefiable gases, that is, with the largest van der Waals forces of cohesion, are those which are most strongly adsorbed.

The second type of adsorption is referred to as **activated adsorption** or **chemisorption;** *the heats of adsorption are much higher than for van der Waals adsorption,* the values being 10 to 100 kcal. per mole. Chemisorption occurs in limited cases only, and it is generally observed at moderately high temperatures. *As the temperature is raised the van der Waals adsorption, for an* *appropriate gas and solid, may pass over into chemisorption.* As the name implies, chemisorption probably involves forces of interaction between the adsorbent and the gas that are chemical in nature, as distinct from the physical forces responsible for van der Waals adsorption. This accounts for the larger heat changes associated with the former type of adsorption.

Chemisorption or activated adsorption is highly specific in character, depending on the chemical properties of the gas and adsorbent. Consequently, many gas-solid systems do not exhibit chemisorption at any temperature. The adsorption of oxygen or of carbon monoxide on tungsten is chemical in nature, as is evident from the fact that an oxide or carbonyl, respectively, of tungsten can be distilled from the surface. Similarly, when oxygen is chemisorbed on charcoal, carbon monoxide and dioxide are obtained by raising the temperature and pumping off the adsorbed gas. Chemisorption also occurs with hydrogen and carbon monoxide on zinc oxide-chromium sesquioxide mixtures, and with hydrogen on nickel and copper. It is probable that in the activated (chemisorption) of hydrogen the molecules are partly, or completely, dissociated into hydrogen atoms which are held to the surface atoms by forces of a chemical nature, that is, by electron sharing. Although the word "activated" was not intended to imply any particular activity of the adsorbed substance, the adsorbed hydrogen is nevertheless active chemically, presumably because it is almost in the state of free atoms. It is for this reason that chemisorption is important in relation to catalytic action on surfaces (§ 61d).

56d. The Langmuir Adsorption Isotherm.—Since chemical forces fall off very rapidly with distance, it is probable that chemisorption does not extend beyond a single layer of gas molecules on the surface of the solid. It is to be anticipated, therefore, as first pointed out by I. Langmuir (1916), that chemisorbed gas layers are in general only one molecule in thickness. Although direct experimental evidence is difficult to obtain, because of the uncertainty concerning the area of the surface, it seems to have been definitely established in a number of cases that there is a single layer of adsorbed molecules. When van der Waals adsorption occurs, the forces can extend from one layer of molecules to another, and so it is possible, in fact probable, that the gas adsorbed on the surface is several molecular layers in thickness, especially at relatively low temperatures and moderately high pressures. However, when the temperatures are sufficiently high for chemisorption to be evident, the van der Waals adsorption is usually negligibly small.

By supposing that a unimolecular layer only of gas can be adsorbed on the surface of a solid, Langmuir was able to derive an adsorption isotherm relating the pressure of the gas to the extent of adsorption. Consider an adsorbing surface exposed to a gas; molecules of gas will strike the surface and will adhere for an appreciable time, while other gas molecules will tend to evaporate from the surface. When a state of adsorption equilibrium is attained, the rate at which the gas molecules strike the surface and are held there, i.e., the rate of adsorption, will be equal to the rate of evaporation under the given conditions. It can be shown by means of the kinetic theory of gases that, at constant temperature, gas molecules strike a surface at a rate proportional to the pressure p of the gas. If at any instant a fraction θ of the adsorbing surface is already covered with gas molecules, the fraction $1 - \theta$ of the surface will be bare. Since only a single layer of molecules can be adsorbed, it follows that only those molecules striking the bare parts of the surface can be retained, i.e., adsorbed; hence,

$$\text{Rate of adsorption of gas molecules} = kp(1 - \theta), \qquad (56.3)$$

where k is a proportionality constant. The rate at which gas molecules evaporate from the surface will be proportional to the extent θ to which it is covered with these molecules; consequently,

$$\text{Rate of evaporation of gas molecules} = k'\theta, \qquad (56.4)$$

where k' is another constant. At equilibrium the rate of adsorption and evaporation, as given by equations (56.3) and (56.4), will be equal, so that

$$kp(1 - \theta) = k'\theta$$

$$\theta = \frac{kp}{kp + k'}. \qquad (56.5)$$

If the surface can become covered with a uniform layer of gas, one molecule in thickness, the amount of gas a adsorbed per unit mass of adsorbent is directly proportional to the fraction θ of the surface covered, i.e., $a = k''\theta$, where k'' is the proportionality constant. Inserting the value of θ given by equation (56.5), and dividing through numerator and denominator by k', the result is

$$a = \frac{(kk''/k')p}{(k/k')p + 1}$$

$$= \frac{k_1 p}{k_2 p + 1}, \qquad (56.6)$$

where k_1 and k_2 are constants.

It is seen that equation (56.6) relates the extent of adsorption to the pressure of the gas, at constant temperature; it is consequently known as the **Langmuir adsorption isotherm.** In order to test this isotherm by means of experimental data, equation (56.6) may be rearranged so as to give

$$\frac{p}{a} = \frac{1}{k_1} + \frac{k_2}{k_1} p.$$

Since $1/k_1$ and k_2/k_1 are constants, it follows from this equation that if p/a is plotted against the pressure p, a straight line should be obtained; that this is so is shown by the results in Fig. 114 for the adsorption of ethylene gas on charcoal. Numerous instances of adsorption have been found to satisfy the Langmuir isotherm; where deviations occur they can be accounted for in various ways, particularly by nonuniformity of the surface leading to simultaneous adsorptions of different types. It should be understood that equation (56.6) can be expected to apply only when there is adsorption of a single uniform layer of molecules.

Two special cases of the Langmuir isotherm are of interest. If the gas pressure is very low, it is possible to neglect k_2p in comparison with unity in the denominator of equation (56.6); under these conditions this becomes

$$a = k_1p. \tag{56.7}$$

Since k_1 is a constant, it is evident that the extent of adsorption should be directly proportional to the pressure; it can be readily seen from Fig. 113

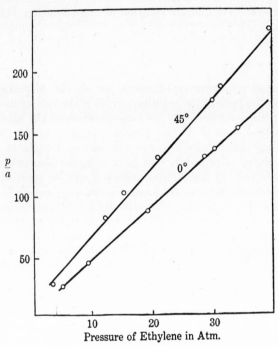

FIG. 114.   Langmuir adsorption isotherms

that this is the case at very low pressures. On the other hand, at high pressures, unity may be neglected in comparison with k_2p; equation (56.6) then reduces to

$$a = \frac{k_1}{k_2}. \tag{56.8}$$

According to this result, the amount of gas adsorbed, at any temperature, should reach a constant limiting value at high pressures; this condition arises when the surface is completely covered by a unimolecular layer of gas molecules.

The Langmuir isotherm thus takes the form $a = k_1 p$ at low pressures [equation (56.7)] and $a = k_1/k_2$ at high pressures [equation (56.8)]; consequently, over a limited range of intermediate pressures an expression of the type

$$a = kp^n,$$

where n lies between zero and unity, may be expected to hold. This result is, of course, identical with the adsorption isotherm of equation (56.1).

56e. Adsorption from Solutions: The Gibbs Equation.—A significant equation in connection with adsorption at the surface of a solution was first derived by J. Willard Gibbs (1878); it is usually referred to as the **Gibbs adsorption equation.** For a dilute solution of concentration c this equation may be written as

$$S = -\frac{c}{RT} \cdot \frac{d\gamma}{dc}, \tag{56.9}$$

where S is the *excess concentration* of solute per sq. cm. of surface, as compared with that in the bulk of the solution; $d\gamma/dc$ is the rate of increase of the surface tension of the solution with the concentration of the solute; R is the familiar gas constant, and T is the absolute temperature. According to equation (56.9), any solute which causes the surface tension of the solvent to decrease, i.e., $d\gamma/dc$ is negative, will have a higher concentration in the surface than in the bulk of the solution, since S will be positive. In other words, *a substance which decreases the tension at an interface will be adsorbed at that interface.* If $d\gamma/dc$ is positive, the dissolved substance raising the surface tension, then S will have a negative value; the concentration of the solute will thus be lower in the surface than in the body of the solution. This behavior, known as **negative adsorption,** has been observed with some electrolytes.

When a finely powdered porous substance, such as charcoal or silica gel, is added to a solution, the area of the interface is very large, and the possible extent of adsorption is considerable. In this case the Gibbs adsorption equation applies to the surface of contact between the solid and the solution; hence, $d\gamma/dc$ refers, strictly, to the influence of concentration on the solid-liquid interfacial tension. Very little information is available concerning such interfacial tensions, but as an approximation it may be assumed that the influence of concentration is the same as on the corresponding air-liquid surface tension. The latter is, of course, the quantity commonly referred to as the surface tension of the liquid, as described in Chapter V. It may be supposed, therefore, as a rough general rule, that a particular substance will be adsorbed from solution by a solid adsorbent if that substance reduces the surface tension of the solvent.

Water has a high surface tension, and most solutes reduce the value; hence, the great majority of substances are positively adsorbed from aqueous solution by such an adsorbent as charcoal. The surface tension of ethanol (Table XIX) is much lower than that of water; consequently most solutes will decrease the surface tension of ethanol less than they do that of water. It is to be expected, therefore, that a given solute will generally be more readily adsorbed from aqueous than from alcoholic solution. This anticipation has been confirmed in many cases, although exceptions are known.

There is evidence that in some instances adsorption from solution leads to the formation of a single layer of solute molecules on the surface of the solid, analogous to that in the chemisorption of a gas. In this event, an equation similar to the Langmuir isotherm will be applicable to the effect of concentration on the extent of adsorption from solution; the appropriate

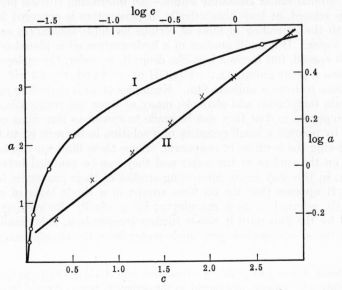

FIG. 115. Adsorption of acetic acid by charcoal

isotherm is obtained by replacing the pressure p in equation (56.6) by the concentration. For most purposes, however, the empirical isotherm, now taking the form

$$a = kc^n, \tag{56.10}$$

is found to be adequate for adsorption from solution over a considerable range of concentration; as before, a is the amount of solute adsorbed by unit mass of adsorbent from a solution of concentration c; k and n are constants for the given adsorbent and solute. Taking logarithms of equation (56.10) it is seen that

$$\log a = \log k + n \log c, \tag{56.11}$$

so that $\log a$ against $\log c$ should give a linear plot. The data in Fig. 115, for the adsorption of acetic acid from aqueous solution at 25° C, are in agreement with equation (56.11); curve I is the plot of a against c, while II shows the variation of $\log a$ with $\log c$.

It is apparent from curve I in Fig. 115 that the *relative extent* of adsorption, as compared with the concentration of the solution, is large in dilute solutions. This is a matter of importance in quantitative analytical chemistry, since it renders difficult the removal by washing of the last traces of solute adsorbed by a precipitate. In order to minimize the errors due to adsorption, precipitation should be carried out in hot solution, when the extent of adsorption is decreased; the conditions should be adjusted so that the particles formed are relatively large, and hence have a comparatively small exposed area.

56f. Unimolecular Insoluble Films.—An interesting surface phenomenon which is related, at least theoretically, to adsorption is observed in connection with the spreading of films of certain insoluble substances on the surface of water. If a small amount of a hydrocarbon oil is placed on water it does not spread, but forms a lens-like drop; if, however, the molecules of the oil possess a polar group, e.g., —CH_2OH or —COOH, the oil will spread on the surface to form a uniform film. Examples of such spreading oils are the long-chain fatty acids and alcohols; many of these are really solids at ordinary temperatures, but they can be made to spread as thin films on a water surface by pouring a small quantity of a solution in benzene on to the water and allowing the benzene to evaporate. Since these films are insoluble, they remain on the surface of the water and they can be confined between glass barriers; in this way many interesting studies of their properties have been made. It appears that the oil films consist of a single layer of molecules, frequently referred to as a **monolayer;** by gradually diminishing the area covered by the film until it resists further compression, it is possible to determine the area occupied by a single molecule in the closely packed monolayer.

Problem: When 5.19×10^{-5} g. of palmitic acid ($C_{15}H_{31}COOH$), in the form of a dilute solution in benzene, was spread on the surface of water, it could be compressed to an area of 265 sq. cm. before the resisting force increased sharply. Calculate the area occupied by a single molecule in the closely packed layer.

The molecular weight of palmitic acid is 256, and hence the 5.19×10^{-5} g. contain $5.19 \times 10^{-5}/256$ moles, or $6.02 \times 10^{23} \times 5.19 \times 10^{-5}/256$ individual molecules, since there are 6.02×10^{23}, i.e., the Avogadro number, molecules per mole of any substance. The area occupied by these molecules in the closely packed monolayer is 265 sq. cm.; hence,

$$\text{Area per single molecule} = \frac{265 \times 256}{6.02 \times 10^{23} \times 5.19 \times 10^{-5}} = 21.7 \times 10^{-16} \text{ sq. cm.}$$

It is a very striking fact that the area of surface per single molecule was found to be almost constant, namely, about 21 sq. Å, i.e., 21×10^{-16} sq. cm., for a series of long-chain compounds with polar end-groups, such as fatty acids, alcohols, methyl ketones, amides, etc., independent of their chain length. The simplest interpretation of these results is that *the oil films consist of a single layer in which the molecules are arranged almost vertically;* the polar end-groups are attracted by, and hence are "dissolved" in, the water, while the long, insoluble hydrocarbon chains project from the surface, as indicated diagrammatically in Fig. 116. If the film consists of an oriented monolayer, as suggested, it is evident that the area per molecule in the close-packed film, as derived above, should be equal to the cross-sectional area of a hydrocarbon chain. The value will thus be independent of the chain length, and also largely of the nature of the polar end-group, as found experimentally. By the foregoing arguments the area of cross section of a hydrocarbon chain should thus be about 20 sq. Å; this has been confirmed by X-ray diffraction studies of crystals of long-chain compounds. Many results of interest have been obtained in the study of monolayers, but it is not possible to discuss them here.

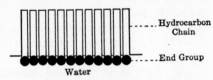

FIG. 116. Monolayer on the surface of water

THE COLLOIDAL STATE

57a. General Properties of Colloidal Systems.—In a true solution, such as one of sugar or a salt in water, the particles of solute distributed in the solvent consist essentially of single molecules or ions. On the other hand, a suspension contains particles that are large enough to be seen by the naked eye or, at least, in the microscope. Between these two extremes are to be found the **colloidal systems**; the important characteristic of the colloidal state is *the presence of particles which are larger than molecules but not large enough to be seen in the microscope.* It is obviously impossible to draw a distinct line between true (molecular) solutions and colloidal solutions, at one extreme, and between colloidal solutions and suspensions, at the other extreme. There is a gradual transition from one type of system to the other; nevertheless, colloidal systems have certain properties which, as a general rule, place them in a more or less separate category.

The upper limit of size of particles in the colloidal state may be taken as approximately the lower limit of microscopic visibility, i.e., 2×10^{-5} cm. or 0.2 μ,* whereas the lower limit is roughly 5×10^{-7} cm. or 5 mμ. The latter figure is about the same as the diameters of certain complex molecules of high molecular weight, e.g., proteins, starch, rubber and other polymers. It is not surprising, therefore, that solutions of such substances, although they probably contain single molecular particles, show colloidal behavior.

The essential properties of colloidal solutions can be ascribed to the fact that the ratio of surface area to volume of the particles is very large. In a true solution the system consists of one phase only, and there is no true surface of separation between the molecular particles of solute and solvent. Colloidal solutions, however, are two-phase systems, and for each particle there is a definite surface of separation between it and the liquid medium.

* The symbol μ is used to represent a *micron*, which is 10^{-6} meter or 10^{-4} cm.; a millimicron, represented by mμ, is equal to 10^{-3} μ or 10^{-7} cm.

At this interface characteristic properties, such as adsorption and electrical potential, are evident. When the total surface area is relatively small, as with suspensions, where the particles are relatively large, the effect of these properties is not marked, but in colloidal systems the surface area, for a given quantity of material, is so large that they play an important part. For example, the total surface area of 1 cc. of solid in the form of a cube of 1 cm. edge is 6 sq. cm.; when divided into cubes of 10^{-6} cm. edge, which approximates to the dimensions of the particles in many colloidal systems, the total area of the same volume of material is increased a million fold, i.e., to 6×10^6 sq. cm. It is to be expected, therefore, that the surface will influence the behavior of colloidal solutions.

The two phases involved in a colloidal system may be distinguished by the terms **disperse phase,** for *the phase forming the particles,* and **dispersion medium** for *the medium in which the particles are distributed (or dispersed).* So far it has been assumed that the dispersion medium is a liquid; such colloidal systems are called **sols.** In other cases the medium may be solid or even gaseous; similarly, the disperse phase may be solid, liquid or gaseous, thus leading to a number of possible types of colloidal systems. **Smokes** and **dusts,** for example, consist of solid particles dispersed in a gaseous medium, whereas in **fog, mist** and **cloud** the disperse phase is liquid and the dispersion medium is a gas. Many minerals contain gas, liquid or solid dispersed in a solid medium, and ruby glass consists of fine particles of gold dispersed in glass. A **foam** is a two-phase system of gas dispersed in a liquid. If, in a liquid medium, the disperse phase is solid and the particles are relatively large, a **suspension** is obtained, but if the disperse phase is a liquid the result is an **emulsion.** In these systems the particles of disperse phase are somewhat larger than in true colloidal solutions, but they possess certain properties analogous to those of the latter. Although many of the systems referred to in this paragraph are of considerable interest, they will not all be discussed; most attention will be paid to those in which the dispersion medium is a liquid, e.g., sols and emulsions.

Colloidal solutions with a liquid dispersion medium, i.e., sols, may be divided roughly into two categories, referred to as **lyophobic** (Greek: *liquid hating*) and **lyophilic** (*liquid loving*) sols. If water is the dispersion medium, as it is in most of the systems to be considered in this chapter, the terms **hydrophobic** and **hydrophilic,** respectively, are sometimes employed. As the names imply, lyophobic sols are relatively unstable compared with lyophilic sols; in the former type, small quantities of electrolytes are able to cause the coagulation and precipitation of the dispersed particles, but the latter are not affected unless large amounts of electrolyte are added. Upon evaporation or cooling of lyophobic systems, solids are obtained which cannot be reconverted into sols by reversing the physical change, i.e., by adding solvent or by warming, respectively. Lyophilic sols, however, are generally reversible in this respect, and consequently they behave like true solutions to some extent. This is in agreement with the view that in many lyophilic sols, e.g., of proteins, the dispersed particles are actually large single molecules. Typical examples of lyophobic sols are those of metals, sulfur, sulfides and silver halides; on the other hand, sols of gums, starches and proteins provide instances of lyophilic systems. As in most cases of colloidal behavior, it is not possible to draw a sharp line of demarcation between lyophobic and lyophilic sols; colloidal solutions of a number of metallic hydroxides, for instance, possess intermediate properties.

57b. Preparation of Colloidal Solutions.—Many substances, particularly those of high molecular weight forming lyophilic sols, pass into colloidal solution when they are warmed with a suitable dispersion medium. Instances of the preparation of colloidal solutions in this manner are gelatin and starch in water, and rubber in benzene. Lyophobic sols, however, have generally to be prepared by special methods which yield particles of the appropriate size; various procedures have been used, and these may be considered under the headings of "condensation methods" and "dispersion methods."

I. Condensation Methods.—The essential principle of these methods is that the materials from which the sol is prepared are originally present in true solution, as ions or molecules; as a result of a chemical reaction between them, insoluble particles of colloidal size are obtained. The experimental conditions, particularly as regards the concentrations of electrolytes, must be closely controlled in order to prevent the growth and consequent precipitation of the small particles. Chemical reactions of various types have been used for the preparation of colloidal solutions by the condensation method. Metal sols have been obtained by the *reduction* of solutions of their soluble salts or oxides; the reducing agents employed for this purpose are nonelectrolytes, e.g., hydrogen, carbon monoxide, formaldehyde, hydrazine and hydroxylamine. Sols of gold, silver, platinum, iridium and palladium have been prepared in this manner. The presence of a small amount of gum arabic acts as a stabilizing agent (§ 57f). *Oxidation* has also been used to prepare colloidal solutions; for example, an aqueous solution of hydrogen sulfide can be oxidized by oxygen or by sulfur dioxide to yield a sulfur sol. Selenium sols have been obtained in a similar manner from hydrogen selenide solution.

Sols of the oxides or hydroxides of weakly electropositive metals, such as iron, aluminum, chromium, tin, thorium, zirconium, etc., have been obtained by *hydrolysis* of their salts in aqueous solution. The bases corresponding to these metals are all weak, and hence the salts are considerably hydrolyzed in solution. By suitable adjustment of the conditions, the hydrated oxides are not precipitated but remain in a state of colloidal dispersion. The hydrolytic reaction is a type of double decomposition (or metathesis), and other double decomposition reactions have been employed for the production of colloidal solutions. The passage of hydrogen sulfide through solutions of mercuric cyanide or arsenious oxide leads to the formation of colloidal mercuric or arsenious sulfide, respectively. In each case the other product is a very weak electrolyte; a strong electrolyte would have caused the sulfide particles to coagulate. Silver halide sols can be obtained by mixing dilute solutions of an alkali halide and a silver salt, one or other being present in very slight excess. One of the best known inorganic sols, that of silicic acid, is generally prepared by a double decomposition reaction between dilute solutions of sodium silicate and hydrochloric acid.

II. Dispersion Methods.—In these methods the starting material consists of the substance in the massive form; by means of suitable devices it is then disintegrated into particles of colloidal dimensions which remain for some time in the dispersed state. In this connection the principle of **peptization** is frequently used; this term refers to the direct disintegration (or dispersion) of a substance into particles of colloidal size by an added agent, the latter being known as a **peptizing agent.** In the preparation of lyophilic sols, such as those of gelatin or starch, the dispersion medium, i.e., water, is itself the peptizing agent. Incompletely nitrated cellulose is peptized by various organic solvents, e.g., mixtures of ethanol and ether; in this case the product is the familiar "collodion" sol. In other cases, however, a peptizing agent must be present in addition; freshly precipitated substances, such as the hydrated oxides of metals, can frequently be peptized to the colloidal state by dilute solutions of alkali hydroxides. In general, the presence of a common ion encourages peptization, provided the total concentration of electrolyte is not too great; thus, alkali hydroxides peptize hydroxides, hydrogen sulfide peptizes sulfides, and the chloride ion can peptize freshly precipitated silver chloride.

Many substances can be reduced to colloidal size in a *colloid mill,* consisting of a series of closely spaced discs, each rotating at a very high speed in a direction opposite to that of its immediate neighbors. The dispersion medium, together with the substance to be dispersed, and a stabilizing agent are passed through the mill; after a time a colloidal solution results.

A process which involves both dispersion and condensation makes use of *electrical disintegration;* a direct current electric arc is struck between wires of platinum, gold or silver immersed in water, and a sol of the metal is obtained. The high temperature of the arc causes the metal to vaporize, and the vapor is then condensed by the water to form colloidal particles. Electrolytes should generally be absent from the liquid, although traces of alkali hydroxide are advantageous. The electrical method of preparing sols has been modified so that it can be used for nonmetals as well as for metals. The electrodes are of iron or aluminum, which do not disintegrate, and the material to be dispersed is suspended, in the form of granules or foil, in the liquid through which the arc is passed. Sols in organic dispersion media have been prepared in this manner.

57c. Purification of Colloidal Solutions.—Two main procedures have been applied to the removal from sols of substances in true solution; both methods depend on the relatively large size of the colloidal dispersed particles. The process known as **dialysis** (T. Graham, 1861) utilizes the fact that the great majority of *substances in true solution can pass through a parchment (or similar) membrane while colloidal particles are retained.* It should be noted that the dialyzing membrane does not act merely as a sieve, retaining the larger particles; this sieve action is, no doubt, partly responsible for dialysis, but the difference in the relative rates of diffusion of the dissolved and dispersed (colloidal) particles is probably the most important factor. Colloidal particles diffuse very slowly, chiefly because of their relatively large dimensions, while molecules and ions in true solution diffuse much more rapidly.

Various forms of dialyzers and a variety of dialyzing materials have been used for the purification of colloidal solutions. In addition to parchment, membranes of cellophane, cellulose nitrate and cellulose acetate have been found satisfactory; these may be in the form of an elongated tube, or as a bag or thimble. The colloidal solution is placed inside the tube or bag, and this is suspended in a vessel containing water; the latter is changed either periodically or continuously, as the dissolved molecules pass out from the interior of the dialyzer into the surrounding water.

In **electrodialysis** the removal of electrolytes is facilitated by means of an electric field. The colloidal solution containing the unwanted electrolyte is placed between two dialyzing membranes, with pure water in a compartment on each side. By means of electrodes placed in these compartments an E.M.F. is applied which causes the ions to migrate out of the colloidal solution into the water; the latter is replaced continuously or as required.

The second important method for purifying sols is known as **ultrafiltration** (H. Bechhold, 1907). The pores of even the best filter papers permit the passage of colloidal particles, but *by impregnating filter papers with suitable substances the pores can be made small enough to retain particles of colloidal dimensions*. The impregnating substance may be collodion or gelatin hardened by formaldehyde. The colloidal solution is poured on to the filter, which is supported so as to increase its strength, and the passage of the liquid is facilitated by pressure or suction. The size of the pores in the ultrafilter depends on the paper and on the concentration of the solution used to impregnate it. In this way a series of graded ultrafilters, of varying pore size, can be prepared; by means of them a colloidal solution may not only be purified from dissolved material, but it may be separated into fractions containing particles of different size.

57d. Optical Properties of Sols.—Colloidal particles are too small to be seen in the microscope; nevertheless, their presence can be made evident by optical means. If a strong beam of light is passed through a medium which is "optically clear," that is, it contains no particles larger than about 10^{-7} cm., the path of the light cannot be easily detected. If particles of larger, e.g., colloidal, size are present, however, they will scatter the light, and as a result the beam is rendered visible. Most true solutions are optically clear, but colloidal solutions scatter light, producing what is known as the **Tyndall effect.** The path of the light through the sol, which is rendered visible as a result of the scattering, is called the **Tyndall beam.**

In the instrument known as the **ultramicroscope,** invented by H. Siedentopf and R. Zsigmondy (1903), the scattered light in the Tyndall beam is observed in a microscope. In this way the presence of individual particles in a colloidal solution become apparent as flashes of scattered light. Although the particles themselves are actually too small to be visible in the microscope, the light scattered by them can be seen in the ultramicroscope; particles as small as 5 to 10 mμ diameter can be detected in this manner.

The principle of the slit ultramicroscope is illustrated diagrammatically in Fig. 117; a narrow, powerful beam of parallel or slightly convergent light, from an arc lamp, is passed at right angles to the direction of the microscope through a cell upon which the instrument is focussed. If the solution in the cell is optically clear, the microscopic field will appear completely dark. On the other hand, if it contains a colloidal solution, the particles scatter the light, some of which passes vertically into the microscope; each particle thus appears as a small disc of light on a black background. Other forms of ultramicroscope have been designed, but the one just described is the most satisfactory.

The size of the luminous reflections seen in the ultramicroscope bears no relation to the actual size of the particles; it is possible, nevertheless, to utilize the ultramicroscope to determine the dimensions of colloidal particles. If

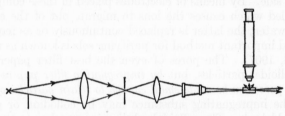

Fig. 117.   Slit ultramicroscope

the total weight of material dispersed in a given volume of sol is known, and the density of the particles is assumed to be the same as in the macroscopic (massive) state, the total volume of the dispersed phase can be calculated. To determine the volume or size of each particle it is required to find the number of particles in a given quantity of the sol. The counting is carried out by diluting the sol to a definite extent, if necessary, and noting the number of particles visible in the ultramicroscope; the observations are repeated many times and the average taken. From a knowledge of the volume of sol in the field of the ultramicroscope, the number of particles in a given volume can be calculated. All the information is thus available for determining the dimensions of the particles, which are generally assumed to be spherical.

When observed in the ultramicroscope colloidal particles are seen to be undergoing continuous and rapid motion in all directions; in other words, the particles exhibit Brownian movement (§ 12k). The vertical distribution of colloidal particles under the influence of gravity, when equilibrium is attained, should be given by an expression identical with equation (12.28). By determining the numbers of particles at different levels in a gold sol, by means of the ultramicroscope, a value of the Avogadro number has been obtained which is in excellent agreement with that derived in other ways.

57e. Hydrophobic Sols: Electrical Properties.—In considering the electrical properties of aqueous sols, it is convenient to treat lyophobic (hydrophobic) sols separately from those possessing lyophilic character. When a hydrophobic sol is placed in an electric field the particles move definitely in one direction or another; this means that *colloidal particles are electrically charged with respect to the dispersion medium.* The phenomenon of *the migration of colloidal particles under the influence of an electrical potential* is called **electrophoresis.** The movement of particles in an electric field can be observed in the ultramiscrocope, but a more convenient method is to use the apparatus shown in Fig. 118; the lower part of the U-tube contains the sol covered by the pure dispersion medium, e.g., water, into which dip platinum electrodes connected to a source of E.M.F. If the boundary between the sol and the pure water is sharp and visible, its rate of motion, which is equal to the speed of electrophoresis of the dispersed particles, can be determined. Special methods, such as causing the surface to fluoresce in ultraviolet light, are sometimes employed to render the boundary visible. The potential gradient in volts per cm. can be derived from the applied E.M.F. and the dimensions of the apparatus; hence, the velocity of the particles under a fall of potential of 1 volt per cm., i.e., the **electrophoretic mobility,** may be calculated. The sign of the charge carried by the particles can, of course, be determined by observing the direction in which the boundary moves.

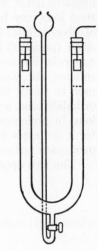

Sols of metallic hydroxides and hydrated oxides, and of basic dyestuffs usually contain positively charged particles, whereas in sols of metals, sulfur, metallic sulfides, acidic hydroxides and acidic dyestuffs the particles carry negative charges. In some cases the sign of the electrical charge depends on the method of preparing the colloidal solution, but one particular type is usually more stable than the other. In spite of the varying nature of the dispersed particles, the electrophoretic mobilities for aqueous

Fig. 118. Measurement of electrophoresis

sols almost always lie within the range of 2 to 4×10^{-4} cm. per sec. It is of interest to note that the mobilities of ordinary ions, with the exception of hydrogen and hydroxyl ions, are about 4 to 8×10^{-4} cm. per sec. Since colloidal particles migrate with a velocity comparable to that of electrolytic ions, sols might be expected to possess appreciable electrical conductance; however, this is not the case, because the number of particles in a colloidal solution is very small in comparison with an electrolytic solution at a reasonable concentration.

The electrical charge carried by colloidal particles is of fundamental importance, because it is probable that without it lyophobic sols would be extremely unstable, as will be seen later. The question of the origin of the charge is therefore of some interest. It has been frequently observed that small quantities of electrolytes are associated with colloidal systems; if they are removed by persistent dialysis, or in other ways, the sol becomes unstable, and the dispersed particles grow in size and are eventually precipitated. It appears, therefore, that in many instances traces of ions present in the sol are responsible for both the charge and stability of the colloidal system. It was mentioned in § 57b, II, for example, that metal sols prepared by the arc method are stabilized by the presence of small amounts of alkali hydroxide. Further, if a dilute solution of a silver salt is added to a slight excess of dilute potassium iodide solution, a negatively charged sol of silver iodide is obtained; however, if the dilute iodide solution is added to excess of the silver nitrate, a positively charged sol results. If the two solutions are mixed in exactly equivalent amounts, the silver iodide sol is unstable, and complete precipitation occurs.

In the light of these experimental facts, the stability and charge of the negative silver iodide sol formed in the presence of an excess of iodide (negative) ions may be attributed to the adsorption of these ions by the particles of silver iodide; the positive sols are similarly stabilized by the adsorption of silver (positive) ions, since the latter are in excess in the solution. As a general rule, ionizable (electrovalent) solids, such as silver halides, hydroxides, sulfides, etc., appear to have a preference for adsorbing ions which are common to them; thus a colloidal silver halide will tend to adsorb either silver or halide ions, a metallic hydroxide will adsorb ions of the metal or hydroxyl ions, in preference to others, and so on. Such behavior is not unreasonable, for it indicates a natural tendency for the electrovalent crystal to extend its own space lattice, which already consists of ions (§ 19b).

The two oppositely charged silver iodide sols may be represented as

$$[AgI]I^- \mid K^+ \quad \text{and} \quad [AgI]Ag^+ \mid NO_3^-$$

where [AgI] represents a small particle of silver iodide; in the first case it has adsorbed iodide ions, giving a negative charge, while in the second case silver ions are adsorbed and the particle has a positive charge. In both cases the ions of opposite sign, viz., K^+ and NO_3^-, respectively, will remain in solution; these will be mainly in proximity to the colloidal particle because of the electrostatic attraction. The structure to the left of the dotted line thus represents the dispersed particle itself, while to the right the nature of the ion present in excess on the solution side is indicated. It should be clearly understood that although only one ion is shown to the left and one to the right of the dotted line, actually many ions of both kinds are probably adsorbed by the colloidal particle; the ions given in the formula represent the particular species present in excess.

Hydrated ferric oxide sols have been prepared both positively and negatively charged; the particles of the former, obtained in the presence of excess of ferric ions, probably adsorb and are stabilized by these ions, viz., $[Fe_2O_3 \cdot xH_2O]Fe^{+++}$, while in the latter, which is formed when hydroxyl ions are in excess, the particles may be represented by $[Fe_2O_3 \cdot xH_2O]OH^-$. In each case, oppositely charged ions, e.g., Cl^- and Na^+, respectively, remain on the solution side of the particle. It was stated earlier that sols of hydrated metallic oxides can often be obtained by using alkali hydroxide as a peptizing agent; here also, preferential adsorption of the hydroxyl ion probably accounts for the formation of negatively charged colloidal particles. Similarly, since negatively charged sulfide sols are stabilized by hydrogen sulfide, adsorption of sulfide ions may be responsible, e.g., $[As_2S_3]S^{--}$.

Although adsorption of a common ion is undoubtedly not the only way whereby a colloidal particle acquires its charge and stability, there appears to be satisfactory evidence that this is often the case. Metallic sols, which are usually negatively charged, are probably stabilized by the adsorption of hydroxyl ions; the presence of small quantities of these ions has a beneficial effect in the arc method of preparing these sols, as mentioned above. It is probably true to state, in general, that *the charge and stability of lyophobic colloidal particles in an aqueous sol are due to the preferential adsorption of a particular ion.* In view of this conclusion it can be understood why the complete removal of all electrolytes often leads to instability of a colloidal system.

57f. Precipitation by Electrolytes.—Although traces of electrolyte are apparently essential to the stability of lyophobic sols, at least in water, somewhat larger amounts cause the particles to aggregate and form a visible precipitate; the phenomenon is known as **precipitation** or **coagulation.** Many experiments have been made on the precipitating effects of various electrolytes on different sols; the results depend on the conditions, to some extent, but two definite conclusions have been drawn. First, *the ion which is effective in causing precipitation of a sol is the one whose charge is of opposite sign to that of the colloidal particles;* and second, *the precipitating effect increases markedly with increasing valence of the ion.* These statements concerning the influence of sign and valence on the precipitation of a colloidal solution are included under the title of the **Hardy-Schulze rule** (H. Schulze, 1882; W. B. Hardy, 1900).

TABLE LXVII. MINIMUM ELECTROLYTE CONCENTRATIONS FOR PRECIPITATION

Ferric Oxide Sol (Positive)			Arsenious Sulfide Sol (Negative)		
Electrolyte	Anion Valence	Min. Conc.	Electrolyte	Cation Valence	Min. Conc.
KCl	1	103	NaCl	1	51
KBr	1	138	KNO$_3$	1	50
KNO$_3$	1	131	$\frac{1}{2}$K$_2$SO$_4$	1	63
K$_2$CrO$_4$	2	0.325	MgSO$_4$	2	0.81
K$_2$SO$_4$	2	0.219	BaCl$_2$	2	0.69
K$_3$Fe(CN)$_6$	3	0.096	AlCl$_3$	3	0.093

The data in Table LXVII show the minimum concentrations, in millimoles per liter, of various electrolytes required to cause precipitation of a positively charged ferric oxide sol and of a negatively charged arsenious sulfide sol. In each case it is evident that the result of increasing the valence of the ion of opposite sign to that of the charged particles is to bring about a very marked decrease in the quantity of electrolyte required to cause precipitation; the precipitating effect thus increases with increasing valence of the ion. A change in the valence of the ion of the same sign as the colloidal particle has only a relatively small influence, as is evident from the results for the precipitation of the arsenious sulfide sol.

The precipitating effect of an electrolyte is probably due to the adsorption of an ion of sign opposite to that of the colloidal particle. When the charge carried by the ion adsorbed in this manner just neutralizes the charge on the particles, the resulting uncharged particles can unite to form a visible precipitate. If this argument is correct then the precipitation of a given sol should require the adsorption of electrically equivalent amounts of ions of different valences; that is to say, the amounts of uni-, bi-, and tri-valent ions adsorbed should be in the ratio of 3 to 1.5 to 1, since the charges are 1, 2 and 3, respectively, per ion. The actual ratios of the ionic concentrations *in solution* necessary for the precipitation of arsenious sulfide sol, for example, are seen from Table LXVII to be about 600 to 9 to 1. It should be noted, however, that these figures give the ratios of the ionic concentrations in solution, whereas the calculated ratios of 3 to 1.5 to 1 refer to the amounts of the ions actually *adsorbed* by the colloidal particles. It is an experimental fact, as may be seen from Fig. 115, or from the adsorption isotherm equation (56.10), that since n is less than unity, the amount of substance adsorbed from solution increases less rapidly than does the concentration in the solution. It would not be unreasonable, therefore, if the ratios of the ionic concentrations in solution were 1 to 9 to 600 in order for the amounts actually adsorbed to be in the ratios of 1 to 1.5 to 3. The concept of the adsorption of oppositely charged ions thus provides a satisfactory qualitative explanation, at least, of the experimental facts relating to the precipitation of lyophobic sols by electrolytes.

The addition of a lyophilic substance to a lyophobic sol frequently renders the latter less sensitive to the precipitating effect of electrolytes; this is an illustration of the phenomenon of **protective action,** the lyophilic substance being a **protective colloid.** It appears that the protective (lyophilic) colloid, such as gelatin, albumin, gums, etc., is able in some manner, not clearly understood, to confer upon lyophobic sols its property of stability to electrolytes. Although lyophilic sols are the most effective protective agents, certain other substances also exert protective action.

The relative protective effects of different substances can be expressed quantitatively in terms of what is known as the **gold number** (R. Zsigmondy, 1901); this is defined as the dry weight in milligrams of protective material which when added to 10 ml. of a standard gold sol (0.0053 to 0.0058 per cent) is just sufficient to prevent color change from red to blue on the addition of 1 ml. of a 10 per cent solution of sodium chloride. The color change referred to is due to coagulation of the particles, and hence the gold number is a measure of the quantity of protective colloid which just fails to prevent precipitation by the electrolyte (sodium chloride). It follows, therefore, that the smaller the gold number the greater the protective action of the given substance. Gelatin has a very small gold number, and hence is a very good protective colloid; egg albumin and gum arabic are less effective, while potato starch has relatively little protective action.

57g. Electrokinetic (Zeta) Potential.—The electrical properties of colloids, and other related phenomena, can be most clearly understood by a more detailed consideration of the electrical condition of a surface. It was suggested by H. von Helmholtz (1879) that an **electrical double layer,** of positive and negative charges, is generally formed at the surface of separation between two phases. According to modern views, at a solid-liquid interface, this double layer is made up of a layer of charges, i.e., ions in aqueous solution, which are firmly held to the solid, and a more diffuse mobile layer, extending into the solution. The resultant (net) charge of the diffuse layer is equal in magnitude but of opposite sign to that of the firmly held, or fixed, layer. A simplified schematic representation of the structure of the double layer is shown in Fig. 119; in one case it is supposed that the fixed part of the double layer is positively charged, while in the other case it is negatively charged. Because of the electrical charges, there is a difference of potential between the dotted line, representing the separation of fixed and diffuse double layers,

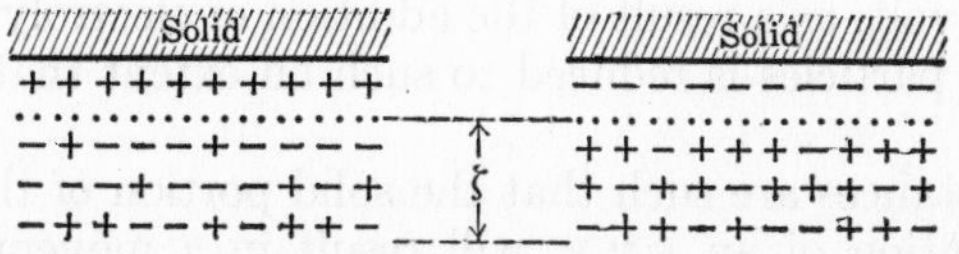

FIG. 119. Representation of electrical double layer

and the bulk of the solution. This has been called the **electrokinetic potential;** it is often referred to by the noncommittal name of **zeta potential,** because it is represented by the Greek letter *zeta, ζ.*

The electrical double layer described above presumably exists at all solid-liquid interfaces, and it is undoubtedly formed at the surface of a colloidal particle. The fixed part of the layer then corresponds to the ions adsorbed by the particle and to which it owes its charge; the diffuse portion is represented by the oppositely charged ions in the solution, as described in § 57e. The dotted line employed earlier in the formulation of the colloidal particle, e.g., in $[AgI]I^- \mid K^+$, corresponds to the dotted line between the fixed and diffuse layers in Fig. 119. It is probably the presence of electrical double layers surrounding all the particles that accounts for the stability of a colloidal system; the mutual repulsion of these layers prevents the particles from approaching sufficiently closely for them to coalesce. When an ion of opposite charge to that of the colloidal particle is adsorbed, the double layer (electrokinetic) potential is decreased. As a result, the mutual repulsion of the particles is diminished and coalescence, with consequent precipitation, becomes possible.

When an E.M.F. is applied to an electrical double layer there must be a displacement of the oppositely charged layers relative to one another; the actual movement will presumably take place at the region indicated by the dotted line in Fig. 119, since this represents the separation between the two charged layers. In the case of a sol, the layer attached to the colloidal particle is free to move, together with the particle itself, in an applied field, thus producing the phenomenon of electrophoresis, described above. It is to be expected that there should be a connection between the velocity of electrophoresis and the zeta potential acting at the surface of the colloidal particle. By treating the double layer as a simple electrical condenser, the relationship

$$\zeta = \frac{4\pi\eta u}{D}$$

can be derived; ζ is the electrokinetic (zeta) potential, u is the electrophoretic mobility of the particle, i.e., under a potential of 1 volt per cm., and η and D are the viscosity and dielectric constant, respectively, of the dispersion medium. Utilizing the electrophoretic mobilities already determined, viz., 2 to 4×10^{-4} cm. per sec. for most colloidal particles, the corresponding electrokinetic potentials are found to be from 0.03 to 0.06 volt when water is the dispersion medium. Experiments have shown that when this potential falls below about 0.02 volt, as a result of the addition of electrolytes, the repulsion between colloidal particles is reduced to such an extent that coagulation can occur.

If the circumstances are such that the solid portion of the surface cannot move, the application of an E.M.F. will result in a movement of the other portion of the double layer; since this is attached to the liquid, it is accompanied by a movement of the liquid itself. This is the basis of the phenomenon of **electroosmosis**, i.e., *the passage of liquid through a porous diaphragm under the influence of an applied electric field.* If two portions of a liquid, e.g., water, are separated by a porous diaphragm, and an E.M.F. is applied between electrodes placed on each side of the diaphragm, there will be a flow of liquid from one side to the other. A porous diaphragm is actually a mass of small capillaries, and the same type of electroosmotic flow has been observed through glass capillary tubes. In each case, the charged layer attached to the solid cannot move, and so the diffuse layer in the liquid phase, together with the liquid, moves when an electric field is applied. The direction of the electroosmotic flow depends on the charge of the diffuse part of the double layer; in moderately pure water most solids acquire a negative charge, so that the diffuse layer has a resultant positive charge. The flow of water through the diaphragm is thus generally in the direction of the (positive) current. The presence of electrolytes, however, can influence the rate and even the direction of flow. As in the case of precipitation by electrolytes, the most effective ions are those of sign opposite to that carried by the solid, and their influence increases markedly with increasing valence.

It is possible to calculate the value of the zeta potential from a study of electroosmosis, but a more convenient method is to make use of another electrokinetic phenomenon, namely, the **streaming potential;** this is *the production of a potential difference when a liquid is forced through a porous membrane or capillary tube.* The separation of the oppositely charged layers of the electrical double layer, due to the forcible passage of liquid, results in a difference of potential between the two sides of the membrane or the ends of the capillary tube. The streaming potential effect may thus be regarded as the reverse of electroosmosis, for in the latter the application of a potential difference, i.e., an E.M.F., causes a flow of liquid, while in the former the flow of liquid produces a potential difference. The streaming potential can be readily measured by placing identical reversible, e.g., calomel, electrodes (§ 49d) at each end of a capillary tube, and determining the difference of potential that results when water or an aqueous solution is forced through the tube.

By considering the electrical double layer as a simple condenser, as before, it has been found that the streaming potential S is related to the electrokinetic (zeta) potential ζ by

$$\zeta = \frac{4\pi\eta\kappa S}{PD},$$

where P is the pressure applied to the streaming liquid, whose specific conductance is κ (§ 46a); η and D are the viscosity and dielectric constant, respectively, of the liquid. The values of the electrokinetic potential obtained by means of this equation, from measurements of the streaming potential, are of the order of 0.02 to 0.05 volt, which is similar to that found for colloidal particles. If electrolytes are added to the water the streaming potentials, and hence the zeta potentials, are changed. In agreement with the conclusions already drawn, ions of high valence, with a charge of opposite sign to that carried by the solid material of the tube through which the liquid streams, have a very marked effect in reducing, and eventually reversing the sign of, the electrokinetic potential.

In the foregoing discussion the interface has been treated as one between a solid and a liquid; however, it is probable that a similar electrical double layer exists at a liquid-liquid interface. It would be difficult to observe electroosmosis and the streaming potential under these conditions, since it would not be easy to prepare a fairly rigid porous diaphragm made of liquid. However, electrophoresis can be readily observed when very small droplets of one liquid are suspended in another, e.g., water; the application of an E.M.F. results in the movement of the droplets in one direction or another. A particular case of this type occurs with a mercury sol; the particles are undoubtedly very minute drops of liquid mercury dispersed in water. It will be seen shortly (§ 57m) that emulsions also fall into the category of liquid-liquid systems, and these exhibit the electrophoretic effect.

57h. Properties of Lyophilic Sols: Viscosity and Electrophoresis.—The chief lyophilic substances, e.g., starch, proteins, etc., are naturally occurring, and their colloidal properties are probably of biological importance. The study of lyophilic sols is, however, very complicated and the results are often difficult to interpret; nevertheless, there are some definite conclusions which will be considered. One of the most striking differences between lyophobic and lyophilic sols is the high viscosity of the latter; this is attributed to the extensive solvation (hydration) of the lyophilic particles, so that there is increased resistance to flow under the action of a shearing force. It is perhaps significant in connection with the idea that lyophilic particles are solvated that solid gelatin and agar, which form lyophilic sols readily in water, are able to take up large quantities of water to form jelly-like masses (§ 57l); rubber takes up benzene in a similar manner.

Particles of lyophilic sols exhibit electrophoretic migration in an electric field, but the direction of movement is often, especially with proteins and related substances, very sensitive to changes in the hydrogen ion concentration of the medium. Proteins are complex amino-acids, and hence are amphoteric in nature (§ 53i); they consequently possess both acidic and basic functions. The charge carried by a protein particle is governed by the particular property which is effective in the given environment. If the solution

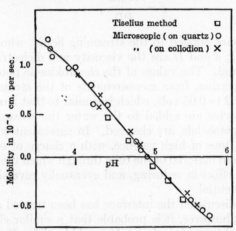

FIG. 120.   Mobility of horse serum albumin (Abramson, Gorin and Moyer)

is relatively acid, the protein molecule will behave as a base, and will take up protons from the acid, thus acquiring a positive charge; for example, if the amphoteric molecule is represented by XH, it will ionize in acid solution, thus

$$XH + H_3O^+ = HXH^+ + H_2O,$$

giving a positively charged colloidal particle. If, however, the solution is relatively alkaline, the protein will act as an acid and will transfer a proton to the hydroxyl ion, or other base, thus

$$XH + OH^- = X^- + H_2O,$$

so that the particles will be negatively charged.

As may be imagined, there is a certain hydrogen ion concentration, or pH, at which the acidic and basic functions of a protein molecule balance one another exactly; the two ionizations depicted above then take place to the same extent. This condition occurs at the **isoelectric point** of the particular protein (see § 53i); *at this* pH *value a lyophilic (protein) sol will exhibit no electrophoretic movement.* The isoelectric point varies with the nature of the substance; thus, it is at a pH of 2.6 for lecithin, 4.7 for gelatin, 7.0 for hemoglobin and 4.9 for horse serum albumin. At lower pH values the particles have positive charges and move in the direction of an applied field; at higher pH values they carry negative charges and move in the opposite direction. The effect of pH on the electrophoretic mobility of protein particles is brought out clearly by the results in Fig. 120, which have been obtained by different methods with horse serum albumin at various pH's; the isoelectric point is seen to occur at pH 4.9.

The fact that different proteins have different electrophoretic mobilities at a given pH has been utilized by A. Tiselius (1937) to design a special apparatus which uses the same principle as, but is a considerable refinement over, the U-tube form in Fig. 118. It is known as the **Tiselius apparatus,** and it permits the identification and even the separation of proteins present in a mixture, such as in the lyophilic sol blood plasma. When an E.M.F. is applied to the sol in the Tiselius apparatus, separate boundaries are formed, due to the different speeds of the different protein particles; by the use of special optical devices each boundary produces a characteristic peak on a photographic plate (Fig. 121). From the position of the peak, which is determined by the electrophoretic mobility, the nature of the protein can be identified; further, the area under the peak is a measure of the amount present in the sol. One difficulty inherent in the Tiselius procedure is the fact that two proteins having the same mobility at the given pH will be indistinguishable and will produce one boundary only. It is sometimes possible to effect a separation by changing the pH, but some biological sols are so sensitive to such changes that the results may be of no value.

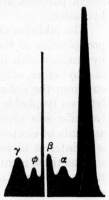

FIG. 121. Separation of proteins in blood plasma (Longsworth, Shedlovsky and MacInnes)

57i. Stability of Lyophilic Sols.—Small amounts of electrolytes have no coagulating effect on lyophilic sols, even though the zeta potentials are altered; some sols are actually stable at their isoelectric points, when the electrokinetic potential is zero. It is evident that some factor, in addition to the charge, i.e., the double layer potential, must play a part in determining the stability of lyophilic sols; this factor is believed to be the solvation of the particles, referred to in § 57h as the cause of the high viscosity of lyophilic sols. If alcohol or acetone is added to a lyophilic sol in water, the system becomes sensitive to electrolytes, thus behaving like a lyophobic sol. This action is attributed to the removal of the stabilizing layer of water molecules by the alcohol or acetone; the stability of the resulting unhydrated "bare" particles is now dependent upon the zeta potential, and hence electrolytes can bring about coagulation.

It appears, therefore, that the stability of a lyophilic sol in water, i.e., a hydrophilic sol, is determined by two factors, viz., the layer of water molecules, i.e., **hydration,** and the electric charge, i.e., the zeta potential. If the water molecules are removed, then oppositely charged ions can neutralize the charge and so cause precipitation to occur. On the other hand, when the electric charge is neutralized, as at the isoelectric point, precipitation can be brought about by the addition of small amounts of alcohol which removes the layer of water molecules. In some sols, e.g., gelatin, both stabilizing factors are effective and can operate more or less independently. In other cases, one factor apparently predominates; for example, a casein sol is very unstable at the isoelectric point, indicating that hydration plays a relatively minor part in maintaining the stability. It is probable, however, that the extent of hydration depends on the charge, and when the charges on the casein particles are neutralized there may be an accompanying decrease of hydration.

The addition of large amounts of electrolyte to lyophilic sols results in a precipitation of the dispersed substance. The effect is called "salting out," by analogy with the influence of electrolytes on true solutions, such as those of ethyl ether, ethyl acetate and aniline in water; the behavior is quite different from the ordinary coagulation produced by small quantities of electrolytes on lyophobic sols. In the light of the interpretation of the stability of lyophilic sols given above, it is probable that the precipitation by large amounts of electrolytes is due to dehydration of the dispersed particles. It is of interest to mention that the salting out of soluble organic substances, such as those mentioned above, is attributed to a somewhat similar dehydration. The removal of the electrolyte from the coagulated lyophilic sol results in the return of the substance to the colloidal state; such is not the case with lyophobic sols.

The coagulating effect of a given salt depends on the nature of its ions, and the salts of a given metal, for instance, can be arranged in order of their decreasing ability to cause precipitation of lyophilic substances from colloidal solution. The resulting arrangement is called the **Hofmeister series** (F. Hofmeister, 1891) or the **lyotropic series**; the order of anions, for a given cation, is

$$SO_4^{--} > C_2H_3O_2^- > Cl^- > NO_3^- > ClO_3^- > I^- > CNS^-,$$

while that of cations, which have a smaller influence than anions, is

$$Mg^{++} > Ca^{++} > Sr^{++} > Ba^{++} > Li^+ > Na^+ > K^+.$$

It is of interest to note that these series are very similar to those observed for the influence of ions on the salting out of soluble organic substances.

57j. Molecular Weights of Protein Particles: The Ultracentrifuge.—It was shown in § 12h that by studying the distribution under the influence of gravity of suspended particles undergoing Brownian movement, it was possible to determine the Avogadro number, e.g., by equation (12.27) or (12.28). For this purpose it was necessary to know the actual mass m of the particles, and this was derived from the radius and density. Since the Avogadro number N is now known with considerable accuracy, it is possible to reverse the calculations, and thus to determine the "molecular weight," i.e., the value of Nm, of the dispersed particles of a colloidal system. With protein sols, it is probable that each particle is a single molecule, and so the result may be taken as the actual molecular weight of the protein.

Although, in principle, distribution of the particles under the influence of gravity could be used for protein particles, the results would not be satisfactory for a number of reasons. By means of the **ultracentrifuge,** designed by T. Svedberg (1925), a considerable improvement is possible; in outline, the apparatus (Fig. 122) consists of a rotor A, revolving at high speed about the axis BB; a cell C contains the experimental solution through which a beam of light can pass and then fall on a photographic plate P. By rapidly rotating the colloidal solution in this manner a force approaching a half-million times gravity can be applied to the particles. When equilibrium is attained, the distribution of particles at various levels is given by an expression exactly analogous to equation (12.27), with the exception that the gravitational factor $g(h_2 - h_1)$ is replaced by the corresponding centrifugal term $\frac{1}{2}\omega^2(x_1^2 - x_2^2)$, where ω is the angular velocity of rotation of the sol, i.e., 2π times the number of rotations per sec., and x_1 and x_2 are the respective distances of the two levels from the axis of rotation. The condition of equilibrium is then given by

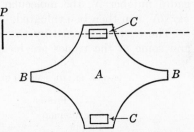

FIG. 122. Principle of the ultracentrifuge

$$\ln \frac{n_1}{n_2} = \frac{M\omega^2(x_1^2 - x_2^2)}{2RT}\left(1 - \frac{d'}{d}\right), \qquad (57.1)$$

where mN has been replaced by the molecular weight M; d and d' are the densities of the particles and of the medium, respectively.

If the amount of light absorbed at any level of the solution is proportional to the number of particles at that level, the ratio n_1/n_2 can be estimated at two depths x_1 and x_2 from the blackening of the photographic plate P, upon which the beam of light passing through the cell C impinges (Fig. 122).* From a knowledge of the speed of rotation of the ultracentrifuge, ω can be derived, and hence all the information is available for the calculation of the molecular weight M by means of equation (57.1).

Instead of using the "sedimentation equilibrium" method, as described above, an alternative, more rapid, procedure, known as the "sedimentation velocity" method can be employed to give the molecular weight. It is applicable to the conditions that exist before the attainment of equilibrium. The equation used for this purpose is

$$\ln \frac{x}{x'} = \frac{2\omega^2 r^2(d - d')}{9\eta}(t - t'), \qquad (57.2)$$

---

* In modern forms of the apparatus, methods other than light absorption are used.

where x and x' may be taken as the distances of a particular layer, e.g., the boundary of the sol particles, from the axis of rotation at the times t and t'; η is the viscosity of the medium, and r is the radius of the particles in the sol; ω, d and d' have the same significance as before. The position of the boundary after various time intervals is indicated by means of the beam of light passing through the cell. It is thus possible to calculate the particle radius r from equation (57.2), and then $\frac{4}{3}\pi r^3$ gives the volume, assuming the particle to be spherical. Knowing the density d of the material and the Avogadro number N, the molecular weight of the particle, which is equal to $\frac{4}{3}\pi r^3 dN$, can then be evaluated.

The results obtained by the two methods are in satisfactory agreement, and some of the values are recorded in Table LXVIII; particle molecular

TABLE LXVIII.   MOLECULAR WEIGHTS OF PROTEIN PARTICLES

Protein	Molecular Weight
Egg albumin	40,000
Insulin	41,000
Hemoglobin (human)	63,000
Serum albumin (horse)	70,000
Serum globulin (human)	176,000
Edestin	310,000
Thyroglobulin	630,000
Hemocyanins	4×10^5 to 6×10^6

weights varying from a minimum of about 20,000 to over 6,000,000 have been observed. It should be remembered that these are true molecular weights only if the particles in the sol consist of single molecules.

57k. The Donnan Equilibrium.—Since a protein sol is, in a sense, a molecular solution, it should be possible to determine the molecular weights of the particles by osmotic pressure measurements (§ 30d). However, apart from errors due to traces of electrolytes remaining in the solution, it is necessary to take into consideration the **Donnan equilibrium** (F. G. Donnan, 1911); this arises when a large, nondiffusible ion, e.g., a protein ion, is separated by a diffusion membrane from a diffusible salt. Suppose a solution of sodium chloride of concentration c_1 is separated by a membrane from a solution of a salt NaR of concentration c_2, where R^- is a nondiffusible ion. At equilibrium, a certain amount x of sodium and chloride ions will have passed through the membrane, so that the final state will be as represented below.

Equilibrium State

$$\underset{c_1 - x}{\text{Na}^+} \quad \underset{c_1 - x}{\text{Cl}^-} \quad \bigg| \quad \underset{c_2 + x}{\text{Na}^+} \quad \underset{c_2}{\text{R}^-} \quad \underset{x}{\text{Cl}^-}$$

The condition of electrical neutrality must apply on both sides of the membrane, and so the total concentration of positive ions is equal to that of the negative ions in each solution. At equilibrium the molar free energy of any substance which is present on both sides of the membrane must be the same

(§ 26c) on each side; this will apply, in particular, to the sodium chloride. Consequently, according to equation (31.7)

$$F^0 + RT \ln a_{NaCl(1)} = F^0 + RT \ln a_{NaCl(2)},$$

where a_{NaCl} represents the activity of the sodium chloride, and the symbols (1) and (2) refer to the solutions in equilibrium on the two sides of the membrane. It follows from this result that

$$a_{NaCl(1)} = a_{NaCl(2)}$$

or

$$a_{Na^+(1)} \times a_{Cl^-(1)} = a_{Na^+(2)} \times a_{Cl^-(2)}, \tag{57.3}$$

since the activity of the salt may be taken as the geometric mean of the activities of its component ions (§ 50a). If the solutions are dilute, the ionic activities may be replaced by the corresponding concentrations; if the symbol (1) refers to the solution on the left-hand side of the membrane, and (2) to the solution on the right-hand side, equation (57.3) leads to the result

$$(c_1 - x)(c_1 - x) = (c_2 + x)x,$$

$$\frac{x}{c_1} = \frac{c_1}{c_2 + 2c_1}. \tag{57.4}$$

It is clear from this equation that the presence of the nondiffusible ion R^- influences the extent of diffusion of the sodium chloride. The fraction x/c_1 represents the proportion of sodium chloride initially present on one side of the membrane which has diffused through to the other side when equilibrium is attained; this is seen to be smaller the larger the concentration c_2 of the nondiffusible ion. If c_2 is small in comparison with the salt concentration c_1, the former may be neglected in comparison with $2c_1$ in equation (57.4); under these conditions, x becomes equal to $\frac{1}{2}c_1$, so that the sodium chloride is almost equally distributed on both sides of the membrane.

Problem: A 0.01 molar solution of NaR, where R is a nondiffusible ion, is placed on one side of a membrane; on the other side is placed (i) 0.01 molar NaCl, (ii) 1.0 molar NaCl. Calculate the ratio of NaCl on the two sides when equilibrium is attained in each case.

At equilibrium, the concentration of NaCl on the left-hand side of the membrane is $c_1 - x$, while that on the right-hand side, i.e., on the side containing the nondiffusible ion, is x; the ratio is $(c_1 - x)/x$, and it is readily shown by equation (57.4)

$$\frac{c_1 - x}{x} = \frac{c_1 + c_2}{c_1},$$

where c_2 is the concentration of NaR.

(i) In this case, c_1 is 0.01 and c_2 is 0.01; hence, the required ratio is

$$\frac{c_1 + c_2}{c_1} = \frac{0.01 + 0.01}{0.01} = \frac{2}{1}.$$

(ii) The value of c_1 is now 1.0, while c_2 is still 0.01; hence

$$\frac{c_1 + c_2}{c_1} = \frac{1.0 + 0.01}{1.0} = \frac{1.01}{1}.$$

The osmotic pressure across the membrane may be calculated by assuming the approximate van't Hoff relationship $\Pi = RTc$, where in the present case c is the difference in the molar concentrations on the two sides of the membrane; hence, for the equilibrium state represented above,

$$\Pi = RT\{[(c_2 + x) + c_2 + x] - [(c_1 - x) + (c_1 - x)]\}$$
$$= 2RT(c_2 - c_1 + 2x). \tag{57.5}$$

If the sodium chloride had been equally distributed on both sides of the membrane, or if there had been no electrolyte, the osmotic pressure would have been $2RTc_2$. The difference between this value and that given by equation (57.5) accounts for the difficulty in determining the molecular weight of a protein by measurement of osmotic pressure. It can be seen that if $2x$ is practically equal to c_1, the osmotic pressure given by equation (57.5) becomes equal to the ideal value $2RTc_2$. As seen above, if the salt concentration c_1 is large in comparison with the concentration c_2 of the nondiffusible ion, x becomes equal to $\frac{1}{2}c_1$, i.e., $2x$ is equal to c_1. Consequently, the effect of the Donnan equilibrium on the osmotic pressure can be largely eliminated by using a high salt concentration in conjunction with a diffusion membrane. This is the condition frequently used for the determination of the molecular weight of a protein by osmotic pressure measurement.

In these calculations it has been assumed for the sake of simplicity that the diffusible salt has an ion in common, viz., the Na^+ ion, with the substance NaR. A Donnan equilibrium will apply, however, even if this is not the case, e.g., if the electrolyte is potassium chloride, although the situation will now be complicated by the diffusion of Na^+, K^+ and Cl^- ions.

There have been numerous applications of the Donnan equilibrium in connection with the interpretation of biological and other phenomena; reference to one of these will be made below.

571. The Properties of Gels.—Under certain conditions it is possible to coagulate a sol, particularly a lyophilic sol, in such a manner as to yield *a semi-rigid, jelly-like mass which includes the whole of the liquid present in the sol;* this product is known as a **gel**. The properties of gels divide them into two types, namely, **elastic gels** and **nonelastic gels**. A typical elastic gel is that of gelatin, obtained by cooling the lyophilic sol that results when this substance is warmed with water. Other lyophilic sols, provided they are not too dilute, yield elastic gels upon cooling; examples are agar, starch and pectin sols in water. Such familiar food products as gelatin jellies, fruit jams and jellies, and cornstarch puddings are gels of this type. Solutions of soaps, which form a special group of colloidal substances possessing appreciable electrical conductance, also set to elastic gels.

The best known example of a nonelastic gel is that of silicic acid, usually known as silica gel; this is obtained by mixing solutions of sodium silicate and hydrochloric acid at appropriate concentrations. Under some conditions the whole system sets to a gel immediately, but in other cases the setting process takes a little time. Similar gels of other hydrated oxides, e.g., ferric oxide, have been prepared. The familiar gelatinous precipitates of metallic hydroxides or hydrated oxides, such as those of iron, aluminum, chromium, tin and lead, are probably related to the nonelastic gels; these precipitates are, however, not true gels because they do not include the whole of the water present.

The elastic and nonelastic gels are distinguished primarily by their behavior upon dehydration and rehydration. Partial dehydration of an elastic (gelatin) gel leads to the formation of an elastic solid from which the original sol may be readily regenerated by the addition of water, and warming if necessary. A nonelastic (silica) gel, on the other hand, becomes glassy or falls to a powder, and loses its elasticity on drying. When a gelatin gel is dehydrated, the vapor pressure decreases continuously, and rehydration by exposure to water vapor takes place almost reversibly over the whole range from completely dry to wet gel. Dehydration of a silica gel is quite different; the vapor pressure exhibits discontinuities, and upon rehydration there is reversibility only for the almost dry gel. The essential difference between elastic and nonelastic gels is attributed to the rigidity of the walls of the capillaries formed when the latter gels are dehydrated, whereas with the former gels these walls are flexible. Dehydrated silica gel is so honeycombed with fine capillaries that it is a most valuable adsorbing agent, as mentioned earlier.

After an elastic gel has taken up as much liquid, e.g., water, as possible from the vapor phase, it can still imbibe considerable amounts when actually placed in the liquid. The phenomenon is referred to as **imbibition** or **swelling,** because of the marked increase in the dimensions of the gel. The swelling of gels is influenced by electrolytes, the effect of various ions corresponding exactly with the lyotropic or Hofmeister series, referred to in § 57i. If ions are arranged in order of their ability to inhibit swelling, the order will be identical with that given previously. When swelling is considerable, as in solutions of iodides and thiocyanates, the gel often disperses to form a sol spontaneously; in other cases, the sol is formed by warming the gel. The Hofmeister series may thus be taken as giving the order of temperature to which a swollen gel must be heated, in the presence of various ions, before it is transformed into a sol. Similarly, the same series, in reverse, gives the order of temperatures to which the sol must be cooled before it sets to a gel.

The swelling of elastic protein gels has been explained by means of the Donnan equilibrium. Except at the isoelectric point, a protein consists of an ionized substance with a large nondiffusible ion, and if the substance is in gel form, the gel will act as a Donnan membrane. As a result, when equilibrium is established the total ionic concentration will be greater within the gel than in the solution in which the gel is placed [equation (57.4)]; osmotic flow will, therefore, occur and water will be drawn into the gel, thus causing swelling to take place.

Nonelastic gels do not exhibit the phenomenon of swelling, although when moderately dry they are capable of taking up appreciable quantities of liquid without undergoing any marked volume change. The liquid evidently enters the pores of the gel, and since the walls are rigid, as noted above, the volume of the gel does not alter. Another characteristic difference between elastic and nonelastic gels arises in connection with the imbibition of liquid; in the former case the imbibition is selective, while in the latter it is more general. Thus, a gelatin gel will take up water but not alcohol, while silica gel will absorb both; in general, a nonelastic gel will take up any liquid by which it is wetted (§ 17b).

There is ample evidence that the transition from sol to gel, and the reverse, takes place gradually, at least with elastic gels; this suggests that there is no essential difference in the structure of sol and gel. The view widely accepted at the present time is that in the course of gelation, i.e., formation of the gel, the particles in the sol gradually unite to form short chains or threads; these become interlocked, so that the viscosity of the system increases, and eventually a semi-solid form is acquired. Part of the dispersion medium may exist as water of hydration of the chains of particles, but the major portion is believed to be held by capillary forces between the threads. This theory of the formation of gel from sol gives a satisfactory picture of the structure of a gel. The same type of structure, of *interlocking solvated threads enclosing the liquid dispersion medium,* is probably applicable to both elastic and nonelastic gels; the difference between them depends on the physical and chemical nature of the material constituting the disperse phase, i.e., the particles of the sol, which forms the threads.

57m. Emulsions.—An **emulsion** consists of *small drops of one liquid dispersed in another liquid;* the globules or droplets of dispersed liquid are from 0.1 to 1 μ in diameter, and hence are larger than those found in sols. Common examples of emulsions are milk and mayonnaise, which consist of small drops of liquid fat dispersed in an aqueous medium; in cod-liver oil emulsions used in pharmacy globules of water are dispersed in the oil. If a hydrocarbon oil is shaken with water, or if a liquid which is immiscible or partially miscible with water, e.g., aniline or nitrobenzene, is distilled in steam, or if a solution of the organic liquid in alcohol or acetone is poured into an excess of water, a faintly milky system is often obtained; this is a weak emulsion of the **oil in water** type. In these emulsions the disperse phase consists of small drops of oil dispersed in water. The term "oil" is used in connection with emulsions to represent the organic substance insoluble in water, since this is frequently, but not necessarily, a hydrocarbon oil, a vegetable oil, or other liquid fat. In some emulsions the water is in the form of droplets dispersed in a continuous medium of oil; these are known as the **water in oil** type of emulsions.

Several methods are available for distinguishing between emulsions of the two types; the simplest is to place a small quantity of the emulsion under a microscope and to stir into it a drop of either oil or water. If the emulsion is the oil in water type, the water will mix readily but not the oil, since the former is the continuous medium. On the other hand, a water in oil emulsion mixes freely with oil but not with water.

Emulsions are generally unstable unless a third substance, known as an **emulsifying agent,** is present; such an agent makes possible the preparation of emulsions containing relatively large proportions of disperse phase. The most frequently employed emulsifying agents fall into three categories; first, certain long-chain compounds with polar groups, such as the soaps and long-chain sulfonic acids and sulfates, which are now classified under the general heading of **detergents.** It may be noted that the cleansing action of these detergents is ascribed to their emulsifying properties; by breaking up grease and oil into minute droplets they facilitate their removal together with the accompanying dirt. The second group of emulsifying agents are lyophilic substances, such as proteins, gums and agar; in milk, for example, the emulsifying agent is the protein casein, while in mayonnaise the stability of the emulsion is largely due to the presence of egg albumin. The third category of emulsifiers consists of certain insoluble powders, e.g., basic sulfates of iron, copper or nickel, lead sulfate, ferric oxide and lamp black.

The soaps of alkali metals favor the formation of oil in water emulsions, but those of higher valence metals, such as the alkaline earth metals, zinc, iron and aluminum, yield water in oil emulsions. It is for this reason that an emulsion of a hydrocarbon oil in water, with a sodium or potassium soap as emulsifier, may be converted into a water in oil emulsion by the addition of a salt of a bi- or tri-valent metal. The latter substance reacts with the alkali metal soap, producing a soap of the higher valence metal which stabilizes the water in oil type of emulsion.

57n. Stability of Emulsions.—Because of the forces of surface tension at an interface, the latter tends to become as small as possible (§ 17a); in an emulsion, however, the area of separation between the droplets of disperse phase and the dispersion medium is very large. This means that the interfacial tension is small, and it seems to be the function of the emulsifying agent to decrease the tension at the oil-water interface. Emulsifiers of the detergent type, e.g., soap, usually consist of a hydrocarbon chain and a polar group; when added to an oil and water system, the hydrocarbon chain will attach itself to the oil while the polar group will be attracted to the water (§ 56f). There will then be two interfaces to consider, viz., one between the oil and soap (I), and the other between soap and the water (II). If the interfacial tension at the former, i.e., γ_I, is greater than that of the latter, i.e., γ_{II}, the oil-soap interface (I) will tend to have a smaller area than the soap-water interface, as shown in Fig. 123A. This condition can be realized if the water surrounds the oil, and hence an oil in water type of emulsion will be stabilized. If the relative values of the two interfacial tensions are reversed, as in Fig. 123B, a water in oil type of emulsion will have preferred stability.

The foregoing considerations provide a basis for the interpretation of the behavior of different soaps in stabilizing emulsions of different types. If the soap is preferentially adsorbed, or wetted, by the water, or, in more general terms, has a greater attraction for the water than for the oil, the water-soap interfacial tension γ_{II} will be reduced, in accordance with the requirement of the Gibbs equation (56.9); an oil in water emulsion will then be stable. The soaps of the alkali metals are of this type, and so their influence in stabilizing oil in water emulsions can be understood. On the other hand, it is an experimental fact that the soaps of calcium, magnesium and other high valence metals, have a greater attraction for oil than for water; in this event, the oil-soap interfacial tension γ_I is diminished, and the water in oil type of emulsion will be preferred.

Such "dilute" emulsions as are obtained in the absence of an emulsifying agent possess properties similar to those of lyophobic sols. The globules show Brownian movement, provided they are not too large; they carry a negative electrical charge, and can be "coagulated" by electrolytes, particu-

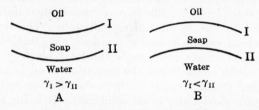

FIG. 123. The stability of emulsions

larly by positive ions of high valence. The droplets exhibit electrophoresis, and the mobility is of the same order as for colloidal particles, viz., about 4×10^{-4} cm. per sec. for a potential gradient of 1 volt per cm. The electrokinetic potential at the oil-water interface, calculated from the electrophoretic mobility, is about 0.05 volt. It is probable that these "dilute" emulsions owe their stability to the existence of this potential at the interface.

It is of interest to note that emulsions stabilized by an emulsifying agent resemble lyophilic, rather than lyophobic, sols. They can be obtained with relatively high concentrations, have a high viscosity, and are not greatly affected by electrolytes, unless they react chemically with the emulsifier. An excess of electrolyte may "salt out" the latter, and so cause the emulsion to become unstable.

Emulsions may be "broken," that is, converted into two separate liquid layers, in several ways; the process is sometimes referred to as **demulsification**. Chemical destruction of the emulsifying agent is effective in this respect; for example, the addition of an acid converts a soap into the corresponding fatty acid which is not an emulsifier. Physical methods, such as heating, freezing and centrifuging, are often employed for breaking emulsions. The conversion of cream into butter by churning is an example of the breaking of an emulsion of fat in water; in the separation of cream from milk use is made of centrifuging to bring about demulsification.

READING REFERENCES

1. **Electrodialysis.** Kendall and Fuelnegg, *Journal of Chemical Education*, **8,** 1634 (1931).
2. **Colloids** (historical). Gortner, *ibid.*, **11,** 279 (1934).
3. **Surface energy experiment.** Caldwell, *ibid.*, **12,** 444 (1935).
4. **Silicic acid gels.** Hurd, *ibid.*, **14,** 84 (1937).
5. **Chromatographic analysis.** Cassidy, *ibid.*, **16,** 88 (1939).
6. **Electrokinetic phenomena.** Horowitz, *ibid.*, **16,** 519 (1939).
7. **Demonstration of adsorption.** Smith, *ibid.*, **18,** 432 (1941).
8. **Colloids in daily life.** Hauser, *ibid.*, **18,** 590 (1941).
9. **Unimolecular films.** Kuehner, *ibid.*, **19,** 27 (1942).
10. **Electroosmosis.** Porter, *ibid.*, **19,** 533 (1942).
11. **Wetting agents.** Sluhan, *ibid.*, **20,** 38 (1943).
12. **Wetting and spreading.** Bircher, *ibid.*, **20,** 428 (1943).
13. **Chromatographic adsorption.** Eliel, *ibid.*, **21,** 583 (1944).

REVIEW QUESTIONS

1. Define the term adsorption and illustrate with reference to the adsorption of gases by solids. Show by means of an equation and a figure how the adsorption varies with the pressure of the gas.

2. Describe the characteristic properties of the two main types of gaseous adsorption.

3. Derive the Langmuir adsorption isotherm, stating the assumptions upon which it is based. Show how the isotherm may be tested by a graphical method.

4. To what form does the Langmuir isotherm reduce (a) at low pressures, (b) at high pressures? What is the significance of the result in the latter case?

5. Write down the Gibbs adsorption equation. Show how it leads to an understanding of adsorption from solution. Why are substances adsorbed from water often dissolved out again by ethanol?

6. State the isotherm generally employed to represent adsorption from solutions of different concentrations. Explain its meaning.

7. What types of substances form unimolecular films (monolayers) on water? Describe some of the important properties of such films.

8. What are the characteristic properties of colloidal solutions? How do they differ from true solutions?

9. Define the terms disperse phase, dispersion medium, sol, lyophobic, and lyophilic. Describe the chief methods for the preparation of colloidal solutions.

10. Explain the purification of colloidal solutions by (a) dialysis, (b) electrodialysis, (c) ultrafiltration.

12. What is the Tyndall effect? How is it utilized in the ultramicroscope to render colloidal particles visible?

13. Describe the phenomenon of electrophoresis. To what is it due and how is it studied? What is the magnitude of electrophoretic mobilities?

14. Explain the influence of small amounts of ions in favoring the stability of colloidal systems. What suggestions have been made concerning the structure of colloidal particles?

15. Describe the effect of appreciable concentrations of electrolytes on colloidal solutions. How are the results explained?

16. Define and explain the terms protective action, protective colloid, gold number.

17. Describe the structure of the electrical double layer at a solid-liquid surface. How may the results be applied to colloidal particles?

18. What is electroosmosis? How is it affected by electrolytes, and how are the results explained?

19. Explain how the electrokinetic (zeta) potential can be determined from (a) electrophoresis, (b) streaming potential.

20. Describe the electrophoretic properties of lyophilic sols. How are they utilized for the separation of proteins? What is meant by the isoelectric point of a protein sol?

21. What are the factors which determine the stability of a lyophilic sol? Give reasons.

22. What is meant by the lyotropic (Hofmeister) series as regards (a) the precipitating effect of an ion, (b) the swelling of gels?

23. Describe the ultracentrifuge method for determining the particle molecular weights of proteins.

24. What is the Donnan membrane equilibrium? Explain its importance in connection with the measurement of the osmotic pressure of a protein sol.

25. Write an account of the properties and structure of (a) elastic gels, (b) nonelastic gels.

26. What is an emulsion? Describe the two main types of emulsions. How may they be distinguished?

27. Describe the three main types of emulsifying agents. Give examples of their action.

28. Show how the stability of emulsions can be accounted for in terms of interfacial tensions.

29. Dilute unstabilized emulsions are said to resemble lyophobic sols, while stabilized emulsions are like lyophilic sols. Justify this statement.

PROBLEMS

I

1. In the adsorption of carbon monoxide on mica at $90°$ K, the volume of gas adsorbed, reduced to S.T.P., was 1.082 ml. and 1.769 ml., for a constant weight of mica, at pressures of 5.60×10^{-4} and 5.45×10^{-3} mm., respectively. By means of (a) the classical adsorption isotherm, equation (56.1), and (b) the Langmuir equation (56.6), calculate the volume adsorbed, measured at S.T.P., by the same weight of mica at a pressure of 10^{-3} mm.

2. In the measurements described in the preceding problem, a limiting adsorption of 2.00 ml. (at S.T.P.) of carbon monoxide was approached as the pressure was increased. Assuming the formation of a single layer of carbon monoxide molecules, each with an effective diameter of 3.5 Å, estimate the area of the mica.

3. In the adsorption of acetic acid from aqueous solution by charcoal the following results were obtained at equilibrium:

| c | 0.365 | 0.84 | 1.45 | 2.06 | 3.50 g. per liter |
| a | 0.186 | 0.230 | 0.250 | 0.286 | 0.324 g. per g. |

Test the validity of (a) the classical adsorption equation (56.10), (b) the Langmuir adsorption isotherm, by means of these data.

4. The spherical particles in a mercury sol have a diameter of 22×10^{-7} cm. A liter of the sol contains 0.080 g. of mercury; how many particles are present in 1 ml. of the sol, and what is their total area?

5. A quantity of gold sol containing 50 mg. of gold per liter was diluted 1000 times and examined in the ultramicroscope. The total number of particles observed in twenty successive counts was 65, the field of vision having an area of 1.2×10^{-5} sq. cm., with a light beam depth of 2.0×10^{-3} cm. Assuming the gold particles to be spherical, and to have the same density as solid gold (19.3 g. per cc.), calculate their mean radius.

6. In an experiment with an aqueous protein sol in the ultracentrifuge, the ratio n_1/n_2 was estimated photographically to be 1.82 at equilibrium for distances x_1 and x_2 of 4.24 and 4.01 cm., at 22° C. The speed of the rotor was 152 rotations per sec. The density of the solvent may be taken as unity, and that of the protein particles as 1.33. Calculate the particle molecular weight of the protein.

7. A 0.005 molal solution of Congo red (NaR), which is the salt of a nondiffusible ion (R^-), was placed on one side of a membrane, and 0.015 molal sodium chloride on the other side. Determine the concentrations of Na^+, Cl^- and R^- ions on the two sides of the membrane at equilibrium.

8. A solution of 0.0422 g. of a spreading compound, consisting of a single hydrocarbon chain with a polar end group, was made in 25.05 g. benzene. When ten drops of this solution, each weighing 2.06×10^{-3} g., was placed on water, the resulting film began to show marked resistance to further compression when the area was 286 sq. cm. Estimate the approximate molecular weight of the compound.

II

1. The following results were obtained for the adsorption of carbon dioxide on a constant weight of charcoal at 0° C at various pressures:

p	25.1	137.4	416.4	858.6 mm.
a	0.77	1.78	2.26	2.42 mg.

Employ these data to test the validity of (a) the classical adsorption equation (56.1), (b) the Langmuir adsorption equation.

2. From the slope of the line plotted according to the Langmuir equation, in the preceding problem, estimate the value of k_1/k_2, and hence the limiting adsorption, according to equation (56.8). If the diameter of the molecule of carbon dioxide is 3.5 Å, determine the surface area of the charcoal, assuming the formation of a unimolecular layer.

3. In the adsorption of acetic acid from aqueous solution by charcoal, the values of the amounts a adsorbed were found to be 0.467×10^{-3} and 2.48×10^{-3} mole per g. of charcoal, when the equilibrium concentrations c of the solution were 0.0181 and 0.882 mole per liter, respectively. One liter of a 0.250 molar solution of acetic acid was shaken with 50 g. of charcoal; calculate the concentration of the residual solution at equilibrium, assuming the adsorption equation (56.10).

4. A ferric oxide sol, known to contain particles of an average radius of 40×10^{-7} cm., was diluted 5000 fold; upon examination in the ultramicroscope, in which the field of vision had a volume of 2.4×10^{-8} cc., a total of 72 particles were observed in 25 successive counts. Assuming the particles to be spherical, and to have a density of 5.2, determine the concentration of the original solution.

5. Calculate the number of ferric oxide particles present in 1 ml. of the sol referred to in the preceding problem. What is their total area?

6. In an experiment with an aqueous protein sol in the ultracentrifuge, the ratio n_1/n_2 was estimated photographically to be 1.13 at equilibrium for distances x_1 and x_2 of 4.12 and 4.04 cm., respectively, at 20° C. The speed of the rotor was 172 rota-

tions per sec. The density of the solvent may be taken as unity, and that of the protein particles as 1.36. Calculate the particle molecular weight of the protein.

7. In a membrane distribution experiment with potassium chloride and the potassium salt KR, of the nondiffusible ion R$^-$, it was found at equilibrium that the solution on one side of the membrane contained 0.0298 mole KCl per liter, while on the other side there were 0.0222 mole KCl and 0.0178 mole KR per liter. Neglecting activity corrections, how close are these results to those expected theoretically?

8. When 5.13×10^{-5} g. of tristearin, i.e., the triglyceryl ester of stearic acid, $C_3H_5(COOC_{17}H_{35})_3$, was spread upon water, it was found that the film showed appreciable resistance to further compression when the area was 220 sq. cm. Calculate the area of cross section per single molecule of tristearin. What conclusion may be drawn from the result concerning the orientation of the molecules on the surface of water? (Note that the molecule of tristearin has three hydrocarbon chains.)

CHAPTER XVIII

KINETICS OF CHEMICAL REACTIONS

ORDER OF REACTION

58a. Chemical Kinetics.—Every chemical reaction takes place at a definite rate depending on the experimental conditions; the most important of these are the concentrations (or pressures) of the reacting substances, temperature, the presence of a catalyst, and radiation, e.g., light of suitable wave length. Some reactions are so rapid that they appear to be instantaneous, e.g., the neutralization of an acid by a base in aqueous solution, while others are so slow at ordinary temperatures, e.g., the combination of hydrogen and oxygen, in the absence of a catalyst, that no detectable change would be observed in many years. Between these two extremes there are many processes, involving both inorganic and organic compounds, taking place with measurable velocities at temperatures that are easily accessible in the laboratory. Many reactions involving gases, such as the combination of hydrogen and oxygen, are extremely slow at ordinary temperatures, but occur with appreciable velocities when the temperature is raised to about 600° C or more. It is the study of the rates of chemical reactions and of

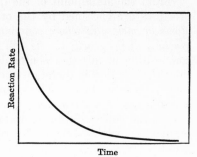

FIG. 124. Change of rate of reaction with time

the influence of conditions on these rates that constitute the experimental basis of the subject of **reaction kinetics.**

By the law of mass action, considered in § 32b, the rate of a chemical reaction is proportional to the concentrations (or pressures) of the reacting substances; since the latter are being continuously consumed in the course of the reaction, their concentrations (or pressures) must be decreasing steadily. It follows, therefore, that the reaction rate must vary with time, somewhat in the manner of Fig. 124, the process becoming slower and slower as the reactants are used up. It is obviously not a simple matter to define the general rate of a given reaction, and so in practice the rate is considered at a particular instant; by a simple mathematical treatment it is possible to obtain certain constants that are characteristic of the reaction at each temperature.

In the study of chemical kinetics it is convenient to classify reactions according to their **molecularity**; this is *the number of atoms or molecules taking part in each act leading to chemical reaction.* If one molecule only is involved, the reaction is said to the **unimolecular**; an illustration of this type of process is the decomposition of nitrogen pentoxide, either in the gas phase or in solution, viz.,

$$N_2O_5 = N_2O_4 + \tfrac{1}{2}O_2.$$

The dissociation of gaseous hydrogen iodide has been shown to be a **bimolecular** reaction, since two molecules take part, thus

$$2HI = H_2 + I_2,$$

and *not* $HI = \tfrac{1}{2}H_2 + \tfrac{1}{2}I_2$. Another type of bimolecular reaction is the hydrolysis of an ester, e.g.,

$$CH_3COOC_2H_5 + H_2O = CH_3COOH + C_2H_5OH.$$

If three molecules are involved in each chemical act, the process is said to be **termolecular**; an instance of this type is the reaction

$$2NO + O_2 = 2NO_2.$$

From the standpoint of the quantitative consideration of reaction rates, processes are classified by the **order of the reaction,** that is, *the number of atoms or molecules whose concentrations (or pressures) determine the rate (or kinetics) of the reaction.* As will be seen presently, the rate of thermal decomposition of nitrogen pentoxide is directly proportional to its concentration; the reaction is therefore said to be of the **first order,** as well as unimolecular, as seen above. The hydrolysis of an ester in dilute aqueous solution is also a first order reaction, although the process is bimolecular; the reason is that the concentration of water, which is one of the reactants, does not change appreciably because it is present in large excess. The rate of the reaction is then determined by the concentration of one molecule only, viz., that of the ester.

The dissociation of hydrogen iodide is a **second order** reaction, as well as being bimolecular; experiments have shown that the reaction rate is proportional to the *square* of the hydrogen iodide concentration, indicating that the concentrations of two molecules are involved. The reaction between nitric oxide and oxygen, represented above, is **third order,** and also termolecular. It is seen that the molecularity and the order of a reaction are often identical, although in certain cases they are different; both quantities are important in connection with the problems of the detailed mechanisms of chemical reactions. This is one of the main purposes of the study of reaction kinetics.

It is hardly necessary to emphasize the fact that chemical processes are not always simple; complications due to reversible reactions, or to two or more reactions occurring consecutively, or to other causes, often arise. It will be convenient, however, to consider in the first place what have been called **isolated reactions,** which are free from secondary effects; the influence of disturbing factors will be referred to later. Further, it is desirable to distinguish clearly between **homogeneous reactions,** which take place entirely in one phase, either gas or solution, and **heterogeneous reactions,** involving two phases, e.g., gas and solid, or solution and solid. The treatment will be restricted first to homogeneous reactions. As already indicated, temperature alters the rate of a reaction, and so it will be assumed that the temperature remains constant while a particular reaction is being studied; subsequently the influence of temperature will be examined in some detail.

Various procedures have been used for following the rates of chemical reactions; both physical and chemical methods have been applied to determine the quantities of the reacting substances still remaining, or of the products that have been formed, after a series of time intervals. The particular procedure adopted depends on the nature of the reactants and the products, and also on the temperature. Illustrations of the different methods are given below in connection with the consideration of reactions of various types.

58b. Reactions of the First Order.—In a first order reaction the rate is directly proportional to the concentration of the reacting substance; this condition can be expressed mathematically by

$$-\frac{dc}{dt} = kc, \tag{58.1}$$

where c is the concentration of the reacting substance, and k is a proportionality constant. According to equation (58.1), the rate of decrease of the concentration with time, i.e., $-dc/dt$, at any instant represented by the time t, is proportional to the concentration c, at that instant. The proportionality constant k is called the **velocity constant** or **rate constant** or, more generally, the **specific reaction rate.** The reason for the latter title can be readily seen in the following manner. The left-hand side of equation (58.1) represents the reaction rate; hence, k is equal to the reaction rate for unit concentration, that is, when c on the right-hand side is unity. The specific reaction rate is a constant for the given reaction at a definite temperature; it is evident from equation (58.1) that the reaction rate at any instant is obtained upon multiplying this constant by the concentration of the reactant at that instant.

Although equation (58.1) is the fundamental characteristic equation for a first order reaction, it is convenient for practical purposes to put it in another form. Suppose a is the initial concentration of the reacting substance, i.e., the amount in moles initially present in a given volume, and let x be the decrease (or change) after the lapse of time t; the amount remaining in the given volume will then be $a - x$, and this may be identified with the concentration c at any instant. Making this substitution in equation (58.1), the result is

$$-\frac{d(a - x)}{dt} = k(a - x),$$

and since the initial concentration a is a constant, $-d(a - x)/dt$ is equal to dx/dt; hence

$$\frac{dx}{dt} = k(a - x), \tag{58.2}$$

where dx/dt is an alternative expression for the reaction rate at any instant. Upon slight rearrangement of equation (58.2), it is possible to carry out the integration of this equation

$$k \int_0^t dt = \int_0^x \frac{dx}{a - x}, \tag{58.3}$$

remembering that when t is zero, i.e., at the beginning of the reaction, the amount x of reactant that has undergone change is zero, whereas after time t, the amount changed is x; the result of the integration is

$$k = \frac{1}{t} \ln \frac{a}{a - x} = \frac{2.303}{t} \log \frac{a}{a - x}. \tag{58.4}$$

This is known as the **kinetic equation** for a reaction of the first order; it provides a means for calculating the specific reaction rate of the given process at a definite temperature.

Before proceeding to consider examples of first order reactions it is of interest to examine some general consequences of equation (58.4). It is seen, in the first place, that the quantity $a/(a - x)$ is a *ratio* of concentrations, and so its value will be independent of the units used to express these concentrations, provided the same units are used for a and x. This fact makes the evaluation of the first order velocity constant particularly simple, for the values of a and $a - x$ can be given in moles per liter, as ml. of a volumetric reagent, as the partial pressure of a gas, or in other ways. Further, since $a/(a - x)$ is a number, independent of the concentration units, it follows from equation (58.4) that the specific reaction rate k has the dimensions of reciprocal time, i.e., t^{-1}; if the time t is given in seconds, as is generally the case, k is expressed in sec.$^{-1}$ units.

Another important characteristic of first order reactions can be derived from equation (58.4) by evaluating the time taken to complete a definite fraction of the reaction; for example, let $t_{0.5}$ be the time required for the concentration of the reacting substance to be reduced to half its initial value, i.e., for x to be equal to $\frac{1}{2}a$. Upon insertion of this value for x into equation (58.4), it is seen that

$$t_{0.5} = \frac{2.303}{k} \log 2 = \frac{0.693}{k}. \tag{58.5}$$

It is evident, therefore, that for any given first order reaction $t_{0.5}$ is a constant, independent of the initial concentration. In other words, the time required to reduce the concentration (or pressure) of the reacting substance to half of its initial value is a constant quantity, for a given first order reaction; thus, it will take the same time to reduce the amount of reactant from

1 mole to 0.5 mole, in a given volume, as is required to decrease the amount from 0.001 to 0.0005 mole, in the same volume. In general, *the time to complete any definite fraction of the reaction is independent of the initial concentration;* this is one of the most striking properties of a first order reaction. It is of interest to mention that the decay of a radioactive element may be regarded as a first order process; it shows the characteristic property of a definite period of half-change which is independent of the initial amount of the particular element.

58c. Examples of First Order Reactions.—The application of equation (58.4) may be illustrated by reference to one of the best known first order reactions, namely the decomposition of nitrogen pentoxide. In the gaseous reaction the over-all process may be represented by

$$N_2O_5(g) = N_2O_4(g) + \tfrac{1}{2}O_2(g),$$

intermediate steps being ignored; for every molecule of pentoxide decomposed there is a net increase of one-half molecule in the reacting system. The partial pressure of the nitrogen pentoxide decomposed, equivalent to x, should thus be equal to double the increase of gas pressure at constant volume, as the reaction proceeds. Unfortunately, the situation is complicated somewhat by the dissociation of the N_2O_4 into $2NO_2$, which causes a further increase of pressure; from a knowledge of the equilibrium constant of this reaction, however, the necessary allowance can be made. It is thus possible from measurements of the total pressure at various times t to determine the partial pressure x of the nitrogen pentoxide decomposed. The initial pressure, expressed in the same units, gives the corresponding value of a, and hence it is possible to calculate the specific rate k by means of equation (58.4). The results obtained in this manner at 35° C are given in Table LXIX (F. Daniels

TABLE LXIX.   DECOMPOSITION OF GASEOUS NITROGEN PENTOXIDE AT 35° C

Initial Pressure $a = 308.2$ mm.

t	x	k sec.$^{-1}$	t	x	k sec.$^{-1}$
1200 sec.	53.8 mm.	1.60×10^{-4}	3600 sec.	121.4 mm.	1.39×10^{-4}
1800	72.7	1.49	6000	171.0	1.33
2400	90.0	1.43	8400	206.8	1.33
3000	106.0	1.40	12000	244.6	1.30

and E. H. Johnston, 1921); the approximate constancy of the k values for various time intervals indicates that the reaction is of the first order.

It may be mentioned that the decomposition of nitrogen pentoxide has also been studied in solution; by choosing a suitable solvent, the N_2O_4 and NO_2 can be retained in the solution while the oxygen is evolved and its volume measured. As seen from the equation for the reaction, every molecule of oxygen produced means two molecules of pentoxide decomposed; hence, the extent of decomposition x at any time t can be obtained. The corresponding value of a, in the same units, is derived from the final volume of oxygen when the nitrogen pentoxide has been completely decomposed.

Instead of calculating the individual values of k from the data at each time interval, a graphical method may be employed to cover the whole of the reaction period. By rearrangement, equation (58.4) becomes

$$t = \frac{2.303}{k} \log a - \frac{2.303}{k} \log (a - x), \qquad (58.6)$$

and since the first term on the right-hand side is constant, it can be seen that the plot of t against $\log (a - x)$ should be linear if the reaction is first order; the slope of the straight line will be equal to $-2.303/k$, thus enabling the

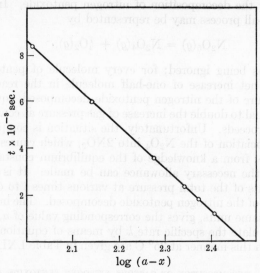

FIG. 125.   Decomposition of gaseous nitrogen pentoxide

rate constant k to be evaluated. The data in Table LXIX are plotted in this manner in Fig. 125; the points are seen to fall close to a straight line. The slope of this line is -1.706×10^4, and consequently k is 1.35×10^{-4}, in agreement with the mean value from Table LXIX.

A different type of first order reaction, as noted earlier, is the hydrolysis of an ester in aqueous solution. Frequently the reaction is too slow to be studied, but the rate is measurable in the presence of a small amount of mineral acid. The latter substance acts as a catalyst; it does not appear in the equation for the reaction, e.g., the hydrolysis of methyl acetate, thus

$$CH_3COOCH_3 + H_2O = CH_3COOH + CH_3OH,$$

and its concentration remains unchanged throughout the reaction. Further, the water is present in such large excess that the concentration of this substance is virtually constant. The kinetics of the reaction are then determined solely by the concentration of the ester; hence, the process is of the first order, and equation (58.4) should be applicable. In order to follow the course of the reaction, a definite volume of the reacting solution, consisting of the ester dissolved in water containing the catalyst, e.g., 0.05 N hydrochloric acid, is withdrawn and titrated with standard alkali. The amount of the titration is equivalent to the total of the hydrochloric acid and the acetic acid produced in the hydrolytic reaction. The titration T_0 at the commencement is equivalent to the catalyst alone, and if T_t is the titration after time t, the difference $T_t - T_0$ is a measure of the acetic acid formed, and hence of the ester decomposed; consequently, $T_t - T_0$ may be identified with x in equation (58.4). After the lapse of sufficient time, when the reaction is virtually complete, the titration T_∞ is equivalent to the catalyst and the acetic acid formed by the hydrolysis of the whole of ester; the difference $T_\infty - T_0$ is thus equivalent to a, the initial concentration of ester. Substitution of these values for a and x in equation (58.4) then gives for the first order reaction

$$k = \frac{2.303}{t} \log \frac{T_\infty - T_0}{T_\infty - T_t}.$$

The results of an actual experiment on the hydrolysis of methyl acetate at 25° C, using 0.05 N hydrochloric acid as catalyst, are recorded in Table LXX;

TABLE LXX. HYDROLYSIS OF METHYL ACETATE AT 25° C

t sec.	T ml.	k sec.$^{-1}$
0	$24.36 = T_0$	—
1200	25.85	5.62×10^{-5}
4500	29.32	5.46
7140	31.72	5.44
∞	$47.15 = T_\infty$	—

in accordance with what has been already stated, the value of k is independent of the units employed for expressing a and x, and so the concentration of the alkali used for the titration is immaterial. The approximate constancy of the results in the last column supports the view that the reaction is first order, in spite of the fact that two molecules of reactant, apart from the catalyst, are involved.

Another reaction of the same type is the hydrolysis or "inversion" of sucrose, viz.,

$$C_{12}H_{22}O_{11} + H_2O = C_6H_{12}O_6 + C_6H_{12}O_6,$$

sucrose   dextrose   levulose

which is also catalyzed by acids. The course of the reaction can be followed by measuring, in a polarimeter, the angle of rotation of polarized light; sucrose rotates the plane of polarization to the right, whereas the mixture of dextrose and levulose produced upon hydrolysis has a rotation in the opposite direction. If α_0 and α_∞ are the angles of rotation, including the correct signs, at the beginning and when the reaction is complete, respectively, and α_t is the value after time t, then $\alpha_0 - \alpha_\infty$ is proportional to the initial amount a

of sucrose, and $\alpha_0 - \alpha_t$ is equivalent to $a - x$, the amount still remaining after the time t. It follows then from equation (58.4) that

$$k = \frac{2.303}{t} \log \frac{\alpha_0 - \alpha_\infty}{\alpha_0 - \alpha_t},$$

and it has been verified that the experimental values of k calculated from this expression are constant over the whole period of the inversion process.

58d. Reactions of the Second Order.—The rate of a second order reaction depends on two concentration terms; these may both refer to the same reactant, as in the dissociation of gaseous hydrogen iodide, or to two different reactants. If the two reacting molecules are the same, the general reaction would be written as

$$2A \rightarrow \text{products},$$

and the rate would be given by the expression

$$-\frac{dc_A}{dt} = kc_A^2, \tag{58.7}$$

where c_A is the concentration of the reactant A at any time t. If a is the initial amount, in moles, of the reactant A present in a given volume, and x is the amount which has been removed by reaction after the lapse of time t, the quantity $a - x$ remaining may be identified with c_A in equation (58.7); the latter thus becomes

$$-\frac{d(a - x)}{dt} = \frac{dx}{dt} = k(a - x)^2.$$

Upon integration between the limits of t from 0 to t, and of x from 0 to x, as before, the result is

$$k = \frac{1}{t}\left(\frac{1}{a - x} - \frac{1}{a}\right) = \frac{1}{t} \cdot \frac{x}{a(a - x)}. \tag{58.8}$$

A second order reaction involving one molecule of each of two different reacting substances A and B may be represented by

$$A + B \rightarrow \text{products},$$

so that the reaction rate is given by

$$-\frac{dc_A}{dt} = -\frac{dc_B}{dt} = kc_A c_B \tag{58.9}$$

in place of equation (58.7). If a and b represent the initial molar amounts of A and B, respectively, in a given volume, and x is the amount of each that has reacted after time t, the concentrations c_A and c_B will be $a - x$ and $b - x$, respectively; equation (58.9) then becomes

$$\frac{dx}{dt} = k(a - x)(b - x), \tag{58.10}$$

which upon integration, by the method of partial fractions, yields

$$k = \frac{1}{t(a - b)} \ln \frac{b(a - x)}{a(b - x)} = \frac{2.303}{t(a - b)} \log \frac{b(a - x)}{a(b - x)}. \tag{58.11}$$

An examination of equations (58.8) and (58.11) shows that the second order rate constant differs from that for a first order reaction in being dependent on the units employed to express the concentrations. It can be seen that there is one more concentration term in the denominator than in the numerator, and so the specific reaction rate is expressed in conc.$^{-1}$ time^{-1} units. If the time is in seconds, and the concentrations in moles per liter, the specific rate will be in (moles/liter)$^{-1}$ sec.$^{-1}$ or liters mole^{-1} sec.$^{-1}$.

The time taken for the initial concentration of the reactants in a bimolecular reaction to be reduced by a definite fraction may be readily calculated; the time $t_{0.5}$ for the concentration, which is taken as being the same for A and B, to be reduced to one-half of its initial value, is given by substituting $\frac{1}{2}a$ for x in equation (58.8). The result is

$$t_{0.5} = \frac{1}{ka}, \tag{58.12}$$

so that the time is inversely proportional to the initial concentration of the reactants; hence, the greater the initial concentration the smaller the time required to reduce it to one-half. The same relationship applies for the completion of any other definite fraction of the reaction. The difference in this respect between first and second order reactions is very striking, and permits them to be distinguished from one another.

58e. Examples of Second Order Reactions.—Although the dissociation of hydrogen iodide is a second order process, its study is rendered somewhat complicated by the fact that the reaction is reversible, and so requires special treatment (§ 58i). There are relatively few gas reactions that are definitely of the second order, free from secondary effects; among these, mention may be made of the combination of hydrogen and ethylene to yield ethane. The reaction rate in this case may be followed by measurement of the decrease of pressure.

There are, however, a large number of processes taking place in solution that are kinetically of the second order; one of the most familiar of these is the alkaline hydrolysis, or saponification, of an ester, e.g.,

$$CH_3COOC_2H_5 + OH^- = CH_3COO^- + C_2H_5OH.$$

This differs from the hydrolysis in acid solution considered in § 58c, because the two reactants are present in more or less similar amounts; the concentrations of both change appreciably during the reaction, and hence affect the reaction rate. The course of the reaction has been followed in several different ways: one method makes use of the fact that the removal of the hydroxyl ions and their replacement by acetate ions is accompanied by a decrease in the conductance of the reacting system. From this decrease, the extent of the reaction can be calculated. In the second method, definite quantities of the reacting solution are withdrawn from time to time, and the amount of alkali $b - x$ that remains is determined by titration. If the initial concentrations of ester and hydroxide, i.e., a and b, are known, the value of $a - x$ may be obtained, and hence the specific rate k can be calculated from equation (58.11). Some experimental data for the reaction between ethyl ace-

TABLE LXXI.   ALKALINE HYDROLYSIS OF ETHYL ACETATE AT 15.8° C

$$a = 0.01211 \text{ mole per liter}$$
$$b = 0.02578$$

t sec.	$a - x$ mole liter^{-1}	$b - x$ mole liter^{-1}	k liter mole^{-1} sec.$^{-1}$
224	0.00889	0.02256	5.74×10^{-2}
377	0.00734	0.02101	5.74
629	0.00554	0.01921	5.68
816	0.00454	0.01821	5.68

tate (A) and sodium hydroxide (B) at 15.8° C are recorded in Table LXXI; the results in the final column are seen to be constant, within the limits of experimental error.

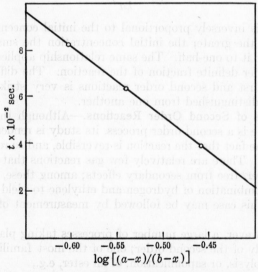

FIG. 126.   Alkaline hydrolysis of ethyl acetate

The measurements of second order reactions may also be treated in a graphical manner; thus, if equation (58.11) is written in the form

$$t = \frac{2.303}{k(a - b)} \log \frac{b}{a} + \frac{2.303}{k(a - b)} \log \frac{a - x}{b - x},$$

it is seen that since a and b are constants, the plot of t against $\log [(a - x)/(b - x)]$ should be a straight line of slope equal to $2.303/k(a - b)$. The results of Table LXXI are plotted in Fig. 126; the slope of the line is -2970, and hence the over-all value of k is found to be 5.68×10^{-2}, in agreement with the figures in the table.

Other second order reactions taking place in solution are the interaction of alkyl halides with tertiary amines, e.g.,

$$C_2H_5I + C_6H_5N(CH_3)_2 = C_6H_5N(CH_3)_2(C_2H_5)^+ + I^-,$$

and of alkyl iodides with sodium phenoxide, e.g.,

$$RI + C_6H_5ONa = C_6H_5OR + Na^+ + I^-,$$

where R varies from CH_3 to C_8H_{17}. The progress of both these types of processes can be followed by titration, with silver nitrate, of the iodide ions produced in the reaction.

58f. Reactions of the Third Order.—A third order reaction may involve three molecules, e.g., $A + B + C$, whose concentrations are changing in the course of the reaction, or there may be two molecules of one substance and one of another, e.g., $2A + B$, or three molecules of a single substance, e.g., $3A$, may be concerned. In the most general case, i.e.,

$$A + B + C \rightarrow \text{products},$$

the reaction rate at any instant is given by

$$-\frac{dc_A}{dt} = -\frac{dc_B}{dt} = -\frac{dc_C}{dt} = kc_A c_B c_C. \tag{58.13}$$

If a, b and c are the amounts of the three reactants present initially in a given volume, and x is the decrease in each case after the lapse of time t, it follows from equation (58.13) that the reaction can be expressed in the form

$$\frac{dx}{dt} = k(a - x)(b - x)(c - x). \tag{58.14}$$

This equation can be integrated in the usual manner, but the result is rarely used. The special case will be considered, therefore, in which the three concentration terms c_A, c_B and c_C are equal; equation (58.14) then becomes

$$\frac{dx}{dt} = k(a - x)^3,$$

which upon integration gives

$$k = \frac{1}{2t} \left\{ \frac{1}{(a - x)^2} - \frac{1}{a^2} \right\}. \tag{58.15}$$

A comparison of this expression with equation (58.8) for a bimolecular reaction reveals a general form which is applicable to reactions of second and higher orders.

It will be evident from equation (58.15) that the value of the rate constant depends on the units employed for the concentration terms; since there are always two more such terms in the denominator than in the numerator, k will have the dimensions of conc.$^{-2}$ time^{-1}.

If it is assumed that the concentrations are all equal, so that equation (58.15) holds, the time to complete a definite fraction of the reaction can be calculated in the usual manner. Thus, when half the reaction is completed, x is equal to $\frac{1}{2}a$, and the corresponding time $t_{0.5}$ is given by equation (58.15) as

$$t_{0.5} = \frac{3}{2ka^2}. \tag{58.16}$$

The time to complete one-half or, in fact, any definite fraction, of the reaction is thus inversely proportional to the square of the initial concentration of the reactants.

Only five homogeneous gas reactions are definitely known to be of the third order; these are all termolecular reactions involving two molecules of nitric oxide, the other reactant being a molecule of hydrogen, deuterium, oxygen, chlorine or bromine. The reaction with chlorine, for example, is

$$2NO + Cl_2 = 2NOCl,$$

so that the rate is proportional to the square of the nitric oxide concentration (or pressure) and to the first power of the concentration (or pressure) of the chlorine gas. It may be remarked, incidentally, that for gas reactions in general, concentrations may be replaced by pressures if the deviations from ideal behavior are not large.

A number of third order reactions in solution have been described, but the results are somewhat in doubt. For example, the interaction of stannous and ferric salts was at one time thought to be of the third order; it appears, however, that it is more probably of the second order, the presence of the ions introducing a complicating effect. Similar considerations apply to other reactions which are apparently third order.

58g. Reactions Occurring in Stages.—It is generally accepted at the present time that reactions of the third order or, more correctly, termolecular reactions, are uncommon, and that processes of still higher order, involving more than three molecules, are either extremely rare or do not occur at all. For a reaction to be termolecular it would be necessary for three of the proper molecules to come together at one instant, and for the arrangement to be suitable for the reaction to take place (§ 59c); this occurrence is evidently rare, as is apparent from the scarcity of third order or termolecular processes. The fact that the only known third order gas reactions involve two molecules of nitric oxide is commonly attributed to the formation of an intermediate double molecule $(NO)_2$ which has an appreciable life; the reaction will then require an encounter between one of these molecules and a molecule of the other reactant, e.g., oxygen, chlorine, etc. The reaction would then really be bimolecular, thus

$$(NO)_2 + Cl_2 = 2NOCl,$$

although it would still be kinetically of the third order, since the rate will depend on the square of the NO concentration.

It would appear, therefore, that except in very unusual circumstances, *a reaction of the fourth or higher order is improbable, and even those of the third order are not of frequent occurrence.* An exception to this general statement arises for reactions in solution when the solvent is itself one of the reactants; since the solvent molecules are relatively close together, it is possible for two such molecules to be involved in a simultaneous encounter with one or two molecules of another reactant. However, although such reactions between four molecules might take place in solution, the order would probably be not more than second, because the solvent does not appear in the expression for the reaction rate.

In view of the foregoing considerations, it is evident that many reactions, for which the over-all process may involve more than three or four molecules, must occur in stages. A simple case in point is the reaction between nitric oxide and hydrogen which is kinetically of the third order; the rate is proportional to the square of the pressure of nitric oxide and to the first power of that of the hydrogen. The complete reaction, however, requires two molecules of hydrogen, viz.,

$$2NO + 2H_2 = N_2 + 2H_2O,$$

and so the reaction probably takes place in two stages, the first being

$$2NO + H_2 = N_2 + H_2O_2,$$

followed by

$$H_2O_2 + H_2 = 2H_2O.$$

The exact nature of the stages is not known with certainty, but from the reaction kinetics it can be concluded definitely that one of them involves $2NO + H_2$, and the reactions given above appear to be reasonable.

Another illustration of similar behavior is provided by the reaction between hydrogen peroxide and hydrogen iodide in aqueous solution; the over-all process is

$$H_2O_2 + 2H_3O^+ + 2I^- = 4H_2O + I_2,$$

but kinetic measurements indicate that the reaction is of the second order, the rate being directly proportional to the concentrations of hydrogen peroxide and of the iodide ions. The process evidently occurs in stages, and the following have been suggested; first,

$$H_2O_2 + I^- = H_2O + IO^-,$$

followed by the establishment of the equilibrium of the weak hypoiodous acid,

$$IO^- + H_3O^+ \rightleftharpoons HIO + H_2O,$$

and finally by the reaction

$$HIO + H_3O^+ + I^- = 2H_2O + I_2,$$

which may well take place in stages.

When a reaction occurs in stages, *the rate is determined by the slowest of these stages*, provided the others are relatively rapid. In this event, *the kinetics and order of the reaction are really those of the slowest stage;* this is frequently known as the **rate-determining stage** of the complete reaction. Thus, in the reaction between nitric oxide and hydrogen, the rate-determining stage is known from the kinetics to involve $2NO + H_2$; similarly, in the interaction of hydrogen peroxide and hydrogen iodide in solution, the rate-determining reaction occurs between a molecule of peroxide and an iodide ion. It happens in these two instances that the slow stage which determines the reaction kinetics is the first one, but this is not necessarily always the case; it may be any one of the stages of the complete process. It will be seen, therefore, that a study of reaction kinetics has led to the conclusion that even moderately complex reactions occur in stages, and the order of the reaction gives an indication of the nature of the slowest, or rate-determining, stage.

It may, and often does, happen that two or more of the stages of a reaction are fairly slow; the kinetics of the process will then not be simple. If one of the slow stages involves one molecule of a given reactant, while the other involves two of these molecules, the reaction rate will appear to depend on a power of the concentration lying between one and two. When the successive stages of a reaction are known, and they are not too complicated, it is possible to derive complete kinetic equations which take the various stages into consideration. This aspect of the subject will be considered briefly in § 58k.

58h. Determination of Order of Reaction.—It is opportune, at this point, to review the chief methods for determining the order of a reaction.

I. Method of Trial.—The most obvious method is to determine the amount of reactant decomposed after various intervals of time and to insert the data in the equations for first, second and third order reactions. The equation giving the most constant value for the specific reaction rate for a series of time intervals is the one corresponding most closely to the correct order of the reaction.

A modification of this procedure is to use a graphical method based on the respective rate equations, such as is depicted in Figs. 125 and 126. In general, if the reactants are all present at the same molar concentration, the expression for the rate of a reaction of the nth order, at any instant, when the concentration is c, is

$$-\frac{dc}{dt} = kc^n. \tag{58.17}$$

For $n = 1$, this equation gives upon rearrangement and integration

$$t = \text{constant} - \frac{2.303}{k} \log c, \tag{58.18}$$

while for n equal to or greater than 2,

$$t = \text{constant} + \frac{1}{k(n-1)} \cdot \frac{1}{c^{n-1}}. \tag{58.19}$$

According to equation (58.18), the plot of t against $\log c$ will be a straight line for a first order reaction; this is, of course, equivalent to the result of equation (58.6), since $a - x$ is the same as the concentration c of reactant at any instant. For reactions of higher order, on the other hand, the plot of t against $1/c^{n-1}$ will be linear, where n is the order of the reaction; this result follows directly from equation (58.19), since $k(n - 1)$ is a constant for each reaction. For a second order ($n = 2$) process, therefore, a straight line will be obtained if $1/c$ is plotted against the time; for a third order ($n = 3$) reaction, the plot of $1/c^2$ against time will be linear.

II. Time to Complete a Definite Fraction of the Reaction.—It has been seen from equations (58.5), (58.12) and (58.16), respectively, that the time taken to complete half the reaction is independent of the initial concentration for a first order reaction; it is inversely proportional to this concentration for a second order reaction, while it is inversely proportional to its square for a third order reaction. In general, therefore, if the reaction is of the nth order, $t_{0.5}$ is inversely proportional to a^{n-1}, where a is the initial concentration; hence, the product of a^{n-1} and $t_{0.5}$ should be constant. By varying the initial concentrations of the reactants, and measuring the time taken to decompose the same fraction, e.g., one-half, of the amounts initially present, it is possible to derive the order of the reaction.

Problem: In the decomposition of gaseous acetaldehyde at 518° C, the time taken to decompose half the material was found to be 410 sec. when the initial pressure was 363 mm., and 880 sec. for an initial pressure of 169 mm. What is the apparent order of the reaction?

Since the time $t_{0.5}$ is not constant, the reaction is obviously not of the first order. If the reaction were of the second order ($n = 2$), then the product of the initial concentration (or pressure), i.e., $a^{2-1} = a$, and $t_{0.5}$ should be constant; in the present case the products are 148,830 and 148,720. The values are sufficiently alike to indicate that the reaction is of the second order.

III. The Differential Method.—For two different concentrations c_1 and c_2 of the reactants, equation (58.17) becomes

$$-\frac{dc_1}{dt} = kc_1^n \quad \text{and} \quad -\frac{dc_2}{dt} = kc_2^n,$$

and by taking logarithms, it is easily shown that

$$n = \frac{\log(-dc_1/dt) - \log(-dc_2/dt)}{\log c_1 - \log c_2}. \tag{58.20}$$

The values of dc_1/dt and dc_2/dt are best obtained by plotting the variation of concentration c of the reactant, or reactants, with time during the course of the reaction, and determining the slopes, i.e., dc/dt, of the curve for two different values, c_1 and c_2, of the concentration. The result given by equation (58.20) is independent of the units used to express the concentration (or pressure), provided, of course, that the same units are used throughout.

If the reaction involves more than one substance it is not necessary that they should all have the same initial concentration. For two reactants A and B, the general expression for the reaction rate is

$$-\frac{dc}{dt} = k c_A^m c_B^n,$$

where m and n are the numbers of molecules of A and B, respectively, whose concentrations affect the reaction rate; the total order of the reaction is $m + n$. In one set of experiments, c_A is varied while c_B is kept constant; application of equation (58.20) then gives the value of m. In a second set of experiments, c_A is maintained constant while c_B is varied, and hence n can be evaluated; the sum of m and n gives the order of the reaction.

Problem: In the reaction between NO and H_2, the value of $-dp/dt$ was found to be 1.50 mm. sec.$^{-1}$ for a pressure of 359 mm. of NO, and 0.25 mm. sec.$^{-1}$ for a pressure of 152 mm., the pressure of H_2 being constant. On the other hand, when the pressure of NO was kept constant, $-dp/dt$ was 1.60 mm. sec.$^{-1}$ for a H_2 pressure of 289 mm., and 0.79 mm. sec.$^{-1}$ for a pressure of 147 mm. Determine the order of the reaction.

The concentrations are expressed in terms of partial pressures, and hence the $-dc/dt$ and c terms in equation (58.20) may be replaced by $-dp/dt$ and p, respectively. The order m of the reaction with respect to NO is then obtained from the first set of data, viz.,

$$m = \frac{\log 1.50 - \log 0.25}{\log 359 - \log 152} \approx 2.$$

The second set of data give the order n of the reaction with respect to H_2; thus,

$$n = \frac{\log 1.60 - \log 0.79}{\log 289 - \log 147} \approx 1.$$

The reaction is thus of the second order with respect to NO, and of the first order with respect to H_2; the whole process is thus of the third order.

58i. Opposing Reactions.—As mentioned at the outset, the treatment so far has been applied to simple or isolated reactions; some reference will now be made to certain of the complications that frequently arise. In the first case, the process may be reversible, in the chemical sense, so that forward and reverse reactions occur simultaneously. The simplest form of this type of process is that in which both reactions are of the first order; thus,

$$A \underset{k'}{\overset{k}{\rightleftharpoons}} B,$$

where k and k' are the specific rates of the forward and reverse reactions, respectively. As stated in § 32b, the ratio k/k' is equal to the equilibrium constant for the given system. If a is the concentration of A at the commencement of the experiment, and there is initially no B present, then after the lapse of time t, the concentrations of A and B will be $a - x$ and x, respectively; the *net rate of reaction* in the forward direction will be given by

$$\frac{dx}{dt} = k(a - x) - k'x, \tag{58.21}$$

where $k(a - x)$ is the actual rate in the forward direction and $k'x$ is that of the reverse reaction. When the system reaches equilibrium the rates of the two reactions are equal (§ 32b), so that

$$k(a - x_e) = k'x_e, \tag{58.22}$$

where x_e is the amount of B formed, or of A decomposed, at equilibrium. Substituting the value of k' derived from equation (58.22) into (58.21), the result is

$$\frac{dx}{dt} = k(a - x) - \frac{kx}{x_e}(a - x_e) = \frac{ka}{x_e}(x_e - x). \tag{58.23}$$

Upon integration, recalling that $x = 0$ when $t = 0$, and $x = x$ when $t = t$, it is found that

$$\frac{ka}{x_e} = \frac{1}{t}\ln\frac{x_e}{x_e - x}. \tag{58.24}$$

By means of equation (58.24) it is possible to derive the specific rate k of the forward reaction, by following the course of the reaction in a suitable manner; the amount of B formed at equilibrium, i.e., x_e, must be determined by allowing sufficient time to elapse. Incidentally, it is seen from equation (58.22) that ka/x_e is equal to $k + k'$; the latter quantity is therefore also given by (58.24). This equation thus provides a means for evaluating both k and k', the specific rates of the forward and reverse reactions, respectively, from the experimental data.

Methods similar to that just described have been used for the treatment of more complicated reactions; one of these, to which reference may be made, is the dissociation of gaseous hydrogen iodide, viz.,

$$2HI(g) \rightleftharpoons H_2(g) + I_2(g).$$

If the initial concentration of the hydrogen iodide is a, and x is the extent of decomposition after time t has elapsed, the concentration of hydrogen iodide at this time will be $a - x$; the concentrations of hydrogen and iodine will both be $\frac{1}{2}x$, since two molecules of hydrogen iodide produce one molecule of hydrogen and one of iodine upon decomposition. It is found, therefore, that the net rate of the forward reaction is given by

$$\frac{dx}{dt} = k(a - x)^2 - k'(\tfrac{1}{2}x)^2, \tag{58.25}$$

where k and k' are the specific rates of forward and reverse reactions. At equilibrium the rates of these two reactions will be equal, so that

$$k(a - x)^2 = k'(\tfrac{1}{2}x_e)^2, \tag{58.26}$$

and if the value of k' derived from this expression is inserted in equation (58.25), the result can be integrated to give

$$k = \frac{x_e}{2a(a - x_e)t} \ln \frac{x(a - 2x_e) + ax_e}{a(x_e - x)} \tag{58.27}$$

for the specific rate of the forward reaction. By the use of equations (58.26) and (58.27) it is thus possible to evaluate both k and k' from the experimental measurements. Because the dissociation of hydrogen iodide is not accompanied by a change of volume (or pressure), the course of the reaction is followed by rapidly cooling the reaction system and analyzing the mixture.

58j. Equilibrium Constant and Specific Reaction Rate.—For any reversible reaction, the equilibrium constant K is equal to the ratio of the specific rates of forward and reverse reactions; that is,

$$K = \frac{k}{k'}, \tag{58.28}$$

as already mentioned. This relationship is actually implied in equations (58.22) and (58.26), and hence the values of k and k' derived above cannot be used to verify equation (58.28). However, for some reactions it has been found possible to obtain k and k' separately by studying the forward and reverse reactions in the early stages, when the extent of the opposing reaction is negligible. The values derived in this way, therefore, do not involve any reference to equilibrium. If the equilibrium constant is subsequently determined by analysis of the reacting system when equilibrium is attained, it is possible to verify equation (58.28).

The necessary information for this purpose has been obtained for the esterification of acetic acid by ethanol, and the reverse reaction, i.e., the hydrolysis of ethyl acetate, viz.,

$$CH_3COOH + C_2H_5OH \rightleftharpoons CH_3COOC_2H_5 + H_2O,$$

in the presence of hydrochloric acid as catalyst. Thus, from observations on the early stages of the direct reaction k was found to be 2.38×10^{-4}, while for the reverse reaction k' was 8.15×10^{-5}, the opposing process being ignored in each case. It follows, therefore, that

$$K = \frac{k}{k'} = \frac{2.38 \times 10^{-4}}{8.15 \times 10^{-5}} = 2.92.$$

The equilibrium constant derived from analysis of the system at equilibrium, in the presence of the same concentration of hydrochloric acid, was found to be 2.84. The agreement is as good as could be expected, the difference being probably due to the fact that the solutions do not behave ideally. It will be noted that the equilibrium constant given here is appreciably lower than that in § 34a; this is to be attributed to the change in the medium resulting from the presence of the hydrochloric acid.

58k. Consecutive Reactions.—In accordance with the statements in § 58g, the great majority of reactions involving three or more molecules actually take place in a series of successive stages. If one of the stages is relatively slow and rate-determining, the kinetics of the reaction are simple, as already explained. It is of interest, however, to examine the subject of consecutive reactions when the different stages have specific rates of similar magnitude. The simplest case arises when there are two successive stages of the first order, viz.,

$$A \xrightarrow{k_1} B \xrightarrow{k_2} C,$$

where k_1 and k_2 are the two rate constants. If a is the initial concentration of the reactant A, and c_A, c_B and c_C represent the concentrations of A, B and C, respectively, after the lapse of time t from the commencement of the reaction, it can be readily seen that

$$a = c_A + c_B + c_C. \tag{58.29}$$

The decomposition of A is a first order process, and hence the rate of its disappearance at any instant is given by

$$-\frac{dc_A}{dt} = k_1 c_A. \tag{58.30}$$

Utilizing the fact that c_A is equal to a when t is zero, and equal to c_A when t is equal to t, integration of equation (58.30) gives the result

$$c_A = a e^{-k_1 t}, \tag{58.31}$$

which is really another form of equation (58.4). The rate at which the concentration of B increases, i.e., dc_B/dt, is equal to the difference between the rate of its formation from A, by equation (58.30), i.e., $k_1 c_A$, and the rate of its decomposition into C, which is $k_2 c_B$; hence

$$\frac{dc_B}{dt} = k_1 c_A - k_2 c_B. \tag{58.32}$$

Introduction of the result of equation (58.31) and subsequent integration leads to the expression

$$c_B = a \cdot \frac{k_1}{k_2 - k_1} (e^{-k_1 t} - e^{-k_2 t}). \tag{58.33}$$

The equations (58.31) and (58.33) thus give the values of c_A and c_B at any instant; from these results together with equation (58.29), the corresponding concentration c_C is obtained. In order to determine k_1 and k_2 it is necessary to know any two of the concentrations; thus, if c_A and c_B are found by experiment at any instant, k_1 and k_2 can be readily evaluated from equations (58.31) and (58.33).

An outstanding example of consecutive first order reactions is provided by the radioactive disintegration series; however, the number of stages is so large that the treatment is rendered difficult. A simple case is the acid hydrolysis of an ester of a dibasic acid, e.g., diethyl succinate or diethyl tartrate; the two ester groups are hydrolyzed in turn, thus providing two successive first order reactions. The values of k_1 and k_2 can here be determined independently, as well as by using the equations given above. By making measurements on the diethyl ester in the early stages of the acid hydrolysis, before an appreciable amount of the intermediate monoethyl ester has formed. it is possible to obtain satisfactory values of k_1; the method used is similar to that described in § 58c in connection with the acid hydrolysis of ethyl acetate. A separate set of experiments, with the same acid catalyst, are now made with the monoethyl ester; this is free from complications, and the specific rate k_2 can be calculated from the results.

The consecutive reactions encountered in practice are frequently more complex than those given above, and the mathematical analysis may not be possible. Where one or more of the intermediate substances are present in very small amount only, a special device may be used which permits a considerable simplification of the problem. Reference to this will be made in § 63g as applied to photochemical reactions.

581. Chain Reactions.—A special type of successive reaction phenomenon is encountered in connection with what are known as chain reactions. If atoms of chlorine are introduced, in a suitable manner, e.g., by exposure of chlorine gas to light (§ 63c), into a mixture of hydrogen and chlorine gases, two successive rapid reactions apparently take place, viz.,

$$Cl + H_2 = HCl + H,$$

followed by reaction of the hydrogen atom produced in this manner with the chlorine molecules,

$$H + Cl_2 = HCl + Cl.$$

As a result of these two reactions a molecule of hydrogen and one of chlorine have been combined to yield two molecules of hydrogen chloride, but a chlorine atom has been regenerated, and this can set off the combination of further hydrogen and chlorine molecules. The introduction of a few chlorine atoms can thus initiate a chain of consecutive reactions, the two stages depicted above repeating themselves until the reactants are used up. The series of successive processes is referred to as a **chain reaction.** Although it might appear that a chain has unlimited length, ending only when the hydrogen and chlorine have reacted completely, there are always factors operative which tend to terminate or "break" the chains. In the reaction under consideration, for example, removal of the **chain carriers,** that is, the hydrogen and chlorine *atoms,* by any of the processes

$$2H = H_2, \quad 2Cl = Cl_2, \quad \text{and} \quad H + Cl = HCl,$$

will result in the termination of a chain.

The chain carriers are frequently atoms or other chemically active species, e.g., free radicals, and their destruction occurs most readily at the walls of the containing vessel or, in fact, at any solid surface. For this reason, the introduction of powdered glass or silica into the reaction vessel is often found to decrease the rate of the reaction, because greater facilities are available for chain breaking. In general, if an increase in the ratio of the surface area to the volume of the vessel decreases the rate of a process, a chain reaction is probably taking place, with the chains being broken at the surface. In some chain reactions, however, the chain termination is brought about mainly by some process taking place within the gas; in cases of this kind, increase of pressure often has the effect of decreasing the reaction rate.

Another test for chain reactions, especially those in the gas phase, is based on the observation that traces of certain substances, e.g., nitric oxide and propylene, are able to reduce the rate of a chain process; the function of these **inhibitors** is apparently to remove the atoms or radicals that would normally act as chain carriers. The phenomenon of "knocking" in the internal combustion engine is associated with a special type of chain which occurs in the reaction between hydrocarbons and oxygen at certain pressures. The presence of small amounts of lead tetraethyl results in the formation of compounds which are able to break the chains, thus permitting a normal type of explosion to take place.

Chain reactions play an important part in many oxidation processes, e.g., of hydrocarbons, carbon monoxide, hydrogen, hydrogen sulfide, phosphine, phosphorus vapor and methanol. It is a remarkable fact that such an apparently simple reaction as the combination of hydrogen and oxygen to form water at 500° to 600° C, is actually a complex process involving reaction chains.

In the decomposition by heat of the vapors of many organic compounds, free radicals frequently act as chain carriers. For example, in the thermal decomposition of acetaldehyde, the first stage apparently involves the formation of the CH_3 and CHO radicals, thus

$$CH_3CHO = CH_3 + CHO.$$

The CHO probably decomposes into H and CO, and plays a minor part, but the free methyl radical appears to act as a chain carrier according to the reactions

$$CH_3 + CH_3CHO = CH_4 + CH_3CO$$

$$CH_3CO = CO + CH_3.$$

The chains may be terminated by the combination of two CH_3 radicals, of two CH_3CO radicals, or of a CH_3 with a CH_3CO radical. By applying the well established methods of chemical kinetics to the series of reactions involved in the formation, continuation and termination of reaction chains, it is possible to derive equations expressing the over-all reaction rate in terms of the concentration of the reacting substance and the specific rate constants of the various stages. In certain cases these expressions reduce to remarkably simple forms in spite of the complexity of the actual reactions. It is possible, for example, for a chain reaction to appear to be kinetically of the first order; consequently, it is necessary to exercise caution in the interpretation of results of reaction kinetics, especially if there are reasons for believing that chains are involved.

THEORY OF REACTION RATES

59a. The Effect of Temperature on Reaction Rate: Energy of Activation.— Increase of temperature almost invariably increases the rate of a chemical reaction to a marked extent; for homogeneous processes the specific rate is usually increased by a factor of about two or three for every 10° rise of temperature. The results in Table LXXII, for instance, show the effect of temperature on the rates of two entirely different reactions; they are (I) the decomposition of dibromosuccinic acid in aqueous solution, and (II) the decomposition of nitrogen pentoxide vapor. The actual change of the specific rate varies with the nature of the reaction, but the data in Table LXXII may

TABLE LXXII.   INFLUENCE OF TEMPERATURE ON SPECIFIC REACTION RATE

I		II	
Temp.	Specific Rate	Temp.	Specific Rate
15° C	9.67×10^{-6}	25° C	3.46×10^{-5}
60°	6.54×10^{-4}	45°	4.19×10^{-4}
101°	3.18×10^{-2}	65°	4.87×10^{-3}

be regarded as more or less typical. A rise of about 40° in the temperature is seen to increase the reaction rate from fifty to one hundred fold, in the examples given. It can be readily understood, therefore, why many reactions which are immeasurably slow at ordinary temperatures, e.g., the combination of hydrogen and oxygen, take place with great rapidity as the temperature is raised.

The most satisfactory method for expressing the influence of temperature on reaction velocity can be derived by plotting the logarithm of the specific rate, i.e., log k, against the reciprocal of the absolute temperature, i.e., against $1/T$. An illustration of this type of plot, for the decomposition of gaseous hydrogen iodide, is shown in Fig. 127; it is seen that the experimental points fall on a straight line, and the same general result has been obtained for almost all reactions. It is evident, therefore, that the variation of the rate constant of a reaction with temperature can be expressed by means of an equation of the form

$$\log k = a - \frac{b}{T}, \tag{59.1}$$

where a and b are constants for the given reaction; T is the absolute temperature. For purposes of the subsequent treatment (§ 59b, c), it is convenient to write equation (59.1) in the exponential form, involving the Boltzmann factor $e^{-E/RT}$ (see § 12g), where R is the gas constant; thus,

$$k = Ae^{-E/RT}, \tag{59.2}$$

where the constants A and E are related to a and b, respectively; this is one form of the **Arrhenius equation** (S. Arrhenius, 1889). For reasons which will appear later, A is sometimes called the **frequency factor,** while E is the **energy of activation** of the reaction.

Upon taking logarithms of equation (59.2), it is found that

$$\log k = \log A - \frac{E}{2.303RT}, \tag{59.3}$$

which is identical in form with the experimental equation (59.1); it requires the plot of $\log k$ against $1/T$ to be linear, the slope being equal to $-E/2.303R$.

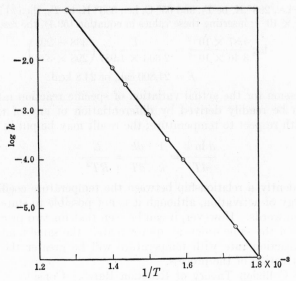

FIG. 127. Decomposition of hydrogen iodide

The constant E, which is characteristic of the reaction and determines the influence of temperature on the reaction rate, can thus be calculated from the value of this slope. The slope of the straight line in Fig. 127 is -9.70×10^3, and if R is taken as 1.987 cal., it follows that for the thermal decomposition of hydrogen iodide E is 44,300 cal., or 44.3 kcal.

An alternative method of evaluating E is to take the specific rates k_1 and k_2 for two temperatures T_1 and T_2, and insert them in equation (59.3); if the two resulting expressions are subtracted from one another, it is found that

$$\log \frac{k_2}{k_1} = \frac{E}{2.303R} \left(\frac{T_2 - T_1}{T_1 T_2} \right). \tag{59.4}$$

Consequently, if the specific rates at two temperatures are known, the value of E can be readily calculated. It may be noted that this expression is similar in form to equation (36.5) which gives the variation with temperature of the equilibrium constant of a reversible reaction. Just as ΔH is an energy quantity in the latter equation, so also is E * in equations (59.3) and (59.4), as may be readily shown. The ratio k_2/k_1 on the left-hand side of equation (59.4) is dimensionless, and since R has the dimensions of energy per degree (§ 11f), it is evident that E must be an energy term. For the present purpose E is almost invariably expressed in calories or, better, in kilocalories. The characteristic property E for a given reaction is thus an energy quantity, as indicated above.

Problem: Using the data for 25° and 65° C in Table LXXII, calculate E, the energy of activation, for the decomposition of nitrogen pentoxide.

Let 25° C, i.e., 298° K, be T_1, and 65° C, i.e., 338° K, be T_2; then k_1 is 3.46×10^{-5} and k_2 is 4.87×10^{-3}; inserting these values in equation (59.4), the result is

$$\log \frac{4.87 \times 10^{-3}}{3.46 \times 10^{-5}} = \frac{E}{2.303 \times 1.987} \left(\frac{338 - 298}{298 \times 338} \right)$$

$$E = 24{,}800 \text{ cal., or } 24.8 \text{ kcal.}$$

An expression for the actual variation of specific reaction rate with temperature can be readily derived by differentiation of any of the foregoing equations with respect to temperature; the result may be put in the form

$$\frac{d \ln k}{dT} = \frac{1}{k} \cdot \frac{dk}{dT} = \frac{E}{RT^2}.$$

There is evidently a relationship between the temperature coefficient dk/dT and the energy of activation, although it is not possible to state the connection simply in words. However, it can be seen that for two reactions having specific rates of the same order, at approximately the same temperature, the increase of reaction rate with temperature will be greater the greater the energy of activation of the process.

59b. The Collision Theory of Reaction Rates.—Consider a bimolecular reaction between a molecule of A and one of B; for the reaction to occur it is obvious that these two molecules must collide. By the use of equation (12.24) it is possible to calculate the number of such collisions taking place between the molecules of A and B at a given temperature and concentration (or pressure); if this result is compared with the number of molecules reacting, as determined by direct experiment, the number of collisions is almost invariably found to be very much greater. For example, at a temperature of 556° K and a concentration of 1 mole per liter, the number of molecules of hydrogen iodide that collide with each other is calculated to be 6×10^{31} per ml. per sec., assuming a collision diameter of 3.5×10^{-8} cm. (§§ 12i, 12j). From experiments on the bimolecular dissociation of hydrogen iodide at the same temperature and pressure (concentration), it is found that the number of molecules reacting is only about 2×10^{14} per ml. per sec. This means that only one collision in every 10^{17} is effective in bringing about dissociation.

* As will be evident shortly, E, like ΔH, is an energy *difference*; it is the common practice, however, to omit the Δ symbol.

Another apparent discrepancy arises when the effect of temperature is considered; it can be shown from the kinetic theory of gases, e.g., by differentiation of equation (12.24), that a 10° rise of temperature increases the number of binary collisions, i.e., collisions between two molecules, by about 2 per cent, while the rate of a chemical reaction is increased by 200 to 300 per cent.

The experimental facts can be accounted for, however, if it is postulated that reaction occurs when two molecules collide *only if they possess energy in excess of a certain amount;* all other collisions are fruitless and do not lead to reaction. The minimum energy which the molecules must acquire before they can react upon collision is equal, as a first approximation, to the energy of activation E, as derived above from the effect of temperature on reaction rate. It was seen in § 12g that in consequence of the mutual impacts of molecules of gas, there is a continuous interchange of energy between them; as a result there are always a few molecules possessing energies that are greatly in excess of the normal or average value (Fig. 12). It is thus possible to have collisions between molecules having the high energy of activation E necessary for reaction, but the number of such collisions will be a very small fraction of the total number of collisions taking place in the gas. This accounts for the fact that only a small proportion of the collisions are effective in leading to reaction, as mentioned above. As the temperature is increased, the number of molecules possessing a certain high energy increases rapidly, and although the total number of collisions is not much changed, the proportion of effective collisions will obviously be greatly increased. The marked effect of temperature on reaction rate can be explained in this manner.

If the molecules A and B taking part in a given reaction could be treated as rigid spheres, possessing only (kinetic) energy of translation, the activation energy would then be restricted to translational energy along the direction in which the molecules collide. In this event, the proportion of collisions in which the molecules possess energy in excess of the minimum amount E required for the reaction is equal to the Boltzmann factor $e^{-E/RT}$ (§ 12g). If Z represents the total number of collisions, as given by equation (12.21) or (12.24), the actual number of collisions leading to reaction should thus be equal to $Ze^{-E/RT}$, since this product gives the number of effective collisions. When the two reacting molecules are the same, as in the dissociation of hydrogen iodide, the number of molecules reacting is, of course, equal to twice the number of collisions, and allowance should be made for this fact. Comparison of the theoretical expression $Ze^{-E/RT}$ with the experimental equation (59.2) shows that the former is, at least, of the correct form; the frequency factor A in the Arrhenius equation is seen to be equivalent to the collision frequency Z, according to the arguments given above.

As stated earlier, the number of molecules of hydrogen iodide colliding per second at 556° K and a concentration of 1 mole per liter is 6×10^{31} per ml.; this is equal to $2Z$, calculated from equation (12.21). Since the activation energy for this reaction was found to be 44,300 cal., it follows that the exponential Boltzmann factor $e^{-E/RT}$, which gives the fraction of effective collisions, at 556° K is $e^{-44,300/2 \times 556}$, the value of R being taken, with sufficient accuracy, as 2 cal. This fraction is found to be 5×10^{-18}, and hence the number of molecules reacting per ml. should be the product of the total number of molecules colliding, i.e., 6×10^{31} per ml., and the Boltzmann factor 5×10^{-18}, that is, 3×10^{14} molecules per ml. The result is in good agreement with the value given above, i.e., 2×10^{14} molecules per ml., calculated from the experimental data on the dissociation of hydrogen iodide at 556° K and a concentration of 1 mole per liter. Since the value of E used in the foregoing calculations was based on rate measurements over a range of temperatures, equally satisfactory agreement between the observed and calculated reaction rates could be obtained at other temperatures.

It is true that for the dissociation of hydrogen iodide, and also for the combination of hydrogen and gaseous iodine, and in a few other cases, the product of the collision number Z and the exponential factor $e^{-E/RT}$ gives results which agree with the observed reaction rates within a factor of ten. In many other instances, however, the calculated and observed values differ considerably. For the combination of two molecules of ethylene the discrepancy is a factor of about 2,000, while in the reaction between ethanol and acetic anhydride vapors at 79° C, and between carbonyl sulfide and water vapor at about 300° C, the calculated rates are too large by a factor of 10^5 to 10^6.

In seeking for an explanation of these discrepancies it must be remembered that the identification of $Ze^{-E/RT}$ with the reaction rate is based on the supposition that the reacting molecules behave as rigid spheres, and that the activation energy is translational in character. When the reacting molecules are relatively simple, as in the decomposition of hydrogen iodide or in the combination of hydrogen and iodine, they approximate to rigid spheres, and the calculations given above are roughly applicable. For more complex molecules, on the other hand, the approximation of rigid spheres is not satisfactory, and account must be taken of various forms of rotational and vibrational energy (§ 12m) in addition to the translational energy. The molecules acquire the high energy necessary for reaction as a result of interchanges upon impact, but the energy must be properly distributed among the various rotations and vibrations before the reaction can take place. The number of collisions is still given by the value of Z, but the simple factor $e^{-E/RT}$ no longer determines the probability that a collision will result in reaction. No direct method has yet been devised for calculating the fraction of fruitful collisions in the general case of molecules that are not rigid spheres, and so other approaches to the problem have been developed.

59c. The Activated-Complex Theory of Reaction Rates.—One of the most significant treatments of the theory of reaction rates is based on the concept of the existence of an **activated complex** or **activated state** as an intermediate state in all chemical reactions. In a reaction involving two or more molecules, the reactants, possessing sufficient energy, must approach one another closely; there must then be an appropriate rearrangement of valence bonds and energy so as to give the activated complex characteristic of the given reaction. The activated complex is regarded as a molecule which does not differ from normal molecules, except in one respect; it has a transient existence only, and breaks up at a definite rate to yield the products of the reaction. The bimolecular decomposition of hydrogen iodide, for example, might be represented as follows:

$$
\begin{array}{ccccc}
\text{H} \quad \text{H} & & \text{H} \text{----} \text{H} & & \text{H}\text{---}\text{H} \\
| \quad + \quad | & \rightarrow & \vdots \quad \vdots & \rightarrow & + \\
\text{I} \quad \text{I} & & \text{I} \text{----} \text{I} & & \text{I}\text{---}\text{I} \\
\text{Reactants} & & \text{Activated} & & \text{Products} \\
& & \text{Complex} & &
\end{array}
$$

Even in a unimolecular reaction, in which a single molecule takes part in each chemical act, it is necessary for some rearrangement of atoms and energy to occur, giving the requisite activated complex, before reaction can take place. The activation energy of a reaction is then defined as *the additional energy which the reactant molecules must acquire in order to form the activated complex for the reaction*. In other words, it is *the difference in energy of the activated complex and the reactants*.

By supposing that an equilibrium exists between reacting molecules and the activated complex, which decomposes at a definite rate, viz.,

Reactants $\rightleftharpoons$ Activated State $\rightarrow$ Products,

it has been found possible to derive an equation for the specific rate of any reaction, namely

$$
k = \frac{RT}{Nh} K^{\ddagger}, \tag{59.5}
$$

where R and T have their usual significance; N is the Avogadro number, h is Planck's quantum theory constant (§ 9b), and $K^{\ddagger}$ is the equilibrium constant of the equilibrium between activated state and the reactants (H. Eyring, 1935). In one important development of equation (59.5), the equilibrium constant $K^{\ddagger}$ is expressed in terms of the partition functions (§ 38c) of the substances concerned; the treatment lies beyond the scope of this book, and so it will not be discussed here. Another approach, which has considerable interest, is to utilize the familiar thermodynamic equations (37.8) and (26.6), i.e.,

$$
\Delta F^{0} = -RT \ln K \qquad \text{and} \qquad \Delta F^{0} = \Delta H^{0} - T\Delta S^{0},
$$

to derive the general expression

$$
K = e^{-\Delta F^{0}/RT} = e^{\Delta S^{0}/R} e^{-\Delta H^{0}/RT}. \tag{59.6}
$$

If the corresponding result for the equilibrium constant $K^{\ddagger}$ is inserted in equation (59.5), it is seen that

$$
k = \frac{RT}{Nh} e^{-\Delta F^{\ddagger}/RT} \tag{59.7}
$$

$$
= \frac{RT}{Nh} e^{\Delta S^{\ddagger}/R} e^{-\Delta H^{\ddagger}/RT}, \tag{59.8}
$$

where $\Delta F^{\ddagger}$, $\Delta S^{\ddagger}$ and $\Delta H^{\ddagger}$ are the standard free energy, entropy and heat of activation, respectively; these quantities represent the difference between the values of the respective thermodynamic functions for the activated complex and the reactants, all the substances being in their standard states of unit activity. Because of the transient nature of the activated complex, there is no hope of being able to determine its thermodynamic properties by direct measurement; useful information can nevertheless be obtained in other ways. It should be noted, incidentally, that the factor RT/Nh in equations (59.5), (59.7) and (59.8) is a universal constant, apart from the temperature, and contains no reference to the reacting substances or to the activated state.

It is seen that according to equation (59.7) *the specific rate of a reaction, at a given temperature, is determined by* $\Delta F^{\ddagger}$, *the free energy of activation.* This is a result of outstanding significance; among other matters, it is evident that *the higher the free energy of activation, the slower the reaction rate at a given temperature.* In equation (59.8) the free energy factor has been replaced by factors involving the entropy and heat of activation. The latter may be identified, at least approximately, with the experimental activation energy E, so that

$$k = \frac{RT}{Nh} e^{\Delta S^{\ddagger}/R} e^{-E/RT}, \tag{59.9}$$

and if this is compared with the Arrhenius equation (59.1), it is seen that the two expressions become identical if the frequency factor A of the latter is represented by

$$A = \frac{RT}{Nh} e^{\Delta S^{\ddagger}/R}. \tag{59.10}$$

In the simple collision theory of reaction rates, discussed in § 59b, the factor A was regarded as equivalent to the collision number Z, but in the present treatment it is seen to have a different meaning. However, for simple molecules, which may be treated as rigid spheres, the value of A as given by equation (59.10) comes out to be the same as the collision frequency. For simple molecules, therefore, the two theories are identical, as they should be. With more complex reactants, when the simple collision theory fails, equation (59.10) is still satisfactory. When the reacting molecules contain relatively large numbers of atoms, the formation of the activated state is usually accompanied by a large decrease of entropy, that is, $\Delta S^{\ddagger}$ has a fairly large *negative* value. In this case the quantity $e^{\Delta S^{\ddagger}/R}$ in equation (59.10) is small, and since RT/Nh is the same for all reactions, it follows that the frequency factor A will be much less than it would be for simple reactants. This accounts for the fact that the experimental value of A is often less than the collision number Z by factors as large as 10^6, as stated in § 59b.

The theory of *unimolecular reactions* is essentially the same as that described above, and equations (59.5), (59.7), etc., are applicable to such reactions. It is, nevertheless, important to consider how the molecules acquire the energy that is necessary before the activated state can be formed. Like all other molecules, those taking part in unimolecular reactions must obtain the energy of activation as the result of interchanges in collisions with other molecules. However, if the molecules decomposed immediately after acquiring the requisite minimum (activation) energy, the reaction rate would be dependent on the number of collisions, and hence on the *square* of the concentration [cf. n^2 in equation (12.21)]. In other words, the reaction would be kinetically of the second order. Nevertheless, first order gas reactions are not uncommon, and the cause of the apparent discrepancy will now be considered.

In order to account for the fact that certain reactions, such as the decomposition of nitrogen pentoxide, are of the first order, it has been suggested that after the molecule of reactant acquires sufficient energy in the course of a collision there is an appreciable delay before decomposition occurs. This delay is presumably due to the necessity for the energy to be distributed in such a way as to form the activated complex appropriate to the reaction. In the period which elapses between the acquisition of the energy and the breaking up of the activated molecule, another collision may ensue in which a large proportion of the energy is removed; if this happens, the molecule will not decompose. It is thus seen that a fraction only of the molecules which acquire sufficient energy to react actually succeed in doing so. By a simple mathematical treatment, based on the postulate of activation by collision, followed by a delay before decomposition, it can be shown that provided the gas concentration is relatively high, the reaction rate will be directly proportional to this concentration, as required for a first order process. At low concentrations (or pressures), on the other hand, the theory requires the unimolecular reaction to behave kinetically as second order; this has been verified experimentally.

59d. Prediction of Reaction Rates.—One of the purposes of the theory of reaction rates is to be able to predict the rate of a reaction from a knowledge of the properties of the substances involved. An examination of the Arrhenius equation (59.2) shows that the problem falls into two parts; first, the determination of the frequency factor A, and second, the estimation of the activation energy E. A solution to the first part of the problem is given by equation (59.10), but the theoretical calculation of E is much more difficult. Some progress has been made in this connection by means of quantum (wave) mechanics, but the complex subject is still in the early stages of development. Another method for assessing energies of activation is to make use of the information that is available concerning the strengths of various valence bonds. From a consideration of the nature of the reactants and the products, and the strengths of the bonds that are broken and formed in the course of the reaction, it is often possible to make a fairly reliable estimate of the magnitude of the activation energy. This procedure requires considerable experience and knowledge of the theory of reaction rates.

There is one type of reaction for which it is a simple matter to derive a minimum value, at least, for the energy of activation; it can be shown that for an endothermic reaction, i.e., one accompanied by an absorption of heat, and for which ΔH is positive, the energy of activation E must be at least equal to the change ΔH in the heat content for the complete reaction. In Fig. 128 are depicted the energies of reactants, activated state and the products, for exothermic and endothermic reactions, respectively. Since the energy of the activated state must always be in excess of that of both the reactants and the products, it is obvious that for the endothermic reaction, the energy

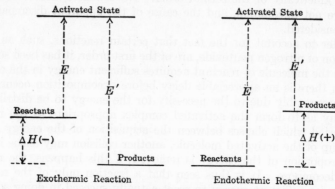

FIG. 128. Energy of activation

of activation E must be at least as great as ΔH. In other words, *the activation energy of an endothermic reaction must be greater than the heat change accompanying the reaction;* frequently the difference is quite large, but there is no simple method for its estimation.

For an exothermic reaction there is no connection whatever between the activation energy and the over-all heat of reaction. However, in the case of a reversible reaction, if E has been determined for the reaction in one direction, the value of E' for the other direction can be readily derived from a knowledge of ΔH for the complete reaction. The activated state is the same for the reaction in either direction, and hence it can be seen from Fig. 128 that

$$E - E' = \Delta H, \tag{59.11}$$

so that one activation energy can be calculated if the other is known.

Problem: For the dissociation of gaseous hydrogen iodide, the energy of activation is 44.3 kcal.; determine the activation energy for the reverse reaction, utilizing the fact that ΔH for the formation of a mole of hydrogen iodide from hydrogen and gaseous iodine is -1.35 kcal.

The data given are

$$2HI(g) = H_2(g) + I_2(g) \qquad\qquad E = 44.3 \text{ kcal.}$$
$$\tfrac{1}{2}H_2(g) + \tfrac{1}{2}I_2(g) = HI(g) \qquad\qquad \Delta H = -1.35 \text{ kcal.}$$

and from the latter result, it follows that

$$2HI(g) = H_2(g) + I_2(g) \qquad\qquad \Delta H = 2 \times 1.35 = 2.70 \text{ kcal.}$$

Combination of this value of ΔH with E for the forward reaction gives E' for the reverse reaction, by equation (59.11), as

$$E' = E - \Delta H = 44.3 - 2.70 = 41.6 \text{ kcal.}$$

The same result may be obtained directly from Fig. 129.

In view of the difficulty in deriving the activation energy from theoretical considerations, it is necessary in most cases to obtain the value from measurements of the reaction rate at various temperatures, as explained in § 59a. The problem is then to estimate the frequency factor A for the given reaction, as defined by equation (59.10). The value of R is 8.31×10^7 ergs deg.$^{-1}$ mole^{-1}, N is 6.02×10^{23} mole^{-1} and h is 6.62×10^{-27} erg sec.; hence

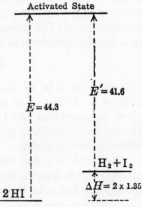

FIG. 129. Activation energies in the $2HI = H_2 + I_2$ reaction

$$A = 2.1 \times 10^{10} T e^{\Delta S^{\ddagger}/R} \text{ sec.}^{-1} \quad (59.12)$$

There is some uncertainty in assessing $\Delta S^{\ddagger}$ the standard entropy of activation, but from various considerations it is known that for *bimolecular reactions* it usually lies within the range of about -10 to -40 cal. deg.$^{-1}$ mole^{-1}, if the standard state is taken as corresponding to a concentration of 1 mole per liter; with this standard state the specific reaction rate is given in the familiar (mole/liter)$^{-1}$ sec.$^{-1}$ units. If these extreme values for $\Delta S^{\ddagger}$ are inserted into equation (59.12), it follows that for a bimolecular reaction A may be between about $10^8 T$ and $10^2 T$, so that, utilizing the Arrhenius type of equation,

$$k = 10^2 T e^{-E/RT} \quad \text{to} \quad 10^8 T e^{-E/RT} \text{ liter mole}^{-1} \text{ sec.}^{-1} \quad (59.13)$$

For simple reacting molecules, such as hydrogen iodide, the frequency factor approaches the higher limit, but with increasing complexity the trend is toward the lower value.

It is evident from equation (59.13) that the rate of a bimolecular reaction is not determined solely by the energy of activation, since the frequency factor can vary over a considerable range. As stated earlier, it is really the *free energy of activation* that is the determining factor. Nevertheless, it is possible to state that for a series of similar reactions, in which the frequency factor does not vary greatly, the higher the energy of activation the slower the reaction at the same temperature. It is found, as a rough approximation, that for a chemical reaction to have an appreciable rate at normal temperatures, i.e., about $300°$ K, the activation energy must be about 20 kcal., but if the rate does not become measurable until about $600°$ K, the activation energy will be about 40 kcal.

Problem: Estimate the specific rate of the bimolecular dissociation of hydrogen iodide in liters mole^{-1} sec.$^{-1}$ units at $556°$ K, the activation energy being 44.3 kcal.

Since the reacting molecules are simple, it is probable that k is given by the upper limit in equation (59.13), i.e., $k = 10^8 T e^{-E/RT}$; hence, taking R as 2 cal.,

$$k = 10^8 \times 556 \times e^{-44,300/2 \times 556} = 2.8 \times 10^{-7} \text{ liter mole}^{-1} \text{ sec.}^{-1}$$

(The experimental result at 556° K is 3.5×10^{-7} liter mole^{-1} sec.$^{-1}$)

For *unimolecular reactions* the situation with regard to the entropy of activation is somewhat simpler than for bimolecular reactions; in the majority of unimolecular processes the activated complex has about the same entropy as the reacting molecule, so that $\Delta S^\ddagger$ is approximately zero. The expression for A, the frequency factor, then reduces to RT/Nh, and the equation for the specific rate is, from (59.9),

$$k = 2 \times 10^{10} T e^{-E/RT} \text{ sec.}^{-1} \tag{59.14}$$

The value of k is, of course, independent of the concentration units, as explained in § 58b. For certain reactions the rates are much slower than is given by equation (59.14), but for a large proportion of unimolecular reactions this equation gives specific rates in fair agreement with those observed experimentally.

It should be noted that if the process under consideration involves chains of appreciable length, the rate constants derived from equations (59.13) and (59.14) are liable to be much too low.

Problem: Estimate the specific rate of the unimolecular decomposition of nitrogen pentoxide at 45° C; the activation energy for the reaction is 24.7 kcal.

Since T is $273 + 45 = 318°$ K, equation (59.14), with R equal to 2 cal., gives

$$k = 2 \times 10^{10} \times 318 \times e^{-24,700/2 \times 318} = 0.9 \times 10^{-4} \text{ sec.}^{-1}$$

(The experimental result is 4.9×10^{-4} sec.$^{-1}$, more than five times the estimated value; however, the latter is of the correct order, which is as much as may be expected.)

The equations derived above have referred primarily to gas reactions, but they are probably applicable also to reactions in solution. In a number of cases, e.g., the decomposition of nitrogen pentoxide, the same reactions have been carried out in the gas phase and in an inert solvent; the rates in the two cases have been found to be approximately equal. If there is a tendency for compound formation to take place between the solvent and the reactants, the results may be different.

HETEROGENEOUS GAS REACTIONS

60a. Kinetics of Heterogeneous Reactions.—The study of the kinetics of heterogeneous reactions between gases taking place on the surfaces of solids has led to the discovery that in addition to reactions of apparently simple orders, there are others of zero or fractional order. In some cases, further, the reaction is inhibited, instead of accelerated, by increasing the concentration of one of the reacting gases, while in other cases the products may have a retarding influence. The equations for the kinetics of surface reactions may best be developed by following the method of I. Langmuir (1916), as described in connection with the adsorption of gases in § 56d.

Consider, first, the case of a *unimolecular reaction*, involving a single gaseous reactant on the surface of a solid. The rate of reaction will evidently be proportional to the concentration of adsorbed gas on the surface; for a given surface, this is proportional to θ, the fraction of the surface covered by the adsorbed gas. The value of θ is given by equation (56.5) as

$$\theta = \frac{kp}{kp + k'}, \tag{60.1}$$

where k and k' are constants, and p is the pressure of the gas. The rate of reaction, represented by the general expression dx/dt, is directly proportional to θ, and consequently, by the same procedure as was used in deriving equation (56.6) from (56.5), it follows that

$$\frac{dx}{dt} = \frac{k_1 p}{k_2 p + 1} \tag{60.2}$$

where k_1 and k_2 are constants.* It is apparent from this result that although the surface reaction is unimolecular, it does not behave, in general, as if it were kinetically of the first order.

At low gas pressures, $k_2 p$ in the denominator of equation (60.2) may be neglected in comparison with unity; hence, the rate equation becomes

$$\frac{dx}{dt} = k_1 p, \tag{60.3}$$

which is the expression for a first order reaction. It is evident, therefore, that a heterogeneous unimolecular reaction is kinetically of the first order only when the reacting gas pressure is low, that is, when the surface of the solid is only sparsely covered. Instances of such behavior are found for the decomposition of phosphine on glass, porcelain and silica surfaces, of nitrous oxide on gold, of hydrogen iodide on platinum, and of formic acid vapor on glass, platinum, and other surfaces.

At sufficiently high pressures, when the surface of the solid is almost completely covered with adsorbed gas, it is possible to neglect unity in comparison with $k_2 p$ in equation (60.2); this equation then becomes

$$\frac{dx}{dt} = \frac{k_1}{k_2} = \text{constant.} \tag{60.4}$$

The rate of the reaction will now be constant, independent of the pressure; such a reaction is said to be kinetically of **zero order**. The decomposition of

* These values of k_1 and k_2 are, of course, different from those in equation (56.6), because the proportionality constant is not the same.

hydrogen iodide on a gold surface, and of ammonia on surfaces of molybdenum or tungsten, are found to be reactions of zero order, the rates being independent of the pressure over a considerable range. The physical interpretation of this constancy of the reaction rate is that the surface is virtually covered with the reacting gas, and changing the pressure does not have any appreciable effect on the surface concentration of reacting molecules; the rate of decomposition is consequently almost independent of the pressure.

According to equations (60.3) and (60.4) the rate of a surface reaction is proportional to the first power of the gas pressure, at low pressures, and to the zero power at high pressures; it is thus possible to write the general equation

$$\frac{dx}{dt} = kp^n, \tag{60.5}$$

where n varies from unity to zero as the pressure is increased. It can be understood, therefore, why certain surface reactions, such as the decomposition of stibine on an antimony surface, are kinetically of a fractional order, viz., 0.6 in this case. This fractional order would undoubtedly vary with the pressure of the reacting gas, as has been observed in the decomposition of phosphine on a molybdenum surface.

For a *bimolecular reaction* involving two gaseous molecules, it is necessary for the two molecules to be adsorbed adjacent to one another on the surface of the solid. The probability of this occurrence, which determines the reaction rate, is proportional to θ^2, for a single reactant, and to $\theta_A\theta_B$ for two reacting molecules; θ_A and θ_B represent the fractions of the surface covered by the reactants A and B, respectively. If neither of the gases is strongly adsorbed, then at low pressures θ_A and θ_B are proportional to the respective pressures [see equation (56.7)]; the rate of the reaction is then given by

$$\frac{dx}{dt} = k\theta_A\theta_B = k_1 p_A p_B, \tag{60.6}$$

where k and k_1 are constants. Under these conditions the bimolecular heterogeneous reaction would be kinetically of the second order. This type of behavior has been observed for the reaction of ethylene and hydrogen on a copper surface, of hydrogen and carbon dioxide on platinum, and of nitric oxide and oxygen on glass, at low pressures.

The variation with temperature of the specific rate of a simple surface reaction, of the type considered above, can usually be represented by an expression of the form of equation (59.2), viz., $k = Ae^{-E/RT}$, where E is the energy of activation. As will be seen later (§ 61d), the activation energy for a heterogeneous reaction is, however, in general, quite different from that for the same reaction taking place in a homogeneous, e.g., gas, phase. Further, although the frequency factor A is still given by equations (59.10) and (59.12), the entropy of activation cannot be estimated in a simple manner, and equations (59.13) and (59.14) are usually not applicable.

If one of the reacting substances is strongly adsorbed, so that it occupies most of the surface, the kinetics of the process is completely changed. In fact, as the pressure of the more strongly adsorbed gas is increased the rate of the surface reaction actually decreases, as will be shown in the following section.

60b. Retardation of Surface Reactions.—Consider a bimolecular heterogeneous reaction between one molecule of a gaseous reactant A and one of a reactant B; if the gas A is strongly adsorbed, the fraction θ_A of the surface covered by this reactant at the pressure p_A is given by equation (60.1) as

$$\theta_A = \frac{kp_A}{kp_A + k'}. \tag{60.7}$$

The fraction of the surface covered by the reactant B is small, and hence the fraction of the surface that is bare may be taken as equal to $1 - \theta_A$; by equation (60.7) this is

$$1 - \theta_A = \frac{k'}{kp_A + k'}.$$

For a strongly adsorbed gas, k' may be neglected in comparison with kp_A, and hence

$$1 - \theta_A = \frac{k'}{kp_A}. \tag{60.8}$$

The rate of the surface reaction between A and B will depend on the rate at which the B molecules can reach the bare parts of the surface, because there are always A molecules available in the vicinity for reaction to occur. The rate of adsorption of the B molecules on the bare surface, and hence the reaction rate, is proportional to the product of the pressure of the gas B, i.e., p_B, and the fraction $1 - \theta_A$ of the surface that is bare; hence, making use of equation (60.8),

$$\frac{dx}{dt} = k_1 p_B(1 - \theta_A) = k_2 \frac{p_B}{p_A}. \tag{60.9}$$

The rate of reaction should thus be proportional to p_B, the pressure of the feebly adsorbed gas, and *inversely proportional* to p_A, the pressure of the strongly adsorbed reactant. *The reacting gas A thus retards the rate of the surface reaction because it virtually monopolizes the surface and makes it more difficult for B to be adsorbed.* A number of instances of this type of kinetics are known; in the combination of carbon monoxide and oxygen on a platinum or a quartz glass surface, the former gas is strongly adsorbed and retards the reaction. In the ethylene-hydrogen reaction on copper at low temperatures, the rate is inversely proportional to the pressure of ethylene; on a nickel surface the hydrogen is strongly adsorbed and retards the formation of ethane.

Not only can one of the reactants retard a heterogeneous reaction by being strongly adsorbed, but a reaction product can function in a similar manner. The principle is identical with that described above; by occupying a large proportion of the surface the product prevents access of the reactant or reactants. As in the preceding case, the rate of reaction is proportional to the pressure of the reacting gas, assuming a single reactant, and to the fraction of bare surface; this leads to a result analogous to equation (60.9), where p_A now represents the pressure of the strongly adsorbed product. Examples of retardation by a reaction product are the thermal decomposition of nitrous and nitric oxides on a platinum surface, when oxygen is strongly adsorbed, and of ammonia, also on platinum, when hydrogen gas is the strongly adsorbed product. The familiar reaction between sulfur dioxide and oxygen on a platinum catalyst is retarded by the product, sulfur trioxide, which is strongly adsorbed.

There are many other cases of unusual kinetics of surface reactions. Sufficient has been stated, however, to indicate the general nature of the results, and it is unnecessary to treat the subject further at present.

CATALYSIS

61a. The Criteria of Catalysis.—The term **catalysis** is applied generally to cases in which *the rate of a chemical reaction is accelerated by the presence of a substance which is itself unchanged chemically in the process.* The substance causing the acceleration is called a **catalyst.** In some cases an added substance retards the rate of a reaction; this is referred to as **negative catalysis.** Many types of catalyzed reactions, both homogeneous and heterogeneous, are known, but in spite of their many differences there are certain characteristics common to them all; these will now be considered briefly.

(i) *The catalyst is unchanged chemically at the end of the reaction.* The total amount of the catalyst is the same at the end as at the beginning of the reaction; hence, it must be unchanged chemically, although it frequently undergoes a change in physical form. For example, manganese dioxide employed to catalyze the decomposition of potassium chlorate can be changed from relatively large crystals to a fine powder, and platinum gauze used as a catalyst for the oxidation of ammonia shows considerable roughening after a few weeks. Since the catalyst undergoes a physical alteration, it probably takes part *chemically* in a certain stage of the reaction and is regenerated, also chemically, in another stage.

(ii) *A small quantity of catalyst is often sufficient to bring about a considerable amount of reaction.* Since the catalyst is not used up in the course of the reaction, a small quantity will often bring about the combination of large quantities of reactants. In some cases minute traces of catalyst are sufficient to cause considerable acceleration of certain reactions, but as a general rule, in a homogeneous reaction that does not involve a chain mechanism, the rate of a catalytic action is proportional to the concentration of the catalyst. For many heterogeneous reactions, also, the rate increases roughly in proportion to the area of the catalyst surface, although the same material in different forms may have quite different activities (§ 61e).

(iii) *The catalyst does not affect the position of equilibrium in a reversible reaction.* Since a catalyst is unchanged chemically at the end of the reaction, it can contribute no appreciable energy to the system; consequently, it follows from thermodynamics that the same position of equilibrium should be ultimately attained whether a catalyst is present or not. This theoretical expectation has been verified experimentally. The function of the catalyst, therefore, is to speed up the attainment of equilibrium without affecting the value of the equilibrium constant. An important consequence of this fact is, that for a reversible process, the catalyst must affect the rates of the forward and reverse reactions to the same extent, since the equilibrium constant K is equal to the ratio k/k' of the respective specific rates (§ 58j). Consequently, a good catalyst for the forward reaction will also accelerate the reverse change. In illustration may be quoted the fact that the same catalyst, namely hydrochloric acid, can be employed to facilitate the esterification of an organic acid and also the hydrolysis of the corresponding ester. Other instances will be found in later parts of the present chapter.

There are some cases, e.g., in the esterification process just mentioned, in which the catalyst, i.e., the hydrochloric acid, appears to affect the equilibrium constant (§ 58j); the reason for this lies in the fact that the acid changes the medium to such an extent that the activities differ markedly from the concentrations. If the true equilibrium constants, involving the activities, were evaluated they would be found to be independent of the catalyst.

(iv) *The catalyst does not initiate the reaction; it merely accelerates a reaction that is already occurring, although perhaps extremely slowly.* The criterion that a given reaction should be possible is that the process should be accompanied by a decrease of free energy (§ 37c), but the fact that the reaction is possible gives no indication of whether it will take place at an appreciable rate. If the *free energy of activation* of the reaction, which may bear no relationship to the over-all free energy, is large, the reaction may be so slow as to be undetectable; nevertheless, it is probably true to say that the reaction is taking place. *The function of a catalyst, which speeds up the reaction, is to make the same over-all process take place by an alternative path involving a smaller free energy of activation.* The catalyzed reaction invariably occurs in stages, and the free energy of activation of the slowest of these stages must be appreciably less than for the reaction in the absence of a catalyst. If the frequency factor A in the Arrhenius equation or, in other words, the entropy of activation, is taken as roughly constant, the reaction rate is determined essentially by the energy (heat) of activation. It is possible to state the foregoing conclusions in the following approximate form: *a catalyst causes a given reaction to take place in such stages that the slowest has an activation energy considerably less than for the uncatalyzed reaction.* Experimental data will be quoted later which support this theoretical deduction.

Consider a reaction involving a substance A and a substance B to give AB, viz.,

$$A + B = AB.$$

If the free energy ΔF for this reaction is negative under the experimental conditions, the process will be possible theoretically, but it may be very slow. Suppose a catalyst C is added which accelerates the formation of AB; the reaction may occur in the following relatively rapid stages,

$$A + C = AC$$

$$AC + B = AB + C,$$

so that the result is the formation of AB, the catalyst C being regenerated. The substance AC, which acts as an intermediate and permits the reaction to take place in stages with low activation energies, is sometimes referred to as an **intermediate compound,** although it is not always a stable compound capable of isolation. Sometimes the intermediate substance can be identified as a known compound, as, for instance, in the combination of hydrogen and oxygen on a copper catalyst. It has been proved that the reaction occurs in the stages

$$2Cu + \tfrac{1}{2}O_2 = Cu_2O \quad \text{and} \quad Cu_2O + H_2 = H_2O + Cu,$$

so that the intermediate is the familiar substance cuprous oxide. The same is true in the conversion of ethanol to diethyl ether in the presence of sulfuric acid as catalyst; the intermediate compound is then ethyl sulfuric acid in solution. In other cases, however, the intermediate substance may exist on a surface or it may have a transitory existence only, so that it will not be identical with any known compound. This is probably true for the hydrolysis of esters, the inversion of cane sugar, and similar processes catalyzed by acids or bases (§ 61b). For the heterogeneous gas reactions occurring on the surface of a solid catalyst, the intermediate state is probably represented by the reacting molecules adsorbed on the surface.

61b. Homogeneous Catalysis.—Catalytic processes may be considered in separate categories, depending on whether the catalyst is part of the same phase as the reactants, i.e., **homogeneous catalysis,** or whether it forms a separate phase, i.e., **heterogeneous catalysis.** There may be a further subdivision according as the reactants are in the gaseous or liquid phase. Catalyzed homogeneous gas reactions are not very common; one of the best known is the use of nitric oxide to catalyze the combination of sulfur dioxide and oxygen in the "lead chamber" process. Nitric oxide is also able to catalyze the reaction between carbon monoxide and oxygen. The reactions may be written as

$$\tfrac{1}{2}O_2 + NO = NO_2 \quad \text{and} \quad NO_2 + SO_2 = NO + SO_3,$$

$$\tfrac{1}{2}O_2 + NO = NO_2 \quad \text{and} \quad NO_2 + CO = NO + CO_2,$$

the nitrogen dioxide being the intermediate compound. It is probable, however, that the actual reactions are much more complicated than these equations would imply.

Another type of catalyzed homogeneous gas reaction is the thermal decomposition of ethers and aldehydes in the presence of iodine as catalyst.

Approximate activation energies for the iodine-catalyzed and uncatalyzed decompositions of a number of ethers have been calculated from measurements of the reaction rates at several temperatures (C. N. Hinshelwood, 1929); the results, which are of interest, are recorded in Table LXXIII. It

TABLE LXXIII. ACTIVATION ENERGIES FOR THE THERMAL DECOMPOSITION OF ETHERS

Substance Decomposed	Uncatalyzed	Catalyzed
Methyl ethyl ether	54.5 kcal.	38.0 kcal.
Diethyl ether	53.0	34.3
Diisopropyl ether	61.0	28.5

is seen that the activation energies of the catalyzed reactions are 16.5 to 32.5 kcal. less than for the uncatalyzed reactions. At a temperature of 800° K, in the vicinity of which the latter were studied, the increase in reaction rate would be given approximately by a factor of $e^{16,500/2 \times 800}$ to $e^{32,500/2 \times 800}$, i.e., about 10^4 to 10^8.

There are many instances of homogeneous catalysis in solution, and perhaps the most important examples are those generally included under the heading of **acid-base catalysis.** It has long been known that hydrogen ions are able to accelerate the inversion of cane sugar, the hydrolysis of esters, and other reactions in aqueous solution; similarly, hydroxyl ions were found to be particularly effective for the mutarotation of glucose, the conversion of acetone into diacetone alcohol, etc. In the course of recent years, however, it has become evident that for certain reactions which are catalyzed by hydrogen ions, e.g., hydrolysis of ortho-esters, all acids in the widest sense (§ 53a), that is, all substances with a tendency to give up a proton, can act as catalysts; this is known as **general acid catalysis.** Similarly, **general base catalysis,** in which all bases, that is, all substances capable of taking up a proton, can act as catalysts, has been shown to occur with certain reactions primarily catalyzed by hydroxyl ions. For some processes, e.g., the mutarotation of glucose,* the hydrolysis of simple esters and the enolization of acetone, both acids and bases have been found to have catalytic action, although bases are, in general, more effective than the corresponding acids. It is of interest to note that it was the discovery of the phenomena of general acid and base catalysis that led to the development of the concept of acids and bases treated in § 53a.

By determining the rates of the catalyzed reactions under various conditions and carrying out a mathematical analysis of the results, it is possible to determine the catalytic effects of individual acids and bases, including those of water, hydrogen ions, hydroxyl ions, undissociated molecules of acids and bases, anions of weak acids, and cations of weak bases. The general conclusions reached from these measurements is that *the catalytic efficiency of an acid or base for a given reaction is related to the dissociation constant of the acid or base* (§ 53c). The dissociation constant is a measure of the tend-

* The mutarotation is a spontaneous change in the angle of rotation of the plane of polarization of light observed with solutions of glucose (dextrose); it is due to an isomeric change of an α-form to a β-form, or vice versa.

ency of an acid to lose, or of a base to gain, a proton; it appears, therefore, that the addition and removal of protons play an essential part in the mechanism of the catalyzed reactions under consideration.

The mutarotation of glucose, for example, probably involves the addition of a proton, from the acid catalyst, to the molecule at one point, followed, or accompanied, by the removal of a proton, by the basic catalyst, from another point in the molecule. Thus, if GH represents α-glucose and HG is the isomeric β-glucose, the catalyzed change may be represented by

$$H^+ + GH \rightarrow H\overset{+}{G}H \rightarrow HG + H^+,$$

the first proton being supplied by an acid while the one discarded is removed by a base; the intermediate compound $H\overset{+}{G}H$ probably exists as an ion in solution, although it cannot be isolated. It may be noted, in connection with this proposed mechanism, that in the absence of water the base pyridine is a poor catalyst for the mutarotation of tetramethylglucose, and so also is the acid m-cresol; a mixture of pyridine and m-cresol is, however, a powerful catalyst.

It is probable that all reactions catalyzed by acids or bases, or both, involve a somewhat similar mechanism, viz., the addition of a proton to one part of the molecule and its removal from another part. In hydrolytic reactions a molecule of water is probably added at the same time as the proton, and the resulting intermediate breaks up when (or after) the other proton is removed. If the rate of the addition process is relatively slow, compared with the removal of the proton, the reaction will be of the acid-catalyzed type; if the reverse is the case, then bases will be the effective catalysts. On the other hand, if the addition and removal of the proton take place with somewhat similar rates, both acids and bases will act catalytically.

Among other homogeneous catalyzed reactions in solution reference may be made to the decomposition of hydrogen peroxide in the presence of halogen and halide ions. If a halide ion, preferably in acid solution, is added to hydrogen peroxide, a steady state is soon reached in which the halogen and halide ion concentrations remain constant, and the net reaction is the decomposition of the peroxide. Careful study of the mechanisms of the processes involved has shown that at the steady state two "compensating reactions" occur at the same rate. For example, when the bromine-bromide ion system is the catalyst, the processes, each of which undoubtedly takes place in at least two stages, are

$$H_2O_2 + 2H_3O^+ + 2Br^- = Br_2 + 4H_2O$$

$$Br_2 + H_2O_2 + 2H_2O = O_2 + 2H_3O^+ + 2Br^-,$$

with the result that the peroxide is decomposed catalytically. In these reactions it is not possible to identify the "intermediate compound," except perhaps as bromine molecules. It must be remembered, however, that these equations represent over-all reactions; it appears from a study of the detailed stages that HBrO may be regarded as the intermediate compound in each case.

61c. Negative Catalysis and Inhibition.—A substance that is able to diminish, rather than increase, the rate of reaction is said to be a **negative catalyst** or **inhibitor**. The oxidation of sodium sulfite solution by oxygen gas is inhibited by small amounts of various organic compounds, e.g., alcohols, aniline and benzaldehyde; similarly, the oxidation of benzaldehyde and of other aldehydes is inhibited by anthracene, diphenylamine and other substances. It has been proved that these oxidations are actually chain reactions (§ 581), and the function of the inhibitors in these instances is to terminate the reaction chains by combining with, and thus destroying, the chain carriers.

Negative catalysis in gas reactions is probably to be ascribed similarly to the breaking of reaction chains. Reference was made earlier to the use of lead tetraethyl to reduce "knocking" in the internal combustion engine, and of the property of nitric oxide and propylene of terminating chains. These are all examples of inhibition or negative catalysis. In the case of tetraethyl lead the actual inhibitor is probably finely divided lead dioxide, formed by oxidation, which reacts with and destroys the chain carriers.

61d. Heterogeneous Catalysis Involving Gases.—Reactions between gaseous substances in the presence of a solid catalyst are very common; in fact, the heterogeneous processes considered from the standpoint of their kinetics in § 60a fall into this category. These reactions are all catalyzed by the material of the surface upon which they occur; in the absence of the solid the reaction rates are usually smaller. A number of processes of industrial importance, such as the combination of nitrogen and hydrogen to form ammonia, the oxidation of ammonia, the reduction of carbon monoxide to methanol, and many reactions involving hydrocarbons, require the use of suitable solid catalysts. Some reactions which were at one time thought to be completely homogeneous have been found to take place, at least partly, on the walls of the containing vessel; thus, the combination of ethylene and bromine vapor is inhibited if the interior of the glass reaction vessel is coated with paraffin, but it occurs even more rapidly if stearic acid is used. The formation of ethylene bromide is evidently a heterogeneous reaction which is catalyzed by a glass or a stearic acid surface, but not by paraffin.

In a catalyzed reaction between two gases taking place on the surface of a solid, it is probably necessary that the reacting molecules should be first adsorbed at adjacent points on the surface (§ 60a). If these adsorbed molecules have sufficient energy, they may combine to form the activated complex for the process (§ 59c); this differs from the activated complex of the corresponding homogeneous reaction in being also adsorbed by the catalyst surface. The adsorbed activated complex then decomposes at a definite rate, forming the reaction products which are finally desorbed from the surface and pass into the gas phase. *The basis of heterogeneous catalysis is consequently adsorption, at adjacent positions on the surface, of molecules with sufficient energy to form the adsorbed activated complex.* If one of the reactants is very strongly adsorbed it will prevent access of the other to the surface, and consequently the reaction will be retarded, as explained in § 60b. On the other hand, if neither of the gases is adsorbed to any appreciable extent, the probability of the reacting molecules being adjacent to one another on the surface will be small, and the catalytic effect will not be great. The ideal conditions for catalysis are that both gases should be adsorbed to a moderate extent, but neither so strongly that it covers virtually the whole of the surface.

If the catalyzed reaction is unimolecular in character, involving a single molecular species, e.g., the decomposition of hydrogen iodide on gold or platinum, or of ammonia on tungsten or molybdenum, the process involves the adsorption of a molecule of reactant with sufficient energy to form the adsorbed activated complex. The latter then decomposes and the products are desorbed, as described above. Since there is only one reacting substance it would seem that strong adsorption would be advantageous; the larger the amount of surface covered the greater the probability of the formation of the adsorbed activated complex, and hence also the greater the reaction rate.

Both experimental and theoretical considerations lead to the view that the type of adsorption which is a necessary prerequisite to surface catalysis is that referred to in § 56c as chemisorption or activated adsorption. The more general, van der Waals, type of adsorption involves forces that are too feeble to have any appreciable influence on chemical reaction. The stronger forces of a chemical nature operative in chemisorption tend to bring about a partial loosening of the bonds in the adsorbed reacting molecules; the result is that a much smaller amount of energy is sufficient to form the activated complex for the reaction. It is to be expected, therefore, that the activation energy of a surface reaction should be less than for the corresponding homogeneous reaction; that this is the case is indicated by the results in Table LXXIV. It is the marked decrease in the energy of activation that is

TABLE LXXIV.   ACTIVATION ENERGIES OF HOMOGENEOUS AND HETEROGENEOUS REACTIONS

| Decomposition of | Surface | Activation Energy | |
		Heterogeneous	Homogeneous
Hydrogen iodide	Platinum	25.0 kcal.	44.0 kcal.
	Gold	14.0	
Nitrous oxide	Platinum	32.5	58.5
	Gold	29.0	
Ammonia	Tungsten	39.0	~80
	Osmium	47.0	

the main reason for the greatly increased rates of catalyzed reactions. Another important factor is the large surface area of the catalyst, since this permits a greater concentration of the activated complex, but calculations have shown that the reduction of activation energy, as compared with the homogeneous reaction, is chiefly responsible for the acceleration of heterogeneous processes.

61e. Properties of the Catalytic Surface: Active Centers.—The catalytic activity of a surface, like chemisorption, is specific in nature; there is, in other words, no universal catalyst for all reactions. Some reactions are accelerated by one substance, while others require a surface of an entirely different material. In spite of the many variations, certain generalizations can be made. The metals copper and nickel, in particular, have a strong attraction for hydrogen; hydrogen gas is chemisorbed on surfaces of these metals, and it probably exists there in a form approaching that of the separated atoms. It is consequently not surprising to find that copper and nickel are among the best catalysts for reactions involving the addition to or removal of hydrogen from a molecule, i.e., hydrogenation and dehydrogenation processes. For example, if ethanol vapor is passed over a copper or nickel catalyst at 300° to 400° C, it is dehydrogenated, with the formation of acetaldehyde; thus,

$$CH_3CH_2OH = CH_3CHO + H_2.$$

Similar reactions, involving removal of hydrogen from various alcohols and other organic compounds, are also catalyzed by copper and nickel. In the reduction of carbon monoxide to methanol, which is a hydrogenation process, viz.,

$$CO + 2H_2 = CH_3OH,$$

the catalyst usually employed is a mixture of zinc oxide and chromium sesquioxide; this mixture is known to exhibit marked chemisorption of hydrogen.

Aluminum oxide, in an appropriate physical form, adsorbs water vapor very strongly; this substance is consequently found to be a valuable catalyst for dehydration processes, involving the removal of the elements of water from a molecule of an organic compound. Thus, when ethanol vapor is passed over a surface of alumina the product is ethylene,

$$CH_3CH_2OH = CH_2 : CH_2 + H_2O.$$

If zinc oxide is used in place of aluminum oxide, the product is acetaldehyde, as might have been anticipated; since zinc oxide is able to chemisorb hydrogen, the dehydrogenation process would take place in preference to dehydration.

In addition to the chemical nature of the catalyst, the state of its surface is of great importance in determining the rate of a heterogeneous reaction. Not the whole of the surface is catalytically active, for the reaction apparently takes place at certain points only. These are generally known as **active centers** (H. S. Taylor, 1925), and in the preparation of a catalytic material it is desirable that there should be as large a number as possible of such active centers.

There is much evidence which indicates the existence of points or centers of special activity on the surface of a catalyst. Ethylene and hydrogen, for instance, are both adsorbed by a copper surface, and there they react to form ethane; a trace of mercury reduces the amount of ethylene adsorbed to about 80 per cent, and that of hydrogen to 5 per cent of their respective values on a clean surface. At the same time, however, the rate of production of ethane, by the combination of ethylene and hydrogen, is decreased to less than 0.5 per cent of its initial value. The fact that the catalytic activity is diminished by the mercury to a much greater extent than is the adsorption of the reacting gases, shows that chemical reaction occurs at only a small fraction of the centers of adsorption. If all the parts of the surface were equally active for catalysis, the adsorption and reaction should be affected to the same extent.

Different reactions apparently occur at different active centers on a given surface, for it has been found that the reaction between carbon dioxide and hydrogen on a platinum catalyst can be largely inhibited, while on the same surface the decomposition of nitrous oxide is hardly affected. The exact nature of the active centers is not known, but it is believed that they are partially isolated atoms or groups of atoms situated at lines of discontinuity, such as the edges of crystals, at the boundaries between crystal grains, or at cracks or imperfections in the small crystals constituting the surface.

61f. Promoters.—It sometimes happens that a mixture of two catalysts is more effective than either alone, e.g., zinc and chromium oxides in the reduction of carbon monoxide to methanol. Such a mixture is known as a **mixed catalyst**. In the extreme case, a small quantity of a material, which is itself either noncatalytic or a feeble catalyst, is able to increase very appreciably the activity of a given catalyst; a substance of this kind is referred to as a **promoter**. Many examples of promoter action are known, and several are of industrial importance. In the combination of nitrogen and hydrogen, the catalyst that has been used is iron, promoted by the addition of small amounts of potassium and aluminum oxides.

Attempts have been made to explain promoter action by changes in the spacing of the crystal lattice, and consequently of the active centers of the catalytic surface, and also by changes in the adsorptive power of the catalyst. It has been established experimentally that chemisorption occurs more readily at a promoted than at an unpromoted surface, but it is doubtful if this alone will account for promoter action. There are probably several factors which are simultaneously operative; these may include the number, spacing and effectiveness of the catalytically active centers.

61g. Retardation and Poisoning.—It was seen in § 60b that if either one of the reactants or one of the products of a reaction is strongly adsorbed by the catalyst, the rate of the reaction may be considerably decreased. This is the phenomenon of **retardation,** the retarding effect being proportional to a simple power of the pressure (or concentration) of the retarding substance. In other cases, purely extraneous materials, often present in very minute amounts, are able to inhibit catalyzed reactions to a marked extent; such substances are called **catalytic poisons**. An example of poisoning was given in § 61e in connection with the ethylene-hydrogen reaction on copper; traces of mercury reduce very greatly the efficiency of the catalyst. In the manufacture of sulfur trioxide from sulfur dioxide and oxygen, arsenic compounds act as poisons for the platinum catalyst; it was this fact which was the cause of the failure of the early attempts to establish this process on the industrial scale. The vanadium pentoxide catalyst, largely used at the present time, is much less sensitive to poisons.

The behavior of a catalytic poison is evidently based on its strong adsorption at the active centers, thus preventing access of the reacting substances. Since these centers constitute a fraction only of the total surface, it is clear that a small amount of poison may have a very considerable effect in reducing the efficiency of a catalyst. The fact that such is actually the case may be taken as proof of the existence of active centers on the catalyst surface.

61h. Heterogeneous Reactions in Solution.—The decomposition of hydrogen peroxide in aqueous solution can be catalyzed by various metals. If the surface of the metal is greatly increased, by the use of the catalyst in the colloidal form, the rate of the decomposition is considerably accelerated. The reactions are found to be kinetically of the first order, and the catalysts are particularly susceptible to the action of poisons, such as hydrogen sulfide, hydrogen cyanide, mercuric chloride and iodine. The poisoning action is probably due to the preferential adsorption of the poison, so that the hydrogen peroxide does not have access to the surface of the colloidal particles.

The most important heterogeneous catalyzed reactions occurring in solution are those in which the catalysts are the **enzymes** derived from living organisms. These substances are protein in nature, and hence they exist in the colloidal form in solution; the catalytic action is thus to be regarded as heterogeneous in character. Each enzyme is specific for a given reaction, although in the case of reversible processes, enzymes, like other catalysts, are able to accelerate both forward and reverse reactions. Further, like the colloidal metals, which they resemble in some respects, enzymes are readily poisoned by traces of the same substances that poison the former catalysts.

The rate of an enzyme reaction is proportional to the concentration of the reactant, referred to as the **substrate,** provided this concentration is small; the reaction kinetics are then quite normal. However, at high concentrations of the substrate, the reaction rate becomes independent of the concentration; the reaction is then of zero order. The behavior is analogous to that observed with some homogeneous gas reactions on solid surfaces (§ 60a); when the surface is almost completely covered with reactant, the rate becomes independent of the pressure (or concentration) of the latter. In the case of the enzyme action, similarly, the process will become of zero order when the surface of the colloidal particle, or such parts of it as are catalytically active, is covered with substrate. Even if the concentration of the latter is increased beyond this point there can be no further increase in the rate of the reaction, for the given quantity of enzyme.

READING REFERENCES

1. **Ammonia catalysis.** Emmett, *Journal of Chemical Education,* **7,** 2571 (1930).
2. **Acid-base catalysis.** Livingston, *ibid.,* **7,** 2887 (1930).
3. **Chain reactions.** Crist, *ibid.,* **8,** 504 (1931).
4. **Rate of inversion of cane sugar.** Montgomery, *ibid.,* **8,** 940 (1931).
5. **Catalyzed organic reactions.** Mitchell, *ibid.,* **9,** 59 (1932).
6. **Molecular fragments in oxidation processes.** Bates, *ibid.,* **9,** 1219 (1932).

7. **Catalytic decomposition of ethanol.** Morris, *ibid.*, **9,** 1730 (1932).
8. **Reaction mechanisms.** Steffens, *ibid.*, **12,** 115 (1935).
9. **Kinetics of some inorganic reactions.** Treffers, *ibid.*, **14,** 74 (1937).
10. **Catalysis in the hydrocarbon field.** Gilbert, *ibid.*, **18,** 435 (1941).
11. **Catalysis.** Komarewsky, *ibid.*, **19,** 563 (1942).
12. **Experiments in reaction kinetics.** Wistar and Nelson, *ibid.*, **21,** 94 (1944).

REVIEW QUESTIONS

1. Distinguish between the molecularity and the order of a reaction. Why are these quantities important?
2. Derive the characteristic equation of a first order reaction. How does the specific rate depend on the concentration units?
3. Give examples of a first order reaction, (*a*) in the gas phase, (*b*) in solution. State how the reactions are studied.
4. Derive the characteristic equation for a second order reaction, in which the reactants are (*a*) at the same concentration, (*b*) at different concentrations. What are the units of the specific reaction rate?
5. Give an example of a second order reaction and state how the specific rate may be determined.
6. Derive the characteristic equation for a third order reaction in which the reactants are at the same concentration. Give examples of such reactions.
7. Why are reactions involving more than three molecules believed to take place in stages? What stage determines the rate of such a reaction? Give examples.
8. How may the order of a reaction be determined by a graphical procedure?
9. Show that the time taken to complete a definite fraction, e.g., half, of a reaction is a function of the initial concentration, depending on the order of the reaction.
10. Describe the differential method for determining the order of a reaction. Explain its use in connection with the nitric oxide-hydrogen reaction.
11. Derive the rate equation for a reversible reaction in which both forward and reverse reactions are (*a*) first order, (*b*) second order.
12. How may the relationship between the specific rates of forward and reverse reactions, and the equilibrium constant of a reversible reaction be tested?
13. In the simultaneous consecutive reactions $A \rightarrow B \rightarrow C$, how are the amounts of A, B, and C present at any instant related to the specific rates?
14. Explain, with examples, what is meant by a chain reaction. How can the reaction chains be broken?
15. Give an equation which represents the variation of specific reaction rate with temperature. Explain the significance of the various factors. How may the equation be tested graphically?
16. Outline the collision theory of reaction rates. When does it succeed, and why does it fail?
17. Describe the activated complex theory of reaction rates. Show that it leads to the expectation that the free energy of activation, in general, determines the rate of a reaction.
18. Show that the activated complex theory can be applied where the simple collision theory fails.
19. Explain how it is possible for the reacting molecules in a unimolecular reaction to acquire their activation energy in collisions, although the process is kinetically of the first order.

20. What is known about the activation energy of an endothermic reaction? How are the activation energies of the two directions of a reversible reaction related?

21. How is it possible to predict the specific rate of (a) a bimolecular, (b) a unimolecular, reaction?

22. Derive the general equation for a unimolecular heterogeneous gas reaction. To what does this equation reduce at (a) high, (b) low, gas pressures? Why do reactions of apparently fractional order occur?

23. How is it possible for a reactant or a product to retard the rate of a surface reaction? Derive an equation to show the nature of this effect.

24. State and explain the four criteria of catalysis.

25. Explain the intermediate compound theory of catalysis in its most general form.

26. Describe the nature of general acid and general base catalysis. How are these forms of catalysis explained?

27. Give examples of heterogeneous catalysis involving gases. How are such reactions explained? What is believed to be the main cause of the increased reaction rate?

28. How does the chemical nature of the catalyst sometimes determine the type of reaction catalyzed? Give examples.

29. What are active centers? Give evidence for their existence on a catalyst surface.

30. Explain, with examples, the following terms: promoter, negative catalysis, catalytic poison.

31. Give a brief account of enzyme reaction from the standpoint of catalysis.

PROBLEMS

I

1. The following results were obtained in the decomposition of nitrogen pentoxide in carbon tetrachloride solution at 40° C. The reaction rate was followed by measuring the amount of decomposition x in terms of the volume of oxygen liberated after various times t sec.

t	600	1200	1800	2400	3000	∞ sec.
x	6.30	11.40	15.53	18.90	21.70	34.75 cc.

Show by calculation and graphically that the reaction is first order; determine the value of the specific rate and state the units. What is the time required to reduce the concentration to half its initial value?

2. In the thermal decomposition of gaseous acetaldehyde the amount decomposed, x, was indicated by the increase, Δp, of pressure in a closed vessel; the results were as follows:

t	42	105	242	480	840 sec.
Δp	34	74	134	194	244 mm.

The initial pressure, a, of acetaldehyde in the same vessel was 363 mm. Show graphically and by calculation that the reaction is of the second order.

3. In the thermal decomposition of nitrous oxide at 760° C, the time required to decompose half the reactant was 255 sec. when the initial pressure was 290 mm., and 212 sec. at an initial pressure of 360 mm. What is the order of the reaction under these conditions? Calculate the time required to decompose half the reactant when the initial pressure is 1 atm.

4. In the reaction between equal molar concentrations of bromine and fumaric acid in aqueous solution, the reaction rate, $-dc/dt$, is represented by 0.0106 units, when the concentration of the reactants is expressed by 8.37 in the same units. When the concentration has fallen to 3.66 the reaction rate is equivalent to 0.0022 in the same units. What is the order of the reaction?

5. In a reversible reaction of the type $A \rightleftharpoons B$, the following results were obtained:

t	180	300	420	1440	∞ sec.
x	0.20	0.33	0.43	1.05	1.58 $(= x_e)$

In the same units the initial concentration of A, i.e., a, was 1.89. Calculate the specific rates of the direct and reverse reactions.

6. For the decomposition of nitrous oxide, the specific rate in liter mole^{-1} sec.$^{-1}$ units is 0.135 at 694° C and 3.70 at 812° C. Calculate the activation energy for this reaction, and evaluate A in the Arrhenius equation $k = Ae^{-E/RT}$. What would be the specific rate of the reaction at 550° C?

II

1. The following results were obtained in the decomposition of malonic acid vapor; the increase of pressure, Δp, is a measure of the amount, x, of the reactant decomposed.

t	600	1200	2100	3360	∞ sec.
Δp	37.0	67.0	108.0	155.0	302.0 mm.

Show by calculation and graphically that the reaction is of the first order; determine the value of the specific rate and state the units. What is the time required to decompose half the reactant?

2. In the saponification of 0.01 molar methyl acetate by 0.01 molar sodium hydroxide at 25° C the following results were obtained:

t	180	300	420	600	900 sec.
x	2.60	3.66	4.50	5.36	6.37 $\times 10^{-3}$ mole liter^{-1}

Show graphically and by calculation that the reaction is of the second order. Determine the value of the specific rate, and state the units.

3. In the reaction between equimolar amounts of nitric oxide and hydrogen, the times taken to reduce the pressure to half the initial value, for different initial pressures, p, were as follows:

p	263	227	192 mm.
$t_{0.5}$	78	102	141 min.

What is the order of the reaction?

4. In the thermal decomposition of nitrogen dioxide the reaction rate, $-dc/dt$, for an initial concentration of 0.0225 mole liter^{-1} was 0.0033, whereas for an initial concentration of 0.0162 mole liter^{-1} the rate was 0.0016. Determine the order of the reaction.

5. In a reversible reaction of the type $A \rightleftharpoons B$, the following results were obtained:

t	2160	3900	6000	9600	∞ sec.
x	3.70	6.07	7.98	10.28	13.29 $(= x_e)$

In the same units the initial concentration of A, i.e., a, was 18.23. Calculate the specific rates of the direct and reverse reactions.

6. The specific rate of the unimolecular decomposition of nitrous oxide on a gold surface is 2.21×10^{-4} sec.$^{-1}$ at 990° C and 4.28×10^{-5} sec.$^{-1}$ at 834° C. Calculate the activation energy for this reaction, and evaluate A in the Arrhenius equation $k = A e^{-E/RT}$. Determine the specific reaction rate on the same surface at 1100° C. (The activation energy for the heterogeneous reaction may be compared with the result for the homogeneous reaction in problem I, 6.)

CHAPTER XIX

PHOTOCHEMISTRY

The Laws of Photochemistry

62a. Introduction.—The subject of **photochemistry** is concerned mainly with *the characteristics of chemical reactions resulting from exposure of a system to radiation*, although certain related topics are generally considered under the same heading. The term "radiation," strictly speaking, refers to electromagnetic vibrations ranging from the low frequency electric (radio) waves, through the infrared, visible and ultraviolet portions of the spectrum to the high frequency X-rays and γ-rays. The radiations of photochemical interest, however, are generally restricted to those lying in the visible and ultraviolet regions, that is, in the wave length range from 8000 Å to 2000 Å. Reactions of many types, e.g., synthesis, decomposition, polymerization, isomeric change, oxidation and reduction, can be brought about by exposure to light of suitable wave length.

There is one respect in which some, but not all, photochemical reactions differ from ordinary chemical processes, usually referred to as "thermal" or "dark" reactions. The latter, as seen in § 37c, are always accompanied by a decrease of free energy of the reacting system; *certain photochemical processes, however, involve an increase of the free energy.* Illustrations of such reactions are provided by the conversion of oxygen into ozone, the decomposition of ammonia, and the polymerization of anthracene. One of the most important of all photochemical processes, from the biological and other standpoints, namely the photosynthesis of carbohydrates and oxygen from carbon dioxide and water, falls into the same category. In all these reactions some of the energy of the radiation is converted into free energy of the products; when the source of light is removed, however, the system tends to return to its original state, since this process is accompanied by a decrease of free energy. The change may, nevertheless, take place extremely slowly at ordinary temperatures, as in the case of the reaction between carbohydrates and oxygen to regenerate carbon dioxide and water. On the other hand, if the reverse (dark) reaction is rapid, it may occur simultaneously with the photochemical reaction, and this leads to a state of photochemical equilibrium.

62b. The Absorption of Radiation.—It is to be expected that there should be some relationship between the light absorbed and the chemical change occurring in a photochemical reaction. Such a connection can be stated in terms of the generalization first proposed by T. von Grotthuss (1817) and rediscovered by J. W. Draper (1841). It is usually known as the **Grotthuss-Draper law,** and may be put in the following form: *only those radiations which*

are absorbed by the reacting system are effective in producing chemical change.
It should be clearly understood that although photochemical reaction can
result only from the absorption of radiation, it does not follow that all, or any,
of the light absorbed is effective chemically.   In certain cases some or all of the
light absorbed is converted into heat; that is to say, the energy of the radiation
is transformed into kinetic energy of translation of the absorbing molecules.
In other instances, *the absorbed radiation is re-emitted as light of the same or
another frequency;* this emission of radiation, which occurs simultaneously with
the absorption, is known as **fluorescence.**

The relationship between the extent of light absorption and the depth, or
thickness, of the absorbing material is given, for a pure substance, by **Lambert's law** (1760); this law states that *equal fractions of the incident radiation
are absorbed by successive layers of equal thickness of the light-absorbing substance.*   The mathematical representation of this statement is

$$I = I_0 e^{-kl}, \tag{62.1}$$

where I_0 is the intensity of the incident light, and I is its intensity after the
passage through l cm. of the given material; the constant k, which is characteristic of the latter, is known as its **absorption coefficient.**   It refers to light
of a particular wave length, its value varying with the wave length of the absorbed radiation.   The intensity $I_{abs.}$ of the light absorbed is equal to the
difference between the intensities of the incident (I_0) and the transmitted
(I) radiation; thus,

$$I_{abs.} = I_0 - I = I_0(1 - e^{-kl}). \tag{62.2}$$

The light-absorbing properties of a substance are often described in terms of
its **extinction coefficient** ϵ; this is defined by an alternative form of Lambert's
law equation (62.1), viz.,

$$I = I_0 10^{-d}. \tag{62.3}$$

It can be readily shown from equations (62.1) and (62.3) that

$$k = 2.303\epsilon, \tag{62.4}$$

which provides the connection between the absorption and extinction coefficients.

If the absorbing substance is in solution, the relationship between the intensities of the incident and transmitted radiations is given by **Beer's law**
(1852), which is an extension of Lambert's law; this law may be put in the
alternative forms

$$I = I_0 e^{-kcl} \qquad \text{or} \qquad I = I_0 10^{-\epsilon cl}, \tag{62.5}$$

where c is the concentration of the solution.   The corresponding expressions
for the light absorbed are

$$I_{abs.} = I_0(1 - e^{-kcl}) = I_0(1 - 10^{-\epsilon cl}). \tag{62.6}$$

The absorption and extinction coefficients of the dissolved substance are k
and ϵ, respectively; they are related to each other by an expression identical

with equation (62.4). Most solutions obey Beer's law if dilute, but divergences are observed in more concentrated solutions. The law has been used, in conjunction with light absorption measurements, to determine the quantity of a given light-absorbing substance in solution for analytical purposes.

Problem: Light of definite wave length was passed through a cell 5.0 cm. thickness containing a 0.01 molar solution of a given substance; it was found that the intensity of the transmitted light was 0.245 of the incident light. Calculate the extinction coefficient of the dissolved substance.

For this problem it is convenient to use equation (62.5), in which c is 0.01, and l is 5.0; I/I_0 is 0.245, and hence,

$$\frac{I}{I_0} = 10^{-\epsilon cl} \quad \text{or} \quad 0.245 = 10^{-\epsilon \times 0.01 \times 5.0}.$$

Taking logarithms, the result is

$$\log 0.245 = -0.05\epsilon$$

$$\epsilon = 12.22.$$

If the absorption coefficient k is required, it is best derived from ϵ by the use of equation (62.4).

62c. The Law of the Photochemical Equivalent.—One of the most fruitful generalizations in photochemistry is the **law of the photochemical equivalent,** first proposed by A. Einstein (1905, 1912); according to this law, *each molecule taking part in a chemical reaction, which is a direct result of the absorption of light, takes up one quantum of the radiation causing the reaction.* If ν is the frequency of the absorbed radiation in vibrations per sec., i.e., in sec.$^{-1}$ units, the corresponding quantum is equal to $h\nu$ ergs (§ 9b), where h, the Planck constant, is equal to 6.62×10^{-27} erg sec.; this is the amount of energy absorbed per molecule if the Einstein law is obeyed. The energy E absorbed per mole is then $Nh\nu$, where N is the Avogadro number, 6.02×10^{23}, i.e., the number of molecules in 1 mole; that is,

$$E = Nh\nu \text{ ergs per mole.} \tag{62.7}$$

The frequency ν of the radiations in sec.$^{-1}$ is equal to c/λ, where c is the velocity of light, i.e., 3.0×10^{10} cm. per sec., and λ is the wave length in cm.; it is more usual to express the wave length of the radiation in Ångström units, i.e., 10^{-8} cm., and so it is possible to write

$$\nu = \frac{c}{\lambda} \times 10^8,$$

when equation (62.7) becomes

$$E = \frac{Nhc}{\lambda} \times 10^8 \text{ ergs per mole,}$$

where λ is the wave length in Ångströms. It is more convenient to state the energy in calories or kilocalories, and since 1 cal. is equivalent to 4.184×10^7 ergs, it follows that

$$E = \frac{Nhc}{\lambda} \times \frac{10^8}{4.184 \times 10^7} \text{ cal. per mole.}$$

Upon inserting the known values of N, h and c, the result is

$$E = \frac{2.859}{\lambda} \times 10^5 \text{ kcal. per mole.} \qquad (62.8)$$

The quantity E, that is, the energy absorbed per mole of reacting substance, is sometimes referred to as one **einstein** of radiation of the given wave length λ. The value is seen to decrease with increasing wave length, so that the absorption of energy per mole (or per molecule) is greater at the violet or ultraviolet end of the spectrum and smaller at the red end. The values of the einstein for radiations of different wave lengths, at intervals of 1000 Å, in the spectral region of photochemical interest are given in Table LXXV.

TABLE LXXV. VALUES OF THE EINSTEIN AT DIFFERENT WAVE LENGTHS

Wave Length	Color Region	E
2000 Å	Ultraviolet	142.95 kcal.
3000	Ultraviolet	95.30
4000	Violet	71.48
5000	Blue-green	57.18
6000	Yellow-orange	47.65
7000	Red	40.84
8000	Near infrared	35.74

62d. The Spectra of Molecules.—By combining the results of the Grotthuss-Draper and the Einstein laws of photochemistry, it is possible to draw certain conclusions as to the type of radiation likely to be chemically active. It is known that only light which is absorbed can produce photochemical change, and hence the first point to consider is the nature of the light absorbed by the reacting substance; this information is provided by the spectrum of the substance. It was seen in § 9c that the (absorption) spectrum of an atom is due to the absorption of radiation which causes one of the outermost electrons to be raised from a lower to a higher energy level. The frequency of the spectral line, in wave numbers, corresponding to any particular electronic transition is equal to the resulting energy change divided by the product of the Planck constant and the velocity of light [equation (9.8)].

With *molecules*, the situation as regards the spectrum is more complicated; a molecule possesses rotational and vibrational, as well as electronic, energy, all of which are quantized, that is to say, they have a series of definite values or levels only, and do not vary continuously. When a molecule absorbs radiation it can, therefore, do so in several ways. In the first place, the absorption may be such as to change only the rotational energy from one level to another; the energy change in this case is small, and it can be shown that the corresponding spectrum, known as the **rotational spectrum,** lies in the far infrared (long wave length) region of the spectrum, viz., about 10^6 Å. By equation (62.8), the energy absorbed per mole in this region is about 300 cal.; this is obviously insufficient to provide the energy of activation for a reacting molecule, i.e., about 40 kcal. or more, or to dissociate a molecule by direct breaking of a bond, which would require about 50 to 100 kcal. per mole. It is evident, therefore, that absorption of radiation in the far infrared spectrum cannot have any chemical effects. The energy absorbed in this region, taken up as rotational energy, ultimately appears in the form of heat, that is, as kinetic energy of translational motion.

If the molecule absorbs energy sufficient to produce a change from one vibrational level to another, the corresponding spectrum appears in the near infrared portion of the spectrum. Each vibrational transition is usually accompanied by a number of different changes in the rotational energy, and the resulting spectrum, consisting of a band made up of a series of closely spaced lines, is called the **vibration-rotation spectrum.** For most molecules the vibration-rotation bands appear in that region of the infrared spectrum with wave lengths from about 10,000 to 30,000 Å. According to the law of the photochemical equivalent, the energy of the einstein of absorbed radiation in this wave length range is roughly 28.6 kcal. to 9.5 kcal. per mole. The higher of these values might conceivably be sufficient to bring about chemical reaction in certain cases, but as a general rule it is to be expected that the radiations which molecules absorb in the near infrared will not be active photochemically. Actually no direct chemical reactions resulting from the absorption of radiations in the infrared (vibration-rotation) spectrum have been observed.

Although it has no immediate connection with the problems of photochemistry, it may be mentioned that symmetrical diatomic molecules, such as H_2, N_2, O_2, etc., do not exhibit rotation or vibration-rotation spectra. For certain reasons, these substances do not absorb radiation in the infrared region of the spectrum.

A third type of spectrum, exhibited by *all* molecules, is due to a change in the electronic energy; when there is an absorption of radiation of relatively high energy, one of the electrons is raised from one energy level to another, thus giving rise to a system of bands known as the **electronic spectrum.** Each band represents a particular change in the vibrational energy accompanying the given electronic transition; the small rotational energy changes which occur at the same time account for the fine structural lines of the band. If the absorbing substance has no visible color, its electronic spectrum lies in the ultraviolet, that is to say, the wave length of the absorbed radiation is less than 4000 Å, and hence the energy absorbed will be greater than 70 kcal. per mole (see Table LXXV). It is obvious that such radiations are likely to produce photochemical action. When a substance has a visible color its electronic spectrum is in the visible region, so that the wave length of the absorbed radiation must lie within the range of 4000 Å to 8000 Å. The corresponding energy is 70 kcal. to 35 kcal. per mole, which is often sufficient to bring about photochemical reaction, especially with gaseous reactants, such as chlorine, bromine, iodine vapor, and nitrogen dioxide.

It follows from the foregoing discussion that a particular molecule will only absorb radiation whose wave length happens to lie within the range of one or other of the three types of spectra described above. If it is outside or between these ranges, for the given molecule, the radiation cannot be absorbed. Further, if the light is to be active photochemically, the wave length must fall within the electronic spectrum of at least one of the reacting substances. As stated earlier, however, the absorption of radiation is not necessarily accompanied by chemical reaction; whether the latter occurs or not depends on various circumstances.

62e. Electronic Spectrum and Molecular Dissociation.—A more detailed examination of the electronic spectrum of a gaseous substance in the ultraviolet or visible regions of the spectrum reveals certain information that is of great photochemical significance. It was stated above that this spectrum consists of a series of bands representing changes of vibrational energy associated with the electronic transition. It is found in some cases that these bands crowd closer and closer together toward the shorter wave length portion of the spectrum, and at a certain point they merge into a region of continuous absorption with no banded structure. These observations have been interpreted in the following manner. The vibrational energy of a molecule increases with decreasing wave length, the vibrations within the molecule becoming more and more vigorous. Ultimately a point is reached when the energy of the absorbed radiation is so great that the molecule flies apart; in other words, the absorbed energy is sufficient to bring about dissociation of the molecule. As there is now no definite vibration, there are no vibrational bands and the spectrum is continuous. It follows, consequently, that *the absorption of radiation lying within the continuous region of the spectrum of a given molecule should be accompanied by dissociation of that molecule.*

There is much evidence in favor of the explanation just given of the continuous portion of the electronic spectrum, but one aspect only will be referred to here. If the arguments are correct, the energy corresponding to the wave length at which the continuous region commences should be related to the energy required to dissociate the molecule; this has been confirmed in a number of instances. In the spectrum of chlorine gas the banded region of the electronic spectrum passes into one of continuous absorption at a wave length of 4785 Å; according to equation (62.8) the energy absorbed must then be 59.7 kcal. per mole. The products of dissociation of a chlorine molecule are two chlorine atoms, although one of these is not a normal atom, but an "excited atom," in which one of the outer electrons occupies a higher level than normal; the excess energy is known from the spectrum of atomic chlorine to be 2.5 kcal. per gram atom. If this energy is subtracted from the value equivalent to the absorbed radiation, the difference, i.e., 57.2 kcal., should represent the energy required to dissociate 1 mole of chlorine into normal atoms. The heat of dissociation of molecular chlorine derived from thermal measurements, which are probably less accurate than the spectroscopic studies, is 57.0 kcal. The agreement in this and other instances is sufficiently good to establish the view that absorption of light in the continuous spectrum of any gaseous molecule is accompanied by dissociation of that molecule.

PHOTOCHEMICAL REACTIONS

63a. The Quantum Yield or Efficiency.—The results of a photochemical process are frequently expressed by means of the **quantum efficiency** or **quantum yield** of the reaction; this is defined as *the number of moles of the light-absorbing substance that react for each einstein of absorbed radiation.*[*] By the law of the photochemical equivalent, *one mole* of the substance should be involved in the reaction which is a *direct result* of the absorption of light, for each einstein absorbed. It is to be expected, therefore, that if the only reaction which occurred in a given process was the one associated with the light absorption, the quantum yield should be unity. In certain cases (see Table LXXVI) the quantum yields are found to be very close to this value, but in the majority of instances the results differ from unity. In general, quantum efficiencies of one, two or three are the most common, that is, one, two or three moles react for each einstein absorbed, but for some photochemical reactions the yields are very large or very small.

The apparent discrepancy between the Einstein law of the photochemical equivalent and the experimental results can, however, be readily explained. The view is now held that the law applies to what is called the **primary process** of the reaction, in which the light is actually absorbed; that is why the phrase *"direct result* of the absorption of light" is included in the statement of the law (§ 62c). One mole of the light-absorbing substance reacts in the primary process for every einstein, or one molecule per quantum, of absorbed radiation. It frequently happens, however, that the products of the primary process are involved in subsequent thermal (dark) reactions, referred to as the **secondary processes,** in which the molecules of reactant take part. As a result, the *total number* of moles reacting for each einstein of radiation absorbed may differ from unity. In other words, although the quantum efficiency of the primary photochemical process is unity, the over-all yield, as determined from the ultimate results of the reaction, may be quite different. The actual value of the quantum yield provides information which makes it possible to understand the nature of the secondary processes; this will be made clear shortly, when specific photochemical reactions are considered.

The experimental determination of the quantum yield constitutes one of the main aspects of the study of photochemical changes. For this purpose it is convenient to represent the quantum yield by the expression

$$\text{Quantum yield (or efficiency)} = \frac{\text{Number of moles reacting}}{\text{Number of cinsteins absorbed}}, \quad (63.1)$$

[*] An alternative, equivalent definition is the number of *molecules* reacting for each *quantum* of absorbed radiation.

which is, of course, equivalent to the definition given earlier. The number of moles of the light-absorbing substance that react in a given time can be determined by familiar analytical procedures, adapted to the materials concerned and the experimental conditions. The measurement of the number of einsteins, i.e., of the energy, absorbed requires some consideration. Since the value of the einstein depends on the wave length (or frequency) of the radiation [equation (62.8)], it is desirable in photochemical work that light of a definite wave length, i.e., monochromatic light, or light falling within a narrow range of wave lengths, should be used. Much of the older photochemical research is of little value because of failure to observe this condition. The energy of the monochromatic radiation is determined most accurately by means of a thermopile, made up of a large number of junctions of two dissimilar metals. The radiations are converted into heat, and the E.M.F. produced by the resulting thermoelectric effect is observed; this provides a measure of the energy of the radiation falling on the thermopile. The measurements are made with and without the reacting system, and the difference gives the amount of energy actually absorbed by the latter.

Problem: Radiation of wave length 2540 Å was passed through a cell containing 10 ml. of a 0.0495 molar solution of oxalic acid (together with 0.01 molar uranyl sulfate); after the absorption of 8.81×10^8 ergs of radiation, the concentration of the oxalic acid was reduced to 0.0383 molar. Calculate the quantum yield for the photochemical decomposition of oxalic acid at the given wave length.

The magnitude of the einstein for radiation of 2540 Å is given by equation (62.8); this is in kcal., and upon multiplying by $4.184 \times 10^7 \times 10^3$ the result will be in ergs, i.e.,

$$E = \frac{2.859}{2540} \times 10^5 \times 4.184 \times 10^{10} \text{ ergs.}$$

The number of einsteins absorbed in the experiment is obtained if the 8.81×10^8 ergs is divided by this value of the einstein. The concentration of the oxalic acid is decreased by $0.0495 - 0.0383 = 0.0112$ mole per liter; the quantity of oxalic acid decomposed in 10 ml., the volume of the cell, is therefore 1.12×10^{-4} mole. Hence by equation (63.1)

$$\text{Quantum yield} = \frac{1.12 \times 10^{-4} \times 2.859 \times 4.184 \times 10^{15}}{8.81 \times 10^8 \times 2540}$$

$$= 0.599.$$

For many purposes the accuracy of the thermopile is not required, and the energy of the absorbed light is determined by means of an **actinometer**; this is a device for using a photochemical reaction to estimate the absorbed energy. One of these, which has been used in recent years, is the uranyl oxalate actinometer, consisting of a dilute solution of oxalic acid containing uranyl sulfate. When exposed to ultraviolet or violet light, within the range of about 2540 to 4350 Å, the oxalic acid is decomposed; the extent of decomposition at the conclusion of the experiment is determined by titration with permanganate. The uranyl oxalate actinometer has been standardized with radiations of various wave lengths, and from the amount of oxalic acid decomposed the amount of energy absorbed can be evaluated. As before, the measurements are made with and without the reacting system in the path of the light; the difference in the energies taken up by the actinometer is equal to the energy absorbed by the reacting substance.

The quantum yields of a number of photochemical reactions of different types are given in Table LXXVI; the approximate wave length, or range of

TABLE LXXVI. QUANTUM YIELDS OF PHOTOCHEMICAL REACTIONS

Reaction	Wave Length	Yield
Gas Phase		
$2NH_3 = N_2 + 3H_2$	$\sim$2100 Å	$\sim$0.2
$CH_3COCH_3 = CO + C_2H_6$	$\sim$3000	$\sim$0.3
$2NO_2 = 2NO + O_2$	4050	0.7
" " "	3660	1.5
$2HI = H_2 + I_2$	2070–2820	2
$2HBr = H_2 + Br_2$	2070–2530	2
$2Cl_2O = 2Cl_2 + O_2$	3130–4360	3.5
$CO + Cl_2 = COCl_2$	4000–4360	$\sim$10³
$H_2 + Cl_2 = 2HCl$	$\sim$4000	$\sim$10⁵
Liquid Phase		
Maleic acid $\rightarrow$ fumaric acid	2000–2800	$\sim$0.04
$2Fe^{++} + I_2 = 2Fe^{+++} + 2I^-$	5790	1
$CH_2ClCOOH + H_2O = CH_2OHCOOH + HCl$	2537	1
$2HI = H_2 + I_2$	3000	1.84
$2H_2O_2 = 2H_2O + O_2$	3100	>7

wave length, of the effective radiation is given in each case. In some instances the quantum efficiency is seen to be a small integer; this is explained by a simple secondary process following the primary light absorption stage. The large quantum yields, e.g., 10^3 for the reaction between carbon monoxide and chlorine, and 10^5 for the hydrogen-chlorine reaction, are attributed to chain reactions. The low yields, on the other hand, are due either to recombination of the products or to the removal of energy from the light-absorbing molecule before it has time to react. Instances of the various types of behavior are described in the succeeding sections.

63b. The Decomposition of Hydrogen Iodide and Hydrogen Bromide.— The photochemical decomposition of hydrogen iodide has been studied with radiations of wave lengths of 2070, 2530 and 2820 Å; the quantum yield was found to be very close to 2.0 moles of hydrogen iodide decomposed per einstein of absorbed energy in each case (E. Warburg, 1918). The electronic spectrum of hydrogen iodide is continuous in the region from about 3320 Å to less than 2000 Å wave length; hence, it is clear, from the arguments in § 62e, that, in the experiments referred to, the absorption of radiation must be accompanied by dissociation of the absorbing molecule. The primary photochemical stage may be represented by the equation

$$(1) \quad HI + h\nu = H + I,$$

where $h\nu$ represents a single quantum of radiation which is absorbed by a molecule of hydrogen iodide, in accordance with the law of the photochemical equivalent. The hydrogen and iodine atoms formed in this manner can react in several ways, but there are reasons for stating that the most important secondary chemical processes are

$$(2) \quad H + HI = H_2 + I$$
$$(3) \quad I + I \; = I_2.$$

The over-all photochemical process is obtained by adding the primary and secondary stages, i.e., reactions (1), (2) and (3); thus,

$$2HI + h\nu = H_2 + I_2,$$

so that two molecules of hydrogen iodide should be dissociated for each quantum, or two moles for each einstein, of radiation absorbed, as found experimentally. The observed results can thus be interpreted by means of the proposed mechanism.

As the photochemical decomposition of hydrogen iodide proceeds, the quantum yield is found to fall appreciably below 2.0; the reason is that as the iodine molecules accumulate, the thermal reaction

$$H + I_2 = HI + I$$

becomes appreciable. Since this reaction regenerates hydrogen iodide, it will evidently cause a decrease in the over-all efficiency of the photochemical process.

The results of the photochemical dissociation of hydrogen bromide are very similar to those for hydrogen iodide; the quantum yield is initially about 2.0, but it falls off as the proportion of molecular bromine increases. The mechanism of the reaction is presumably analogous to that proposed above for hydrogen iodide; the process involving the regeneration of hydrogen bromide, by the reaction between hydrogen atoms and bromine molecules, probably occurs more readily than does the corresponding reaction with iodine.

63c. The Hydrogen-Chlorine and Hydrogen-Bromine Reactions.—One of the most interesting, if perplexing, photochemical processes is the long known reaction occurring between hydrogen and chlorine gases upon exposure to visible or ultraviolet light of wave length less than about 5460 Å; actually the most effective radiation is that of wave length less than 4785 Å, that is, in the region of continuous absorption of the electronic spectrum of molecular chlorine. The quantum efficiency of the photochemical hydrogen-chlorine reaction is exceptionally high; it varies somewhat with the conditions, but values from 10^4 to 10^6 are not uncommon, in the absence of oxygen, with light of less than 4800 Å wave length.

Since the photochemically active radiation falls within the region of continuous absorption of chlorine, the primary stage of the reaction is undoubtedly the dissociation of one molecule per quantum, i.e.,

$$(1) \quad Cl_2 + h\nu = 2Cl,$$

in agreement with the Einstein law, and this is followed by the stages

$$(2) \quad Cl + H_2 = HCl + H \qquad and \qquad (3) \quad H + Cl_2 = HCl + Cl.$$

The regeneration of the chlorine atom in reaction (3), after the production of two molecules of hydrogen chloride, permits reactions (2) and (3) to occur again, so that a reaction chain is propagated, as explained in § 581. It is seen, therefore, that once the process has been started by the absorption of a single quantum, a very large number of molecules of hydrogen chloride can be formed as a result of the continued repetition of reactions (2) and (3). This accounts for the high observed quantum yield.

The actual efficiency of the photochemical hydrogen-chlorine reaction is determined by the length of the reaction chains, i.e., the number of times reactions (2) and (3) can be repeated, on the average, before the chain is broken by the removal of either the hydrogen or chlorine atom which is propagating the chain. There is no general agreement concerning the nature of the chief chain-breaking process, but the most probable appears to be the recombination of chlorine atoms to form molecules; this reaction occurs largely at the walls of the reaction vessel. It might be supposed that the chains could also be broken by the combination of two hydrogen atoms or of a hydrogen and a chlorine atom; since the concentration of hydrogen atoms is much smaller than that of chlorine atoms, these processes will occur to a lesser extent than the reaction between two chlorine atoms.

In the presence of small amounts of oxygen the quantum yield for the photochemical combination of hydrogen and chlorine is greatly reduced; the primary process and the chain-propagating reactions, viz., (1), (2) and (3), are the same as before, but the chain-breaking reactions, upon which the chain length and the quantum yield depend, are quite different. Both chlorine atoms and hydrogen atoms can react with oxygen, ultimately producing chlorine dioxide and water, respectively, so that there are two additional processes whereby the chain carriers can be removed from the reacting system. It can thus be readily understood why the efficiency of the formation of hydrogen chloride is much less in the presence of oxygen than in its absence.

It is somewhat surprising, at first sight, to find that the corresponding hydrogen-bromine reaction has a quantum yield as small as 0.01 molecules of hydrogen bromide per quantum of absorbed radiation at ordinary temperatures, although it increases somewhat as the temperature is raised. From the fact that the active radiation lies in the continuous region of the spectrum of bromine vapor, it is evident that the primary stage is the dissociation

$$(1) \quad Br_2 + h\nu = 2Br.$$

This is probably followed, as in the chlorine reaction, by the secondary stage,

$$(2) \quad Br + H_2 = HBr + H,$$

but here the resemblance ceases. The activation energy for the reaction between chlorine atoms and molecular hydrogen is small, and the process occurs very rapidly, thus permitting the propagation of chains. The corresponding reaction between bromine atoms and molecular hydrogen is endothermic to the extent of about 17 kcal., and hence the activation energy must be at least equal to this value (§ 59d); this means that the reaction will undoubtedly be slow. There is, consequently, in this case no chain mechanism. Further, because the bromine atoms react slowly with hydrogen molecules, they tend to recombine to regenerate bromine molecules; thus the efficiency of the formation of hydrogen bromide, occurring through reaction (2), may fall below one molecule per quantum, as is actually the case. If the temperature is raised, the rate of reaction (2) is increased, and so the over-all quantum yield is also increased to some extent.

63d. Decomposition of Ammonia.—Ammonia gas can be decomposed by radiations of wave length from 1600 to 2200 Å; the quantum yield is about 0.15 molecule per quantum, or 0.15 mole per einstein, at 20° C, and about 0.5 at 400° C, the value depending somewhat on the pressure. The electronic spectrum of ammonia in the region of the photochemically active radiation indicates that the primary stage of the reaction involves dissociation, probably

$$NH_3 + h\nu = NH_2 + H.$$

The final products of the reaction are nitrogen, hydrogen and hydrazine, which result from the secondary processes

$$NH_2 + NH_2 = N_2 + 2H_2 \quad \text{and} \quad NH_2 + NH_2 = N_2H_4,$$

as well as from the combination of hydrogen atoms. The quantum efficiency for the decomposition of ammonia should thus have a maximum value of unity; the fact that it is less suggests that the products of the primary stage, i.e., NH_2 and H, recombine to some extent to form ammonia, so that not every molecule absorbing a quantum succeeds in taking part in the secondary reactions following the initial decomposition.

The photochemical decomposition of ammonia and the hydrogen-bromine reactions have one feature in common; the primary stage in each case, i.e., decomposition of ammonia and bromine molecules, is a process involving an *increase* of free energy. Consequently, if the products of this stage are not removed rapidly by subsequent, i.e., secondary, processes, they are liable to recombine, since this reaction would be accompanied by a decrease of free energy.

63e. Reactions Involving Excited Molecules.—The photochemical processes described so far have all involved dissociation as the primary stage; some reference will now be made to reactions in which the active radiation falls within the discontinuous or banded spectral region of the absorbing molecule. In these cases the primary stage is not dissociation, but the formation of an "excited" or "activated" molecule possessing energy in excess of the normal due chiefly to the increase in the electronic energy (§ 62d). The excited molecule may then react when it collides with another molecule, as with anthracene in solution (§ 63f), or it may lose its energy if it does not, or is unable to, react or combine within a short time. If the excited molecule possesses sufficient energy for dissociation to be feasible as a result of a rearrangement of the energy in the molecule, there is always a possibility that this will occur; the dissociation may then take place spontaneously or in a collision with another molecule which may be of the same kind or different. The life of an excited molecule is usually about 10^{-7} to 10^{-8} sec., and hence it can undergo many vibrations and rotations before dissociating; the spectrum will thus exhibit definite structure, in spite of the ultimate dissociation. Behavior of this type has been referred to as "predissociation."

Acetone vapor can be decomposed photochemically over a range of wave lengths in the ultraviolet region; some of these lie within the continuous spectrum of acetone, and the primary photochemical process is then the dissociation of the molecule. However, photochemical decomposition, although with a low quantum yield, does occur with light that is absorbed in the banded portion of the spectrum, so that the primary stage is presumably the formation of an excited molecule; thus, indicating the excited molecule by an asterisk,

$$CH_3COCH_3 + h\nu = CH_3COCH_3^*.$$

The excited molecule has sufficient energy to decompose after a short time required for the rearrangement of the energy; this probably occurs spontaneously and the products are ethane and carbon monoxide, i.e.,

$$CH_3COCH_3^* = C_2H_6 + CO.$$

If decomposition does not occur, the excess energy of the excited molecule is lost either by the re-emission of energy as fluorescence, or by conversion into kinetic energy, i.e., into heat, in a nonreactive collision.

Another instance of the "predissociation" phenomenon is provided by the hydrogen-bromine reaction (§ 63c); the rate of reaction is almost the same in the discontinuous, i.e., banded, as in the continuous portion of the bromine spectrum, provided the energy in the former case is sufficient to dissociate the molecule into normal atoms. In the discontinuous region the primary process is the formation of excited Br_2^* molecules, and these subsequently dissociate, probably as the result of a collision, viz.,

$$Br_2 + h\nu = Br_2^* \qquad \text{and} \qquad Br_2^* + X = 2Br + X,$$

where X is any molecule, not necessarily bromine.

An example of where dissociation apparently takes place when an excited molecule collides with another molecule of the same species is the photochemical decomposition of nitrosyl chloride in the discontinuous region of light absorption. The first stage is the production of an excited molecule NOCl*, and this reacts when it encounters another nitrosyl chloride molecule, i.e.,

$$NOCl^* + NOCl = 2NO + Cl_2,$$

thus accounting for a quantum yield of approximately two.

63f. The Dimerization of Anthracene: Photochemical Equilibrium.—A photochemical reaction that presents a number of particularly interesting aspects is the dimerization, or doubling, of the anthracene molecule, i.e.,

$$2C_{14}H_{10} = C_{28}H_{20},$$
$$\text{anthracene} \quad \text{dianthracene}$$

occurring when a solution of anthracene in benzene, or other inert solvent, is exposed to ultraviolet light. In dilute solution the reaction is accompanied by emission of part of the absorbed radiation in the form of fluorescence, and the quantum yield of the dimerization reaction is then small. As the concentration of the anthracene is increased, the fluorescence falls off and the

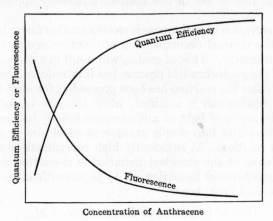

Concentration of Anthracene

FIG. 130. Dimerization and fluorescence of anthracene in solution

quantum efficiency of the dimerization increases, at the same time, toward a limiting value; when the latter is attained there is very little fluorescence (Fig. 130). This behavior can be accounted for by a simple mechanism. The primary process associated with the absorption of the radiation by a molecule A of anthracene is the formation of an excited molecule A* in which one of the electrons occupies a higher energy level than in the normal molecule; thus, the primary stage is

$$A + h\nu = A^*.$$

This is followed by combination of the excited molecule with another molecule of anthracene, to form a molecule A_2 of dianthracene, i.e.,

$$A^* + A = A_2.$$

When the concentration of anthracene is small, a large proportion of the excited molecules lose their energy as fluorescence, i.e., by the emission of light, before they can encounter another anthracene molecule with which to react. The fluorescence will then be considerable while the quantum efficiency for the formation of dianthracene will be small. At higher concentrations, however, the frequency of collisions between A* and A molecules is increased, and consequently fewer excited molecules lose their energy by the emission of radiation. The quantum efficiency thus increases while the fluorescence diminishes correspondingly.

If every excited A* molecule succeeded in combining with another molecule to form A_2, the quantum yield would be two; the maximum observed value is, however, about 0.5. The probable reason for the difference is that some of the A* molecules lose their energy as a result of colliding with solvent molecules; this is a possibility which must always be taken into consideration for photochemical reactions in solution. The energy of the absorbed radiation that is lost in this manner ultimately appears in the form of heat.

As the concentration of anthracene increases another factor becomes operative, namely, the thermal decomposition of dianthracene to regenerate two molecules of anthracene. This, of course, will result in a decrease of the overall efficiency of the photochemical process, but it introduces a new feature into the situation. After the reaction has been proceeding for some time a state of **photochemical equilibrium** is attained, when the rate of formation of A_2 as a result of the action of light on anthracene is exactly balanced by the rate at which A_2 dissociates into simple anthracene molecules as a result of the thermal (dark) reaction. At sufficiently high concentrations of anthracene, when little or none of the absorbed radiation is re-emitted as fluorescence, the rate of photochemical formation of A_2 is proportional to the intensity $I_{abs.}$ of the absorbed light; hence,

$$\text{Rate of formation of dianthracene} = kI_{abs.},$$

where k is a constant. It should be noted that the rate of the photochemical process depends only on the energy of the absorbed light, and is apparently independent of the concentration of the anthracene molecules. Actually, of course, the light absorption itself depends on the concentration, in accordance with Beer's law, equation (62.6). The rate of the thermal dissociation of A_2 into anthracene molecules is proportional to the concentration of the former, in accordance with the usual requirements for a unimolecular (thermal) reaction; hence,

$$\text{Rate of dissociation of dianthracene} = k'c_{A_2},$$

where k' is the specific rate of the dissociation reaction, and c_{A_2} is the concentration of dianthracene. At the photochemical equilibrium state the rates of formation and decomposition of dianthracene are equal, so that

$$kI_{abs.} = k'c_{A_2}$$

$$c_{A_2} = \frac{k}{k'} I_{abs.}. \tag{63.2}$$

The equilibrium concentration of A_2 should thus be proportional to the intensity of the absorbed light; if this intensity is kept constant, the value of

c_{A_2} at equilibrium should be independent of the concentration of anthracene. These results emphasize the fact that the ordinary equilibrium constant is not applicable to photochemical equilibrium; the latter is determined by the absorption of energy by the reacting system, and as soon as the source of radiation is removed the system would immediately begin to change toward its normal, or thermal, equilibrium state.

63g.—The Photochemical Stationary State.—A somewhat different type of equilibrium, generally referred to as a photochemical **stationary state** or steady state, occurs in many reactions under the influence of light. It appears that for any species, such as atoms or radicals, produced in the course of the primary or secondary processes, whose concentrations are never large, a steady state is attained soon after the commencement of the reaction. The rate of formation of the atoms or radicals is then equal to their rate of removal. For example, in the photochemical hydrogen-chlorine reaction, chlorine atoms are formed in reactions (1) and (3), as recorded in § 63c, and are removed by reaction (2) and also by the chain-terminating reaction; the sum of the rates of the first two processes is then equal to that of the latter two, when the stationary state is attained. Similarly, the rate of formation of hydrogen atoms by reaction (2) will be equal to the rate of their removal by reaction (3). The use of such results as these, based on the idea of the stationary state, has helped in explaining the complex kinetics of many photochemical reactions.

Problem: Derive an expression for the rate of formation of HCl in the H_2-Cl_2 photochemical reaction, utilizing the method of the photostationary state; the assumption is made that Cl atoms are removed by a monatomic wall reaction, represented by (4) $Cl + wall \rightarrow \frac{1}{2}Cl_2$.

Chlorine atoms are formed in reactions (1) and (3), in § 63c; the rate of the former reaction is proportional to the intensity of the absorbed radiation, i.e., $k_1 I_{abs.}$, while for the latter the rate is $k_3 c_H c_{Cl_2}$. Chlorine atoms are removed from the system by reactions (2) and (4), the rates being $k_2 c_{Cl} c_{H_2}$ and $k_4 c_{Cl}$, respectively. In the photostationary states the total rate of formation of Cl atoms is equal to the rate of their removal, so that

$$k_1 I_{abs.} + k_3 c_H c_{Cl_2} = k_2 c_{Cl} c_{H_2} + k_4 c_{Cl}.$$

Hydrogen atoms are formed in reaction (2) and removed in (3); equating the rates of the two reactions, for the photostationary state,

$$k_2 c_{Cl} c_{H_2} = k_3 c_H c_{Cl_2}.$$

If this equation is added to the preceding one, the result is

$$k_1 I_{abs.} = k_4 c_{Cl}$$

$$c_{Cl} = k_1 I_{abs.}/k_4.$$

The rate of formation of HCl is the sum of the rates of reactions (2) and (3); hence,

$$\frac{dc_{HCl}}{dt} = k_2 c_{Cl} c_{H_2} + k_3 c_H c_{Cl_2}.$$

The rates of these two reactions are equal, as seen above; consequently,

$$\frac{dc_{HCl}}{dt} = 2k_2 c_{Cl} c_{H_2},$$

and upon insertion of the expression for c_{Cl} just derived, it follows that

$$\frac{dc_{HCl}}{dt} = \frac{2k_1k_2}{k_4} I_{abs}.c_{H_2}.$$

The rate of formation of HCl should thus be proportional to the intensity of the absorbed light and to the H_2 concentration (or pressure); this is in agreement with experiment provided the Cl_2 pressure is not too low.

It may be mentioned that an analogous stationary state, as regards the rates of formation and removal of atoms or free radicals, probably occurs also with certain purely thermal reactions. The concept has been applied with success to account for the kinetics of such processes as the thermal combination of hydrogen and bromine, in which hydrogen and bromine atoms are concerned, and the decomposition of organic compounds, in which free radicals are involved.

63h. Photosensitized Reactions.—In some photochemical processes the reacting substance is itself unable to absorb the radiation directly, but a suitable atom or molecule, known as a **sensitizer,** absorbs the radiation and passes it on to the reacting molecule. Processes of this type are known as **photosensitized reactions.** A hydrogen molecule, for instance, is unable to absorb the radiation of wave length 2537 Å that is produced in the passage of an electrical discharge through mercury vapor, e.g., in a mercury vapor lamp. Consequently, this radiation cannot bring about dissociation of the hydrogen, in spite of the fact that the value of the einstein corresponding to 2537 Å, i.e., 113 kcal., is more than would be required, namely 103 kcal., to dissociate 1 mole of hydrogen molecules into atoms. If a small amount of mercury vapor is added to the hydrogen gas, however, exposure to the 2537 Å radiation immediately leads to dissociation. The reaction is photosensitized by the mercury in the following manner. The atoms of mercury in the vapor are able to absorb the radiation, thus forming electronically excited Hg^* atoms, possessing 113 kcal. per gram atom of excess energy. When these excited atoms collide with hydrogen molecules the 103 kcal. required for dissociation are transferred to the latter, and the reaction

$$Hg^* + H_2 = Hg + 2H$$

takes place; the additional 10 kcal. are converted into kinetic energy of translation, that is, into heat.

When hydrogen is mixed with oxygen, carbon monoxide, ethylene, nitrous oxide or nitrogen, and a small amount of mercury vapor added, exposure to ultraviolet light of 2537 Å wave length leads to a variety of photosensitized hydrogenation reactions. With oxygen, one of the products isolated is hydrogen peroxide, in addition to water. Mercury vapor is also able to sensitize the decomposition of ammonia, water, ethanol and acetone, and the conversion of oxygen into ozone, by means of the 2537 Å radiation.

Examples of photosensitization in solution are known; in the uranyl oxalate actinometer (§ 63a) the uranyl salt acts as a sensitizer for the photodecomposition of the oxalic acid. In the absence of the uranium compound the quantum efficiency is very low, generally less than 0.01, but for the sensitized reaction it is about 0.5. Uranyl salts also sensitize the photochemical decomposition of formic acid solutions, and ferric salts sensitize the oxidation of potassium ferrocyanide in alkaline solution and other reactions.

The most outstanding illustration of photosensitization is the action of chlorophyll in permitting carbon dioxide and water to react in sunlight, with the eventual formation of carbohydrates and oxygen; this is the process of **photosynthesis** occurring in green plants under the influence of visible light of almost any wave length from 4000 to 7000 Å. Neither water nor carbon dioxide absorbs radiations in the visible region, but chlorophyll absorbs over almost the whole range, and particularly in the blue-violet (4700 Å) and red (6500 to 7000 Å) regions. The energy of the light absorbed by the chlorophyll is evidently transferred to the carbon dioxide and water, so that the reaction

$$CO_2 + H_2O = \tfrac{1}{6}(C_6H_{12}O_6) + O_2$$

can occur. It is a remarkable fact, however, that this process requires energy to the extent of 112 kcal. per mole of carbon dioxide reacting, and yet, in the presence of chlorophyll, it can take place in red light of 7000 Å wave length, which corresponds to only 41 kcal. per mole (Table LXXV).

The photosynthetic process is evidently a very complex one, and it probably occurs in several stages. Since the value of the einstein for red light is 41 kcal., while the formation of carbohydrate requires 112 kcal. per mole of carbon dioxide, the maximum quantum efficiency for the reaction in red light will be 41/112, i.e., 0.37, molecule of carbon dioxide per quantum of absorbed radiation. The experimental value does not exceed 0.1, and so less than one-third of the absorbed energy is actually utilized in photosynthesis.

Brief reference may also be made to photosensitization of an entirely different type. When a silver halide is exposed to visible light of short wave length, e.g., from green to violet, or to ultraviolet radiation, decomposition occurs; thus, with silver bromide the primary process is

$$AgBr + h\nu = Ag + Br,$$

which provides the basis for the action of the photographic plate. Normally, the silver halides are not appreciably affected by red or yellow light, but the addition of certain dyestuffs, which act as photosensitizers, makes possible the preparation of photographic plates that are responsive to red and even infrared radiations.

63i. Chemiluminescence.—The term **luminescence** is used to describe *the emission of visible radiation that is due to some cause other than temperature;* in other words, luminescence may be regarded as light without heat, or "cold light." At temperatures below about 500° C a body does not normally emit visible or ultraviolet radiation to any appreciable extent, but if by some means it is made to do so, it is described as **luminescent**. The phenomenon of fluorescence, in which radiation absorbed by a molecule is re-emitted at the same or another wave length is an example of luminescence. When the emission of light, at a temperature at which light rays are not normally to be expected, is the result of a chemical reaction, the effect is known as **chemiluminescence**. In a sense chemiluminescence may be regarded as the reverse of photochemical reaction; in the latter the absorption of radiation leads to chemical change, while in the former a chemical reaction is accompanied by the emission of visible radiation.

Many chemical oxidations are associated with luminescence; one of the most familiar is the glow of the element phosphorus and of its trioxide in air. Many Grignard reagents exhibit chemiluminescence when oxidized by air or oxygen, but not when hydrogen peroxide is the oxidizing agent. The oxidation of alkaline aqueous solutions of 5-aminophthalic hydrazide, and of other cyclic hydrazides, by various substances, including hydrogen peroxide, is accompanied by spectacular luminescence. Reference may also be made to the cold light produced by several living organisms; this occurs when a protein derivative, known as luciferin, is oxidized by atmospheric oxygen in the presence of the enzyme luciferase.

The explanation of chemiluminescence probably lies in the formation of one of the products of the reaction in an electronically excited state, in which it has more energy than a normal molecule at the same temperature. The loss of this additional energy then results in the emission of radiation of the appropriate wave length, in accordance with the requirements of the quantum theory. In chemiluminescence the energy is such that this wave length falls within the visible region of the spectrum.

READING REFERENCES

1. **Chemical actions of light.** Bodenstein, *Journal of Chemical Education*, **7**, 518 (1930).

2. **Luminescence experiments.** Huntress, Stanley and Parker, *ibid.*, **11**, 142 (1934).

3. **Photosensitized reactions.** Livingston, *ibid.*, **11**, 400 (1934).

4. **Luminescence.** Cottman, *ibid.*, **14**, 236 (1937).

5. **The glow of nitrogen.** Ewing, *ibid.*, **14**, 487 (1937).

6. **Infra-red spectra.** Barnes and Bonner, *ibid.*, **14**, 564 (1937); **15**, 25 (1938).

7. **Luminescence.** Johnson, *ibid.*, **17**, 295 (1940).

8. **Hydrogen-chlorine reaction.** Ferguson and Moore, *ibid.*, **20**, 41 (1943).

9. **Chemiluminscence.** Leedy, *ibid.*, **21**, 142 (1944).

REVIEW QUESTIONS

1. In what respect do certain photochemical reactions differ from thermochemical reactions?

2. State and explain the following laws: Grotthuss-Draper law, Lambert's law, Beer's law. What is their importance to photochemistry?

3. State the law of photochemical equivalence. What is an einstein? Derive an expression giving the value of the einstein in terms of the wave length of the absorbed radiation.

4. Write an account of the three types of spectra exhibited by molecules.

5. What is the significance of continuous absorption in the spectrum of a molecule? How may this be used to determine heats of dissociation? Why is the molecular spectrum important in relation to the mechanism of photochemical reactions?

6. What is the quantum yield of a photochemical reaction? How may it be determined?

7. Distinguish between the primary and secondary processes in a photochemical reaction. How does the distinction permit the explanation of reactions with very high or very low quantum yields?

8. Describe and explain the photochemical decomposition of hydrogen bromide and hydrogen iodide.

9. Describe the important aspects of the hydrogen-chlorine photochemical reaction. Why does the reaction have a high quantum yield, while that of the hydrogen-bromine reaction is low?

10. Explain the low quantum yield in the photochemical decomposition of ammonia.

11. Give examples of photochemical reactions which occur in the discontinuous (banded) region of the spectrum of the reacting molecules.

12. Describe the photochemical dimerization of anthracene in solution, with special reference to (a) fluorescence, (b) the photochemical equilibrium.

13. What is meant by the photochemical stationary state? How is the concept utilized in deriving the kinetics of photochemical reactions?

14. What is a photosensitized reaction? Explain, with examples, the occurrence of reactions photosensitized by mercury.

15. Describe some of the important features of the photosynthesis of carbohydrates in nature.

16. What is the basis of chemiluminescence? Describe the phenomenon with examples.

PROBLEMS

I

1. When light of a definite wave length is passed through a 0.001 molar solution of a given substance in a cell of 10 cm. thickness, a fraction 0.24 of the incident light is absorbed. What is the concentration of the solution of the same substance which, when placed in the same cell, gives 35 per cent absorption at the same wave length, assuming Beer's law? What is the extinction coefficient of the solute at the given wave length?

2. Calculate the value of the einstein corresponding to ultraviolet radiation of wave length 1750 Å.

3. The energy of cadmium atoms which have become excited by the absorption of light of 3262 Å is unable to bring about dissociation of hydrogen molecules. Explain this result.

4. The spectrum of bromine molecules shows continuous absorption commencing at a wave length of 5107 Å. The photochemical dissociation of molecular bromine results in the formation of a normal atom and an excited atom, the excess energy of the latter being 10.4 kcal. per g. atom. Calculate the heat of dissociation of a mole of bromine to form normal atoms.

5. Calculate the number of ergs of radiation of wave length 2820 Å required to decompose one millimole of hydrogen iodide. The quantum yield may be taken as two molecules per quantum.

II

1. When light of definite wave length was passed through a cell 5.5 cm. thickness containing a gas, a fraction 0.64 of the incident light was absorbed. Calculate the extinction coefficient of the gas. What thickness would be required to absorb a further fraction 0.64 of the emergent light?

2. Calculate the maximum wave length of the radiation which would have sufficient energy to dissociate hydrogen molecules into normal atoms. The known value of the heat of dissociation is 103 kcal. per mole.

3. In the reaction between Na_2 molecules, present to a small extent in sodium vapor, and chlorine atoms sufficient energy is liberated to excite sodium atoms to such an extent that they subsequently emit the D-line radiation of wave length 5890 Å. What is the minimum value of $-\Delta H$ in kcal. for the Na_2-Cl reaction?

4. The spectrum of molecular iodine shows continuous absorption commencing at 4995 Å. The photochemical dissociation results in the formation of a normal and an excited iodine atom, the excess energy of the latter being 21.72 kcal. per g. atom. Calculate the molar heat of dissociation of iodine to form normal atoms.

5. The exposure of o-nitrobenzaldehyde ($NO_2C_6H_4CHO$) to suitable radiation results in an isomeric change in which o-nitrosobenzoic acid (NOC_6H_4COOH) is formed. The absorption of 6.17×10^7 ergs at 3660 Å results in the formation of 9.72×10^{-6} mole of the acid. Calculate the quantum yield.

MISCELLANEOUS PROBLEMS

1. From distribution measurements it has been estimated that K_c for the equilibrium between double and single molecules of benzoic acid, i.e., $(C_6H_5COOH)_2 \rightleftharpoons 2C_6H_5COOH$, in benzene solution is 0.00219 at 10° and 0.0103 at 40° C. Calculate the heat change accompanying the dissociation of the double molecules.

2. The E.M.F. of a cell consisting of a quinhydrone electrode, in a solution made by mixing 20 ml. of a 0.01 N weak acid (HA) and 30 ml. of a 0.01 N solution of its salt NaA, combined with a 0.1 N KCl calomel electrode, was found to be +0.1126 volt at 25° C. What is the dissociation constant of the acid HA?

3. The density of oxygen at several pressures at 0° C (273.16° K) was found to be as follows:

d	1.42897	1.07149	0.71415	0.35699 g. per liter
P	1	$\frac{3}{4}$	$\frac{1}{2}$	$\frac{1}{4}$ atm.

Find the limiting "normal" density of oxygen, and from this and the molecular weight (32.000), calculate an accurate value for the molar gas constant R.

4. The critical temperature, pressure and volume of nitrous oxide are 36.5° C, 71.7 atm. and 0.45 g. per ml., respectively. Determine the pressure at which 2.4 moles of this gas will occupy 5.0 liters at 45° C, according to the van der Waals equation.

5. The equivalent conductances at infinite dilution Λ_0 of barium chloride, sodium sulfate and sodium chloride are 140.0, 129.9 and 126.5 ohms^{-1} cm.^{2}, respectively, at 25° C. The solubility of barium sulfate at this temperature is 0.00251 g. per liter. Calculate the specific conductance of the saturated solution, exclusive of that of the water.

6. The heat of fusion of monoclinic sulfur at its melting point 119° C is 13 cal. per g. The density of the solid is 1.96 and that of the liquid 1.80 g. per ml. Calculate the pressure at which monoclinic sulfur melts at 151° C. (The experimental value is 1290 atm.)

7. In an experiment with an iodine coulometer, it was found that the passage of 3666.5 coulombs resulted in the liberation of 4.8222 g. of iodine. Calculate the value of the faraday. (Atomic weight of iodine, 126.92.)

8. In a Dumas experiment, the weight of the globe with air at 21° C was 52.181 g.; when filled with a vapor at 100° C it was 53.630 g., and with water, 278.2 g. The atmospheric pressure was 750 mm. Calculate the molecular weight of the vaporized substance.

9. Cesium chloride has a body-centered cubic crystal lattice. Show that there is the equivalent of one molecule of CsCl per unit cube. The density of the salt is 3.97 g. per cc.; calculate the length of the edge of a unit cube (d_{100}).

10. For the reaction $C(s) + CO_2(g) = 2CO(g)$ the value of ΔH is +40.3 kcal., which may be assumed to be independent of temperature. The standard molar entropies at 25° C are 1.36 E.U. for carbon, 51.07 E.U. for carbon dioxide, and 47.32 E.U. for carbon dioxide. Calculate the equilibrium constant at 600° C.

11. It takes 1 min. 16 sec. for 42 ml. of oxygen to pass through a small hole in a metal plate. What is the molecular weight of a gas which takes 2 min. 12 sec. to pass through the same hole under the same conditions?

12. A solution of silver nitrate was electrolyzed with a silver anode. **Before electrolysis,** exactly 100 g. of the solution contained 0.1788 g. of silver nitrate. After electrolysis, resulting in the deposition of 0.0322 g. of silver in a coulometer, 20.09 g. of the anode solution contained 0.06227 g. of silver nitrate. Calculate the transference numbers of the Ag^+ and NO_3^- ions.

13. The vapor pressure of benzene is 271 mm. at 50° C, and that of toluene is 93 mm. Assuming ideal behavior, calculate the compositions of the vapor in equilibrium with mixtures containing 0.25, 0.5 and 0.75 mole fraction of benzene. Plot a curve showing the weight composition of the vapor against that of the liquid; what conclusions can be drawn from the curve?

14. Sodium carbonate may be regarded as the sodium salt of the monobasic acid $NaHCO_3$ with K_a equal to 5.62×10^{-11} at 25° C. Find the pH and degree of hydrolysis of 0.1 M sodium carbonate at 25°.

15. A volume 1.425 l. of gas A at 762 mm. pressure together with 0.556 l. of gas B at 645 mm., both at 15° C, were put into a vessel of 1.00 l. What will be the total pressure of the mixed gases at 55° C?

16. The boiling point of formic acid HCOOH is 101° C and its heat of vaporization is 120 cal. per g. Assuming Trouton's rule, calculate the approximate extent of association of formic acid into double molecules at its boiling point.

17. A gas at 25° C is expanded adiabatically from 200 atm. to 10 atm. If the final temperature is −185° C, what is the probable atomicity, i.e., number of atoms per molecule, of the gas?

18. Show that the reaction in the cell Ag, AgCl(s), KCl soln., $Cl_2(g)$, Pt is the formation of solid silver chloride from its elements. Given that ΔH for the reaction is −30.3 kcal., and that the standard molar entropies at 25° C are 10.3 E.U. for silver, 53.31 E.U. for chlorine gas, and 23.4 E.U. for silver chloride, calculate the standard E.M.F. of the cell. (The experimental value at 25° is +1.136 volt.)

19. A solution of 3.80 g. of sulfur in 100 g. of carbon disulfide boils 0.361° above the pure solvent. Given that the boiling point of the latter is 46.3° C and the heat of vaporization is 84.1 cal. per g., determine the molecular weight of the sulfur. What conclusion can be drawn from the result?

20. Potassium chloride has a face-centered cubic lattice of the NaCl-type. By the use of X-rays of known wave length it is found that the edge of the unit cube (d_{100}) is 3.145×10^{-8} cm. The density of the crystal is 1.989 g. per cc. Calculate the Avogadro number.

21. Evaluate ΔH, ΔF^0 and K_p at 1000° K for the reaction $CO(g) + H_2O(g) = CO_2(g) + H_2(g)$, given that ΔH is +11.2 kcal. at 25° C. The standard molar entropies at 25° and the heat capacities at constant pressure are as follows:

	S^0	C_P
$CO(g)$	47.32 E.U. per mole	$6.76 + 0.000606T$ cal. deg.$^{-1}$
$H_2O(g)$	45.17	$8.22 + 0.00015T$
$CO_2(g)$	51.07	$7.70 + 0.0053T$
$H_2(g)$	31.23	$6.85 + 0.00028T$

At what temperature would it be possible to mix equal molar amounts of the reactants and products without the system changing at equilibrium?

22. The E.M.F. of the cell Pt, H_2 (1 atm.), KOH (0.01 M) || HCl (0.01 M), H_2 (1 atm.), Pt is +0.5874 at 25° C. Assuming activity coefficients of unity, as an approximation, evaluate the ionic product of water.

23. The vapor pressure of liquid bromine at 20° C is 173 mm. Calculate the free

energy change in calories accompanying the transfer of one mole of bromine, treated as an ideal gas, from a saturated solution at 20° C to the gas at 1 atm. pressure.

24. The relative lowering of vapor pressure of mercury produced by dissolving 1.00 g. of sodium in 280 g. of mercury is 0.962. Assuming mercury to be monatomic, what is the atomicity of sodium?

25. The energy of certain γ-rays, which is 25.27×10^{11} ergs per einstein, is able to disintegrate deuterium nuclei, viz., ${}^2_1D + \gamma = {}^1_1H + {}^1_0n$, the products having translational energy equivalent to 4.08×10^{11} ergs per g. atom. The atomic weights of H and D are 1.00813 and 2.01473, respectively, on the physical scale. Calculate the mass of the neutron on the same scale.

26. A conductance cell containing 0.01 N potassium chloride ($\Lambda = 141.3$ ohms^{-1} cm.^{2}) has a resistance of 2573 ohms at 25° C. The same cell filled with 0.2 N acetic acid has a resistance of 5085 ohms. Calculate the equivalent conductance of the acetic acid solution.

27. The densities of phosphine (PH_3) at 0° C and various pressures are as follows:

d	1.5307	1.1454	0.76190	0.38012 g. per liter
P	1	$\frac{3}{4}$	$\frac{1}{2}$	$\frac{1}{4}$ atm.

Calculate the atomic weight of phosphorus, by the method of limiting densities.

28. From the following ΔH data determine the heat of formation of anhydrous sulfuric acid from its elements: $S(s) + O_2(g) = SO_2(g)$, -70.9; $SO_2(g) + aq = SO_2(aq)$, -8.5; $\frac{1}{2}H_2(g) + \frac{1}{2}Br_2(g) = HBr(g)$, -8.7; $HBr(g) + aq = HBr(aq)$, -19.9; $H_2(g) + \frac{1}{2}O_2(g) = H_2O(l)$, -68.4; $H_2SO_4(l) + aq = H_2SO_4(aq)$, -20.5; $SO_2(g) + Br_2(g) + 2H_2O + aq = H_2SO_4(aq) + 2HBr(aq)$, -51.3 kcal.

29. A solution of cadmium sulfate ($a_{Cd^{++}} = 0.5$) and sulfuric acid ($a_{H^+} = 0.1$) is electrolyzed, so that cadmium is deposited on the cathode and oxygen on a platinum anode, at which the overvoltage is 0.45. Taking E^0 for Cd, Cd^{++} as $+0.441$, for Pt, O$_2$, OH$^-$ as -0.401, and K_w as 10^{-14}, calculate the decomposition voltage.

30. Light of wave length 2537 Å and incident intensity of 9.25×10^5 ergs per sec. is passed through a cell of 5.5 cm. thickness containing a gas of extinction coefficient 2.35, with concentrations expressed in moles per liter. The capacity of the cell was 122 cc. and the gas pressure was 10 cm. at 22° C. After passing the light for 1 hr. 15 min., it was found that 8.5×10^{-5} mole of the gas had reacted; what is the quantum yield of the process?

31. The activation energy of the reaction $2NO_2 = 2NO + O_2$ is 32 kcal. The value of ΔH for this reaction is $+28$ kcal. Explain why nitric oxide and oxygen react rapidly at ordinary temperatures.

32. The melting point of phenol is 41.0° C and its heat of fusion is 24.9 cal. per g. Upon melting the specific volume increases by 0.0159 cc. per g. Calculate the melting point of phenol at 100 atm. pressure.

33. How long would it take to plate an area of 12.5 sq. cm. with a layer of silver of 1 mm. thickness, using a current of 0.500 amp.? The density of silver is 10.5 g. per cc.

34. The solubility of iodine in water is 0.001341 mole per liter at 25° and 0.004160 mole per liter at 60°. Calculate the mean heat of solution per gram in the saturated solution.

35. If the equilibrium constant of the reaction $Fe^{++} + Hg^{++} \rightleftharpoons Fe^{+++} + \frac{1}{2}Hg_2^{++}$ is 120 at 25°, and the standard potential of the Pt, Fe^{++}, Fe^{+++} electrode is -0.771 volt, determine the standard potential of Pt, Hg$_2^{++}$, Hg^{++}.

36. Plot the logarithms of the vapor pressures of benzene against $1/T$ from 30° to 80° C, from the data in Table XVI. Determine the heat of vaporization of benzene at 20° intervals.

37. If a liquid obeys Trouton's law, show that it is possible to calculate the approximate vapor pressure at any temperature (or boiling point at any pressure) if the normal boiling point is known. The normal boiling point of benzene is 80.1° C; at what temperature would it boil at 551 mm.? (The experimental value is 70° C.)

38. When 0.375 g. formic acid (HCOOH) vapor was placed in a vessel of 78.5 ml. capacity at 50° C the pressure was 14.90 mm., while at 70° C the pressure was 18.10 mm. Calculate the heat of dissociation of double molecules to single molecules in the vapor.

39. Calculate the energy liberated in the formation of 1 g. atom of deuterium (atomic weight 2.01473) from a neutron, a proton and an electron. The atomic weight of the hydrogen atom is 1.00813, and the mass of the neutron on the same (physical) scale is 1.00893.

40. What concentration of acetic acid ($K_a = 1.75 \times 10^{-5}$) may be present in 0.10 N lactic acid ($K_a = 1.37 \times 10^{-4}$) so as to have the same pH as that of the lactic acid solution alone? Explain why one acid may be mixed with another and yet leave the hydrogen ion concentration unaffected.

41. The distribution coefficient of ammonia between water and chloroform is about 26.0. An aqueous solution containing 0.025 M copper sulfate at equilibrium contains a total of 0.38 mole per liter of ammonia, while a chloroform solution contains 0.0112 mole per liter. Calculate how much ammonia is present in the free state in the aqueous solution, and hence derive the formula of the complex ion $Cu(NH_3)_x^{++}$.

42. A liquid, immiscible with water, when distilled in steam gave a distillate containing 22.4 per cent by weight of the liquid at 98.5° C, when the external pressure was 755 mm. Given that the heat of vaporization of water is 539 cal. per g. near its boiling point, calculate the molecular weight of the liquid.

43. The solubilities of sodium sulfate, expressed as g. Na_2SO_4 per liter, at several temperatures are as follows: 25°, 29.0; 30°, 40.1; 35°, 49.5; 40° C, 48.1. Below the transition point (32.4° C) the solid phase is $Na_2SO_4 \cdot 10H_2O$, and above it is Na_2SO_4 anhydrous. Calculate the heat of hydration of Na_2SO_4 to $Na_2SO_4 \cdot 10H_2O$ in the saturated solution in the vicinity of the transition point.

44. A balloon of capacity 5 million liters was filled with helium gas at 750 mm. pressure and 22° C. Upon ascending into the atmosphere, the temperature fell to −12° C, while the external pressure decreased at the same time to 122 mm. What weight of helium would have to be released to maintain the volume constant?

45. Show that when the extent of light absorption is small, i.e., at low concentration or for small extinction coefficient, Beer's law leads to the result that the intensity of the absorbed light is directly proportional to that of the incident light and the concentration of the solution. (Note that e^{-x} is equal to $1 - x$, when x is small.)

46. The photochemical oxidation of carbonyl chloride ($COCl_2$) by oxygen is believed to occur in the following stages: the primary (photochemical) stage $COCl_2 + h\nu = COCl + Cl$ is followed by the secondary (thermal) reactions: $COCl + O_2 = CO_2 + ClO$; $COCl_2 + ClO = CO_2 + Cl_2 + Cl$; $COCl + Cl_2 = COCl_2 + Cl$; and $Cl + Cl = Cl_2$. Assuming the principle of the photostationary state, derive an expression for the rate of formation of carbon dioxide. Utilize the result of problem 45 to simplify the expression for low light absorption.

47. A molar solution of cadmium chloride of pH 5.0 is electrolyzed, using a cadmium cathode and a platinum anode; what products might be expected at the two electrodes at ordinary temperatures? (The hydrogen overvoltage at cadmium is 0.48, and the oxygen overvoltage at platinum is 0.45 volt.)

48. When one mole of ethanol and one mole of propionic acid were mixed and allowed to come to equilibrium at 50° C, it was found that 0.73 mole of ester (ethyl

propionate) and 0.73 mole of water were formed. How much ester will be produced when a mixture of one mole of ethanol, two moles of the acid and three moles of water come to equilibrium at 50° C?

49. The cell Ag, AgCN(s) in 0.1 N KCN $\|$ AgNO$_3$ (a_{Ag^+} = 0.1), Ag has an E.M.F. of 1.224 volt at 25° C. What is the silver ion activity in the cyanide solution? The solubility product of silver cyanide is about 10^{-12}; account for its ready solubility in alkali cyanide solutions.

50. In the spectrum of molecular hydrogen continuous absorption commences at a wave length of 849 Å. The products of dissociation are a normal atom and one with excitation energy of 234.0 kcal. per g. atom. Calculate the molar heat of dissociation of hydrogen to form normal atoms.

51. The vapor pressure of benzene at 75° C is 651 mm., and that of a solution of a nonvolatile substance is 620 mm. at the same temperature. The normal boiling point of benzene is 80.1° C; calculate the boiling point of the solution.

52. A saturated solution of silver chloride placed in a conductance cell, whose constant was 0.1802 cm.$^{-1}$, had a resistance of 67,950 ohms at 25° C. The resistance of the water used as solvent was 212,180 ohms in the same cell. Calculate the solubility of the silver chloride in water at 25°, in g. per liter, and also its solubility product, assuming the salt to be completely dissociated in the saturated solution. (The ion conductances are 61.92 for Ag$^+$ and 76.34 ohms^{-1} cm.^{2} for Cl$^-$ at infinite dilution.)

53. The osmotic pressure of a 0.5 molal solution of sucrose in water is 12.86 atm. at 20° C. Calculate the vapor pressure of the solution at 20°, and the lowering of the freezing point. The vapor pressure of pure water at 20° is 17.535 mm.; the heat of fusion of ice is 79.8 cal. per g., and the density of water may be taken as unity.

54. At what concentration will a solution of formic acid (K_a = 1.774 $\times$ 10^{-4}) have a pH of 3.00? What will be the degree of dissociation of the acid? How many grams of sodium formate (NaHCO$_2$) must be added to 1 liter of this solution to change the pH to 5.00?

55. A mixture consisting initially of 7.94 moles of hydrogen and 5.30 moles of iodine vapor is heated at 445° C, and 9.52 moles of hydrogen iodide are formed at equilibrium. Calculate the equilibrium composition of a mixture which consists initially of 8.07 moles of hydrogen and 9.27 moles of iodine.

56. The following results were obtained in the decomposition of nitrous oxide on a gold surface; x represents the percentage decomposition of the amount initially present.

t	900	1800	3180	3900 sec.
x	16.5	32	50	57 per cent

Show that the reaction is kinetically of the first order. How long will it take to decrease the amount of nitrous oxide to 25 per cent of the initial value?

57. The transition point of rhombic (α) to monoclinic (β) sulfur is 95.6° C. The difference between the specific volumes, i.e., $v_\beta - v_\alpha$, is +0.0126 cc. per g. The transition point increases 4.5° per 100 atm. increase of pressure. Calculate the heat of transition per gram.

58. The freezing point depressions of potassium chloride and magnesium sulfate solutions at various molalities are as follows:

Molality		0.005	0.01	0.02	0.05	0.10	0.20
KCl	$\Delta T_f =$	0.0182°	0.0361°	0.0712°	0.175°	0.345°	0.678°
MgSO$_4$		0.01570°	0.0300°	0.0570°	0.131°	0.246°	0.454°

Calculate the van't Hoff factor i and the osmotic coefficient g at each molality. Plot the values of g against the ionic strength, and state the conclusion to be drawn.

59. The heat of vaporization of chloroform ($CHCl_3$) is 59 cal. per g. at the boiling point 61.3° C. At what pressure will chloroform boil at 61.0° C?

60. A solution containing 7.148 g. of potassium chloride in 100 g. is electrolyzed, using a silver chloride cathode and a silver anode. After passage of current, resulting in the deposition of 2.4835 g. of silver, it was found that 125.66 g. cathode solution contained 7.7668 g. of potassium chloride in 100 g. of solution, while 121.41 g. anode solution contained 6.509 g. of salt in 100 g. of solution. Calculate the transference numbers of K^+ and Cl^- ions from the data for each solution separately.

61. A liquid, insoluble in water, was steam distilled at two different external pressures. When the latter was 759 mm., the distillation occurred at 95° C, when the vapor pressure of water is 634 mm. At an external pressure of 650 mm., distillation occurred at 92° C, when the vapor pressure of water is 580 mm. Estimate the heat of vaporization and the boiling point of the liquid. (The former may be assumed to be independent of temperature.)

62. For the reaction $\frac{1}{2}H_2(g) + \frac{1}{2}I_2(g) = HI(g)$, the value of ΔH is $+6.0$ kcal. at 25° C. The standard molar entropies are 31.23 E.U. for hydrogen, 62.29 E.U. for iodine vapor (I_2), and 49.40 E.U. for hydrogen iodide. Calculate the standard free energy of formation of hydrogen iodide at 25° C. If ΔH is assumed to remain constant, what is the value of the equilibrium constant at 445° C?

63. The E.M.F. of the cell Ag, 0.01 M $AgNO_3$ || 0.01 M KBr, AgBr(s), Ag is -0.586 volt at 25°. Taking the activity coefficients of the ions in the 0.01 M solutions to be 0.90, determine the solubility product of silver bromide. Estimate its solubility in a 0.01 M silver nitrate solution.

64. The heat of combustion ΔH of sucrose ($C_{12}H_{22}O_{11}$) is -1350.0 kcal. per mole, while that of hydrogen is -68.4, and carbon -94.0 kcal. Calculate the heat of formation of sucrose. Derive a general formula for calculating the heat of formation of the compound $C_xH_yO_z$ from its heat of combustion.

65. For two successive first order reactions $A \xrightarrow{k_1} B \xrightarrow{k_2} C$, show that if $k_1 \gg k_2$ the rate of formation of C is determined by k_2, while if $k_2 \gg k_1$ it is determined by k_1, so that the slowest stage is rate-determining for the formation of C. (See § 58k. Note that $dc_C/dt = k_2 c_B$.)

66. By means of the standard potentials in Table LVI, calculate ΔF^0 and the equilibrium constants for the reactions (a) $Fe^{+++} + Br^- = Fe^{++} + \frac{1}{2}Br_2(l)$; and (b) $Fe^{+++} + I^- = Fe^{++} + \frac{1}{2}I_2(s)$. What conclusions may be drawn concerning the oxidation of bromide and iodide ions, respectively, by ferric ions?

67. In the reaction between ethyl acetate and a small excess of sodium hydroxide in aqueous solution, 100 ml. portions were removed from time to time and titrated with 0.1 N acid; the results were as follows:

Time	0	294	624	1695	∞ sec.
Titration	26.18	22.16	18.20	12.87	6.44 ml.

Show that the reaction is second order, and determine the value of the specific rate in liter mole^{-1} sec.$^{-1}$ units.

68. It was found that 1 g. of charcoal took up 0.770 g. of carbon dioxide at 0° C when the equilibrium pressure was 25.1 mm., and 2.48 g. at an equilibrium pressure of 858.6 mm. What weight of gas would be expected to be taken up when 1 g. of charcoal is placed in 1 liter of carbon dioxide which is initially at a pressure of 0.75 atm. at 0° C?

69. In a Victor Meyer experiment, 0.185 g. of a liquid when vaporized caused the displacement of 25.6 ml. of air, collected over water, measured at 20° C and an atmos-

pheric pressure of 762 mm. The air in the apparatus may be taken as 40 per cent saturated, while the saturation vapor pressure of water is 17.5 mm. at 20° C. Determine the molecular weight of the vaporized liquid.

70. The absorption coefficients of oxygen and nitrogen are 0.0489 and 0.0239, respectively, at 0° C. Taking the molal depression constant of water as 1.86°, estimate the lowering of the freezing point of pure water when in equilibrium with air at atmospheric pressure. (The other gases may be neglected.)

71. The E.M.F. of the cell Zn, $ZnCl_2$ soln., $Hg_2Cl_2(s)$, Hg is 1.0009 volt at 25° C and 1.0000 volt at 0° C. Write the reaction occurring in the cell, and determine ΔF, ΔH and ΔS at 25° C.

72. What is the maximum hydrogen ion concentration of a solution of a nickel salt ($a_{Ni^{++}} = 0.1$) from which the deposition of nickel on the cathode during electrolysis would not be accompanied by hydrogen evolution? The standard Ni, Ni^{++} potential is $+0.236$, and the hydrogen overvoltage on nickel is 0.21 volt.

73. The gases oxygen and carbon monoxide were found to have exactly the same densities at the following pairs of pressures at 293.0° K:

p_{O_2}	572.27	361.87	182.34 mm.
p_{CO}	653.96	413.44	208.30 mm.

Extrapolate the ratios to zero pressure of carbon monoxide, and hence calculate the molecular weight of carbon monoxide and the atomic weight of carbon.

74. The distribution of an organic acid between water (c_1) and benzene (c_2) was found to be as follows at 20° C:

c_1	0.0150	0.0195	0.0289 mole per liter
c_2	0.242	0.412	0.970

The saturation solubility of the acid (molecular weight 118) in water at 20° is 3.80 g. per liter; estimate its solubility in benzene.

75. Silver crystallizes in a face-centered cubic lattice form; the d_{100} edge of the unit cube is 4.08×10^{-8} cm. Show that there are four silver atoms per unit cell, and hence calculate the density of silver.

76. The viscosity of ammonia gas is 91.8×10^{-6} poise at 0° C. Calculate (a) the mean free path, (b) the mean collision diameter, of the molecules, at 0° C and 1 atm. pressure. Assuming the collision diameter to remain constant, calculate the number of collisions taking place in 1 sec. between ammonia molecules in 1 ml. of gas at 25° C and 0.2 atm. pressure.

77. Calculate the value of $e^{-E/RT}$ at the temperatures 20° C and 60° C with E equal to 23.2 kcal. Show that the ratio at the two temperatures is sufficient to account for an observed twelve-fold increase of reaction rate between these temperatures.

78. The vapor pressure of acetone CH_3COCH_3 is 115.6 mm. at 10° and 147.1 mm. at 15° C. Assuming the heat of vaporization to remain constant, estimate the normal boiling point, by two methods, and the critical temperature of acetone.

79. A 0.001 N solution of aniline hydrochloride is 14 per cent hydrolyzed at 25° C. Calculate the hydrolysis constant of the salt and the dissociation constant of aniline.

80. For the equilibrium $Fe(s) + H_2O \rightleftharpoons FeO(s) + H_2$ the value of K_p is 1.62 at 1200° K. At this temperature and 1 atm. pressure, steam is 7.45×10^{-4} per cent dissociated into hydrogen and oxygen. Calculate the oxygen dissociation pressure of ferrous oxide at 1200° K, and the standard free energy of formation of one mole of this oxide from its elements at this temperature.

81. The density of the nonpolar liquid hexane C_6H_{14} is 0.6603 g. per ml. at 20° C.

Estimate its dielectric constant, utilizing the refraction equivalents of carbon 2.42 ml., and hydrogen 1.10 ml.

82. A current of dry air was passed through a saturator containing 7.452 g. of a nonvolatile solute in 120.0 g. of water; the loss in weight was 1.2122 g. The same volume of air passing through pure water at the same temperature caused the vaporization of 1.2746 g. What was the molecular weight of the solute? Estimate the osmotic pressure of the solution.

83. The vapor pressures of iodobenzene (C_6H_5I) and water at several temperatures are as follows:

Temp.	80°	90°	100°	110° C
H_2O	355.1	525.8	760.0	1075.0 mm.
C_6H_5I	21.8	33.5	50.2	73.9 mm.

Draw the vapor pressure curves for these two substances, and determine the temperatures at which iodobenzene will distil in steam at external pressures of 500, 700 and 900 mm. Calculate the composition of the distillate in each case. What conclusion can be drawn from the results?

84. Plot the variation of pH during the course of neutralization of 0.1 N acetic acid ($K_a = 1.752 \times 10^{-5}$) by a strong base. The volume change in the titration may be neglected.

85. The freezing point of benzene is 5.42° C and this is lowered 0.840° by a nonvolatile solute. Calculate (a) the molality of the solution, (b) the osmotic pressure at 5.42° C. The heat of fusion of benzene is 30.3 cal. per g., and the density of liquid benzene is 0.8943 g. per ml. at the freezing point.

86. When 0.232 g. of acetone CH_3COCH_3 was vaporized in a constant volume apparatus containing air, the increase of pressure was 22.4 mm. at 100° C. Another substance gave a pressure increase of 27.8 mm. when 0.326 g. was vaporized in the same apparatus at 100° C. Determine the molecular weight of the latter substance.

87. In the dissociation of solid ammonium carbamate NH_4COONH_2 into $2NH_3(g)$ and $CO_2(g)$, the total gas pressures were 61.3 mm. at 19.9° C, and 124.5 mm. at 30.0° C. Calculate the mean heat of dissociation of ammonium carbamate in the given temperature range.

88. Copper is univalent in cuprocyanide solution; when a current of 0.200 amp. was passed through this (dilute) solution for exactly 2 hr. a weight of 0.7450 g. of copper was deposited on the cathode. The remainder of the current caused the liberation of hydrogen; what volume of moist hydrogen gas was evolved at 18° C and 766 mm.? The vapor pressure of water at 18° C is 15.5 mm.

89. At 727° C, a weight of 0.364 g. of iodine occupied 125 ml. at 752 mm. pressure. Calculate the values of K_p and K_c for the $I_2 \rightleftharpoons 2I$ equilibrium at the given temperature.

90. In the reaction involving the conversion of parahydrogen to orthohydrogen, the times of half change were 648 sec. and 450 sec. for initial pressures of 50 mm. and 100 mm. respectively. What is the apparent order of the reaction?

91. A 1 per cent aqueous solution of hemoglobin had an osmotic pressure of 35.4 mm. of water at 0° C. Calculate the approximate molecular weight of hemoglobin.

92. A given solution in benzene freezes at 5.01° C, compared with 5.42° C for pure benzene. The heat of vaporization of benzene at its boiling point 80.1° C is 95 cal. per g., and the heat of fusion at the freezing point is 30.3 cal. per g. Calculate the temperature at which the given solution will boil at standard atmospheric pressure. What is the vapor pressure of pure benzene at this temperature?

93. Sodium bicarbonate dissociates according to the reaction $2NaHCO_3(s) = Na_2CO_3(s) + H_2O(g) + CO_2(g)$. At 50° C the total dissociation pressure is 0.03947

atm. The water vapor pressure for the $CuSO_4 \cdot 5H_2O \rightleftharpoons CuSO_4 \cdot 3H_2O + 2H_2O(g)$ system is 45.4 mm. at 50° C. Calculate the pressure in atm. of carbon dioxide in equilibrium with a system containing $NaHCO_3$-Na_2CO_3 and $CuSO_4 \cdot 5H_2O$-$CuSO_4 \cdot 3H_2O$.

94. In the reaction between ethyl bromacetate with a small excess of sodium thiosulfate, the rate of the process was followed by removing equal portions of the system after various intervals and titrating the unchanged thiosulfate. The results were as follows:

Time	0	600	1500	2400	4800	∞ sec.
Titration	35.0	27.3	22.1	19.5	16.5	15.0 ml.

Show that the reaction is of the second order.

95. The dissociation pressure of calcium carbonate is 0.073 mm. at 500° C and 1.84 mm. at 600° C. The mean molar heat capacities C_P are 12.27 cal. deg.$^{-1}$ for calcium oxide, 10.9 for carbon dioxide, and 26.37 for calcium carbonate. Calculate the heat of dissociation of the carbonate at 25° C.

96. The melting point of lead is 327.4° C, and the increase of specific volume on melting is 0.003076 cc. per g. The melting point of lead increases 8.03° for 1000 atm. increase of pressure. Calculate the temperature at which a mixture of 5 g. of potassium and 95 g. of lead will melt, assuming ideal behavior, both metals being monatomic.

97. A reversible engine operating between temperatures of 100° and 15° C does 5.64×10^{12} ergs of work in each cycle. How much heat in calories must be taken up at 100° C?

98. A solution contains copper sulfate ($a_{Cu^{++}} = 0.1$) and sulfuric acid ($a_{H^+} = 1.0$). The hydrogen overvoltage at a copper cathode is 0.23 volt, and the standard Cu, Cu^{++} potential is -0.340 volt. What is the copper ion activity when visible hydrogen evolution commences?

99. The heats of combustion of liquid ethanol, acetic acid and ethyl acetate are -327.0, -207.0 and -538.0 kcal., respectively. Calculate the heats of formation of these substances, and the heat change accompanying the liquid-phase reaction $C_2H_5OH + CH_3COOH = CH_3COOC_2H_5 + H_2O$. Explain why the equilibrium constant varies only slightly with temperature.

100. When ammonium carbamate NH_4COONH_2 is heated to 100° C it is virtually completely dissociated into $2NH_3(g) + CO_2(g)$. Calculate (a) the concentrations in moles per liter, (b) the partial pressures in atm., of the gases when 5.62 g. ammonium carbamate are heated in a closed vessel of 7.25 liters capacity at 100° C.

101. Calculate the energy produced in ergs in the self-destruction accompanying the combination of a single electron and a positron. (The mass of an electron is 9.1×10^{-28} g.)

102. Nitric oxide at 99.3 mm. and bromine vapor at 41.6 mm. pressure at 299.4° K are allowed to attain equilibrium at 296.9° K; the total pressure is then 110.5 mm. Calculate K_p, with pressures in atm., for the equilibrium $2NO(g) + Br_2(g) \rightleftharpoons 2NOBr(g)$ at 296.9° K.

103. The freezing point lowerings ΔT_f of several solutions of acetic acid containing m g. of the latter in 1000 g. of benzene are as follows:

m	0.399	0.895	2.894	14.25	30.57 g.
ΔT_f	0.0277°	0.0539°	0.1472°	0.608°	1.254°

The molal depression constant of benzene is 5.12; calculate the apparent molecular weight of the acetic acid at each concentration and plot the values against the molalities. What conclusion can be drawn from the results?

104. An aqueous solution containing one mole of calcium ferrocyanide $Ca_2Fe(CN)_6$ in a liter, density 1.224 g. per ml., has an osmotic pressure of 41.27 atm. at 0° C. The ratio of the vapor pressure of water to that of the solution is 1.033. Calculate the value of the van't Hoff factor i for this solution; the density of water may be taken as unity.

105. The standard molar entropies of hydrogen, bromine gas and hydrogen bromide are 31.23 E.U., 58.67 E.U., and 47.48 E.U., respectively, at 25° C. The molar heat capacities at constant pressure are $6.85 + 0.00028T$, $7.40 + 0.001T$, and $6.80 + 0.00084T$ cal. deg.$^{-1}$, respectively. The heat of formation ΔH per mole of hydrogen bromide is -8.5 kcal. at 25° C. Calculate the equilibrium constant of the reaction $\frac{1}{2}H_2(g) + \frac{1}{2}Br_2(g) \rightleftharpoons HBr(g)$ at 25° and 300° C.

106. The heat of vaporization of benzene is 94.3 cal. per g. at the boiling point at 80.1° C. The density of the liquid at the boiling point is 0.815, and that of the vapor is 0.0026 g. per ml. Calculate the boiling point of benzene at a pressure of 740 mm., by accurate and approximate methods.

107. For the reaction $N_2O_4 \rightleftharpoons 2NO_2$, the value of K_p is 0.6707 at 45° C. What volume would be occupied by 48 g. of gas at 45° C and a pressure of 0.500 atm.?

108. The solubility of magnesium hydroxide is 0.010 g. per liter; calculate the solubility product. What is the ammonia concentration that should just cause the precipitation of the hydroxide from a 0.1 molar solution of magnesium chloride? The activity corrections may be neglected. (The value of K_b for ammonia is 1.74×10^{-5}.)

PHYSICAL CONSTANTS AND CONVERSION FACTORS

1 liter = 1000 ml. = 1000.027 cc.

1 absolute joule = 10^7 ergs

1 international joule = 1.0002×10^7 ergs

1 defined calorie = 4.1833 int. joules

$\qquad = 4.184 \times 10^7$ ergs

1 standard atm. = 76.0 cm. of mercury

$\qquad = 76.0 \times 13.595 \times 980.66 = 1.0132 \times 10^6$ dynes cm.$^{-2}$

Ice point ($0°$ C) = $273.16°$ K

Volume of 1 mole of ideal gas at S.T.P. = 22.414 liters

Gas constant (R) = 0.08205 liter-atm. deg.$^{-1}$ mole^{-1}

$\qquad = 8.314 \times 10^7$ ergs deg.$^{-1}$ mole^{-1}

$\qquad = 1.987$ cal. deg.$^{-1}$ mole^{-1}

$\ln x = 2.3026 \log x$

$2.3026R = 4.576$ cal. deg.$^{-1}$ mole^{-1}

Avogadro number (N) = 6.023×10^{23} molecules mole^{-1}

Boltzmann constant (k) = 1.380×10^{-16} erg deg.$^{-1}$ molecule^{-1}

Faraday (F) = 96,500 int. coulombs g. equiv.$^{-1}$

1 int. volt-coulomb = 1 int. joule = 0.2390 (defined) cal.

Acceleration due to gravity (g) = 980.66 cm. sec.$^{-2}$

Planck constant (h) = 6.624×10^{-27} erg sec.

Velocity of light (c) = 2.998×10^{10} cm. sec.$^{-1}$

ATOMIC WEIGHTS OF FAMILIAR ELEMENTS *

Element	Symbol	At. Wt.	Element	Symbol	At. Wt.
Aluminum	Al	26.97	Iron	Fe	55.85
Antimony	Sb	121.76	Lead	Pb	207.21
Argon	A	39.944	Lithium	Li	6.940
Arsenic	As	74.91	Magnesium	Mg	24.32
Barium	Ba	137.36	Manganese	Mn	54.93
Beryllium	Be	9.02	Mercury	Hg	200.61
Bismuth	Bi	209.00	Molybdenum	Mo	95.95
Boron	B	10.82	Neon	Ne	20.183
Bromine	Br	79.916	Nickel	Ni	58.69
Cadmium	Cd	112.41	Nitrogen	N	14.008
Calcium	Ca	40.08	Oxygen	O	16.000
Carbon	C	12.010	Phosphorus	P	30.98
Cesium	Cs	132.91	Potassium	K	39.096
Chlorine	Cl	35.457	Rubidium	Rb	85.48
Chromium	Cr	52.01	Selenium	Se	78.96
Cobalt	Co	58.94	Silicon	Si	28.06
Copper	Cu	63.57	Silver	Ag	107.880
Fluorine	F	19.00	Sodium	Na	22.997
Gold	Au	197.2	Strontium	Sr	87.63
Helium	He	4.003	Sulfur	S	32.06
Hydrogen	H	1.008	Tin	Sn	118.70
Iodine	I	126.92	Zinc	Zn	65.38

* For other atomic weights, see Table II.

LOGARITHMS

Proportional Parts

No.	0	1	2	3	4	5	6	7	8	9	1	2	3	4	5	6	7	8	9
10	0000	0043	0086	0128	0170	0212	0253	0294	0334	0374	4	8	12	17	21	25	29	33	37
11	0414	0453	0492	0531	0569	0607	0645	0682	0719	0755	4	8	11	15	19	23	26	30	34
12	0792	0828	0864	0899	0934	0969	1004	1038	1072	1106	3	7	10	14	17	21	24	28	31
13	1139	1173	1206	1239	1271	1303	1335	1367	1399	1430	3	6	10	13	16	19	23	26	29
14	1461	1492	1523	1553	1584	1614	1644	1673	1703	1732	3	6	9	12	15	18	21	24	27
15	1761	1790	1818	1847	1875	1903	1931	1959	1987	2014	3	6	8	11	14	17	20	22	25
16	2041	2068	2095	2122	2148	2175	2201	2227	2253	2279	3	5	8	11	13	16	18	21	24
17	2304	2330	2355	2380	2405	2430	2455	2480	2504	2529	2	5	7	10	12	15	17	20	22
18	2553	2577	2601	2625	2648	2672	2695	2718	2742	2765	2	5	7	9	12	14	16	19	21
19	2788	2810	2833	2856	2878	2900	2923	2945	2967	2989	2	4	7	9	11	13	16	18	20
20	3010	3032	3054	3075	3096	3118	3139	3160	3181	3201	2	4	6	8	11	13	15	17	19
21	3222	3243	3263	3284	3304	3324	3345	3365	3385	3404	2	4	6	8	10	12	14	16	18
22	3424	3444	3464	3483	3502	3522	3541	3560	3579	3598	2	4	6	8	10	12	14	15	17
23	3617	3636	3655	3674	3692	3711	3729	3747	3766	3784	2	4	6	7	9	11	13	15	17
24	3802	3820	3838	3856	3874	3892	3909	3927	3945	3962	2	4	5	7	9	11	12	14	16
25	3979	3997	4014	4031	4048	4065	4082	4099	4116	4133	2	3	5	7	9	10	12	14	15
26	4150	4166	4183	4200	4216	4232	4249	4265	4281	4298	2	3	5	7	8	10	11	13	15
27	4314	4330	4346	4362	4378	4393	4409	4425	4440	4456	2	3	5	6	8	9	11	13	14
28	4472	4487	4502	4518	4533	4548	4564	4579	4594	4609	2	3	5	6	8	9	11	12	14
29	4624	4639	4654	4669	4683	4698	4713	4728	4742	4757	1	3	4	6	7	9	10	12	13
30	4771	4786	4800	4814	4829	4843	4857	4871	4886	4900	1	3	4	6	7	9	10	11	13
31	4914	4928	4942	4955	4969	4983	4997	5011	5024	5038	1	3	4	6	7	8	10	11	12
32	5051	5065	5079	5092	5105	5119	5132	5145	5159	5172	1	3	4	5	7	8	9	11	12
33	5185	5198	5211	5224	5237	5250	5263	5276	5289	5302	1	3	4	5	6	8	9	10	12
34	5315	5328	5340	5353	5366	5378	5391	5403	5416	5428	1	3	4	5	6	8	9	10	11
35	5441	5453	5465	5478	5490	5502	5514	5527	5539	5551	1	2	4	5	6	7	9	10	11
36	5563	5575	5587	5599	5611	5623	5635	5647	5658	5670	1	2	4	5	6	7	8	10	11
37	5682	5694	5705	5717	5729	5740	5752	5763	5775	5786	1	2	3	5	6	7	8	9	10
38	5798	5809	5821	5832	5843	5855	5866	5877	5888	5899	1	2	3	5	6	7	8	9	10
39	5911	5922	5933	5944	5955	5966	5977	5988	5999	6010	1	2	3	4	5	7	8	9	10
40	6021	6031	6042	6053	6064	6075	6085	6096	6107	6117	1	2	3	4	5	6	8	9	10
41	6128	6138	6149	6160	6170	6180	6191	6201	6212	6222	1	2	3	4	5	6	7	8	9
42	6232	6243	6253	6263	6274	6284	6294	6304	6314	6325	1	2	3	4	5	6	7	8	9
43	6335	6345	6355	6365	6375	6385	6395	6405	6415	6425	1	2	3	4	5	6	7	8	9
44	6435	6444	6454	6464	6474	6484	6493	6503	6513	6522	1	2	3	4	5	6	7	8	9
45	6532	6542	6551	6561	6571	6580	6590	6599	6609	6618	1	2	3	4	5	6	7	8	9
46	6628	6637	6646	6656	6665	6675	6684	6693	6702	6712	1	2	3	4	5	6	7	7	8
47	6721	6730	6739	6749	6758	6767	6776	6785	6794	6803	1	2	3	4	5	5	6	7	8
48	6812	6821	6830	6839	6848	6857	6866	6875	6884	6893	1	2	3	4	4	5	6	7	8
49	6902	6911	6920	6928	6937	6946	6955	6964	6972	6981	1	2	3	4	4	5	6	7	8
50	6990	6998	7007	7016	7024	7033	7042	7050	7059	7067	1	2	3	3	4	5	6	7	8
51	7076	7084	7093	7101	7110	7118	7126	7135	7143	7152	1	2	3	3	4	5	6	7	8
52	7160	7168	7177	7185	7193	7202	7210	7218	7226	7235	1	2	2	3	4	5	6	7	7
53	7243	7251	7259	7267	7275	7284	7292	7300	7308	7316	1	2	2	3	4	5	6	6	7
54	7324	7332	7340	7348	7356	7364	7372	7380	7388	7396	1	2	2	3	4	5	6	6	7
No.	0	1	2	3	4	5	6	7	8	9	1	2	3	4	5	6	7	8	9

No.	0	1	2	3	4	5	6	7	8	9	1	2	3	4	5	6	7	8	9
55	7404	7412	7419	7427	7435	7443	7451	7459	7466	7474	1	2	2	3	4	5	5	6	7
56	7482	7490	7497	7505	7513	7520	7528	7536	7543	7551	1	2	2	3	4	5	5	6	7
57	7559	7566	7574	7582	7589	7597	7604	7612	7619	7627	1	2	2	3	4	5	5	6	7
58	7634	7642	7649	7657	7664	7672	7679	7686	7694	7701	1	1	2	3	4	4	5	6	7
59	7709	7716	7723	7731	7738	7745	7752	7760	7767	7774	1	1	2	3	4	4	5	6	7
60	7782	7789	7796	7803	7810	7818	7825	7832	7839	7846	1	1	2	3	4	4	5	6	6
61	7853	7860	7868	7875	7882	7889	7896	7903	7910	7917	1	1	2	3	4	4	5	6	6
62	7924	7931	7938	7945	7952	7959	7966	7973	7980	7987	1	1	2	3	3	4	5	6	6
63	7993	8000	8007	8014	8021	8028	8035	8041	8048	8055	1	1	2	3	3	4	5	5	6
64	8062	8069	8075	8082	8089	8096	8102	8109	8116	8122	1	1	2	3	3	4	5	5	6
65	8129	8136	8142	8149	8156	8162	8169	8176	8182	8189	1	1	2	3	3	4	5	5	6
66	8195	8202	8209	8215	8222	8228	8235	8241	8248	8254	1	1	2	3	3	4	5	5	6
67	8261	8267	8274	8280	8287	8293	8299	8306	8312	8319	1	1	2	3	3	4	5	5	6
68	8325	8331	8338	8344	8351	8357	8363	8370	8376	8382	1	1	2	3	3	4	4	5	6
69	8388	8395	8401	8407	8414	8420	8426	8432	8439	8445	1	1	2	2	3	4	4	5	6
70	8451	8457	8463	8470	8476	8482	8488	8494	8500	8506	1	1	2	2	3	4	4	5	6
71	8513	8519	8525	8531	8537	8543	8549	8555	8561	8567	1	1	2	2	3	4	4	5	5
72	8573	8579	8585	8591	8597	8603	8609	8615	8621	8627	1	1	2	2	3	4	4	5	5
73	8633	8639	8645	8651	8657	8663	8669	8675	8681	8686	1	1	2	2	3	4	4	5	5
74	8692	8698	8704	8710	8716	8722	8727	8733	8739	8745	1	1	2	2	3	4	4	5	5
75	8751	8756	8762	8768	8774	8779	8785	8791	8797	8802	1	1	2	2	3	3	4	5	5
76	8808	8814	8820	8825	8831	8837	8842	8848	8854	8859	1	1	2	2	3	3	4	5	5
77	8865	8871	8876	8882	8887	8893	8899	8904	8910	8915	1	1	2	2	3	3	4	4	5
78	8921	8927	8932	8938	8943	8949	8954	8960	8965	8971	1	1	2	2	3	3	4	4	5
79	8976	8982	8987	8993	8998	9004	9009	9015	9020	9025	1	1	2	2	3	3	4	4	5
80	9031	9036	9042	9047	9053	9058	9063	9069	9074	9079	1	1	2	2	3	3	4	4	5
81	9085	9090	9096	9101	9106	9112	9117	9122	9128	9133	1	1	2	2	3	3	4	4	5
82	9138	9143	9149	9154	9159	9165	9170	9175	9180	9186	1	1	2	2	3	3	4	4	5
83	9191	9196	9201	9206	9212	9217	9222	9227	9232	9238	1	1	2	2	3	3	4	4	5
84	9243	9248	9253	9258	9263	9269	9274	9279	9284	9289	1	1	2	2	3	3	4	4	5
85	9294	9299	9304	9309	9315	9320	9325	9330	9335	9340	1	1	2	2	3	3	4	4	5
86	9345	9350	9355	9360	9365	9370	9375	9380	9385	9390	1	1	2	2	3	3	4	4	5
87	9395	9400	9405	9410	9415	9420	9425	9430	9435	9440	0	1	1	2	2	3	3	4	4
88	9445	9450	9455	9460	9465	9469	9474	9479	9484	9489	0	1	1	2	2	3	3	4	4
89	9494	9499	9504	9509	9513	9518	9523	9528	9533	9538	0	1	1	2	2	3	3	4	4
90	9542	9547	9552	9557	9562	9566	9571	9576	9581	9586	0	1	1	2	2	3	3	4	4
91	9590	9595	9600	9605	9609	9614	9619	9624	9628	9633	0	1	1	2	2	3	3	4	4
92	9638	9643	9647	9652	9657	9661	9666	9671	9675	9680	0	1	1	2	2	3	3	4	4
93	9685	9689	9694	9699	9703	9708	9713	9717	9722	9727	0	1	1	2	2	3	3	4	4
94	9731	9736	9741	9745	9750	9754	9759	9763	9768	9773	0	1	1	2	2	3	3	4	4
95	9777	9782	9786	9791	9795	9800	9805	9809	9814	9818	0	1	1	2	2	3	3	4	4
96	9823	9827	9832	9836	9841	9845	9850	9854	9859	9863	0	1	1	2	2	3	3	4	4
97	9868	9872	9877	9881	9886	9890	9894	9899	9903	9908	0	1	1	2	2	3	3	4	4
98	9912	9917	9921	9926	9930	9934	9939	9943	9948	9952	0	1	1	2	2	3	3	4	4
99	9956	9961	9965	9969	9974	9978	9983	9987	9991	9996	0	1	1	2	2	3	3	3	4
No.	0	1	2	3	4	5	6	7	8	9	1	2	3	4	5	6	7	8	9

ANSWERS TO PROBLEMS

Chapter I

I

1. Cl in proportions of $1 : 2 : 4$ combine with fixed wt. of S. **2.** 2.21 parts by wt. of Cl should combine with 1 part of S. **3.** 12. **4.** 2.828×10^{-23} g. **5.** 140.13; 3. **6.** 132.9.

II

1. O in proportions of $2 : 3 : 4$ combine with fixed wt. of N. **2.** 1.71 parts by wt. of O should combine with 1 part of N. **3.** 19. **4.** 4.652×10^{-23} g. **5.** 126.84; 4. **6.** 79.19.

Chapter II

I

1. 24; chromium. **2.** 208; 82. **3.** 75.65% of lighter, 24.35% of heavier isotope.
4. -5.714; -5.946. **5.** 2.72×10^{19}. **6.** Remaining nuclei are ^{12}C, ^{14}N, ^{13}C, ^{17}O, ^{23}Na, ^{24}Mg, ^{35}Cl, ^{42}Ca, which are stable (see Table IV). **7.** ^{30}P, ^{12}C, ^{24}Na, ^{38}K.

II

1. 3.352×10^{-8} cm. **2.** 5α, 2β. **3.** 10.853. **4.** -3.167; -2.480; -3.923. **5.** 17.0047.
6. Remaining nuclei are ^{11}B, ^{16}O, ^{15}N, ^{19}F, ^{19}F, ^{20}Ne, ^{28}Si, ^{38}A, which are stable (see Table IV). **7.** ^{27}Si, ^{13}C, ^{8}Be, ^{28}Si.

Chapter III

I

1. 15,233.022 cm.$^{-1}$, 3.027×10^{-12} ergs; 20,564.58 cm.$^{-1}$, 4.087×10^{-12} ergs; 23,032.33 cm.$^{-1}$, 4.577×10^{-12} ergs; 24,372.84 cm.$^{-1}$, 4.843×10^{-12} ergs. **5.** H—O; C—F; C—F.

II

2. 2.179×10^{-11} ergs. **5.** HF; NH_3; H_2O.

Chapter IV

I

1. 73.0° C. **2.** 5×10^{20}. **3.** 1.154 g. per l. **4.** (a) H_2, 0.625; N_2, 0.208; NH_3, 0.167;
(b) H_2, 475.0 mm.; N_2, 158.1 mm.; NH_3, 126.9 mm.; (c) 2.95 l. **5.** (a) 5.06×10^4,
(b) 4.66×10^4 cm. per sec. **6.** 8 moles H_2 to 1 mole O_2. **7.** (a) 0.960×10^{-5} cm.,
(b) 3.08×10^{-8} cm., (c) 6.04×10^{28}. **8.** 7.3×10^{23}. **9.** High temp. (a) 1.15, (b) 1.17;
normal temp. (a) 1.40 or 1.29, (b) 1.33. **10.** (a) 319, (b) 452 atm. **11.** 44.006; 12.006.
12. 0.468 liter.

II

1. 93.0 cm. **2.** (a) 0.0170, (b) 1.02×10^{22}. **3.** 1.327 g. per l. **4.** (a) PCl_5, 0.408;
PCl_3, 0.296; Cl_2, 0.296; (b) PCl_5, 0.498 atm.; PCl_3, 0.361 atm.; Cl_2, 0.361 atm.
5. (a) 4.82×10^4, (b) 4.44×10^4 cm. per sec. **6.** 97.8. **7.** (a) 1.02×10^{-5} cm.,
(b) 2.97×10^{-8} cm., (c) 5.41×10^{28}. **8.** 7.7×10^{23}. **9.** (a) 8.25; (b) 6.25;
3.25 cal. deg.$^{-1}$ mole^{-1}. **10.** (a) 63.5, (b) 45.8 atm. **11.** 34.002; 30.978. **12.** 57.1; 0.611.

Chapter V

I

1. 0.455; 0.114 g. per ml. **2.** 195° C; 281 ml. per mole; 37 (or 51) atm. **3.** 0.246; 2.67 $\times$ 10^{-2} in liter, atm., mole units. **4.** 40.3 mm. **5.** 2.25; 2.23 cm. deg.$^{-1}$; 76.08° C. **6.** 166 cal. per g. **7.** (a) 1.49, (b) 0.715, (c) 0.780 g. per ml. **8.** 126.6; 131.6. **9.** 12.0 $\times$ 10^{-3} poise. **10.** 22.1; 22.33. **11.** 2.16. **12.** 1.32 $\times$ 10^{-18} e.s.-cm. units (or 1.32 debye units).

II

1. 0.442; 0.118 g. per ml. **2.** 127° C; 170.4 ml. per mole; 53 (or 73) atm. **3.** 1.37; 3.19 $\times$ 10^{-2} in liter, atm., mole units. **4.** 0.1223 g. **5.** 101; 97.5 cal. per g. **6.** 48.3 cm. **7.** One ether oxygen atom (—O—) and one ketonic atom (=O). **8.** $CHCl_3$ to $(C_2H_5)_2O$ is 1.67 to 1. **9.** 1.16 to 1. **10.** Two. **11.** 24.8; 1.493. **12.** 1.05 $\times$ 10^{-18} e.s.-cm. units (or 1.05 debye units).

Chapter VI

I

1. $d_{100} : d_{110} : d_{111} = 1 : 0.702 : 1.13$. **2.** 10.7°; 15.2°; 9.2°. **3.** 6.1 $\times$ 10^{23}. **4.** 3.7 $\times$ 10^{-4} cal. deg.$^{-1}$ g.$^{-1}$; 270. **5.** 16.7(04)° C. **6.** 676; 596 cal. per g.

II

1. 19.9°; 30.7°. **2.** 5.0°; 7.1°; 4.4°. **3.** 0.582 $\times$ 10^{-8} cm. **4.** 4.39 $\times$ 10^{-4}; 1.48 $\times$ 10^{-3} cal. deg.$^{-1}$ g.$^{-1}$. **5.** 3.40 $\times$ 10^{-3} cc. per g.; v_s is larger. **6.** 58.9 cal. per g.

Chapter VII

I

1. 729 cal. **2.** 1.43 $\times$ 10^{11}. **3.** $-118.7°$ C. **4.** ΔH is larger by 1086 cal.; ΔE is larger by 1185 cal. **5.** -31.5; -15.9; -67.6; -34.4 kcal. **6.** -85.7 kcal. **7.** 14.2 kcal. **8.** -101.9 kcal. **9.** (a) -22.56, (b) -86.0 kcal. **10.** -52.25 kcal. **11.** $40.6 + 2.83 \times 10^{-3}T - 2.75 \times 10^{-6}T^2$ kcal.

II

1. 770 cal. **2.** 0.198 liter. **3.** 101. **4.** ΔE is larger by 2225 cal.; ΔH is larger by 874 cal. **5.** 8.3; 41.2; -310.3; -149.4 kcal. **6.** -14.9 kcal. **7.** -327.2 kcal. **8.** -335.2 kcal. **9.** (a) -24.4, (b) -129.9 kcal. **10.** -8.8 kcal. **11.** $-9.85 - 0.27 \times 10^{-3}T + 2.12 \times 10^{-6}T^2$ kcal.

Chapter VIII

I

1. -0.27 cal. deg.$^{-1}$. **2.** -2.906 cal. deg.$^{-1}$ **3.** 9.31 cal. deg.$^{-1}$ mole^{-1}. **4.** -32.08 cal. deg.$^{-1}$. **5.** 0.355. **6.** $+46.8$ cal. **7.** -13.7 cal. deg.$^{-1}$; $+137$ cal.

II

1. 4.08-fold increase. **2.** 60.6° C. **3.** $+2.54$ cal. deg.$^{-1}$. **4.** $+14.01$ cal. deg.$^{-1}$. **5.** 3.83 $\times$ 10^6. **6.** $+1.87 \times 10^{11}$. **7.** -50 cal. deg.$^{-1}$; -35.4 kcal.

Chapter IX

I

1. 215.8 mm. **2.** 63.5. **3.** 4.02; 3.86. **4.** (a) 26.5, (b) 24.0; 19.9 atm. **5.** $-0.55°$ C. **6.** Mol. wts. are 117 and 168; association occurs in solution. **7.** Three. **8.** -954 cal. **9.** 0.98.

II

1. 59.5. **2.** 5.16; 5.24. **3.** 500; 40.4. **4.** 0.0417; 2.4. **5.** 29.8 atm. **6.** Mol. wt. in water 61.2; in benzene 125; association occurs in benzene solution. **7.** 3.76; 0.75. **8.** 79.7 mole % of substance. **9.** 0.958.

CHAPTER X

I

1. 1.1×10^{-5}. **2.** 43.6 N_2, 43.6 O_2, 12.8 NO in mole %. **3.** 0.64×10^{-7}; 0.992%. **4.** 1.17×10^{-10}. **5.** 0.396 mole acid, 0.396 mole amylene, 0.614 mole ester. **6.** 1.22 g. single, 10.98 g. double molecules. **7.** H_2, 0.936; H_2O, 0.064 atm. **8.** NH_3, 0.173; H_2S, 0.623 atm. **9.** 35.60 kcal. **10.** 167.5.

II

1. 6.55. **2.** HI, 4.38 moles; H_2, 0.31 mole; I_2, 0.31 mole. **3.** CO_2, 98.6; CO, 0.93; O_2, 0.47 mole %. **4.** 73.2. **5.** Ethanol, 1.9; Acid, 56.4; Ester, 34.6; Water, 7.1% by wt. **6.** 7.86×10^{-4} mole NO_2 per l. **7.** CO, 0.322; CO_2, 0.178 atm. **8.** NH_3, 0.32; H_2S, 0.07 atm. **9.** -5.67 kcal. **10.** 0.436.

CHAPTER XI

I

1. 2.82 kcal. **2.** -20.30 kcal. **3.** Greater than 12.8 atm. **4.** -71.5 kcal. **5.** $+6.9$ kcal., 8.8×10^{-6}; -47.4 kcal., 5.5×10^{34}; -27.2 kcal., 8.5×10^{19}. **6.** -60.4; -59.6 cal. deg.$^{-1}$. **7.** 5.2×10^{-34}.

II

1. 0.70 kcal. **2.** 9.89 kcal. **3.** Less than 0.083 atm. **4.** -49.0 kcal. **5.** -18.4 kcal., 3.05×10^{13}; -7.3 kcal., 2.24×10^5; -16.5 kcal., 1.24×10^{12}. **6.** -34.9; 44.4 cal. deg.$^{-1}$. **7.** 7.1×10^{16}.

CHAPTER XII

I

1. 3.77×10^{-2} **2.** -3.08 kcal.; 0.0250 g. **3.** H_2, 54.8; O_2, 45.2 mole %. **4.** 253.9 mm.; C_6H_6, 59.0; $C_2H_4Cl_2$, 41.0 mole %. **5.** H_2O, 84.4; $C_6H_5NO_2$, 15.6% by wt. **6.** $c_1/\sqrt{c_2}$ is approx. constant at 2.4×10^{-2}. **7.** 3.46; 3.56 g. per l.

II

1. 1.021 g. **2.** -3.44 kcal.; 0.032. **3.** NH_3, 99.81; N_2, 0.043, H_2, 0.148 mole %. **4.** Benzene, 22.0; toluene, 78.0% by wt. **5.** 203. **6.** Approx. constancy of $c_1/\sqrt{c_2}$ (about 1.2) shows double molecules in benzene. **7.** 0.177 g.

CHAPTER XIII

I

1. 0.0025 amp. too low. **2.** 0.490; 0.510. **3.** 0.284; 0.716. **4.** 0.390. **5.** 8.40 cm.$^{-1}$; 4.21×10^{-3} ohm^{-1} cm.$^{-1}$. **6.** 12.08 cm.$^{-1}$; 252.6 ohm cm. **7.** 138.35 ohm^{-1} cm.^{2}. **8.** 383.01 ohm^{-1} cm.^{2}. **9.** 0.1036; 0.1031. **10.** NH_4^+, 73.46, 7.61×10^{-4}; Cl^-, 76.24 ohm^{-1} cm.^{2}, 7.90×10^{-4} cm. sec.$^{-1}$. **11.** 117.3 ohm^{-1} cm.^{2}. **12.** 1.49×10^{-6} ohm^{-1} cm.$^{-1}$.

II

1. 586. **2.** 0.326, 0.674. **3.** 0.448, 0.552. **4.** 0.389. **5.** 4.25 cm.; 2.29 cm.$^{-1}$. **6.** 3.04×10^{-4} ohm^{-1} cm.$^{-1}$. **7.** 60.8 ohm^{-1} cm.^{2}. **8.** 382.18 ohm^{-1} cm.^{2}. **9.** 0.1993; 0.1980. **10.** Na^+, 0.3963, 5.19×10^{-4}; Cl^-, 0.6037, 7.91×10^{-4} cm. sec.$^{-1}$. **11.** 140.2 ohm^{-1} cm.^{2}. **12.** 1.57×10^{-4}.

CHAPTER XIV

I

1. $Pb + 2AgCl(s) = PbCl_2(s) + 2Ag$; -22.60; -25.16 kcal.   **2.** $H_2(g) + Hg_2Cl_2(s)$ $= 2Hg + 2H^+ + 2Cl^-$; $Zn + Sn^{++++} = Zn^{++} + Sn^{++}$.   **3.** $Fe(CN)_6^{\equiv} + \frac{1}{2}I_2(s)$ $= Fe(CN)_6^{\equiv} + I^-$; $+0.180$ volt; -4.15 kcal.   **4.** Left to right; greater than 1104. **5.** 0.113, right to left. **6.** (a) 0.03848, (b) 0.07696 volt. **7.** $+0.461$, $+1.376$, $+1.837$, spontaneous; -0.397, $+0.301$, -0.096, not spontaneous.   **8.** 0.0708 molal; $Fe^{+++}/Fe^{++} = 1.60$. **9.** -0.0256 volt. **10.** 0.490, 0.510. **11.** -0.0237 volt.

II

1. $Zn + Hg_2SO_4(s) + 7H_2O(l) = ZnSO_4 \cdot 7H_2O(s) + 2Hg$; -65.81; -82.03 kcal. **2.** $H_2(g) + PbSO_4(s) = Pb + 2H^+ + SO_4^{--}$; $Cd + 2Ce^{++++} = Cd^{++} + 2Ce^{+++}$. **3.** $Cu + 2Fe^{+++} = Cu^{++} + 2Fe^{++}$; $+0.431$; -19.87 kcal. **4.** Left to right; less than 5.18×10^{-8}. **5.** 4.15×10^3; left to right. **6.** (a) -0.1419, (b) -0.07095. **7.** -0.712, -0.521, -1.233; -0.704, -0.2366, -0.941 volt. **8.** 0.0895 molal; $(Hg^{++})^2/(Hg_2^{++})$ $= 17.8$. **9.** 1.034. **10.** 0.827; 0.173. **11.** 0.270 atm.

CHAPTER XV

I

1. 0.025; 0.10; 0.15.   **2.** (a) 0.921, (b) 0.743.   **3.** 7.4×10^{-13}; 1.6×10^{-4}. **4.** (a) 1.7×10^{-2}, (b) 3.0×10^{-7} neglecting activity correction; 8.0×10^{-7} allowing for activity coefficients.   **5.** 6.4×10^{-4} mole per l.   **6.** 2.04×10^{-5}; 1.98×10^{-5}. **7.** (a) 0.132; 7.59×10^{-14}; 13.12; (b) 3.02×10^{-5}; 3.31×10^{-10}; 9.48. (c) 1.45×10^{-10}; 6.92×10^{-5}; 4.16. **8.** (a) -0.079; 14.08; (b) 2.61; 11.39; (c) 10.11; 3.89; (d) 2.00; 12.00; (e) 12.00; 2.00. **9.** 1.54×10^{-3}, 2.812; 1.57×10^{-3}, 2.81. **10.** 5.61×10^{-5}; 4.25.

II

1. 0.05; 0.30; 0.75.   **2.** (a) 0.847, (b) 0.762.   **3.** 2.81×10^{-13}; 2.3×10^{-2}. **4.** (a) 1.5×10^{-4}; (b) 1.9×10^{-9} neglecting activity correction; 3.0×10^{-9} allowing for activity coefficients.   **5.** 7.4×10^{-5} mole per l.   **6.** 7.42×10^{-5}; 7.12×10^{-5}. **7.** (a) 0.355; 2.82×10^{-14}; 13.55; (b) 5.25×10^{-3}; 1.91×10^{-12}; 11.72; (c) 1.62×10^{-11}; 6.17×10^{-4}; 3.21. **8.** (a) -0.13; 14.13; (b) 5.28; 8.72; (c) 8.48; 5.52; (d) 1.30; 12.70; (e) 12.70; 1.30. **9.** 2.366×10^{-2}, 1.626; 2.74×10^{-2}, 1.56. **10.** 1.38×10^{-10}; 9.86.

CHAPTER XVI

I

1. (a) 5.71×10^{-11}; 7.56×10^{-5};   7.88;   (b) 8.42×10^{-5}; 2.90×10^{-2};   11.46. **2.** (a) 5.81×10^{-10}; 1.70×10^{-4}; 5.47; (b) 6.3×10^{-6}; 5.6×10^{-3}; 2.95. **3.** 3.59×10^{-4}; 6.44×10^{-9}; 1.57×10^{-6}. **4.** 3.32×10^{-5}; 5.76×10^{-3}; 7.00. **5.** 4.58; (a) -0.30, (b) $+0.54$. **6.** 3.73. **7.** 6.84. **8.** 4.13. **9.** 2.81; 8.81; the second; phenol phthalein.

II

1. (a) 1.60×10^{-10}; 5.66×10^{-5};   8.45;   (b) 1.40×10^{-5}; 8.37×10^{-3};   11.22. **2.** (a) 2.0×10^{-11}; 4.5×10^{-5}; 6.35; (b) 2.5×10^{-5}; 1.1×10^{-2}; 2.66. **3.** 1.43×10^{-4}; 2.04×10^{-10}; 1.00×10^{-14}. **4.** 18.5%; 0.0343.   **5.** 0.0844 mole acid, 0.1156 mole salt per l.; (a) -0.35, (b) $+0.41$. **6.** 4.79. **7.** 0.50. **8.** 5.93. **9.** 9.21; thymol phthalein or phenol phthalein.

CHAPTER XVII

I

1. (a) 1.23, (b) 1.33. **2.** 6.6×10^4 sq. cm. (treating gas molecules as spheres packed side by side).   **3.** (a) Plot $\log c$ against $\log a$, (b) plot c/a against c.   **4.** 1.06×10^{12};

16.1 sq. cm. **5.** 1.66×10^{-6} cm. **6.** 68,400. **7.** 0.0086 (Na^+), 0.0086 (Cl^-); 0.0114 (Na^+), 0.0064 (Cl^-), 0.005 (R^-) molal. **8.** 153.

II

1. (a) Plot $\log a$ against $\log p$, (b) plot p/a against p. **2.** 0.391 (slope); 2.56 mg.; 4.29×10^4 sq. cm. (treating gas molecules as spheres packed side by side). **3.** 0.186 mole per l. **4.** 0.836 g. per l. **5.** 6×10^{11}; 1.21×10^2 sq. cm. **6.** 29,600. **7.** Exact. **8.** 63.5×10^{-16} sq. cm.; three hydrocarbon chains parallel to each other and perpendicular to surface of water.

CHAPTER XVIII
I

1. $k = 3.33, 3.31, 3.29, 3.27, 3.27 \times 10^{-4}$ (3.27×10^{-4} sec.$^{-1}$); 2.12×10^3 sec. **2.** $k = 6.78, 6.72, 6.66, 6.59, 6.73 \times 10^{-6}$; plot of t against $1/(a - x)$ is linear. **3.** Second; 99 sec. **4.** Second. **5.** 6.38×10^{-4} sec.$^{-1}$; 1.25×10^{-4} sec.$^{-1}$. **6.** 58,500 cal.; 2.2×10^{12} liter mole^{-1} sec.$^{-1}$; 6.6×10^{-4} liter mole^{-1} sec.$^{-1}$.

II

1. $k = 2.18, 2.09, 2.11, 2.14 \times 10^{-4}$ (2.13×10^{-4} sec.$^{-1}$); 3.25×10^3 sec. **2.** $k = 0.195$, 0.192, 0.195, 0.193, 0.195 (0.194 liter mole^{-1} sec.$^{-1}$); plot of t against $1/(a - x)$ is linear. **3.** Third. **4.** Second. **5.** 1.12×10^{-4} sec.$^{-1}$; 0.42×10^{-4} sec.$^{-1}$. **6.** 29,200 cal.; 25 sec.$^{-1}$; 5.5×10^{-4} sec.$^{-1}$

CHAPTER XIX
I

1. 1.57×10^{-3} molar; 11.92. **2.** 163.4 kcal. per mole. **3.** $E = 87.64$ kcal. per mole, which is less than the 103 kcal. required for dissociation. **4.** 45.6 kcal. **5.** 2.12×10^9.

II

1. 0.0807; additional 5.5 cm., or total of 11.0 cm. **2.** 2776 Å. **3.** 48.5 kcal. **4.** 35.52 kcal. **5.** 0.51.

INDEX